Haese Mat
specialists in mathe

MW01069256

Cambridge IGCSE™

International

Mathematics

(0607)
Extended

second edition

Michael Haese

Mark Humphries

Ngoc Vo

CAMBRIDGE IGCSE INTERNATIONAL MATHEMATICS (0607) EXTENDED
second edition

Michael Haese   B.Sc.(Hons.), Ph.D.
Mark Humphries   B.Sc.(Hons.)
Ngoc Vo   B.Ma.Sc.

Published by Haese Mathematics
152 Richmond Road, Marleston, SA 5033, AUSTRALIA
Telephone: +61 8 8210 4666
Email: info@haesemathematics.com.au
Web: www.haesemathematics.com.au

National Library of Australia Card Number & ISBN 978-1-925489-65-1

© Haese & Harris Publications 2018

First Edition	2009
Reprinted	2010, 2011, 2012, 2014, 2015 (twice), 2016, 2017
Second Edition	2018
Reprinted	2020, 2021

Cartoon artwork by John Martin.

Fractal artwork on the cover copyright by Jaroslaw Wierny, *www.fractal.art.pl*

Artwork by Brian Houston, Bronson Mathews, and Charlotte Frost.

Computer software by Yi-Tung Huang, Huda Kharrufa, Brett Laishley, Bronson Mathews, Linden May, Joshua Douglass-Molloy, Jonathan Petrinolis, and Nicole Szymanczyk.

Production work by Sandra Haese, Bradley Steventon, Nicholas Kellett-Southby, and Cashmere Collins-McBride.

Typeset in Australia by Deanne Gallasch and Charlotte Frost. Typeset in Times Roman 10.

Printed in China by Prolong Press Limited.

Acknowledgements: The authors and publishers would like to thank Cambridge Assessment International Education for their assistance and support in the preparation of this book. Questions from past exam papers are reproduced by permission of Cambridge Assessment International Education. Cambridge Assessment International Education bears no responsibility for the example answers to questions taken from its past question papers which are contained in this publication. The example answers to past exam questions were written by the authors.

Maps that have been provided by OpenStreetMap are available freely at www.openstreetmap.org. Licensing terms can be viewed at www.openstreetmap.org/copyright.

While every attempt has been made to trace and acknowledge copyright, the authors and publishers apologise for any accidental infringement where copyright has proved untraceable. They would be pleased to come to a suitable agreement with the rightful owner.

Disclaimer: All the internet addresses (URLs) given in this book were valid at the time of printing. While the authors and publisher regret any inconvenience that changes of address may cause readers, no responsibility for any such changes can be accepted by either the authors or the publisher.

FOREWORD

This book has been written to cover the '*Cambridge IGCSE*™ *International Mathematics (0607) Extended*' syllabus for examination from 2020.

The course springs from the principles that students should develop a good foundation of mathematical skills and that they should learn to develop strategies for solving open-ended problems. It aims to promote a positive attitude towards Mathematics and a confidence that leads to further enquiry.

References to the syllabus are made throughout but the book can be used as a full course in its own right, as a preparation for GCE Advanced Level Mathematics or IB Diploma Mathematics, for example. The book has been endorsed by Cambridge Assessment International Education.

The textbook and interactive online features provide an engaging and structured package, allowing students to explore and develop their confidence in mathematics. The material is presented in a clear, easy-to-follow style, free from unnecessary distractions, while effort has been made to contextualise questions so that students can relate concepts to everyday use. In this second edition, many of the chapters have been reordered and restructured, allowing for a more logical progression of ideas and difficulty.

Seven chapters of 'assumed knowledge' are accessible online for those who want to ensure that they have the prerequisite levels of understanding for the course. To reflect one of the main aims of the course, the last two chapters in the book are devoted to multi-topic questions, and investigations and modelling. Review exercises appear at the end of each chapter, and answers are given at the end of the book.

The accompanying digital book is accessed through our Snowflake platform. It contains ◀) *Self Tutor* software (see p. 5), geometry and graphics software, demonstrations and simulations, and the assumed knowledge chapters. The digital book is a complete copy of the text of the book, so students can view it on a home computer or tablet and keep the textbook at school.

The Cambridge International Mathematics examinations are in the form of three papers: one a non-calculator paper, another requiring the use of a graphics calculator, and a third paper containing an investigation and a modelling question. This book supports all three papers.

The book can be used as a scheme of work but it is expected that the teacher will choose the order of topics. Exercises in the book range from routine practice and consolidation of basic skills, to problem solving exercises that are quite demanding.

In this changing world of mathematics education, we believe that the contextual approach shown in this book, with the associated use of technology, will enhance the students' understanding, knowledge and appreciation of mathematics, and its universal application.

We welcome your feedback.

Email: info@haesemathematics.com.au
Web: www.haesemathematics.com.au   *PMH, MH, NV*

4

ABOUT THE AUTHORS

Michael Haese completed a BSc at the University of Adelaide, majoring in Infection and Immunity, and Applied Mathematics. He completed Honours in Applied Mathematics, and a PhD in high speed fluid flows. Michael has a keen interest in education and a desire to see mathematics come alive in the classroom through its history and relationship with other subject areas. He is passionate about girls' education and ensuring they have the same access and opportunities that boys do. His other interests are wide-ranging, including show jumping, cycling, and agriculture. He has been the principal editor for Haese Mathematics since 2008.

Mark Humphries completed a degree in Mathematical and Computer Science, and an Economics degree at the University of Adelaide. He then completed an Honours degree in Pure Mathematics. His mathematical interests include public key cryptography, elliptic curves, and number theory. Mark enjoys the challenge of piquing students' curiosity in mathematics, and encouraging students to think about mathematics in different ways. He has been working at Haese Mathematics since 2006, and is currently the writing manager.

Ngoc Vo completed a BMaSc at the University of Adelaide, majoring in Statistics and Applied Mathematics. Her mathematical interests include regression analysis, Bayesian statistics, and statistical computing. Ngoc has been working at Haese Mathematics as a proof reader and writer since 2016.

ONLINE FEATURES

With the purchase of a new textbook, you will gain 27 months subscription to our online product. This subscription can be renewed for a small fee.

Access is granted through **SNOWFLAKE**, our book viewing software that can be used in your web browser or may be installed to your tablet or computer.

Students can revisit concepts taught in class and undertake their own revision and practice online.

COMPATIBILITY

For iPads, tablets, and other mobile devices, some of the interactive features may not work. However, the digital version of the textbook can be viewed online using any of these devices.

REGISTERING

You will need to register to access the online features of this textbook.

Visit www.haesemathematics.com.au/register and follow the instructions. Once registered, you can:
- activate your digital textbook
- use your account to make additional purchases.

To activate your digital textbook, contact Haese Mathematics. On providing proof of purchase, your digital textbook will be activated. **It is important that you keep your receipt as proof of purchase.**

For general queries about registering and subscriptions:
- Visit our **SNOWFLAKE** help page: http://snowflake.haesemathematics.com.au/help
- Contact Haese Mathematics: info@haesemathematics.com.au

ONLINE VERSION OF THE TEXTBOOK

The entire text of the book can be viewed online, allowing you to leave your textbook at school.

SELF TUTOR

Self tutor is an exciting feature of this book.

The ◀) *Self Tutor* icon on each worked example denotes an active online link.

> Simply 'click' on the ◀) *Self Tutor* (or anywhere in the example box) to access the worked example, with a teacher's voice explaining each step necessary to reach the answer.
>
> Play any line as often as you like. See how the basic processes come alive using movement and colour on the screen.

Example 6   ◀) *Self Tutor*

An equilateral triangle has sides of length 8 cm. Find the height of the triangle, to the nearest mm.

We draw an altitude which *bisects* the base.

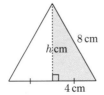

$h^2 + 4^2 = 8^2$ {Pythagoras}

$\therefore\ h^2 + 16 = 64$

$\therefore\ \ h^2 = 48$

$\therefore\ \ h = \sqrt{48}$ {as $h > 0$}

$\therefore$ the height of the triangle ≈ 6.9 cm.

See **Chapter 9, Pythagoras' theorem**, p. 149

INTERACTIVE LINKS

Throughout your digital textbook, you will find interactive links to:

- Graphing software
- Statistics software
- Games
- Demonstrations
- Printable pages

Click anywhere you see one of these icons.

ICON

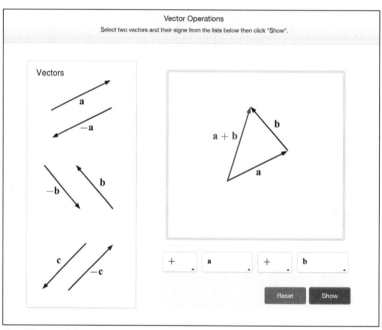

See **Chapter 34**, **Vectors**, p. 599

GRAPHICS CALCULATOR INSTRUCTIONS

Printable calculator instruction booklets are available for the **Casio fx-9860G Plus**, **Casio fx-CG20**, and the **TI-84 Plus CE**. Click on the relevant icon below.

CASIO
fx-9860G Plus

CASIO
fx-CG20

TI-84 Plus CE

When additional calculator help may be needed, specific instructions can be printed from icons within the text.

GRAPHICS
CALCULATOR
INSTRUCTIONS

ASSUMED KNOWLEDGE

Click on the icon to obtain the Assumed Knowledge chapters.

ASSUMED
KNOWLEDGE

1 NUMBER
A Exponent notation
B Roots
C Order of operations
D Primes and composites
E Highest common factor
F Lowest common multiple
G Operations with fractions
H Rounding numbers

2 PERCENTAGE AND RATIO
A Percentage
B One quantity as a percentage of another
C Ratio
D Writing ratios as fractions
E Using ratios to divide quantities
F Equal ratios
G Proportions

3 UNITS
A Units of length
B Units of area
C Units of volume
D Units of capacity
E Units of mass

4 TIME
A Units of time
B Time calculations
C 24-hour time

5 GEOMETRY
A Angles
B Lines and line segments
C Polygons
D Symmetry
E Congruence of figures
F Congruent triangles
G Circles

6 STATISTICS
Interpreting graphs and tables

7 ALGEBRA
A Algebraic notation
B The language of mathematics
C Collecting like terms
D Generalising arithmetic
E Algebraic products

TABLE OF CONTENTS

1   EXPONENTS   **13**
A   Exponent or index notation   13
B   The Fundamental Theorem of Arithmetic   15
C   Exponent or index laws   16
D   Zero and negative exponents   20
E   Standard form   23
    Review set 1A   27
    Review set 1B   27

2   ALGEBRA: EXPANSION   **29**
A   The distributive law   30
B   The product $(a+b)(c+d)$ 31
C   Difference between two squares   34
D   Perfect squares expansion   36
E   Further expansion   38
    Review set 2A   40
    Review set 2B   40

3   ALGEBRA: FACTORISATION   **41**
A   Algebraic common factors   42
B   Factorising with common factors   43
C   Difference between two squares
    factorisation   46
D   Perfect squares factorisation   48
E   Expressions with four terms   50
F   Factorising $x^2 + bx + c$ 50
G   Factorising $ax^2 + bx + c,\ a \neq 1$ 53
H   Miscellaneous factorisation   55
    Review set 3A   56
    Review set 3B   56

4   STATISTICAL GRAPHS   **57**
A   Graphs of categorical data   58
B   Comparing categorical data   62
C   Line graphs   66
    Review set 4A   68
    Review set 4B   70

5   ALGEBRA: LINEAR EQUATIONS   **73**
A   Maintaining balance   74
B   Inverse operations   75
C   Linear equations   76
D   Equations with a repeated unknown   79
E   Rational equations   81
F   Problem solving   83
    Review set 5A   85
    Review set 5B   86

6   SETS AND VENN DIAGRAMS   **87**
A   Set notation   87
B   Complement of a set   90
C   Intersection and union   91
D   Special number sets   92
E   Interval notation   94
F   Venn diagrams   96
G   Venn diagram regions   99
H   Problem solving with Venn diagrams   103
    Review set 6A   106
    Review set 6B   107

7   ANGLES AND POLYGONS   **109**
A   Angle theorems   109
B   Parallel lines   112
C   Triangles   116
D   Isosceles triangles   119
E   The interior angles of a polygon   122
F   The exterior angles of a polygon   124
    Review set 7A   125
    Review set 7B   127

8   SURDS AND OTHER RADICALS   **129**
A   Surds   130
B   Power equations   131
C   Properties of radicals   132
D   Simplest form   134
E   Operations with radicals   134
F   Divisions involving surds   137
    Review set 8A   139
    Review set 8B   140

9   PYTHAGORAS' THEOREM   **141**
A   Pythagoras' theorem   142
B   The converse of Pythagoras' theorem   146
C   Problem solving   147
    Review set 9A   152
    Review set 9B   153

10 FORMULAE   **155**
A   Formula construction   156
B   Substituting into formulae   157
C   Rearranging formulae   159
D   Rearrangement and substitution   163
    Review set 10A   165
    Review set 10B   166

11 *MEASUREMENT:*
PERIMETER AND AREA   **167**
A   Perimeter   167
B   Area of polygons   172
C   Area of a circle   175
     Review set 11A   180
     Review set 11B   181

12 *MEASUREMENT: SOLIDS AND*
CONTAINERS   **183**
A   Surface area   183
B   Volume   190
C   Capacity   197
D   Density   199
     Review set 12A   201
     Review set 12B   203

13 *APPLICATIONS OF PERCENTAGE*   **205**
A   Finding a percentage of a quantity   205
B   Percentage increase and decrease   206
C   Finding the original amount   209
D   Profit and loss   210
E   Chain percentage problems   211
F   Simple interest   213
G   Compound interest   215
     Review set 13A   217
     Review set 13B   218

14 *COORDINATE GEOMETRY*   **219**
A   The Cartesian plane   220
B   The distance between two points   222
C   Midpoints   225
D   Gradient   227
E   Parallel and perpendicular lines   231
F   Collinear points   233
G   Using coordinate geometry   233
     Review set 14A   235
     Review set 14B   236

15 *SPEED, DISTANCE, AND TIME*   **237**
A   Speed, distance, and time   237
B   Travel graphs   240
     Review set 15A   243
     Review set 15B   244

16 *STRAIGHT LINES*   **245**
A   Vertical and horizontal lines   245
B   Properties of a straight line   246
C   Gradient-intercept form   249
D   General form   250

E   Finding the equation of a line   252
F   Lines of symmetry   257
     Review set 16A   258
     Review set 16B   260

17 *SIMULTANEOUS EQUATIONS*   **261**
A   Graphical solution   262
B   Solution by equating values of y 263
C   Solution by substitution   264
D   Solution by elimination   265
E   Problem solving with
     simultaneous equations   268
     Review set 17A   270
     Review set 17B   270

18 *ONE-VARIABLE STATISTICS*   **271**
A   Variables used in statistics   273
B   Organising data   275
C   Measuring the centre of discrete data 283
D   Measuring the spread of discrete data 289
E   Estimating the centre of data in
     class intervals   292
F   Cumulative frequency   295
     Review set 18A   300
     Review set 18B   302

19 *TWO-VARIABLE ANALYSIS*   **305**
A   Correlation   306
B   Line of best fit by eye   309
C   Linear regression   312
     Review set 19A   316
     Review set 19B   317

20 *ALGEBRAIC FRACTIONS*   **319**
A   Evaluating algebraic fractions   320
B   Simplifying algebraic fractions   321
C   Multiplying and dividing
     algebraic fractions   325
D   Adding and subtracting
     algebraic fractions   327
     Review set 20A   330
     Review set 20B   331

21 *SIMILARITY*   **333**
A   Similar figures   333
B   Similar triangles   337
C   Problem solving   340
D   Areas of similar objects   343
E   Volumes of similar objects   345
     Review set 21A   347
     Review set 21B   349

22	TRIGONOMETRY	351
A	Labelling right angled triangles	352
B	The trigonometric ratios	354
C	Finding side lengths	356
D	Finding angles	358
E	Problem solving	359
F	True bearings	366
G	The angle between a line and a plane	368
H	The angle between two planes	370
	Review set 22A	372
	Review set 22B	373

23	QUADRATIC EQUATIONS	375
A	Equations of the form $x^2 = k$	376
B	Solving equations by factorisation	377
C	The quadratic formula	381
D	Problem solving	383
	Review set 23A	386
	Review set 23B	387

24	TRANSFORMATION GEOMETRY	389
A	Translations	390
B	Reflections	392
C	Rotations	395
D	Enlargements and reductions	397
E	Stretches	399
F	The inverse of a transformation	402
G	Combinations of transformations	403
	Review set 24A	404
	Review set 24B	406

25	FUNCTIONS	407
A	Mapping diagrams	407
B	Functions	410
C	Function notation	412
D	Composite functions	414
E	The absolute value function	415
F	Reciprocal functions	419
G	Graphs of functions	421
H	Transforming functions	423
I	Inverse functions	427
	Review set 25A	429
	Review set 25B	431

26	POLYNOMIAL FUNCTIONS	433
A	Quadratic functions	434
B	Graphs of quadratic functions	435
C	Axes intercepts	440
D	Axis of symmetry of a quadratic	444
E	Vertex of a quadratic	445
F	Finding a quadratic function	447
G	Problem solving with quadratic functions	449

H	Cubic functions	450
	Review set 26A	454
	Review set 26B	455

27	SEQUENCES	457
A	Number sequences	458
B	Formulae for sequences	459
C	Geometric sequences	462
D	The difference method for sequences	463
	Review set 27A	468
	Review set 27B	469

28	EXPONENTIALS	471
A	Rational exponents	471
B	Exponential functions	473
C	Graphs of exponential functions	474
D	Exponential equations	477
E	Problem solving with exponential functions	479
F	Exponential modelling	481
	Review set 28A	482
	Review set 28B	484

29	LOGARITHMS	485
A	Logarithms	485
B	The logarithmic function	487
C	Laws of logarithms	488
D	Logarithms in base 10	490
E	Logarithmic equations	492
F	Solving exponential equations	494
	Review set 29A	495
	Review set 29B	496

30	ADVANCED TRIGONOMETRY	497
A	The unit circle	498
B	The multiples of 30° and 45°	502
C	The area of a triangle	504
D	The sine rule	506
E	The cosine rule	509
F	Problem solving with the sine and cosine rules	512
G	Graphs from the unit circle	514
H	Trigonometric functions	515
I	Transformations of trigonometric functions	517
	Review set 30A	520
	Review set 30B	521

31	CIRCLE GEOMETRY	523
A	Angle in a semi-circle theorem	524
B	Chords of a circle theorem	526
C	Radius-tangent theorem	528

D   Tangents from an external point
      theorem   531
E   Angle between a tangent and a chord
      theorem   533
F   Angle at the centre theorem   535
G   Angles subtended by the same arc
      theorem   537
H   Cyclic quadrilaterals   539
I   Tests for cyclic quadrilaterals   542
      Review set 31A   545
      Review set 31B   547

32 PROBABILITY   **549**
A   Probability   550
B   Experimental probability   552
C   Expectation   556
D   Sample space and events   557
E   Theoretical probability   559
F   The addition law of probability   563
G   Independent events   565
H   Dependent events   568
      Review set 32A   571
      Review set 32B   573

**33 VARIATION AND
      POWER MODELLING**   **575**
A   Direct variation   576
B   Powers in direct variation   579
C   Inverse variation   582
D   Powers in inverse variation   586
E   Power models   587
      Review set 33A   590
      Review set 33B   591

34 VECTORS   **593**
A   Directed line segment representation   594
B   Vector equality   595
C   Vector addition   596
D   Vector subtraction   599
E   Vectors in component form   601
F   Operations in component form   604
G   Scalar multiplication   607
H   Parallel vectors   608
      Review set 34A   611
      Review set 34B   612

35 INEQUALITIES   **613**
A   Linear inequalities   614
B   Solving linear inequalities   614
C   Sign diagrams   617
D   Quadratic inequalities   619
E   Solving inequalities using technology 621

F   Linear inequalities in the Cartesian plane   622
      Review set 35A   626
      Review set 35B   627

36 MULTI-TOPIC QUESTIONS   **629**

**37 INVESTIGATION AND MODELLING
      QUESTIONS**   **637**
A   Investigation questions   637
B   Modelling questions   640

ANSWERS   **643**

INDEX   **736**

SYMBOLS AND NOTATION USED IN THIS BOOK

$\mathbb{N}$	the set of positive integers and zero, $\{0, 1, 2, 3, ...\}$
$\mathbb{Z}$	the set of integers, $\{0, \pm1, \pm2, \pm3, ...\}$
$\mathbb{Z}^+$	the set of positive integers, $\{1, 2, 3, ...\}$
$\mathbb{Q}$	the set of rational numbers
$\mathbb{Q}'$	the set of irrational numbers
$\mathbb{R}$	the set of real numbers
$\{x_1, x_2, ...\}$	the set with elements $x_1, x_2, ...$
$n(A)$	the number of elements in the finite set A
$\{x \mid ......$	the set of all x such that
$\in$	is an element of
$\notin$	is not an element of
$\varnothing$ or $\{\ \}$	the empty (null) set
U	the universal set
$\cup$	union
$\cap$	intersection
$\subseteq$	is a subset of
$\subset$	is a proper subset of
A'	the complement of the set A
$a^{\frac{1}{n}}, \sqrt[n]{a}$	a to the power of $\frac{1}{n}$, nth root of a (if $a \geqslant 0$ then $\sqrt[n]{a} \geqslant 0$)
$a^{\frac{1}{2}}, \sqrt{a}$	a to the power $\frac{1}{2}$, square root of a (if $a \geqslant 0$ then $\sqrt{a} \geqslant 0$)
$\|x\|$	the modulus or absolute value of x, that is $\begin{cases} x \text{ for } x \geqslant 0, & x \in \mathbb{R} \\ -x \text{ for } x < 0, & x \in \mathbb{R} \end{cases}$
$\equiv$	identity or is equivalent to
$\approx$	is approximately equal to
$\cong$	is congruent to
$>$	is greater than
$\geq$ or $\geqslant$	is greater than or equal to
$<$	is less than
$\leq$ or $\leqslant$	is less than or equal to
u_n	the nth term of a sequence or series
$f : x \mapsto y$	f is a function under which x is mapped to y
$f(x)$	the image of x under the function f
f^{-1}	the inverse function of the function f
$\log x$	logarithm to the base 10 of x
$\log_a x$	logarithm to the base a of x
sin, cos, tan	the circular functions
$A(x, y)$	the point A in the plane with Cartesian coordinates x and y
AB	$\begin{cases} \text{the line segment with endpoints A and B} \\ \text{the distance from A to B} \\ \text{the line containing points A and B} \end{cases}$
$\widehat{A}$	the angle at A
$C\widehat{A}B$	the angle between CA and AB
$\triangle ABC$	the triangle whose vertices are A, B, and C
$\mathbf{v}$	the vector $\mathbf{v}$
$\overrightarrow{AB}$	the vector represented in magnitude and direction by the directed line segment from A to B
$\|\mathbf{a}\|$	the magnitude of vector $\mathbf{a}$
$\|\overrightarrow{AB}\|$	the magnitude of $\overrightarrow{AB}$
$P(A)$	probability of event A
$P(A')$	probability of event "not A"
$x_1, x_2, ...$	observations of a variable
$f_1, f_2, ...$	frequencies with which the observations $x_1, x_2, x_3, ...$ occur
$\overline{x}$	mean of the values $x_1, x_2, ...$
$\sum f$	sum of the frequencies $f_1, f_2, ...$
r	Pearson's correlation coefficient
r^2	coefficient of determination

Exponents

1

Contents:

A Exponent or index notation [E1.4, E1.9]
B The Fundamental Theorem
 of Arithmetic [E1.9]
C Exponent or index laws [E1.9, E2.4]
D Zero and negative exponents [E1.9, E2.4]
E Standard form [E1.9]

Opening problem

Amedeo Avogadro (1776 - 1856) first proposed that the volume of a gas, at a given pressure and temperature, is proportional to the number of atoms or molecules present, regardless of the nature of the gas.

In 1865, **Johann Josef Loschmidt** estimated that one gram of hydrogen contains 6.02×10^{23} atoms. This number of atoms is now called one **mole** of a substance.

French physicist **Jean Perrin**, who earned a Nobel Prize in Physics, named the number in honour of Avogadro in 1909, for his work in the field of molecular theory.

Amedeo Avogadro

Things to think about:

a How can we write 6.02×10^{23} as an ordinary number?

b How many atoms would be in one tonne of hydrogen gas?

c Can you find the mass of 10^{30} atoms of hydrogen?

A EXPONENT OR INDEX NOTATION [E1.4, E1.9]

The use of **exponents**, also called **powers** or **indices**, allows us to write products of factors and also to write very large or very small numbers quickly.

Rather than writing $2 \times 2 \times 2$, we can write such a product as 2^3. We call this **exponent** or **index notation**.

We say that 2 is the **base** and that 3 is the **exponent**, **power**, or **index**.

2^3 reads   *"two cubed"* or
                "two to the power three".

$$2^3 \xleftarrow{\hspace{1cm}} \text{exponent, power, or index}$$

base

> If n is a positive integer, then a^n is the product of n factors of a.
> $$a^n = \underbrace{a \times a \times a \times a \times a \times a \times .... \times a}_{n \text{ factors}}$$

Example 1
◀️) **Self Tutor**

Find the integer equal to: **a** 3^4 **b** $2^4 \times 3^2 \times 7$

a 3^4	**b** $2^4 \times 3^2 \times 7$
$= 3 \times 3 \times 3 \times 3$	$= 2 \times 2 \times 2 \times 2 \times 3 \times 3 \times 7$
$= 81$	$= 1008$

Consider the following patterns:

$(-1)^1 = -1$ $(-2)^1 = -2$
$(-1)^2 = -1 \times -1 = 1$ $(-2)^2 = -2 \times -2 = 4$
$(-1)^3 = -1 \times -1 \times -1 = -1$ $(-2)^3 = -2 \times -2 \times -2 = -8$
$(-1)^4 = -1 \times -1 \times -1 \times -1 = 1$ $(-2)^4 = -2 \times -2 \times -2 \times -2 = 16$

The patterns lead us to conclude that:

> - A **negative** base raised to an **odd** power is **negative**.
> - A **negative** base raised to an **even** power is **positive**.

Example 2
◀️) **Self Tutor**

Simplify:

a -4^2 **b** $(-4)^2$ **c** -2^3 **d** $(-2)^3$

a -4^2	**b** $(-4)^2$	**c** -2^3	**d** $(-2)^3$
$= -4 \times 4$	$= -4 \times -4$	$= -2 \times 2 \times 2$	$= -2 \times -2 \times -2$
$= -16$	$= 16$	$= -8$	$= -8$

EXERCISE 1A

1 Find the integer equal to:

   a 2^3 **b** 2^4 **c** 3^3 **d** 2×5^2
   e $2^2 \times 5^2$ **f** $3^3 \times 5$ **g** $3^2 \times 5 \times 7$ **h** $2^2 \times 3^3 \times 11$

2 Use your calculator to write each product as a natural number:

   a $2^5 \times 3^3 \times 11^2$ **b** $2^2 \times 5^4 \times 7^5$ **c** $3^4 \times 7^2 \times 11^3$ **d** $2^3 \times 3^4 \times 5^2 \times 11$

3 Write in exponent form:

    a $2 \times 3 \times 3$ **b** $2 \times 5 \times 5 \times 5$ **c** $2 \times 2 \times 2 \times 5 \times 7$ **d** $3 \times 3 \times 3 \times 7 \times 7$

    e $3 \times 3 \times 3 \times 3 \times 5 \times 5$ **f** $7 \times 7 \times 7 \times 7 \times 7 \times 11 \times 11 \times 11$

4 Simplify:

    a -3^2 **b** $(-3)^2$ **c** -1^3 **d** $(-1)^3$

    e $(-5)^2$ **f** -5^2 **g** $(-2)^4$ **h** -2^4

    i $(-3)^3$ **j** -3^3 **k** $-(-3)^3$ **l** $-(-4)^3$

5 Simplify:

    a $2^3 \times 3^2 \times (-1)^5$ **b** $(-1)^4 \times 3^3 \times 2^2$ **c** $(-2)^3 \times (-3)^4$

6 Use your calculator to evaluate the following, recording the entire display:

    a 2^8 **b** $(-5)^4$ **c** -3^5 **d** $(-7)^6$

    e -7^6 **f** 1.05^{12} **g** -0.623^{11} **h** $(-2.11)^{17}$

7 Write in exponent form with 2 as a base:

    a 4   **b** 16   **c** 64   **d** 4096

8 Write in exponent form with 3 as a base:

    a 27   **b** 81   **c** 729   **d** 59 049

9 By considering $3^1, 3^2, 3^3, 3^4, 3^5, ...$ and looking for a pattern, find the last digit of 3^{33}.

10 What is the last digit of 7^{77}?

11 Find n if:

    a $5^4 = n$ **b** $n^3 = 343$ **c** $11^n = 161\,051$ **d** $(0.6)^n = 0.046\,656$

B THE FUNDAMENTAL THEOREM OF ARITHMETIC [E1.9]

> Apart from order, every composite number can be written as a **product of prime factors** in **one and only one way**.

For example, $72 = 2 \times 2 \times 2 \times 3 \times 3$ is the only way of writing 72 as the product of prime factors. Using exponent notation, we write $72 = 2^3 \times 3^2$. We call this a **prime factorisation** and say the number is written in **prime factored form**.

Example 3   ◀) *Self Tutor*

Write 600 as the product of prime factors in exponent form.

2	600
2	300
2	150
3	75
5	25
5	5
	1

$$\therefore \quad 600 = 2 \times 2 \times 2 \times 3 \times 5 \times 5$$
$$= 2^3 \times 3 \times 5^2$$

EXERCISE 1B

1 Write the following as powers of a prime:

    a 8   **b** 27   **c** 125   **d** 128

    e 343   **f** 729   **g** 361   **h** 1331

2 Express as the product of prime factors in exponent form:

    a 54   **b** 108   **c** 360   **d** 228

    e 196   **f** 756   **g** 936   **h** 1225

    i 588   **j** 945   **k** 910   **l** 1274

Activity

Click on the icon to play a game which involves writing numbers as the product of prime factors. See if you can get the highest score in your class.

GAME

C | EXPONENT OR INDEX LAWS   *[E1.9, E2.4]*

Discovery 1   *Discovering exponent laws*

We can discover some laws for exponents by considering several examples and looking for patterns.

WORKSHEET

What to do:

1 Copy and complete:

$$2^2 \times 2^3 = (2 \times 2) \times (2 \times 2 \times 2) = 2^5$$

  a $5^4 \times 5^2 = \boxed{} = \boxed{}$

  b $a^3 \times a^4 = \boxed{} = \boxed{}$

In general, $a^m \times a^n = \boxed{}$.

2 Copy and complete:

$$\frac{2^5}{2^3} = \frac{2 \times 2 \times \cancel{2} \times \cancel{2} \times \cancel{2}}{\cancel{2} \times \cancel{2} \times \cancel{2}} = 2^2$$

  a $\dfrac{3^6}{3^4} = \boxed{} = \boxed{}$

  b $\dfrac{a^5}{a^2} = \boxed{} = \boxed{}$

In general, $\dfrac{a^m}{a^n} = \boxed{}$.

3 Copy and complete:

  a $(2^2)^3 = 2^2 \times 2^2 \times 2^2 = (2 \times 2) \times (2 \times 2) \times (2 \times 2) = \boxed{}$

  b $(3^2)^4 = \boxed{} = \boxed{} = \boxed{}$

  c $(a^4)^3 = \boxed{} = \boxed{} = \boxed{}$

In general, $(a^m)^n = \boxed{}$.

4 Copy and complete the following:

a $(ab)^4 = ab \times ab \times ab \times ab = a \times a \times a \times a \times b \times b \times b \times b =$ ☐

b $(ab)^3 =$ ☐ $=$ ☐ $=$ ☐

c $(2a)^5 =$ ☐ $=$ ☐ $=$ ☐

In general, $(ab)^n =$ ☐ .

5 Copy and complete:

a $\left(\dfrac{a}{b}\right)^2 = \dfrac{a}{b} \times \dfrac{a}{b} \quad = \dfrac{a \times a}{b \times b} \quad =$ ☐

b $\left(\dfrac{a}{b}\right)^3 = \dfrac{a}{b} \times \dfrac{a}{b} \times \dfrac{a}{b} =$ ☐ $=$ ☐

c $\left(\dfrac{a}{b}\right)^4 =$ ☐ $=$ ☐ $=$ ☐

In general, $\left(\dfrac{a}{b}\right)^n =$ ☐ for $b \neq 0$.

From **Discovery 1** you should have found these **exponent laws** for **positive exponents**:

> If m and n are positive integers, then:
>
> - $a^m \times a^n = a^{m+n}$ — To **multiply** numbers with the **same base**, keep the base and **add** the exponents.
>
> - $\dfrac{a^m}{a^n} = a^{m-n}, \ a \neq 0$ — To **divide** numbers with the **same base**, keep the base and **subtract** the exponents.
>
> - $(a^m)^n = a^{m \times n}$ — When **raising** a **power** to a **power**, keep the base and **multiply** the exponents.
>
> - $(ab)^n = a^n b^n$ — To **expand** a **product** to a power, raise each factor to the power.
>
> - $\left(\dfrac{a}{b}\right)^n = \dfrac{a^n}{b^n}$ provided $b \neq 0$. — To **expand** a **quotient** to a power, raise both the numerator and denominator to the power.

Example 4   ◀) *Self Tutor*

Simplify using the laws of exponents:

a $2^3 \times 2^2$ **b** $x^4 \times x^5$

a $\quad 2^3 \times 2^2$ **b** $\quad x^4 \times x^5$
$\quad = 2^{3+2}$ $\quad = x^{4+5}$
$\quad = 2^5$ $\quad = x^9$
$\quad = 32$

When multiplying numbers with the same base, keep the base and add the exponents.

EXERCISE 1C

1 Simplify using the exponent laws:

   a $3^2 \times 3^3$ **b** $2^2 \times 2^2$ **c** $5^2 \times 5^4$ **d** $3^4 \times 3^3$

   e 7×7^4 **f** $(-2)^2 \times (-2)$ **g** $x \times x$ **h** $y \times y^2$

   i $a \times a^4$ **j** $n^2 \times n$ **k** $x^3 \times x^6$ **l** $y^3 \times y^5$

Example 5   ◀) Self Tutor

Simplify using the exponent laws:

  a $\dfrac{3^5}{3^3}$ **b** $\dfrac{p^7}{p^3}$

> When dividing numbers with the same base, keep the base and subtract the exponents.

  a $\dfrac{3^5}{3^3} = 3^{5-3}$ **b** $\dfrac{p^7}{p^3} = p^{7-3}$

         $= 3^2$ $= p^4$

         $= 9$

---

2 Simplify using the exponent laws:

   a $\dfrac{2^4}{2^2}$ **b** $\dfrac{3^3}{3}$ **c** $\dfrac{7^5}{7^2}$ **d** $\dfrac{10^4}{10^3}$

   e $\dfrac{x^6}{x^2}$ **f** $\dfrac{y^9}{y^5}$ **g** $c^6 \div c^4$ **h** $b^8 \div b^5$

> For a power to a power, keep the base and multiply the exponents.

Example 6   ◀) Self Tutor

Simplify using the exponent laws:

  a $(2^3)^2$ **b** $(x^4)^5$

  a $(2^3)^2 = 2^{3\times2}$ **b** $(x^4)^5 = x^{4\times5}$

           $= 2^6$ $= x^{20}$

           $= 64$

---

3 Simplify using the exponent laws:

   a $(2^2)^3$ **b** $(10^4)^2$ **c** $(3^3)^2$ **d** $(2^4)^3$

   e $(x^5)^2$ **f** $(p^3)^3$ **g** $(t^3)^4$ **h** $(z^2)^6$

4 Simplify using the exponent laws:

   a $c^2 \times c^4$ **b** $b^8 \div b^3$ **c** $(y^5)^3$ **d** $y^4 \times y^6$

   e $q \times q^6$ **f** $(z^6)^5$ **g** $t^{10} \div t^7$ **h** $a^2 \times a^n$

   i $g^4 \div g$ **j** $n^2 \times n^3 \times n^5$ **k** $(k^4)^2 \div k$ **l** $(p^2)^2 \times p^2$

5 Copy and complete, replacing each □ with a number or operation:

   a $(7^2)^{□} = 7^6$ **b** $2^4 \,□\, 2 = 2^3$ **c** $2^2 \,□\, 2^7 = 2^9$

   d $(x^{□})^4 = x^{12}$ **e** $a^5 \,□\, a^5 = a^{10}$ **f** $5^9 \,□\, 5^3 = 5^6$

6   Simplify using the exponent laws:

  a $\dfrac{5a^3}{a}$ **b** $3q^2 \times 5q$ **c** $8x^2y \times 2xy^3$ **d** $\dfrac{21t^3}{3t^2}$

Example 7   ◀ッ) *Self Tutor*

Remove the brackets and simplify:

  a $(ab)^5$ **b** $(2xy)^3$

  a $(ab)^5$
    $= a^5b^5$

  b $(2xy)^3$
    $= 2^3 \times x^3 \times y^3$
    $= 8x^3y^3$

Raise each factor to the given power.

---

7   Remove the brackets and simplify:

  a $(pq)^2$ **b** $(xy)^4$ **c** $(ab)^6$ **d** $(abc)^3$

  e $(2a)^3$ **f** $(3d)^5$ **g** $(2k)^5$ **h** $(5gh)^2$

Example 8   ◀ッ) *Self Tutor*

Remove the brackets and simplify:

  a $\left(\dfrac{m}{n}\right)^4$ **b** $\left(\dfrac{2}{b}\right)^3$

  a $\left(\dfrac{m}{n}\right)^4$
    $= \dfrac{m^4}{n^4}$

  b $\left(\dfrac{2}{b}\right)^3 = \dfrac{2^3}{b^3}$
    $= \dfrac{8}{b^3}$

Raise both the numerator and the denominator to the given power.

---

8   Remove the brackets and simplify:

  a $\left(\dfrac{a}{b}\right)^2$ **b** $\left(\dfrac{b}{2}\right)^3$ **c** $\left(\dfrac{j}{k}\right)^4$ **d** $\left(\dfrac{2}{z}\right)^4$

  e $\left(\dfrac{4}{x}\right)^2$ **f** $\left(\dfrac{2}{b}\right)^5$ **g** $\left(\dfrac{q}{2}\right)^4$ **h** $\left(\dfrac{3}{b}\right)^3$

Example 9   ◀ッ) *Self Tutor*

Express in simplest form, without brackets:

  a $(3a^3b)^4$ **b** $\left(\dfrac{x^2}{2y}\right)^3$

  a $(3a^3b)^4 = 3^4 \times (a^3)^4 \times b^4$
    $= 81 \times a^{3\times4} \times b^4$
    $= 81a^{12}b^4$

  b $\left(\dfrac{x^2}{2y}\right)^3 = \dfrac{(x^2)^3}{2^3 \times y^3}$
    $= \dfrac{x^{2\times3}}{8 \times y^3}$
    $= \dfrac{x^6}{8y^3}$

9 Express in simplest form, without brackets:

a $(2b^4)^3$

b $\left(\dfrac{3}{x^2y}\right)^2$

c $(5a^4b)^2$

d $\left(\dfrac{m^3}{2n^2}\right)^4$

e $\left(\dfrac{3a^3}{b^5}\right)^3$

f $(2m^3n^2)^5$

g $\left(\dfrac{4a^4}{b^2}\right)^2$

h $(5x^2y^3)^3$

D   ZERO AND NEGATIVE EXPONENTS   [E1.9, E2.4]

For all positive integers n, a^n is defined as the product of n factors of a:

$$a^n = \underbrace{a \times a \times a \times .... \times a}_{n \text{ factors}}$$

But what if n is 0 or negative? In the following **Discoveries** we will see how to define zero and negative exponents in a way that preserves the exponent laws we have already established.

Discovery 2   *The zero exponent law*

What to do:

1 State the value of:

a $\dfrac{2}{2}$

b $\dfrac{7}{7}$

c $\dfrac{-5}{-5}$

d $\dfrac{-23}{-23}$

2 Copy and complete: When a non-zero value is divided by itself, the result is always ......

For any $a \neq 0$, $\dfrac{a^3}{a^3} = ...$

3 Use an exponent law to show that $\dfrac{a^3}{a^3} = a^0$.

4 Hence complete: $a^0 = ...$ for all $a \neq 0$.
Check your answer by evaluating 2^0 and 5^0 on your calculator.

Discovery 3   *Negative exponents*

What to do:

1 Consider the fraction $\dfrac{7^3}{7^5}$.

a   By expanding and then cancelling common factors, show that $\dfrac{7^3}{7^5} = \dfrac{1}{7^2}$.

b   Use an exponent law to show that $\dfrac{7^3}{7^5} = 7^{-2}$.

c   Hence copy and complete: $7^{-2} = ...$

2 Use the fact that $a^0 = 1$ to copy and complete: $a^{-n} = a^{0-n} = \dfrac{a^0}{\square} = \dfrac{\square}{\square}$.

From the **Discoveries** on the previous page, you should have found:

- The **zero exponent law**: $a^0 = 1$ for all $a \neq 0$.

- The **negative exponent law**:   If a is any non-zero number and n is an integer, then $a^{-n} = \dfrac{1}{a^n}$.

  This means that a^n and a^{-n} are **reciprocals** of one another.

  In particular, notice that $a^{-1} = \dfrac{1}{a}$.

Using the negative exponent law, $\left(\frac{2}{3}\right)^{-4} = \dfrac{1}{\left(\frac{2}{3}\right)^4}$

$$= \dfrac{1^4}{\left(\frac{2}{3}\right)^4} \qquad \{1^4 = 1\}$$

$$= \left(\dfrac{1}{\frac{2}{3}}\right)^4 \qquad \{\text{expansion law}\}$$

$$= \left(\tfrac{3}{2}\right)^4 \qquad \{\text{simplifying}\}$$

So, in general: $\left(\dfrac{a}{b}\right)^{-n} = \left(\dfrac{b}{a}\right)^n$ provided $a \neq 0,\ b \neq 0$.

Example 10   ◄)) *Self Tutor*

Simplify, giving answers in simplest rational form:

a $2^0 - 2^{-2}$ **b** $\left(\tfrac{3}{5}\right)^{-2}$

"Simplest rational form" means "as a fraction in lowest terms".

a $2^0 - 2^{-2}$

$= 1 - \dfrac{1}{2^2}$

$= \tfrac{3}{4}$

b $\left(\tfrac{3}{5}\right)^{-2} = \left(\tfrac{5}{3}\right)^2$

$= \dfrac{5^2}{3^2}$

$= \dfrac{25}{9}$

EXERCISE 1D

1 Simplify:

a 7^0 **b** 41^0 **c** x^0 **d** 5×2^0

e $8 + 10^0$ **f** $6 - 6^0$ **g** 11×11^0 **h** $p^6 \times p^0$

i $(2^3)^0$ **j** $(2^0)^3$ **k** 7×3^0 **l** $(7 \times 3)^0$

2 Simplify:

a $\dfrac{n^2}{n^2}$ **b** $\dfrac{k^6}{k^6}$ **c** $\dfrac{xy}{y}$ **d** $\dfrac{a^3b^2}{b^2}$

3 Write as a power with a negative exponent:

a $\dfrac{3}{3^3}$ **b** $\dfrac{5^2}{5^3}$ **c** $\dfrac{2^3}{2^5}$ **d** $\dfrac{3^2}{3^4}$ **e** $\dfrac{7^4}{7^5}$

4 Simplify:

  a 5^{-1} **b** 4^{-1} **c** 8^{-1} **d** 10^{-1} **e** 3^{-2}

  f 2^{-2} **g** 11^{-2} **h** 7^{-2} **i** 3^{-3} **j** 2^{-7}

5 Simplify:

  a $3^1 - 3^{-1}$ **b** $3^0 + 3^{-1}$ **c** $7^0 - 7^{-1}$ **d** $5^0 + 5^1 - 5^{-1}$

6 Write as a fraction:

  a x^{-1} **b** k^{-1} **c** t^{-3} **d** r^{-5}

7 Simplify, giving answers in simplest rational form:

  a $\left(\frac{1}{3}\right)^{-1}$ **b** $\left(\frac{1}{5}\right)^{-1}$ **c** $\left(\frac{3}{7}\right)^{-1}$ **d** $\left(\frac{5}{2}\right)^{-1}$

  e $\left(\frac{1}{10}\right)^{-1}$ **f** $\left(\frac{5}{6}\right)^{-2}$ **g** $\left(2\frac{1}{4}\right)^{-2}$ **h** $\left(\frac{2}{3}\right)^{-3}$

Example 11   ◀) **Self Tutor**

Write without brackets or negative exponents:

  a $8ab^{-1}$ **b** $8(ab)^{-1}$

  a $8ab^{-1} = \frac{8a}{1} \times \frac{1}{b}$ **b** $8(ab)^{-1} = 8 \times \frac{1}{ab}$

            $= \frac{8a}{b}$ $= \frac{8}{ab}$

---

8 Write without brackets or negative exponents:

  a $2x^{-1}$ **b** $(2x)^{-1}$ **c** $(3q)^{-1}$ **d** $3q^{-1}$

  e $7a^{-2}$ **f** $\left(\frac{1}{t}\right)^{-2}$ **g** $(5z)^{-2}$ **h** $(5z^{-2})^{-1}$

  i st^{-1} **j** $(st)^{-1}$ **k** gh^{-3} **l** $(gh)^{-3}$

  m $4cd^{-2}$ **n** $(4cd)^{-2}$ **o** $\frac{(cd)^3}{2^{-2}}$ **p** $(7m^{-3})^{-1}$

9 Write using powers of 2, 3, and 5 only:

  a 16 **b** $\frac{1}{16}$ **c** 25 **d** $\frac{1}{25}$

  e 81 **f** $\frac{1}{81}$ **g** $\frac{1}{1024}$ **h** $\frac{1}{2^a}$

  i $\frac{9}{25}$ **j** $\frac{32}{81}$ **k** $2\frac{2}{5}$ **l** $9\frac{3}{8}$

Discussion

- Can we *always* cancel the common factor of x in $\frac{2x}{x}$?

- Discuss how to simplify $\frac{x}{x}$ using the exponent laws. By considering the case where $x = 0$, explain why 0^0 is undefined.

E | STANDARD FORM   [E1.9]

There are many situations where we need to describe very large and very small numbers. For example:

- There are about $75\,000\,000\,000\,000$ cells in the human body.

- A glass of tap water contains about $0.000\,04$ grams of chlorine.

Numbers with so many digits can be hard to comprehend and operate with. We can use **standard form** or **scientific notation** to write these numbers in a way that is easier to understand.

> **Standard form** involves writing a given number as *a number between* 1 *and* 10, multiplied by an *integer power of* 10. It has the form
>
> $$a \times 10^n \quad \text{where} \quad 1 \leqslant a < 10 \quad \text{and } n \text{ is an integer.}$$

Consider the pattern alongside.

Notice that each time we divide by 10, the exponent or index of 10 decreases by one.

$$\div 10 \begin{cases} 10\,000 = 10^4 \\ 1000 = 10^3 \\ 100 = 10^2 \\ 10 = 10^1 \\ 1 = 10^0 \\ \frac{1}{10} = 10^{-1} \\ \frac{1}{100} = 10^{-2} \\ \frac{1}{1000} = 10^{-3} \end{cases}$$

So, when a number is written in standard form:

- If the original number is greater than or equal to 10, then n is **positive**.

- If the original number is less than 1, then n is **negative**.

- If the original number is between 1 and 10, we write the number as it is and multiply it by 10^0, which is 1.

To write a number larger than 10, we start with a number between 1 and 10, then multiply it by a positive power of 10.

> To multiply a number by 10^n, $n > 0$, shift the decimal point n places to the **right**.

For example:
$$27 = 2.7 \times 10$$
$$580 = 5.8 \times 100 = 5.8 \times 10^2$$
$$3040 = 3.04 \times 1000 = 3.04 \times 10^3$$

To write a number smaller than 1, we start with a number between 1 and 10, then *divide* it by a power of 10.

> To multiply a number by 10^{-n}, $n > 0$, shift the decimal point n places to the **left**.

For example:
$$0.75 \qquad\qquad 0.0006$$
$$= 7.5 \div 10 \qquad = 6 \div 10\,000$$
$$= 7.5 \times \frac{1}{10^1} \qquad = 6 \times \frac{1}{10^4}$$
$$= 7.5 \times 10^{-1} \qquad = 6 \times 10^{-4}$$

EXERCISE 1E.1

1 Write as powers of 10:

a 100	**b** 1000	**c** 10	**d** 100 000
e 0.1	**f** 0.01	**g** 0.0001	**h** 100 000 000

2 The following values are all equal to $53\,000$. Which of them is written in standard form?

    A 53×10^3 **B** 0.53×10^5 **C** 5.3×10^4 **D** $53\,000 \times 10^0$

3 Copy and complete to write the following numbers in standard form:

    a $376 = 3.76 \times 10^{\cdots\cdots}$ **b** $8000 = \ldots\ldots \times 10^3$ **c** $0.04 = \ldots\ldots \times 10^{-2}$

    d $0.005\,07 = 5.07 \times 10^{\cdots\cdots}$ **e** $9\,040\,000 = \ldots\ldots \times 10^6$ **f** $0.000\,000\,23 = 2.3 \times 10^{\cdots\cdots}$

Example 12   ◀️ *Self Tutor*

Express in standard form:

    a $4\,500\,000$ **b** $0.000\,592$

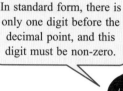

> In standard form, there is only one digit before the decimal point, and this digit must be non-zero.

    a $4\,500\,000 = 4.5 \times 10^6$ **b** $0.000\,592$

                                                                      $= 5.92 \div 10^4$

                                                                      $= 5.92 \times \dfrac{1}{10^4}$

                                                                      $= 5.92 \times 10^{-4}$

---

4 Express in standard form:

    a 425 **b** $425\,000$ **c** 4.25 **d** 0.425

    e 20.1 **f** $20\,100$ **g** $0.002\,01$ **h** $2\,010\,000$

    i 3870 **j** 0.0387 **k** $38\,700\,000$ **l** $0.000\,387$

5 Express in standard form:

    a The circumference of the Earth is approximately $40\,075$ kilometres.

    b Bacteria are single cell organisms, some of which have a diameter of 0.0004 mm.

    c There are typically 40 million bacteria in a gram of soil.

    d The probability that your six numbers will be selected for Lotto on Saturday night is $0.000\,000\,141\,62$.

    e Superfine sheep have wool fibres as low as 0.01 mm in diameter.

    f The central temperature of the Sun is 15 million degrees Celsius.

Example 13   ◀️ *Self Tutor*

Write as an ordinary decimal number:

    a 3.2×10^2 **b** 5.76×10^{-5}

    a 3.2×10^2 **b** 5.76×10^{-5}

           $= 3.20 \times 100$ $= 000005.76 \div 10^5$

           $= 320$ $= 0.000\,057\,6$

---

6 Write as an ordinary decimal number:

    a 5×10^4 **b** 3×10^3 **c** 1.8×10^7 **d** 8.1×10^2

    e 6.5×10^5 **f** 1.1×10^1 **g** 2.75×10^8 **h** 8×10^6

7 Write as an ordinary decimal number:

  a 3×10^{-2} **b** 9×10^{-5} **c** 7×10^{-3} **d** 4.1×10^{-4}

  e 8.2×10^{-6} **f** 7.61×10^{-1} **g** 3.25×10^{-7} **h** 2×10^{-8}

8 Express as ordinary decimal numbers:

  a The wavelength of blue light is about 4.75×10^{-7} m.

  b The estimated world population for 2017 was 7.53×10^{9} people.

  c Physicists in Japan created a model bull which is only 1.2×10^{-5} m long.

  d The length of the Earth's equator is approximately 4.01×10^{4} km.

  e A mosquito weighs about 1.5×10^{-6} kg.

9 Write in standard form:

  a 18.17×10^{6} **b** 0.934×10^{11} **c** 0.041×10^{-2}

10 Answer the **Opening Problem** on page **13**.

11 Which number is larger:

  a 2.2×10^{8} or 5.8×10^{6} **b** 7.71×10^{-7} or 3.5×10^{-5}

  c 4.9×10^{-3} or 4.9×10^{3} **d** 6.2×10^{8} or 6.41×10^{8}

  e 1.006×10^{-6} or 1.01×10^{-6} **f** 9×10^{-8} or 0?

Example 14   ◀ *Self Tutor*

Simplify the following, giving your answer in standard form:

  a $(5 \times 10^{4}) \times (4 \times 10^{5})$ **b** $(8 \times 10^{5}) \div (2 \times 10^{3})$ **c** $8.7 \times 10^{8} - 3 \times 10^{7}$

  a $\quad (5 \times 10^{4}) \times (4 \times 10^{5})$

  $\quad = 5 \times 4 \times 10^{4} \times 10^{5}$

  $\quad = 20 \times 10^{4+5}$

  $\quad = 2 \times 10^{1} \times 10^{9}$

  $\quad = 2 \times 10^{10}$

  b $\quad (8 \times 10^{5}) \div (2 \times 10^{3})$

  $\quad = \dfrac{8 \times 10^{5}}{2 \times 10^{3}}$

  $\quad = \dfrac{8}{2} \times 10^{5-3}$

  $\quad = 4 \times 10^{2}$

  c $\quad 8.7 \times 10^{8} - 3 \times 10^{7}$

  $\quad = 8.7 \times 10^{8} - 0.3 \times 10^{8}$

  $\quad = 8.4 \times 10^{8}$

---

12 Simplify the following, giving your answer in standard form:

  a $(2 \times 10^{5}) \times (3 \times 10^{2})$ **b** $(4 \times 10^{3}) \times (6 \times 10^{3})$ **c** $(8 \times 10^{5}) \times (5 \times 10^{6})$

  d $(9 \times 10^{9})^{2}$ **e** $(3 \times 10^{4}) \times (3 \times 10^{-9})$ **f** $(7 \times 10^{-3})^{2}$

  g $(8 \times 10^{2}) \div (2 \times 10^{3})$ **h** $(6 \times 10^{7}) \div (3 \times 10^{-4})$ **i** $(2 \times 10^{9}) \div (8 \times 10^{5})$

13 Simplify the following, giving your answer in standard form:

  a $3 \times 10^{8} + 6 \times 10^{8}$ **b** $6.4 \times 10^{5} - 5.9 \times 10^{5}$

  c $2 \times 10^{5} + 7 \times 10^{4}$ **d** $3.6 \times 10^{-4} + 1.7 \times 10^{-5}$

  e $5.81 \times 10^{4} - 1.4 \times 10^{3}$ **f** $7 \times 10^{6} + 2.3 \times 10^{8}$

  g $3.54 \times 10^{-7} + 8.5 \times 10^{-9}$ **h** $1.05 \times 10^{-5} - 8.2 \times 10^{-6}$

> To add or subtract numbers in standard form, express the numbers with the same power of 10.

14 The table alongside shows the production of cereals for some European regions in 2015.

Region	Cereal production (tonnes)
Finland	3.7×10^6
France	7.2×10^7
Lithuania	6.1×10^6
Luxembourg	1.8×10^5
Poland	2.8×10^7
Switzerland	8.9×10^5
United Kingdom	2.5×10^7

    a Which of the regions listed produced the most cereals?

    b Find, in standard form, the cereal production of the United Kingdom in kilograms.

    c Find, in standard form, the combined cereal production of Poland and Lithuania.

    d How much more cereal did Finland produce than Switzerland?

    e How many *times* more cereal did France produce than Luxembourg?

STANDARD FORM ON A CALCULATOR

Calculators use standard form to display very large and very small numbers. However, if we wish, we can tell the calculator to give all its answers in standard form.

GRAPHICS
CALCULATOR
INSTRUCTIONS

EXERCISE 1E.2

1 Calculate the following, giving each answer in standard form. The decimal part should be written correct to 2 decimal places.

    a $0.0003 \times 0.01 \div 5000$ **b** $375 \times 220 \times 290\,000$ **c** $8\,760\,000 \times 25\,000$

    d $800 \times 740 \times 67\,800$ **e** $0.002\,12 \div 3\,400\,000$ **f** $0.019 \times 0.000\,27 \times 0.02$

2 Find in standard form, with the decimal part correct to 2 decimal places:

    a $(2.81 \times 10^5) \times (3.4 \times 10^4)$ **b** $(9.81 \times 10^{-4})^2$ **c** $\dfrac{3.43 \times 10^{-6}}{7 \times 10^7}$

    d $(8.66 \times 10^{-3}) \times (7.5 \times 10^{-5})$ **e** $\dfrac{1}{2.5 \times 10^6}$ **f** $(7.59 \times 10^4)^3$

3 For the following, give answers in standard form correct to 3 significant figures:

    a How many millimetres are there in 479.8 kilometres?

    b How many seconds are there in one year?

    c How many seconds are there in a millennium?

    d How many kilograms are there in 0.5 milligrams?

4 If a rocket travels at 3600 km/h, how far will it travel in:

    a 1 day   **b** 1 week   **c** 2 years?

Give your answers in standard form with decimal part correct to 2 decimal places. Assume that 1 year = 365 days.

5 Light travels at a speed of 3×10^8 metres per second. How far will light travel in:

    a 1 minute   **b** 1 day   **c** 1 year?

Give your answers in standard form with decimal part correct to 2 decimal places. Assume that 1 year = 365 days.

Review set 1A

1 Simplify using the exponent laws:

  a $k^3 \times k^6$ **b** $(b^4)^3$ **c** $\dfrac{p^{13}}{p^5}$

2 Express as a power of 5:

  a $5^4 \times 5^3$ **b** $(5^3)^2$ **c** 1

3 Simplify using the exponent laws:

  a $\dfrac{6b^4}{2b^2}$ **b** $3m^2 \times (-m)$ **c** $2x^2y \times 3xy^2$

4 Express in simplest form, without brackets:

  a $(5x)^2$ **b** $(3mn)^3$ **c** $\left(\dfrac{p}{2q}\right)^4$

5 Simplify:

  a 8^0 **b** 13×13^0 **c** $7 - 5^0$

6 Simplify:

  a 9^{-1} **b** 6^{-2} **c** 10^{-3}

7 Simplify, using the exponent laws:

  a $5^{-2} \times 5$ **b** $b^7 \div b^{-2}$ **c** $(x^4)^{-2}$

8 Express in simplest form, without brackets or negative exponents:

  a $(5c)^{-1}$ **b** $7k^{-2}$ **c** $(4d^2)^{-3}$

9 Write in standard form:

  a 9 **b** $34\,900$ **c** 0.0075

10 Write as an ordinary decimal number:

  a 2.81×10^6 **b** 2.81×10^0 **c** 2.81×10^{-3}

11 Simplify, giving your answer in standard form:

  a $(6 \times 10^3) \times (7.1 \times 10^4)$ **b** $(2.4 \times 10^6) \div (4 \times 10^2)$

  c $1.5 \times 10^5 + 2.8 \times 10^6$ **d** $7.1 \times 10^{-2} - 9.5 \times 10^{-3}$

12 The Earth orbits around the Sun at a speed of approximately 1.07×10^5 km/h. How far does the Earth move, relative to the Sun, in:

  a 1 day   **b** 1 week   **c** 1 year?

Give your answers in standard form with decimal part correct to 2 decimal places. Assume that 1 year = 365 days.

Review set 1B

1 Simplify using the exponent laws:

  a $x^3 \times x^3$ **b** $\dfrac{c^{12}}{c^7}$ **c** $(d^{11})^3$

2 Simplify, using the exponent laws:

    a $3^2 \times 3^6$ **b** $2^5 \div 2^5$ **c** $(y^3)^{-1}$

3 Copy and complete, replacing each $\square$ and $\triangle$ with a number or operation:

    a $3^5 \,\square\, 3^2 = 3^3$ **b** $(x^3)^{\square} = x^6$ **c** $(4a)^{\square} \times a^3 = 64a^{\triangle}$

4 Express in simplest form, without brackets:

    a $(-2x)^3$ **b** $(3m^2)^2$ **c** $\left(\dfrac{m}{4n}\right)^3$

5 Simplify:

    a $21^0 - 3$ **b** y^0 **c** $\left(\dfrac{3}{5}\right)^3$

6 Remove the brackets and simplify:

    a $\left(\dfrac{c}{d}\right)^2$ **b** $\left(\dfrac{q}{4}\right)^3$ **c** $\left(\dfrac{ab}{8}\right)^2$

7 Simplify, giving answers in simplest rational form:

    a $\left(\dfrac{4}{5}\right)^{-1}$ **b** $\left(\dfrac{2}{7}\right)^{-2}$ **c** $\left(3\tfrac{1}{3}\right)^{-2}$

8 Write without brackets or negative exponents:

    a $a^{-2}b$ **b** $(5a^{-2})^2$ **c** $(5p^{-3})^{-1}$

9 Write in standard form:

    a 263.57 **b** $0.000\,511$ **c** $863\,400\,000$

10 Write as an ordinary decimal number:

    a 2.78×10^0 **b** 3.99×10^7 **c** 2.081×10^{-3}

11 Simplify, giving your answer in standard form:

    a $(8 \times 10^3)^2$ **b** $(3.6 \times 10^5) \div (6 \times 10^{-2})$

    c $6.8 \times 10^4 + 7.03 \times 10^4$ **d** $5.8 \times 10^{-3} - 8 \times 10^{-5}$

12 How many kilometres are there in 0.21 millimetres? Give your answer in standard form.

Algebra: Expansion

2

Contents:

A	The distributive law	[E2.7]
B	The product $(a + b)(c + d)$	[E2.7]
C	Difference between two squares	[E2.7]
D	Perfect squares expansion	[E2.7]
E	Further expansion	[E2.7]

Opening problem

Each month, Jasmin earns $10 from her father for washing the family car, and $18 from her grandfather for mowing his lawns.

Things to think about:

a Can you explain why the total amount Jasmin earns each year is:

    i $(12 \times 10 + 12 \times 18)$ dollars   **ii** $12(10 + 18)$ dollars?

b Can you explain *why* $12(10 + 18) = 12 \times 10 + 12 \times 18$?

c Now suppose Jasmin earns $$x$ each month for washing the family car.

    Can you explain why $12(x + 18) = 12x + 216$?

d What mathematical rules can we use to remove brackets from expressions?

We use algebra to solve problems with unknown variables, to generalise situations with formulae, and to develop more complicated mathematical theories.

In this Chapter we consider mathematical expressions which include brackets, and what rules we can use to **expand** the brackets.

A   THE DISTRIBUTIVE LAW   [E2.7]

In the **Opening Problem**, suppose Jasmin earns $x each month for washing the family car, and \$18 per month for mowing her grandfather's lawns.

- Each month she earns $(x + 18)$ dollars, so in the whole year she earns $12(x + 18)$ dollars.
- Over a year, she earns $(12 \times x)$ dollars for washing the car, and (12×18) dollars for mowing the lawns.

We can hence conclude that $12(x + 18) = 12 \times x + 12 \times 18$.

In the expression $12(x + 18)$, we say that 12 is the **coefficient** of the expression in brackets.

To produce the expression on the right hand side, we multiply the coefficient by each term within the brackets.

This process is called the **distributive law**:

$$a(b + c) = ab + ac$$

We can explain why the distributive law works using geometry:

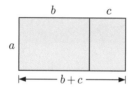

The overall area is $a(b + c)$.

However, this could also be found by adding the areas of the two small rectangles: $ab + ac$.

So, $a(b + c) = ab + ac$. {equating areas}

Example 1   ◀) *Self Tutor*

Expand the following:

a $3(4x + 1)$ **b** $2x(5 - 2x)$ **c** $-2x(x - 3)$

a $3(4x + 1)$
$= 3 \times 4x + 3 \times 1$
$= 12x + 3$

b $2x(5 - 2x)$
$= 2x(5 + -2x)$
$= 2x \times 5 + 2x \times -2x$
$= 10x - 4x^2$

c $-2x(x - 3)$
$= -2x(x + -3)$
$= -2x \times x + -2x \times -3$
$= -2x^2 + 6x$

> Multiply the coefficient by each term within the brackets.

With practice, you should not need to write all of these steps.

Having expanded the brackets in an expression, we can often simplify it by collecting like terms.

Example 2

◀)) **Self Tutor**

Expand and simplify:

a $2(3x - 1) + 3(5 - x)$

b $x(2x - 1) - 2x(5 - x)$

Notice in **b** that the minus sign in front of $2x$ affects *both* terms inside the following bracket.

a $\quad 2(3x - 1) + 3(5 - x)$
$\quad = 6x - 2 + 15 - 3x$
$\quad = 3x + 13$

b $\quad x(2x - 1) - 2x(5 - x)$
$\quad = 2x^2 - x - 10x + 2x^2$
$\quad = 4x^2 - 11x$

EXERCISE 2A

1 Expand and simplify:

a $3(x + 1)$	**b** $2(5 - x)$	**c** $5(x + 2)$	**d** $4(3 - x)$
e $4(a + 2b)$	**f** $3(2x + y)$	**g** $5(x - y)$	**h** $6(-x^2 + y^2)$
i $-2(x + 4)$	**j** $-3(2x - 1)$	**k** $x(x + 3)$	**l** $2x(x - 5)$
m $-3(x + 2)$	**n** $-4(x - 3)$	**o** $-(7 - 2x)$	**p** $-2(x - y)$
q $a(a + b)$	**r** $-a(a - b)$	**s** $x(2x - 1)$	**t** $-x(2 - x)$

2 Expand and simplify:

a $3(x - y + 1)$ **b** $-(x^2 + x - 4)$ **c** $2(a - 3b - ab)$

d $3x(2x + y - 1)$ **e** $2x(x^2 - x - 2)$ **f** $-3x(x + 1 - x^2)$

3 Expand and simplify:

a $1 + 2(x + 2)$ **b** $13 - 4(x + 3)$ **c** $3(x - 2) + 5$

d $4(3 - x) - 10$ **e** $x(x - 1) + x$ **f** $2x(3 - x) + x^2$

g $2a(b - a) + 3a^2$ **h** $4x - 3x(x - 1)$ **i** $7x^2 - 5x(x + 2)$

4 Expand and simplify:

a $3(x - 4) + 2(5 + x)$ **b** $2a + (a - 2b)$ **c** $2a - (a - 2b)$

d $3(y + 1) + 6(2 \quad y)$ **e** $2(y - 3) - 4(2y + 1)$ **f** $3x - 4(2 - 3x)$

g $2(b - a) + 3(a + b)$ **h** $x(x + 4) + 2(x - 3)$ **i** $x(x + 4) - 2(x - 3)$

j $x^2 + x(x - 1)$ **k** $-x^2 - x(x - 2)$ **l** $x(x + y) - y(x + y)$

m $-4(x - 2) - (3 - x)$ **n** $5(2x - 1) - (2x + 3)$ **o** $4x(x - 3) - 2x(5 - x)$

B   THE PRODUCT $(a + b)(c + d)$ [E2.7]

The product $(a + b)(c + d)$ has two **factors**, $(a + b)$ and $(c + d)$.

We can evaluate this product by using the distributive law several times.

$(a + b)(c + d) = a(c + d) + b(c + d)$
$\qquad\qquad\quad = ac + ad + bc + bd$

So, $(a + b)(c + d) = ac + ad + bc + bd$

The final result contains four terms:

This is sometimes called the **FOIL** rule.

ac is the product of the   **First**   terms of each bracket.
ad is the product of the   **Outer**   terms of each bracket.
bc is the product of the   **Inner**   terms of each bracket.
bd is the product of the   **Last**   terms of each bracket.

Example 3   ◀ﻩ **Self Tutor**

Expand and simplify:

  a $(x + 3)(x + 2)$ **b** $(2x + 1)(3x - 2)$

a $(x + 3)(x + 2)$

    $= x \times x + x \times 2 + 3 \times x + 3 \times 2$
    $= x^2 + 2x + 3x + 6$
    $= x^2 + 5x + 6$

b $(2x + 1)(3x - 2)$

    $= 2x \times 3x + 2x \times -2 + 1 \times 3x + 1 \times -2$
    $= 6x^2 - 4x + 3x - 2$
    $= 6x^2 - x - 2$

With practice you should not need the second line of working.

EXERCISE 2B

1   Consider the figure alongside.
    Write an expression for the area of:

    a   rectangle 1   **b**   rectangle 2
    c   rectangle 3   **d**   rectangle 4
    e   the overall rectangle.

    What can you conclude?

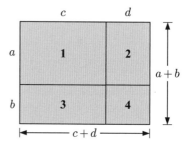

2   Expand and simplify:

    a $(x + 3)(x + 7)$ **b** $(x + 5)(x - 4)$ **c** $(x - 3)(x + 6)$
    d $(x + 2)(x - 2)$ **e** $(x - 8)(x + 3)$ **f** $(2x + 1)(3x + 4)$
    g $(1 - 2x)(4x + 1)$ **h** $(4 - x)(2x + 3)$ **i** $(3x - 2)(1 + 2x)$
    j $(5 - 3x)(5 + x)$ **k** $(7 - x)(4x - 1)$ **l** $(1 - 3x)(2x + 3)$

Example 4

$\blacktriangleleft$ Self Tutor

Expand and simplify:

  a $(x+3)(x-3)$ **b** $(3x-5)(3x+5)$

What do you notice about the two middle terms?

  a $(x+3)(x-3)$
     $= x^2 - 3x + 3x - 9$
     $= x^2 - 9$

  b $(3x-5)(3x+5)$
     $= 9x^2 + 15x - 15x - 25$
     $= 9x^2 - 25$

3   Expand and simplify:

  a $(x+2)(x-2)$ **b** $(a-5)(a+5)$ **c** $(4+x)(4-x)$

  d $(2x+1)(2x-1)$ **e** $(5a+3)(5a-3)$ **f** $(4+3a)(4-3a)$

Example 5

$\blacktriangleleft$ Self Tutor

Expand and simplify:

  a $(3x+1)^2$ **b** $(2x-3)^2$

  a $(3x+1)^2$
     $= (3x+1)(3x+1)$
     $= 9x^2 + 3x + 3x + 1$
     $= 9x^2 + 6x + 1$

  b $(2x-3)^2$
     $= (2x-3)(2x-3)$
     $= 4x^2 - 6x - 6x + 9$
     $= 4x^2 - 12x + 9$

4   Expand and simplify:

  a $(x+3)^2$ **b** $(x-2)^2$ **c** $(3x-2)^2$

  d $(1-3x)^2$ **e** $(3-4x)^2$ **f** $(5x-y)^2$

Example 6

$\blacktriangleleft$ Self Tutor

Expand and simplify: $(x+2)(x-3) + 5(x+4)$

    $(x+2)(x-3) + 5(x+4)$
  $= x^2 - 3x + 2x - 6 + 5x + 20$
  $= x^2 + 4x + 14$

5   Expand and simplify:

  a $(x+5)(x+1) + 2(x-2)$ **b** $4(x+2) + (x-3)(x+6)$

  c $(2a+5)(a-6) + a(a+7)$ **d** $(3x+5)(2x-3) - x(x+3)$

  e $(2x+3)(x+2) + (x+6)(x-5)$ **f** $(y+7)(y-4) - (y+1)(y+3)$

  g $(k+2)(k-5) - (2k+1)(k-3)$ **h** $(x+2)(x-2) + (x+6)(x-6)$

C DIFFERENCE BETWEEN TWO SQUARES [E2.7]

Consider the product $(a+b)(a-b)$.

Using the FOIL rule to expand this product,

$$(a+b)(a-b)$$
$$= a^2 - ab + ab - b^2$$
$$= a^2 - b^2$$

The middle two terms add to zero.

Thus,
$$(a+b)(a-b) = a^2 - b^2$$

This is called the **difference between two squares** expansion, because the expression on the right hand side is the difference between the two squares a^2 and b^2.

GEOMETRIC DEMONSTRATION

In the figure alongside,
shaded area = area of large square − area of small square
$$= a^2 - b^2$$

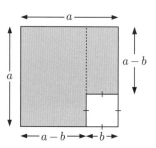

If the rectangle on the right hand side is rotated and placed on top of the remaining shaded area, we form a new rectangle.

$\therefore$ shaded area $= (a+b)(a-b)$

$\therefore$ $(a+b)(a-b) = a^2 - b^2$ {equating areas}

DEMO

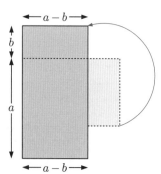

Example 7   ◀) Self Tutor

Expand and simplify:

 a $(x+5)(x-5)$ **b** $(3-y)(3+y)$

a $(x+5)(x-5)$	**b** $(3-y)(3+y)$
$= x^2 - 5^2$	$= 3^2 - y^2$
$= x^2 - 25$	$= 9 - y^2$

Example 8

◆)) *Self Tutor*

Expand and simplify:

  a $(2x - 3)(2x + 3)$ **b** $(5 - 3y)(5 + 3y)$ **c** $(3x + 4y)(3x - 4y)$

a $(2x - 3)(2x + 3)$	**b** $(5 - 3y)(5 + 3y)$	**c** $(3x + 4y)(3x - 4y)$
$= (2x)^2 - 3^2$	$= 5^2 - (3y)^2$	$= (3x)^2 - (4y)^2$
$= 4x^2 - 9$	$= 25 - 9y^2$	$= 9x^2 - 16y^2$

EXERCISE 2C

1 Expand and simplify using the rule $(a + b)(a - b) = a^2 - b^2$:

  a $(x + 2)(x - 2)$ **b** $(x - 2)(x + 2)$ **c** $(2 + x)(2 - x)$

  d $(2 - x)(2 + x)$ **e** $(x + 1)(x - 1)$ **f** $(1 - x)(1 + x)$

  g $(x + 7)(x - 7)$ **h** $(c + 8)(c - 8)$ **i** $(d - 5)(d + 5)$

  j $(x + y)(x - y)$ **k** $(4 + d)(4 - d)$ **l** $(5 + e)(5 - e)$

2 Expand and simplify:

  a $(2x - 1)(2x + 1)$ **b** $(3x + 2)(3x - 2)$ **c** $(4y - 5)(4y + 5)$

  d $(2y + 5)(2y - 5)$ **e** $(3x + 1)(3x - 1)$ **f** $(1 - 3x)(1 + 3x)$

  g $(2 - 5y)(2 + 5y)$ **h** $(3 + 4a)(3 - 4a)$ **i** $(4 + 3a)(4 - 3a)$

  j $(2a + b)(2a - b)$ **k** $(a - 2b)(a + 2b)$ **l** $(4x + y)(4x - y)$

  m $(4x + 5y)(4x - 5y)$ **n** $(2x + 3y)(2x - 3y)$ **o** $(7x - 2y)(7x + 2y)$

3   **a** Use the difference between two squares expansion to show that:

      i $43 \times 37 = 40^2 - 3^2$ **ii** $24 \times 26 = 25^2 - 1^2$

  b Evaluate without using a calculator:

      i 18×22 **ii** 49×51 **iii** 103×97.

Discovery   *The product of three consecutive integers*

Con was trying to multiply $19 \times 20 \times 21$ without a calculator. Aimee told him to "cube the middle integer and then subtract the middle integer" to get the answer.

What to do:

1 Find $19 \times 20 \times 21$ using a calculator.

2 Find $20^3 - 20$ using a calculator. Does Aimee's rule work?

3 Check that Aimee's rule also works for:

  a $4 \times 5 \times 6$ **b** $9 \times 10 \times 11$ **c** $49 \times 50 \times 51$

4 Let the middle of three consecutive integers be x. The other integers must be $(x - 1)$ and $(x + 1)$. Use the difference between two squares expansion to help prove Aimee's rule.

D | PERFECT SQUARES EXPANSION   [E2.7]

$(a+b)^2$ and $(a-b)^2$ are called **perfect squares**.

Notice that
$$(a+b)^2 = (a+b)(a+b)$$
$$= a^2 + ab + ab + b^2 \qquad \text{\{using "FOIL"\}}$$
$$= a^2 + 2ab + b^2$$

The middle two terms are identical.

Thus, we can state the perfect square expansion rule:

$$(a+b)^2 = a^2 + 2ab + b^2$$

We can remember this rule as follows:

> *Step 1*: Square the *first term*.
> *Step 2*: Add twice the product of the *first* and *last terms*.
> *Step 3*: Add on the square of the *last term*.

Notice that
$$(a-b)^2 = (a+(-b))^2$$
$$= a^2 + 2a(-b) + (-b)^2$$
$$= a^2 - 2ab + b^2$$

Once again, we have the square of the first term, twice the product of the first and last terms, and the square of the last term.

Example 9   ◀)) Self Tutor

Expand and simplify:

  a $(x+3)^2$ **b** $(x-5)^2$

  a $(x+3)^2$
      $= x^2 + 2 \times x \times 3 + 3^2$
      $= x^2 + 6x + 9$

  b $(x-5)^2$
      $= (x+-5)^2$
      $= x^2 + 2 \times x \times (-5) + (-5)^2$
      $= x^2 - 10x + 25$

EXERCISE 2D

1 Consider the figure alongside.
Write an expression for the area of:

  a square 1   **b** rectangle 2   **c** rectangle 3

  d square 4   **e** the overall square.

What can you conclude?

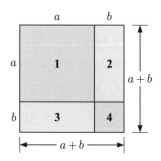

2 Use the rule $(a+b)^2 = a^2 + 2ab + b^2$ to expand and simplify:

  a $(x+5)^2$ **b** $(x+4)^2$ **c** $(x+7)^2$

  d $(a+2)^2$ **e** $(3+c)^2$ **f** $(5+x)^2$

3 Expand and simplify:

   a $(x-3)^2$ **b** $(x-2)^2$ **c** $(y-8)^2$

   d $(a-7)^2$ **e** $(5-x)^2$ **f** $(4-y)^2$

Example 10   ◀) *Self Tutor*

Expand and simplify using the perfect square expansion rule:

   a $(5x+1)^2$ **b** $(4-3x)^2$

   a $(5x+1)^2$
        $= (5x)^2 + 2 \times 5x \times 1 + 1^2$
        $= 25x^2 + 10x + 1$

   b $(4-3x)^2$
        $= (4 + -3x)^2$
        $= 4^2 + 2 \times 4 \times (-3x) + (-3x)^2$
        $= 16 - 24x + 9x^2$

---

4 Expand and simplify:

   a $(3x+4)^2$ **b** $(2a-3)^2$ **c** $(3y+1)^2$

   d $(2x-5)^2$ **e** $(3y-5)^2$ **f** $(7+2a)^2$

   g $(1+5x)^2$ **h** $(7-3y)^2$ **i** $(3+4a)^2$

Example 11   ◀) *Self Tutor*

Expand and simplify:

   a $(2x^2+3)^2$ **b** $5-(x+2)^2$

   a $(2x^2+3)^2$
        $= (2x^2)^2 + 2 \times 2x^2 \times 3 + 3^2$
        $= 4x^4 + 12x^2 + 9$

   b $5-(x+2)^2$
        $= 5 - [x^2 + 4x + 4]$
        $= 5 - x^2 - 4x - 4$
        $= 1 - x^2 - 4x$

> The square brackets in the second line remind us that the minus in front of the brackets affects *all* terms within them.

---

5 Expand and simplify:

   a $(x^2+2)^2$ **b** $(y^2-3)^2$ **c** $(3a^2+4)^2$

   d $(1-2x^2)^2$ **e** $(x^2+y^2)^2$ **f** $(x^2-a^2)^2$

6 Expand and simplify:

   a $3x+1-(x+3)^2$ **b** $5x-2+(x-2)^2$

   c $(x+2)(x-2)+(x+3)^2$ **d** $(x+2)(x-2)-(x+3)^2$

   e $(3-2x)^2-(x-1)(x+2)$ **f** $(1-3x)^2+(x+2)(x-3)$

   g $(2x+3)(2x-3)-(x+1)^2$ **h** $(4x+3)(x-2)-(2-x)^2$

   i $(1-x)^2+(x+2)^2$ **j** $(1-x)^2-(x+2)^2$

Activity

Any even number can be written in the form $2a$ where a is an integer.

Any odd number can be written in the form $2a + 1$ where a is an integer.

What to do:

Suppose p and q are positive integers, and that $p^2 + q^2$ is divisible by 4. Prove that p and q are both even.

Hint: Consider the 4 possible cases, one of which is when p and q are both even.

E | FURTHER EXPANSION   [E2.7]

In this Section we expand more complicated expressions by repeated use of the expansion laws.

Consider the expansion of $(a + b)(c + d + e)$.

Now $(a + b)(c + d + e)$ {Compare with $\Box(c + d + e)$

$= (a + b)c + (a + b)d + (a + b)e$ $= \Box c + \Box d + \Box e$}

$= ac + bc + ad + bd + ae + be$

Notice that there are 6 terms in this expansion. Each term in the first bracket is multiplied by each term in the second bracket.

2 terms in the first bracket $\times$ 3 terms in the second bracket $\longrightarrow$ 6 terms in the expansion.

Example 12   ◀)) Self Tutor

Expand and simplify: $(2x + 3)(x^2 + 4x + 5)$

$(2x + 3)(x^2 + 4x + 5)$

$= 2x^3 + 8x^2 + 10x$ {$2x \times$ all terms in 2nd bracket}

$\quad + 3x^2 + 12x + 15$ {$3 \times$ all terms in 2nd bracket}

$= 2x^3 + 11x^2 + 22x + 15$ {collecting like terms}

Each term in the first bracket is multiplied by each term in the second bracket.

Example 13   ◀)) Self Tutor

Expand and simplify: $(x + 2)^3$

$(x + 2)^3 = (x + 2) \times (x + 2)^2$

$= (x + 2)(x^2 + 4x + 4)$ {perfect square expansion}

$= x^3 + 4x^2 + 4x$ {$x \times$ all terms in 2nd bracket}

$\quad + 2x^2 + 8x + 8$ {$2 \times$ all terms in 2nd bracket}

$= x^3 + 6x^2 + 12x + 8$ {collecting like terms}

EXERCISE 2E

1 Expand and simplify:

 a $(x+2)(x^2+x+4)$
       b $(x+3)(x^2+2x-3)$

 c $(x+3)(x^2+2x+1)$
       d $(x+1)(2x^2-x-5)$

 e $(2x+3)(x^2+2x+1)$
      f $(2x-5)(x^2-2x-3)$

 g $(x+5)(3x^2-x+4)$
       h $(4x-1)(2x^2-3x+1)$

2 Expand and simplify:

 a $(x+1)^3$
   b $(x+3)^3$
   c $(x-4)^3$
   d $(x-3)^3$

 e $(3x+1)^3$
   f $(2x-3)^3$
   g $(x+1)^4$
   h $(1-x)^4$

Example 14
                  🔊 **Self Tutor**

Expand and simplify:

 a $x(x+1)(x+2)$
     b $(x+1)(x-2)(x+2)$

The product of three brackets is not required in the syllabus.

 a $x(x+1)(x+2)$
   $= (x^2+x)(x+2)$ {all terms in first bracket $\times\ x$}
   $= x^3+2x^2+x^2+2x$ {expanding remaining factors}
   $= x^3+3x^2+2x$ {collecting like terms}

 b $(x+1)(x-2)(x+2)$
   $= (x+1)(x^2-4)$ {difference between two squares}
   $= x^3-4x+x^2-4$ {expanding factors}
   $= x^3+x^2-4x-4$

---

3 Expand and simplify:

 a $x(x+2)(x+4)$
   b $x(x-3)(x+2)$
   c $x(x-4)(x-5)$

 d $2x(x+2)(x+5)$
   e $3x(x-2)(3-x)$
   f $-x(2+x)(6-x)$

 g $-3x(3x-1)(x+4)$
  h $x(1-5x)(2x+3)$
  i $(x-2)(x+2)(x-3)$

4 Expand and simplify:

 a $(x+4)(x+3)(x+2)$
      b $(x-3)(x-2)(x+4)$

 c $(x-3)(x-2)(x-5)$
      d $(2x-3)(x+3)(x-1)$

 e $(3x+5)(x+1)(x+2)$
      f $(4x+1)(3x-1)(x+1)$

 g $(2-x)(3x+1)(x-7)$
      h $(x-2)(4-x)(3x+2)$

5 State how many terms you would obtain by expanding the following:

 a $(a+b)(c+d)$
       b $(a+b+c)(d+e)$

 c $(a+b)(c+d+e)$
      d $(a+b+c)(d+e+f)$

 e $(a+b+c+d)(e+f)$
     f $(a+b+c+d)(e+f+g)$

 g $(a+b)(c+d)(e+f)$
     h $(a+b+c)(d+e)(f+g)$

Review set 2A

1 Expand and simplify:

  a $3(2+x)$ **b** $-(4x-2)$ **c** $3x(x+3)$

2 Expand and simplify:

  a $7+4(x-2)$ **b** $3-2(x+4)$ **c** $-4(2x-3)-(x+1)$

3 Expand and simplify:

  a $(x+4)(x+7)$ **b** $(x+8)(x-2)$ **c** $(1-x)(5x+6)$

  d $(2a-3)(a-9)$ **e** $(4x+1)(1-3x)$ **f** $(4x+1)(5x-4)$

4 Expand and simplify:

  a $(x+3)(x+2)+3(x-4)$ **b** $(n-3)(n+5)-(n-2)(n+3)$

5 Expand and simplify:

  a $(x+4)^2$ **b** $(x-10)^2$ **c** $(2x+5)^2$

  d $(3-4x)^2$ **e** $(x+2y)^2$ **f** $(2x-1)^3$

6 Expand and simplify:

  a $(x+9)(x-9)$ **b** $(3x+2)(3x-2)$ **c** $(1-7x)(1+7x)$

7 Expand and simplify:

  a $(x+4)(x^2+x-7)$ **b** $(4x-3)(x^2-x-5)$ **c** $-(x-1)(2-x+x^2)$

Review set 2B

1 Expand and simplify:

  a $-3(x+4)$ **b** $x(y+3)$ **c** $2a(a-5)$

2 Expand and simplify:

  a $4(x-2)+3(2x-1)$ **b** $x(x+1)-4(x-2)$ **c** $-(3-x)+x(x+3)$

3 Expand and simplify:

  a $(x+9)(x-4)$ **b** $(2x-7)(x+6)$ **c** $(2a-3)(a-4)$

  d $(x+3)(x-8)$ **e** $(a+b)(2a-b)$ **f** $(4x+1)(3x-2)$

4 Expand and simplify:

  a $(y+3)^2$ **b** $(3x+2)^2$ **c** $(4a-b)^2$

5 Expand and simplify:

  a $(5-x)(5+x)$ **b** $(3y+4)(3y-4)$ **c** $(4x+1)(1-4x)$

6 Expand and simplify:

  a $-4(x+2)-(x+1)^2$ **b** $5(y-3)+(y+5)(y-5)$

7 Expand and simplify:

  a $(x+4)^2(x-2)$ **b** $(x+2)(x-3)^2$ **c** $(x-5)^3$

  d $(x^2-3x+4)(2-x)$ **e** $-(x-2)^2(1+x)$ **f** $(x-3)^4$

Algebra: Factorisation

3

Contents:

A   Algebraic common factors

B   Factorising with common factors   [E2.8]

C   Difference between two squares factorisation   [E2.8]

D   Perfect squares factorisation   [E2.8]

E   Expressions with four terms   [E2.8]

F   Factorising $x^2 + bx + c$ [E2.8]

G   Factorising $ax^2 + bx + c$, $a \neq 1$ [E2.8]

H   Miscellaneous factorisation   [E2.8]

Opening problem

A square garden plot is surrounded by a path 1 m wide. The sides of the garden plot have length x m, as shown.

The landscaper needs to know the area of the path so that he can order enough pebbles to cover it.

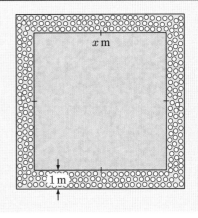

Things to think about:

a   Can you explain why the area of the path can be expressed as:

    i $[(x+2)^2 - x^2]$ m²   **ii** $(4x+4)$ m²?

b   Can you use an expansion law in *reverse* to explain why $(x+2)^2 - x^2 = 2(2x+2)$?

Factorisation is the reverse process of expansion.

expansion

$$3(x+2) \quad = \quad 3x+6$$

factorisation

A ALGEBRAIC COMMON FACTORS

In previous years you should have seen how numbers can be expressed as the product of factors.

A number which is a factor of two or more numbers is called a **common factor** of these numbers.
The **highest common factor** of a set of numbers is the largest factor that is common to all of them.

For example: $30 = 2 \times 3 \times 5$ and $140 = 2 \times 2 \times 5 \times 7$.

∴   2 and 5 are the common factors of 30 and 140.

∴   the highest common factor (HCF) of 30 and 140 is $2 \times 5 = 10$.

The same method can be used to find the HCF of **algebraic products** which contain variables.

Example 1   ◀) *Self Tutor*

Find the highest common factor of:

a $8a$ and $12b$ **b** $4x^2$ and $6xy$

Write each term
as a product of
its **factors**!

a $8a = 2 \times 2 \times 2 \times a$ **b** $4x^2 = 2 \times 2 \times x \times x$

$12b = 2 \times 2 \times 3 \times b$ $6xy = 2 \times 3 \times x \times y$

∴ HCF $= 2 \times 2$ ∴ HCF $= 2 \times x$

$= 4$ $= 2x$

EXERCISE 3A

1 Find the missing factor:

a $3 \times \square = 6a$ **b** $3 \times \square = 15b$ **c** $2 \times \square = 8xy$

d $2x \times \square = 8x^2$ **e** $\square \times 2x = 2x^2$ **f** $\square \times 5x = -10x^2$

g $-a \times \square = ab$ **h** $\square \times a^2 = 4a^3$ **i** $3x \times \square = -9x^2y$

2 Find the highest common factor of the following:

a $2a$ and 6 **b** $5c$ and $8c$ **c** $8r$ and 27

d $12k$ and $7k$ **e** $3a$ and $12a$ **f** $5x$ and $15x$

g $25x$ and $10x$ **h** $24y$ and $32y$ **i** $36b$ and $54d$

3 Find the HCF of the following:

a $23ab$ and $7ab$ **b** abc and $6abc$ **c** $36a$ and $12ab$

d $9r$ and r^3 **e** $3q$ and qr **f** $4r$ and $8r^2$

g $3pq$ and $6pq^2$ **h** $2a^2b$ and $6ab$ **i** $6xy$ and $18x^2y^2$

j $15a$, $20ab$ and $30b$ **k** $12wxz$, $12wz$, $24wxyz$ **l** $24p^2qr$, $36pqr^2$

Example 2   ◀) *Self Tutor*

Find the HCF of $3(x + 3)$ $3(x + 3) = (x + 3) \times 3$
and $(x + 3)(x + 1)$. $(x + 3)(x + 1) = (x + 3) \times (x + 1)$
                                   ∴ HCF $= (x + 3)$

4 Find the HCF of:

    a $5(x+2)$ and $(x+8)(x+2)$

    b $2(x+5)^2$ and $6(x+9)(x+5)$

    c $3x(x+4)$ and $x^2(x+2)$

    d $6(x+1)^2$ and $2(x+1)(x-2)$

    e $2(x+3)^2$ and $4(x+3)(x-7)$

    f $4x(x-3)$ and $6x(x-3)^2$

Activity   ***Algebraic common factor maze***

Instructions:

1 Start at the green starting cell.

2 You may move horizontally or vertically to an adjacent cell if it has a common factor, other than 1, with the cell you are currently on.

3 Find a path to the exit.

PRINTABLE
MAZE

$6m$	$2a$	3	$9c^2$	$3c$	c^2	np	$2p^2$
$4m$	mn	$6n$	$5c$	25	$5m$	n	$4p$
$8y$	xy	n	$6x$	$2x^2$	mn	$6n^2$	4
$7y$	21	$3z$	$5x$	$3y$	z^2	$3p$	p
ab	$5b$	yz	xy	$15x$	yz	p^2	$3b$
$4a$	$9q$	$3q$	q^2	63	$7y$	b^2	b
12	9	10	$10b$	12	$8b$	$9b$	3
$6a$	a^2	$5a$	$3a$	$4x$	xy	$2x$	x^2

start → (row with 12) p → exit

B | *FACTORISING WITH COMMON FACTORS*   *[E2.8]*

> **Factorisation** is the process of writing an expression as a **product** of its **factors**.
>
> **Factorisation** is the reverse process of expansion.

When we expand an expression, we remove its brackets.

When we factorise an expression, we insert brackets.

$3(x+2)$ is the product of two factors, 3 and $(x+2)$.

expansion

$$3(x+2) = 3x + 6$$

factorisation

To factorise an algebraic expression involving a number of terms, we look for the HCF of the terms. We write it in front of a set of brackets, then use the reverse of the distributive law to complete the factorisation.

For example: $5x^2$ and $10xy$ have HCF $= 5x$.

$$\therefore \quad 5x^2 + 10xy = 5x \times x + 5x \times 2y$$
$$= 5x(x + 2y)$$

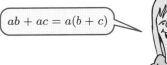

$ab + ac = a(b + c)$

An expression is **fully factorised** if none of its algebraic factors can be factorised further.

For example: $4a + 12 = 2(2a + 6)$ is not fully factorised since $(2a + 6)$ still has the common factor 2.

$\qquad\qquad\quad 4a + 12 = 4(a + 3)$ is fully factorised.

EXERCISE 3B

1 Copy and complete:

   a $2x + 4 = 2(x + ...)$ **b** $3a - 12 = 3(a - ......)$

   c $15 - 5p = 5(...... - p)$ **d** $18x + 12 = 6(...... + 2)$

   e $4x^2 - 8x = 4x(x - ......)$ **f** $2m + 8m^2 = 2m(...... + 4m)$

You can check your factorisations by expanding back out!

2 Copy and complete:

   a $4x + 16 = 4(...... + ...)$ **b** $10 + 5d = 5(...... + ...)$

   c $5c - 5 = 5(...... - ......)$ **d** $cd + de = d(...... + ...)$

   e $6a + 8ab = ...(3 + 4b)$ **f** $6x - 2x^2 = ...(3 - x)$

   g $7ab - 7a = ...(b - 1)$ **h** $4ab - 6bc = ...(2a - 3c)$

Example 3   ◀) Self Tutor

With practice the middle line is not necessary.

Fully factorise:

   a $3a + 6$ **b** $ab - 2bc$

   a $3a + 6$ **b** $ab - 2bc$

      $= 3 \times a + 3 \times 2$ $= a \times b - 2 \times b \times c$

      $= 3(a + 2)$ {HCF $= 3$} $= b(a - 2c)$ {HCF $= b$}

3 Fully factorise:

   a $3a + 3b$ **b** $8x - 16$ **c** $3p + 18$ **d** $28 - 14x$

   e $7x - 14$ **f** $12 + 6x$ **g** $ac + bc$ **h** $12y - 6a$

   i $5a + ab$ **j** $bc - 6cd$ **k** $7x - xy$ **l** $xy + y$

   m $a + ab$ **n** $xy - yz$ **o** $3pq + pr$ **p** $cd - c$

Example 4   ◀) Self Tutor

Fully factorise:

   a $8x^2 + 12x$ **b** $3y^2 - 6xy$

   a $8x^2 + 12x$ **b** $3y^2 - 6xy$

      $= 2 \times 4 \times x \times x + 3 \times 4 \times x$ $= 3 \times y \times y - 2 \times 3 \times x \times y$

      $= 4x(2x + 3)$ {HCF $= 4x$} $= 3y(y - 2x)$ {HCF $= 3y$}

4 Fully factorise:

   a $x^2 + 2x$ **b** $5x - 2x^2$ **c** $4x^2 + 8x$ **d** $14x - 7x^2$

   e $6x^2 + 12x$ **f** $x^3 + 9x^2$ **g** $x^2y + xy^2$ **h** $4x^3 - 6x^2$

   i $9x^3 - 18xy$ **j** $a^3 + a^2 + a$ **k** $2a^2 + 4a + 8$ **l** $3a^3 - 6a^2 + 9a$

Example 5   ◆ッ *Self Tutor*

Fully factorise:

   a $-2a + 6ab$ **b** $-2x^2 - 4x$

   a $-2a + 6ab$
      $= 6ab - 2a$ {Write with $6ab$ first.}
      $= 2 \times 3 \times a \times b - 2 \times a$
      $= 2a(3b - 1)$ {HCF $= 2a$}

   b $-2x^2 - 4x$
      $= -2 \times x \times x + -2 \times 2 \times x$
      $= -2x(x + 2)$ {HCF $= -2x$}

5   Fully factorise:

   a $-9a + 9b$ **b** $-3 + 6b$ **c** $-8a + 4b$

   d $-7c + cd$ **e** $-a + ab$ **f** $-6x^2 + 12x$

   g $-5x + 15x^2$ **h** $-2b^2 + 4ab$ **i** $-a + a^2$

6   Fully factorise:

   a $-6a - 6b$ **b** $-4 - 8x$ **c** $-3y - 6z$

   d $-9c - cd$ **e** $-x - xy$ **f** $-5x^2 - 20x$

   g $-12y - 3y^2$ **h** $-18a^2 - 9ab$ **i** $-16x^2 - 24x$

Example 6   ◆ッ *Self Tutor*

Fully factorise:

   a $2(x + 3) + x(x + 3)$ **b** $x(x + 4) - (x + 4)$

   a $2(x + 3) + x(x + 3)$ {HCF $= (x + 3)$}
      $= (x + 3)(2 + x)$

   b $x(x + 4) - (x + 4)$ {HCF $= (x + 4)$}
      $= x(x + 4) - 1(x + 4)$
      $= (x + 4)(x - 1)$

7   Fully factorise:

   a $2(x - 7) + x(x - 7)$ **b** $a(x + 3) + b(x + 3)$ **c** $4(x + 2) - x(x + 2)$

   d $x(x + 9) + (x + 9)$ **e** $a(b + 4) - (b + 4)$ **f** $a(b + c) + d(b + c)$

   g $a(m + n) - b(m + n)$ **h** $x(x + 3) - x - 3$

Example 7   ◆ッ *Self Tutor*

Fully factorise $(x - 1)(x + 2) + 3(x - 1)$

    $(x - 1)(x + 2) + 3(x - 1)$ {HCF $= (x - 1)$}
  $= (x - 1)[(x + 2) + 3]$
  $= (x - 1)(x + 5)$

We use square brackets in the second line to help distinguish them.

8 Fully factorise:

   a $(x+3)(x-5) + 4(x+3)$
           b $5(x-7) + (x-7)(x+2)$

   c $(x+6)(x+4) - 8(x+6)$
          d $(x-2)^2 - 6(x-2)$

   e $(x+2)^2 - (x+2)(x+1)$
      f $5(a+b) - (a+b)(a+1)$

   g $3(a-2)^2 - 6(a-2)$
          h $(x+4)^2 + 3(x+4)(x-1)$

   i $x(x-1) - 6(x-1)(x-5)$
      j $3(x+5) - 4(x+5)^2$

9 Jake has factorised $12x^2 - 18xy$ as $6(2x^2 - 3xy)$.

   a Explain why Jake has not factorised the expression fully.

   b Fully factorise $12x^2 - 18xy$.

C DIFFERENCE BETWEEN TWO SQUARES FACTORISATION   *[E2.8]*

Discovery   *The difference between two squares*

In the diagram alongside, a square with side length b has been cut from a square with side length a.

WORKSHEET

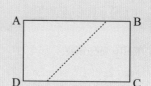

What to do:

1 Explain why the green shaded area is given by $a^2 - b^2$.

2 Copy the above diagram, or print the **worksheet** by clicking on the icon. Cut along the dotted line.

3 Rearrange the two trapezia to form a rectangle as shown.

4 Find, in terms of a and b, the lengths of AB and BC.

5 Hence find the area of the rectangle in the form $(......)(......)$.

6 What can be deduced by comparing the areas in **1** and **5**?

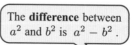

We know the expansion of $(a+b)(a-b)$ is $a^2 - b^2$.

$\therefore$ the factorisation of $a^2 - b^2$ is $(a+b)(a-b)$.

$$a^2 - b^2 = (a+b)(a-b)$$

> The **difference** between a^2 and b^2 is $a^2 - b^2$.

In contrast, the **sum** of two squares does not factorise into real factors.

For example:

- $x^2 - 9$ is the difference between two squares, so $x^2 - 9 = (x+3)(x-3)$.
- $x^2 + 9$ is the sum of two squares, which does not factorise into real factors.

When factorising algebraic expressions, we do not always just use numbers which are *perfect* squares.

For example, even though 7 is not a perfect square, we can still factorise $x^2 - 7$ by writing $7 = (\sqrt{7})^2$.

$$x^2 - 7 = x^2 - (\sqrt{7})^2$$
$$= (x + \sqrt{7})(x - \sqrt{7})$$

Example 8   ◀) *Self Tutor*

Fully factorise:

  a $9 - x^2$
                     b $4x^2 - 25$

  a $9 - x^2$
       $= 3^2 - x^2$
       $= (3 + x)(3 - x)$

  b $4x^2 - 25$
       $= (2x)^2 - 5^2$
       $= (2x + 5)(2x - 5)$

EXERCISE 3C

1 Fully factorise:

  a $x^2 - y^2$ **b** $p^2 - q^2$ **c** $n^2 - m^2$

  d $x^2 - 4$ **e** $4 - x^2$ **f** $x^2 - 81$

  g $25 - x^2$ **h** $64 - a^2$ **i** $4x^2 - 1$

  j $9x^2 - 16$ **k** $4x^2 - 9$ **l** $36 - 49x^2$

  m $x^2 - 4y^2$ **n** $a^2b^2 - 36$ **o** $16x^2 - 9y^2$

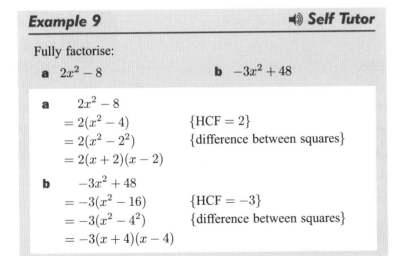

Example 9   ◀) *Self Tutor*

Fully factorise:

  a $2x^2 - 8$
                     b $-3x^2 + 48$

  a $2x^2 - 8$
       $= 2(x^2 - 4)$ {HCF = 2}
       $= 2(x^2 - 2^2)$ {difference between squares}
       $= 2(x + 2)(x - 2)$

  b $-3x^2 + 48$
       $= -3(x^2 - 16)$ {HCF = -3}
       $= -3(x^2 - 4^2)$ {difference between squares}
       $= -3(x + 4)(x - 4)$

Always look to remove a common factor first.

---

2 Fully factorise:

  a $12 - 3x^2$ **b** $2x^2 - 18$ **c** $3x^2 - 27$

  d $-2x^2 + 8$ **e** $3x^2 - 75$ **f** $-5x^2 + 5$

  g $8x^2 - 18$ **h** $-27x^2 + 75$ **i** $3x^2 - 12y^2$

Example 10
◀)) *Self Tutor*

Factorise using the difference between two squares:

a $(3x + 2)^2 - 9$ **b** $(x + 2)^2 - (x - 1)^2$

a $(3x + 2)^2 - 9$
$= (3x + 2)^2 - 3^2$
$= [(3x + 2) + 3][(3x + 2) - 3]$
$= [3x + 5][3x - 1]$

b $(x + 2)^2 - (x - 1)^2$
$= [(x + 2) + (x - 1)][(x + 2) - (x - 1)]$
$= [x + 2 + x - 1][x + 2 - x + 1]$
$= [2x + 1][3]$
$= 3(2x + 1)$

3 Factorise using the difference between two squares:

a $(x + 1)^2 - 4$ **b** $(2x + 1)^2 - 9$ **c** $(1 - x)^2 - 16$

d $(x + 3)^2 - 4x^2$ **e** $4x^2 - (x + 2)^2$ **f** $9x^2 - (3 - x)^2$

g $(2x + 1)^2 - (x - 2)^2$ **h** $(3x - 1)^2 - (x + 1)^2$ **i** $4x^2 - (2x + 3)^2$

4 Answer the **Opening Problem** on page **41**.

Example 11
◀)) *Self Tutor*

Factorise into linear factors: **a** $x^2 - 11$ **b** $(x + 3)^2 - 5$

Linear factors are factors of the form $ax + b$.

a $x^2 - 11$
$= x^2 - (\sqrt{11})^2$
$= (x + \sqrt{11})(x - \sqrt{11})$

b $(x + 3)^2 - 5$
$= (x + 3)^2 - (\sqrt{5})^2$
$= [(x + 3) + \sqrt{5}][(x + 3) - \sqrt{5}]$
$= [x + 3 + \sqrt{5}][x + 3 - \sqrt{5}]$

5 If possible, factorise into linear factors:

a $x^2 - 3$ **b** $x^2 + 4$ **c** $x^2 - 15$ **d** $7 - x^2$

6 If possible, factorise into linear factors:

a $(x + 1)^2 - 6$ **b** $(x + 2)^2 + 6$ **c** $(x - 2)^2 - 7$ **d** $(x + 3)^2 - 17$

e $(x - 4)^2 + 9$ **f** $4x^2 - (1 - x)^2$

7 Write 391 as the difference between two squares. Hence write a factor pair of 391.

D   PERFECT SQUARES FACTORISATION   [E2.8]

We have seen the perfect square expansions

$$(a + b)^2 = a^2 + 2ab + b^2 \qquad \text{and} \qquad (a - b)^2 = a^2 - 2ab + b^2$$

We can reverse this process to factorise perfect squares:

$$a^2 + 2ab + b^2 = (a + b)^2 \qquad \text{and} \qquad a^2 - 2ab + b^2 = (a - b)^2$$

A perfect square must contain two squares a^2 and b^2, and a middle term which is $\pm 2ab$. The sign of the middle term indicates whether the perfect square is $(a+b)^2$ or $(a-b)^2$.

For example, $x^2 + 10x + 25$ is a perfect square because it contains two squares x^2 and 5^2, and a middle term $2 \times x \times 5$.

Example 12   ◀)) *Self Tutor*

Use perfect square rules to fully factorise:

    a $x^2 + 10x + 25$ **b** $x^2 - 14x + 49$

    a $x^2 + 10x + 25$ **b** $x^2 - 14x + 49$

            $= x^2 + 2 \times x \times 5 + 5^2$ $= x^2 - 2 \times x \times 7 + 7^2$

            $= (x+5)^2$ $= (x-7)^2$

EXERCISE 3D

1 Determine whether each expression is a perfect square:

    a $x^2 + 4x + 1$ **b** $9 - 6x + x^2$ **c** $x^2 - 2x - 1$

    d $x^2 - 4x + 4$ **e** $x^2 + 8x - 16$ **f** $x^2 - 5x + 25$

2 Fully factorise:

    a $x^2 + 6x + 9$ **b** $x^2 + 8x + 16$ **c** $x^2 - 6x + 9$

    d $x^2 - 8x + 16$ **e** $x^2 + 2x + 1$ **f** $x^2 - 10x + 25$

    g $y^2 + 18y + 81$ **h** $m^2 - 20m + 100$ **i** $t^2 + 12t + 36$

Example 13   ◀)) *Self Tutor*

Fully factorise:

    a $9x^2 - 6x + 1$ **b** $-8x^2 - 24x - 18$

    a $9x^2 - 6x + 1$ **b** $-8x^2 - 24x - 18$

            $= (3x)^2 - 2 \times 3x \times 1 + 1^2$ $= -2(4x^2 + 12x + 9)$ {HCF $= -2$}

            $= (3x - 1)^2$ $= -2([2x]^2 + 2 \times 2x \times 3 + 3^2)$

                                              $= -2(2x + 3)^2$

3 Fully factorise:

    a $9x^2 + 6x + 1$ **b** $4x^2 - 4x + 1$ **c** $9x^2 + 12x + 4$

    d $25x^2 - 10x + 1$ **e** $16x^2 + 24x + 9$ **f** $25x^2 - 20x + 4$

    g $9x^2 - 42x + 49$ **h** $36x^2 + 60x + 25$ **i** $4x^2 - 28x + 49$

4 Fully factorise:

    a $2x^2 + 4x + 2$ **b** $2x^2 - 12x + 18$ **c** $4x^2 - 32x + 64$

    d $-x^2 + 2x - 1$ **e** $-2x^2 - 8x - 8$ **f** $-3x^2 - 30x - 75$

5 Explain why:

    a $x^2 + 12x + 36$ is never negative   **b** $x^2 + 4 \geqslant 4x$ for all real x.

E   EXPRESSIONS WITH FOUR TERMS   [E2.8]

Some expressions with four terms do not have an overall common factor, but can be factorised by pairing the four terms.

For example, $\underbrace{ab + ac}_{} + \underbrace{bd + cd}_{}$

$= a(b + c) + d(b + c)$ {factorising each pair separately}
$= (b + c)(a + d)$ {removing the common factor $(b + c)$}

Example 14   ◆)) Self Tutor

Sometimes it is necessary to reorder the terms first.

Factorise:

a $x^2 + 2x + 5x + 10$ **b** $3x + x^2 - 3 - x$

a $\underbrace{x^2 + 2x}_{} + \underbrace{5x + 10}_{}$ **b** $3x + x^2 - 3 - x$
$= x(x + 2) + 5(x + 2)$ $= \underbrace{x^2 + 3x}_{} \underbrace{- x - 3}_{}$
$= (x + 2)(x + 5)$ $= x(x + 3) - (x + 3)$
    $= x(x + 3) - 1(x + 3)$
    $= (x + 3)(x - 1)$

EXERCISE 3E

1 Factorise:

a $2a + 2 + ab + b$ **b** $4d + ac + ad + 4c$ **c** $ab + 6 + 2b + 3a$
d $mn + 3p + np + 3m$ **e** $x^2 + 3x + 7x + 21$ **f** $x^2 + 5x + 4x + 20$
g $2x^2 + x + 6x + 3$ **h** $3x^2 + 2x + 12x + 8$ **i** $20x^2 + 12x + 5x + 3$

2 Factorise:

a $x^2 - 4x + 5x - 20$ **b** $x^2 - 7x + 2x - 14$ **c** $x^2 - 3x - 2x + 6$
d $x^2 - 5x - 3x + 15$ **e** $x^2 + 7x - 8x - 56$ **f** $2x^2 + x - 6x - 3$
g $3x^2 + 2x - 12x - 8$ **h** $4x^2 - 3x - 8x + 6$ **i** $9x^2 + 2x - 9x - 2$

F   FACTORISING $x^2 + bx + c$ [E2.8]

A **quadratic trinomial** is an algebraic expression of the form $ax^2 + bx + c$ where x is a variable and a, b, c are constants, $a \neq 0$.

In this Section we learn to factorise quadratic trinomials for which $a = 1$. They have the form $x^2 + bx + c$.

Consider the expansion

$$(x + 2)(x + 5) = x^2 + \quad 5x + 2x \quad + \quad 2 \times 5 \qquad \{\text{using FOIL}\}$$
$$= x^2 + \quad (5 + 2)x \quad + \quad 2 \times 5$$
$$= x^2 + (\textbf{sum of 2 and 5})x + (\textbf{product of 2 and 5})$$
$$= x^2 + 7x + 10$$

So, to factorise $x^2+7x+10$, we need two numbers whose sum is 7 and whose product is 10. The numbers are 2 and 5, so $x^2 + 7x + 10 = (x + 2)(x + 5)$.

$$x^2 + bx + c = (x + p)(x + q)$$
$$\text{where } p + q = b \text{ and } pq = c.$$

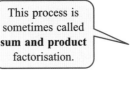 This process is sometimes called **sum and product** factorisation.

Example 15   ◀) *Self Tutor*

Factorise: $x^2 + 11x + 24$

We need to find two numbers which have sum $= 11$ and product $= 24$.

We consider the factor pairs of 24:

Factor pair	1×24	2×12	3×8	4×6
Sum of factors	25	14	11	10

The numbers we want are 3 and 8.

$\therefore$ $x^2 + 11x + 24 = (x + 3)(x + 8)$

 Most of the time we can find the two numbers mentally.

EXERCISE 3F

1 Find two numbers which have:

   a product 12 and sum 7   **b** product 15 and sum 8   **c** product 16 and sum 10

   d product 18 and sum 11   **e** product -21 and sum 4   **f** product -21 and sum -4

   g product -12 and sum -4 **h** product -30 and sum 13.

2 Factorise:

   a $x^2 + 4x + 3$ **b** $x^2 + 14x + 24$ **c** $x^2 + 10x + 21$

   d $x^2 + 15x + 54$ **e** $x^2 + 9x + 20$ **f** $x^2 + 8x + 15$

   g $x^2 + 10x + 24$ **h** $x^2 + 9x + 14$ **i** $x^2 + 6x + 8$

Example 16   ◀) *Self Tutor*

Factorise: $x^2 - 7x + 12$

sum $= -7$ and product $= 12$

$\therefore$ the numbers are -3 and -4

$\therefore$ $x^2 - 7x + 12 = (x - 3)(x - 4)$

 The sum is negative but the product is positive, so both numbers must be negative.

3 Factorise:

   a $x^2 - 3x + 2$ **b** $x^2 - 4x + 3$ **c** $x^2 - 5x + 6$

   d $x^2 - 14x + 33$ **e** $x^2 - 16x + 39$ **f** $x^2 - 19x + 48$

   g $x^2 - 11x + 28$ **h** $x^2 - 14x + 24$ **i** $x^2 - 20x + 36$

Example 17   ◀) *Self Tutor*

Factorise: **a** $x^2 - 2x - 15$ **b** $x^2 + x - 6$

a sum $= -2$ and product $= -15$
   $\therefore$ the numbers are -5 and $+3$
   $\therefore$ $x^2 - 2x - 15 = (x - 5)(x + 3)$

b sum $= 1$ and product $= -6$
   $\therefore$ the numbers are $+3$ and -2
   $\therefore$ $x^2 + x - 6 = (x + 3)(x - 2)$

Since the product is negative, the numbers must be opposite in sign.

4 Factorise:

a $x^2 - 7x - 8$	**b** $x^2 + 4x - 21$	**c** $x^2 - x - 2$	**d** $x^2 - 2x - 8$
e $x^2 + 5x - 24$	**f** $x^2 - 3x - 10$	**g** $x^2 + 3x - 54$	**h** $x^2 + x - 72$
i $x^2 - 4x - 21$	**j** $x^2 - x - 6$	**k** $x^2 - 7x - 60$	**l** $x^2 + 7x - 60$
m $x^2 + 3x - 18$	**n** $x^2 - 7x - 18$	**o** $x^2 - 12x - 45$	

5 Factorise:

a $x^2 + 7x + 6$	**b** $x^2 - 2x - 63$	**c** $x^2 - 11x + 18$	**d** $x^2 + 6x - 16$
e $x^2 - 5x + 4$	**f** $x^2 + 12x + 35$	**g** $x^2 - x - 20$	**h** $x^2 - 9x - 22$
i $x^2 + 8x - 48$	**j** $x^2 - 3x - 28$	**k** $x^2 + 13x$	**l** $x^2 - 14x + 49$

Example 18   ◀) *Self Tutor*

Fully factorise: $-6x + 72 - 3x^2$

$\quad -6x + 72 - 3x^2$
$= -3x^2 - 6x + 72$ {rewrite the terms in order}
$= -3(x^2 + 2x - 24)$ {HCF $= -3$}
$= -3(x + 6)(x - 4)$ {sum $= 2$, product $= -24$
                   $\therefore$ the numbers are 6 and -4}

Always look for common factors.

6 Fully factorise:

a $2x^2 + 10x + 8$	**b** $3x^2 - 21x + 18$	**c** $2x^2 + 14x + 24$
d $-x^2 + 4x - 3$	**e** $-x^2 + 4x - 4$	**f** $-x^2 - 2x + 3$
g $-2x^2 + 44x - 240$	**h** $4x^2 - 8x - 12$	**i** $-3x^2 + 42x - 99$
j $2x^2 - 2x - 180$	**k** $3x^2 - 6x - 24$	**l** $-2x^2 - 18x - 40$
m $x^3 - 7x^2 - 8x$	**n** $-4x^2 + 24x - 36$	**o** $7x^2 + 21x - 70$
p $-5x^2 + 30x + 80$	**q** $x^3 - 3x^2 - 28x$	**r** $x^4 + 2x^3 + x^2$

7 Fully factorise:

a $54 - x^2 - 3x$	**b** $14x + 2x^2 + 20$	**c** $-x^2 - 21 - 10x$
d $4x - 96 + 2x^2$	**e** $18x - 3x^2 - 27$	**f** $-20x + 2x^2 + 42$
g $126 - 2x^2 + 4x$	**h** $20x - 2x^2 - 50$	**i** $x^2 - x^3 + 2x$

G | *FACTORISING* $ax^2 + bx + c$, $a \neq 1$ *[E2.8]*

So far we have considered the factorisation of quadratic trinomials of the form $ax^2 + bx + c$ where:

- $a = 1$,   for example $x^2 + 5x + 6 = (x+3)(x+2)$
- a is a common factor,   for example $2x^2 + 10x + 12 = 2(x^2 + 5x + 6)$
  $$= 2(x+3)(x+2)$$

- we have a perfect square or difference between two squares,
  for example $4x^2 - 9 = (2x)^2 - 3^2$
  $$= (2x+3)(2x-3)$$

Factorising a quadratic trinomial such as $8x^2 + 22x + 15$ appears to be more complicated because it does not fall into any of these categories. We therefore need to develop a method for factorising this type of expression.

FACTORISATION BY "SPLITTING" THE MIDDLE TERM

Using the FOIL rule, we see that $(2x+3)(4x+5)$
$$= 8x^2 + 10x + 12x + 15$$
$$= 8x^2 + 22x + 15$$

We will now *reverse* the process to factorise the quadratic trinomial $8x^2 + 22x + 15$.

$$8x^2 + 22x + 15$$
$$= 8x^2 + 10x + 12x + 15 \qquad \{\text{"splitting" the middle term}\}$$
$$= (8x^2 + 10x) + (12x + 15) \qquad \{\text{grouping in pairs}\}$$
$$= 2x(4x+5) + 3(4x+5) \qquad \{\text{factorising each pair separately}\}$$
$$= (4x+5)(2x+3) \qquad \{\text{completing the factorisation}\}$$

But how do we know how to correctly "split" the middle term? How do we determine that $22x$ should be written as $+10x + 12x$ rather than $+15x + 7x$ or $+20x + 2x$?

When looking at $8x^2 + 10x + 12x + 15$, we notice that $8 \times 15 = 120$ and $10 \times 12 = 120$.

So, for $8x^2 + 22x + 15$, we need two numbers whose *sum* is 22 and whose *product* is $8 \times 15 = 120$. These numbers are 10 and 12.

Likewise, for $6x^2 + 19x + 15$ we need two numbers with sum 19 and product $6 \times 15 = 90$.

These numbers are 10 and 9, so $6x^2 + 19x + 15$
$$= 6x^2 + 10x + 9x + 15$$
$$= (6x^2 + 10x) + (9x + 15)$$
$$= 2x(3x+5) + 3(3x+5)$$
$$= (3x+5)(2x+3)$$

> The order in which the "split" terms are written does not matter.

The following procedure is used to factorise $ax^2 + bx + c$ by "splitting" the middle term:

Step 1:   Find two numbers p and q such that $p + q = b$ and $pq = ac$.

Step 2:   Replace bx by $px + qx$.

Step 3:   Complete the factorisation.

Example 19   ◀ঙ Self Tutor

Factorise by "splitting" the middle term:

   a $6x^2 + 19x + 10$ **b** $3x^2 - x - 10$

  a In $6x^2 + 19x + 10$, $ac = 60$ and $b = 19$.

      We need two numbers with product 60 and sum 19. These are 4 and 15.

$$\therefore\quad 6x^2 + 19x + 10$$
$$= 6x^2 + 4x + 15x + 10 \qquad \text{\{"splitting" the middle term\}}$$
$$= 2x(3x + 2) + 5(3x + 2) \qquad \text{\{factorising in pairs\}}$$
$$= (3x + 2)(2x + 5) \qquad \text{\{taking out the common factor\}}$$

  b In $3x^2 - x - 10$, $ac = -30$ and $b = -1$.

      We need two numbers with product -30 and sum -1. These are 5 and -6.

$$\therefore\quad 3x^2 - x - 10$$
$$= 3x^2 + 5x - 6x - 10 \qquad \text{\{"splitting" the middle term\}}$$
$$= x(3x + 5) - 2(3x + 5) \qquad \text{\{factorising in pairs\}}$$
$$= (3x + 5)(x - 2) \qquad \text{\{taking out the common factor\}}$$

EXERCISE 3G

1 Fully factorise:

a $2x^2 + 5x + 3$	**b** $2x^2 + 7x + 5$	**c** $7x^2 + 9x + 2$
d $3x^2 + 7x + 4$	**e** $3x^2 + 13x + 4$	**f** $3x^2 + 8x + 4$
g $8x^2 + 14x + 3$	**h** $21x^2 + 17x + 2$	**i** $6x^2 + 5x + 1$
j $6x^2 + 19x + 3$	**k** $10x^2 + 17x + 3$	**l** $14x^2 + 37x + 5$

2 Fully factorise:

a $2x^2 - 9x - 5$	**b** $3x^2 + 5x - 2$	**c** $3x^2 - 5x - 2$
d $2x^2 + 3x - 2$	**e** $2x^2 + 3x - 5$	**f** $5x^2 - 14x - 3$
g $5x^2 - 8x + 3$	**h** $11x^2 - 9x - 2$	**i** $3x^2 - 7x - 6$
j $2x^2 - 3x - 9$	**k** $3x^2 - 17x + 10$	**l** $5x^2 - 13x - 6$
m $3x^2 + 10x - 8$	**n** $2x^2 + 17x - 9$	**o** $2x^2 + 9x - 18$
p $2x^2 + 11x - 21$	**q** $15x^2 + x - 2$	**r** $21x^2 - 62x - 3$

3 Fully factorise:

a $15x^2 + 19x + 6$	**b** $15x^2 + x - 6$	**c** $15x^2 - x - 6$
d $30x^2 - 38x + 12$	**e** $18x^2 - 12x + 2$	**f** $48x^2 + 72x + 27$
g $16x^2 + 12x + 2$	**h** $16x^2 + 4x - 2$	**i** $40x^2 - 10x - 5$
j $32x^2 - 24x + 4$	**k** $25x^2 + 25x + 6$	**l** $25x^2 - 25x + 6$
m $25x^2 - 10x - 8$	**n** $25x^2 - 149x - 6$	**o** $36x^2 + 24x - 5$
p $36x^2 + 11x - 5$	**q** $36x^2 + 9x - 10$	**r** $36x^2 + 52x - 3$

H   MISCELLANEOUS FACTORISATION   [E2.8]

When asked to factorise an expression:

Look for any **common factors** to take out.

If the expression has 2 or 3 terms, look for:

- **difference between two squares**
  $$a^2 - b^2 = (a + b)(a - b)$$

- **perfect squares**
  $$a^2 + 2ab + b^2 = (a + b)^2$$
  $$a^2 - 2ab + b^2 = (a - b)^2$$

- **sum and product type $x^2 + bx + c$**
  $$x^2 + bx + c = (x + p)(x + q) \quad \text{where} \quad p + q = b \quad \text{and} \quad pq = c$$

- **sum and product type $ax^2 + bx + c, \ a \neq 0 \text{ or } 1$**
  - Find two numbers p and q such that $p + q = b$ and $pq = ac$.
  - "Split the middle term" to replace bx by $px + qx$.
  - Complete the factorisation.

If the expression has 4 terms, look to **group in pairs**.

EXERCISE 3H

1 Fully factorise:

   a $3x^2 + 2x$ **b** $x^2 - 81$ **c** $2p^2 + 8$ **d** $3b^2 - 75$

   e $2x^2 - 32$ **f** $n^4 - 4n^2$ **g** $x^2 - 8x - 9$ **h** $d^2 + 6d - 7$

   i $x^2 + 8x - 9$ **j** $4t + 8t^2$ **k** $3x^2 - 108$ **l** $2g^2 - 12g - 110$

   m $4a^2 - 9d^2$ **n** $5a^2 - 5a - 10$ **o** $2c^2 - 8c + 6$ **p** $x^4 - x^2$

   q $d^4 + 2d^3 - 3d^2$ **r** $x^3 + 4x^2 + 4x$

2 Fully factorise:

   a $x^2 - 6x + 9$ **b** $x^2 - 121$ **c** $x^2 - 2x + 1$ **d** $y^2 + 10y + 25$

   e $x^2 + 22x + 121$ **f** $x^2 - 2xy + y^2$ **g** $1 - x^2$ **h** $25y^2 - 1$

   i $49y^2 - 36z^2$ **j** $4d^2 + 28d + 49$ **k** $4ab^2 - ac^2$ **l** $2\pi R^2 - 2\pi r^2$

3 Fully factorise:

   a $ab + ac - 2a$ **b** $a^2b^2 - 2ab$ **c** $18x - 2x^3$

   d $x^2 + 14x + 49$ **e** $4a^3 - 4ab^2$ **f** $x^3y - 4xy$

   g $4x^4 - 4x^2$ **h** $(x - 2)y - (x - 2)z$ **i** $(x + 1)a + (x + 1)b$

   j $(x - y)a + (x - y)$ **k** $x(x + 2) + 3(x + 2)$ **l** $x^3 + x^2 + x + 1$

4 Fully factorise:

   a $7x - 35y$ **b** $2g^2 - 8$ **c** $-5x^2 - 10x$ **d** $m^2 + 3mp$

   e $a^2 + 8a + 15$ **f** $m^2 - 6m + 9$ **g** $5x^2 + 5xy - 5x^2y$ **h** $xy + 2x + 2y + 4$

   i $y^2 + 5y - 9y - 45$ **j** $2x^2 + 10x + x + 5$ **k** $3y^2 - 147$ **l** $3p^2 - 3q^2$

   m $4c^2 - 1$ **n** $3x^2 + 3x - 36$ **o** $2bx - 6b + 10x - 30$

5 Fully factorise, if possible:

  a $12 - x^2$ **b** $12 - 11x - x^2$ **c** $-2x^2 - 6 + 8x$

  d $14 - x^2 - 5x$ **e** $(x+1)^2 - 2$ **f** $4x^2 - 2x^3 - 2x$

  g $(a+b)^2 - 9$ **h** $(x+2)^2 - 4$ **i** $(x-1)^2 + 4$

6 Fully factorise:

  a $2x^2 + 17x + 21$ **b** $2x^2 + 11x + 15$ **c** $4x^2 + 12x + 5$ **d** $12x^2 + 13x + 3$

  e $6x^2 - 29x - 5$ **f** $16x^2 + 8x + 1$ **g** $25x^2 - 16$ **h** $12x^2 - 71x - 6$

  i $12x^2 - 38x + 6$ **j** $9x^2 + 3x - 12$ **k** $12x^2 - 29x + 15$ **l** $36x^2 + 3x - 14$

Review set 3A

1 Fully factorise:

  a $3x^2 - 12x$ **b** $15x - 6x^2$ **c** $2x^2 - 98$

  d $x^2 - 6x + 9$ **e** $a^2 + 2ab + b^2$ **f** $(x+2)^2 - 3(x+2)$

2 If possible, factorise into linear factors:

  a $x^2 - 10$ **b** $x^2 + 16$ **c** $(x-4)^2 - 13$

3 Fully factorise:

  a $5x - 5 + xy - y$ **b** $3x + 7 + 6bx + 14b$ **c** $2xy - z - 2xz + y$

4 Fully factorise:

  a $x^2 + 10x + 21$ **b** $x^2 + 4x - 21$ **c** $x^2 - 4x - 21$

  d $6 - 5x + x^2$ **e** $4x^2 - 8x - 12$ **f** $-x^2 - 13x - 36$

5 Fully factorise:

  a $8x^2 + 22x + 15$ **b** $12x^2 - 20x + 3$ **c** $12x^2 - 7x - 10$

Review set 3B

1 Fully factorise:

  a $5ab + 10b^2$ **b** $3x^2 - 12$ **c** $x^2 + 8x + 16$

  d $2a^2 - 4ab + 2b^2$ **e** $3x^3 + 6x^2 - 9x$ **f** $(x-3)^2 - 3x + 9$

2 If possible, factorise into linear factors:

  a $x^2 - 81$ **b** $2x^2 - 38$ **c** $x^2 + 25$

3 Fully factorise:

  a $x^2 + 12x + 35$ **b** $x^2 + 2x - 35$ **c** $x^2 - 12x + 35$

  d $2x^2 - 4x - 70$ **e** $30 - 11x + x^2$ **f** $-x^2 + 12x - 20$

4 Fully factorise:

  a $cd + 9 + 3d + 3c$ **b** $(4-x)(x+2) - 3(4-x)$ **c** $6x^2 - 17x + 12$

5 Fully factorise:

  a $12x^2 + 5x - 2$ **b** $12x^2 + x - 6$ **c** $24x^2 + 28x - 12$

Statistical graphs

4

Contents:

A Graphs of categorical data   [E11.3]
B Comparing categorical data   [E11.3]
C Line graphs   [E11.3]

Opening problem

Petrice is a potter who lives in Cheshire. She sells her ceramics on the internet. The multiple bar chart shows her sales over a 4 year period, both within the United Kingdom and internationally.

Things to think about:

a What is the *trend* of the sales within the United Kingdom?

b How would you compare the international sales with those within the United Kingdom?

c Petrice's work was featured in a European ceramics magazine. Which year do you think this was? Explain your answer.

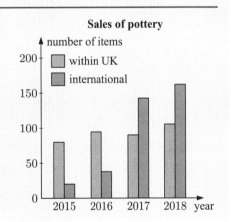

When we construct a statistical investigation, we collect information called **data**.

There are several different types of data that we can collect:

Categorical data is data which can be placed in categories.

Numerical data is data which can be written as numbers:

- **Discrete** numerical data takes exact number values, and results from **counting**.
- **Continuous** numerical data takes numerical values within a continuous range, and usually results from **measuring**.

Statistical graphs are used to display data in a form that is not only more visually appealing, but also easier to understand.

In this Chapter we consider different kinds of graphs which can be used to analyse and compare data.

Throughout the Chapter you can use technology to help you draw graphs.

A   GRAPHS OF CATEGORICAL DATA   [E11.3]

Categorical data is data which can be placed in categories.

For example, suppose the students in Alan's class are asked to name their favourite subject. The data collected is categorical data. The possible categories may include Mathematics, Art, Science, Music, and English.

We organise categorical data using a **tally and frequency table**, and display the data using a **bar chart**, a **pictogram**, or a **pie chart**.

BAR CHART

A **bar chart** is a popular method of displaying statistical data. The information may be displayed either vertically or horizontally. The height (if vertical) or length (if horizontal) of each bar indicates the frequency of the category it represents. All bars have the same width.

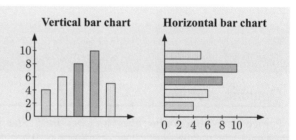

Example 1   ◀)) *Self Tutor*

The students in Alan's class were asked their favourite subject. The possible responses were Mathematics (Ma), Art (A), Science (S), Music (Mu), and English (E):

$$\text{A} \quad \text{Mu} \quad \text{Ma} \quad \text{Mu} \quad \text{E} \quad \text{Ma} \quad \text{S} \quad \text{A}$$
$$\text{Mu} \quad \text{S} \quad \text{Mu} \quad \text{Ma} \quad \text{A} \quad \text{Mu} \quad \text{Ma} \quad \text{Mu}$$

a Construct a tally and frequency table to organise the data.

b Draw a vertical bar chart to display the data.

a

Favourite subject	Tally	Frequency
Mathematics	||||	4
Art	|||	3
Science	||	2
Music	＼＼＼ |	6
English	|	1
	Total	16

b

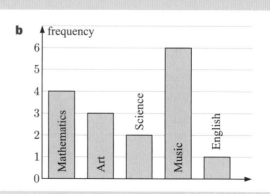

PICTOGRAM

A **pictogram** is set out in the same way as a bar chart, but pictures are used instead of bars to represent the quantities involved.

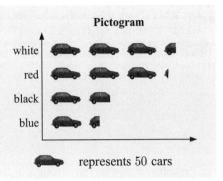

Example 2   🔊 *Self Tutor*

This table shows the number of chickens competing in each category of a show.

Category	Number of chickens
Rhode Island Red	30
Silkie	10
Australorp	13
ISA Brown	22
Cornish	11
Orpington	8
Leghorn	19

Draw a pictogram to represent the data.

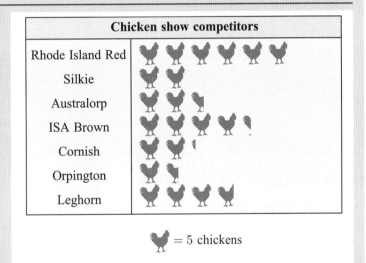

PIE CHART

In a **pie chart**, a circle is divided into sectors which represent the categories. The size of each sector is proportional to the frequency of the category it represents, so its sector angle can be found as a fraction of 360°.

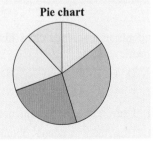

Example 3   ◀⁄)) *Self Tutor*

The table shows the results when the Year 10 students at a school were asked "What is your favourite fruit?"

Construct a pie chart to display this data.

Fruit	Frequency
Orange	13
Apple	21
Banana	10
Pineapple	7
Pear	9
Total	60

There are 60 students in the sample, so each student is represented by $\frac{1}{60}$th of 360° or 6° on the pie chart.

We calculate the sector angles:

$13 \times 6° = 78°$ for Orange
$21 \times 6° = 126°$ for Apple
$10 \times 6° = 60°$ for Banana
$7 \times 6° = 42°$ for Pineapple
$9 \times 6° = 54°$ for Pear.

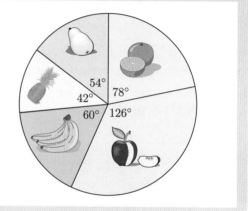

EXERCISE 4A

1 The graph shows the attendances at various Friday night events at an Arts festival.

   a Which event was most popular?

   b How many more people attended the Drama than attended the Modern Dance?

   c What percentage of people went to see the Jazz group?

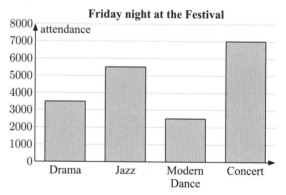

2 Students in a science class obtained the following levels of achievement:

   D C C A A C C D C B C C C D
   B C C C C E B A C C B C B C

   a Draw a tally and frequency table to organise the data.

   b How many students obtained a C?

   c What fraction of students obtained a B?

   d Draw a horizontal bar chart to display the data.

3 People visiting the local show were asked whether they preferred the sideshows (S), the farm animals (F), the ring events (R), the cats (C), or the wood chopping (W).

The results were: S R W S S   W F C C S   R S F W S   R S R W S   S R R R F

   a Draw a tally and frequency table for the data.

   b What percentage of people preferred the wood chopping?

   c Draw a vertical bar chart to display the data.

4 The 20 players in a football team voted to decide who should be their captain. The results are given in the table alongside.

   a Draw a horizontal bar chart to display the data.

   b Which candidate received the most votes?

   c What percentage of the team voted for:

      i Luke   **ii** Greg or Steve?

Candidate	Votes
Cameron	3
Greg	7
Luke	4
Steve	6

5 At a school camp, the students selected their favourite ice cream flavour out of chocolate (C), strawberry (S), vanilla (V), and lime (L).

The results were:

     C V C S S   V L S C V   C V S L V   S C C V V   C S L C V

     V C L S C   C C V L S   S L V C V   C L C S C   L C V L C

> The most common response is called the *mode*.

   a Organise this data into a tally and frequency table.

   b How many students chose vanilla?

   c What percentage of the students chose lime?

   d Find the most common response.

   e Draw a vertical bar chart to display the data.

6 This pictogram shows the number of flights leaving an airport each day for a week.

Departures

| Monday |
| Tuesday |
| Wednesday |
| Thursday |
| Friday |
| Saturday |
| Sunday |

= 5 flights

   a How many flights left on Thursday?

   b What day shows the greatest number of departures?

   c How many flights left over the weekend?

7 Jessica recorded the activities of people using a path for one hour on Sunday morning.

Draw a pictogram to represent the results, using

  to represent 4 people.

Activity	Number of people
Walking	36
Jogging	19
Cycling	26
Rollerblading	13

8 This table shows the types of cards sold by a stationery store in one day. Given that the store sold 64 cards in total:

   a Find the number of "get well" cards sold.

   b Draw a pictogram to represent the data, using

   ▱ to represent 5 cards.

   c What percentage of cards sold were wedding cards?

Type of card	Number sold
Anniversary	8
Birthday	27
Get Well	
Thank You	10
Wedding	12

9 A survey of eye colour in a group of 30 teenagers revealed these results:

   a Illustrate the results on a pie chart.

   b What percentage of the group have: **i** green eyes   **ii** blue or grey eyes?

Eye colour	Blue	Brown	Green	Grey
Number of students	9	12	2	7

10 This bar chart shows the different types of traffic fines handed out by a police officer over one week.

   a How many fines did the police officer hand out in total?

   b Draw a pie chart to illustrate this data.

   c Determine whether each statement is true or false:

   i The most common fine was for drink driving.

   ii Fines for speeding were about one quarter of all fines.

   iii More than half of the fines were either for seatbelt or mobile phone offences.

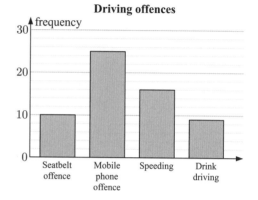

11 In a pie chart on *favourite leisure activities*, the sector angle for *ice skating* is $34°$. This sector represents 136 people.

   a The sector angle for *watching television* is $47°$. How many of the people surveyed selected *watching television*?

   b If 38 people selected *visiting friends*, what sector angle would represent them?

   c In total, how many people were surveyed?

12 90 people were asked their opinions of a new sports stadium. The table alongside gives some of the results.

Given that "Fair" would occupy $100°$ of a pie chart of the responses:

   a Complete the table.

   b Draw a pie chart to display the data.

Response	Frequency
Excellent	8
Good	30
Fair	
Poor	

B   COMPARING CATEGORICAL DATA   [E11.3]

To understand the significance of the results we collect, we often need to compare two data sets.

For example, in **Example 1** we studied the favourite subjects of students in Alan's class. We now also consider the students in Bill's class, whose favourite subjects are shown in the table alongside.

Favourite subject	Frequency
Mathematics	3
Art	5
Science	2
Music	2
English	4
Total	16

MULTIPLE BAR CHART

To compare the results from Alan's class and Bill's class, we can draw a bar chart for each data set on the same axes. This is known as a **multiple bar chart**. A different colour is used for each data set, and a legend is included so we can see clearly which data set is which.

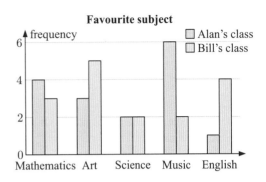

COMPOSITE BAR CHART

Alternatively, we can place the results for Bill's class on top of those for Alan's class, so that each subject is represented by a single bar split into segments. This is known as a **composite bar chart**.

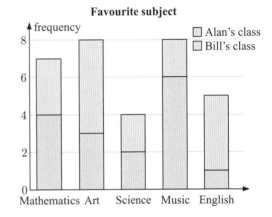

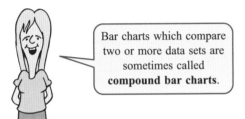

Bar charts which compare two or more data sets are sometimes called **compound bar charts**.

Example 4   ◀)) *Self Tutor*

This bar chart shows the number of girls and boys visiting a playground on Friday, Saturday, and Sunday.

a How many:
  i girls visited the playground on Friday
  ii boys visited the playground on Saturday
  iii children visited the playground on Sunday?

b On what day was the percentage of girls visiting the playground the highest?

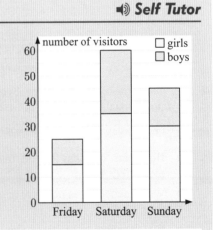

---

a **i** 15 girls visited the playground on Friday.
  ii $60 - 35 = 25$ boys visited the playground on Saturday.
  iii 45 children visited the playground on Sunday.

b Percentage of girls visiting on Friday $= \frac{15}{25} \times 100\% = 60\%$

Percentage of girls visiting on Saturday $= \frac{35}{60} \times 100\% \approx 58.3\%$

Percentage of girls visiting on Sunday $= \frac{30}{45} \times 100\% \approx 66.7\%$

The percentage of girls visiting the playground was highest on Sunday.

EXERCISE 4B

1 The students in classes A and B were asked whether they live north, east, south, or west of their school. This bar chart shows their responses.

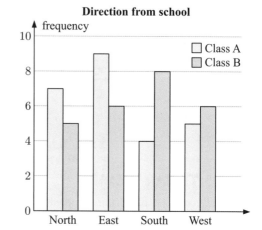

a How many students from class A live south of the school?

b How many students from class B live west of the school?

c Find the most common response for:
   i class A   **ii** class B.

d In which class are there more students who live north of the school?

e What percentage of students who live east of the school are from class B?

2

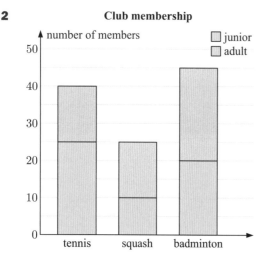

This bar chart shows the number of tennis, squash, and badminton members at a local sports club.

a State the number of:
   i junior tennis members
   ii adult badminton members.

b Does squash have more junior members or adult members?

c For which sport is the percentage of adult members highest?

d The sports club charges $15 for each junior member, and $25 for each adult member. Find the total amount received by the club for memberships.

3 Hillsvale School and Redstone School each have 40 international students. This bar chart shows the countries that these international students come from.

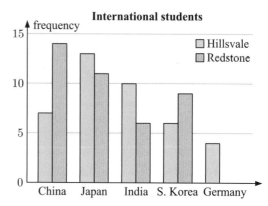

a How many of Hillsvale's international students come from India?

b Which school does not have any students from Germany?

c Which school has more students from:
   i China   **ii** Japan?

4 The data alongside shows the drinks purchased by students at recess and lunch time.

Recess

Drink	Frequency
Orange juice	8
Soft drink	12
Milkshake	5
Water	6

Lunch

Drink	Frequency
Orange juice	20
Soft drink	23
Milkshake	15
Water	5

Frank drew this bar chart to represent the data.

a Describe two mistakes Frank has made.

b Redraw the chart so that it is correct.

c Were more orange juices sold during recess or lunch?

d What percentage of drinks purchased at lunch time were milkshakes?

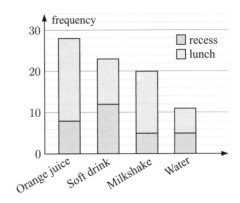

5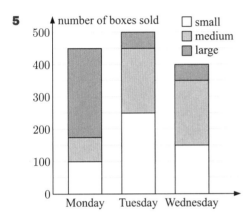

This bar chart shows the number of small, medium, and large boxes of popcorn sold at a cinema over three days.

a On which day was the most boxes of popcorn sold?

b What percentage of popcorn boxes sold on Wednesday were small or medium?

c Which size box was most popular on Tuesday?

d On which day do you think the cinema discounted the price of large popcorn? Explain your answer.

6 30 children and 30 adults were asked which section of the newspaper they enjoyed most.

Section	Children	Adults
News	5	10
Sport	7	9
Comics	10	4
Puzzles	8	7

a Draw a multiple bar chart to display the data.

b Which newspaper section was most popular with:
   i children   **ii** adults?

c Which section has the most difference in popularity between children and adults? Discuss your answer.

7 On a particular day, a fire truck and an ambulance each received 20 call-outs. The data alongside shows the location of each call-out.

a Draw a composite bar chart to display the data.

b Which type of location was most common for:
   i the fire truck   **ii** the ambulance?

c Which vehicle was called out to more offices?

Location	Fire truck	Ambulance
House	6	9
Apartment	2	4
Office	5	2
Factory	7	5

C   LINE GRAPHS   [E11.3]

The table below shows the number of customers in a city restaurant at hourly intervals:

Time	10 am	11 am	12 pm	1 pm	2 pm	3 pm	4 pm	5 pm	6 pm	7 pm	8 pm
Number of customers	12	22	20	29	25	16	10	13	27	35	20

We can use a **line graph** to display this data. We plot each data point on a grid, then join the points with straight line segments.

Displaying data on a line graph enables us to see **trends** in the data.

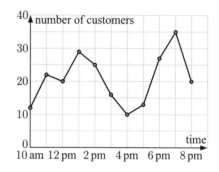

Example 5   ◀)) Self Tutor

The circumference of Warren's head was measured every 2 years from birth.

Age (years)	0	2	4	6	8	10
Head circumference (cm)	35	40	42	44	45	46

a Draw a line graph of Warren's head circumference over time.
b Describe the trend of the graph.

a

head circumference (cm)
46
42
38
34
30
age (years)
0   2   4   6   8   10

b Warren's head circumference increased quickly at first. The rate slowed down over time, and we would expect that once Warren reaches adulthood it would stop increasing altogether.

EXERCISE 4C

1

Volume of water in lake
26 000 Ml
25 000
24 000
23 000
22 000
21 000
20 000

Mar Apr May Jun Jul Aug Sep

a What information is contained in the line graph alongside?

b How much water was in the lake at the start of:
   i April   **ii** August?

c Over which month did the water volume:
   i increase most   **ii** decrease most?

d What was the maximum water volume during this period?

e What was the percentage increase in water volume from the start of March to the start of June?

2 The number of squirrels in a region of forest was recorded at yearly intervals.

Year	2011	2012	2013	2014	2015	2016	2017	2018
Number of squirrels	300	378	455	482	490	488	491	490

    a Draw a line graph to display the data.

    b Describe how the squirrel population has changed over time.

3 Peter recorded the distance he walked each day during February:

Day	1	2	3	4	5	6	7	8	9	10	11	12	13	14
Distance (km)	3.82	4.68	4.69	2.41	3.22	3.25	4.09	5.90	3.76	5.70	2.82	1.89	2.50	4.25

Day	15	16	17	18	19	20	21	22	23	24	25	26	27	28
Distance (km)	4.93	4.67	3.48	2.92	4.25	3.42	3.42	3.84	4.77	2.77	3.08	2.28	4.38	5.01

    a Draw a line graph to display the data.

    b On how many days during February did Peter walk more than 4 km?

    c On which day was Peter most active?

4 The table below shows Jana's heart rate during a 60 minute gym session.

Time (minutes)	0	5	10	15	20	25	30	35	40	45	50	55	60
Heart rate (beats per minute)	50	80	95	112	120	142	130	145	158	152	165	160	135

    a Draw a line graph to display the data.

    b At what time was Jana's heart rate highest?

    c Describe the trend of the data.

5 The water consumption for a household is recorded each quarter for two years.

Year	2017				2018			
Quarter	1	2	3	4	1	2	3	4
Usage (litres × 1000)	59.4	63.2	75.8	70.5	60.3	62.2	79.5	74.3

A **quarter** is 3 months.

    a Draw a line graph to display the data.

    b In which quarter of the year does the household use:

       i most water   **ii** least water?

    Give an explanation for your answers.

6 Leah owns a homewares shop. The table below shows the quarterly profit made by the shop over three years, in thousands of dollars.

	2014				2015				2016			
Quarter	1	2	3	4	1	2	3	4	1	2	3	4
Profit ($ × 1000)	27	20	18	35	31	23	24	42	34	32	29	47

    a Draw a line graph to display the data.

    b In which quarter does the shop generally make most profit? Can you explain why this may occur?

    c Describe the long-term trend of the data.

Discussion   *Misleading graphs*

Some people may try to trick or mislead others by the way they draw their graphs.

For example, Kelly owns two shops. One of them is managed by John, and the other by Wei Li. Last year John's shop earned a profit of \$45 000, whereas Wei Li's profit was \$38 000.

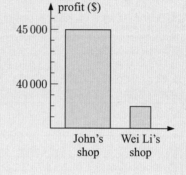

John draws this graph to show the profits earned by the two shops, and gives it to Kelly.

What to do:

1 Discuss the misleading features of John's graph.

2 Why do you think John has drawn the graph like this?

3 Discuss the misleading features of these graphs:

a

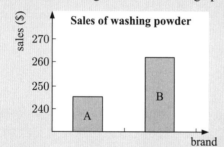

b

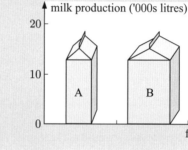

c

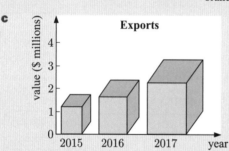

d

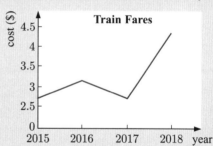

Activity   *Using spreadsheets to graph data*

Click on the icon to obtain this Activity.

USING
SPREADSHEETS

Review set 4A

1 A survey of hair colour in a class of 40 students revealed the results in the table.

  a Construct a horizontal bar chart to display this data.

  b Which was the most common hair colour?

  c What percentage of students in the class have black or blond hair?

Hair colour	Frequency
Red	4
Brown	17
Black	11
Blond	8

2 **a** In the pictogram, what does 🥛 represent?

   b On which day were the milk sales:
      i greatest   **ii** least?
   c How much milk was sold on:
      i Thursday   **ii** Friday?

Quick Mart milk sales	
Monday	🥛🥛🥛🥛
Tuesday	🥛🥛🥛▫
Wednesday	🥛🥛▫
Thursday	🥛🥛🥛
Friday	🥛🥛🥛🥛🥛▫
Saturday	🥛🥛🥛▫

🥛 represents 10 litres sold

3 Farmer Jane owns the assortment of animals shown in the table.

   a Display this data on a vertical bar chart.
   b What fraction of animals on the farm are horses?
   c Name the three most common animals on the farm.
   d What percentage of animals on the farm are:
      i chickens   **ii** birds?

Animal	Number
Chickens	12
Cows	35
Donkeys	4
Ducks	10
Geese	5
Goats	24
Horses	11
Sheep	19

4 A chemical engineer is performing a reaction using large quantities of liquid. The line graph shows the volume of liquid in the collection tank over a 24 hour period. During the day, three samples of the liquid were taken for quality control.

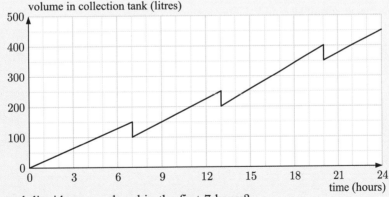

   a How much liquid was produced in the first 7 hours?
   b How much liquid was sampled each time for quality control?
   c What was the total amount of liquid produced by the reaction over the whole day?

5 The table alongside shows the results of a Mathematics competition for students at School A.

   a How many students from School A took part in the competition?

   b Draw a pie chart to display the data.

Result	Frequency
High distinction	52
Distinction	89
Credit	118
Participation	101

c This pie chart shows the competition results for students at School B.

Comment on the validity of this statement:

"School B had more students who scored a Distinction than School A."

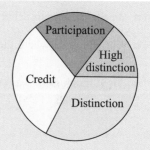

6 This bar chart shows the leg injuries received by two rugby teams during a season.

   a How many calf injuries were received by:

     i the Panthers   **ii** the Tigers?

   b Which team suffered the most ankle injuries?

   c Which injury was most common for:

     i the Panthers   **ii** the Tigers?

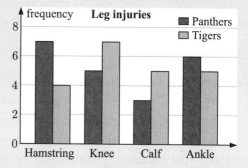

7 A group of children at a summer camp were asked which sport they wanted to play. The choices were tennis, swimming, cricket, basketball, and athletics.

   a Draw a composite bar chart to display the data.

   b Was tennis more popular with girls or boys?

   c What percentage of children who chose athletics were boys?

   d Which sport was most popular overall?

Sport	Girls	Boys
Tennis	8	6
Swimming	6	9
Cricket	5	6
Basketball	4	5
Athletics	7	4

8 The attendances at a football team's home games are shown below.

Game	1	2	3	4	5	6	7	8	9	10	11	12
Attendance (× 1000)	37	34	48	30	33	24	30	18	26	13	17	16

   a Draw a line graph to display the data.

   b Describe the trend in the data.

Review set 4B

1 The bar graph shows the crude oil reserves for the top five oil producing countries in the world.

   a How many billion barrels of crude oil do these countries have in total?

   b How many more barrels does Saudi Arabia hold than Iraq?

   c What percentage of the crude oil is held by Iran?

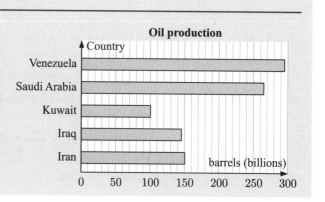

2 Sixty people whose houses had been burgled were asked where they were at the time of the burglary. The responses are shown alongside.

Response	Frequency
At home	12
At work	20
Shopping	5
On holidays	10
Visiting friends	13
Total	60

   a Draw a vertical bar chart to display the data.

   b What percentage of people were shopping when they were burgled?

3 On a spring day in Brighton, Ebony used a thermometer to measure the temperature in her bedroom. Her results are shown in the line graph below:

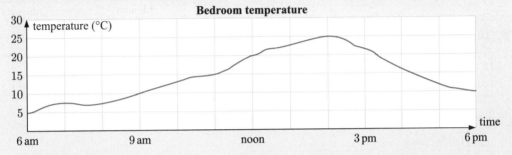

Bedroom temperature

   a Find the temperature at:

     i 9 am   **ii** noon.

   b **i** What was the maximum temperature during the day?

     ii At what time did this maximum temperature occur?

   c Was the temperature increasing or decreasing at 4 pm? Explain your answer.

   d By how much did the temperature vary during the 12-hour period.

4 Answer the **Opening Problem** on page **57**.

5

Month	House sales
April	40
May	15
June	30
July	28
August	13
September	30

This table shows the number of houses sold by Bill Black Real Estate in a six month period.

Draw a pictogram to display the data, where 🏠 represents 10 houses.

6 This bar chart shows the time Megan spent in different stages of sleep over 3 nights.

    a How much sleep did Megan get on Monday?

    b How much more light sleep did Megan get on Tuesday than on Wednesday?

    c What type of sleep did Megan get the least of on Tuesday?

    d On which night did Megan get the greatest percentage of deep sleep?

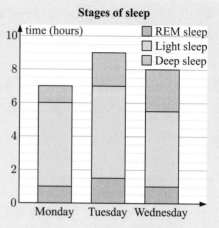

7 This table shows Lisbon's daily rainfall over a two week period.

Day	1	2	3	4	5	6	7	8	9	10	11	12	13	14
Rainfall (mm)	3.4	2.3	4.0	3.1	6.5	5.2	0	4.7	10.3	12.5	11.6	13.5	15.0	11.1

Lewis constructed this line graph to represent the data:

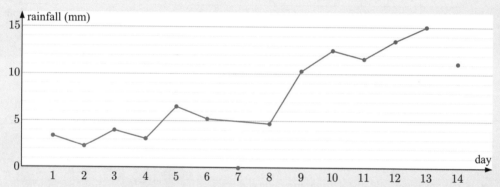

    a Describe two mistakes Lewis has made.

    b Redraw the line graph correctly.

    c Describe the trend of the data.

8 Huw owns a flower shop. The table below shows the total cost of supplying, as well as the sales for each flower type, for the past year.

Flower	Roses	Carnations	Tulips	Orchids	Azaleas	Lilies
Cost ($)	17 000	15 000	8000	7000	5000	8000
Sales ($)	35 000	25 000	16 000	15 000	15 000	14 000

    a Draw two pie charts to display the data.

    b Which two flower types account for more than half of the total costs?

    c Which two flower types account for half of the total sales?

    d Huw needs to reduce his workload, so he decides to stop selling one type of flower. Which flower type would you recommend he stop selling? Explain your answer.

Algebra: Linear equations

5

Contents:

A	Maintaining balance	
B	Inverse operations	
C	Linear equations	[E2.3]
D	Equations with a repeated unknown	[E2.3]
E	Rational equations	[E2.3]
F	Problem solving	

Opening problem

Mrs May set her class the following challenge:

Find a fraction whose numerator is 4 more than its denominator, and the value of the fraction is equal to $\frac{1}{3}$.

"That's impossible!" Stan said, "If the numerator is more than the denominator, the value of the fraction must be greater than 1!"

Things to think about:

a Can you explain why Stan is wrong?

b Can you use algebra to solve the problem?

Equations are a fundamental part of mathematics, and an important tool for problem solving. The use of equations dates back to Ancient Egypt, where the scribe **Ahmes** recorded a series of problems which were solved using equations.

> An **equation** is a mathematical sentence which indicates that two expressions have the same value.
>
> The expressions are connected by an *equal* sign $=$.
>
> The **left hand side** (LHS) of an equation is on the left of the $=$ sign.
>
> The **right hand side** (RHS) of an equation is on the right of the $=$ sign.

We can often convert a worded problem into an equation, then follow a formal procedure to **solve** the equation and hence the problem.

A **solution** of an equation is a value of the variable which makes the equation true.

For example: Consider the equation $\underbrace{5x - 3}_{\text{LHS}} = \underbrace{2x + 6}_{\text{RHS}}$.

$$\text{When } x = 3, \quad \text{LHS} = 5(3) - 3 \quad \text{and} \quad \text{RHS} = 2(3) + 6$$
$$= 15 - 3 \qquad\qquad\qquad = 6 + 6$$
$$= 12 \qquad\qquad\qquad\quad = 12 \quad \text{also.}$$

So, $x = 3$ is a solution of the equation.

A MAINTAINING BALANCE

For any equation, the LHS must always equal the RHS. We can therefore think of an equation as a set of scales that must always be in **balance**.

The balance of an equation is maintained provided we perform the same operation on **both sides** of the equals sign.

Discussion

Will the balance of an equation be maintained if we:
- add the same amount to both sides
- multiply both sides by the same amount
- subtract the same amount from both sides
- divide both sides by the same amount?

To maintain the balance, whatever operation we perform on one side of the equation, we must also perform on the other.

Example 1   ◀⟩ **Self Tutor**

Write down the equation which results when:
  a 3 is added to both sides of $x - 3 = 8$
  b 4 is taken from both sides of $2x + 4 = 18$
  c both sides of $5x = 15$ are divided by 5
  d both sides of $\frac{x}{4} = -7$ are multiplied by 4.

a
$$x - 3 = 8$$
$$\therefore \ x - 3 + 3 = 8 + 3$$
$$\therefore \ x = 11$$

b
$$2x + 4 = 18$$
$$\therefore \ 2x + 4 - 4 = 18 - 4$$
$$\therefore \ 2x = 14$$

c
$$5x = 15$$
$$\therefore \ \frac{5x}{5} = \frac{15}{5}$$
$$\therefore \ x = 3$$

d
$$\frac{x}{4} = -7$$
$$\therefore \ \frac{x}{4} \times 4 = -7 \times 4$$
$$\therefore \ x = -28$$

EXERCISE 5A

1 Write down the equation which results when we add:

    a 3 to both sides of $x - 3 = 2$ **b** 9 to both sides of $x - 9 = 0$

    c 4 to both sides of $5x - 4 = 11$ **d** 5 to both sides of $7x - 5 = x + 1$.

2 Write down the equation which results when we subtract:

    a 1 from both sides of $x + 1 = 5$ **b** 6 from both sides of $2x + 6 = 10$

    c 5 from both sides of $3x + 5 = 2$ **d** 9 from both sides of $4x + 9 = 3x + 11$.

3 Write down the equation which results when we multiply both sides of:

    a $\dfrac{x}{2} = 8$ by 2   **b** $\dfrac{x - 1}{5} = 1$ by 5

    c $\dfrac{3x}{7} = 2$ by 7   **d** $\dfrac{3x - 4}{4} = -10$ by 4.

4 Write down the equation which results when we divide both sides of:

    a $4x = -40$ by 4   **b** $-2x = 18$ by -2

    c $3(2 - x) = 15$ by 3   **d** $-5(2x - 1) = -55$ by -5.

B   INVERSE OPERATIONS

An **inverse operation** is a mathematical operation which **undoes** the effect of another.

- Addition and subtraction are inverse operations.
- Multiplication and division are inverse operations.

Example 2
◀◉ *Self Tutor*

State the inverse of:

    a $\times 4$ **b** $\div 7$ **c** $+ 6$ **d** $- 3$

    a The inverse of $\times 4$ is $\div 4$.   **b** The inverse of $\div 7$ is $\times 7$.

    c The inverse of $+ 6$ is $- 6$.   **d** The inverse of $- 3$ is $+ 3$.

We can use inverse operations to solve simple equations. To keep the equation balanced, we must perform the same operation on both sides of the equation.

Example 3
◀◉ *Self Tutor*

Solve each equation using a suitable inverse operation:

    a $x + 6 = 13$ **b** $y - 4 = -1$ **c** $4g = 20$ **d** $\dfrac{h}{7} = -6$

  a $x + 6 = 13$ **b** $y - 4 = -1$

      $\therefore\ x + 6 - 6 = 13 - 6$ $\therefore\ y - 4 + 4 = -1 + 4$

             $\therefore\ x = 7$ $\therefore\ y = 3$

c $4g = 20$

$\therefore \quad \dfrac{4g}{4} = \dfrac{20}{4}$

$\therefore \quad g = 5$

d $\dfrac{h}{7} = -6$

$\therefore \quad \dfrac{h}{7} \times 7 = -6 \times 7$

$\therefore \quad h = -42$

EXERCISE 5B

1 State the inverse of:

    a $+3$ **b** -8 **c** $\times 2$ **d** $\div 5$

    e $+12$ **f** $\div 6$ **g** -5 **h** $\times 9$

    i $+\frac{2}{3}$ **j** $\div 13$ **k** $\times 15$ **l** $-\frac{4}{5}$

2 Simplify:

    a $x - 3 + 3$ **b** $x + 5 - 5$ **c** $x \div 12 \times 12$ **d** $x \times 9 \div 9$

    e $p + 4 - 4$ **f** $3q \div 3$ **g** $\dfrac{8r}{7} \times 7$ **h** $\dfrac{2s}{3} \div \dfrac{2}{3}$

3 Solve for x using a suitable inverse operation:

    a $x + 4 = 10$ **b** $\dfrac{x}{10} = 1$ **c** $x - 9 = -2$ **d** $2x = 12$

    e $x - 5 = 1$ **f** $x + 2 = 0$ **g** $\dfrac{x}{7} = -5$ **h** $5x = -55$

    i $\dfrac{x}{8} = -4$ **j** $-20x = 60$ **k** $x + 5 = -2$ **l** $x - 7 = -16$

    m $\dfrac{x}{-3} = 3$ **n** $x - 4 = 0$ **o** $-9x = -81$ **p** $x + 9 = -9$

C   LINEAR EQUATIONS   [E2.3]

Linear equations are equations in which the variable is raised only to the power 1.

All linear equations can be written in the form $ax + b = 0$ where a and b are constants, $a \neq 0$, and x is the variable.

To solve simple linear equations, we follow these steps:

Step 1:   Consider how the expression involving the unknown has been **built up**.

For example, for the equation $2x + 3 = 8$, the LHS is built up by starting with x, multiplying by 2, then adding 3.

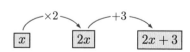

Step 2:   **Isolate the unknown** by performing **inverse operations** in the **reverse order**.

To isolate x, we first subtract 3 from both sides, then divide both sides by 2.

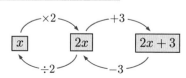

Example 4   ◄)) *Self Tutor*

Solve for x: $4x - 5 = 25$

$$4x - 5 = 25$$
$$\therefore \ 4x - 5 + 5 = 25 + 5 \qquad \text{\{adding 5 to both sides\}}$$
$$\therefore \ 4x = 30 \qquad \text{\{simplifying\}}$$
$$\therefore \ \frac{4x}{4} = \frac{30}{4} \qquad \text{\{dividing both sides by 4\}}$$
$$\therefore \ x = 7\tfrac{1}{2} \qquad \text{\{simplifying\}}$$

Check: LHS $= 4\left(7\tfrac{1}{2}\right) - 5 = 30 - 5 = 25 =$ RHS   ✓

Check your answer by substituting back into the original equation.

EXERCISE 5C

1 Solve for x:

    a $2x + 1 = 5$ **b** $4x + 7 = 27$ **c** $3x + 7 = 19$

    d $3x + 1 = -23$ **e** $5x - 9 = 11$ **f** $8x - 3 = 0$

    g $2x - 7 = -4$ **h** $2x - 11 = 23$ **i** $7 + 8x = -9$

    j $6 + 3x = 0$ **k** $8 + 13x = 34$ **l** $11 + 4x = -6$

2 Solve for x:

    a $15 - 2x = 7$ **b** $2 - 3x = 8$ **c** $1 - 4x = -15$

    d $4 - 5x = -21$ **e** $16 - 8x = 0$ **f** $22 - 3x = 1$

    g $14 - x = -1$ **h** $19 - 4x = -9$ **i** $-5x + 12 = -8$

Example 5   ◄)) *Self Tutor*

Solve for x: $\dfrac{x}{4} + 5 = -8$

$$\frac{x}{4} + 5 = -8$$
$$\therefore \ \frac{x}{4} + 5 - 5 = -8 - 5 \qquad \text{\{subtracting 5 from both sides\}}$$
$$\therefore \ \frac{x}{4} = -13 \qquad \text{\{simplifying\}}$$
$$\therefore \ \frac{x}{4} \times 4 = -13 \times 4 \qquad \text{\{multiplying both sides by 4\}}$$
$$\therefore \ x = -52 \qquad \text{\{simplifying\}}$$

Check: LHS $= \dfrac{-52}{4} + 5 = -13 + 5 = -8 =$ RHS   ✓

With practice, you should not need to write all the steps.

3 Solve for x:

    a $\dfrac{x}{2} + 1 = 3$ **b** $\dfrac{x}{2} - 5 = 6$ **c** $\dfrac{x}{8} + 3 = 5$

    d $\dfrac{x}{3} - 4 = -1$ **e** $\dfrac{x}{3} - 4 = -11$ **f** $\dfrac{x}{6} + 2 = -2$

    g $\dfrac{x}{9} - 7 = 0$ **h** $\dfrac{x}{7} + 5 = -3$ **i** $\dfrac{x}{11} + 31 = 33$

Example 6   ◀⑴ *Self Tutor*

Solve the equation: $\dfrac{2x-3}{3} = -2$

$$\dfrac{2x-3}{3} = -2$$

$\therefore \quad \dfrac{2x-3}{3} \times 3 = -2 \times 3$ {multiplying both sides by 3}

$\therefore \quad 2x - 3 = -6$

$\therefore \quad 2x - 3 + 3 = -6 + 3$ {adding 3 to both sides}

$\therefore \quad 2x = -3$

$\therefore \quad \dfrac{2x}{2} = \dfrac{-3}{2}$ {dividing both sides by 2}

$\therefore \quad x = -\dfrac{3}{2}$

Check: LHS $= \dfrac{2(-\frac{3}{2}) - 3}{3} = \dfrac{-6}{3} = -2 =$ RHS   ✓

4 Solve for x:

a $\dfrac{x+1}{3} = 4$
b $\dfrac{4x-1}{5} = 7$
c $\dfrac{2x-5}{2} = 1$

d $\dfrac{3x+1}{4} = -5$
e $\dfrac{5x+6}{-2} = 7$
f $\dfrac{2x+1}{-5} = 11$

g $\dfrac{11x-1}{8} = -7$
h $\dfrac{6x-2}{-5} = -2$
i $\dfrac{11+4x}{3} = -11$

Example 7   ◀⑴ *Self Tutor*

Solve the equation: $3(2x-1) = -21$

$$3(2x-1) = -21$$

$\therefore \quad \dfrac{3(2x-1)}{3} = \dfrac{-21}{3}$ {dividing both sides by 3}

$\therefore \quad 2x - 1 = -7$

$\therefore \quad 2x - 1 + 1 = -7 + 1$ {adding 1 to both sides}

$\therefore \quad 2x = -6$

$\therefore \quad \dfrac{2x}{2} = \dfrac{-6}{2}$ {dividing both sides by 2}

$\therefore \quad x = -3$

Check: LHS $= 3(2(-3) - 1) = 3(-7) = -21 =$ RHS   ✓

5 Solve for x:

a $2(x-1) = 18$
b $3(2x+1) = 15$
c $5(2x-7) = 10$

d $4(3x-5) = -28$
e $-4(3x-2) = 44$
f $7(3x-7) = -49$

g $6(3x-2) = 12$
h $-5(4x+1) = -15$
i $-6(3+8x) = -18$

6 Solve the following equations:

a $3a + 5 = 14$

b $\dfrac{x}{8} - 1 = 55$

c $\dfrac{3x - 1}{2} = 7$

LEARNING
ALGEBRA

d $4(x + 5) = 24$

e $6(n - 2) = 12$

f $5a + 9 = -31$

g $\dfrac{2x - 5}{4} = 0$

h $\dfrac{x}{5} - 3 = 12$

i $\dfrac{x + 15}{3} = 6$

j $5(2n - 1) = -35$

k $\dfrac{3k + 5}{2} = 13$

l $-8(5z + 1) = 24$

D EQUATIONS WITH A REPEATED UNKNOWN   [E2.3]

If the unknown or variable appears more than once in the equation, we need to take extra steps in its solution.

DEMO

For example, consider the equation $3x + 1 = x + 7$.

In this case the unknown appears twice, once on each side of the equation.

We can represent the equation $3x + 1 = x + 7$ using the set of scales shown.

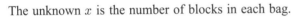

The unknown x is the number of blocks in each bag.

We can add or subtract bags or blocks on both sides of the scales to maintain the balance.

Removing a bag is like subtracting x from both sides. This gives us the equation $2x + 1 = 7$.

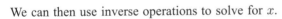

We can then use inverse operations to solve for x.

In general, we follow these steps to solve equations:

Step 1:   If necessary, expand any brackets and collect like terms.

Step 2:   If necessary, remove the unknown from one side of the equation. Remember to balance the other side.

Step 3:   Use inverse operations to isolate the unknown and solve the equation.

Example 8   ◀) *Self Tutor*

Solve for d: $2d + 3(d - 1) = 7$

$2d + 3(d - 1) = 7$

$\therefore \ 2d + 3d - 3 = 7$ {expanding brackets}

$\therefore \quad 5d - 3 = 7$ {collecting like terms}

$\therefore \qquad 5d = 10$ {adding 3 to both sides}

$\therefore \qquad d = 2$ {dividing both sides by 5}

Check: LHS $= 2(2) + 3(2 - 1) = 4 + 3 = 7 =$ RHS   ✓

EXERCISE 5D

1 Solve:

a $2x + 3x = 10$ **b** $5x + 4 + 3x = -36$

c $3x - 6 - 2x + 7 = 16$ **d** $4y - 9 + 3y - 5 = -14$

e $t + \dfrac{t}{3} = 8$ **f** $d - \dfrac{d}{5} = -8$

g $2x + \dfrac{x}{3} = -14$ **h** $\dfrac{x}{2} - \dfrac{x}{3} = 2$

Remember to check your solution by substituting it into the equation.

2 Solve for x:

a $3(x - 2) - x = 12$ **b** $5(x - 3) + 4x = -6$

c $2(3x + 2) - x = -6$ **d** $-2(4x + 3) + 2x = 12$

e $3(x + 2) + 2(x + 4) = -1$ **f** $4(5x - 3) - 3(2x - 5) = 17$

Example 9   ◀ Self Tutor

Solve for x: $3x + 2 = x + 14$

$$3x + 2 = x + 14$$
$\therefore \quad 2x + 2 = 14$ {subtracting x from both sides}
$\therefore \quad 2x = 12$ {subtracting 2 from both sides}
$\therefore \quad x = 6$ {dividing both sides by 2}

Check: LHS $= 3(6) + 2 = 18 + 2 = 20$
           RHS $= 6 + 14 = 20$ ✓

---

3 Solve:

a $2x - 1 = 5 + x$ **b** $3x + 1 = x + 5$ **c** $2x - 6 = 7x + 14$
d $4x - 5 = 2x + 1$ **e** $7x + 7 = 3x + 23$ **f** $x - 6 = 5x + 4$

4 Solve:

a $x + 2 = 4 - x$ **b** $2x + 5 = 10 - 3x$ **c** $2 + 7x = 3 - 3x$
d $3x - 11 = 9 - 2x$ **e** $8 - 9x = 3 - 4x$ **f** $9 - 3x = 5 - 6x$

Example 10   ◀ Self Tutor

Solve for x: $3(x + 2) = x - 1$

$$3(x + 2) = x - 1$$
$\therefore \quad 3x + 6 = x - 1$ {expanding the brackets}
$\therefore \quad 2x + 6 = -1$ {subtracting x from both sides}
$\therefore \quad 2x = -7$ {subtracting 6 from both sides}
$\therefore \quad x = -\dfrac{7}{2}$ {dividing both sides by 2}

Check: LHS $= 3\left(\left(-\dfrac{7}{2}\right) + 2\right) = 3\left(-\dfrac{3}{2}\right) = -\dfrac{9}{2}$
           RHS $= \left(-\dfrac{7}{2}\right) - 1 = -\dfrac{9}{2}$ ✓

5 Solve:

a $2(x + 1) = x + 5$ **b** $3(t - 2) = t + 4$ **c** $6(2x - 3) = x - 7$

d $4(3y - 1) = 2y + 1$ **e** $2(a - 5) = 5 - 3a$ **f** $8(p + 2) = 1 + 3p$

6 Try to solve these equations. How many values of a satisfy each equation?

a $7(a + 3) = 21 + 7a$ **b** $3(a + 1) = 4 + 3a$

7 Solve the following equations:

a $4 - x = 2(x + 1) + 1$ **b** $3x + 1 = 2(1 - 3x) + 19$

c $10 - x = 5(x - 3) + 7$ **d** $7 + 6p = 3 + 2(1 - p)$

8 Solve for x:

a $3(x - 5) = 5x + 1$ **b** $x - 2 + 4(x - 1) = 2$

c $4 - 3x - (x + 5) = 3$ **d** $3x - 2(x + 3) - 4x = 0$

e $3(x - 6) = 2(2 - x) + 3$ **f** $2(x - 8) = 3(x - 5)$

g $4(2x + 3) - 10 = 5(3 - x)$ **h** $7 - (2 - 3x) = 12 - (5 - 4x)$

Activity 1 $\qquad\qquad$ *Solving equations*

Click on the icon to practise solving linear equations.

LEARNING ALGEBRA

E $\quad$ *RATIONAL EQUATIONS* $\qquad\qquad$ *[E2.3]*

Rational equations are equations involving fractions. To solve rational equations, we write all the fractions in the equation with the same **lowest common denominator (LCD)**, and then equate the numerators.

For fractions whose denominators involve the variable, the lowest common denominator is found in the same way as for numerical fractions.

For example: • in $\dfrac{x}{4} = \dfrac{x + 1}{6}$ the LCD is 12   • in $\dfrac{5}{3x} = \dfrac{7}{9}$ the LCD is $9x$

Example 11 $\qquad\qquad$ ◀) Self Tutor

Solve for x: $\dfrac{x}{2} = \dfrac{3 + x}{5}$

$\dfrac{x}{2} = \dfrac{3 + x}{5}$ has LCD $= 10$

$\therefore \dfrac{x}{2} \times \dfrac{5}{5} = \dfrac{2}{2} \times \left(\dfrac{3 + x}{5}\right)$ {creating a common denominator}

$\therefore 5x = 2(3 + x)$ {equating numerators}

$\therefore 5x = 6 + 2x$ {expanding brackets}

$\therefore 3x = 6$ {subtracting $2x$ from both sides}

$\therefore x = 2$ {dividing both sides by 3}

Notice the use of brackets.

EXERCISE 5E

1 Solve for x:

a $\dfrac{x}{2} = \dfrac{5}{9}$

b $\dfrac{x-1}{5} = \dfrac{x}{10}$

c $\dfrac{x}{3} = \dfrac{x+1}{2}$

d $\dfrac{x+2}{5} = \dfrac{3x-1}{4}$

e $\dfrac{3x}{4} = \dfrac{6-x}{5}$

f $\dfrac{2x-5}{4} = \dfrac{3x-1}{-2}$

g $\dfrac{x+5}{2} = 1 - x$

h $\dfrac{2x+7}{3} = x + 4$

i $\dfrac{2x+9}{2} = x - 8$

Example 12   ◀) Self Tutor

Solve for x: $\dfrac{1}{2x} = -3$

$\dfrac{1}{2x} = -3$

$\therefore \dfrac{1}{2x} = -3 \times \dfrac{2x}{2x}$ $\{\text{LCD} = 2x\}$

$\therefore 1 = -6x$ $\{\text{equating numerators}\}$

$\therefore x = -\tfrac{1}{6}$ $\{\text{dividing both sides by } -6\}$

---

2 Solve for x:

a $\dfrac{1}{x} = 3$

b $\dfrac{1}{x} = -4$

c $\dfrac{3}{2x} = 1$

d $-\dfrac{1}{3x} = 2$

e $\dfrac{3}{x} = \dfrac{2}{7}$

f $\dfrac{6}{5} = \dfrac{4}{x}$

g $\dfrac{4}{3x} = \dfrac{8}{7}$

h $\dfrac{7}{2x} = -\dfrac{1}{8}$

Example 13   ◀) Self Tutor

Solve for x: $\dfrac{3x+1}{x-1} = -2$

$\dfrac{3x+1}{x-1} = \dfrac{-2}{1}$

$\therefore \dfrac{3x+1}{x-1} = \dfrac{-2 \times (x-1)}{1 \times (x-1)}$ $\{\text{LCD} = x-1\}$

$\therefore 3x+1 = -2(x-1)$ $\{\text{equating numerators}\}$

$\therefore 3x+1 = -2x+2$ $\{\text{expanding brackets}\}$

$\therefore 5x+1 = 2$ $\{\text{adding } 2x \text{ to both sides}\}$

$\therefore 5x = 1$ $\{\text{subtracting 1 from both sides}\}$

$\therefore x = \tfrac{1}{5}$ $\{\text{dividing both sides by 5}\}$

---

3 Solve for x:

a $\dfrac{1}{x+3} = 1$

b $\dfrac{3}{1-x} = 2$

c $\dfrac{2}{3-x} = \dfrac{1}{2}$

d $\dfrac{-1}{x+2} = \dfrac{2}{3}$

e $\dfrac{2x+1}{x-4} = 4$

f $\dfrac{2x}{x+4} = 3$

g $\dfrac{-3}{2x-1} = 5$

h $\dfrac{4x+1}{x+2} = -3$

4 Solve for x:

a $\dfrac{x}{4} - 3 = \dfrac{2x}{3}$

b $\dfrac{x}{8} + \dfrac{x+2}{2} = -1$

c $\dfrac{2x-1}{3} - \dfrac{5x-6}{6} = -2$

d $\dfrac{2x-7}{3} - 1 = \dfrac{x-4}{6}$

e $\dfrac{x+1}{3} + \dfrac{x-2}{6} = \dfrac{x+4}{12}$

f $\dfrac{2x+1}{4} - \dfrac{1-4x}{2} = \dfrac{3x+7}{6}$

Activity 2   *Identities*

An **identity** is an equation which is always true no matter what value the variable takes.

For example, $2x + 3x = 5x$ is true for all values of x, so this equation is an identity.

What to do:

1 Decide whether the following equations are identities:

a $x + 2 = 2 + x$

b $x - x = 0$

c $3 + x = 3x$

d $x \times 1 = x$

e $0 \times x = 0$

f $4 - x = x - 4$

g $\dfrac{x}{-1} = -x$

h $\dfrac{x}{5} = 5x$

i $\dfrac{x}{x} = 1$

2 For the equations in **1** which are *not* identities, find the value(s) of x which make the equation true.

F   PROBLEM SOLVING

Many problems can be translated into **algebraic equations**. To solve problems using algebra, we follow these steps:

Step 1:   Decide on the unknown quantity and allocate it a variable such as x.

Step 2:   Translate the problem into an equation.

Step 3:   Solve the equation by isolating the variable.

Step 4:   Check that the solution satisfies the original problem.

Step 5:   Write the answer in sentence form, describing how the solution relates to the original problem.

Example 14   ◀) *Self Tutor*

The sum of 3 consecutive even integers is 132. Find the smallest integer.

Let x be the smallest even integer.

$\therefore$ the next is $x + 2$, and the largest is $x + 4$.

So, $x + (x+2) + (x+4) = 132$ {their sum is 132}

$\therefore \quad 3x + 6 = 132$

$\therefore \quad 3x + 6 - 6 = 132 - 6$ {subtracting 6 from both sides}

$\therefore \quad 3x = 126$

$\therefore \quad \dfrac{3x}{3} = \dfrac{126}{3}$ {dividing both sides by 3}

$\therefore \quad x = 42$

$\therefore$ the smallest integer is 42.

Example 15
🔊 *Self Tutor*

If twice a number is subtracted from 11, the result is 4 more than the number.
What is the number?

Let x be the number.

$$\therefore \quad 11 - 2x = x + 4$$
$$\therefore \quad 11 - 2x + 2x = x + 4 + 2x \qquad \{\text{adding } 2x \text{ to both sides}\}$$
$$\therefore \quad 11 = 3x + 4$$
$$\therefore \quad 11 - 4 = 3x + 4 - 4 \qquad \{\text{subtracting 4 from both sides}\}$$
$$\therefore \quad 7 = 3x$$
$$\therefore \quad \frac{7}{3} = \frac{3x}{3} \qquad \{\text{dividing both sides by 3}\}$$
$$\therefore \quad x = 2\tfrac{1}{3}$$

So, the number is $2\tfrac{1}{3}$.

EXERCISE 5F

1 When a number is doubled, the result is 18. Find the number.

2 When 6 is added to a number, the result is 11. Find the number.

3 When a number is trebled and the result is decreased by 5, the answer is 19. Find the number.

4 Two consecutive integers have a sum of 173. Find the numbers.

5 Three consecutive integers add to 108. Find the smallest of them.

6 When a number is decreased by 1 and the resulting number is halved, the answer is 45. Find the number.

7 Three times a number is equal to 17 minus the number. Find the number.

8 Cat food tins are sold in packs of 6. Rachel bought 42 tins in total. How many packs did she buy?

9 Julian's sister owns 3 more shirts than he does. Between them they own 15 shirts. How many shirts does Julian own?

10 A plane flying from Liverpool to Madrid is carrying 30 rows of passengers, as well as 12 crew members. There are 222 people on board the plane, and every seat is taken. How many passengers are in each row?

11 Drew, Paige, and Henry went to a birthday party. Drew ate 7 more sweets than Paige, and Henry ate 2 fewer sweets than Paige. Between them they ate 20 sweets. How many sweets did Paige eat?

12 During a volleyball training session, Keela drank twice as much water as Carol, and Xavier drank 100 ml more water than Keela. Between them they drank 3 litres of water. How much water did Carol drink?

13 In a cricket match, Emma scored 5 fewer runs than Alex, and Alex scored three times as many runs as Toni. Between them they scored 93 runs. How many runs did each player score?

14 Solve the **Opening Problem** on page **73**.

Example 16

◀) *Self Tutor*

Cans of sardines are sold in two sizes. Small cans cost $2 each, and large cans cost $3 each.
If 15 cans of sardines were bought for a total of $38, how many small cans were bought?

Size	Cost per can	Number bought	Value
small	$2	x	$2x$
large	$3	$15 - x$	$3(15 - x)$
		15	$38

$2x + 3(15 - x) = 38$

$\therefore \ 2x + 45 - 3x = 38$ {expanding brackets}

$\therefore \ \ 45 - x = 38$

$\therefore \ \ -x = -7$ {subtracting 45 from both sides}

$\therefore \ \ x = 7$

So, 7 small cans were bought.

15 Isaac is going to boarding school. He buys school shirts at $35 each and trousers at $49 each. Altogether he buys 9 items, and their total cost is $357. How many shirts does he buy?

16 I have 36 coins in my pocket, all of which are 5-cent or 10-cent coins. If their total value is $3.20, how many 5-cent coins do I have?

17 Oranges cost 25 cents each and apples cost 30 cents each. I bought 5 more oranges than apples, and the total cost was $4.55. How many apples did I buy?

18 Ellie is now four times as old as her son. In 5 years' time she will be three times as old as her son. How old is Ellie's son now?

19 Four years ago, Adrian was one quarter of his brother's age. In two years' time, his age doubled will equal his brother's age. How old is Adrian now?

Review set 5A

1 Find the equation which results when:

   a 2 is added to both sides of $3x - 2 = -11$

   b 9 is subtracted from both sides of $4x + 9 = -1$.

2 Solve for x:

   a $10x - 7 = 13$ **b** $5 + 4x = 29$ **c** $3 - 2x = 9$

   d $4x + 7 = -1$ **e** $4x - 5 = 5x - 6$ **f** $\dfrac{5x + 4}{3} = -2$

3 Solve for x:

   a $7x - 6 = 6x - 1$ **b** $4(5x + 1) = 14$

   c $3x + 2(3 - x) = -3$ **d** $4x - 2(3x - 1) = 5 - 7x$

   e $3(x + 6) - 4(4 - 2x) = 7x + 6$ **f** $9 - 5(x - 1) = 2(x + 4)$

4 Solve for x:

   a $\dfrac{x + 3}{5} = \dfrac{x - 4}{2}$ **b** $\dfrac{4}{3x} = \dfrac{10}{7}$ **c** $\dfrac{3}{2 - x} = \dfrac{2}{3}$

   d $\dfrac{x + 6}{3 - 2x} = -1$ **e** $\dfrac{x}{2} + 2x = \dfrac{3x - 1}{4}$ **f** $\dfrac{x + 1}{3} - \dfrac{x}{6} = \dfrac{2x - 3}{2}$

5 When a number is increased by 11 and the result is doubled, the answer is 48. Find the number.

6 The sum of three consecutive integers is 63. Find the smallest of the integers.

7 When 7 times a certain number is decreased by 11, the result is 31 more than the number. Find the number.

8 I have 25 coins consisting of 5-cent and 50-cent pieces. If the total value is $7.10, how many 5-cent coins do I have?

Review set 5B

1 Solve for x:

   a $3x + 5 = 17$ **b** $\dfrac{x}{4} + 1 = -11$ **c** $5 + 2x = 3$

2 Solve for x:

   a $2x + 1 = x + 8$ **b** $x - 4 = 5x - 1$ **c** $3(x - 3) = 8 - x$

3 Solve for x:

   a $3(4 - x) - 2x = -13$ **b** $3x - 5 = 3 - x$

   c $2(4x - 3) + x = 3(2x - 1) + 2$ **d** $2(x - 3) - 3(4 - x) = 4(2x - 5)$

4 Ms Maxwell wrote the equation $\dfrac{x}{3} + 2 = 7$ on the board. She told her class there were *two* good ways to solve the equation.

   a The first method is to first multiply *each* term in the equation by 3.

      i Find the equation that results when *each* term is multiplied by 3.

      ii Hence solve the equation.

   b The second method is to first subtract 2 from each side of the equation.

      i Find the equation that results when 2 is subtracted from both sides of $\dfrac{x}{3} + 2 = 7$.

      ii Hence solve the equation.

   c Do the two methods give the same answer?

5 Solve for x:

   a $\dfrac{x - 3}{4} = \dfrac{2x}{5}$ **b** $\dfrac{3}{5x} = -\dfrac{7}{8}$ **c** $\dfrac{2}{x + 5} = \dfrac{6}{7}$

   d $\dfrac{1 - 3x}{4} = \dfrac{x - 2}{2}$ **e** $\dfrac{2x + 1}{3} - \dfrac{4 - x}{6} = -2$

6 The sum of two consecutive odd integers is 36. Find the larger integer.

7 Five more than a certain number is nine less than three times the number. Find the number.

8 Writing pads cost $1.35 each and pens cost $0.85 each. I bought twice as many pens as pads, and the total cost was $18.30. How many pads did I buy?

9 Sadao likes collecting action figures. In total he has 44 figures belonging to three categories. He has 2 more transformers than chogokin, and he has 1 more anime figure than transformers. How many chogokin does Sadao have?

Sets and Venn diagrams

6

Contents:

A	Set notation	[E9.1, E9.2]
B	Complement of a set	[E9.2]
C	Intersection and union	[E9.4]
D	Special number sets	[E1.1, E9.2]
E	Interval notation	[E2.1, E9.2]
F	Venn diagrams	[E9.3]
G	Venn diagram regions	[E9.3]
H	Problem solving with Venn diagrams	[E9.3, E9.4]

Opening problem

A survey of 50 tea-drinkers found that 32 people surveyed put milk in their tea, 19 put sugar in their tea, and 10 put both milk and sugar in their tea.

Things to think about:

a How can we represent this information using a diagram?

b How many of the people surveyed have their tea with:

  i milk but not sugar   **ii** milk or sugar

  iii neither milk nor sugar?

A   SET NOTATION   [E9.1, E9.2]

A **set** is a collection of numbers or objects.

Each object is called an **element** or **member** of the set.

When we record a set, we write its members within curly brackets, with commas between them.

We often use a capital letter to represent a set so that we can refer to it easily.

For example: E is the set of all IGCSE students who study English.

                P is the set of all prime numbers less than 10.

These sets could be written in the form: $E = \{$IGCSE students who study English$\}$
$P = \{2, 3, 5, 7\}$

where the curly brackets are read as "the set of".

SET NOTATION

> $\in$ means   "is an element of"   or   "is in"
> $\notin$ means   "is not an element of"   or   "is not in"
> $n(A)$ means   "the number of elements in set A".

For example, if $M = \{4, 8, 12, 16, 20, 24, 28\}$ then $12 \in M$, $19 \notin M$, and $n(M) = 7$.

FINITE AND INFINITE SETS

> Set A is a **finite set** if $n(A)$ has a particular defined value.
> If A has an endless number of elements, we say it is an **infinite set**.

EQUAL SETS

> Two sets are **equal** if they contain exactly the same elements.

For example, $\{2, 3, 5, 7\} = \{5, 3, 7, 2\}$.

SUBSETS

> Set A is a **subset** of set B if every element of A is also an element of B. We write $A \subseteq B$.

For example, if $A = \{1, 3, 6\}$ and $B = \{1, 2, 3, 5, 6, 7\}$, then every element of A is also an element
of B. A is a subset of B, and we write $A \subseteq B$.

> A is a **proper subset** of B if every element of A is also an element of B, but $A \neq B$.
> We write $A \subset B$.

EMPTY SET

> The **empty set** $\varnothing$ or $\{ \ \}$ is a set which contains no elements.

For example, the set of multiples of 5 between 1 and 4 is the empty set.

The empty set is a subset of all other sets.

Example 1   ◀) Self Tutor

Let P be the set of all multiples of 6 less than 20, and Q be the set of all
even numbers less than 20.
- **a** List the elements of P and Q.
- **b** True or false?   **i** $10 \in P$ **ii** $10 \notin Q$ **iii** $12 \in P$
- **c** Find: **i** $n(P)$ **ii** $n(Q)$.
- **d** Is $P \subseteq Q$?

> **a** $P = \{6, 12, 18\}$, $Q = \{2, 4, 6, 8, 10, 12, 14, 16, 18\}$
>
> **b** **i** 10 is not an element of P, so $10 \in P$ is false.
>
>   **ii** 10 is an element of Q, so $10 \notin Q$ is false.
>
>   **iii** 12 is an element of P, so $12 \in P$ is true.
>
> **c** **i** $n(P) = 3$ {P has 3 elements}
>
>   **ii** $n(Q) = 9$ {Q has 9 elements}
>
> **d** Every element of P is also an element of Q, so $P \subseteq Q$.

EXERCISE 6A

1 List the elements of each set:

   a {days of the week}   **b** {letters in the word FOOTBALL}

   c {prime numbers less than 20}   **d** {vowels}

   e {factors of 21}

2 Decide whether each set is finite or infinite. Explain your answers.

   a {counting numbers}   **b** {factors of 123 456}   **c** {stars in the universe}

3 Let $S = \{2, 3, 5, 8, 11, 12\}$ and $T = \{2, 4, 5, 12\}$.

   a Find: **i** $n(S)$ **ii** $n(T)$.

   b True or false?

       i $5 \in S$ **ii** $5 \in T$ **iii** $12 \notin T$ **iv** $4 \notin S$

   c Is $T \subseteq S$?

4 Suppose $A = \{$positive square numbers less than 10$\}$, $B = \{$composite numbers less than 20$\}$,
    and $C = \{$factors of 36$\}$.

   a List the elements of: **i** A **ii** B **iii** C.

   b Find: **i** $n(A)$ **ii** $n(B)$ **iii** $n(C)$.

   c True or false?   **i** $A \subseteq B$ **ii** $A \subseteq C$

5 The subsets of $\{a, b\}$ are $\varnothing$, $\{a\}$, $\{b\}$ and $\{a, b\}$.

   a List all subsets of $\{a\}$.   **b** List all subsets of $\{a, b, c\}$.

   c Predict the number of subsets of $\{a, b, c, d\}$ without listing them.

6 For each set S, list the elements of S and hence state $n(S)$:

   a $S = \{$factors of 6$\}$ **b** $S = \{$multiples of 6$\}$

   c $S = \{$factors of 17$\}$ **d** $S = \{$multiples of 17$\}$

   e $S = \{$prime numbers less than 20$\}$ **f** $S = \{$composite numbers between 10 and 30$\}$

7 Let A be the set of colours on spinner 1, and
    B be the set of colours on spinner 2.

   a List the elements of A and B.

   b Is green $\in B$?

   c Find: **i** $n(A)$ **ii** $n(B)$.

   d Is $A \subseteq B$?

Spinner 1

Spinner 2

8 Suppose $F = \{2, 3, 5, 6, 7, 10, 11, 12\}$, $G = \{10, 5, x, 2, 12\}$, and $G \subseteq F$.
What possible values could x have?

9 Suppose $A = \{0, 2, -2, 16, -4, 8, 4\}$ and $B = \{x + 4, \ x^2\}$.
If B is a subset of A, find the possible values of x.

10 Suppose $A = \{\text{prime numbers between 20 and 30}\}$, $B = \{\text{even numbers between 20 and 30}\}$,
$C = \{\text{composite numbers between 20 and 30}\}$, and $D = \{\text{multiples of 18 between 20 and 30}\}$.
   a List the elements of each set.
   b Find: **i** $n(A)$ **ii** $n(D)$.
   c Which of the sets listed are:
      i subsets of A **ii** proper subsets of C?
   d True or false?   **i** $23 \in C$ **ii** $27 \notin A$ **iii** $25 \in B$

B   COMPLEMENT OF A SET   [E9.2]

When we are dealing with sets:

> The **universal set** U is the set of all elements we are considering.

For example, if we are considering the letters of the English alphabet, the universal set is:

$U = \{\text{a, b, c, d, e, f, g, h, i, j, k, l, m, n, o, p, q, r, s, t, u, v, w, x, y, z}\}$

From this universal set we can define subsets of U, such as $V = \{\text{vowels}\} = \{\text{a, e, i, o, u}\}$ and
$C = \{\text{consonants}\} = \{\text{b, c, d, f, g, h, j, k, l, m, n, p, q, r, s, t, v, w, x, y, z}\}$.

> The **complement** of a set A is the set of all elements of U that are *not* elements of A.
> The complement of A is written A'.

For example:
- if $U = \{1, 2, 3, 4, 5, 6, 7, 8, 9\}$ and $A = \{2, 3, 5, 7\}$, then $A' = \{1, 4, 6, 8, 9\}$
- if $U = \{\text{letters of the English alphabet}\}$, $V = \{\text{vowels}\}$, and $C = \{\text{consonants}\}$, then $V' = C$ and $C' = V$.

EXERCISE 6B

1 Let $U = \{1, 2, 3, 4, 5, 6, 7, 8, 9\}$. Find the complement of:
   a $A = \{2, 4, 6\}$ **b** $B = \{1, 3, 5, 7, 9\}$
   c $C = \{8, 4, 7, 3\}$ **d** $D = \{1, 2, 3, 7, 8, 9\}$

For any set A,
$A \cup A' = U$.

2 Suppose $U = \{\text{whole numbers between 0 and 20}\}$, $P = \{\text{factors of 12}\}$,
and $Q = \{\text{prime numbers between 10 and 20}\}$. List the elements of:
   a P **b** Q **c** P' **d** Q'

3 Alongside is a list of sports played at a school.

Let K be the set of sports that involve hitting a ball with a bat or racquet.

a List the elements of:

    i U **ii** K **iii** K'.

b What do the elements of K' represent?

> **SPORTS**
> Rugby
> Athletics
> Volleyball
> Baseball
> Cricket
> Archery
> Netball
> Tennis

4 **a** Suppose $U = \{2, 3, 4, 5, 6, 7, 8\}$, $A = \{2, 3, 4, 7\}$, and $B = \{2, 5\}$. Find:

    i $n(U)$ **ii** $n(A)$ **iii** $n(A')$ **iv** $n(B)$ **v** $n(B')$.

  b Copy and complete: For any set S within a universal set U, $n(S) + n(S') = \ldots\ldots$

C   INTERSECTION AND UNION   *[E9.4]*

INTERSECTION

> The **intersection** of two sets A and B is the set of elements that are in **both** set A **and** set B.
>
> The intersection of sets A and B is written $\boldsymbol{A \cap B}$.

For example, if $A = \{2, 5, 7, 9\}$ and $B = \{3, 5, 9, 10\}$, then $A \cap B = \{5, 9\}$.

> Two sets A and B are **disjoint** if they have no elements in common. In this case $A \cap B = \varnothing$.

UNION

> The **union** of two sets A and B is the set of elements that are in **either** set A **or** set B.
>
> The union of sets A and B is written $\boldsymbol{A \cup B}$.

> Elements in both A and B **are included** in the union of A and B.

For example, if $A = \{2, 5, 7, 9\}$ and $B = \{3, 5, 9, 10\}$, then $A \cup B = \{2, 3, 5, 7, 9, 10\}$.

Example 2   ◀) *Self Tutor*

Let $P = \{b, c, f, g, h\}$ and $Q = \{c, d, g, i\}$. Find:

  a $P \cap Q$ **b** $P \cup Q$.

  a $P \cap Q = \{c, g\}$ {c and g are elements of both sets}

  b $P \cup Q = \{b, c, d, f, g, h, i\}$ {elements of either P or Q}

EXERCISE 6C

1 Suppose $A = \{1, 3, 5, 7\}$ and $B = \{3, 5, 6, 9\}$. Find:

  a $A \cap B$ **b** $A \cup B$.

2 Find $P \cap Q$ and $P \cup Q$ for:

    a $P = \{$Dragons, Tigers, Roosters, Raiders$\}$, $Q = \{$Tigers, Storm, Dragons, Knights$\}$

    b $P = \{1, 3, 6, 10, 15\}$, $Q = \{1, 4, 9, 16\}$

    c $P = \{d, e, g, k, m\}$, $Q = \{g, h, l, m, p\}$

3 Let $A = \{$blue, green, yellow$\}$, $B = \{$green, red, pink$\}$, and $C = \{$orange, blue, black$\}$. Which pair of sets is disjoint?

4 Suppose $X = \{$prime numbers less than 20$\}$ and $Y = \{$factors of 20$\}$.

    a List the elements of X and Y.

    b Find: **i** $X \cap Y$ **ii** $n(X \cap Y)$ **iii** $X \cup Y$ **iv** $n(X \cup Y)$.

5 Sarah has gardenias and roses in her garden in New Zealand. Her gardenias flower every year from September to December, and her roses flower from October to March. Let G be the set of months when the gardenias flower, and R be the set of months when the roses flower.

    a State the universal set U in this case.

    b List the elements of G and R.

    c Find $G \cap R$. What does this set represent?

    d Find $G \cup R$. What does this set represent?

    e Find $(G \cup R)'$. What does this set represent?

6 Suppose $A = \{$multiples of 4 which are less than 10$\}$ and $B = \{$factors of 16$\}$.

    a List the elements of A and B.

    b Is $A \subseteq B$?

    c Find: **i** $A \cap B$ **ii** $A \cup B$.

    d Copy and complete: "If $A \subseteq B$, then $A \cap B = $ ...... and $A \cup B = $ ......"

7   **a** Let $U = \{1, 2, 3, 4, 5, 6, 7, 8\}$, $X = \{1, 3, 5, 7\}$, and $Y = \{2, 4, 6, 8\}$. Find:

        i $X \cap Y$ **ii** $X \cup Y$.

    b Let A be a set in the universal set U. Find:

        i $A \cap A'$ **ii** $A \cup A'$.

D   *SPECIAL NUMBER SETS*   *[E1.1, E9.2]*

Following is a list of some special number sets you should be familiar with. They are all endless, so they are infinite sets.

• $\mathbb{N} = \{0, 1, 2, 3, 4, 5, 6, 7, ...\}$ is the set of all **natural** or **counting numbers**.

• $\mathbb{Z} = \{0, \pm 1, \pm 2, \pm 3, \pm 4, ...\}$ is the set of all **integers**.

- $\mathbb{Z}^+ = \{1, 2, 3, 4, 5, 6, 7, ...\}$ is the set of all **positive integers**.

- $\mathbb{Q}$ is the set of all **rational numbers**, or numbers which can be written in the form $\frac{p}{q}$ where p and q are integers, $q \neq 0$.

  For example:
  - $\frac{1}{3}, \frac{15}{32}, \frac{-5}{4}$ are all rational
  - 5 is rational as $5 = \frac{5}{1}$ or $\frac{20}{4}$
  - $0.\dot{8}$ is rational as $0.\dot{8} = \frac{8}{9}$
  - $-2\frac{1}{4}$ is rational as $-2\frac{1}{4} = \frac{-9}{4}$
  - 0.431 is rational as $0.431 = \frac{431}{1000}$
  - $\sqrt{9}$ is rational as $\sqrt{9} = \frac{3}{1}$
  - All decimal numbers that terminate or recur are rational numbers

- $\mathbb{Q}'$ is the set of all **irrational numbers**, or numbers which cannot be written in rational form.

  For example: $\sqrt{2}$, $\sqrt[3]{7}$, and π are all irrational.

- $\mathbb{R}$ is the set of all **real numbers**, which are all numbers that can be placed on the number line.

$\mathbb{R}$ includes all rational and irrational numbers.
$\frac{2}{0}$ and $\sqrt{-5}$ cannot be placed on a number line, and so are not real.

EXERCISE 6D

1 Copy and complete:

Number	$\mathbb{N}$	$\mathbb{Z}$	$\mathbb{Q}$	$\mathbb{R}$
19	✓	✓	✓	✓
$-\frac{2}{3}$				
$\sqrt{7}$				
5.6389				
$\sqrt{16}$				
2π				
-11				
$\frac{6}{0}$				
$\sqrt{-2}$				

2 Determine whether each statement is true or false:

  a $3 \in \mathbb{Z}^+$
  b $6 \in \mathbb{Z}$
  c $\frac{3}{4} \in \mathbb{Q}$
  d $\sqrt{2} \notin \mathbb{Q}$

  e $-\frac{1}{4} \notin \mathbb{Q}$
  f $2\frac{1}{3} \in \mathbb{Z}$
  g $0.3684 \in \mathbb{R}$
  h $\frac{1}{0.1} \in \mathbb{Z}$

3 Determine whether each number is rational:

  a 8
  b -8
  c $2\frac{1}{3}$
  d $-3\frac{1}{4}$

  e $\sqrt{3}$
  f $\sqrt{400}$
  g 9.176
  h $\pi - \pi$

Example 3   ◀)) *Self Tutor*

Show that $0.\dot{3}\dot{6} = 0.36363636....$ is a rational number.

Let $x = 0.\dot{3}\dot{6} = 0.36363636....$

$\therefore$ $100x = 36.363636.... = 36 + x$

$\therefore$ $99x = 36$ and so $x = \frac{36}{99} = \frac{4}{11}$

So, $0.\dot{3}\dot{6}$ is actually the rational number $\frac{4}{11}$.

---

4 Show that these numbers are rational:

    a $0.\dot{7}$ **b** $0.\dot{4}\dot{1}$ **c** $0.\dot{3}2\dot{4}$

5 Explain why:

    a 0.527 is a rational number   **b** $0.\dot{9}$ is an integer.

6 Give examples to show that these statements are false:

    a The sum of two irrationals is irrational.   **b** The product of two irrationals is irrational.

7 True or false?

    a $\mathbb{N} \subseteq \mathbb{Z}$ **b** $\mathbb{R} \subseteq \mathbb{Q}$ **c** $\mathbb{Z} \subseteq \mathbb{Q}$.

E INTERVAL NOTATION   *[E2.1, E9.2]*

To describe the set of all integers between 3 and 8, we can list the set as $\{4, 5, 6, 7\}$ or illustrate the set as points on a number line. Alternatively, we can write the set using **interval notation** as $\{x \mid 3 < x < 8, \ x \in \mathbb{Z}\}$.

We read this as "the set of all integers x such that x lies between 3 and 8".

> The notation $\{x \mid ......\}$ is used to describe "the set of all x such that ......".

Interval notation is very useful if the set contains a large or infinite number of elements and listing them would be time consuming or impossible.

The set of all *real numbers* between 3 and 8 would be written as $\{x \mid 3 < x < 8, \ x \in \mathbb{R}\}$.

Unless stated otherwise, we *assume* we are dealing with *real* numbers. Thus, the set can also be written as $\{x \mid 3 < x < 8\}$.

Open circles indicate that 3 and 8 are not included.

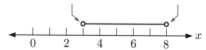

The set of all real numbers between 3 and 8 *inclusive* would be written as $\{x \mid 3 \leqslant x \leqslant 8, \ x \in \mathbb{R}\}$ or just $\{x \mid 3 \leqslant x \leqslant 8\}$.

Filled in circles indicate that 3 and 8 are included.

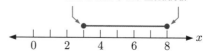

Example 4   ◀) **Self Tutor**

Represent on a number line:

   a $1 \leqslant x < 5$ **b** $x < 0$ or $x \geqslant 4$

a ![number line a]   **b** ![number line b]

EXERCISE 6E

1 Represent on a number line:

  a $x > 5$ **b** $x \geqslant 1$ **c** $x \leqslant 2$ **d** $x < -1$

  e $-2 \leqslant x \leqslant 2$ **f** $-3 < x \leqslant 4$ **g** $1 \leqslant x < 6$ **h** $-1 < x < 0$

  i $x < 0$ or $x \geqslant 3$ **j** $x \leqslant -1$ or $x \geqslant 2$ **k** $x < 2$ or $x > 5$ **l** $x \leqslant -2$ or $x > 0$

2 Write in interval notation:

  a
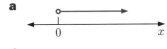

  b

  c

  d
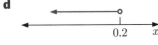

  e
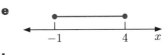

  f
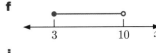

  g
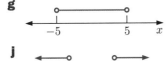

  h

  i
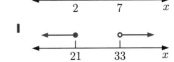

  j

  k

  l

Example 5   ◀) **Self Tutor**

Write down the meaning of the interval notation, and list the elements of the set:

  a $\{x \mid -2 \leqslant x \leqslant 1, \ x \in \mathbb{Z}\}$ **b** $\{x \mid x > 2, \ x \in \mathbb{N}\}$

  a $\{x \mid -2 \leqslant x \leqslant 1, \ x \in \mathbb{Z}\}$ is the set of integers greater than or equal to -2 and less than or equal to 1.

     $\therefore \ \ x \in \{-2, -1, 0, 1\}$

  b $\{x \mid x > 2, \ x \in \mathbb{N}\}$ is the set of natural numbers greater than 2.

     $\therefore \ \ x \in \{3, 4, 5, 6, ...\}$

3 Write down the meaning of the interval notation:

  a $\{x \mid x > 4\}$ **b** $\{x \mid x \leqslant 5, \ x \in \mathbb{N}\}$ **c** $\{y \mid 0 < y < 8, \ y \in \mathbb{Z}\}$

  d $\{x \mid 1 \leqslant x \leqslant 4, \ x \in \mathbb{R}\}$ **e** $\{t \mid 2 < t < 7, \ t \in \mathbb{Z}^+\}$ **f** $\{n \mid n \leqslant 3 \text{ or } n > 6\}$

4 List the elements of the set:

  a $\{x \mid 1 < x \leqslant 6, \ x \in \mathbb{Z}\}$ **b** $\{x \mid x \leqslant 5, \ x \in \mathbb{Z}\}$ **c** $\{x \mid x \geqslant 3, \ x \in \mathbb{Z}\}$

  d $\{x \mid -3 \leqslant x \leqslant 5, \ x \in \mathbb{N}\}$ **e** $\{x \mid x < -4, \ x \in \mathbb{Z}\}$ **f** $\{x \mid x > 6, \ x \in \mathbb{Z}^+\}$

Example 6   ◆⟩ *Self Tutor*

Write in interval notation:

a $\{-3, -2, -1, 0, 1, 2, 3, 4, ...\}$

b

c

a The elements of the set are all integers, so we know $x \in \mathbb{Z}$.
$\{-3, -2, -1, 0, 1, 2, ...\} = \{x \mid x \geqslant -3, \ x \in \mathbb{Z}\}$

b $\{x \mid 1 \leqslant x \leqslant 5, \ x \in \mathbb{N}\}$ **c** $\{x \mid -3 \leqslant x < 6\}$
or $\{x \mid 1 \leqslant x \leqslant 5, \ x \in \mathbb{Z}\}$

5 Write in interval notation:

a $\{-5, -4, -3, -2, -1\}$ **b** $\{0, 1, 2, 3, 4, 5\}$ **c** $\{4, 5, 6, 7, 8, ...\}$
d $\{...., -3, -2, -1, 0, 1\}$ **e** $\{-5, -4, -3, -2, -1, 0, 1\}$ **f** $\{...., 41, 42, 43, 44\}$

6 Write in interval notation:

a    **b**

c 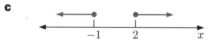   **d**

e    **f**

7 Sketch on a number line:

a $\{x \mid 4 \leqslant x < 8, \ x \in \mathbb{N}\}$ **b** $\{x \mid -5 < x \leqslant 4, \ x \in \mathbb{Z}\}$ **c** $\{x \mid -3 < x \leqslant 5, \ x \in \mathbb{R}\}$
d $\{x \mid x > -5, \ x \in \mathbb{Z}\}$ **e** $\{x \mid x \leqslant 6\}$ **f** $\{x \mid -5 \leqslant x \leqslant 0\}$

8 Determine whether each set is finite or infinite:

a $\{x \mid 1 \leqslant x \leqslant 10, \ x \in \mathbb{Z}\}$ **b** $\{x \mid x < 4, \ x \in \mathbb{Z}\}$ **c** $\{x \mid x > 5, \ x \in \mathbb{Z}^+\}$
d $\{x \mid x < 7, \ x \in \mathbb{Z}^+\}$ **e** $\{x \mid x \leqslant 9, \ x \in \mathbb{N}\}$ **f** $\{x \mid 2 \leqslant x \leqslant 6, \ x \in \mathbb{R}\}$

F VENN DIAGRAMS   [E9.3]

A **Venn diagram** consists of a universal set U represented by a rectangle, and subsets within it that are generally represented by circles.

The Venn diagram alongside shows set A within the universal set U.

The **complement** of A is the shaded region outside the circle.

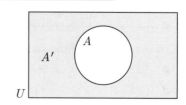

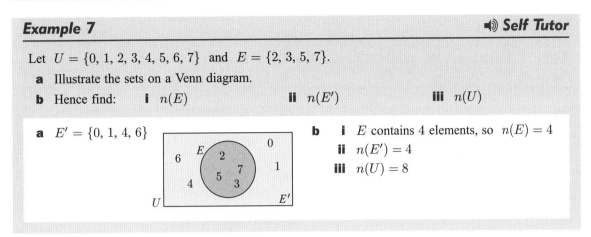

If B is a **subset** of A, then every element of B is also in A.

The circle representing B is placed within the circle representing A.

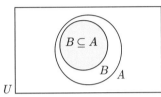

We can use this property to draw a Venn diagram for the special number sets $\mathbb{N}$, $\mathbb{Z}$, $\mathbb{Q}$ and $\mathbb{R}$. In this case $\mathbb{R}$ is the universal set, and $\mathbb{N} \subseteq \mathbb{Z} \subseteq \mathbb{Q} \subseteq \mathbb{R}$.

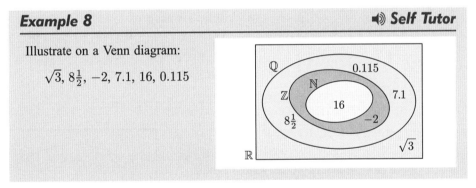

If two sets A and B have elements in common, but neither is a subset of the other, the circles for the sets overlap.

The **intersection** of A and B is the region which is in *both* circles.

$$A \cap B = \{x \mid x \in A \ \textbf{and} \ x \in B\}$$

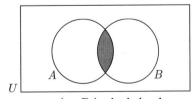

$A \cap B$ is shaded red.

The **union** of sets A and B is the region which is in *either* circle.

$$A \cup B = \{x \mid x \in A \ \textbf{or} \ x \in B\}$$

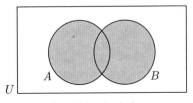

$A \cup B$ is shaded orange.

Example 9
◀)) *Self Tutor*

Let $U = \{x \mid 0 \leqslant x \leqslant 10, \ x \in \mathbb{Z}\}$, $A = \{2, 3, 5, 7\}$, and $B = \{1, 3, 6, 7, 8\}$.
a Find $A \cap B$ and $A \cup B$.   **b** Illustrate A and B on a Venn diagram.

a $A \cap B = \{3, 7\}$

$A \cup B = \{1, 2, 3, 5, 6, 7, 8\}$

b

EXERCISE 6F

1 Suppose $U = \{x \mid x \leqslant 8, \ x \in \mathbb{Z}^+\}$ and $A = \{\text{prime numbers} \leqslant 8\}$.

     a List the set A'.   **b** Show set A on a Venn diagram.   **c** Find $n(A)$ and $n(A')$.

2 Suppose $U = \{\text{letters of the English alphabet}\}$ and

                $V = \{\text{letters of the English alphabet which are vowels}\}$.

Illustrate set V on a Venn diagram.

3

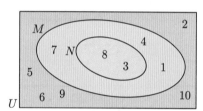

a List the elements of:

     i U **ii** N **iii** M.

b Find $n(N)$ and $n(M)$.

c Is $M \subseteq N$?

4 Suppose the universal set $U = \mathbb{R}$.

     a Copy the given Venn diagram, and label the sets $\mathbb{R}$, $\mathbb{Q}$, $\mathbb{Z}$, and $\mathbb{N}$. Place these numbers on the Venn diagram:

        $\frac{1}{2}, \sqrt{2}, 0.\dot{3}, -5, 5\frac{1}{4}, 0, 10$, and

        $0.213\,700\,561\,8.....$ which does not terminate or recur.

     b True or false?

        i $\mathbb{N} \subseteq \mathbb{Z}$ **ii** $\mathbb{Z} \subseteq \mathbb{Q}$ **iii** $\mathbb{N} \subseteq \mathbb{Q}$

     c Shade the region representing the set of irrationals $\mathbb{Q}'$.

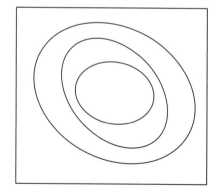

5 Show these sets on a Venn diagram:

     a $U = \{\text{triangles}\}$, $E = \{\text{equilateral triangles}\}$, $I = \{\text{isosceles triangles}\}$

     b $U = \{\text{quadrilaterals}\}$, $P = \{\text{parallelograms}\}$, $R = \{\text{rectangles}\}$

     c $U = \{\text{quadrilaterals}\}$, $P = \{\text{parallelograms}\}$, $R = \{\text{rectangles}\}$, $H = \{\text{rhombuses}\}$

     d $U = \{\text{quadrilaterals}\}$, $P = \{\text{parallelograms}\}$, $T = \{\text{trapezia}\}$

     e $U = \{\text{triangles}\}$, $I = \{\text{isosceles triangles}\}$, $R = \{\text{right angled triangles}\}$,

        $E = \{\text{equilateral triangles}\}$

6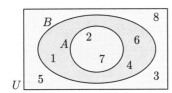

a List the elements of:
 i A **ii** B **iii** U
 iv $A \cap B$ **v** $A \cup B$.
b Find:
 i $n(A)$ **ii** $n(B)$ **iii** $n(U)$
 iv $n(A \cap B)$ **v** $n(A \cup B)$.

7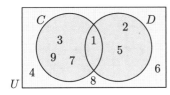

a List the elements of:
 i C **ii** D **iii** U
 iv $C \cap D$ **v** $C \cup D$.
b Find:
 i $n(C)$ **ii** $n(D)$ **iii** $n(U)$
 iv $n(C \cap D)$ **v** $n(C \cup D)$.

8 Let $U = \{1, 2, 3, 4, 5, 6\}$, $A = \{1, 2, 3, 4\}$, and $B = \{3, 4, 5, 6\}$.
 a Find $A \cap B$ and $A \cup B$.   **b** Illustrate A and B on a Venn diagram.

9 Let $U = \{3, 4, 5, 6, 7, 8, 9\}$, $A = \{3, 5, 7, 9\}$, and $B = \{4, 6, 8\}$.
 a Find $A \cap B$ and explain what this means about A and B.
 b Illustrate the sets on a Venn diagram.

10 Illustrate on a Venn diagram: $U = \{4, 5, 6, 7, 8, 9, 10\}$, $A = \{6, 7, 9, 10\}$, $B = \{5, 6, 8, 9\}$

11 Suppose $U = \{x \mid x \leqslant 30, \ x \in \mathbb{Z}^+\}$,
       $A = \{\text{factors of } 30\}$, and $B = \{\text{prime numbers} \leqslant 30\}$.
 a List the elements of set:
  i A **ii** B **iii** $A \cap B$ **iv** $A \cup B$.
 b Find:
  i $n(A)$ **ii** $n(B)$ **iii** $n(A \cap B)$ **iv** $n(A \cup B)$.
 c Show that $n(A \cup B) = n(A) + n(B) - n(A \cap B)$.
 d Illustrate the sets on a Venn diagram.

12 Suppose $U = \{x \mid x \leqslant 30, \ x \in \mathbb{Z}^+\}$,
        $A = \{\text{prime numbers} \leqslant 30\}$,
        $B = \{\text{multiples of } 5 \leqslant 30\}$
    and $C = \{\text{odd numbers} \leqslant 30\}$
Use the Venn diagram shown to display the
elements of the sets.

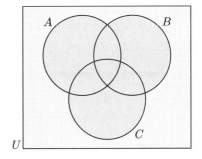

G **VENN DIAGRAM REGIONS**   **[E9.3]**

We can use Venn diagrams to help illustrate regions such as the union or intersection of sets.

The regions of a Venn diagram can be used to verify **set identities**. These are equations involving sets which are true for *all* sets.

Examples of set identities include:

$$A \cup A' = U \qquad\qquad A \cap A' = \varnothing$$
$$(A \cup B)' = A' \cap B' \qquad (A \cap B)' = A' \cup B'$$

Example 10   ◀)) *Self Tutor*

On separate Venn diagrams, shade these regions for two intersecting sets A and B:

   a $A \cup B$ **b** $A' \cap B$ **c** $(A \cap B)'$

a 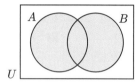   **b** 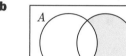   **c**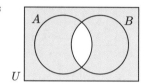

$A \cup B$ means in A, B, or both.

$A' \cap B$ means outside A, intersected with B.

$(A \cap B)'$ means outside the intersection of A and B.

EXERCISE 6G.1

1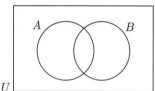

On separate Venn diagrams, shade the region:
   a in A **b** not in A
   c in neither A nor B **d** in A and B
   e in either A or B, but not both.

2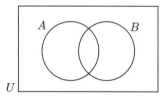

On separate Venn diagrams, shade:
   a B **b** B'
   c $A \cap B'$ **d** $A \cup B'$
   e $(A \cap B)'$ **f** $(A \cup B)'$

PRINTABLE VENN DIAGRAMS

3 Describe in words, the shaded region:

   a 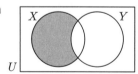   **b** 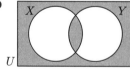   **c**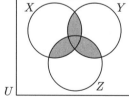

4 On separate Venn diagrams, shade:
   a A **b** B **c** C'
   d $A \cup B$ **e** $B \cap C$ **f** $A \cap B \cap C$
   g $A \cap B' \cap C$ **h** $(A \cup B)'$ **i** $A' \cup (B \cap C)$

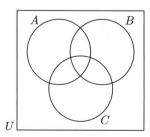

Example 11
●)) *Self Tutor*

Verify that $(A \cup B)' = A' \cap B'$.

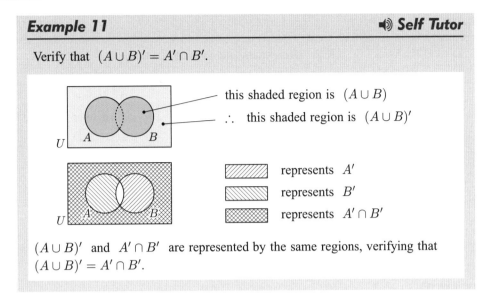

this shaded region is $(A \cup B)$

∴ this shaded region is $(A \cup B)'$

represents A'

represents B'

represents $A' \cap B'$

$(A \cup B)'$ and $A' \cap B'$ are represented by the same regions, verifying that $(A \cup B)' = A' \cap B'$.

5 Verify that:

a $(A \cap B)' = A' \cup B'$

b $A \cup (B \cap C) = (A \cup B) \cap (A \cup C)$

c $A \cap (B \cup C) = (A \cap B) \cup (A \cap C)$

Activity

Click on the icon to practise shading regions representing various subsets. The software includes two and three intersecting sets.

VENN DIAGRAM
REGIONS

Puzzle

Consider the three overlapping sets shown. The universal set contains the smallest positive integers such that each region of the diagram contains exactly one element.

Find the sum of all numbers in the universal set.

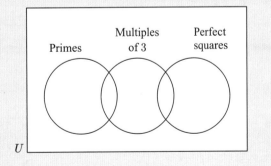

NUMBERS IN REGIONS

For many problems involving Venn diagrams, we are interested in *how many* elements are in each region, but not which elements these are.

To indicate the **number of elements** in a region of a Venn diagram, we write the number in brackets.

Example 12
◄») *Self Tutor*

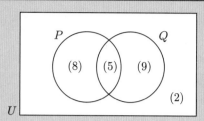

How many elements are there in:

a P **b** Q'

c $P \cup Q$ **d** P, but not Q

e Q, but not P **f** neither P nor Q?

a $n(P) = 8 + 5 = 13$

b $n(Q') = 8 + 2 = 10$

c $n(P \cup Q) = 8 + 5 + 9 = 22$

d $n(P,$ but not $Q) = 8$

e $n(Q,$ but not $P) = 9$

f $n($neither P nor $Q) = 2$

EXERCISE 6G.2

1

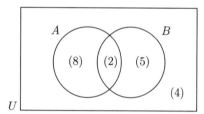

Give the number of elements in:

a B **b** A'

c $A \cup B$ **d** A, but not B

e B, but not A **f** U.

2

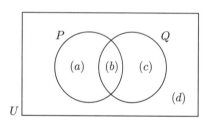

Find, in terms of a, b, c, and d, the number of elements in:

a Q **b** P'

c P or Q, but not both   **d** P and Q

e $(P \cap Q)'$ **f** $(P \cup Q)'$.

3   **a** Find, in terms of a:

        i $n(Q)$ **ii** $n(P \cup Q)$

        iii $n(Q')$ **iv** $n(U)$

   b Given that $n(U) = 43$, find a.

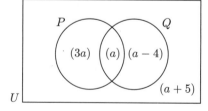

4

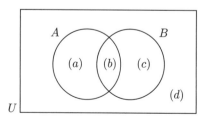

   a Use the Venn diagram to show that:

       $n(A \cup B) = n(A) + n(B) - n(A \cap B)$.

   b Suppose A and B are disjoint events.

       Explain why $n(A \cup B) = n(A) + n(B)$.

PROBLEM SOLVING WITH VENN DIAGRAMS   *[E9.3, E9.4]*

When we solve problems with Venn diagrams, we are generally only interested in the number of individuals in each region, rather than where a particular individual is placed.

Example 13   ◀)) *Self Tutor*

A sports club has 75 members.

42 members play tennis.

53 members play hockey.

27 members play both of these sports.

a Draw a Venn diagram to display this information.

b Hence determine the number of members who play:

   i neither sport   **ii** at least one sport.

a Let T be the set of members who play tennis and H be the set of members who play hockey.

$$n(T \cap H) = 27$$
$$\therefore \quad n(T \cap H') = 42 - 27 = 15$$
$$\text{and} \quad n(T' \cap H) = 53 - 27 = 26$$
$$\therefore \quad n(T' \cap H') = 75 - 27 - 15 - 26 = 7$$

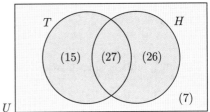

b **i** 7 members play neither sport.

    ii $75 - 7 = 68$ members play at least one sport.

EXERCISE 6H

1 A survey was conducted with a group of teenagers to see how many liked going to the cinema (C) and ice-skating (I). The results are shown in the Venn diagram. Determine the number of teenagers:

  a in the group   **b** who like going to the cinema

  c who like at least one of these activities

  d who only like ice-skating

  e who do not like going ice-skating.

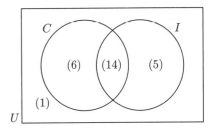

2 This Venn diagram describes the member participation of an outdoor adventure club in rock-climbing (R) and kayaking (K). Determine the number of members:

  a in the club   **b** who go rock-climbing

  c who do not go kayaking

  d who rock-climb but do not go kayaking

  e who do exactly one of these activities.

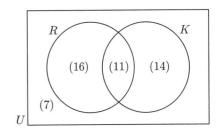

3 A team of 24 swimmers took part in a competition. 15 competed in freestyle (F), 11 competed in backstroke (B), and 6 competed in both of these strokes.

> **a** Display this information on a Venn diagram.
>
> **b** Hence determine the number of swimmers who competed in:
>
> > **i** backstroke but not freestyle   **ii** at least one of these strokes
> >
> > **iii** freestyle but not backstroke   **iv** neither stroke   **v** exactly one of these strokes.

Example 14

◀) *Self Tutor*

In a class of 24 boys, 16 play football (F) and 11 play baseball (B). If two play neither game, how many play both games?

Let $n(F \cap B) = x$

$\therefore\ n(F \cap B') = 16 - x$ and $n(F' \cap B) = 11 - x$.

We know 2 play neither sport.

Since there are 24 boys in total,

$$(16 - x) + x + (11 - x) + 2 = 24$$
$$\therefore\ 29 - x = 24$$
$$\therefore\ x = 5$$

So, 5 play both games.

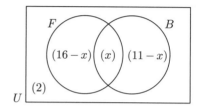

---

4 In a building with 58 apartments, 45 households have children (C), 19 have pets (P), and 5 have neither children nor pets.

> **a** Draw a Venn diagram to display this information.
>
> **b** Hence determine the number of households which:
>
> > **i** do not have children
> >
> > **ii** have children or pets or both
> >
> > **iii** have children or pets but not both
> >
> > **iv** have pets but not children
> >
> > **v** have children but not pets.

5 In a class of 36 girls, 18 play volleyball (V), 13 play badminton (B), and 11 play neither sport. Determine the number of girls who play both sports.

6 At their beachhouse, Anna and Ben have 37 books. Anna has read 21 of them and Ben has read 26 of them. 2 of the books have not been read at all. Find the number of books which have been read by:

> **a** both Anna and Ben   **b** Ben but not Anna.

7 On a particular day, 500 people visited a carnival. 300 people rode the Ferris wheel and 350 people rode the roller coaster. Each person rode at least one of these attractions. Find the number of people who rode:

> **a** both attractions   **b** the Ferris wheel but not the roller coaster.

8 There are 46 shops in the local mall. 25 shops sell clothes, 16 sell shoes, and 34 sell at least one of these items. Find how many shops sell:

> **a** both clothes and shoes   **b** neither clothes nor shoes   **c** clothes but not shoes.

9 All the guests at a barbecue ate either sausages or chicken shashliks. 18 guests ate sausages, 15 ate sausages and chicken shashliks, and 24 ate exactly one of sausages or chicken shashliks. How many guests attended the barbecue?

10   Joe owns an automotive garage which does car services and mechanical repairs. In one week, 18 cars had services or repairs, 9 had services, and 5 had both services and repairs. How many cars had repairs?

11   At a dance school each member studies at least one of classical ballet or modern dance. 72% study classical ballet and 35% study modern dance. What percentage of the students study both classical ballet and modern dance?

12   A group of 28 workers are repairing a road. 9 use machinery, 15 do not use shovels, and 7 do not use either machinery or shovels. How many workers use both machinery and shovels?

Example 15
◀)) **Self Tutor**

In a senior class, all 29 students take one or more of biology, chemistry and physics. The school records show that 15 take biology, 15 take chemistry, 18 take physics, 10 take biology and chemistry, 5 take chemistry and physics, and 7 take biology and physics.

How many students take all three subjects?

Let B, C, and P represent the students taking biology, chemistry, and physics respectively.

We know all students take at least one subject.

Let $n(B \cap C \cap P) = x$

$\therefore \; n(B \cap C \cap P') = 10 - x,$

$n(B \cap C' \cap P) = 7 - x,$

and $n(B' \cap C \cap P) = 5 - x.$

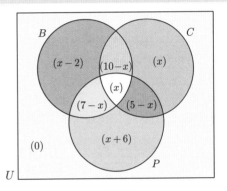

Now $n(B) = 15$, so $n(B \cap C' \cap P') = 15 - x - (10 - x) - (7 - x) = x - 2$

$n(C) = 15$, so $n(B' \cap C \cap P') = 15 - x - (10 - x) - (5 - x) = x$

and $n(P) = 18$, so $n(B' \cap C' \cap P) = 18 - x - (7 - x) - (5 - x) = x + 6$

Since there are 29 students in total,

$$(x - 2) + (10 - x) + x + (7 - x) + x + (5 - x) + (x + 6) = 29$$
$$\therefore \; x + 26 = 29$$
$$\therefore \; x = 3$$

So, 3 students take all three subjects.

---

13   In a small country town there are three restaurants. 42% of the population eat at A, 45% at B, and 41% at C. 15% eat at both A and B, 9% at A and C, and 17% at B and C. 4% eat at all three restaurants.

   a   Display this information on a Venn diagram.

   b   Hence find the percentage of the population who eat at:

   i   none of the restaurants   **ii**   at least one of the restaurants

   iii   exactly one of the restaurants   **iv**   either A or B **v** C only.

14   There are three hairdressing salons S, X and Z, within a large suburban shopping complex. A survey is made of female shoppers within the complex, to determine whether they are clients of S, X, or Z. 83 women are clients of at least one of S, X, or Z. 31 are clients of S, 32 are clients of X, and 49 are clients of Z. Of the women who are clients of S, 10 are also clients of X and 14 are also clients of Z. 12 women are clients of both X and Z. How many women are clients of all three salons?

15 75 supermarkets are surveyed to determine which brands of detergent they sell. All sell at least one of the brands A, B, and C. 55 sell brand A, 57 sell brand B, and 50 sell brand C. 33 supermarkets sell both A and C, while 17 supermarkets sell both A and B but not C. 22 supermarkets sell all three brands.

    a Draw a Venn diagram to display this information.

    b Hence find how many supermarkets sell:

       i both A and C but not B **ii** at least two of these brands.

16 In a school of 145 students, each was asked to choose one or more activities from sport, music, and drama. 76 students chose sport, 64 students chose music, and 40 students chose drama. 12 students chose both music and sport, 7 chose both sport and drama, and 21 chose both music and drama. How many students chose all three activities?

Review set 6A

1   **a** Explain why 1.3 is a rational number.

    b List the set of all prime numbers between 20 and 40.

    c Write a statement describing the meaning of $\{t \mid -1 \leqslant t < 3\}$.

    d Write in interval notation:

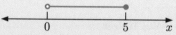

    e Sketch the number set $\{x \mid -2 \leqslant x \leqslant 3,\ x \in \mathbb{Z}\}$.

    f List the proper subsets of $M = \{1, 3, 6, 8\}$.

2

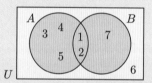

    a List the elements of set:

       i A **ii** B **iii** U

       iv $A \cup B$ **v** $A \cap B$.

    b Find:

       i $n(A)$ **ii** $n(B)$ **iii** $n(A \cup B)$.

3 Sam and Tess are planning a trip around the world together.

$S = \{\text{English, French, German, Spanish}\}$ is the set of languages Sam can speak.

$T = \{\text{English, German, Japanese}\}$ is the set of languages Tess can speak.

Find the following sets, and explain what they mean:

    a $S \cap T$ **b** $S \cup T$ **c** $S \cap T'$

4 Determine whether each statement is true or false:

    a $\sqrt{4000} \in \mathbb{Q}$ **b** $\mathbb{N} \subseteq \mathbb{Z}^{+}$ **c** $\mathbb{Q} \subseteq \mathbb{Z}$

5 Suppose $U = \{x \mid x \leqslant 12,\ x \in \mathbb{Z}^{+}\}$ and $A = \{\text{multiples of 3 which are} \leqslant 12\}$.

    a Show A on a Venn diagram.   **b** List the set A'.   **c** Find $n(A')$.

    d Suppose $C = \{1, 2, 4\}$. Is $C \subseteq A$?

6 Consider $U = \{x \mid x \leqslant 10,\ x \in \mathbb{Z}^{+}\}$, $P = \{2, 3, 5, 7\}$, and $Q = \{2, 4, 6, 8\}$.

    a Show these sets on a Venn diagram.

    b List the elements of: **i** $P \cup Q$ **ii** Q'.

    c Find: **i** $n(P')$ **ii** $n(P \cap Q)$.

    d Determine whether this statement is true or false: $P \cap Q \subseteq P$

7 Describe in words, the shaded region:

a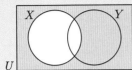

b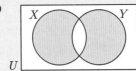

c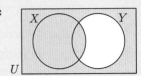

8 Zhe and Michelle are competitive chefs. In the 34 competitions they have both entered, Zhe has won 9 awards and Michelle has won 7 awards. They have both missed out on 22 occasions.

  a Draw a Venn diagram to display this information.

  b Hence determine the number of times that:

    i Zhe has won an award but Michelle has not

    ii Michelle has won an award but Zhe has not.

9

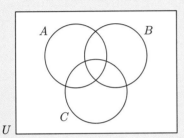

Using separate Venn diagrams like the one shown, shade regions to verify that
$(A \cap B) \cup C = (A \cup C) \cap (B \cup C)$.

10 In a survey at an English airport, 55 travellers said that last year they had been to Spain, 53 to France, and 49 to Germany. 18 had been to Spain and France, 15 to Spain and Germany, and 25 to France and Germany. 10 had been to all three countries.

  a Draw a Venn diagram to illustrate this information.

  b Hence find how many travellers took part in the survey.

Review set 6B

1 Determine whether each statement is true or false:

  a $-2 \in \mathbb{Z}^+$ **b** $\frac{1}{\sqrt{7}} \in \mathbb{Q}$

2 **a** Show that $0.\dot{5}\dot{1}$ is a rational number.

  b Write in interval notation:

  c Sketch the number set $\{x \mid x \leqslant 3 \text{ or } x > 7, \ x \in \mathbb{R}\}$.

3 Consider the universal set $U = \mathbb{R}$.

Copy the given Venn diagram, and label the sets $\mathbb{R}$, $\mathbb{Q}$, $\mathbb{Z}$, and $\mathbb{N}$.

Place these numbers on the Venn diagram:

$-1, \sqrt{2}, 2, 3.1, \frac{\pi}{2}, 4.\dot{2}$

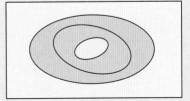

4 Suppose A is the set of all factors of 24 and B is the set of all factors of 18. Find:

  a $A \cap B$ **b** $A \cup B$.

5 Show these sets on a Venn diagram:

    a $U = \{10, 11, 12, 13, 14, 15\}$, $A = \{10, 12, 14\}$, $B = \{11, 12, 13\}$

    b $U = \{\text{quadrilaterals}\}$, $S = \{\text{squares}\}$, $R = \{\text{rectangles}\}$

    c $U = \mathbb{N}$, $A = \{\text{multiples of 2}\}$, $B = \{\text{multiples of 3}\}$, $C = \{\text{multiples of 4}\}$

6 Suppose $U = \{x \mid 12 \leqslant x \leqslant 20,\ x \in \mathbb{Z}\}$, $A = \{12, 14, 16, 18\}$, and $B = \{12, 15, 18\}$.

    a List the elements of:

       i U **ii** A' **iii** B' **iv** $A \cup B$ **v** $A' \cap B'$.

    b Show that $(A \cup B)' = A' \cap B'$.

7 Suppose $U = \{x \mid x \leqslant 10,\ x \in \mathbb{Z}^+\}$, $A = \{\text{primes less than 10}\}$, and
    $B = \{\text{odd numbers between 0 and 10}\}$.

    a Show these sets on a Venn diagram.

    b List the elements of:

       i A' **ii** $A \cap B$.

    c Find:

       i $n(A)$ **ii** $n(B')$ **iii** $n(A \cup B)$.

    d Determine whether each statement is true or false:

       i $A \subset B$ **ii** $A \cap B \subseteq A$

8 On separate Venn diagrams like the one shown, shade the
region representing:

    a B' **b** in A and in B **c** $(A \cup B)'$.

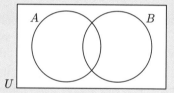

9 A survey was conducted with 120 students in a school to see how many students were members
of extra-curricular clubs. The following results were recorded for the jazz band, drama club, and
rowing team:

        10 students were not members of any of the three clubs

        50 were members of the jazz band

        50 were members of the drama club

        50 were members of the rowing team

        15 were members of the jazz band and drama club

        10 were members of the drama club and rowing team

        20 were members of the jazz band and rowing team.

    a Draw a Venn diagram to display this information.

    b Hence find the number of students who were members of:

       i all three clubs

       ii the jazz band and the rowing team but not the drama club

       iii the rowing team but not the jazz band.

Angles and polygons

7

Contents:

A	Angle theorems	[E5.4]
B	Parallel lines	[E5.4]
C	Triangles	[E5.4]
D	Isosceles triangles	[E5.4]
E	The interior angles of a polygon	[E5.4]
F	The exterior angles of a polygon	[E5.4]

Opening problem

On his birthday, Billy receives a cake in the shape of a regular hexagon. He divides the cake into 4 pieces by making cuts from one corner to each of the other corners as shown.

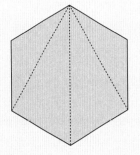

Things to think about:

a Are the four angles at the top of the hexagon equal in size?

b Can you find the size of each angle?

c When a regular hexagon is cut in this way, four triangles are formed. Do any of these triangles contain right angles?

A ANGLE THEOREMS [E5.4]

If we look carefully, we can see **angles** in many objects and situations.

The measurement of angles dates back more than 2500 years and is still very important today in architecture, building, surveying, engineering, navigation, space research, and many other industries.

Research   *Degree measure*

The Babylonian Empire was founded in the 18th century BC by **Hammurabi** in lower Mesopotamia, which is today in southern Iraq. It lasted over a thousand years, finally being absorbed into the Persian Empire of Darius in the 6th century BC.

1 The Babylonians invented the **astrolabe**.
    Find out what an astrolabe measures.

2 How many degrees did the Babylonians decide should be in one full turn? Why did they choose this number?

TERMINOLOGY

- **Complementary angles** have sizes which add to $90°$.

- **Supplementary angles** have sizes which add to $180°$.

- **Adjacent angles** have the same vertex and share a common arm.

ANGLE THEOREMS

Title	Theorem	Figure
Angles at a point	The sum of the sizes of the angles at a point is $360°$.	$a + b + c = 360$
Angles on a straight line	The sum of the sizes of the angles on a line is $180°$. The angles are supplementary.	$a + b = 180$
Angles in a right angle	The sum of the sizes of the angles in a right angle is $90°$. The angles are complementary.	$a + b = 90$
Vertically opposite angles	Vertically opposite angles are equal in size.	$a = b$

EXERCISE 7A

1 Add the following pairs of angles, and state whether they are complementary, supplementary, or neither:

  a 109°, 71°   **b** 67°, 117°   **c** 62°, 28°

  d 155°, 31°   **e** 25°, 55°   **f** 64°, 116°

2 Find the size of the angle complementary to:

  a 15°   **b** 87°   **c** 43°

3 Find the size of the angle supplementary to:

  a 129°   **b** 57°   **c** 90°

4 Classify the following angle pairs as complementary, supplementary, or neither:

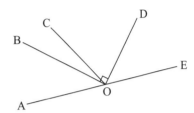

  a $\hat{COA}$ and $\hat{COE}$ **b** $\hat{AOD}$ and $\hat{EOC}$

  c $\hat{BOC}$ and $\hat{COD}$ **d** $\hat{COE}$ and $\hat{DOB}$

5 Copy and complete:

  a The size of the angle complementary to $x°$ is ......

  b The size of the angle supplementary to $y°$ is ......

  c Two lines are perpendicular if they meet at ......

Example 1 ◀)) Self Tutor

Find the value of the unknown:

a 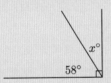   **b** 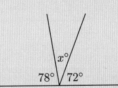   **c**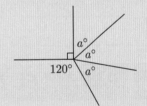

a The angles 58° and $x°$ are complementary.

$\therefore x + 58 = 90$

$\therefore x = 32$

b The three angles are supplementary, so they add to 180°.

$\therefore 78 + x + 72 = 180$

$\therefore x + 150 = 180$

$\therefore x = 30$

c We have five angles at a point, so the sum of the five angles is 360°.

$\therefore 3a + 90 + 120 = 360$

$\therefore 3a + 210 = 360$

$\therefore 3a = 150$

$\therefore a = 50$

6 Find the values of the unknowns:

a 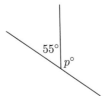   **b** 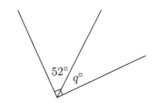   **c**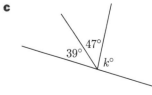

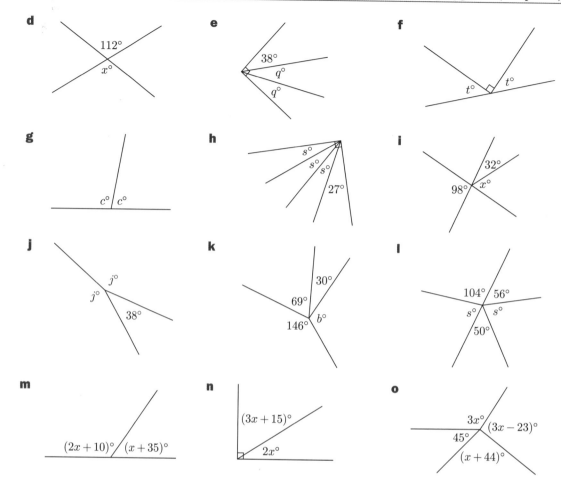

B   PARALLEL LINES   [E5.4]

When two or more straight lines are cut by a transversal, three different angle pairs are formed:

Corresponding angle pairs	Alternate angle pairs	Co-interior angle pairs
The angles marked ● and × are **corresponding angles** because they are both in the *same position*. They are on the *same side* of the transversal and the *same side* of the two straight lines.	The angles marked ● and × are **alternate angles**. They are on *opposite sides* of the transversal and *between* the two straight lines.	The angles marked ● and × are **co-interior angles**. They are on the *same side* of the transversal and *between* the two straight lines. Co-interior angles can also be called **allied angles**.

If *parallel* lines are cut by a transversal, then corresponding, alternate, and co-interior angle pairs have special properties.

Discovery 1   *Angle pairs on parallel lines*

What to do: WORKSHEET

1 Print this worksheet so you can write directly onto it.

2 In each diagram, measure the angles marked.

a

line 1 ——————— *a*
                c / *d*

line 2 ——————— *e* / *f*

b

                                                    line 1
        a
       c *d*
                                        f   line 2
                                 e

c

            a
line 1 ——— *c* | *d*

             e | *f*
line 2 ————————

d

                                       line 2
line 1
                                     f
                                  e
            d
          a *c*

Diagram	Are lines 1 and 2 parallel?	Are the corresponding angles *a* and *e* equal?	Are the alternate angles *c* and *f* equal?	Are the co-interior angles *d* and *f* equal? Are they supplementary?	
				equal	supplementary
a					
b					
c					
d					

3 What can you conclude from your results?   GEOMETRY PACKAGE

4 Click on the icon to further investigate angle pairs on parallel lines, and hence confirm your conclusions.

~~RA~~LLEL LINES THEOREMS

Title	Theorem	Figure
Corresponding angles	When two *parallel* lines are cut by a transversal, angles in corresponding positions are equal in size.	 $a = b$
Alternate angles	When two *parallel* lines are cut by a transversal, angles in alternate positions are equal in size.	$a = b$
Co-interior or allied angles	When two *parallel* lines are cut by a transversal, co-interior angles are supplementary.	$a + b = 180$

Example 2
🔊 *Self Tutor*

Find the value of the unknown, giving a brief reason for your answer:

a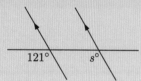

b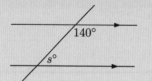

> The special properties only apply if the lines cut are *parallel*.

a Corresponding angles on parallel lines are equal.
∴ $s = 121$

b Co-interior angles on parallel lines are supplementary.
∴ $s + 140 = 180$
∴ $s = 40$

EXERCISE 7B

1 Find, giving brief reasons, the values of the unknowns:

a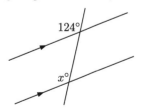

b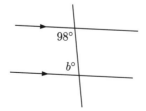

c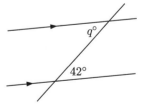

d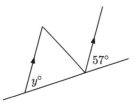

e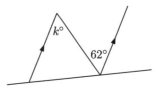

f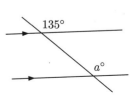

g

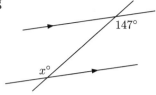

h

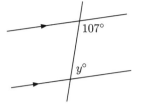

i

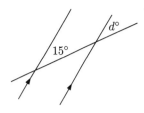

2 Find the values of the unknowns in alphabetical order, giving brief reasons:

a

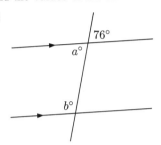

b

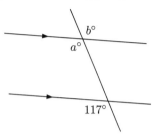

c

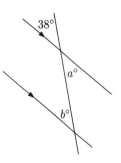

3 Write an equation connecting the unknowns, giving a brief reason:

a

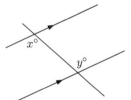

b

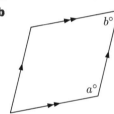

c

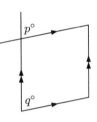

d

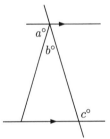

4 The following figures are not drawn to scale.
Decide whether each figure contains a pair of parallel lines, giving brief reasons for your answers:

a

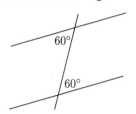

b

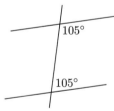

c

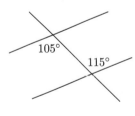

d

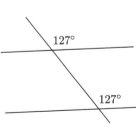

e

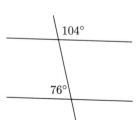

f

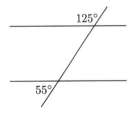

5 Find the values of the unknowns:

a

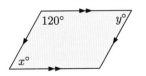

b

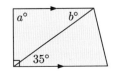

c

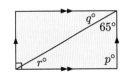

C TRIANGLES　　　　　　　　　　　[E5.4]

A **triangle** is a polygon which has three sides.

All triangles have the following properties:

- The sum of the interior angles of a triangle is 180°.

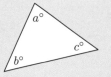

$a + b + c = 180$

GEOMETRY PACKAGE

- Any exterior angle is equal to the sum of the interior opposite angles.

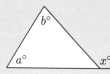

$x = a + b$

GEOMETRY PACKAGE

- The longest side is opposite the largest angle.

Proof that the sum of the angles of a triangle is 180°:

Draw a triangle ABC with angles $a°$, $b°$, and $c°$.

Draw a line segment DE through B which is parallel to AC.

Using equal alternate angles,

$\widehat{ABD} = a°$ and $\widehat{CBE} = c°$.

But $a + b + c = 180$ {angles on a line}

∴ $a + b + c = 180$

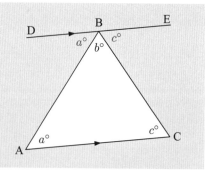

Example 3　　　　　　　　　　◀ Self Tutor

Find the values of the unknowns:

a
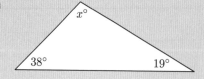

b
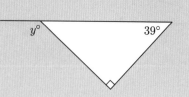

a $x + 38 + 19 = 180$　{angle sum of a triangle}

∴ $x + 57 = 180$

∴ $x = 123$

b $y = 39 + 90$　{exterior angle of a triangle}

∴ $y = 129$

EXERCISE 7C

1 These diagrams are not drawn to scale, but the information on them is correct. Find the values of the unknowns:

a
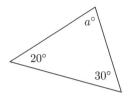

b
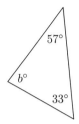

c
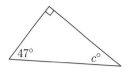

d
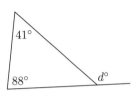

e
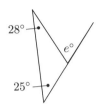

f
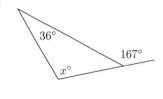

2 State whether the following statements are *true* or *false*:

   a The sum of the angles of a triangle is equal to two right angles.

   b A right angled triangle can contain an obtuse angle.

   c The sum of two angles of a triangle is always greater than the third angle.

   d The two smaller angles of a right angled triangle are supplementary.

3 The following triangles are *not* drawn to scale.
State the longest side of each triangle.

The longest side
is opposite the
largest angle.

a
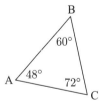

b
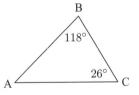

c
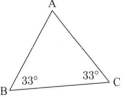

d
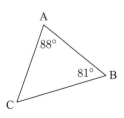

e
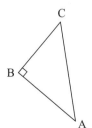

f
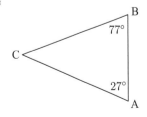

Example 4
◀) **Self Tutor**

Find the values of the variables:

a
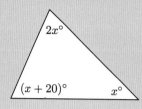

b
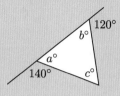

a $2x + x + (x + 20) = 180$ {angle sum of a triangle}

$\therefore \ 4x + 20 = 180$

$\therefore \ 4x = 160$

$\therefore \ x = 40$

b $a = 180 - 140 = 40$ {angles on a line}

Likewise $b = 180 - 120 = 60$

But $a + b + c = 180$ {angle sum of a triangle}

$\therefore \ 40 + 60 + c = 180$

$\therefore \ 100 + c = 180$

$\therefore \ c = 80$

4 Find the values of the variables:

a
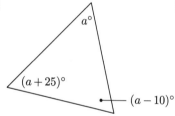

b
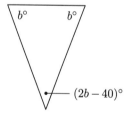

c
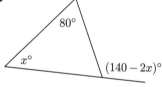

d
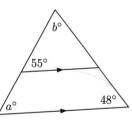

e
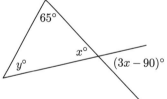

f
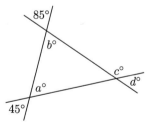

5 For the figure alongside:

  a Explain why $C\widehat{B}D = 90°$.

  b Find the size of $B\widehat{D}C$.

  c Hence find the size of $A\widehat{D}B$.

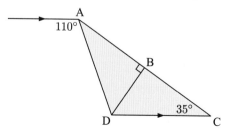

6 The three angles of a scalene triangle are $x°$, $(x - 12)°$, and $(2x + 6)°$. What are the sizes of these angles?

Research

Research the use of triangles in the construction of bridges.

Explain what is meant by the statement *"the triangle is the only rigid polygon"* and how this helps the bridge structure.

D   ISOSCELES TRIANGLES   [E5.4]

An **isosceles triangle** is a triangle in which two sides are equal in length.

The angles opposite the two equal sides are called the **base angles**.

The vertex where the two equal sides meet is called the **apex**.

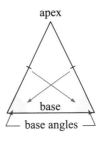

GEOMETRY PACKAGE

THE ISOSCELES TRIANGLE THEOREM

In any isosceles triangle:

- the base angles are equal
- the line joining the apex to the midpoint of the base bisects the vertical angle and meets the base at right angles.

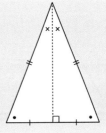

CONVERSES

Discussion

What does the word "converse" mean?

Converse 1:   If a triangle has two equal angles, then it is isosceles.

Converse 2:   The angle bisector of the apex of an isosceles triangle bisects the base at right angles.

Activity

Converses of the isosceles triangle theorem

What to do:

Click on the icon to run the interactive software. Use the software to decide which of the following are also converses of the isosceles triangle theorem:

INTERACTIVE
TRIANGLES

1 If the line joining one vertex to the midpoint of the opposite side is perpendicular to that side, then the triangle is isosceles.

2 If the line joining one vertex to the midpoint of the opposite side bisects the angle at the vertex, then the triangle is isosceles.

3 If a perpendicular to one side of the triangle passes through a vertex and bisects the angle at that vertex, then the triangle is isosceles.

Example 5

◀》 **Self Tutor**

Find x:

a

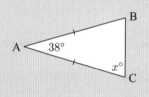

b

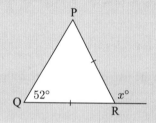

a

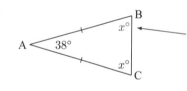

Since AB = AC, the triangle is isosceles.

$\therefore \quad \widehat{ABC} = x°$ {isosceles triangle theorem}

Now $\quad x + x + 38 = 180$ {angle sum of a triangle}

$\therefore \quad 2x + 38 = 180$

$\therefore \quad 2x = 142$

$\therefore \quad x = 71$

b

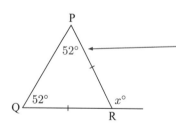

Since PR = QR, the triangle is isosceles.

$\therefore \quad \widehat{QPR} = 52°$ {isosceles triangle theorem}

$\therefore \quad x = 52 + 52$ {exterior angle of a triangle}

$\therefore \quad x = 104$

EXERCISE 7D

1 Find x, giving brief reasons:

a

b

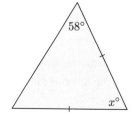

c

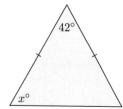

d
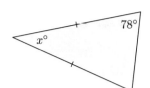

e
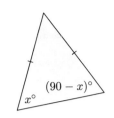

f
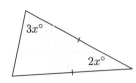

g
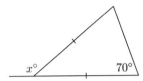

h
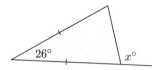

i
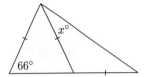

2 Find x, giving brief reasons:

a
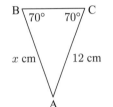

b
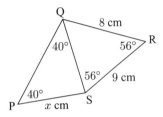

c
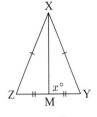

d
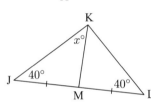

e
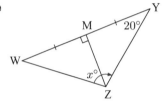

f
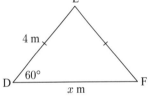

3 The figure alongside has not been drawn to scale, but the information given is correct.

  a Find x.

  b What can be deduced about the triangle?

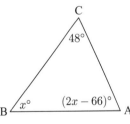

4
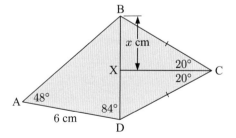

The figure alongside has not been drawn to scale, but the information given is correct.

  a Find $\widehat{ABD}$.

  b What can be deduced about triangle ABD?

  c Find x.

5 Because of its symmetry, a regular pentagon can be constructed from five isosceles triangles.

  a Find the size of angle θ at the centre O.

  b Hence find ϕ.

  c Hence find the measure of one interior angle such as $\widehat{ABC}$.

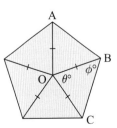

E   THE INTERIOR ANGLES OF A POLYGON [E5.4]

Discovery 2   Angles of an n-sided polygon

We have already seen that the sum of the interior angles of a triangle is $180°$. This fact can be used to find the sum of the interior angles of polygons with more than 3 sides.

What to do:

1 The quadrilateral alongside has been divided into two triangles using a diagonal.

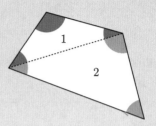

   a Write down the sum of the:

     i red angles   **ii** blue angles.

   b Hence find the sum of the interior angles of the quadrilateral.

2 In the pentagon alongside, one of the vertices is labelled A. All of the diagonals from A are drawn.

Draw similar diagrams for a hexagon, a heptagon (7-gon), and an octagon, drawing diagonals from one vertex only.

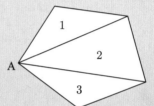

3 Copy and complete the following table:

Polygon	Number of sides	Number of triangles	Angle sum of polygon
quadrilateral	4	2	
pentagon	5	3	
hexagon			
heptagon			
octagon			
20-gon			

4 Copy and complete:

"*The sum of the sizes of the interior angles of any n-sided polygon is ...... $\times 180°$.*"

From the **Discovery** you should have found that:

> The sum of the sizes of the interior angles of any n-sided polygon is $(n-2) \times 180°$.

Example 6   ◀》 *Self Tutor*

Find x:

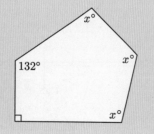

The figure has 5 sides.

$\therefore$ the sum of its interior angles is
$$3 \times 180° = 540°$$

$\therefore \quad x + x + x + 132 + 90 = 540$

$\therefore \quad 3x + 222 = 540$

$\therefore \quad 3x = 318$

$\therefore \quad x = 106$

EXERCISE 7E

1 Find the sum of the angles of:

a

b

c a hexagon

d an octagon

e a polygon with 12 sides

f a 15-gon.

2 Find x:

a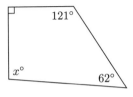

b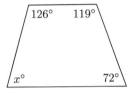

c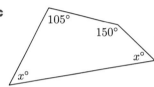

d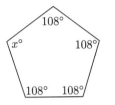

e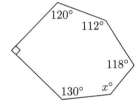

f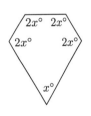

g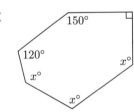

h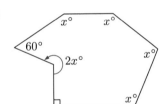

i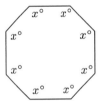

3 A pentagon has three right angles and two other equal angles. Find the size of each of the two equal angles.

4 The sum of the angles of a polygon is $1980°$. How many sides has the polygon?

5 Joanna claims to have found a polygon whose interior angles sum to $2060°$. Comment on Joanna's claim.

6 A **regular** polygon has all sides of equal length and all angles of equal size.

a Copy and complete the table alongside for regular polygons:

Regular polygon	Number of sides	Sum of angles	Size of each angle
triangle			
quadrilateral			
pentagon			
hexagon			
octagon			
decagon			

b Copy and complete:

   i The sum of the angles of an n-sided polygon is ......

   ii The size of each angle of a regular n-sided polygon is ......

c Find the size of each angle of a regular 12-sided polygon.

7 **a** What is the maximum number of reflex angles that a hexagon can have?

   b Draw a hexagon with this number of reflex angles.

8 Answer the **Opening Problem** on page **109**.

9 The figure alongside is a regular heptagon.

   a Find the size of each interior angle.

   b Hence find the value of each of the unknowns.

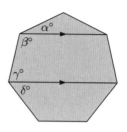

10

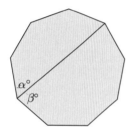

The figure alongside is a regular nonagon.
Find α and β.

Challenge   *Geometric patterns*

Click on the icon to obtain two challenge questions involving geometric patterns.

GEOMETRIC
PATTERNS

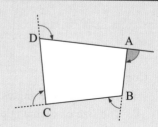

F   THE EXTERIOR ANGLES OF A POLYGON   *[E5.4]*

An **exterior angle** of a polygon is formed by extending one of the sides past a vertex.

Discovery 3   *Exterior angles of a polygon*

The shaded angle is an *exterior angle* of quadrilateral ABCD at vertex A.

Suppose we continued on to extend the other sides to form an exterior angle at each vertex.

The purpose of this Discovery is to find the sum of the exterior angles of a polygon.

What to do:

1 Suppose an ant starts at A, facing B. The ant walks to B, then turns to face C. It does the same at the next two vertices until it returns to A, and then it turns to face B again.

   a Through how many degrees has the ant turned in total?

   b Would your answer change if the ant had walked around a pentagon instead?

2 Write a statement indicating what you have learnt about the sum of the exterior angles of any polygon.

From the **Discovery**, you should have found that:

> The sum of the exterior angles of any polygon is always 360°.

This fact can be used to find the size of an interior angle of a regular polygon.

Example 7 ◀ Self Tutor

A regular polygon has 15 sides. Calculate the size of each interior angle.

For a 15-sided polygon, each exterior angle is $360° \div 15 = 24°$

$\therefore$ each interior angle is $180° - 24° = 156°$

EXERCISE 7F

1 Solve for x:

a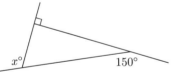

b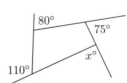

c

2 Calculate the size of each interior angle for these *regular* polygons:

   a pentagon   **b** octagon   **c** decagon

   d 20-sided polygon   **e** 100-sided polygon   **f** n-sided polygon

3 Calculate the number of sides of a regular polygon with exterior angle:

   a 45°   **b** 15°   **c** 2°   **d** $\frac{1}{2}°$

4 Calculate the number of sides of a regular polygon with interior angle:

   a 120°   **b** 150°   **c** 175°   **d** 179°

Review set 7A

1 Copy and complete:

If two parallel lines are cut by a transversal then:

   a the alternate angles are ......   **b** co-interior angles are ......

2 Find x, giving brief reasons:

a
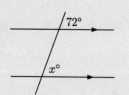

b
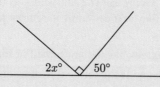

c
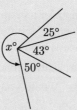

d
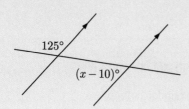

e
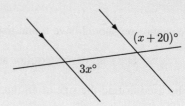

3 Decide if the figure contains parallel lines, giving a brief reason for your answer:

4 Find the value of x:

a

b
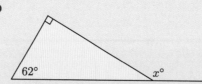

c

5 What can be deduced about triangle ABC shown? Give reasons for your answer.

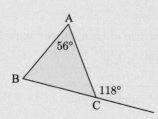

6 Find, giving reasons, the values of the unknowns:

a
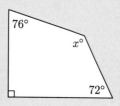

b
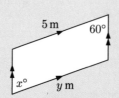

c
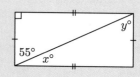

7 Find the value of x, giving reasons:

a
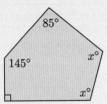

b
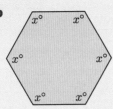

c
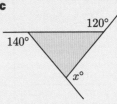

d
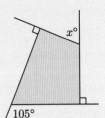

Review set 7B

1 State the values of the unknowns, giving brief reasons:

a
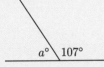

b

c
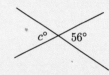

d
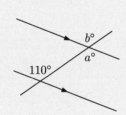

e
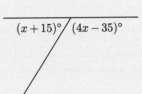

f
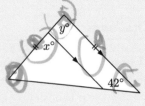

2 Find the value of the unknown, giving brief reasons:

a

b

c
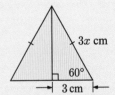

3 Classify each triangle:

a
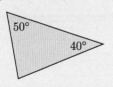

b

c
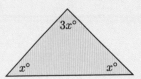

4 Find the values of the unknowns:

a
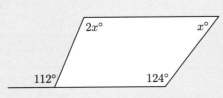

b
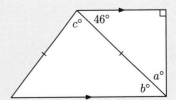

5 Copy and complete:

Polygon	Number of sides	Sum of interior angles	Sum of exterior angles
pentagon			
hexagon			
octagon			

6 Calculate the size of each interior angle for a regular polygon with 18 sides.

7 Solve for x:

a

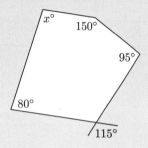

b

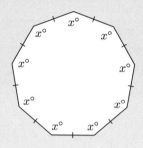

Challenge

1 **a** Find the sum of the angles at A, B, C, D, and E.

   b Repeat with two other "5-point star" diagrams of your choosing.

   c What do you suspect about the angle sum for all "5-point star" diagrams?

   d Use deductive geometry to confirm your suspicion.

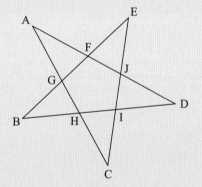

2 Find the sum of the angles at the points of a "7-point star".

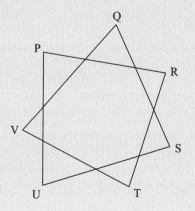

Surds and other radicals

8

Contents:

A	Surds	[E1.10]
B	Power equations	
C	Properties of radicals	[E1.10]
D	Simplest form	[E1.10]
E	Operations with radicals	[E1.10]
F	Divisions involving surds	[E1.10]

Opening problem

Jeremy and Wei were each asked to draw a shape with an area of 15 cm^2. Jeremy drew a $5 \text{ cm} \times 3 \text{ cm}$ rectangle, while Wei drew a square.

Things to think about:

a Can you write the side length of Wei's square as:

   i an exact expression

   ii a decimal approximation?

b If the two shapes are placed on top of one another as shown, can you find:

   i the area covered by Jeremy's shape, but not Wei's shape

   ii the area covered by the two shapes together

   iii the perimeter of the region covered by the two shapes?

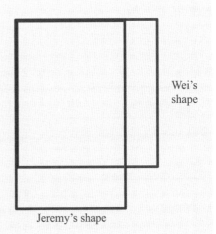

Wei's shape

Jeremy's shape

We have previously seen that the set of real numbers $\mathbb{R}$ can be divided into the rational numbers $\mathbb{Q}$ and the irrational numbers $\mathbb{Q}'$.

In this Chapter we consider **radicals** which are numbers written using the **radical sign** $\sqrt{}$. We are particularly interested in radical numbers which are irrational.

Historical note

Many centuries after Pythagoras, when the Golden Age of the Greeks was past, the writings of the Greeks were preserved, translated, and extended by Arab mathematicians.

The Arabs thought of a square number as growing out of its roots. The roots had to be extracted. The Latin word for "root" is *radix*, from which we get the words "radical" and "radish"! The printed symbol for radix was first R, then r, which was copied by hand as $\sqrt{}$.

In the 9th century AD, the Arab mathematician **Al-Khwarizmi** made a translational error. The Greek word *a-logos* means "irrational" but also means "deaf". So, the Greek *a-logos* was interpreted as "deaf" which in Latin is *surdus*. Hence to this day, irrational radicals like $\sqrt{2}$ are called *surds*.

A SURDS   [E1.10]

A **surd** is a real, irrational number that is written using the radical sign $\sqrt{}$.

$\sqrt{a}$ is the non-negative number such that $\sqrt{a} \times \sqrt{a} = a$.
$\sqrt{a}$ is only real if $a \geqslant 0$.

For example:
- $\sqrt{2}$, $\sqrt{3}$, and $\sqrt{5}$ are surds.
- $\sqrt{4}$ is not a surd, since $\sqrt{4} = \sqrt{2^2} = 2$.
- $\sqrt{\frac{1}{9}}$ is not a surd, since $\sqrt{\frac{1}{9}} = \sqrt{\left(\frac{1}{3}\right)^2} = \frac{1}{3}$.

EXERCISE 8A

1 Determine whether each of the following numbers is a surd. If it is a surd, find its value correct to 4 decimal places.

   a $\sqrt{5}$ **b** $\sqrt{36}$ **c** $\sqrt{72}$ **d** $\sqrt{81}$

   e $\sqrt{200}$ **f** $\sqrt{\frac{1}{10}}$ **g** $\sqrt{\frac{1}{64}}$ **h** $\sqrt{\frac{3}{14}}$

2 Consider the 1000 numbers $\sqrt{1}$, $\sqrt{2}$, $\sqrt{3}$, ..., $\sqrt{1000}$. How many of these numbers are surds?

Example 1   ◀) Self Tutor

Simplify: **a** $\left(\sqrt{2}\right)^3$ **b** $\left(\dfrac{4}{\sqrt{2}}\right)^2$ **c** $\left(3\sqrt{2}\right)^2$

    a $\left(\sqrt{2}\right)^3$ **b** $\left(\dfrac{4}{\sqrt{2}}\right)^2 = \dfrac{4^2}{\left(\sqrt{2}\right)^2}$ **c** $\left(3\sqrt{2}\right)^2$

        $= \sqrt{2} \times \sqrt{2} \times \sqrt{2}$ $= 3\sqrt{2} \times 3\sqrt{2}$

        $= 2\sqrt{2}$ $= \dfrac{16}{2}$ $= 9 \times 2$

                                               $= 8$ $= 18$

3 Simplify:

   a $\left(\sqrt{3}\right)^2$ **b** $\left(\sqrt{3}\right)^3$ **c** $\left(\sqrt{3}\right)^5$ **d** $\left(\dfrac{1}{\sqrt{3}}\right)^2$

   e $\left(\sqrt{5}\right)^2$ **f** $\left(\sqrt{5}\right)^4$ **g** $\left(\dfrac{5}{\sqrt{5}}\right)^2$ **h** $\left(\dfrac{10}{\sqrt{5}}\right)^2$

4 Simplify:

   a $\left(2\sqrt{2}\right)^2$ **b** $\left(4\sqrt{2}\right)^2$ **c** $\left(2\sqrt{3}\right)^2$

   d $\left(3\sqrt{3}\right)^2$ **e** $\left(2\sqrt{5}\right)^2$ **f** $\left(3\sqrt{5}\right)^2$

   g $\left(2\sqrt{7}\right)^2$ **h** $\left(2\sqrt{10}\right)^2$ **i** $\left(7\sqrt{10}\right)^2$

5 Simplify:

   a $3\sqrt{2}\times 4\sqrt{2}$ **b** $5\sqrt{3}\times 2\sqrt{3}$ **c** $7\sqrt{2}\times 5\sqrt{2}$

   d $\left(-4\sqrt{2}\right)^2$ **e** $\left(-7\sqrt{3}\right)^2$ **f** $\sqrt{2}\times\left(-3\sqrt{2}\right)$

   g $\left(-2\sqrt{3}\right)\times\left(-5\sqrt{3}\right)$ **h** $\left(-2\sqrt{7}\right)\times 3\sqrt{7}$ **i** $\sqrt{11}\times\left(-2\sqrt{11}\right)$

B   POWER EQUATIONS

> A **power equation** has the form $x^n = k$ where $n \in \mathbb{R}$, $n \neq 0$.

In this Section we consider cases where $n \in \mathbb{Z}^+$ and $n \geqslant 2$.

You should have seen previously that:

$$\text{If } x^2 = k, \ k > 0, \text{ then } x = \pm\sqrt{k}.$$

More generally, if $x^n = k$ where $n \in \mathbb{Z}^+$, $n > 2$, then:

- if n is odd and $x^n = k$, then $x = \sqrt[n]{k}$
- if n is even and $x^n = k$ where $k > 0$, then $x = \pm\sqrt[n]{k}$.

$\sqrt[n]{k}$ is the nth root of k.

Example 2   ◀ᴵ) *Self Tutor*

Use your calculator to solve for x, giving answers correct to 3 significant figures.

   a $x^2 = 6$ **b** $x^2 = 13, \ x > 0$ **c** $x^3 = 31$

   a $x^2 = 6$ **b** $x^2 = 13, \ x > 0$ **c** $x^3 = 31$

     $\therefore \ x = \pm\sqrt{6}$ $\therefore \ x = \sqrt{13}$ $\therefore \ x = \sqrt[3]{31}$

     $\therefore \ x \approx \pm 2.45$ $\therefore \ x \approx 3.61$ $\therefore \ x \approx 3.14$

GRAPHICS
CALCULATOR
INSTRUCTIONS

EXERCISE 8B

1 Solve for x, giving answers correct to 3 significant figures:

a $x^2 = 11$ **b** $x^2 = -5$ **c** $x^2 = 71$ **d** $x^2 = 89, \ x > 0$

e $x^3 = 8$ **f** $x^3 = 11$ **g** $x^3 = -11$ **h** $x^4 = 81$

i $x^4 = -1$ **j** $x^5 = 23$ **k** $x^5 = -113$ **l** $x^6 = 39.2, \ x > 0$

Example 3   ◀) Self Tutor

Solve for x: $\dfrac{x}{2} = \dfrac{5}{x}$

$$\dfrac{x}{2} = \dfrac{5}{x} \qquad \{\text{LCD} = 2x\}$$

$$\therefore \ \dfrac{x \times x}{2 \times x} = \dfrac{5 \times 2}{x \times 2} \qquad \{\text{to get a common denominator}\}$$

$$\therefore \ x^2 = 10 \qquad \{\text{equating numerators}\}$$

$$\therefore \ x = \pm\sqrt{10}$$

---

2 Solve for x:

a $\dfrac{x}{3} = \dfrac{4}{x}$ **b** $\dfrac{x}{6} = \dfrac{6}{x}$ **c** $\dfrac{1}{x} = \dfrac{x}{3}$ **d** $\dfrac{x}{7} = \dfrac{7}{x}$

e $\dfrac{2}{x} = \dfrac{x}{5}$ **f** $\dfrac{7}{x} = \dfrac{x}{5}$ **g** $\dfrac{x}{2} = \dfrac{8}{x}$ **h** $\dfrac{x}{5} = \dfrac{-2}{x}$

C   PROPERTIES OF RADICALS   [E1.10]

Discovery 1   Properties of radicals

Consider the following observations:

- $\sqrt{4 \times 9} = \sqrt{36} = 6$

  and $\sqrt{4} \times \sqrt{9} = 2 \times 3 = 6$

  so $\sqrt{4} \times \sqrt{9} = \sqrt{4 \times 9}$.

- $\sqrt{\dfrac{36}{4}} = \sqrt{9} = 3$

  and $\dfrac{\sqrt{36}}{\sqrt{4}} = \dfrac{6}{2} = 3$

  so $\dfrac{\sqrt{36}}{\sqrt{4}} = \sqrt{\dfrac{36}{4}}$.

What to do:

1 Test the following *possible* properties of radicals by substituting different values of a and b where $a \geqslant 0$ and $b \geqslant 0$. Use your calculator to evaluate the results.

a $\sqrt{a} \times \sqrt{b} = \sqrt{ab}$ **b** $\sqrt{\dfrac{a}{b}} = \dfrac{\sqrt{a}}{\sqrt{b}}, \ b \neq 0$

c $\sqrt{a + b} = \sqrt{a} + \sqrt{b}$ **d** $\sqrt{a - b} = \sqrt{a} - \sqrt{b}$

2 Summarise the properties which are always true.

From the **Discovery**, you should have found the following properties of radicals:

- If $a \geqslant 0$ and $b \geqslant 0$ then $\sqrt{a}\sqrt{b} = \sqrt{ab}$.

- If $a \geqslant 0$ and $b > 0$ then $\dfrac{\sqrt{a}}{\sqrt{b}} = \sqrt{\dfrac{a}{b}}$.

In general, $\sqrt{a+b} \neq \sqrt{a} + \sqrt{b}$ and $\sqrt{a-b} \neq \sqrt{a} - \sqrt{b}$ for $a \geqslant 0, \ b > 0$.

Example 4   ◀》 Self Tutor

Write in simplest form:

a $\sqrt{2} \times \sqrt{5}$ **b** $3\sqrt{2} \times 4\sqrt{11}$

a $\sqrt{2} \times \sqrt{5}$ **b** $3\sqrt{2} \times 4\sqrt{11} = 3 \times 4 \times \sqrt{2} \times \sqrt{11}$
   $= \sqrt{2 \times 5}$ $= 12 \times \sqrt{2 \times 11}$
   $= \sqrt{10}$ $= 12\sqrt{22}$

With practice you should not need the middle steps.

EXERCISE 8C

1 Simplify:

a $\sqrt{2} \times \sqrt{3}$ **b** $\sqrt{2} \times \sqrt{17}$ **c** $\sqrt{7} \times \sqrt{3}$

d $2\sqrt{2} \times 5\sqrt{3}$ **e** $5\sqrt{2} \times \sqrt{7}$ **f** $-5\sqrt{2} \times 2\sqrt{7}$

g $\left(-\sqrt{7}\right) \times \left(-2\sqrt{3}\right)$ **h** $\left(2\sqrt{3}\right)^2 \times 2\sqrt{5}$ **i** $\left(2\sqrt{2}\right)^3 \times 5\sqrt{3}$

Example 5   ◀》 Self Tutor

Simplify: **a** $\dfrac{\sqrt{75}}{\sqrt{3}}$ **b** $\sqrt{\dfrac{9}{49}}$

a $\dfrac{\sqrt{75}}{\sqrt{3}} = \sqrt{\dfrac{75}{3}}$ **b** $\sqrt{\dfrac{9}{49}} = \dfrac{\sqrt{9}}{\sqrt{49}}$
   $= \sqrt{25}$ $= \dfrac{3}{7}$
   $= 5$

2 Simplify:

a $\dfrac{\sqrt{8}}{\sqrt{2}}$ **b** $\dfrac{\sqrt{3}}{\sqrt{27}}$ **c** $\dfrac{\sqrt{18}}{\sqrt{3}}$ **d** $\dfrac{\sqrt{2}}{\sqrt{50}}$

e $\dfrac{\sqrt{75}}{\sqrt{5}}$ **f** $\dfrac{\sqrt{5}}{\sqrt{75}}$ **g** $\dfrac{\sqrt{18}}{\sqrt{2}}$ **h** $\dfrac{\sqrt{3}}{\sqrt{48}}$

3 Simplify:

a $\sqrt{\dfrac{1}{16}}$ **b** $\sqrt{\dfrac{81}{144}}$ **c** $\sqrt{\dfrac{49}{64}}$ **d** $\sqrt{\dfrac{121}{9}}$

e $\sqrt{6\tfrac{1}{4}}$ **f** $\sqrt{1\tfrac{7}{9}}$ **g** $\sqrt{2\tfrac{14}{25}}$ **h** $\sqrt{7\tfrac{1}{9}}$

Example 6   ◀》 Self Tutor

Write $\sqrt{32}$ in the form $k\sqrt{2}$.

$\sqrt{32} = \sqrt{16 \times 2}$
$\phantom{\sqrt{32}} = \sqrt{16} \times \sqrt{2}$ {using $\sqrt{ab} = \sqrt{a} \times \sqrt{b}$}
$\phantom{\sqrt{32}} = 4\sqrt{2}$

4 Write in the form $k\sqrt{2}$:

     a $\sqrt{8}$ **b** $\sqrt{18}$ **c** $\sqrt{50}$ **d** $\sqrt{98}$

     e $\sqrt{200}$ **f** $\sqrt{288}$ **g** $\sqrt{20\,000}$ **h** $\sqrt{\frac{1}{2}}$

5 Write in the form $k\sqrt{3}$:

     a $\sqrt{12}$ **b** $\sqrt{27}$ **c** $\sqrt{75}$ **d** $\sqrt{\frac{1}{3}}$

6 Write in the form $k\sqrt{5}$:

     a $\sqrt{20}$ **b** $\sqrt{45}$ **c** $\sqrt{125}$ **d** $\sqrt{\frac{1}{5}}$

D   SIMPLEST FORM   *[E1.10]*

A radical is in **simplest form** when the number under the radical sign is the smallest possible integer.

Example 7   ◀)) *Self Tutor*

Write $\sqrt{432}$ in simplest form.

$$\begin{aligned} \sqrt{432} &= \sqrt{2^4 \times 3^3} \\ &= \sqrt{2^4} \times \sqrt{3^3} \\ &= 4 \times 3\sqrt{3} \\ &= 12\sqrt{3} \end{aligned}$$

It may be useful to find the prime factorisation of the number under the radical sign.

EXERCISE 8D

1 Write in simplest form:

     a $\sqrt{12}$ **b** $\sqrt{28}$ **c** $\sqrt{54}$ **d** $\sqrt{60}$

     e $\sqrt{99}$ **f** $\sqrt{52}$ **g** $\sqrt{40}$ **h** $\sqrt{63}$

     i $\sqrt{48}$ **j** $\sqrt{125}$ **k** $\sqrt{147}$ **l** $\sqrt{175}$

     m $\sqrt{176}$ **n** $\sqrt{150}$ **o** $\sqrt{275}$ **p** $\sqrt{2000}$

2 Show that $\dfrac{\sqrt{96}}{\sqrt{6}} = 4$:

     a   by using the rule $\dfrac{\sqrt{a}}{\sqrt{b}} = \sqrt{\dfrac{a}{b}}$ **b**   by first writing $\sqrt{96}$ in simplest form.

E   OPERATIONS WITH RADICALS   *[E1.10]*

We can perform operations with radicals just as we do with ordinary numbers. In particular:

- We can add and subtract "like" radicals in the same way that we add and subtract "like" algebraic terms.
- We can use the usual rules for expanding brackets.

Example 8   ◆⟩ *Self Tutor*

Simplify: **a** $3\sqrt{2} + 4\sqrt{2}$ **b** $5\sqrt{3} - 6\sqrt{3}$

a $\quad 3\sqrt{2} + 4\sqrt{2}$ **b** $\quad 5\sqrt{3} - 6\sqrt{3}$
$= 7\sqrt{2}$ $= -1\sqrt{3}$
$\qquad\qquad\qquad\qquad = -\sqrt{3}$

{Compare with $3x + 4x = 7x$}   {Compare with $5x - 6x = -x$}

EXERCISE 8E

1 Simplify:

a $\sqrt{2} + \sqrt{2}$ **b** $\sqrt{2} - \sqrt{2}$ **c** $3\sqrt{2} - 2\sqrt{2}$

d $2\sqrt{3} - \sqrt{3}$ **e** $5\sqrt{7} + 2\sqrt{7}$ **f** $3\sqrt{5} - 6\sqrt{5}$

g $6\sqrt{2} - 9\sqrt{2}$ **h** $\sqrt{5} + 7\sqrt{5}$ **i** $3\sqrt{2} + 4\sqrt{2} - \sqrt{2}$

j $3\sqrt{2} - 5\sqrt{2} - \sqrt{2}$ **k** $3\sqrt{3} - \sqrt{3} + 2\sqrt{3}$ **l** $3\sqrt{5} + 7\sqrt{5} - 10$

Example 9   ◆⟩ *Self Tutor*

Simplify: **a** $4\sqrt{5} + 3\sqrt{7} - \sqrt{5} + 5\sqrt{7}$ **b** $5\sqrt{2} - 3\sqrt{8}$

a   "like" radicals
$$4\sqrt{5} + 3\sqrt{7} - \sqrt{5} + 5\sqrt{7}$$
"like" radicals
$$= 3\sqrt{5} + 8\sqrt{7}$$

b $\quad 5\sqrt{2} - 3\sqrt{8}$
$= 5\sqrt{2} - 3\sqrt{4 \times 2}$
$= 5\sqrt{2} - 6\sqrt{2}$
$= -\sqrt{2}$

2 Simplify:

a $3\sqrt{2} + 2\sqrt{3} - \sqrt{2} + 5\sqrt{3}$ **b** $7\sqrt{2} - 4\sqrt{3} - 2\sqrt{2} + 3\sqrt{3}$ **c** $-6\sqrt{2} - 2\sqrt{3} - \sqrt{2} + 6\sqrt{3}$

d $2\sqrt{5} + 4\sqrt{2} + 9\sqrt{5} - 9\sqrt{2}$ **e** $3\sqrt{2} - 5\sqrt{7} - \sqrt{2} - 5\sqrt{7}$ **f** $3\sqrt{2} + 4\sqrt{11} - \sqrt{2} - \sqrt{11}$

g $6 - 2\sqrt{2} - \sqrt{2} - 5$ **h** $5\sqrt{3} - 5 + 4\sqrt{3} - 8$

3 Simplify:

a $8\sqrt{2} - \sqrt{8}$ **b** $2\sqrt{3} + 3\sqrt{12}$ **c** $14\sqrt{5} - 2\sqrt{125}$

4 Show that:

a $\sqrt{12} + \sqrt{27} = \sqrt{75}$ **b** $\sqrt{80} - \sqrt{5} = \sqrt{45}$

Example 10   ◆⟩ *Self Tutor*

Simplify: **a** $2\left(2 + \sqrt{3}\right)$ **b** $\sqrt{2}\left(5 - 2\sqrt{2}\right)$

a $\quad 2\left(2 + \sqrt{3}\right)$ **b** $\quad \sqrt{2}\left(5 - 2\sqrt{2}\right)$
$= 2 \times 2 + 2 \times \sqrt{3}$ $= \sqrt{2} \times 5 + \sqrt{2} \times (-2\sqrt{2})$
$= 4 + 2\sqrt{3}$ $= 5\sqrt{2} - 4$

With practice you should not need the middle steps.

5 Expand and simplify:

    a $4(3 + \sqrt{2})$ **b** $3(\sqrt{2} + \sqrt{3})$ **c** $5(4 - \sqrt{7})$ **d** $6(\sqrt{11} - 4)$

    e $\sqrt{2}(1 + \sqrt{2})$ **f** $\sqrt{2}(\sqrt{2} - 5)$ **g** $\sqrt{3}(2 + 2\sqrt{3})$ **h** $\sqrt{3}(\sqrt{3} - \sqrt{2})$

    i $\sqrt{5}(6 - \sqrt{5})$ **j** $\sqrt{5}(2\sqrt{5} - 1)$ **k** $\sqrt{5}(2\sqrt{5} + \sqrt{3})$ **l** $\sqrt{7}(2 + \sqrt{7} + \sqrt{2})$

Example 11
🔊 *Self Tutor*

Expand and simplify: **a** $-\sqrt{3}(2 + \sqrt{3})$ **b** $-\sqrt{2}(\sqrt{2} - \sqrt{3})$

a $-\sqrt{3}(2 + \sqrt{3})$ **b** $-\sqrt{2}(\sqrt{2} - \sqrt{3})$

    $= (-\sqrt{3}) \times 2 + (-\sqrt{3}) \times \sqrt{3}$ $= (-\sqrt{2}) \times \sqrt{2} + (-\sqrt{2}) \times (-\sqrt{3})$

    $= -2\sqrt{3} - 3$ $= -2 + \sqrt{6}$

---

6 Expand and simplify:

    a $-\sqrt{2}(4 + \sqrt{2})$ **b** $-\sqrt{2}(3 - \sqrt{2})$ **c** $-\sqrt{2}(\sqrt{2} - \sqrt{7})$ **d** $-\sqrt{3}(3 + \sqrt{3})$

    e $-\sqrt{3}(5 - \sqrt{3})$ **f** $-\sqrt{3}(2\sqrt{3} + \sqrt{5})$ **g** $-\sqrt{5}(2\sqrt{2} - \sqrt{3})$ **h** $-2\sqrt{2}(\sqrt{2} + \sqrt{3})$

    i $-5\sqrt{2}(4 - 2\sqrt{2})$ **j** $-\sqrt{7}(2\sqrt{7} + 4)$ **k** $-\sqrt{11}(2 - \sqrt{11})$ **l** $-2\sqrt{3}(1 - 2\sqrt{2})$

Example 12
🔊 *Self Tutor*

Expand and simplify: $(3 + \sqrt{5})(1 - \sqrt{5})$

$(3 + \sqrt{5})(1 - \sqrt{5}) = 3 \times 1 + 3 \times (-\sqrt{5}) + \sqrt{5} \times 1 + \sqrt{5} \times (-\sqrt{5})$

                      $= 3 - 3\sqrt{5} + \sqrt{5} - 5$

                      $= -2 - 2\sqrt{5}$

---

7 Expand and simplify:

    a $(1 + \sqrt{2})(5 + \sqrt{2})$ **b** $(3 + \sqrt{2})(3 + \sqrt{2})$ **c** $(\sqrt{2} + 2)(\sqrt{2} - 1)$

    d $(4 - \sqrt{3})(3 + \sqrt{3})$ **e** $(2 + \sqrt{3})(2 - \sqrt{3})$ **f** $(\sqrt{7} + 2)(\sqrt{7} - 3)$

    g $(\sqrt{11} + \sqrt{2})(\sqrt{11} - \sqrt{2})$ **h** $(\sqrt{2} + 1)(3 - \sqrt{2})$ **i** $(6 - 2\sqrt{2})(2 + \sqrt{2})$

Example 13
🔊 *Self Tutor*

Expand and simplify:

    a $(\sqrt{2} + 3)^2$ **b** $(\sqrt{5} - \sqrt{3})^2$

a $(\sqrt{2} + 3)^2$ **b** $(\sqrt{5} - \sqrt{3})^2 = (\sqrt{5} + -\sqrt{3})^2$

    $= (\sqrt{2})^2 + 2\sqrt{2}(3) + 3^2$ $= (\sqrt{5})^2 + 2\sqrt{5}(-\sqrt{3}) + (-\sqrt{3})^2$

    $= 2 + 6\sqrt{2} + 9$ $= 5 - 2\sqrt{15} + 3$

    $= 11 + 6\sqrt{2}$ $= 8 - 2\sqrt{15}$

8 Expand and simplify:

a $\left(1+\sqrt{3}\right)^2$ **b** $\left(\sqrt{2}+5\right)^2$ **c** $\left(3-\sqrt{2}\right)^2$ **d** $\left(1+\sqrt{7}\right)^2$

e $\left(\sqrt{3}-\sqrt{2}\right)^2$ **f** $\left(4-\sqrt{5}\right)^2$ **g** $\left(\sqrt{3}+\sqrt{5}\right)^2$ **h** $\left(3-\sqrt{6}\right)^2$

i $\left(\sqrt{6}-\sqrt{3}\right)^2$ **j** $\left(2\sqrt{2}+3\right)^2$ **k** $\left(3-2\sqrt{2}\right)^2$ **l** $\left(3-5\sqrt{2}\right)^2$

Example 14 ◀)) *Self Tutor*

Expand and simplify:

a $\left(4+\sqrt{2}\right)\left(4-\sqrt{2}\right)$ **b** $\left(2\sqrt{2}+3\right)\left(2\sqrt{2}-3\right)$

a $\left(4+\sqrt{2}\right)\left(4-\sqrt{2}\right) = 4^2 - \left(\sqrt{2}\right)^2$
$= 16 - 2$
$= 14$

b $\left(2\sqrt{2}+3\right)\left(2\sqrt{2}-3\right) = \left(2\sqrt{2}\right)^2 - 3^2$
$= 8 - 9$
$= -1$

9 Expand and simplify:

a $\left(3+\sqrt{2}\right)\left(3-\sqrt{2}\right)$ **b** $\left(\sqrt{3}-1\right)\left(\sqrt{3}+1\right)$ **c** $\left(5+\sqrt{3}\right)\left(5-\sqrt{3}\right)$

d $\left(\sqrt{3}-4\right)\left(\sqrt{3}+4\right)$ **e** $\left(\sqrt{7}-3\right)\left(\sqrt{7}+3\right)$ **f** $\left(2+\sqrt{2}\right)\left(2-\sqrt{2}\right)$

g $\left(\sqrt{7}-5\right)\left(\sqrt{7}+5\right)$ **h** $\left(2\sqrt{5}+6\right)\left(2\sqrt{5}-6\right)$ **i** $\left(3\sqrt{2}+2\right)\left(3\sqrt{2}-2\right)$

j $\left(\sqrt{5}-\sqrt{2}\right)\left(\sqrt{5}+\sqrt{2}\right)$ **k** $\left(\sqrt{3}-\sqrt{7}\right)\left(\sqrt{3}+\sqrt{7}\right)$ **l** $\left(2\sqrt{2}+1\right)\left(2\sqrt{2}-1\right)$

F DIVISIONS INVOLVING SURDS   [E1.10]

When an expression involves division by a surd, we can write the expression with an **integer denominator** which does *not* contain surds. This process is sometimes called **rationalising the denominator**.

For any fraction of the form $\dfrac{b}{\sqrt{a}}$, $a > 0$, we can remove the radical from the denominator by multiplying by $\dfrac{\sqrt{a}}{\sqrt{a}}$.

Example 15 ◀)) *Self Tutor*

Express with an integer denominator: **a** $\dfrac{7}{\sqrt{3}}$ **b** $\dfrac{10}{\sqrt{5}}$ **c** $\dfrac{10}{2\sqrt{2}}$

a $\dfrac{7}{\sqrt{3}}$
$= \dfrac{7}{\sqrt{3}} \times \dfrac{\sqrt{3}}{\sqrt{3}}$
$= \dfrac{7\sqrt{3}}{3}$

b $\dfrac{10}{\sqrt{5}}$
$= \dfrac{10}{\sqrt{5}} \times \dfrac{\sqrt{5}}{\sqrt{5}}$
$= \dfrac{10}{5}\sqrt{5}$
$= 2\sqrt{5}$

c $\dfrac{10}{2\sqrt{2}}$
$= \dfrac{10}{2\sqrt{2}} \times \dfrac{\sqrt{2}}{\sqrt{2}}$
$= \dfrac{10\sqrt{2}}{4}$
$= \dfrac{5\sqrt{2}}{2}$

RADICAL CONJUGATES

The radical expressions $3 + \sqrt{2}$ and $3 - \sqrt{2}$ are identical except for opposite signs in the middle. We call these expressions **radical conjugates**.

> The **radical conjugate** of $a + \sqrt{b}$ is $a - \sqrt{b}$.

We can use radical conjugates to simplify fractions of the form $\dfrac{c}{a + \sqrt{b}}$.

Discovery 2   Radical conjugates

What to do:

1 Expand and simplify:

   a $\left(2 + \sqrt{3}\right)\left(2 - \sqrt{3}\right)$ **b** $\left(\sqrt{3} - 1\right)\left(\sqrt{3} + 1\right)$

   c $\left(a + \sqrt{b}\right)\left(a - \sqrt{b}\right)$ for $b \geqslant 0$ **d** $(\sqrt{a} - b)(\sqrt{a} + b)$ for $a \geqslant 0$.

2 **a** Copy and complete:

      To remove the radicals from the denominator of a fraction, we can multiply the denominator by its ......

   b What must we then do to the numerator of the fraction to ensure we do not change the value of the fraction?

From the **Discovery** above, you should have found that:

> To remove the radicals from the denominator of a fraction, we multiply both the numerator *and* the denominator by the **radical conjugate** of the denominator.

Example 16   ◄ঠ Self Tutor

Write $\dfrac{1 - 2\sqrt{3}}{1 + \sqrt{3}}$ in simplest form.

$$\frac{1 - 2\sqrt{3}}{1 + \sqrt{3}} = \left(\frac{1 - 2\sqrt{3}}{1 + \sqrt{3}}\right)\left(\frac{1 - \sqrt{3}}{1 - \sqrt{3}}\right)$$

$$= \frac{1 - \sqrt{3} - 2\sqrt{3} + 6}{1 - 3} \qquad \{(a + b)(a - b) = a^2 - b^2\}$$

$$= \frac{7 - 3\sqrt{3}}{-2} = \frac{3\sqrt{3} - 7}{2}$$

> We are multiplying by one. This does not change the value of the original expression.

EXERCISE 8F

1 Write with an integer denominator:

  a $\dfrac{1}{\sqrt{5}}$ **b** $\dfrac{2}{\sqrt{2}}$ **c** $\dfrac{5}{\sqrt{3}}$ **d** $\dfrac{1}{\sqrt{8}}$ **e** $\dfrac{\sqrt{2}}{\sqrt{3}}$

  f $\dfrac{4}{\sqrt{7}}$ **g** $\dfrac{1}{2\sqrt{3}}$ **h** $-\dfrac{6}{\sqrt{2}}$ **i** $\dfrac{4}{3\sqrt{2}}$ **j** $\dfrac{3}{\sqrt{6}}$

  k $\dfrac{2\sqrt{5}}{\sqrt{3}}$ **l** $\dfrac{\sqrt{3}}{\sqrt{7}}$ **m** $\dfrac{\sqrt{7}}{3\sqrt{2}}$ **n** $\dfrac{22}{\sqrt{11}}$ **o** $\left(\dfrac{1}{\sqrt{3}}\right)^3$

2 Rationalise the denominator:

a $\dfrac{1}{3-\sqrt{5}}$
b $\dfrac{1}{2+\sqrt{3}}$
c $\dfrac{1}{4-\sqrt{11}}$
d $\dfrac{\sqrt{2}}{5+\sqrt{2}}$

e $\dfrac{\sqrt{3}}{3+\sqrt{3}}$
f $\dfrac{5}{2-3\sqrt{2}}$
g $\dfrac{-\sqrt{5}}{3+2\sqrt{5}}$
h $\dfrac{3-\sqrt{7}}{2+\sqrt{7}}$

3 Write in the form $a+b\sqrt{2}$ where $a,\,b \in \mathbb{Q}$:

a $\dfrac{4}{2-\sqrt{2}}$
b $\dfrac{-5}{1+\sqrt{2}}$
c $\dfrac{1-\sqrt{2}}{1+\sqrt{2}}$
d $\dfrac{\sqrt{2}-2}{3-\sqrt{2}}$

e $\dfrac{\frac{1}{\sqrt{2}}}{1-\frac{1}{\sqrt{2}}}$
f $\dfrac{1+\frac{1}{\sqrt{2}}}{1-\frac{1}{\sqrt{2}}}$
g $\dfrac{1}{1-\frac{\sqrt{2}}{3}}$
h $\dfrac{\frac{\sqrt{2}}{2}+1}{1-\frac{\sqrt{2}}{4}}$

4 Write in simplest form:

a $\dfrac{1-\sqrt{3}}{1+\sqrt{3}}+\dfrac{1+\sqrt{3}}{1-\sqrt{3}}$
b $\dfrac{\sqrt{2}}{3-\sqrt{2}}-\dfrac{3-\sqrt{2}}{3+\sqrt{2}}$
c $\dfrac{2+\sqrt{5}}{3+\sqrt{5}}+\dfrac{2\sqrt{5}}{3-\sqrt{5}}$

5 Find $\sqrt{\dfrac{3+2\sqrt{2}}{3-2\sqrt{2}}}$ giving your answer in the form $a+b\sqrt{2}$ where $a,\,b \in \mathbb{Q}$.

6 **a** We know that in general, $\sqrt{a+b} \neq \sqrt{a}+\sqrt{b}$
Deduce that if $\sqrt{a+b}=\sqrt{a}+\sqrt{b}$ then at least one of a or b is 0.

   b What can be deduced about a and b if $\sqrt{a-b}=\sqrt{a}-\sqrt{b}$?

7 **a** Find the value of $\left(\dfrac{1+\sqrt{5}}{2}\right)^n-\left(\dfrac{1-\sqrt{5}}{2}\right)^n$ for $n=1,\,2,\,3,$ and 4.

   b What do you suspect about $\left(\dfrac{1+\sqrt{5}}{2}\right)^n-\left(\dfrac{1-\sqrt{5}}{2}\right)^n$ for all $n \in \mathbb{Z}^+$?

Activity   *Approximating surds*

Click on the icon to explore a method for numerically approximating surds.

APPROXIMATING
SURDS

Review set 8A

1 Evaluate the following surds correct to 3 decimal places:

a $\sqrt{7}$
b $\sqrt{22}$
c $\sqrt{187}$

2 Simplify:
a $\left(2\sqrt{3}\right)^2$
b $\left(\dfrac{8}{\sqrt{2}}\right)^2$
c $3\sqrt{2} \times 2\sqrt{5}$
d $\sqrt{12\frac{1}{4}}$

3 Simplify:
a $\dfrac{\sqrt{15}}{\sqrt{3}}$
b $\dfrac{\sqrt{35}}{\sqrt{7}}$
c $\dfrac{\sqrt{35}}{\sqrt{5}}$
d $\dfrac{\sqrt{2}}{\sqrt{20}}$

4 Simplify:
a $8\sqrt{11}-10\sqrt{11}+5\sqrt{11}$
b $\sqrt{7}-2\sqrt{3}+5\sqrt{7}-\sqrt{3}$

5 Answer the **Opening Problem** on page **129**.

6 Write $\sqrt{80}$ in simplest form.

7 Expand and simplify:

   a $2\left(\sqrt{3}+1\right)$ **b** $\sqrt{2}\left(3-\sqrt{2}\right)$ **c** $\left(1+\sqrt{7}\right)^2$

   d $\left(2-\sqrt{5}\right)^2$ **e** $\left(5+\sqrt{6}\right)\left(5-\sqrt{6}\right)$ **f** $\left(3+\sqrt{2}\right)\left(1-\sqrt{2}\right)$

8 Write with an integer denominator:

   a $\dfrac{10}{\sqrt{5}}$ **b** $\dfrac{\sqrt{3}+2}{\sqrt{3}+1}$ **c** $\dfrac{1+\sqrt{7}}{1-\sqrt{7}}$

9 Write in the form $a+b\sqrt{5}$, where $a,b \in \mathbb{Q}$:

   a $\dfrac{3}{2-\sqrt{5}}$ **b** $\dfrac{2\sqrt{5}}{\sqrt{5}+1}$ **c** $\dfrac{6}{3+\sqrt{5}}$

10 **a** Simplify $\left(3+\sqrt{2}\right)\left(5-3\sqrt{2}\right)$.   **b** Hence find $\dfrac{9-4\sqrt{2}}{3+\sqrt{2}}$.

   c Check your answer to **b** by simplifying the fraction.

Review set 8B

1 Simplify: **a** $\sqrt{5}\sqrt{2}$ **b** $\dfrac{\sqrt{8}}{\sqrt{2}}$ **c** $\left(3\sqrt{6}\right)^2$

2 Simplify: **a** $\dfrac{\sqrt{3}}{\sqrt{24}}$ **b** $\sqrt{\dfrac{1}{49}}$ **c** $\sqrt{11\tfrac{1}{9}}$

3 Write in simplest form: **a** $\sqrt{44}$ **b** $\sqrt{90}$

4 Simplify:

   a $5\sqrt{2}-\sqrt{5}+\sqrt{2}+3\sqrt{5}$ **b** $6-2\sqrt{7}+5\sqrt{7}-10$

5 Expand and simplify: **a** $\sqrt{7}\left(\sqrt{2}-1\right)$ **b** $\left(5-\sqrt{2}\right)^2$

6 Expand and simplify: **a** $\left(\sqrt{3}+\sqrt{2}\right)^2$ **b** $\left(2-\sqrt{5}\right)\left(2+\sqrt{5}\right)$

7 Write with an integer denominator:

   a $\dfrac{8}{\sqrt{3}}$ **b** $\sqrt{\dfrac{7}{13}}$ **c** $\dfrac{4-\sqrt{5}}{3+\sqrt{5}}$

8 Write in the form $a+b\sqrt{3}$ where $a,b \in \mathbb{Q}$:

   a $\dfrac{18}{5-\sqrt{3}}$ **b** $\dfrac{1}{\sqrt{3}-2}$ **c** $\dfrac{-\sqrt{3}}{3+\sqrt{3}}$

9 **a** Evaluate: **i** $\sqrt{20}\times\sqrt{5}$ and $\dfrac{\sqrt{20}}{\sqrt{5}}$ **ii** $\sqrt{3}\times\sqrt{12}$ and $\dfrac{\sqrt{3}}{\sqrt{12}}$

   b Suppose a and b are positive integers, and that $\sqrt{a}\times\sqrt{b}$ is an integer.
   Prove that $\dfrac{\sqrt{a}}{\sqrt{b}}$ is rational.

10 Write in simplest form: $\dfrac{1-\sqrt{2}}{3+\sqrt{2}}-\dfrac{2\sqrt{2}}{3-\sqrt{2}}$

Pythagoras' theorem

Contents:

A	Pythagoras' theorem	[E5.6]
B	The converse of Pythagoras' theorem	[E5.6]
C	Problem solving	[E5.6, E5.7]

Opening problem

The Louvre Pyramid in Paris, France has a square base with edges 35 m long. The pyramid is 20.6 m high.

Things to think about:

a What right angles can you find in the construction of the pyramid?

b Can you find the length of the slant edges of the pyramid?

Historical note

For many centuries people have used right angled corners to construct buildings and to divide land into rectangular fields. They have done this quite accurately by relatively simple means.

Over 3000 years ago the Egyptians knew that a triangle with sides in the ratio $3 : 4 : 5$ was right angled. They used a loop of rope with 12 knots equally spaced along it to make corners in their building construction.

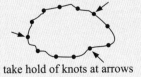
take hold of knots at arrows

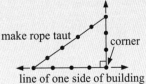
make rope taut   corner

line of one side of building

Around 500 BC, the Greek mathematician **Pythagoras of Samos** proved a rule which connects the sides of a right angled triangle. According to legend, he discovered the rule while studying the tiled palace floor as he waited for an audience with the ruler Polycrates.

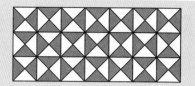

A PYTHAGORAS' THEOREM   [E5.6]

A **right angled triangle** is a triangle which has a right angle as one of its angles.

The side **opposite** the right angle is called the **hypotenuse**. It is the **longest** side of the triangle.

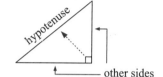

PYTHAGORAS' THEOREM

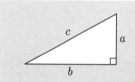

In a right angled triangle with hypotenuse of length c, and other sides of length a and b,

$$c^2 = a^2 + b^2.$$

In geometric form, Pythagoras' theorem states:

In any right angled triangle, the area of the square on the hypotenuse is equal to the sum of the areas of the squares on the other two sides.

Look back at the tile pattern in the **Historical note** above. Can you see this figure in the pattern?

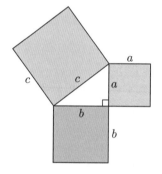

WORKSHEET

There are over 400 different proofs of Pythagoras' theorem. One of them is presented below.

Proof:

On a square we draw 4 identical right angled triangles, as illustrated. A smaller square is formed in the centre.

Suppose the hypotenuse of each triangle has length c, and the other two side lengths are a and b.

The total area of the large square
   $= 4 \times$ area of one triangle + area of smaller square

$$\therefore \quad (a+b)^2 = 4 \times \tfrac{1}{2}ab + c^2$$
$$\therefore \quad a^2 + 2ab + b^2 = 2ab + c^2$$
$$\therefore \quad a^2 + b^2 = c^2$$

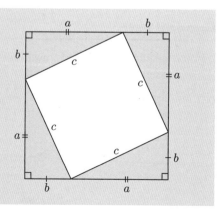

We can use Pythagoras' theorem to find side lengths in right angled triangles.

Example 1
◀)) **Self Tutor**

Find the unknown, giving your answers to 3 significant figures where necessary.

a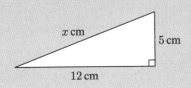

b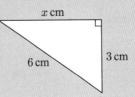

a $x^2 = 12^2 + 5^2$ {Pythagoras}

∴ $x^2 = 144 + 25$

∴ $x^2 = 169$

∴ $x = \sqrt{169}$ {as $x > 0$}

∴ $x = 13$

b $x^2 + 3^2 = 6^2$ {Pythagoras}

∴ $x^2 + 9 = 36$

∴ $x^2 = 27$

∴ $x = \sqrt{27}$ {as $x > 0$}

∴ $x \approx 5.20$

We reject the negative answer as the length of a side must be positive!

EXERCISE 9A

1 Find the length of the hypotenuse in each right angled triangle. Give your answers to 3 significant figures where necessary.

a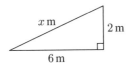

b

c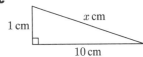

2 Find, correct to 2 decimal places where necessary, the length of the unknown side in each right angled triangle.

a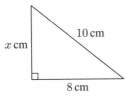

b

c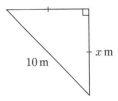

3 Find the length of the unknown side in each right angled triangle.

a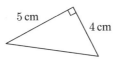

b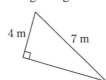

c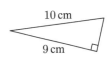

Example 2   ◀ッ **Self Tutor**

Find x in simplest surd form:

a
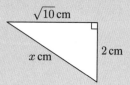

b
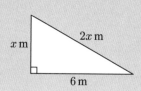

a	$x^2 = 2^2 + (\sqrt{10})^2$	{Pythagoras}	**b**	$(2x)^2 = x^2 + 6^2$	{Pythagoras}
	$\therefore\ x^2 = 4 + 10$			$\therefore\ 3x^2 = 36$	
	$\therefore\ x^2 = 14$			$\therefore\ x^2 = 12$	
	$\therefore\ x = \sqrt{14}$	{as $x > 0$}		$\therefore\ x = \sqrt{12}$	{as $x > 0$}
				$\therefore\ x = 2\sqrt{3}$	

4 Find x in simplest surd form:

a
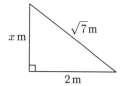

b
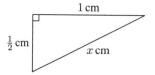

c
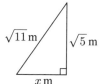

d
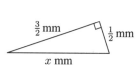

e

f
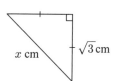

5 Find the value of x:

a
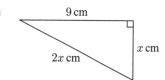

b
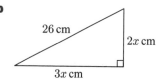

c
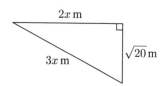

Example 3   ◀ッ **Self Tutor**

Find the unknowns:

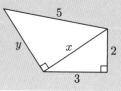

By leaving x in surd form, our answer for y is exact.

$$x^2 = 3^2 + 2^2 \quad \{\text{Pythagoras}\} \qquad y^2 + (\sqrt{13})^2 = 5^2 \quad \{\text{Pythagoras}\}$$
$$\therefore\ x^2 = 9 + 4 \qquad\qquad\qquad\quad \therefore\ y^2 + 13 = 25$$
$$\therefore\ x^2 = 13 \qquad\qquad\qquad\qquad\quad \therefore\ y^2 = 12$$
$$\therefore\ x = \sqrt{13} \quad \{\text{as } x > 0\} \qquad\qquad \therefore\ y = \sqrt{12} \quad \{\text{as } y > 0\}$$

6 Find the unknown lengths:

a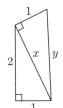

b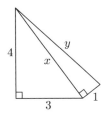

c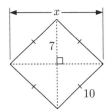

d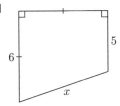

e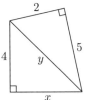

f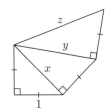

7 Find the length AC:

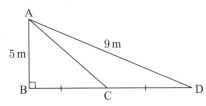

8 Use the figure below to show that $\sqrt{2} + \sqrt{8} = \sqrt{18}$:

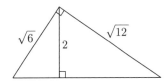

9 Find the distance AB in each figure:

a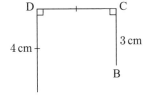

b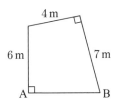

c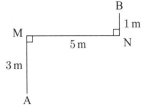

Activity   *Pythagorean triples*

The simplest right angled triangle with sides of integer length is the
3-4-5 triangle.

The numbers 3, 4, and 5 satisfy the rule $3^2 + 4^2 = 5^2$.

> The set of positive integers $\{a, b, c\}$ is a **Pythagorean triple** if it obeys the rule
> $a^2 + b^2 = c^2$.

What to do:

1 Show that these sets of integers are Pythagorean triples:

   a $\{5, 12, 13\}$ **b** $\{7, 24, 25\}$ **c** $\{8, 15, 17\}$

2 Determine whether the following are Pythagorean triples:

   a $\{6, 8, 10\}$ **b** $\{16, 30, 34\}$ **c** $\{5, 6, 7\}$

   d $\{14, 48, 50\}$ **e** $\{1, 2, 3\}$ **f** $\{20, 48, 52\}$

3 Find k given that the following are Pythagorean triples:

   a $\{8, 15, k\}$ **b** $\{k, 24, 26\}$ **c** $\{14, k, 50\}$

   d $\{15, 20, k\}$ **e** $\{k, 45, 51\}$ **f** $\{11, k, 61\}$

4 Explain why there are infinitely many Pythagorean triples of the form:

   a $\{3k, 4k, 5k\}$ where $k \in \mathbb{Z}^+$

   b $\{2n+1, \ 2n^2+2n, \ 2n^2+2n+1\}$ where $n \in \mathbb{Z}^+$.

B   THE CONVERSE OF PYTHAGORAS' THEOREM   [E5.6]

If we are given the lengths of three sides of a triangle, the **converse of Pythagoras' theorem** gives us a simple **test** to determine whether the triangle is right angled.

THE CONVERSE OF PYTHAGORAS' THEOREM

If a triangle has sides of length a, b, and c units where $a^2 + b^2 = c^2$, then the triangle is right angled.

PYTHAGORAS SIMULATION

Example 4	◀ *Self Tutor*

Is the triangle with sides 8 cm, 9 cm, and 12 cm right angled?

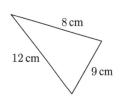

The two shorter sides have lengths 8 cm and 9 cm.

Now $\quad 8^2 + 9^2 = 64 + 81 = 145$

whereas $\quad 12^2 = 144$

$\therefore \quad 8^2 + 9^2 \neq 12^2$

$\therefore$ the triangle is not right angled.

EXERCISE 9B

1 The following figures are not drawn to scale. Which of the triangles are right angled?

  a
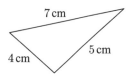

  b
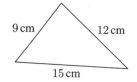

  c
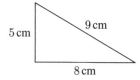

  d
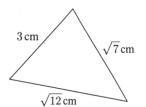

  e
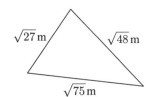

  f
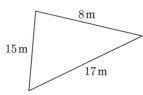

2   The following triangles are not drawn to scale. If any of them are right angled, find the right angle.

a
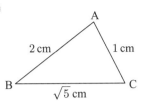

b
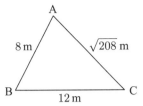

c
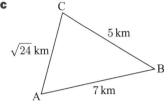

3   Meredith is trying to make a scarf by cutting some cloth into a right angled triangle. The triangle she makes has side lengths 40 cm, 42 cm, and 58 cm. Is Meredith's triangle right angled?

4   Phil is concerned that the street lamp outside his house is not quite at right angles to the ground.

He marks a point A on the lamp 1.5 m from its base, and a point B on the ground 2 m from the lamp's base. Using a tape measure, he finds that the distance between A and B is 2.40 m.

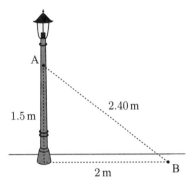

  a   What assumptions has Phil made?

  b   Is the street lamp at right angles to the ground?

5
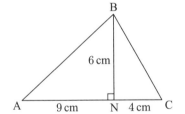

Triangle ABC has altitude BN which is 6 cm long.
AN = 9 cm and NC = 4 cm.
Is triangle ABC right angled at B?

C *PROBLEM SOLVING*   *[E5.6, E5.7]*

Right angled triangles occur in many practical problems. In these situations we can apply Pythagoras' theorem to help find unknown side lengths.

The problem solving approach involves the following steps:

> *Step 1*:   Draw a neat, clear diagram of the situation.
> *Step 2*:   Mark known lengths and right angles on the diagram.
> *Step 3*:   Use a symbol such as x to represent the unknown length.
> *Step 4*:   Write down Pythagoras' theorem for the given information.
> *Step 5*:   Solve the equation.
> *Step 6*:   Where necessary, write your answer in sentence form.

The following geometrical figures contain right angled triangles:

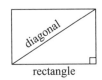
rectangle

Each corner of a **rectangle** is a right angle. We can construct a diagonal to form a right angled triangle.

square   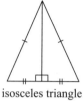 rhombus

In a **square** and a **rhombus**, the diagonals bisect each other at right angles.

isosceles triangle   equilateral triangle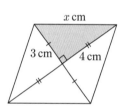

In an **isosceles triangle** and an **equilateral triangle**, the altitude bisects the base at right angles.

Example 5   ◀) *Self Tutor*

A rhombus has diagonals of length 6 cm and 8 cm. Find the length of its sides.

The diagonals of a rhombus bisect at right angles.

Let each side of the rhombus have length x cm.

$$\therefore \quad x^2 = 3^2 + 4^2 \qquad \{\text{Pythagoras}\}$$
$$\therefore \quad x^2 = 25$$
$$\therefore \quad x = \sqrt{25} \qquad \{\text{as } x > 0\}$$
$$\therefore \quad x = 5$$

Thus the sides are 5 cm in length.

EXERCISE 9C

1 A rectangle has sides of length 8 cm and 3 cm. Find the length of its diagonals.

2 The longer side of a rectangle is three times the length of the shorter side. Each diagonal of the rectangle is 10 cm long. Find the dimensions of the rectangle.

3 A rectangle with diagonals of length 20 cm has sides in the ratio $2 : 1$. Find the:

   a perimeter   **b** area of the rectangle.

4 A rhombus has sides of length 6 cm. One of its diagonals is 10 cm long. Find the length of the other diagonal.

5 A square has diagonals of length 10 cm. Find the length of its sides.

6 A rhombus has diagonals of length 8 cm and 10 cm. Find its perimeter.

7 On the grid there are four towns A, B, C, and D. The grid lines are 5 km apart. Find the distance from:

   a A to B   **b** B to C   **c** C to D

   d D to A   **e** A to C   **f** B to D.

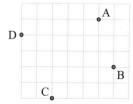

Give all answers correct to 3 significant figures.

8 When the feet of a fireman's ladder are placed 1.6 m from a wall, the ladder just reaches a window which is 4.3 m from the ground. How long is the ladder?

9 A cyclist is 32 km east and 18 km south of her starting point. She wants to return to her starting point in a direct line.

    a How far is the cyclist in a direct line from her starting point?

    b How long will it take her to return to her starting point if she can ride at 36 km per hour?

10 To check that his set square was right angled, Roger measured its sides. The two shorter sides were 8 cm and 11.55 cm long, and the longest side was 14.05 cm long. Is the set square right angled?

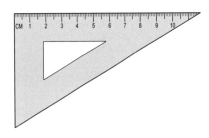

11 Two trains A and B leave the station at the same time. Train A travels north at a constant speed of 45 km per hour. Train B travels east at a constant speed of 70 km per hour.

    a How far will each train have travelled after 3 hours?

    b Find the distance between A and B after 3 hours.

12 A large flagpole is held to the ground by six cables, as illustrated. If the cables have to be replaced, what length of cabling must be purchased?

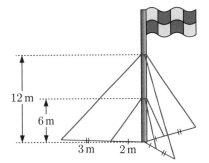

13 A street is 8 m wide, and there are street lights positioned either side of the street every 20 m. How far is street light X from street light:

    a A   **b** B   **c** C   **d** D?

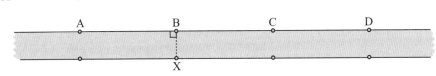

Example 6
🔊 *Self Tutor*

An equilateral triangle has sides of length 8 cm. Find the height of the triangle, to the nearest mm.

We draw an altitude which *bisects* the base.

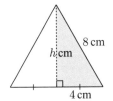

$h^2 + 4^2 = 8^2$ {Pythagoras}

$\therefore \ h^2 + 16 = 64$

$\therefore \ \ h^2 = 48$

$\therefore \ \ h = \sqrt{48}$ {as $h > 0$}

$\therefore$ the height of the triangle ≈ 6.9 cm.

---

14 Find the height of an equilateral triangle with sides of length 10 cm.

15 An isosceles triangle has equal sides measuring 10 cm, and a base which is 12 cm long. Find the length of the altitude of the triangle from the apex to the base.

16 Find the length of the truss AB in the roof structure shown:

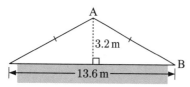

17 How high is the roof above the walls in the roof structure shown?

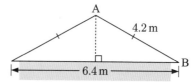

18 An equilateral triangle has an altitude of length 16 cm. Find the length of each side.

19 Ella's house is 2.5 km in a straight line from her school gate. To get to school, Ella walks down Bernard Street, then turns 90° and walks down Thompson Road until she reaches the school gate. She walks twice as far along Bernard Street as she does along Thompson Road. How far does Ella walk along Bernard Street?

20 Boat A is currently 10 km east of boat B. If boat A travels 6 km north and boat B travels 2 km west, how far apart are the boats now?

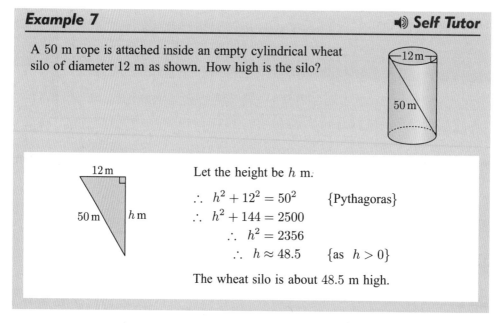

Example 7   ◀⟩ **Self Tutor**

A 50 m rope is attached inside an empty cylindrical wheat silo of diameter 12 m as shown. How high is the silo?

Let the height be h m.

∴ $h^2 + 12^2 = 50^2$ {Pythagoras}

∴ $h^2 + 144 = 2500$

∴ $h^2 = 2356$

∴ $h \approx 48.5$ {as $h > 0$}

The wheat silo is about 48.5 m high.

21 A cone has a slant height of 17 cm, and a base radius of 8 cm. How high is the cone?

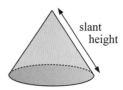

22 A cylindrical drinking glass has radius 3 cm and height 10 cm. Can a 12 cm long thin stirrer be placed in the glass so that it will stay entirely within the glass?

23 A 20 cm nail just fits inside a cylindrical can. Three identical spherical balls need to fit entirely within the can. What is the maximum radius each ball could have?

Example 8
◀)) **Self Tutor**

A room is 6 m by 4 m, and has a height of 3 m. Find the distance from a corner point on the floor to the opposite corner point on the ceiling.

The required distance is AD. We join BD.

In $\triangle$BCD, $x^2 = 4^2 + 6^2$ {Pythagoras}
In $\triangle$ABD, $y^2 = x^2 + 3^2$ {Pythagoras}

$\therefore\ y^2 = 4^2 + 6^2 + 3^2$
$\therefore\ y^2 = 61$
$\therefore\ y \approx 7.81$ {as $y > 0$}

$\therefore$ the distance is about 7.81 m.

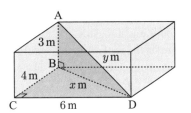

24 A cubic die has sides of length 2 cm. Find the distance between opposite corners of the die. Leave your answer in surd form.

2 cm

25 A room is 5 m by 3 m and has a height of 3.5 m. Find the distance from a corner point on the floor to the opposite corner of the ceiling.

26 Can an 8.5 m long piece of timber be stored in a rectangular shed which is 6 m by 5 m by 2 m high?

Example 9
◀)) **Self Tutor**

A pyramid of height 40 m has a square base with edges of length 50 m. Determine the length of the slant edges.

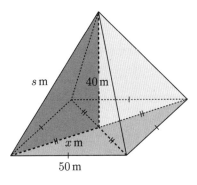

Let a slant edge have length s m.

Let half of a diagonal have length x m.

Using

x m
50 m
x m
50 m

$(2x)^2 = 50^2 + 50^2$ {Pythagoras}
$\therefore\ 4x^2 = 5000$
$\therefore\ x^2 = 1250$

Using

s m
40 m
x m

$s^2 = x^2 + 40^2$ {Pythagoras}
$\therefore\ s^2 = 1250 + 1600$
$\therefore\ s^2 = 2850$
$\therefore\ s \approx 53.4$ {as $s > 0$}

Each slant edge is about 53.4 m long.

27 An Egyptian Pharaoh wishes to build a square-based pyramid with all edges of length 100 m. Its apex will be directly above the centre of its base. How high, to the nearest metre, will the pyramid reach above the desert sands?

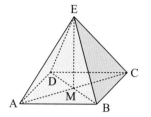

28 In the office building alongside, the entrance is at E. A radio antenna at A, the centre of the roof, receives security signals from the door E. Find the direct distance between the entrance and the antenna.

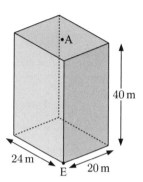

29 Answer the **Opening Problem** on page **141**.

30 In the rectangle shown, point P is 3 cm, 4 cm, and 5 cm from three of the vertices. How far is P from the fourth vertex?

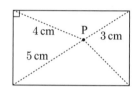

31 An aircraft hangar is semi-cylindrical with diameter 40 m and length 50 m. A helicopter places a cable across the top of the hangar, and one end is pinned to the corner at A. The cable is then pulled tight and pinned at the opposite corner B. Determine the length of the cable, to the nearest cm.

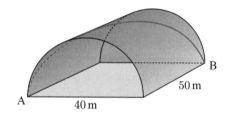

Review set 9A

1 Find x, giving your answer to 2 decimal places where necessary:

a

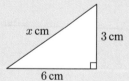

b

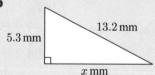

c

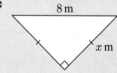

2 A rectangle has sides of length 6 cm and 7 cm. Find the length of the diagonal, to the nearest mm.

3

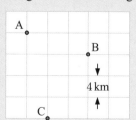

Find, correct to 3 significant figures, the distance from:

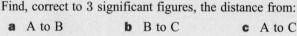

a A to B   **b** B to C   **c** A to C.

4 The given triangles are not drawn to scale. Are either of the triangles right angled? Explain your answers.

a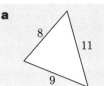

b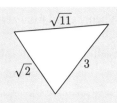

5 A rhombus has diagonals of length 12 cm and 18 cm. Find the length of its sides.

6 A garden gate is 2.4 metres wide and 1.2 metres high. The gate is strengthened by a diagonal strut.

   a How long is the strut?

   b Calculate the length of steel needed for the frame of the gate, including the strut.

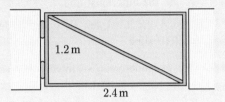

7 Use the figure below to show that $\sqrt{2} + \sqrt{18} = \sqrt{32}$.

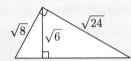

8 Find the length of the truss AB for the roof structure shown.

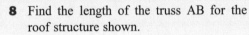

9 The diagonal of a cube is 10 m long. Find the length of its sides.

diagonal

Review set 9B

1 Find the value of x:

a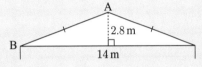

b

c

2 Is triangle ABC right angled? Give evidence to support your answer.

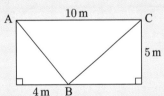

3 A softball diamond has sides of length 30 m. Determine the distance a fielder must throw the ball from second base to reach home base.

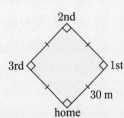

4 When viewed from above, a clothesline has the design shown.

Each of the arms is 1.6 m long.

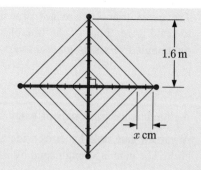

a Find the value of x.

b Calculate the *total* length of:

    i the innermost line

    ii the outermost line.

c Find the total length of cord needed for the clothesline.

5 A 2.5 m ladder reaches three times as far up a vertical wall as the base is out from the wall. How far up the wall does the ladder reach?

6

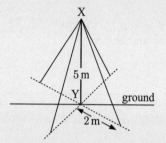

A pole XY is 5 metres tall. Four wires from the top of the pole X connect it to the ground.

Each wire is pegged 2 metres from the base of the pole. Find the total length of the four wires.

7 **a** The vertices of $\triangle$PQR lie on the circumference of a circle. If PQ = 12 cm, QR = 5 cm, and PR = 13 cm, show that the triangle is right angled.

   b State the angle that is the right angle.

8 Marvin the Magnificent is attempting to walk a tightrope across an intersection from one building to another. Using the dimensions given, find the length of the tightrope.

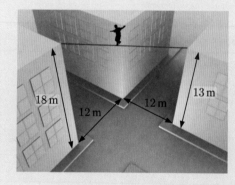

Formulae

10

Contents:

A	Formula construction	[E2.5]
B	Substituting into formulae	[E2.5]
C	Rearranging formulae	[E2.5]
D	Rearrangement and substitution	[E2.5]

Opening problem

In Gaelic football games, teams can score goals worth 3 points each, as well as individual points.

While watching a football game, Josh noticed something unusual about Mayo's score.

Mayo had scored 2 goals and 6 points, which is a total of 12 points, but he also recognised that $2 \times 6 = 12$.

Josh wondered whether there were other football scores with this property.

Things to think about:

a For a score of g goals and p points to have this property, can you explain why $3g + p = gp$?

b Can you *rearrange* this formula to make p the subject?

c By *substituting* different values for g, can you find other scores which have this property?

A **formula** is an equation which connects two or more variables.

For example, the formula $s = \frac{d}{t}$ relates the variables *speed* (s), *distance travelled* (d), and *time taken* (t).

We usually write a formula with one variable on its own on the left hand side. The other variable(s) and constants are written on the right hand side.

The variable on its own is called the **subject** of the formula. We say this variable is written *in terms of* the other variables.

A   FORMULA CONSTRUCTION   [E2.5]

When we **construct** or **derive** a formula to connect related variables, we often start with numerical examples. They help us understand the situation before we generalise the result.

Example 1   ◀)) *Self Tutor*

Write a formula for the amount A in a person's bank account if initially the balance was:

a $5000, and $200 was withdrawn each week for 10 weeks

b $5000, and $200 was withdrawn each week for w weeks

c $5000, and x was withdrawn each week for w weeks

d B, and x was withdrawn each week for w weeks.

We do not simplify the amount in **a** because we want to see how the formula is put together.

a $A = 5000 - 200 \times 10$

b $A = 5000 - 200 \times w$
   $\therefore \ A = 5000 - 200w$

c $A = 5000 - x \times w$
   $\therefore \ A = 5000 - xw$

d $A = B - x \times w$
   $\therefore \ A = B - xw$

EXERCISE 10A

1 Write a formula for the amount A earnt for working:

   a 5 hours at $15 per hour   **b** 5 hours at p per hour   **c** t hours at p per hour.

2 Write a formula for the amount A in a bank account if the initial balance was:

   a $2000, and then $150 was deposited each week for 8 weeks

   b $2000, and then $150 was deposited each week for w weeks

   c $2000, and then d was deposited each week for w weeks

   d P, and then d was deposited each week for w weeks.

3 Write a formula for the total cost C of hiring a plumber given a fixed call-out fee of:

   a $40, plus $60 per hour for 5 hours of work   **b** $40, plus $60 per hour for t hours of work

   c $40, plus x per hour for t hours of work   **d** F, plus x per hour for t hours of work.

4 In a multiple choice mathematics competition, students are awarded 3 points for each question answered correctly, and penalised 1 point for each question answered incorrectly. Write a formula for the number of points P scored by a student who:

   a answers 15 questions and gets 10 of them correct

   b answers 20 questions and gets c of them correct

   c answers a questions and gets c of them correct.

5 A musical recital consists of performances by a number of musicians, with a short break between each performance. Write a formula for the duration D minutes of a recital consisting of:

   a 4 performances of 6 minutes each, with a 2 minute break between performances

   b 5 performances of m minutes each, with a 3 minute break between performances

   c 8 performances of m minutes each, with a b minute break between performances

   d p performances of m minutes each, with a b minute break between performances.

6   A rectangular paddock is fenced into a rectangular array of yards so that each yard is connected by a gate to each adjacent yard. A 2×3 arrangement of yards is shown alongside.

Write a formula for the number of gates G for:

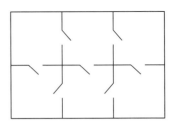

   a a 2×3 arrangement   **b** a 3×5 arrangement

   c a 4×4 arrangement   **d** an $m \times n$ arrangement.

B   SUBSTITUTING INTO FORMULAE   [E2.5]

Suppose a formula contains two or more variables, and we know the value of all but one of them. We can **substitute** the known values into the formula to find the corresponding value of the unknown variable.

> *Step 1*:   Write down the formula.
> *Step 2*:   State the values of the known variables.
> *Step 3*:   Substitute the known values into the formula to form a one variable equation.
> *Step 4*:   Solve the equation for the unknown variable.

Example 2   ◀》 *Self Tutor*

When a stone is dropped from a cliff, the total distance fallen after t seconds is given by the formula $D = \frac{1}{2}gt^2$ metres, where $g = 9.8$ m/s². Find:

a the distance fallen after 4 seconds

b the time, to the nearest $\frac{1}{100}$ th second, taken for the stone to fall 200 metres.

a $D = \frac{1}{2}gt^2$ where $g = 9.8$ and $t = 4$

   $\therefore$ $D = \frac{1}{2} \times 9.8 \times 4^2 = 78.4$

   $\therefore$ the stone has fallen 78.4 metres.

b $D = \frac{1}{2}gt^2$ where $D = 200$ and $g = 9.8$

   $\therefore$ $\frac{1}{2} \times 9.8 \times t^2 = 200$

      $\therefore$ $4.9t^2 = 200$

         $\therefore$ $t^2 = \frac{200}{4.9}$

            $\therefore$ $t = \sqrt{\frac{200}{4.9}}$ {t must be positive}

               $\therefore$ $t \approx 6.39$

   $\therefore$ the time taken is about 6.39 seconds.

EXERCISE 10B

1   The formula for finding the circumference C of a circle with radius r is $C = 2\pi r$. Find:

   a the circumference of a circle of radius 4.2 cm

   b the radius of a circle with circumference 112 cm

   c the diameter of a circle with circumference 400 metres.

2   When a stone is dropped from the top of a cliff, the distance fallen after t seconds is given by the formula $D = \frac{1}{2}gt^2$ metres, where $g = 9.8$ m/s^2. Find:

  a   the distance fallen in the first 2 seconds

  b   the time taken for the stone to fall 100 metres.

3   The area A of a circle with radius r is $A = \pi r^2$. Find:

  a   the area of a circle with radius 6.4 cm

  b   the radius of a circular swimming pool which has an area of 160 m^2.

4   The volume of a cylinder with radius r and height h is given by $V = \pi r^2 h$.
Find:

  a   the volume of a cylindrical tin can with radius 8 cm and height 21.2 cm

  b   the height of a cylinder with radius 6 cm and volume 120 cm^3

  c   the radius, in mm, of a copper pipe with volume 470 cm^3 and length 6 m.

5   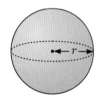   The formula for the surface area A of a sphere with radius r is $A = 4\pi r^2$.
Find:

  a   the surface area of a sphere with radius 7.5 cm

  b   the radius, in cm, of a spherical balloon which has a surface area of 2 m^2.

6   When a car travels a distance d kilometres in time t hours, the average speed for the journey is given by the formula $s = \dfrac{d}{t}$ km/h. Find:

  a   the average speed of a car which travels 250 km in $3\frac{1}{2}$ hours

  b   the distance travelled by a car in $2\frac{3}{4}$ hours if its average speed is 80 km/h

  c   the time taken, to the nearest minute, for a car to travel 790 km at an average speed of 95 km/h.

7   A sphere of radius r has volume given by $V = \frac{4}{3}\pi r^3$. Find:

  a   the volume of a sphere of radius 2.37 m

  b   the radius of a sphere that has volume 2500 cm^3.

8   The *period* or time taken for a simple pendulum to complete one swing is given approximately by $T = \frac{1}{5}\sqrt{l}$ seconds, where l is the length of the pendulum in centimetres. Find:

  a   the time for one complete swing of a pendulum with length 45 cm

  b   the length of a pendulum which has a period of 1.8 seconds.

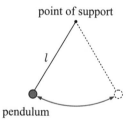

9   The formula $D = 3.56\sqrt{h}$ km gives the approximate distance to the horizon which can be seen by a person with eye level h metres above sea level. Find:

  a   the distance to the horizon for a person whose eye level is 20 m above sea level

  b   how far above sea level a person's eye must be, for the person to be able to see for 25 km.

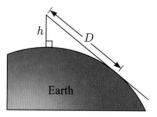

Activity   *Pizza pricing*

Luigi's Pizza Parlour has a "Seafood Special" pizza advertised this week.

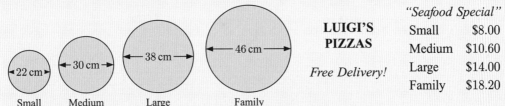

	"Seafood Special"	
LUIGI'S	Small	$8.00
PIZZAS	Medium	$10.60
	Large	$14.00
Free Delivery!	Family	$18.20

Sasha, Enrico, and Bianca each attempted to find Luigi's formula for the price P of each pizza size. The formulae they worked out for a pizza of radius r cm were:

Sasha: $P = \dfrac{17r - 27}{20}$ Enrico: $P = \sqrt{\dfrac{33r - 235}{2}}$ Bianca: $P = 5 + \dfrac{r^2}{40}$.

What to do:

1 Investigate the suitability of each formula.

2 Luigi is introducing a Party size pizza of diameter 54 cm. What do you think his price will be?

C   REARRANGING FORMULAE   *[E2.5]*

In the formula $D = xt + p$, D is expressed in terms of the other variables, x, t, and p. We say that D is the **subject** of the formula.

We can rearrange a formula to make one of the other variables the subject. However, we must do this carefully to ensure that the formula is still true.

> We **rearrange** formulae using the same processes which we use to solve equations. Anything we do to one side we must also do to the other.

Example 3   ◀)) *Self Tutor*

Make y the subject of:

a $2x + 3y = 12$ **b** $x = 5 - cy$

a $2x + 3y = 12$

$\therefore \ 3y = 12 - 2x$ {subtracting $2x$ from both sides}

$\therefore \ y = \dfrac{12 - 2x}{3}$ {dividing both sides by 3}

$\therefore \ y = 4 - \dfrac{2}{3}x$

b $x = 5 - cy$

$\therefore \ x + cy = 5$ {adding cy to both sides}

$\therefore \ cy = 5 - x$ {subtracting x from both sides}

$\therefore \ y = \dfrac{5 - x}{c}$ {dividing both sides by c}

The *subject* of a formula is by itself on the LHS.

EXERCISE 10C

1 Make y the subject of:

  a $x + y = 7$ **b** $x - y = 3$ **c** $x + 2y = 1$

  d $2x + 5y = 10$ **e** $3x + 4y = 20$ **f** $2x - y = 8$

  g $2x + 7y = 14$ **h** $5x + 2y = 20$ **i** $2x - 3y = -12$

2 Make x the subject of:

  a $p + x = r$ **b** $xy = z$ **c** $3x + a = d$

  d $5x + 2y = d$ **e** $ax + by = p$ **f** $y = mx + c$

  g $2 + tx = s$ **h** $p + qx = m$ **i** $6 = a + bx$

3 Make y the subject of:

  a $z = t - 5y$ **b** $c - 2y = p$ **c** $a - 3y = t$

  d $n - ky = 5$ **e** $a - by = n$ **f** $p = a - ny$

  g $4 - xy = c$ **h** $w = 6 - ay$ **i** $-k = m - ty$

Example 4   ◄⑴ Self Tutor

Make z the subject of $c = \dfrac{m}{z}$.

$$c = \frac{m}{z}$$
$$\therefore \; cz = m \qquad \{\text{multiplying both sides by } z\}$$
$$\therefore \; z = \frac{m}{c} \qquad \{\text{dividing both sides by } c\}$$

4 Make z the subject of:

  a $az = \dfrac{b}{c}$ **b** $p = \dfrac{q}{z}$ **c** $\dfrac{a}{z} = d$

  d $\dfrac{3}{d} = \dfrac{2}{z}$ **e** $\dfrac{7}{z} = \dfrac{k}{n}$ **f** $\dfrac{p}{z} = -\dfrac{q}{t}$

  g $\dfrac{z}{2} = \dfrac{a}{z}$ **h** $\dfrac{b}{z} = \dfrac{z}{n}$ **i** $\dfrac{m}{z} = \dfrac{z}{a-b}$

5 Make:

  a a the subject of $F = ma$ **b** r the subject of $C = 2\pi r$

  c d the subject of $V = ldh$ **d** K the subject of $A = \dfrac{b}{K}$

  e h the subject of $A = \dfrac{bh}{2}$ **f** T the subject of $I = \dfrac{PRT}{100}$

  g m the subject of $E = mc^2$ **h** a the subject of $M = \dfrac{a+b}{2}$

6 The surface area of a cylinder with radius r and height h is given by
$A = 2\pi r^2 + 2\pi rh$.
Rearrange this formula to make h the subject.

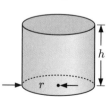

Example 5   ◀) *Self Tutor*

Make t the subject of $s = \frac{1}{2}gt^2$, given that $t > 0$.

$$\frac{1}{2}gt^2 = s \qquad \text{\{rewriting with } t^2 \text{ on the LHS\}}$$
$$\therefore \ gt^2 = 2s \qquad \text{\{multiplying both sides by 2\}}$$
$$\therefore \ t^2 = \frac{2s}{g} \qquad \text{\{dividing both sides by } g\text{\}}$$
$$\therefore \ t = \sqrt{\frac{2s}{g}} \qquad \text{\{as } t > 0\text{\}}$$

7 Make:

   a r the subject of $A = \pi r^2$, given that $r > 0$

   b x the subject of $N = \dfrac{x^2}{a}$

   c k the subject of $M = 5k^2$

   d x the subject of $D = \dfrac{n}{x^3}$

   e x the subject of $y = 4x^2 - 7$, given that $x < 0$

   f Q the subject of $P^2 = Q^2 + R^2$

Example 6   ◀) *Self Tutor*

Make x the subject of $T = \dfrac{a}{\sqrt{x}}$.

$$T = \frac{a}{\sqrt{x}}$$
$$\therefore \ T^2 = \left(\frac{a}{\sqrt{x}}\right)^2 \qquad \text{\{squaring both sides\}}$$
$$\therefore \ T^2 = \frac{a^2}{x}$$
$$\therefore \ T^2 x = a^2 \qquad \text{\{multiplying both sides by } x\text{\}}$$
$$\therefore \ x = \frac{a^2}{T^2} \qquad \text{\{dividing both sides by } T^2\text{\}}$$

8 Make:

   a a the subject of $d = \dfrac{\sqrt{a}}{n}$

   b l the subject of $T = \frac{1}{5}\sqrt{l}$

   c a the subject of $c = \sqrt{a^2 - b^2}$

   d d the subject of $\dfrac{k}{a} = \dfrac{5}{\sqrt{d}}$

   e l the subject of $T = 2\pi\sqrt{\dfrac{l}{g}}$

   f b the subject of $A = 4\sqrt{\dfrac{a}{b}}$

Example 7   ◀) *Self Tutor*

Make x the subject of $ax + 3 = bx + d$.

$$ax + 3 = bx + d$$
$$\therefore \ ax - bx = d - 3 \qquad \text{\{writing terms containing } x \text{ on the LHS\}}$$
$$\therefore \ x(a - b) = d - 3 \qquad \text{\{}x \text{ is a common factor on the LHS\}}$$
$$\therefore \ x = \frac{d - 3}{a - b} \qquad \text{\{dividing both sides by } (a - b)\text{\}}$$

If the variable we wish to make the subject appears more than once, we will need factorisation or expansion.

9 Make x the subject of:

    a $3x + a = bx + c$ **b** $ax = c - bx$ **c** $mx + a = nx - 2$

    d $8x + a = -bx$ **e** $a - x = b - cx$ **f** $rx + d = e - sx$

10 Make x the subject of:

    a $4(x + y) = x + 1$ **b** $5x - z = 2(3 - x)$ **c** $a(x + 5) = b(x - 1)$

    d $k(2x - 1) = x - 7$ **e** $3(xy + 2) = 2x$ **f** $m(1 - 4x) = nx - m$

Example 8   ◀๑) Self Tutor

Make x the subject of $T = \dfrac{a}{x - b}$.

$$T = \frac{a}{x - b}$$

$\therefore \ T(x - b) = a$ {multiplying both sides by $(x - b)$}

$\therefore \ Tx - Tb = a$

$\qquad \therefore \ Tx = a + Tb$ {adding Tb to both sides}

$\qquad \qquad \therefore \ x = \dfrac{a + Tb}{T}$ {dividing both sides by T}

---

11 Make:

    a a the subject of $P = \dfrac{2}{a + b}$ **b** r the subject of $T = \dfrac{8}{q + r}$

    c q the subject of $A = \dfrac{B}{p - q}$ **d** x the subject of $A = \dfrac{3}{2x + y}$

    e y the subject of $M = \dfrac{4}{x^2 + y^2}, \ y > 0$

Example 9   ◀๑) Self Tutor

Make x the subject of $y = \dfrac{3x + 2}{x - 1}$.

$$y = \frac{3x + 2}{x - 1}$$

$\therefore \ y(x - 1) = 3x + 2$ {multiplying both sides by $(x - 1)$}

$\quad \therefore \ xy - y = 3x + 2$

$\quad \therefore \ xy - 3x = y + 2$ {writing terms containing x on LHS}

$\quad \therefore \ x(y - 3) = y + 2$ {factorising}

$\qquad \quad \therefore \ x = \dfrac{y + 2}{y - 3}$ {dividing each side by $(y - 3)$}

---

12 Make x the subject of:

    a $y = \dfrac{x}{x + 1}$ **b** $y = \dfrac{x - 3}{x + 2}$ **c** $y = \dfrac{3x - 1}{x + 3}$

    d $y = \dfrac{5x - 2}{x - 1}$ **e** $y = \dfrac{4x - 1}{2 - x}$ **f** $y = \dfrac{3x + 7}{3 - 2x}$

    g $y = 1 + \dfrac{2}{x - 3}$ **h** $y = -2 + \dfrac{5}{x + 4}$ **i** $y = -3 - \dfrac{6}{x - 2}$

D **REARRANGEMENT AND SUBSTITUTION [E2.5]**

In the Section on formula substitution, the known variables were replaced by numbers, and we then solved an equation to find the unknown.

In situations when we need to perform this process several times, it is quicker to **rearrange** the formula first, and then **substitute**.

Example 10
◀)) Self Tutor

The volume of a cone is given by $V = \frac{1}{3}\pi r^2 h$, where r is the base radius and h is the height.

  a Rearrange this formula to make r the subject.

  b Hence, find the base radius of a cone with:

    i height 6 cm and volume 100 cm³

    ii height 10 cm and volume 200 cm³

    iii height 15 cm and volume 150 cm³.

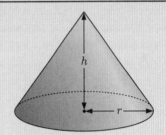

  a $V = \frac{1}{3}\pi r^2 h$

    $\therefore\ 3V = \pi r^2 h$ {multiplying both sides by 3}

    $\therefore\ \dfrac{3V}{\pi h} = r^2$ {dividing both sides by πh}

    $\therefore\ r = \sqrt{\dfrac{3V}{\pi h}}$ {as r must be positive}

  b **i** When $h = 6$ and $V = 100$, $r = \sqrt{\dfrac{3 \times 100}{\pi \times 6}} = \sqrt{\dfrac{50}{\pi}} \approx 3.99$

      So, the base radius is approximately 3.99 cm.

    ii When $h = 10$ and $V = 200$, $r = \sqrt{\dfrac{3 \times 200}{\pi \times 10}} = \sqrt{\dfrac{60}{\pi}} \approx 4.37$

      So, the base radius is approximately 4.37 cm.

    iii When $h = 15$ and $V = 150$, $r = \sqrt{\dfrac{3 \times 150}{\pi \times 15}} = \sqrt{\dfrac{30}{\pi}} \approx 3.09$

      So, the base radius is approximately 3.09 cm.

EXERCISE 10D

1 The area of a sector with radius r and angle θ is given by the formula $A = \dfrac{\theta}{360} \times \pi r^2$.

  a Rearrange this formula to make θ the subject.

  b Hence, find the angle of a sector with:

    i radius 3 cm and area 5 cm²

    ii radius 7 cm and area 45 cm²

    iii radius 8.5 cm and area 135 cm².

2 **a** Make a the subject of the formula $K = \dfrac{d^2}{2ab}$.

   b Find the value of a when:

       i $K = 112,\ d = 24,\ b = 2$ **ii** $K = 400,\ d = 72,\ b = 0.4$

3 The height of a bush after t years is given by the formula $H = 1 + \sqrt{t}$ metres.

   a Rearrange this formula to make t the subject.

   b How long will it take for the bush to reach a height of:

       i 2 m   **ii** 3 m   **iii** 3.5 m?

4 The formula for the volume V of a sphere with radius r is $V = \frac{4}{3}\pi r^3$.

   a Make r the subject of the formula.

   b Find the radius of a sphere which has volume:

       i 40 cm^3 **ii** 800 cm^3 **iii** 1 000 000 cm^3.

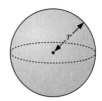

5 An object with constant acceleration a m/s^2 travels s m. Its initial speed is u m/s and its final speed is v m/s. The variables are connected by the formula $v^2 - u^2 = 2as$.

   a Rearrange the formula to make v the subject, where $v \geqslant 0$.

   b Find the final speed of an object which travels:

       i 100 m with initial speed 5 m/s and constant acceleration 2 m/s^2

       ii 1.5 km with initial speed 10 m/s and constant acceleration 0.9 m/s^2.

6 The *winning percentage* of a tennis player who has won w matches and lost l matches is given by the formula $P = \dfrac{w}{w + l} \times 100\%$.

   a Find the winning percentage of a player who has won 10 matches and lost 7 matches.

   b Rearrange the formula to make w the subject.

   c This year Mary has lost 15 matches, with a winning percentage of 37.5%. How many matches has she won?

   d Over his career, Claude has won 84 matches and lost 49 matches. His aim is to increase his winning percentage to 65%. How many consecutive matches must he win to reach his target?

7 Consider two objects with masses m_1 kg and m_2 kg, which are d m apart. The gravitational force between the objects is given by the formula

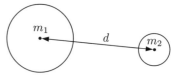

$$F = G\,\frac{m_1 m_2}{d^2}\quad \text{Newtons}$$

where $G \approx 6.67 \times 10^{-11}$ is the universal gravitational constant.

   a The Earth has mass 5.97×10^{24} kg, and the Moon has mass 7.35×10^{22} kg. Given that the Earth and the Moon are approximately 3.82×10^8 m apart, find the gravitational force between them. Give your answer in standard form.

   b Rearrange the formula so that d is the subject.

   c   **i** The Sun has mass 1.99×10^{30} kg. Given that the gravitational force between the Sun and the Earth is 3.54×10^{22} N, find the distance between the Sun and the Earth.

       ii Two planets each have mass 2.32×10^{26} kg, and the gravitational force between them is 1.76×10^{14} N. Find the distance between the planets.

8 Answer the **Opening Problem** on page **155**.

9 According to Einstein's theory of relativity, the mass of a particle is given by the formula

$m = \dfrac{m_0}{\sqrt{1 - \left(\frac{v}{c}\right)^2}}$ where m_0 is the mass of the particle at rest,

v is the speed of the particle, and

c is the speed of light.

a Make v the subject of the formula.

b Find the speed necessary to increase the mass of a particle to three times its rest mass. Give your answer in terms of c.

c A cyclotron increased the mass of an electron to $30m_0$. Given that $c \approx 3 \times 10^8$ m/s, at what speed was the electron travelling?

Review set 10A

1 **a** A trough is initially empty. Write a formula for the volume of water V in the trough if:
  i six 8-litre buckets of water are poured into it
  ii n 8-litre buckets of water are poured into it
  iii n l-litre buckets of water are poured into it.

  b A trough initially contains 25 litres of water. Write a formula for the volume of water V in the trough if n buckets of water, each containing l litres, are poured into it.

2 The formula for the density D of a substance with mass M and volume V is $D = \dfrac{M}{V}$.

  a Find the density of lead given that 350 g of lead occupies 30.7 cm^3.

  b Find the mass of a lump of uranium with density 18.97 g/cm^3 and volume 2 cm^3.

  c Find the volume of a piece of pine timber with mass 6 kg and density 0.65 g/cm^3.

3 Make x the subject of:
  a $mx + n = 3p$
  b $\dfrac{7}{y} = \dfrac{5}{x}$
  c $y = \dfrac{2x - 3}{x - 2}$

4 Make k the subject of:
  a $T = \sqrt{k - l^2}$
  b $P = 2k^2 - r, \ k < 0$

5 Let $A = \dfrac{b}{b + c}$. Find the value of c when:
  a $A = 2, \ b = 6$
  b $A = 3, \ b = -9$
  c $A = -1, \ b = 5$

6 The electric current in a circuit with voltage E volts, resistance r ohms, and load resistance R ohms, is given by the formula $I = \dfrac{E}{r + R}$ amperes.

  a Find the current in a circuit with voltage 24 V, resistance 0.5 ohms, and load resistance 2.5 ohms.

  b Rearrange the formula to make r the subject.

  c Find the resistance of a circuit with current 1.5 amperes, voltage 7.725 V, and load resistance 5 ohms.

7 To convert temperatures from degrees Fahrenheit (°F) to Kelvin (K), we use the formula
$K = \frac{5}{9}(F - 32) + 273.15$.

    a Convert the following temperatures to Kelvin, correct to 1 decimal place:

        i 50°F   **ii** −130°F   **iii** 150°F

    b Rearrange the formula to make F the subject.

    c Convert the following temperatures to degrees Fahrenheit:

        i 313.15 K   **ii** 0 K   **iii** 200 K

Review set 10B

1 Write a formula for the bill $B at a restaurant if there is a charge of:

    a $15 for service, plus $25 per person for 5 people

    b $s for service, plus $25 per person for p people

    c $s for service, plus $m per person for p people.

2 Write a formula for the number of edge pieces E
(excluding corner pieces) in a:

    a 3×5 jigsaw puzzle

    b 4×8 jigsaw puzzle

    c $m \times n$ jigsaw puzzle.

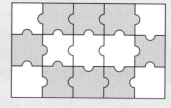

3 Consider the formula $M = p - qr$. Find:

    a M when $p = 19$, $q = -3$, and $r = 6$ **b** r when $M = -2$, $p = 14$, and $q = 2$.

4

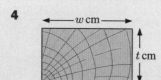

The strength S of a wooden beam is given by $S = 200w^2t$ units,
where w cm is its width and t cm is its thickness.
Find:

    a the strength of a beam of width 16 cm and thickness 4 cm

    b the width of a 5 cm thick beam of strength 60 000 units.

5 Make a the subject of:

    a $B = ad - f$ **b** $\dfrac{Q}{\sqrt{a}} = \dfrac{t}{3}$ **c** $G = \sqrt{\dfrac{5}{a+1}}$

6 The surface area A of a sphere with radius r is given by the formula $A = 4\pi r^2$. If the surface
area of a sphere is 250 cm^2, find its radius correct to 2 decimal places.

7 The kinetic energy of an object with mass m kg which is moving with speed v m/s, is given by
the formula $E = \frac{1}{2}mv^2$ joules, $v \geqslant 0$.

    a Find the kinetic energy of a person with mass 80 kg moving at 5 m/s.

    b Rearrange the formula to make v the subject.

    c A running wombat with mass 25 kg has 800 joules of kinetic energy. Find the speed of the
wombat.

Measurement: Perimeter and area

11

Contents:

A Perimeter   [E7.2, E7.3]
B Area of polygons   [E7.2, E7.5]
C Area of a circle   [E7.3, E7.5]

Opening problem

A javelin throwing arena is illustrated alongside. It has the shape of a sector of a circle of radius 100 m. The throwing line is 5 m from the centre. A white line is painted on the two 95 m straights, and on the circular arcs shown. These arcs mark the throwing line, and throwing distances at 5 m intervals from 45 m to 95 m.

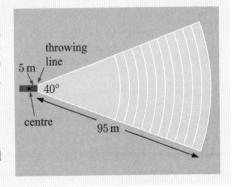

Things to think about:

a Find the total length of the white lines.

b The light green landing area is grassed. Find the total area of grass.

A   PERIMETER   [E7.2, E7.3]

The **perimeter** of a closed figure is the total distance around its **boundary**.

POLYGONS

The perimeter of a **polygon** is the sum of the lengths of its sides.

For example:

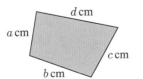

Perimeter $= (a + b + c + d)$ cm

Example 1
◀) **Self Tutor**

Find the perimeter of the following figures:

a

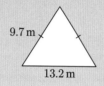
9.7 m
13.2 m

b

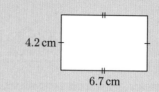
4.2 cm
6.7 cm

a Perimeter $= (2 \times 9.7 + 13.2)$ m
$= 32.6$ m

b Perimeter $= (2 \times 4.2 \ + \ 2 \times 6.7)$ cm
$= (8.4 + 13.4)$ cm
$= 21.8$ cm

CIRCLES

In the case of the circle, the perimeter is given the special name **circumference**.

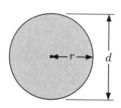
r d

π is an irrational number. It is approximately 3.141 59 ....

Circumference $C = 2\pi r$ or $C = \pi d$

Example 2
◀) **Self Tutor**

Find the perimeter of the following figures:

a

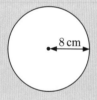
8 cm

b

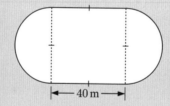
40 m

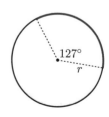
GRAPHICS
CALCULATOR
INSTRUCTIONS

a   Circumference
$= 2\pi r$
$= 2\pi \times 8$ cm
$= 16\pi$ cm
≈ 50.3 cm

b   Perimeter
$=$ circumference of circle $+ \ 2 \times$ length of each straight side
$= ((\pi \times 40) + (2 \times 40))$ m
$= (40\pi + 80)$ m
≈ 206 m

ARC LENGTH

Consider the red arc shown. The angle at the centre of the circle is $127°$.

Since there are $360°$ in the whole circle, the arc makes up $\dfrac{127}{}$ of the circle's circumference.

the arc is $\left(\dfrac{127}{360}\right) \times 2\pi r$.

127°
r

Arc length $l = \left(\dfrac{\theta}{360}\right) \times 2\pi r$

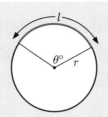

Example 3

◀) **Self Tutor**

Find the perimeter of the sector:

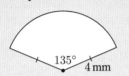

Perimeter
$= (4 + 4) \text{ mm} + \text{length of arc}$
$= 8 \text{ mm} + \left(\frac{135}{360}\right) \times 2 \times \pi \times 4 \text{ mm}$
$\approx 17.4 \text{ mm}$

> The length of an arc is a fraction of the circumference.

EXERCISE 11A

1 Find the perimeter of each figure:

a
9.7 cm

b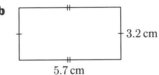
3.2 cm
5.7 cm

c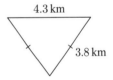
4.3 km
3.8 km

d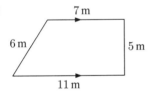
7 m
6 m
5 m
11 m

e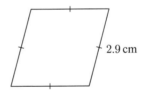
2.9 cm

f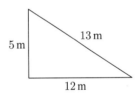
13 m
5 m
12 m

g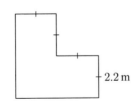
2.2 m

h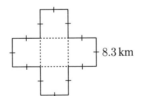
8.3 km

i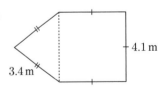
4.1 m
3.4 m

2 Calculate, correct to 3 significant figures, the circumference of a circle with:

a radius 8 cm   **b** radius 0.54 m   **c** diameter 11 cm.

3 Find the perimeter of each figure:

a
3 m

b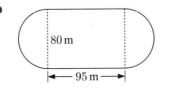
80 m
95 m

c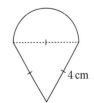
4 cm

4 Find the perimeter of each figure:

a
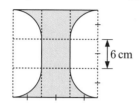
6 cm

b
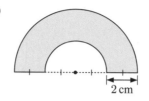
2 cm

c
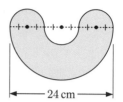
24 cm

5 An isosceles triangle has perimeter 30 cm. If the base is 7.8 cm long, find the length of the equal sides.

6 A rectangle is 16.4 cm by 11.8 cm and has the same perimeter as an equilateral triangle. Find the length of the sides of the triangle.

7 Find the perimeter of the following figures:

a
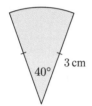
40° 3 cm

b
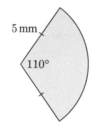
5 mm
110°

c
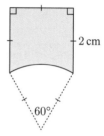
2 cm
60°

8
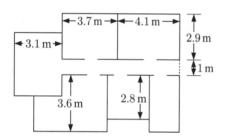
3.7 m, 4.1 m, 3.1 m, 2.9 m, 1 m, 3.6 m, 2.8 m

Find the external perimeter of the house in this plan.

9 Calculate the length of the arc of a circle if:

   a the radius is 12.5 cm and the angle at the centre is 60°

   b the radius is 8.4 m and the angle at the centre is 120°.

10 Write a formula for the perimeter P of the following figures:

a
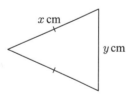
x cm
y cm

b
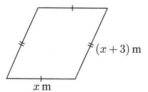
$(x+3)$ m
x m

c
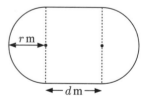
r m
d m

11 The horses on a merry-go-round complete 20 laps during each ride.

   a Find, correct to 1 decimal place, the total distance travelled during a ride by:

     i the black horse   **ii** the white horse.

   b How much farther than the white horse does the black horse travel?

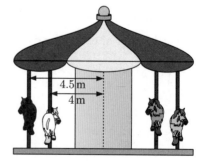
4.5 m
4 m

12 A tennis court has the dimensions shown.

    a What is the perimeter of the court?

    b Find the total length of all the marked lines, not including the net.

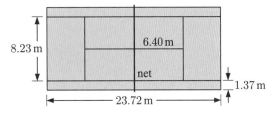

13 A lighting company produces conical lampshades from sectors of circles as illustrated. When the lampshades are made, lace is stitched around the circular base. Determine the total cost of the lace for 1500 lampshades if the lace costs $0.75 per metre.

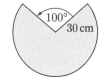

14   **a** Find the length of an arc of a circle of radius 8 cm and angle $120°$.

    b Find the perimeter of a sector of a circle of radius 9 cm and sector angle $80°$.

15 The second hand of a clock is 10 cm long. How far does the tip of the second hand travel in 20 seconds?

16

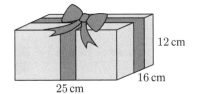

Find the total length of ribbon used to tie the box illustrated. 25 cm of ribbon is required for the bow.

17 At Bushby Park there is a 5 m diameter circular pond which is surrounded by a 1 m wide garden bed, and then a 3 m wide lawn. A safety fence is placed around the lawn with posts every 3 m and a gateway 1.84 m wide. The gate is wrought iron.

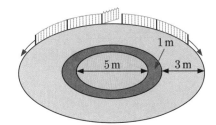

    a How many metres of safety fence are needed?

    b How many posts are needed?

    c If the posts cost $15.75 and the safety fence costs $18.35 per metre, calculate the total cost of the fence (excluding the gate).

Puzzle   *Rope around the Earth*

Consider these two scenarios:

1 A loop of rope is placed tightly around a circular table top.

    1 metre of rope is then added to the loop, and the rope is stretched into a circle so there is a gap between the rope and the table top.

2 A loop of rope is placed tightly around the Earth. Again, 1 metre of rope is then added to the loop, and the rope is stretched into a circle so there is a gap between the rope and the Earth.

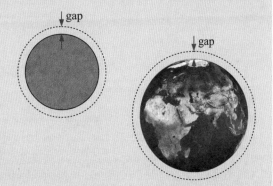

Do you think the gap will be larger in scenario **1** or scenario **2**? Perform some calculations to find out whether you are correct!

B AREA OF POLYGONS   [E7.2, E7.5]

All around us we see surfaces such as walls, ceilings, paths, and sporting fields. All of these surfaces have boundaries which define their shape.

The **area** of a region is the amount of **surface** within its boundaries.

The **area** of surface of a closed figure is measured in terms of the number of square units it encloses.

In previous years you should have seen the following area formulae:

Shape	Figure	Formula
Rectangle	width / length	**Area = length × width**
Triangle	height / base base	**Area = $\frac{1}{2}$ × base × height**
Parallelogram	height / base	**Area = base × height**
Trapezium	a / h / b	**Area = $\left(\dfrac{a+b}{2}\right) \times h$**

DEMO

DEMO

DEMO

Example 4   ◀)) *Self Tutor*

Find the area of:

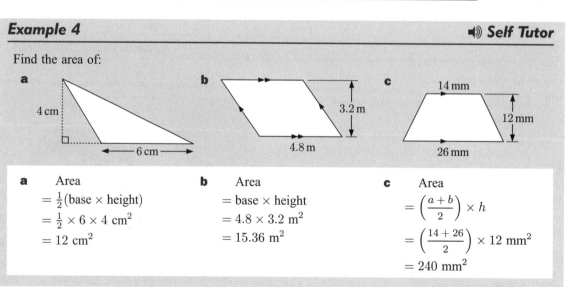

a   Area
$= \frac{1}{2}(\text{base} \times \text{height})$
$= \frac{1}{2} \times 6 \times 4 \text{ cm}^2$
$= 12 \text{ cm}^2$

b   Area
$= \text{base} \times \text{height}$
$= 4.8 \times 3.2 \text{ m}^2$
$= 15.36 \text{ m}^2$

c   Area
$= \left(\dfrac{a+b}{2}\right) \times h$
$= \left(\dfrac{14+26}{2}\right) \times 12 \text{ mm}^2$
$= 240 \text{ mm}^2$

EXERCISE 11B

1 Find the area of the following figures:

a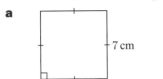

b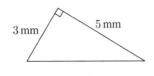

c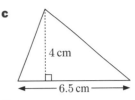

d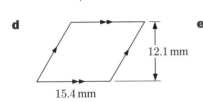

e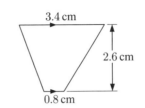

f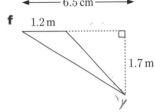

2 Find the area of the following figures:

a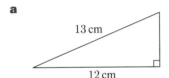

b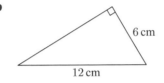

c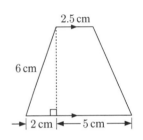

3 Calculate the height h of the following figures:

a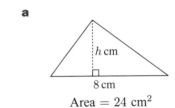
Area = 24 cm²

b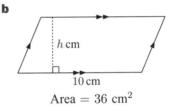
Area = 36 cm²

c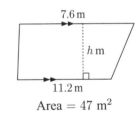
Area = 47 m²

4 A 15 cm by 20 cm rectangle has the same perimeter as a square. Which figure has the greater area? Explain your answer.

5 The Highways Department orders 25 road signs that warn motorists to watch out for squirrels.

  a By assuming the signs are triangular, find the area of metal sheeting (in m²) required for the 25 signs.

  b To allow for wastage when the signs are cut, an extra 20% of the metal is needed. How much metal needs to be purchased?

  c The sheet metal costs \$28.40 per m². What will its cost be?

6 A 4.2 m by 3.5 m tablecloth is used to cover a square table with sides of length 3.1 m. Find the area of the tablecloth which overhangs the edges.

7 A square tile has area 256 cm². How many tiles are needed to cover a floor 4 m × 2.4 m?

8 Find the area of a rhombus which has diagonals of length 12 cm and 8 cm.

9 One diagonal of a rhombus is twice as long as the other diagonal. If the rhombus has area 32 cm², find the length of the shorter diagonal.

10   The area of trapezium ABCD is 204 cm². Find the area of triangle DBC.

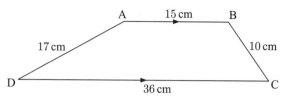

11   Find the area of a kite with diagonals of length: **a**   16 cm and 10 cm   **b** a cm and b cm.

12   Parallelogram ABCD has AB = 10 cm and diagonal DB = 15 cm. If the shortest distance from C to line AB is 8 cm, find the shortest distance from A to DB.

13   Find the area of an equilateral triangle with side length 4.8 cm.

14   Find the side length of an equilateral triangle with area 325 mm².

Example 5   ◀) *Self Tutor*

Find the shaded area:

Shaded area
= area of rectangle − area of triangle
$= (8.6 \times 5.4) \text{ m}^2 - \left(\frac{1}{2} \times 3.7 \times 2.2\right) \text{ m}^2$
$= 42.37 \text{ m}^2$

---

15   Find the shaded area:

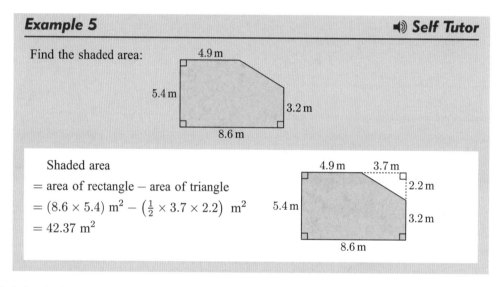

16   The diagram shows the dimensions of a courtyard. It is to be paved with 60 cm square tiles costing $9.40 each.

   a   How many tiles will be needed?

   b   How much will the tiles cost?

17   A chessboard consists of 5 cm squares of blackwood for the black squares, and maple for the white squares. The squares are surrounded by an 8 cm wide blackwood border. Determine the percentage of the board which is made of maple. (There are 64 squares on a chessboard.)

18   Write a formula for the area of each shape:

a

b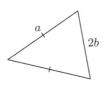

c

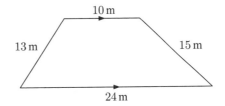

19   Find the area of this trapezium:

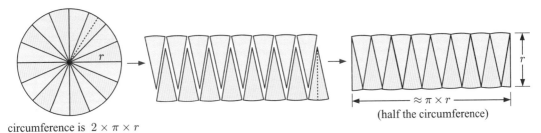

C   AREA OF A CIRCLE   [E7.3, E7.5]

Consider cutting a circle of radius r into 16 equal sectors and arranging them as shown:

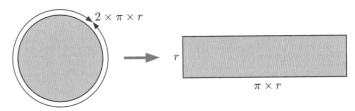

The figure obtained closely resembles a rectangle. The height of the rectangle is the radius of the circle.

The top "edge" is the sum of all the arc lengths of the blue sectors. This is half the circumference of the circle, which is $\frac{1}{2} \times 2\pi r = \pi \times r$.

The bottom "edge" is made up from the arcs of the yellow sectors in a similar way.

If the original circle is cut into thousands of equal sectors and arranged in the same way, the resulting figure is indistinguishable from a rectangle.

DEMO

So, the area of the circle $A = \text{length} \times \text{width}$ of the rectangle

$$\therefore \quad A = \pi \times r \times r$$
$$\therefore \quad A = \pi r^2$$

The area of a circle of radius r is given by   **Area $= \pi r^2$.**

AREA OF A SECTOR

The area of a **sector** is a fraction of the area of the circle it is taken from.

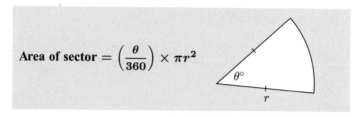

$$\text{Area of sector} = \left(\frac{\theta}{360}\right) \times \pi r^2$$

Example 6   ◄) *Self Tutor*

Find, to 1 decimal place, the shaded area:

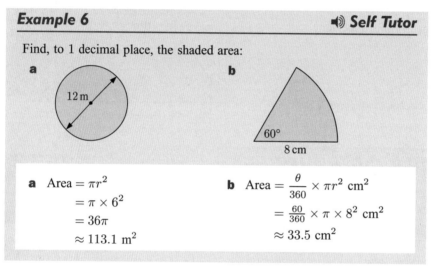

a   Area $= \pi r^2$
      $= \pi \times 6^2$
      $= 36\pi$
      $\approx 113.1 \text{ m}^2$

b   Area $= \dfrac{\theta}{360} \times \pi r^2 \text{ cm}^2$
      $= \dfrac{60}{360} \times \pi \times 8^2 \text{ cm}^2$
      $\approx 33.5 \text{ cm}^2$

EXERCISE 11C

1 Calculate, correct to 3 significant figures, the area of a circle with:

   a radius 10 cm   **b** radius 12.2 m   **c** diameter 9.7 cm.

2 Find the area of each shape:

a 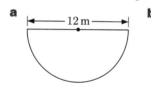 **b** 4 cm **c** 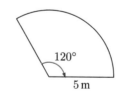 **d**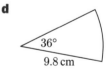

3 Calculate the area of a sector of:

   a radius 5.62 m and angle 80°   **b** radius 8.7 cm and angle 210°.

4 Find, in terms of π:

   a the length of arc AB
   b the perimeter of sector OAB
   c the area of sector OAB.

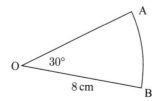

5 Calculate the radius of a circle with:

   a circumference 20 cm   **b** area 20 cm²   **c** area 9π m².

6 Find the angle of a sector with area 30 cm² and radius 12 cm.

7 A circular golfing green has diameter 20 m. The hole must be positioned on the green at least 3 m from its edge. Find the area of the green on which the hole is allowed to be positioned.

8 Find the shaded area:

a

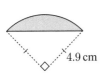

4.9 cm

b

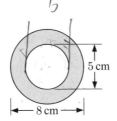

5 cm

8 cm

c

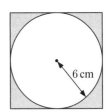

6 cm

d

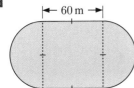

60 m

e

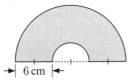

6 cm

f

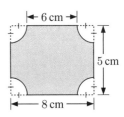

6 cm

5 cm

8 cm

9 A door is in the shape of a rectangle surmounted by a semi-circle. The width of the door is 1.2 m, and the height of the door is 2.5 m. Find the total area of the door.

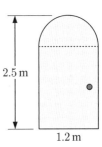

2.5 m

1.2 m

10 A restaurant uses square tables with sides of length 1.3 m, and round tablecloths with diameter 2 m. Determine the percentage of each tablecloth which overhangs its table.

11 6 identical metal discs are stamped out of an 18 cm by 12 cm sheet of copper as illustrated. What percentage of the copper is wasted?

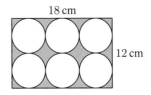

18 cm

12 cm

12 A gravel path 1 m wide is placed around a circular garden bed of diameter 2 m. The gravel costs $7.90 per m².

    a Find the area of the path.   **b** Find the cost of the gravel.

13 Find the perimeter and area of the following shapes:

a

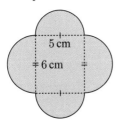

5 cm

6 cm

b

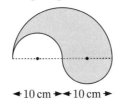

10 cm

10 cm

c

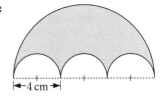

4 cm

14 Answer the **Opening Problem** on page **167**.

Example 7

◀)) *Self Tutor*

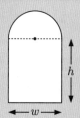

The illustrated door consists of a semi-circle and a rectangle. Find a formula for the area of the door in terms of the width w and height h of the rectangular part.

The area of a rectangle = height × width

$$= hw$$

The radius of the semi-circle is $\dfrac{w}{2}$.

$\therefore$ the area of the semi-circle $= \frac{1}{2} \times$ (area of full circle)

$$= \tfrac{1}{2} \times \pi r^2$$

$$= \tfrac{1}{2} \times \pi \times \left(\dfrac{w}{2}\right)^2$$

$$= \tfrac{1}{2} \times \pi \times \dfrac{w^2}{4}$$

$$= \tfrac{1}{8}\pi w^2$$

$\therefore$ the total area is $A = hw + \frac{1}{8}\pi w^2$

15 Find a formula for the area A of the following regions:

a

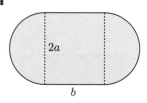

b

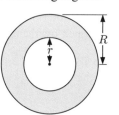

c

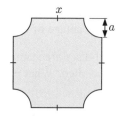

You may need to use Pythagoras' theorem!

d

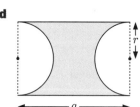

e

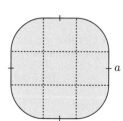

f

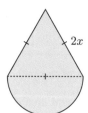

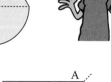

16 A square slice of bread has sides of length 10 cm. A semi-circular piece of ham with diameter 10 cm is placed on the bread, and the bread is cut in half diagonally as illustrated. What percentage of the ham is on side A of the bread?

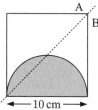

17 A dartboard is divided into 20 equal sections numbered from 1 to 20. Players throw darts at the board, and score points given by the section number that the dart lands in. If a dart lands in the outer "double" ring, the points value of the throw is doubled. If a dart lands in the middle "treble" ring, the points value of the throw is trebled. The central bulls eye has diameter 32 mm, and is worth 25 points. The red centre of the bulls eye has diameter 12 mm, and is worth 50 points.

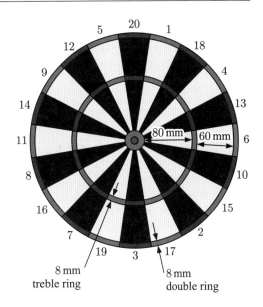

8 mm
treble ring

8 mm
double ring

   a Find the circumference of the dartboard in cm.

   b Find the outer arc length of the "triple 9" section in cm.

   c Find the area in cm², of the region(s) of the dartboard which result in a score of:

      i 50   **ii** 25   **iii** 5

      iv 14   **v** 12

Activity

Sam the sheep

Click on the icon to obtain further problems with area.

SAM THE SHEEP

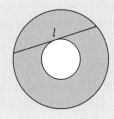

Challenge

1 The rectangle contains 7 semi-circles and 2 quarter circles. What percentage of the rectangle is shaded?

2 A regular hexagon and an equilateral triangle have the same perimeter. Find the ratio of their areas.

3

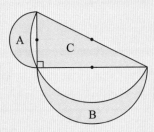

Show that Area A + Area B = Area C.

4 In the figure shown, prove that the (shaded) area of the annulus is $\frac{1}{4}\pi l^2$, where l is the length of a chord of the outer circle which is also a tangent to the inner circle.

5 The figure given represents a rectangular box. The areas of 3 touching faces are 2 cm², 4 cm² and 8 cm². Determine the volume of the box.

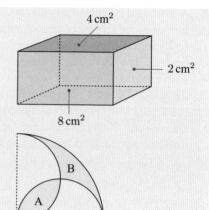

6 Show that the two shaded regions have equal area.

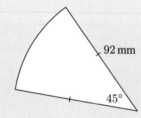

7 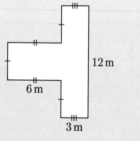 A thin plastic band is used to tie the seven plastic pipes together. If the band is 50 cm long, what is the radius of each pipe?

Review set 11A

1 Find the perimeter and area of each figure:

a

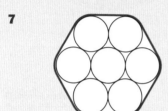

b

92 mm

45°

c

6 cm

8 cm

5 cm

d

2 m

1.8 m

3.6 m

2 A rectangular bathroom measuring 3 m by 2 m is to be decorated on all walls with a single row of patterned tiles. There is a doorway measuring 90 cm wide. Each patterned tile is 15 cm long and costs $5. Find:

    a the total length of patterned tiles required   **b** the total cost of the tiles.

3 A circular playing field has radius 80 metres. The field is surrounded by a fence 10 metres from the edge of the field. Determine the length of the fence.

4 Find the area of:

    a a sector with radius 10 cm and angle 120°

    b a right angled triangle with base 5 cm and hypotenuse 13 cm

    c a circle with diameter 15 cm.

5 The diameter of a car tyre is 50 cm. How many revolutions does the tyre complete if the car travels 2 km?

6 A circle has area 8 m². Find its:

    a radius   **b** circumference.

7 Find the angle of a sector with arc length 32 cm and radius 7 cm.

8 Write a formula for the perimeter P and area A of each figure:

a
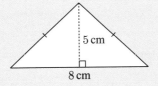

b
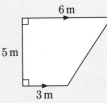

9
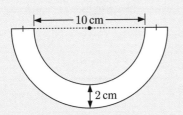

By finding the area of triangle ABC in two different ways, show that $d = \frac{60}{13}$.

Review set 11B

1 Find the perimeter and area of each figure:

a
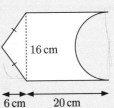

b

c

d

2 Find the perimeter of:

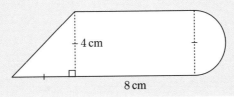

3 Find the shaded area, rounded to 2 decimal places.

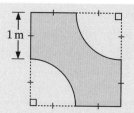

4 Calculate the area in hectares of a rectangular field with sides 300 m and 0.2 km.

5 A sector of a circle has radius 12 cm and angle 135°.

  a What fraction of a whole circle is this sector?

  b Find the perimeter of the sector.

  c Find the area of the sector.

6 A circle has circumference 40.8 m. Find its:

  a radius   **b** area.

7 A security-conscious man builds himself a house on a circle of land with radius 10 m. The circle is surrounded by a moat 3 m wide. A shark swims in the middle of the moat to deter anyone who may attempt to cross it. The shark makes 150 complete circuits of the moat every day. How far does the shark swim every day?

8 Find the formula for the area A of each figure:

  a

  b

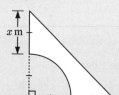

  c

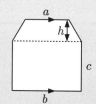

9 Find in terms of π the perimeter and area of the shaded region:

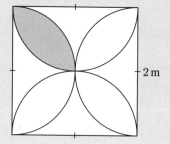

Measurement: Solids and containers

12

Contents:

A	Surface area	[E7.4, E7.5]
B	Volume	[E7.1, E7.4, E7.5]
C	Capacity	[E7.1, E7.4]
D	Density	[E7.1]

Opening problem

Jacob wants to throw a water balloon at his brother. It is a sphere containing 1 litre of water.

Things to think about:

a What is the *volume* of the filled balloon?

b What is the *radius* of the water balloon?

c What is the outer *surface area* of the water balloon?

In this Chapter we consider measurements involving 3-dimensional objects. These may be solids which have **mass**, **surface area**, and **volume**, or containers which can hold a certain **capacity**.

A   SURFACE AREA   [E7.4, E7.5]

SOLIDS WITH PLANE FACES

The **surface area** of a solid with plane faces is the sum of the areas of the faces.

A *plane* face is one which is flat.

The surface area is therefore the same as the area of the **net** required to make the figure.

Example 1   ◀) *Self Tutor*

Find the surface area of:

a

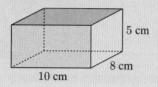

b

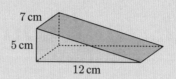

a Surface area $= 2 \times 10 \times 8$ cm$^2 + 2 \times 10 \times 5$ cm$^2 + 2 \times 8 \times 5$ cm^2
$\qquad\qquad\quad = (160 + 100 + 80)$ cm^2
$\qquad\qquad\quad = 340$ cm^2

b

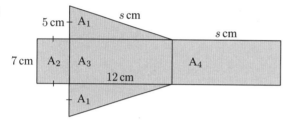

Let the slant edge have length s cm.
$\therefore \ s^2 = 12^2 + 5^2 \qquad$ {Pythagoras}
$\therefore \ s^2 = 169$
$\qquad \therefore \ s = \sqrt{169} = 13 \quad$ {as $s > 0$}

$\begin{aligned} A_1 &= \tfrac{1}{2}bh \\ &= \tfrac{1}{2} \times 12 \times 5 \\ &= 30 \text{ cm}^2 \end{aligned}$
$\qquad$
$\begin{aligned} A_2 &= 7 \times 5 \\ &= 35 \text{ cm}^2 \end{aligned}$
$\qquad$
$\begin{aligned} A_3 &= 12 \times 7 \\ &= 84 \text{ cm}^2 \end{aligned}$
$\qquad$
$\begin{aligned} A_4 &= 13 \times 7 \\ &= 91 \text{ cm}^2 \end{aligned}$

Surface area $= 2 \times A_1 + A_2 + A_3 + A_4$
$\qquad\qquad\quad = 2 \times 30 + 35 + 84 + 91$
$\qquad\qquad\quad = 270$ cm^2

EXERCISE 12A.1

1 Find the surface area of a cube with sides:

   a 3 cm   **b** 4.5 cm   **c** 9.8 mm

2 Find the surface area of the following rectangular prisms:

   a

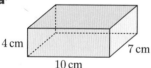

   b

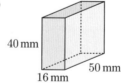

   c

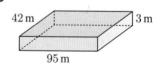

3 Find the surface area of the following triangular prisms:

   a

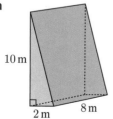

   b

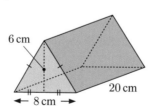

   c

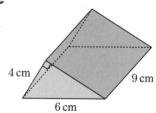

Example 2   ◀)) *Self Tutor*

Find the surface area of the
square-based pyramid:

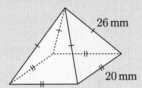

The figure has:

  • 1 square base   • 4 triangular faces

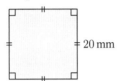

$$h^2 + 10^2 = 26^2 \quad \{\text{Pythagoras}\}$$
$$\therefore \ h^2 + 100 = 676$$
$$\therefore \ \ h^2 = 576$$
$$\therefore \ \ h = 24 \quad \{\text{as } h > 0\}$$

Surface area $= 20 \times 20$ mm^2 $+ \ 4 \times \left(\frac{1}{2} \times 20 \times 24\right)$ mm^2
$\qquad\qquad\quad = (400 + 960)$ mm^2
$\qquad\qquad\quad = 1360$ mm^2

4 Find the surface area of the following square-based pyramids:

a
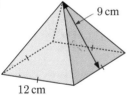

b
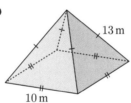

c
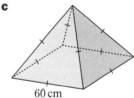

5 Find the surface area of each solid:

a
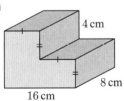

b
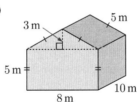

c
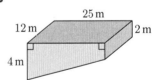

d
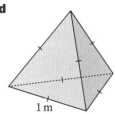

e
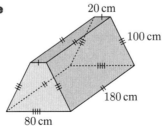

6 A metal pencil box is 20 cm by 15 cm by 8 cm high. Find the total area of metal used to make the
pencil box.

7

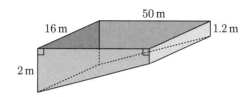

The base and internal walls of the swimming pool shown are tiled. The tiles cost $25 per m².

a   Find the total area of tiles.

b   Find the value of the tiles.

8   A marquee with the dimensions as shown is made from canvas. The marquee has no floor. Find the total cost of the canvas if it costs $31.50 per square metre.

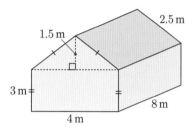

9   An aviary has the shape of a hexagonal prism. Find the area of netting required to cover the aviary, including the floor.

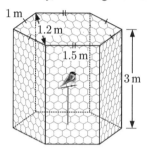

10

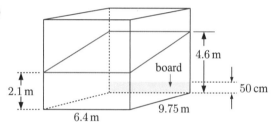

A squash court has the dimensions given. Each shot may strike the floor, or the walls below the red line, except for the board on the front wall. Calculate the total surface playing area of the walls and the floor. Give your answer correct to 4 significant figures.

11   Find a formula for the surface area A of each of the following:

a

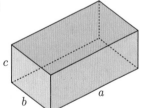

b

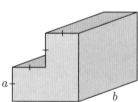

c

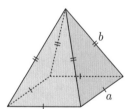

CYLINDERS

The cylinder shown has no top or bottom. If the cylinder is cut, opened out, and flattened, it takes the shape of a rectangle.

The length of the rectangle is the circumference of the cylinder.

The width of the rectangle is the height of the cylinder.

∴   for a hollow cylinder, the outer surface area

$$A = \text{area of rectangle}$$
$$= \text{length} \times \text{width}$$
$$= 2\pi r h$$

DEMO

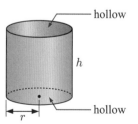

Hollow cylinder (no ends)	Open can (one end)	Solid cylinder (two ends)
hollow h r hollow	hollow h r solid	solid h r solid
$A = 2\pi rh$	$A = 2\pi rh + \pi r^2$	$A = 2\pi rh + 2\pi r^2$

CONES

The curved surface of a cone is made from a sector of a circle. The radius of the sector is equal to the slant height s of the cone. The arc length AB of the sector is equal to the circumference of the base.

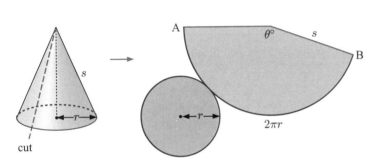

$$\text{arc AB} = 2\pi r$$

$$\therefore \left(\frac{\theta}{360}\right) 2\pi s = 2\pi r$$

$$\therefore \frac{\theta}{360} = \frac{r}{s}$$

$\therefore$ the area of the curved surface
= the area of the sector

$$= \left(\frac{\theta}{360}\right) \pi s^2$$

$$= \frac{r}{s} \times \pi s^2$$

$$= \pi rs$$

Hollow cone (no end)	Solid cone (closed end)
hollow — r s	solid — r s
$A = \pi rs$	$A = \pi rs + \pi r^2$

SPHERES

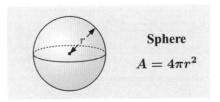

Sphere

$A = 4\pi r^2$

SURFACE AREA
OF A SPHERE

Example 3

◀⬤ *Self Tutor*

Find the surface area of each solid:

a

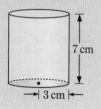

7 cm

3 cm

b

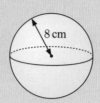

8 cm

a Surface area
$$= 2\pi rh + 2\pi r^2$$
$$= (2 \times \pi \times 3 \times 7 + 2 \times \pi \times 3^2) \text{ cm}^2$$
$$\approx 188 \text{ cm}^2$$

b Surface area
$$= 4\pi r^2$$
$$= 4 \times \pi \times 8^2 \text{ cm}^2$$
$$\approx 804 \text{ cm}^2$$

Example 4

◀⬤ *Self Tutor*

Find the surface area of a solid cone with base radius 5 cm and height 12 cm.

Let the slant height be s cm.

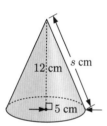

12 cm s cm

5 cm

$$s^2 = 5^2 + 12^2 \qquad \{\text{Pythagoras}\}$$
$$\therefore \ s^2 = 169$$
$$\therefore \ s = \sqrt{169} = 13 \qquad \{\text{as } s > 0\}$$
Now $A = \pi r^2 + \pi rs$
$$\therefore \ A = \pi \times 5^2 + \pi \times 5 \times 13$$
$$\therefore \ A = 90\pi$$
$$\therefore \ A \approx 283$$

The surface area is approximately 283 cm^2.

EXERCISE 12A.2

1 Find the outer surface area of each cylinder:

a solid

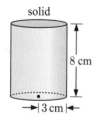

8 cm

3 cm

b can (no top)

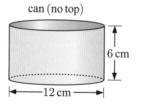

6 cm

12 cm

c solid

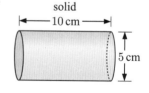

10 cm

5 cm

d well (no top)

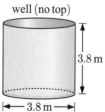

3.8 m

3.8 m

e solid

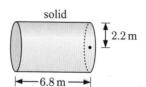

2.2 m

6.8 m

f hollow throughout

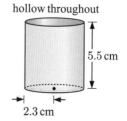

5.5 cm

2.3 cm

2 Find the surface area of each solid:

a

b

c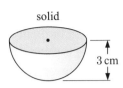

3 Find the *outer* surface area of each cone:

a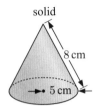

b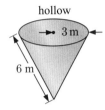

c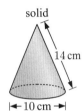

d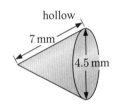

e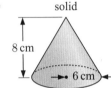

f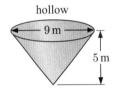

4 Find the total surface area of:

   a a cylinder with base radius 9 cm and height 20 cm

   b a solid cone with base radius and perpendicular height both 10 cm

   c a sphere with radius 6 cm

   d a hemisphere with radius 10 m

   e a cone with base radius 8 cm and vertical angle $60°$.

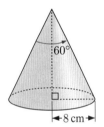

5 A conical piece of filter paper has a base radius of 2 cm, and is 5 cm high.

   a Find the slant height s.

   b Hence find the outer surface area of the filter paper.

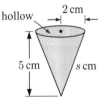

6 A cylindrical tank is 6 m high and has diameter 8 m. Its outer surface (including both ends) is to be painted bright red. Each litre of paint covers 5 m^2. It is purchased in 5 litre cans costing $52.50 each.

   a Find the surface area to be painted.

   b Find the number of cans of paint which must be purchased.

   c What is the cost of the paint?

7 Find:

   a the radius of a sphere with surface area 400 m^2

   b the height of a solid cylinder with radius 10 cm and surface area 2000 cm^2

   c the slant height of a solid cone with base radius 8 m and surface area 850 m^2.

8 We commonly use a sphere to model the Earth, even though it is not a *perfect* sphere. The Earth has a radius of approximately 6400 km.

  a Estimate the surface area of the Earth.

  b 71% of the Earth's surface is covered by water. Estimate this area.

  c China has a land area of 9 706 961 km².

    i What percentage of the surface area of the Earth is China?

    ii What percentage of the *land* area of the Earth is China?

9 Find, correct to 1 decimal place, the surface area of each solid:

  a
      b
      c

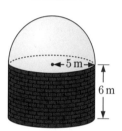
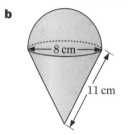
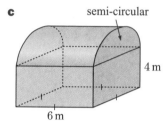

10

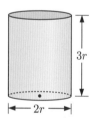

The outside of this observatory needs cleaning. The cost of cleaning the hemispherical glass roof is $4 per square metre, and the cost of cleaning the cylindrical walls is $2.50 per square metre. Find, to the nearest dollar, the total cost of cleaning the observatory.

11 A wedge with angle 20° is cut from the centre of a cylindrical cake of radius 13 cm and height 6 cm. Each side of the wedge, excluding the bottom, is to be covered with icing.

Find the total surface area of cake to be iced.

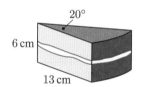

12 Find a formula for the surface area A of each of the following:

  a   **b**   **c**   **d**

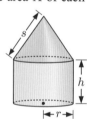
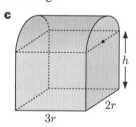
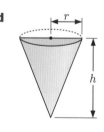

B   VOLUME   [E7.1, E7.4, E7.5]

The **volume** of a solid is the amount of space it occupies.

RECTANGULAR PRISM (CUBOID)

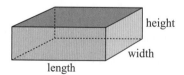

> **Volume = length × width × height**

SOLIDS OF UNIFORM CROSS-SECTION

In the triangular prism alongside, any vertical slice parallel
to the front triangular face will be the same size and shape
as that face. Solids like this are called **solids of uniform
cross-section**. The cross-section in this case is a triangle.

Solid   Cross-section

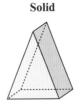

Another example is this hexagonal prism:

Solid   Cross-section

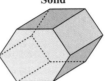

For any solid of uniform cross-section:

> **Volume = area of cross-section × length**

For a **cylinder**, the cross-section is a circle.

Volume = area of circle × height
$$= \pi r^2 \times h$$

> **Volume $= \pi r^2 h$**

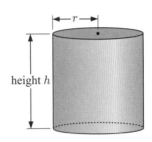

height h

Example 5   ◆)) *Self Tutor*

Find the volume of each solid:

a   **b**   area = 30 cm²   **c**

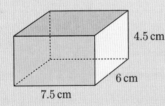 4.5 cm

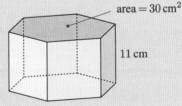   11 cm

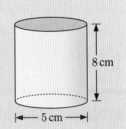   8 cm

6 cm

7.5 cm   ⊢— 5 cm —⊣

a   Volume
= length × width × height
= 7.5 cm × 6 cm × 4.5 cm
= 202.5 cm³

b   Volume
= area of cross-section × height
= 30 cm² × 11 cm
= 330 cm³

c   The base has diameter 5 cm, so the radius is 2.5 cm.
$$V = \pi r^2 h$$
$$= \pi \times 2.5^2 \times 8 \text{ cm}^3$$
$$\approx 157 \text{ cm}^3$$

EXERCISE 12B.1

1 Find the volume of each rectangular prism:

a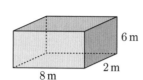
6 m
2 m
8 m

b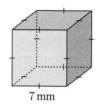
7 mm

c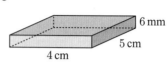
6 mm
5 cm
4 cm

2 Find, rounded to 3 significant figures, the volume of each cylinder:

a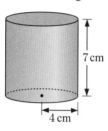
7 cm
4 cm

b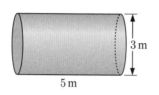
3 m
5 m

c
4 m
70 cm

3 Find the volume of each solid:

a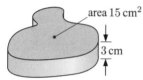
area 15 cm²
3 cm

b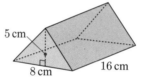
5 cm
8 cm
16 cm

c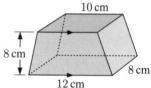
10 cm
8 cm
12 cm
8 cm

d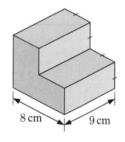
8 cm
9 cm

e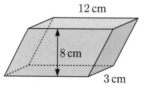
12 cm
8 cm
3 cm

f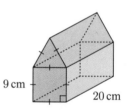
9 cm
20 cm

4 Find the volume of:

a this brick

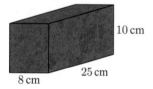
10 cm
25 cm
8 cm

b this coin

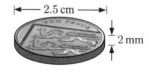
2.5 cm
2 mm

c this wedge of cheese

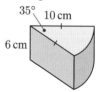
35° 10 cm
6 cm

d this picket

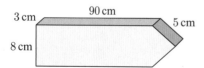
3 cm
90 cm
5 cm
8 cm

e this dumbbell

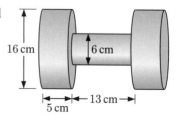
16 cm
6 cm
5 cm
13 cm

5

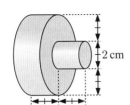

1 m³ of brass is melted down and cast into solid door handles with the shape shown. How many handles can be cast?

6 A swimming pool has internal dimensions shown alongside.

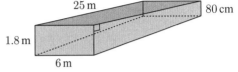

   a Find the area of a trapezium-shaped side.

   b Determine the volume of water required to fill the pool.

7 A concrete tank has an external diameter of 5 m and an internal height of 3 m. The walls and base of the tank are 20 cm thick. The concrete costs \$142 per m³.

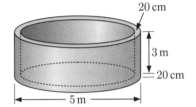

   a Find the volume of concrete required to make:

   i the base   **ii** the walls.

   b Find the total volume of concrete required.

   c Find the cost of the concrete required to make the tank.

8 In the town square, there is a fountain in the middle of a circular pond. The pond is 6 metres in diameter. A concrete wall 30 cm wide and 60 cm high is built around the edge of the pond.

   a Find the area of the top of the wall.   **b** Find the volume of concrete required for the wall.

9 Write a formula for the volume V of each object:

   a   **b**   **c**

   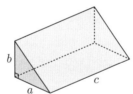   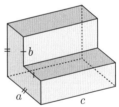

10

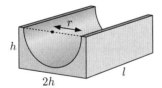

A half-pipe for skating is made with the dimensions shown. Show that the volume of concrete used is given by the formula $V = l(2h^2 - \frac{1}{2}\pi r^2)$.

11 A cylindrical pipe has outside radius R, inside radius r, and length l. Show that the volume of concrete used to make the pipe is given by
$$V = \pi l(R + r)(R - r).$$

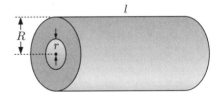

Activity 1   *Packing boxes*

Click on the icon to obtain this Activity.

**PACKING
BOXES**

PYRAMIDS AND CONES

Pyramids and cones are known as **tapered solids**. They have a flat base, and come to a point called the **apex**.

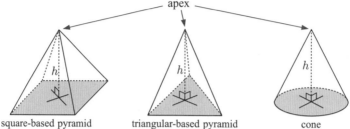

square-based pyramid   triangular-based pyramid   cone

Tapered solids do **not** have a uniform cross-section. For example, we can see that the perpendicular cross-section of a cone is always a circle, but its radius decreases as we move up the cone.

DEMO

The volume of a square-based pyramid is one third of the volume of a prism with the same base area and height.

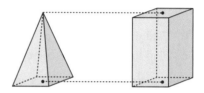

Similarly, the volume of a cone is one third of the volume of a cylinder with the same base area and height.

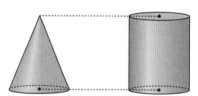

> **Volume of a tapered solid** $= \frac{1}{3} \times$ **area of base** $\times$ **height**

A formal proof of this formula is beyond the scope of this course. It may be demonstrated using water displacement by comparing tapered solids with solids of uniform cross-section with identical bases and the same heights.

Example 6
◀) *Self Tutor*

Find the volume of each solid:

a
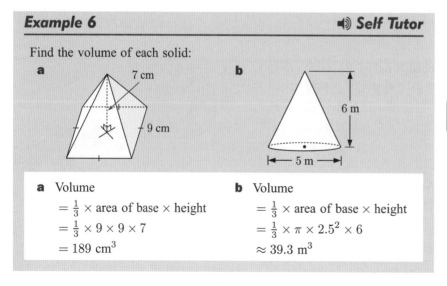
7 cm

9 cm

b

6 m

5 m

The volume of a cone is
$V = \frac{1}{3}\pi r^2 h$.

a Volume
$= \frac{1}{3} \times$ area of base $\times$ height
$= \frac{1}{3} \times 9 \times 9 \times 7$
$= 189 \text{ cm}^3$

b Volume
$= \frac{1}{3} \times$ area of base $\times$ height
$= \frac{1}{3} \times \pi \times 2.5^2 \times 6$
$\approx 39.3 \text{ m}^3$

EXERCISE 12B.2

1 Find the volume of each solid:

a 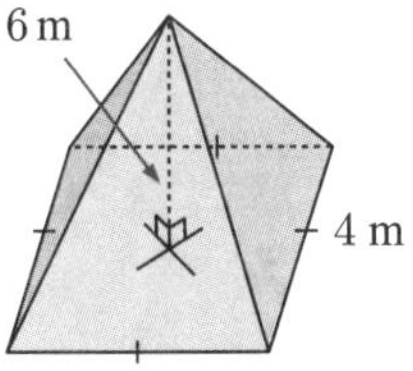
6 m
4 m

b 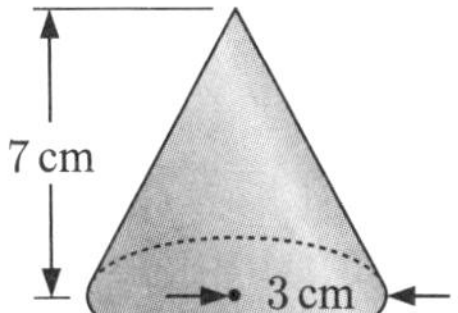
7 cm
3 cm

c 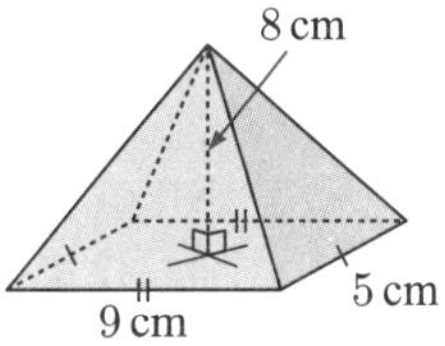
8 cm
9 cm
5 cm

d 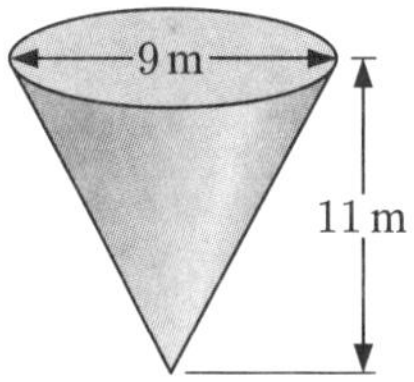
9 m
11 m

2 Use Pythagoras' theorem to help find the volume of each solid:

a 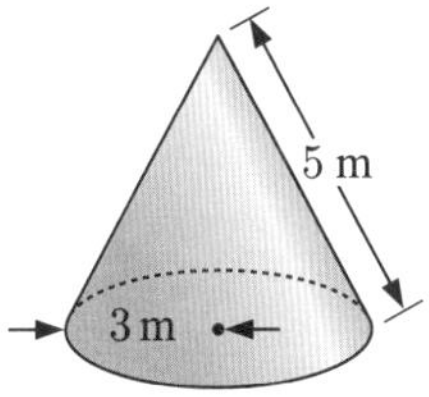
5 m
3 m

b 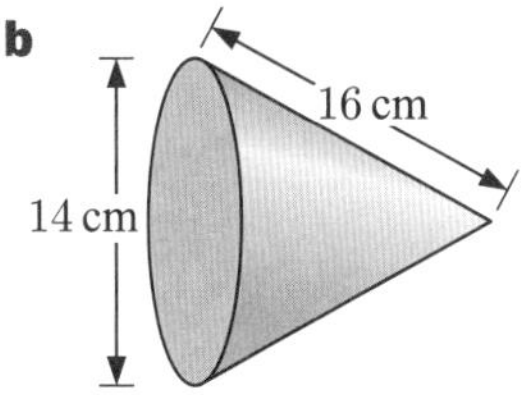
16 cm
14 cm

c 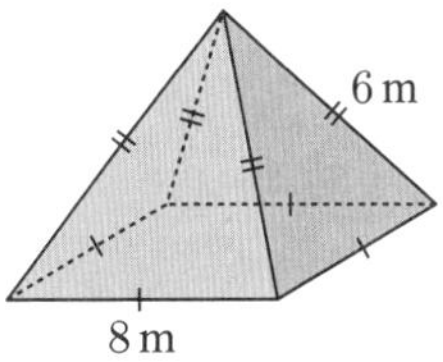
6 m
8 m

d 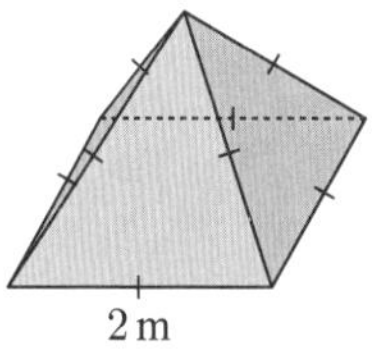
2 m

3 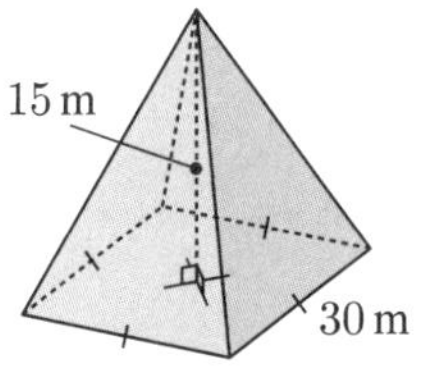
15 m
30 m

The conservatory for tropical plants at the Botanic gardens is a square-based pyramid with sides 30 metres long and height 15 metres. Calculate the volume of air in this building.

4 A conical heap of gravel is 1.4 m high and has a diameter of 2.6 m. Find the volume of the heap.

5 A wax crayon has the dimensions shown. Find the total volume of wax required to make a set of 24 crayons.

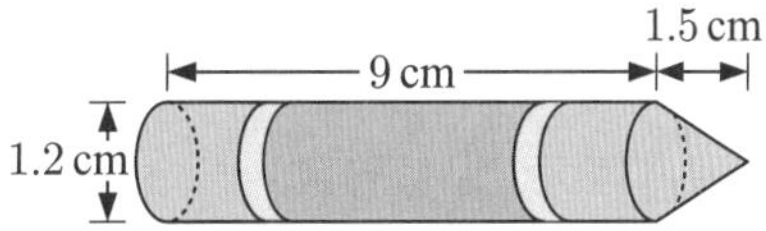
1.5 cm
9 cm
1.2 cm

6 0.6 cubic metres of metal is melted down and cast into garden stakes with the dimensions shown. How many garden stakes can be made?

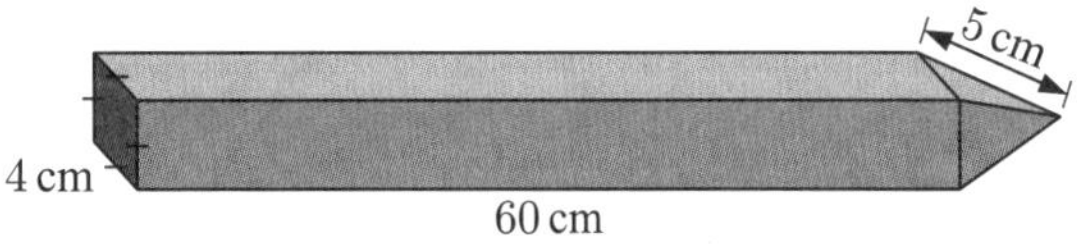
5 cm
4 cm
60 cm

7 A conical heap of garden soil is dumped on a flat surface. If the diameter of the heap equals its height, and its volume is 1.5 m^3, how high is the heap?

8 A cone has height equal to its base diameter d. Write a formula for its volume.

SPHERES

The Greek philosopher **Archimedes** was born in Syracuse in 287 BC. Amongst other discoveries, he found that the volume of a sphere is equal to two thirds of the volume of the smallest cylinder which encloses it.

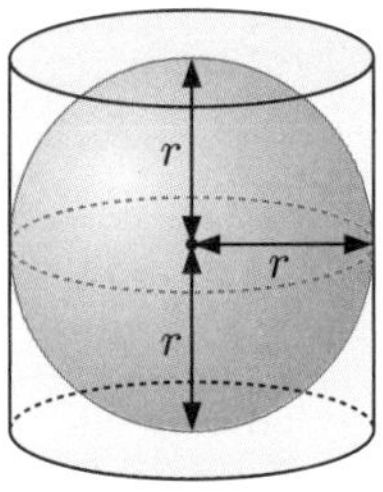
r
r
r

$$\begin{aligned}\text{Volume of cylinder} &= \pi r^2 \times h \\ &= \pi r^2 \times 2r \\ &= 2\pi r^3 \\ \therefore\quad \text{volume of sphere} &= \tfrac{2}{3} \times \text{volume of cylinder} \\ &= \tfrac{2}{3} \times 2\pi r^3 \\ &= \tfrac{4}{3}\pi r^3\end{aligned}$$

Thus $\boldsymbol{V = \frac{4}{3}\pi r^3}$

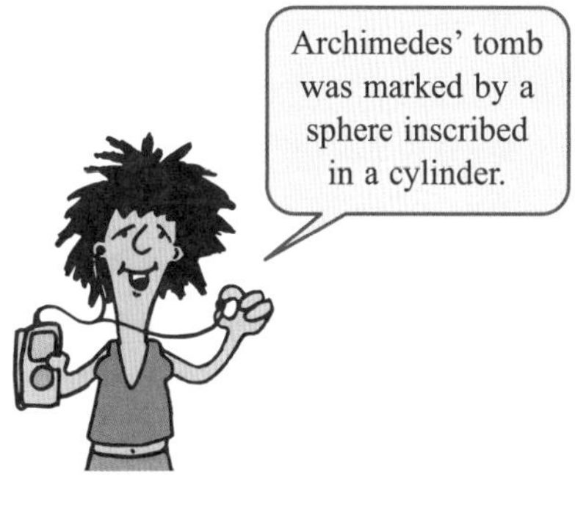
Archimedes' tomb was marked by a sphere inscribed in a cylinder.

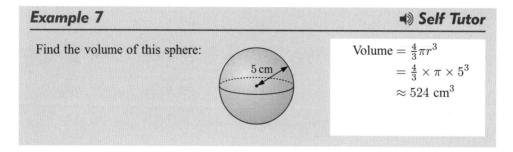

Example 7   ◀ৈ) *Self Tutor*

Find the volume of this sphere:

Volume $= \frac{4}{3}\pi r^3$

$= \frac{4}{3} \times \pi \times 5^3$

≈ 524 cm^3

EXERCISE 12B.3

1 Find the volume of each solid:

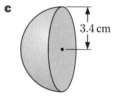 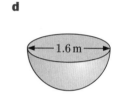

a   4 cm

b   5.8 cm

c   3.4 cm

d   1.6 m

2 Find the volume of each solid:

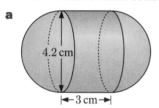

a   4.2 cm |← 3 cm →|

b   6 m   2.5 m

c   3.6 m   4.8 m

3 A beach ball has diameter 1.2 m. Find the volume of air inside the ball.

4 A garden ornament is shaped like a mushroom. The base is a cylinder 8 cm high and 6 cm in diameter. The top of the mushroom is 20 cm in diameter.

What volume of concrete, in m^3, is needed to make 50 mushrooms?

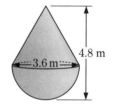

20 cm

8 cm

6 cm

5 A hollow spherical glass bauble contains a winter snowman scene.

The bauble has internal diameter 6.8 cm and external diameter 7.0 cm. What volume of glass was used to make it?

6 A block of lead 3.2 cm × 2.1 cm × 4.6 cm is melted and used to craft solid spheres with radius 6 mm.

a Find the volume of the block of lead.

b Find the volume of each sphere.

c How many spheres can be made?

d What percentage of the lead will be wasted?

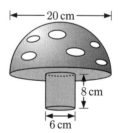

7 Write a formula for the volume of each object:

a

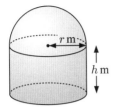

b

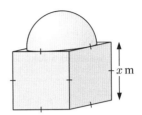

C | CAPACITY [E7.1, E7.4]

The **capacity** of a container is the quantity of fluid or gas used to fill it.

You should remember that the units of volume and capacity are connected:

$$1 \text{ ml} \equiv 1 \text{ cm}^3$$
$$1 \text{ cl} \equiv 10 \text{ cm}^3$$
$$1 \text{ litre} \equiv 1000 \text{ cm}^3$$
$$1000 \text{ litres} \equiv 1 \text{ m}^3$$

Example 8 ◄) Self Tutor

Find the capacity of a 3 m by 2.4 m by 1.8 m tank.

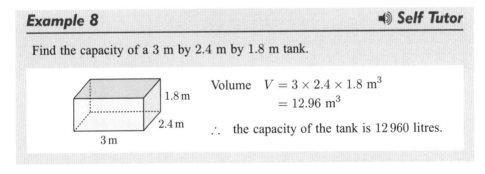

Volume $V = 3 \times 2.4 \times 1.8 \text{ m}^3$
$= 12.96 \text{ m}^3$

∴ the capacity of the tank is 12 960 litres.

EXERCISE 12C

1 Find the capacity of each container:

a

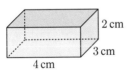

b

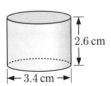

c

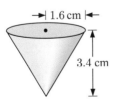

d

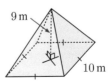

2 How many cylindrical bottles 12 cm high and with 6 cm diameter could be filled from a tank containing 125 litres of detergent?

3 A bottle of perfume is spherical with a diameter of 36 mm. Calculate the capacity of the bottle, in ml.

4 A spherical snow globe is made of glass that is 2 mm thick. If the outer diameter of the globe is 12 cm, find the capacity of its interior.

5 A 1 litre cylindrical can of paint has base radius 5 cm. Find the height of the can.

6 The average depth of water in a lake is 1.7 m. It is estimated that the total surface area of the lake is 1.35 ha.

   a Convert 1.35 ha to m^2.

   b How many litres of water does the lake contain?

7 A car has a rectangular prism petrol tank with dimensions 48 cm by 56 cm by 20 cm.

   a Find the capacity of the petrol tank.

   b The car consumes petrol at an average rate of 8.7 litres per 100 km. How far could it travel on a full tank of petrol?

8

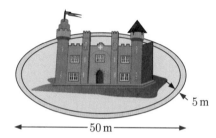

A castle is surrounded by a circular moat which is 5 m wide and 2 m deep. The diameter of the outer edge of the moat is 50 m. Find, in litres, the quantity of water in the moat.

9 The inside of a glass vase consists of a cylinder with diameter 8 cm and depth 15 cm, with a hemisphere below it.
Find the quantity of water that the vase can hold.

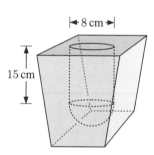

10 Answer the **Opening Problem** on page **183**.

Example 9   ◀) *Self Tutor*

14 400 litres of water is pumped into an empty cylindrical tank with base radius 2 m. How high up the tank will the water level rise?

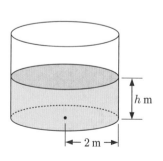

Since 1000 litres $\equiv$ 1 m^3, the volume of water pumped into the tank is 14.4 m^3.

If the water in the cylindrical tank is h m deep,

$$\text{its volume} = \pi \times 2^2 \times h \quad \{V = \pi r^2 h\}$$
$$= 4\pi h \text{ m}^3$$
$$\therefore \ 4\pi h = 14.4 \qquad \{\text{equating volumes}\}$$
$$\therefore \ h = \frac{14.4}{4\pi} \approx 1.15$$

$\therefore$ the water level will rise to 1.15 m.

11 20 000 litres of water is pumped into an empty cylindrical tank with base radius 3 m. How high up the tank will the water level rise?

12 Water enters a cylindrical rainwater tank at 80 litres per minute. The base diameter of the tank is 2.4 m and the height is 4 m.

a Find the capacity of the full tank.

b How high up the tank will the water level rise after 10 minutes?

13 Consider the following three containers:

A

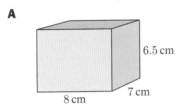

6.5 cm

8 cm

7 cm

B

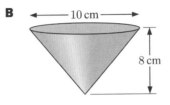

10 cm

8 cm

C

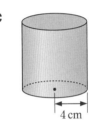

4 cm

Container A is filled with water. The water from container A is poured into container B until it is full, and the remainder is poured into container C. Find the height of the water in container C.

14 Regulation army huts have the dimensions shown. They sleep 36 soldiers, and each soldier has access to 11 000 litres of air space.

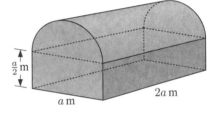

$\frac{a}{2}$ m

a m

$2a$ m

a Find the capacity of the hut in terms of a.

b Hence, find the value of a.

c If each bed and surrounds requires 4 m² of floor space, explain how the 36 soldiers can be accommodated.

15

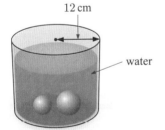

12 cm

water

A cylindrical container with radius 12 cm is partly filled with water. Two spheres with radii 3 cm and 4 cm are dropped into the water and are fully submerged. Find the *exact* increase in height of water in the cylinder.

D DENSITY   [E7.1]

The **mass** of an object is the amount of matter in it.

The **density** of an object is its mass divided by its volume.

$$\text{density} = \frac{\text{mass}}{\text{volume}}$$

Density is commonly measured in grams per cubic centimetre, or g per cm^3.

For example, the density of pure water is 1 g per cm^3.

EXERCISE 12D

1 Find the density of:

    a a substance with mass 83.5 g and volume 66.3 cm^3

    b a substance with mass 10.4 kg and volume 9620 cm^3.

2 Find the density of:

    a a cube of chocolate with side length 2 cm and mass 18 g

    b a 15 cm by 8 cm by 4 cm rectangular block of metal with mass 9.6 kg.

3 What volume is occupied by a lump of metal with mass 3.62 kg and density 11.6 g per cm^3?

4 Find the mass of a sphere of a metal with diameter 5 cm and density 8.7 g per cm^3.

5 A gold ingot with the dimensions shown has mass 12.36 kg.
Find the density of gold.

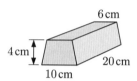

6 A rectangular block of metal has base 7 cm by 5 cm. The block has total mass 1285 g and the metal has density 7.5 g per cm^3. How high is the block?

7 Polystyrene spherical beads have an average diameter of 0.6 cm. The density of polystyrene is 0.15 g per cm^3. Estimate the total number of beads in a box of beads with total mass 8 kg.

8 A rubber tube has the dimensions shown.

    a Find the cross-sectional area of one end of the tube.

    b Hence find the volume of rubber used to make the tube.

    c If the rubber weighs 1500 kg per m^3, find the weight of the tube.

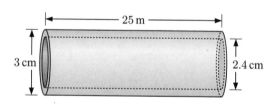

9 Determine the total mass of stone required to build a square-based pyramid with all edges of length 200 m. Assume that the density of the stone is 2.25 tonnes per m^3.

10 Assuming these solids have density d g per cm^3, find formulae for their:

    i surface area A **ii** volume V **iii** mass M.

a

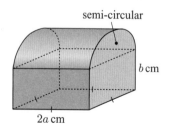

b

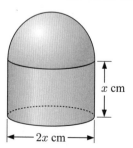

Activity 2   *Making cylindrical bins*

Your business has won a contract to make 40 000 cylindrical bins, each with capacity 50 litres. The bins will be made of plastic 3.4 mm thick and with density 0.64 g per cm^3. The plastic costs \$11.20 per kg.

What to do:

1 Find the formula for the volume V and the outer surface area A in terms of the base radius x and the height h.

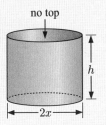

2 Show that the surface area can be written as

$$A = \pi x^2 + \frac{100\,000}{x} \text{ cm}^2.$$

3 Use technology to sketch the function $y = \pi x^2 + \frac{100\,000}{x}$. Hence find the minimum value of y and the value of x when this occurs.

GRAPHING PACKAGE

4 Draw the bin which minimises the amount of plastic needed. Make sure you fully label your diagram.

5 Find the total cost of plastic for the bins.

Review set 12A

1 Find the outer surface area of each solid:

a
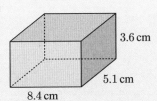
3.6 cm
5.1 cm
8.4 cm

b
19.4 mm
hollow top
38.3 mm
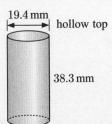

c
2.5 cm
8 cm
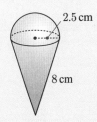

2 Find the volume of each solid:

a
14 cm
12.5 cm
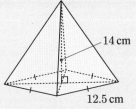

b
8.2 cm
6 cm
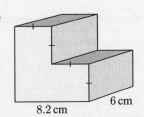

c
5 cm
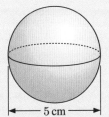

3 A solid cone has radius 5 cm and perpendicular height 8 cm. Find its:

    a volume   **b** surface area.

4 Li has a 10 cm × 8 cm × 5 cm block of clay. She wants to mould 50 clay spheres to use as heads for her figurines. Assuming there is no wastage, find the radius of the spheres Li should make.

5 Soup cans have a base diameter of 7 cm and a height of 10 cm.

   a Exactly how many such cans can be filled from a vat containing 2000 litres of soup?

   b Calculate the total surface area of metal required to make the cans in **a**.

6 A semi-circular tunnel with the cross-section shown is made of concrete. The tunnel is 220 m long, and the concrete costs \$256 per m^3.

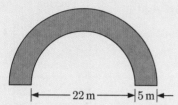

   a Find the cross-sectional area of the tunnel.

   b Find the volume of concrete used in the tunnel.

   c Find the cost of the concrete.

7 **a** Find the capacity of a swimming pool with the dimensions shown.

   b If the pool was filled to a depth 10 cm from the top, how much water would it contain?

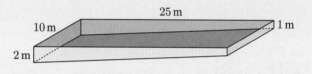

8 A conical heap of sand is twice as wide as it is high. If the sand has volume 2 m^3, find the height of the heap.

9 A wedge with angle $\theta°$ is cut from the centre of a cylindrical cake with radius r and height h. Write an expression for the wedge's:

   a volume

   b surface area.

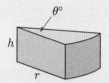

10 The Pyramid of Khufu in Egypt has a square base with sides 230.4 m and a height of 138.8 m.

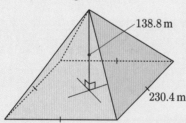

   a Find the total volume of the pyramid.

   b Suppose the pyramid is solid stone. If the stone has density 2.67 tonnes per m^3, find the total mass of stone used. Give your answer in standard form.

   c The King's Chamber in the pyramid is rectangular and measures 10.47 m by 5.23 m by 5.97 m. Find the capacity of the chamber.

Review set 12B

1 Find the outer surface area of each solid:

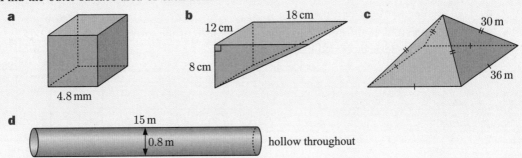

a   4.8 mm

b   18 cm, 12 cm, 8 cm

c   30 m, 36 m

d   15 m, 0.8 m   hollow throughout

2 The moon is approximately spherical with radius 1737 km. Estimate:

   a the distance around the equator of the moon   **b** the surface area of the moon.

3 Find the volume of each solid:

a   12 cm, 3 cm

b   15 cm, 18 cm

c   15 cm

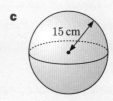

4 The diagram shows the cross-section of a railway cutting that needs to be excavated. The cutting will be 56 m long. Find the volume of soil that needs to be excavated.

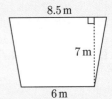

8.5 m, 7 m, 6 m

5 Write a formula for the surface area A of each solid:

a $2x$, x

b $2x$, x

c $3x$, x, x

6 Find the radius of a sphere with surface area 200 cm^2.

7 A solid cone has base radius 2 m and surface area 10π m^2. Find the slant length of the cone.

8

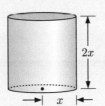

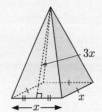

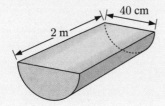

40 cm, 2 m

A horse's drinking trough has the dimensions shown. Water flows into the empty trough at 12 litres per minute for 10 minutes. Will the trough overflow?

9 A clock tower has the dimensions shown. On each side of the tower there is a clock 2 m in diameter. The highest point of the tower is 24 m above ground level.

   a Find the height of the roof pyramid.

   b Find, correct to 3 significant figures, the surface area of the tower excluding the clock faces and base.

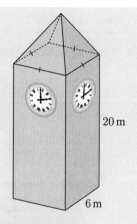

20 m

6 m

10 A block of wood 30 cm by 40 cm by 20 cm has density 0.81 g per cm^3. Its corner is chopped by an axe, and a section removed as shown. Find, to 1 decimal place:

   a the remaining volume of the block

   b the surface area of the remaining block

   c the mass of the remaining block.

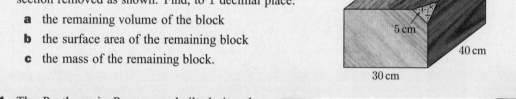

20 cm

5 cm

40 cm

30 cm

11 The Pantheon in Rome was built during the reign of emperor Augustus around 27 BC, and rebuilt by the emperor Hadrian around 126 AD. Its centre is designed as a hemisphere on a cylinder so that a sphere with diameter 43.3 m will fit exactly inside it.

Find the capacity of this chamber in litres.

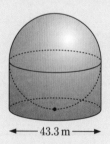

43.3 m

Applications of percentage

13

Contents:

A	Finding a percentage of a quantity	[E1.8]
B	Percentage increase and decrease	[E1.8]
C	Finding the original amount	[E1.8]
D	Profit and loss	[E1.8]
E	Chain percentage problems	[E1.8]
F	Simple interest	[E1.8]
G	Compound interest	[E1.8]

Opening problem

Michelle bought an antique clock for \$1500. It increased in value by 4.8% each year until she sold it 5 years later.

Things to think about:

a How much did Michelle sell the clock for?

b What profit did Michelle make on her investment?

We have previously seen that a **percentage** is a fraction of 100. For example, $20\% = \frac{20}{100} = 0.2$.

In the world around us, we often talk about **percentage change**.

We see percentage changes most often with money, when we talk about discounts, mark-up, interest, and tax.

A · FINDING A PERCENTAGE OF A QUANTITY [E1.8]

> To find a **percentage of a quantity**, we convert the percentage to a **decimal**, then **multiply** to find the required amount.

Example 1   ◀) *Self Tutor*

Find:

    a   35% of $5000   **b**   12.4% of 6 m

a 35% of $5000	**b** 12.4% of 6 m
$= 0.35 \times \$5000$	$= 0.124 \times 600$ cm
$= \$1750$	$= 74.4$ cm

The decimal number we multiply the quantity by is sometimes called the **multiplier**.

EXERCISE 13A

1   Find:

    a   25% of 36   **b**   10% of 70   **c**   20% of 45

    d   36% of $4200   **e**   125% of $600   **f**   95% of 5 tonnes

    g   3.8% of 100 m   **h**   112% of 5000 ml   **i**   0.7% of 2670 tonnes

    j   46.7% of $35 267.20   **k**   15% of 1 hour (in minutes)   **l**   29% of 1 tonne (in kg)

2   Carly has 20 sweets. She gives 35% of them to her sister. How many sweets does Carly give away?

3   88% of seeds in a packet are expected to germinate. If the packet contains 150 seeds, how many are expected to germinate?

4   In Formula One racing, a driver must complete at least 90% of the race distance in order to be classified. How many laps of a 60 lap race must a driver complete to be classified?

5   A marathon runner starts a race with mass 72.0 kg. Despite continual rehydration, he loses 3% of this mass during the race.

    a   How much mass did the runner lose during the race?

    b   Calculate his mass at the end of the race.

6   Petra has a monthly income of $4700. She does not have to pay any tax on the first $2400 she earns, but she has to pay 15% of the remainder as tax.

    a   How much tax does Petra have to pay?

    b   How much does Petra have left after tax?

    c   What percentage of the $4700 does Petra actually pay in tax?

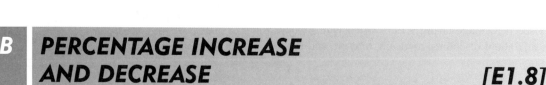

B   PERCENTAGE INCREASE AND DECREASE   *[E1.8]*

If we *increase* an amount by 20% then we have $(100\% + 20\%)$ of the amount

                                                   $= 120\%$ of the amount

                                                   $= 1.2 \times$ the amount.

If we *decrease* an amount by 20% then we have $(100\% - 20\%)$ of the amount

                                                   $= 80\%$ of the amount

                                                   $= 0.8 \times$ the amount.

Example 2

◄) *Self Tutor*

A fruit grower picked 1830 kg of apples last year. This year she expects her crop to be 30% bigger. How many kilograms of apples does she expect to pick this year?

The expected new crop $= (100\% + 30\%)$ of 1830 kg
$$= 130\% \times 1830 \text{ kg}$$
$$= 1.3 \times 1830 \text{ kg}$$
$$= 2379 \text{ kg}$$

She expects to pick 2379 kg.

EXERCISE 13B.1

1 Write down the number we multiply a quantity by to obtain:

  a an increase of 30%   **b** a decrease of 10%   **c** an increase of 15%

  d a decrease of 35%   **e** an increase of 12%   **f** a decrease of 7.5%.

2 The price of vegetables has risen by 20% because of dry weather. How much will Justine need to pay for tomatoes that usually cost $3.50 per kilogram?

3 In 2015 Su-Lin's salary was $48 000. In 2016 it increased by 35% when she was promoted to manager. What was her salary in 2016?

4 Stefan expected to harvest 2000 kg of cherries this year, but bad storms damaged 60% of his crop. What weight of cherries can he expect to harvest now?

5 Marius found that travelling on the new freeway decreased his travelling time to work by 12%. He used to take 50 minutes to get to work. How long does he take now?

6 If Claudia walked to school following the footpaths, she would walk 920 metres. If she walked across the park she could reduce this distance by 16%. How far would she walk then?

Discussion

If an amount is *increased* by 18%, and the resulting amount is then *decreased* by 18%, do we return to the original amount?

FINDING A PERCENTAGE CHANGE

When the size of a quantity changes, we can determine the percentage change by calculating the ratio $\dfrac{\text{new amount}}{\text{old amount}}$.

- If $\dfrac{\text{new amount}}{\text{old amount}} > 1$, then the quantity has **increased**.

- If $\dfrac{\text{new amount}}{\text{old amount}} < 1$, then the quantity has **decreased**.

Example 3   ◀)) *Self Tutor*

Determine the percentage change when:

a 50 kg is increased to 70 kg   **b** $160 is decreased to $120.

a $\dfrac{\text{new amount}}{\text{old amount}} = \dfrac{70 \text{ kg}}{50 \text{ kg}}$

$\qquad\qquad\quad = 1.4$

This corresponds to a 40% increase.

b $\dfrac{\text{new amount}}{\text{old amount}} = \dfrac{\$120}{\$160}$

$\qquad\qquad\quad = 0.75$

This corresponds to a 25% decrease.

EXERCISE 13B.2

1 Find the percentage change when:

    a $20 is increased to $22

    b 80 ml is decreased to 68 ml

    c 45 g is decreased to 27 g

    d 90 cm is increased to 1.35 m.

2 Describe the percentage change in the following situations:

    a The price of a haircut last year was $30. It has since risen to $34.50.

    b 150 people attended a community picnic last year. It rained this year, so only 108 people attended.

    c At his school's sports day, Casey threw the javelin 56.33 m, breaking the previous school record of 52.40 m.

    d John completed a half-marathon in 1 hour and 52 minutes, improving on his previous best time of 2 hours and 8 minutes.

3 Harriot really loves snakes. For her birthday in 2014, she was given a pet carpet python by her uncle. Since then, she has measured its length on her birthday each year.

Year	2014	2015	2016	2017
Length	58 cm	79 cm	94 cm	1.07 m

    a Calculate the percentage by which the snake's length increased from:

       i 2014 to 2015   **ii** 2015 to 2016   **iii** 2016 to 2017.

    b Calculate the overall percentage increase for the 3-year period.

4 The following table shows the populations of some European countries, in millions of people, in 2006 and 2016:

	Germany	Italy	France	Spain	Greece	Portugal	United Kingdom
2006	82.4	58.1	63.6	44.7	11.0	10.5	60.8
2016	82.7	60.6	66.9	46.6	10.7	10.3	65.6

    a Calculate the percentage change in population from 2006 to 2016 for each country.

    b Which country had the:

       i largest percentage increase   **ii** largest percentage decrease in population?

5 A circle's radius is increased by 10%. By what percentage does its area increase?

6 The side lengths of a rectangle are all decreased by 20%. Find the percentage decrease in the rectangle's:

    a perimeter   **b** area.

C   *FINDING THE ORIGINAL AMOUNT*   *[E1.8]*

We have seen how to obtain a percentage of a quantity.

It is also useful to be able to solve the reverse problem, so that if we know a percentage of a quantity, we can calculate the original amount.

Example 4   ◀) *Self Tutor*

Colleen receives 5% commission on the items she sells. In one week she earns $140 commission. Find the value of the items she sold.

Let the value of the items sold be x.

Now 5% of x is $140

$\therefore \quad 0.05 \times x = 140$

$\therefore \quad x = \dfrac{140}{0.05} = 2800$

The value of the items sold was $2800.

EXERCISE 13C

1   Linda scored 80% in her French test. If she received 60 marks, find the total number of marks possible for the test.

2   45% of the students at a school are boys. If there are 279 boys, how many students are at the school?

3   The legs account for 40% of the total weight of a table. If the legs weigh 16 kg, find the total weight of the table.

4   Heidi pays 22% of her monthly income in tax, and spends 5% on petrol. If Heidi pays $1034 each month in tax, find:

    a   her monthly income   **b**   the amount she spends on petrol each month.

5   A walker has travelled 9 km along a trail. If he has completed 80% of the trail, how much further does he still have to go?

Example 5   ◀) *Self Tutor*

In one season, Josephine's camellia grew 25%. It is now 1.68 m tall. How high was the camellia at the start of the season?

Suppose the camellia was x m tall.

Now 125% of x m is 1.68 m

$\therefore \quad 1.25 \times x = 1.68$

$\therefore \quad x = \dfrac{1.68}{1.25} \approx 1.34$

Josephine's camellia was about 1.34 m high at the start of the season.

6 Find the original amount given that:

   a after an increase of 20%, the length was 24 cm

   b after a decrease of 15%, the mass was 51 kg

   c after an increase of 3.6%, the amount was $129.50

   d after an increase of 130%, the capacity was 9200 litres

   e after a decrease of 0.8%, the attendance was 49 600 people.

7 Two years ago, Maria invested a sum of money. It has increased by 12% to reach $1064. What was her original investment?

8 A car is sold for $7560 at a 10% discount. What was the original price of the car?

9 From 1993 to 2013, the recorded number of black rhinoceroses increased by 97.2% to 4880. Estimate the black rhinoceros population in 1993.

10 Joan has just received an electricity bill of $283.50. This is 32.5% less than her previous bill. How much was Joan's previous bill?

D PROFIT AND LOSS   [E1.8]

When running a business, it is important to understand **profit** and **loss**.

> A **profit** occurs if the selling price is *higher* than the cost price.
>
> **Profit = selling price − cost price**
>
> A **loss** occurs if the selling price is *lower* than the cost price.
>
> **Loss = cost price − selling price**

We often express profit or loss as a **percentage of the cost price**.

Profit and loss correspond to a percentage increase or decrease in the price respectively.

Example 6   ◄》 Self Tutor

A bicycle was bought for $240 and sold for $290. Find the:

  a profit   **b** percentage profit.

a Profit = selling price − cost price
     = $290 − $240
     = $50

b Percentage profit = $\frac{\text{profit}}{\text{cost price}} \times 100\%$

     = $\frac{\$50}{\$240} \times 100\%$

     ≈ 20.8%

EXERCISE 13D

1 A tennis racquet bought for $95 was then sold for $132. Find the:

  a profit   **b** percentage profit.

2 Kane bought a lawnmower for $180 and marked it up to $240 to sell in his shop. Find the:

  a profit   **b** percentage profit.

3 A jewellery store buys a bracelet for $70, and sells it for $126. Find the percentage profit.

4 A 25 m roll of carpet was bought wholesale for $435. Over time, the whole roll is sold at $32.50 per metre. Find the:

  a total selling price   **b** profit   **c** percentage profit.

5 Felipe paid $18 200 for a boat, but because of financial difficulties he was soon forced to sell it for $13 600.

  a Find the loss on this sale.   **b** Find the percentage loss.

6 A furniture store has a clearance sale. A sofa costing $1450 is sold for $980. Find the:

  a loss made on the sale   **b** percentage loss.

7 Athos bought a crate containing 11 kg of apricots for $17.60. He sold the apricots in his shop in 1 kilogram bags for $2.85 each.

  a How much did 1 kg of apricots cost Athos?   **b** What was his profit per kilogram?

  c Find his percentage profit.

8 A newly married couple purchased a two-bedroom unit for $126 000. They spent another $14 300 putting in a new kitchen and bathroom. Two years later they had twins and were forced to sell the unit so they could buy a bigger house. Unfortunately, due to a down-turn in the market they received only $107 500 for the sale. Find:

  a the total cost of the unit

  b the percentage loss on the sale.

9 A clothing store bought a shirt for $15, and sold it at a 60% profit. Find the selling price of the shirt.

10 A bicycle is bought for $300 and sold for a 25% loss. Find the selling price of the bicycle.

11 An electrical goods store sells a television for $234, at a 30% profit. What price did the store pay for the television?

12 A fish shop is forced to sell prawns for $22.08 per kg, at a 36% loss. Find the cost price of the prawns.

E CHAIN PERCENTAGE PROBLEMS   [E1.8]

When two or more percentage changes occur in succession, we have a **chain percentage**.

Example 7   ◀ᴺ) *Self Tutor*

A 1.5 litre bottle of soft drink is bought by a deli for $0.80. The deli owner adds 60% mark-up then 15% goods tax. What price does the customer pay (to the nearest 5 cents)?

A 60% mark-up means we multiply by $160\% = 1.6$.

A 15% goods tax means we multiply by $115\% = 1.15$.

$\therefore$ cost to customer $= \$0.80 \times 1.6 \times 1.15$

$= \$1.472$

$\approx \$1.45$ {to the nearest 5 cents}

A **mark-up** increases the price!

EXERCISE 13E

1 Kirsty buys a skirt for $22. She applies a 55% mark-up, then adds 20% goods tax. For what price will Kirsty sell the skirt?

2 On his 5th birthday, Sean was 110 cm tall. He grew by 8% the next year, and by 5% the year after that. How tall was Sean on his 7th birthday?

3 A surfboard manufactured for $300 is sold to a retail shop for a 40% profit. The shop then applies a 20% mark-up. What price does the customer pay?

4 The population of a town was 25 000 in 2016. The population increased by 15% in 2017, and then decreased by 6% in 2018. Find the population of the town in 2018.

5 A fisherman sells a crayfish to a wholesaler for $35. The wholesaler sells it to a fresh fish shop for 60% profit. However, the fish shop is forced to sell the crayfish at a 25% loss. What price does the customer pay?

6 In a particular city it is estimated that, for each additional kilometre from the city centre, the average house price decreases by 4%.

If the average house price 2 km from the city centre is $350 000, find the average house price:

  a　3 km from the city centre   **b**　5 km from the city centre.

7 An art supplies store buys canvases for $40, and applies a 40% mark-up. During a sale, a discount is offered of 12.5% for non-members, and 15% for members. Find the difference in the sale price for non-members and members.

Example 8　　　　　　　　　　　　　🔊 Self Tutor

Over 3 consecutive years, Heather's salary increased by 3%, 6%, and 4%. What is the overall percentage increase in Heather's salary over this period?

Suppose Heather's original salary was x.

Heather's salary after 3 years $= \$x \times 1.03 \times 1.06 \times 1.04$
$$\approx \$x \times 1.135$$

∴　overall, Heather's salary increased by $\approx 13.5\%$.

---

8 Over 2 consecutive years, a company's sales increased by 6% and then increased by 3%. Find the overall percentage increase in sales over this period.

9 A rare book is bought by an antiques dealer, and he marks its price up by 50% for sale. One of his regular customers is interested in buying the book, so the dealer offers the customer a 20% discount. Find the overall percentage mark-up in the price of the book.

10 A baby's weight increased by 28% in the first month then 17% in the second month. The baby weighed 5.4 kg after 2 months. Find the weight of the baby when it was born.

11 Over 2 years, the yield of apples from an apple tree decreased by 13%, then increased by 13%. Does this mean that the yield returned to its original level after 2 years? Explain your answer.

12 Julia's parents have agreed to increase her allowance by 20% each year. Julia thinks her allowance when she is 12 will be 60% higher than when she is 9. Is Julia correct? Explain your answer.

F SIMPLE INTEREST   [E1.8]

If you **borrow** money from a bank, you must repay the loan in full, and also pay an additional charge called **interest**.

By contrast, if you deposit money in the bank, then it will *earn* interest.

One method for calculating interest is called **simple interest**.

Simple interest is interest that is calculated each year as a fixed percentage of the original amount borrowed.

The fixed percentage is called the **interest rate**, and is usually written as a percentage **per annum**, which means "per year".

For problems involving interest, the original amount invested or borrowed is often called the **principal**.

For example, suppose $4000 is borrowed at 10% per annum simple interest.

Each year, the simple interest charge is 10% of $4000 = $400.

Example 9   ◀)) Self Tutor

Find the simple interest payable on a loan of $60 000 borrowed at 9% p.a. for:

a 4 years   **b** 5 months

p.a. means "per annum".

The simple interest charge each year = 9% of $60 000
$$= 0.09 \times \$60\,000$$
$$= \$5400$$

a The simple interest for 4 years
$$= \$5400 \times 4$$
$$= \$21\,600$$

b 5 months is $\frac{5}{12}$ of a year
∴ the simple interest for 5 months
$$= \frac{5}{12} \times \$5400$$
$$= \$2250$$

EXERCISE 13F

1 Find the simple interest charged when:

   a $5000 is borrowed for 1 year at 12% per annum

   b $2500 is borrowed for 2 years at 8% p.a.

2 Find the simple interest earned when:

   a $40 000 is deposited for 5 years at 3% p.a.

   b $250 000 is deposited for 9 months at 2% p.a.

Example 10   ◀ঠ *Self Tutor*

Find the total amount needed to repay a loan of $40 000 borrowed at 9% p.a. simple interest for 5 years.

The simple interest charge each year $= 9\%$ of $\$40\,000$

$$= 0.09 \times \$40\,000$$

$$= \$3600$$

$\therefore$ the simple interest for 5 years $= \$3600 \times 5$

$$= \$18\,000$$

$\therefore$ the total to be repaid $= \$40\,000 + \$18\,000$

$$= \$58\,000$$

Total to be repaid
= original amount
+ interest.

3   Find the total amount needed to repay a loan of:

   a $2400 borrowed for 3 years at 10% p.a. simple interest

   b $8000 borrowed for 7 years at 12% p.a. simple interest.

4   Find the total value of an investment when:

   a $7500 is deposited for $2\frac{1}{2}$ years at 2.2% p.a. simple interest

   b $23 000 is deposited for 4 months at 1.5% p.a. simple interest.

5   Kyle borrows $25 000 at 6% p.a. simple interest for 4 years.

   a   Find the total amount needed to repay the loan.

   b   Calculate the monthly repayment required to pay this loan off in 48 equal instalments.

6   Alice borrows $4700 from a finance company to buy her first car. The rate of simple interest is 17% p.a. and she borrows the money over a 5 year period. Find:

   a   the total amount Alice must repay the finance company

   b   her equal monthly repayments.

7   Richard invests $6000 at 4% p.a. simple interest. At the time he withdraws his investment, Richard receives $7200. For how long did Richard invest his money?

8   Jenny took out a loan at 8% p.a. simple interest for 6 years. She paid a total of $1680 interest on the loan. How much money did she borrow?

9   Suppose Ting Ting invests $\$P$ for n years in an account which pays interest rate r per annum simple interest.

   a   Explain why the total interest earned $\$I$ is given by the formula $I = Prn$.

   b   Use this formula to find:

     i   the interest earned on a $4000 investment for 3 years at 3.6% p.a. simple interest

     ii   the interest rate if a $6000 principal earns $432 simple interest over 4 years

     iii   the time needed for a $5000 investment to earn $525 at 4.2% p.a. simple interest.

G   COMPOUND INTEREST   *[E1.8]*

A more common method for calculating interest is **compound interest**.

If you leave your money in the bank for a period of time, the interest is automatically added to your account.

With compound interest, any interest that is added to your account will also earn interest in the next time period.

Compound interest allows you to earn interest on interest!

> **Compound interest** is calculated as a percentage of the total amount at the end of the previous compounding period.

In this course we will only consider interest which compounds each year.

Suppose $1000 is placed in an account earning interest at a rate of 10% p.a. The interest is allowed to compound itself for three years. We say it is earning "10% p.a. compound interest".

We can show this in a table:

Year	Amount at beginning of year	Compound interest	Amount at end of year
1	$1000	10% of $1000 = $100	$1000 + $100 = $1100
2	$1100	10% of $1100 = $110	$1100 + $110 = $1210
3	$1210	10% of $1210 = $121	$1210 + $121 = $1331

After 3 years there is a total of $1331 in the account. We have earned $331 in compound interest.

Notice that the amount in the account increases by 10% each year. This means that we can use chain percentage calculations to find the balance in the account after a particular time period.

For example, the balance after 3 years $= \$1000 \times 1.1 \times 1.1 \times 1.1$
$$= \$1000 \times 1.1^3$$
$$= \$1331$$

Example 11   ◀ *Self Tutor*

a What will $5000 invested at 8% p.a. compound interest amount to after 3 years?

b How much interest is earned?

a The amount increases by 8% each year.
∴ the total amount after 3 years $= \$5000 \times 1.08^3$
$$= \$6298.56$$

b Interest earned
$$= \$6298.56 - \$5000$$
$$= \$1298.56$$

EXERCISE 13G

1 Sunil invested $4000 at 5% p.a. compound interest. Find the value of the investment after 2 years.

2 Cassandra invested $7000 at 3.5% p.a. compound interest for 2 years. Find:

    a the value of the investment after 2 years   **b** the interest earned.

3 Donna borrows $6500 for 3 years at 4% p.a. compound interest.

    a Find the total amount Donna must repay after 3 years.

    b In total, how much interest will Donna be charged?

4 How much compound interest is earned by investing $9000 for 3 years at 4.5% p.a.?

5 George invests $6200 at 6% p.a. compound interest.

    a Find the balance of the account after 4 years.

    b Find the overall percentage increase in value of the investment.

6 Shelley invests $8500 in an account which pays 3.7% p.a. compound interest.

    a Find the value of the investment after 3 years.

    b How many years will it take for the investment to be worth at least $10 000?

7 You have $8000 to invest for 3 years. You have been offered two investment options:

    Option 1: Invest at 9% p.a. simple interest.

    Option 2: Invest at 8% p.a. compound interest.

    a Calculate the amount accumulated at the end of the 3 years for both options, and decide which option to take.

    b Would you change your decision if you were investing for 5 years?

8 Helen invests $2000 in an account which offers 6% p.a. compound interest in the first 2 years, and then 3.5% p.a. compound interest for each subsequent year.

    a Find the value of the investment after 4 years.

    b Would Helen have been better off investing in an account which paid a constant compound interest rate of 5% p.a.?

9 Warren invests $5000 in an account which pays 4% p.a. compound interest.

    a Explain why the amount in the account after n years is given by the formula $A = 5000 \times 1.04^n$ dollars.

    b Find the amount in the account after: **i** 3 years   **ii** 7 years.

    c How many years will it take for the investment to be worth at least $8000?

Example 12
◀ɔ *Self Tutor*

An investment of $5500 amounted to $8000 after 4 years of compound growth. What was the annual rate of growth?

Suppose the investment was multiplied by x each year

$$\therefore \quad 5500 \times x^4 = 8000$$

$$\therefore \quad x^4 = \frac{8000}{5500}$$

$$\therefore \quad x = \sqrt[4]{\frac{8000}{5500}} \approx 1.098\,201$$

So, the annual growth rate was about 9.82%.

10 An investment of $7000 amounted to $8300 after 3 years of compound growth. What was the annual rate of growth?

11 The value of a car halves in 3 years. Find its annual rate of *depreciation* or loss in value.

12 After 4 years a tractor purchased for $58 500 has a resale value of $35 080. Find its annual rate of depreciation.

Review set 13A

1 Find:

   a 20% of $60   **b** 13% of 400 ml   **c** 160% of 40 kg.

2 **a** Increase $2500 by 16%.   **b** Decrease 65 kg by 10%.

3 In the long jump final, Tran jumped 5.65 m. Lim beat this distance by 7%. How far did Lim jump?

4 Eito purchases a pair of shoes for $200 and sells them at a 45% profit. Find the selling price.

5 Moira bought a car for $4500 but had to sell it for $4000 a few weeks later. Find Moira's percentage loss.

6 A store usually sells an item for $80. Find the sale price of the item if it is discounted by 15%.

7 David purchased a stamp collection for $860. Two years later it was valued at $2410. Calculate the percentage increase in the value of the investment.

8 A publisher sells a book for $20 per copy to a retailer. The retailer marks up the price by 75%, then adds a further 10% for tax. What price does the customer pay?

9 As a result of a redevelopment, the area of a city park was reduced by 15% to 3.4 hectares. Find the original area of the park.

10 Find the simple interest earned by an investment of $4000 at 7% p.a. for 3 years.

11 Raj borrows $5000 from a bank at $8\frac{1}{2}\%$ p.a. simple interest. He will repay the money over a 4 year period, with equal monthly repayments.

   a Find the total amount that Raj must repay the bank.

   b Find Raj's equal monthly repayments.

12 **a** What will an investment of $8000 at 6% p.a. compound interest amount to after 4 years?

   b What part of this is interest?

13 A caravan costing $15 000 depreciates by 16% p.a. each year.

   a Explain why the value of the caravan after n years is given by the formula
$$V = 15\,000 \times 0.84^n \text{ dollars.}$$

   b Find the value of the caravan after 5 years.

   c How many years will it take for the value of the caravan to fall below $5000?

Review set 13B

1 A football stadium has a maximum capacity of 60 000 people. At today's game, 15% of the seats are empty. How many people are at the game?

2 As part of a road safety campaign, fines for all traffic offences will increase by 5%.
Copy and complete the table alongside, showing the changes to each fine.

Offence	Old fine	New fine
Speeding	$200	
Drink driving	$840	
Not wearing seatbelt		$273
Illegal parking		$52.50

3 An item of clothing is marked at $49, but is discounted 15% in a sale. Find the sale price.

4 A soufflé increases in height by 125% while in the oven. If the finished height is 13.5 cm, how tall was the soufflé when it was placed in the oven?

5 Adam bought a motorcycle for $1650 and later sold it for $1300. Find Adam's:

  a loss   **b** percentage loss.

6 A furniture store bought a chair for $380, marked it up by 35%, and then discounted it by 25%. Find:

  a the marked-up price   **b** the discounted price.

7 A company cut its advertising budget by 12%. If the company previously spent $80 000 on advertising, what was the new advertising budget?

8 A toaster is sold to a retailer for $38. The retailer marks it up by 40%, discounts it by 15%, and then adds on a goods tax of 16%. How much does the customer pay?

9 A blender was discounted by 20% and sold for $64. Find the marked price of the blender.

10 A new café opened in January in the city centre. The number of customers visiting the café increased by 8% each month.

  a Find the overall percentage increase in visitors from April to July.

  b Given that the café had 2106 customers in March, how many customers did they have in February?

11 Answer the **Opening Problem** on page **205**.

12 Darren borrows $15 000 from the bank to extend his house. The bank will charge him simple interest of 6.8% p.a. for a 5 year loan. Find the total amount Darren will need to repay.

13 Denise invests $30 000 in an account paying 4.6% p.a. compound interest.

  a Find the value of the investment after 3 years.

  b How many years will it take for the investment to be worth at least $40 000?

Coordinate geometry

14

Contents:

A	The Cartesian plane	[E4.1]
B	The distance between two points	[E4.1, E4.2]
C	Midpoints	[E4.3]
D	Gradient	[E4.1, E4.4]
E	Parallel and perpendicular lines	[E4.5]
F	Collinear points	[E4.5]
G	Using coordinate geometry	[E4.2 - E4.5]

Opening problem

On the given map, Peta's house is located at point P, and Russell lives at point R.

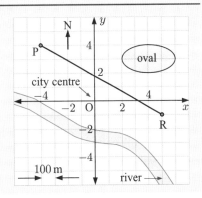

Things to think about:

a How can we describe the *positions* of P and R using ordered pairs of numbers?

b What is the position of the eastern end of the oval?

c How far is Peta's house from Russell's house?

d Which point is midway between Peta's house and Russell's house?

Historical note

History shows that the two Frenchmen **René Descartes** and **Pierre de Fermat** arrived at the idea of **analytical geometry** at about the same time. Descartes' work *La Geometrie* was published first, in 1637, while Fermat's *Introduction to Loci* was not published until after his death.

Today, they are considered the co-founders of this important branch of mathematics which links algebra and geometry.

The initial approaches used by these mathematicians were quite opposite. Descartes began with a line or curve and then found the equation which described it. Fermat, to a large extent, started with an equation and investigated the shape of the curve it described.

Analytical geometry and its use of coordinates enabled **Isaac Newton** to later develop another important branch of mathematics called **calculus**. Newton humbly stated: *"If I have seen further than Descartes, it is because I have stood on the shoulders of giants."*

A THE CARTESIAN PLANE   [E4.1]

The number grid alongside is a **Cartesian plane**, named after **René Descartes**. The numbers or **coordinates** on it allow us to locate the exact position of any point on the plane.

We start with a point of reference O called the **origin**. Through it we draw a horizontal line called the x-axis, and a vertical line called the y-axis.

The x-axis is an ordinary number line with positive numbers to the right of O and negative numbers to the left of O.

The y-axis has positive numbers above O and negative numbers below O.

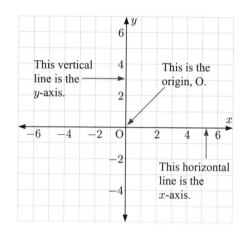

PLOTTING POINTS ON THE CARTESIAN PLANE

To specify the position of a point on the number plane, we use an **ordered pair** of coordinates in the form (x, y).

For example, on the grid alongside we see the point described by the ordered pair of coordinates $(3, 2)$. We say that 3 is the x-**coordinate** and 2 is the y-**coordinate**.

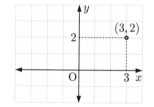

To help us identify particular points, we often refer to them using a capital letter. For example, consider the points A(1, 3), B(4, −3), and C(−4, −2).

To plot the point A(1, 3):

- start at the origin O
- move right along the x-axis 1 unit
- then move upwards 3 units.

To plot the point B(4, −3):

- start at the origin O
- move right along the x-axis 4 units
- then move downwards 3 units.

To plot the point C(−4, −2):

- start at the origin O
- move left along the x-axis 4 units
- then move downwards 2 units.

DEMO

The x-coordinate is always given first. It indicates horizontal movement away from the origin.

QUADRANTS

The x and y-axes divide the Cartesian plane into four regions referred to as **quadrants**. These quadrants are numbered in an **anti-clockwise direction** as shown:

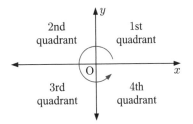

Example 1   ◀》 *Self Tutor*

Plot the points   A(3, 5),   B(−1, 4),   C(0, −3),   D(−3, −2), and   E(4, −2)   on the same set of axes.

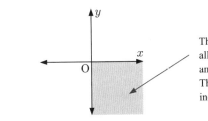

Start at O and move horizontally, then vertically.
→ is positive
← is negative
↑ is positive
↓ is negative.

Example 2   ◀》 *Self Tutor*

On a Cartesian plane, show all the points with positive x-coordinate and negative y-coordinate.

This shaded region contains all points where x is positive and y is negative.
The points on the axes are not included.

This region is the 4th quadrant.

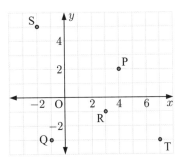

EXERCISE 14A

1   State the coordinates of the points P, Q, R, S, and T:

2 a On the same set of axes, plot the points:

A(2, 5), B(4, −2), C(−5, 0), D(−1, −4), E(−2, 3), F(0, 3), G(5, 1), and H(−5, −1).

b State the quadrant in which each point in **a** lies.

3 State the quadrants in which points have coordinates with:

a the same sign   **b** different signs.

4 On different sets of axes, show all the points with:

a x-coordinate equal to −1   **b** y-coordinate equal to 3

c x-coordinate equal to 0   **d** y-coordinate equal to 0

e negative x-coordinate   **f** positive y-coordinate

g negative x and y-coordinates   **h** negative x-coordinate and positive y-coordinate.

5

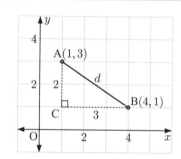

a State the coordinates of P and Q.

b Point R has the same y-coordinate as P, and lies on the y-axis. Find the coordinates of R.

c Find the coordinates of S such that PQRS is a kite.

B   THE DISTANCE BETWEEN TWO POINTS   [E4.1, E4.2]

Suppose we want to find the distance d between the points A(1, 3) and B(4, 1).

By drawing line segments AC and BC along the grid lines, we form a right angled triangle with hypotenuse AB.

$\therefore\ d^2 = 2^2 + 3^2$ {Pythagoras}

$\therefore\ d^2 = 13$

$\therefore\ d = \sqrt{13}$ {as $d > 0$}

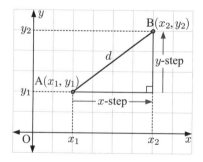

So, the distance between A and B is $\sqrt{13}$ units.

To make the process quicker, we can develop a formula.

To go from $A(x_1, y_1)$ to $B(x_2, y_2)$, we find the

$x\text{-step} = x_2 - x_1$

and $y\text{-step} = y_2 - y_1$.

Using Pythagoras' theorem,

$d^2 = (x\text{-step})^2 + (y\text{-step})^2$

$\therefore\ d = \sqrt{(x\text{-step})^2 + (y\text{-step})^2}$

$\therefore\ d = \sqrt{(x_2 - x_1)^2 + (y_2 - y_1)^2}.$

> The distance d between two points (x_1, y_1) and (x_2, y_2) is given by
> $$d = \sqrt{(x_2 - x_1)^2 + (y_2 - y_1)^2}.$$

Example 3   ◀) *Self Tutor*

Find the distance between A$(-2, 1)$ and B$(3, 4)$.

The distance formula saves us having to graph the points each time we want to find a distance.

$$\text{A}(-2, 1) \qquad \text{B}(3, 4) \qquad \text{AB} = \sqrt{(3 - -2)^2 + (4 - 1)^2}$$

$x_1 \ y_1 \qquad\qquad x_2 \ y_2$

$$= \sqrt{5^2 + 3^2}$$

$$= \sqrt{25 + 9} = \sqrt{34} \text{ units}$$

EXERCISE 14B

1 Find the distance between:

  a A$(3, 1)$ and B$(5, 3)$ **b** C$(-1, 2)$ and D$(6, 2)$ **c** O$(0, 0)$ and P$(-2, 4)$

  d E$(8, 0)$ and F$(2, -3)$ **e** G$(0, -2)$ and H$(0, 5)$ **f** I$(2, 0)$ and J$(0, -1)$

  g R$(1, 2)$ and S$(-2, 3)$ **h** W$(1, -1)$ and Z$(\frac{1}{2}, -2)$.

2 The grid lines in this map are 10 km apart.

  Find the direct distance between:

  a Dalgety Bay and Edinburgh

  b Coatbridge and Dalgety Bay

  c Coatbridge and Edinburgh.

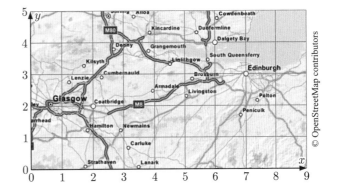

© OpenStreetMap contributors

Example 4   ◀) *Self Tutor*

Consider the triangle formed by the points A$(1, 2)$, B$(2, 5)$, and C$(4, 1)$.

  a Use the distance formula to classify the triangle as equilateral, isosceles, or scalene.

  b Determine whether the triangle is right angled.

a $\text{AB} = \sqrt{(2 - 1)^2 + (5 - 2)^2} \qquad \text{AC} = \sqrt{(4 - 1)^2 + (1 - 2)^2}$

$\qquad = \sqrt{1^2 + 3^2} \qquad\qquad\qquad\quad = \sqrt{3^2 + (-1)^2}$

$\qquad = \sqrt{10} \text{ units} \qquad\qquad\qquad\quad = \sqrt{10} \text{ units}$

$\qquad \text{BC} = \sqrt{(4 - 2)^2 + (1 - 5)^2}$

$\qquad\quad = \sqrt{2^2 + (-4)^2}$

$\qquad\quad = \sqrt{20} \text{ units}$

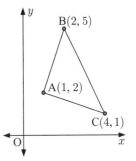

    Since AB $=$ AC, the triangle is isosceles.

b The shortest sides are AB and AC.

    Now $\text{AB}^2 + \text{AC}^2 = 10 + 10$

$\qquad\qquad\qquad\quad = 20$

$\qquad\qquad\qquad\quad = \text{BC}^2$

Using the converse of Pythagoras' theorem, the triangle is right angled. The right angle is at A, opposite the longest side.

3 Use the distance formula to classify triangle ABC as either equilateral, isosceles, or scalene:

    a A(3, −1), B(1, 8), C(−6, 1)   **b** A(1, 0), B(3, 1), C(4, 5)

    c A(−1, 0), B(2, −2), C(4, 1)   **d** A($\sqrt{2}$, 0), B(−$\sqrt{2}$, 0), C(0, −$\sqrt{5}$)

    e A($\sqrt{3}$, 1), B(−$\sqrt{3}$, 1), C(0, −2)   **f** A(a, b), B(−a, b), C(0, 2)

4 Determine whether the following triangles are right angled. If there is a right angle, state the vertex where it occurs.

    a A(−2, −1), B(3, −1), C(3, 3)   **b** A(−1, 2), B(4, 1), C(4, −5)

    c A(1, −2), B(3, 0), C(−3, 2)   **d** A(3, −4), B(−2, −5), C(−1, 1)

Example 5   ◄)) *Self Tutor*

Find b given that A(3, −2) and B(b, 1) are $\sqrt{13}$ units apart. Explain your result using a diagram.

From A to B, x-step $= b - 3$

               y-step $= 1 - -2 = 3$

$\therefore \ \sqrt{(b-3)^2 + 3^2} = \sqrt{13}$

$\therefore \ (b-3)^2 + 9 = 13$ {squaring both sides}

$\therefore \ (b-3)^2 = 4$

$\therefore \ b - 3 = \pm 2$

$\therefore \ b = 3 \pm 2$

$\therefore \ b = 5$ or 1

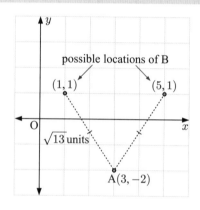

Point B could be at two possible locations:
(5, 1) or (1, 1).

---

5 For each of the cases below, find a and explain the result using a diagram:

    a P(2, 3) and Q(a, −1) are 4 units apart   **b** P(−1, 1) and Q(a, −2) are 5 units apart

    c X(a, a) is $\sqrt{8}$ units from the origin

    d A(0, a) is equidistant from P(3, −3) and Q(−2, 2).

6   **a** Find the relationship between x and y if the point P(x, y) is always:

       i 3 units from O(0, 0)   **ii** 2 units from A(1, 3).

    b Illustrate and describe the set of points (x, y) such that $x^2 + y^2 = 1$.

7 P is at (−5, 9), Q is at (1, 2), and R is on the x-axis. Given that triangle PQR is isosceles, find the possible coordinates of R.

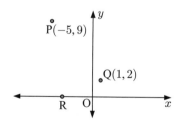

C *MIDPOINTS*   *[E4.3]*

The **midpoint** of line segment AB is the point which lies midway between points A and B.

Consider the points A$(-1, -2)$ and B$(6, 4)$. From the diagram we see that the midpoint of AB is M$(2\frac{1}{2}, 1)$.

The x-coordinate of M is the *average* of the x-coordinates of A and B.

$\therefore$ the x-coordinate of M $= \dfrac{-1+6}{2} = \dfrac{5}{2} = 2\frac{1}{2}$

The y-coordinate of M is the *average* of the y-coordinates of A and B.

$\therefore$ the y-coordinate of M $= \dfrac{-2+4}{2} = 1$

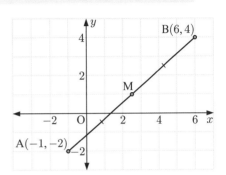

If A(x_1, y_1) and B(x_2, y_2) are two points, then the **midpoint** of AB has coordinates $\left(\dfrac{x_1 + x_2}{2}, \dfrac{y_1 + y_2}{2}\right)$.

DEMO

Example 6   ◀) *Self Tutor*

Find the midpoint of AB given A$(-1, 3)$ and B$(4, 7)$.

A$(-1, 3)$ B$(4, 7)$ The x-coordinate of the midpoint $= \dfrac{x_1 + x_2}{2} = \dfrac{-1+4}{2} = \dfrac{3}{2} = 1\frac{1}{2}$

$x_1 \ y_1$ $x_2 \ y_2$ The y-coordinate of the midpoint $= \dfrac{y_1 + y_2}{2} = \dfrac{3+7}{2} = 5$

So, the midpoint is $(1\frac{1}{2}, 5)$.

EXERCISE 14C

1 Use this diagram only to find the coordinates of the midpoint of the line segment:

    a GA   **b** ED

    c AC   **d** AD

    e CD   **f** GF

    g EG   **h** GD

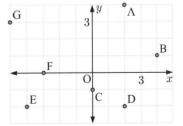

2 Find the coordinates of the midpoint of the line segment joining:

    a $(8, 1)$ and $(2, 5)$ **b** $(2, -3)$ and $(0, 1)$ **c** $(3, 0)$ and $(0, 6)$

    d $(-1, 4)$ and $(1, 4)$ **e** $(5, -3)$ and $(-1, 0)$ **f** $(5, 9)$ and $(-3, -4)$.

Example 7   ◄ **Self Tutor**

Suppose M is the midpoint of AB, where A is $(1, 3)$ and M is $(4, -2)$.
Find the coordinates of B using:
   a the midpoint formula   **b** equal steps.

a Suppose B has coordinates (a, b).

$\therefore \quad \dfrac{a+1}{2} = 4 \quad$ and $\quad \dfrac{b+3}{2} = -2$

$\therefore \quad a + 1 = 8 \quad$ and $\quad b + 3 = -4$

$\therefore \quad a = 7 \quad$ and $\quad b = -7$

$\therefore \quad$ B is $(7, -7)$.

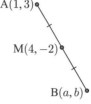

b x-step: $1 \xrightarrow{+3} 4 \xrightarrow{+3} 7$

     y-step: $3 \xrightarrow{-5} -2 \xrightarrow{-5} -7$

    $\therefore$ B is $(7, -7)$.

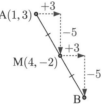

3 M is the midpoint of AB. Find the coordinates of B given:

   a A$(6, 4)$ and M$(3, -1)$ **b** A$(-5, 0)$ and M$(0, -1)$

   c A$(3, -2)$ and M$(1\frac{1}{2}, 2)$ **d** A$(-1, -2)$ and M$(-\frac{1}{2}, 2\frac{1}{2})$

   e A$(7, -3)$ and M$(0, 0)$ **f** A$(3, -1)$ and M$(0, -\frac{1}{2})$.

  Check your answers using *equal steps*.

4 AB is a diameter of a circle with centre C. A is $(3, -2)$ and B is $(-1, -4)$. Find the coordinates of C.

5 PQ is a diameter of a circle with centre $(3, -\frac{1}{2})$. If Q is $(-1, 2)$, find the coordinates of P.

6 The diagonals of parallelogram PQRS bisect each other at X. Find the coordinates of S.

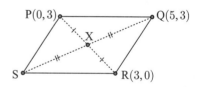

7 Triangle ABC has vertices A$(-1, 3)$, B$(1, -1)$, and C$(5, 2)$. Find the length of the line segment from A to the midpoint of BC.

8 A, B, C, and D are four points on the same straight line. The distances between successive points are equal, as shown. If A is $(1, -3)$, C is $(4, a)$, and D is $(b, 5)$, find the values of a and b.

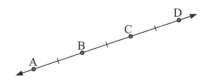

9 The midpoints of the sides of a triangle are $(5, 4)$, $(8, 5)$, and $(6, 0)$. Find the coordinates of the vertices of the triangle.

D | GRADIENT   [E4.1, E4.4]

When looking at line segments drawn on a set of axes, it is clear that different line segments are inclined to the horizontal at different angles. Some appear to be *steeper* than others.

> The **gradient** of a line is a measure of its steepness.

We can calculate the rate at which a line rises or falls by choosing two points on the line, then dividing the vertical step between them by the horizontal step between them.

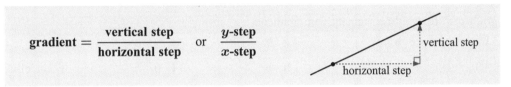

$$\text{gradient} = \frac{\textbf{vertical step}}{\textbf{horizontal step}} \quad \text{or} \quad \frac{\textbf{y-step}}{\textbf{x-step}}$$

In general, we choose the horizontal step to be positive.

- For an upwards sloping line, the vertical step is also positive.

  > **Upward sloping lines** have a **positive gradient**.

- For a downward sloping line, the vertical step is negative.

  > **Downward sloping lines** have a **negative gradient**.

Discussion

Why do you think we define gradient as $\dfrac{y\text{-step}}{x\text{-step}}$ rather than $\dfrac{x\text{-step}}{y\text{-step}}$?

Example 8   ◀》 Self Tutor

Find the gradient of each line segment:

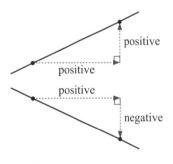

a gradient $= \frac{3}{2}$ **b** gradient $= \frac{-2}{5} = -\frac{2}{5}$

c gradient $= \frac{0}{3} = 0$

d gradient $= \frac{3}{0}$ which is undefined

From the previous Example, we can see that:

- The gradient of all **horizontal** lines is **0**, since the vertical step is 0.
- The gradient of all **vertical** lines is **undefined**, since the horizontal step is 0.

EXERCISE 14D.1

1 State the gradient of each line segment:

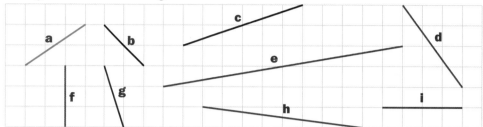

2 On grid paper, draw a line segment with gradient:

   a $\frac{1}{2}$ **b** $\frac{2}{3}$ **c** 1   **d** 2   **e** $-\frac{1}{4}$

   f -3 **g** $-\frac{5}{2}$ **h** 5   **i** 0   **j** undefined

---

Example 9   🔊 Self Tutor

Draw a line through the point $(2, 4)$ with gradient $-\frac{2}{3}$.

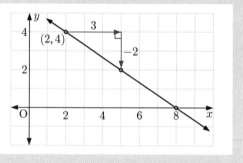

$\text{gradient} = -\frac{2}{3} = \frac{-2}{3}$ ← y-step ← x-step

Choose a positive x-step.

3 Draw a line through the point:

   a $(4, 1)$ with gradient $\frac{3}{2}$ **b** $(3, -1)$ with gradient $\frac{1}{4}$

   c $(-2, 3)$ with gradient $-\frac{1}{5}$ **d** $(0, 4)$ with gradient $-\frac{2}{3}$.

4 On the same set of axes, draw lines through $(2, 3)$ with gradients $\frac{1}{3}$, $\frac{3}{4}$, 2, and 4.

5 On the same set of axes, draw lines through $(-1, 2)$ with gradients 0, $-\frac{2}{5}$, -2, and -5.

THE GRADIENT FORMULA

Although we can find gradients using steps on a diagram, it is often quicker to use a formula.

For points $A(x_1, y_1)$ and $B(x_2, y_2)$, the vertical step is $y_2 - y_1$, and the horizontal step is $x_2 - x_1$.

$\therefore$ the gradient is $\dfrac{y_2 - y_1}{x_2 - x_1}$.

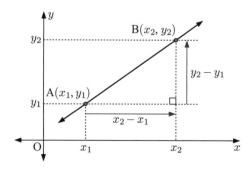

> The **gradient** of the line through (x_1, y_1) and (x_2, y_2) is $\dfrac{y_2 - y_1}{x_2 - x_1}$.

Example 10
🔊 *Self Tutor*

Find the gradient of the line through $(3, -2)$ and $(6, 4)$.

$(3, -2)$ $(6, 4)$
$\uparrow$ $\uparrow$ $\uparrow$ $\uparrow$
x_1 y_1 x_2 y_2

$$\text{gradient} = \frac{y_2 - y_1}{x_2 - x_1}$$

$$= \frac{4 - (-2)}{6 - 3}$$

$$= \frac{6}{3} = 2$$

EXERCISE 14D.2

1 Use the gradient formula to find the gradient of the line through $A(-2, -3)$ and $B(5, 1)$.
Plot the line segment AB on a set of axes to illustrate your answer.

2 Find the gradient of the line segment joining:

a $(2, 3)$ and $(7, 4)$ **b** $(5, 7)$ and $(1, 6)$ **c** $(1, -2)$ and $(3, 6)$

d $(5, 5)$ and $(-1, 5)$ **e** $(3, -1)$ and $(3, -4)$ **f** $(5, -1)$ and $(-2, -3)$

g $(-5, 2)$ and $(2, 0)$ **h** $(0, -1)$ and $(-2, -3)$ **i** $(-1, 7)$ and $(11, -9)$.

Example 11
🔊 *Self Tutor*

Find t given that the line segment joining $(5, -2)$ and $(9, t)$ has gradient $\frac{2}{3}$.

The line segment joining $(5, -2)$ and $(9, t)$ has gradient $= \dfrac{t - (-2)}{9 - 5} = \dfrac{t + 2}{4}$.

$$\therefore \frac{t + 2}{4} = \frac{2}{3}$$

$$\therefore t + 2 = \frac{8}{3}$$

$$\therefore t = \frac{2}{3}$$

3 Find t given that the line segment joining:

a $(-3, 5)$ and $(4, t)$ has gradient 2

b $(5, t)$ and $(10, 12)$ has gradient $-\frac{1}{2}$

c $(3, -6)$ and $(t, -2)$ has gradient 3

d $(t, 9)$ and $(4, 7)$ has gradient $-\frac{3}{5}$

e $(2, 5)$ and (t, t) has gradient $\frac{4}{7}$

f $(t, 2t)$ and $(-3, 12)$ has gradient $-\frac{1}{4}$.

4

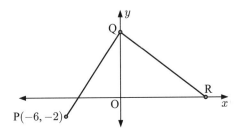

The gradient of PQ is $\frac{3}{2}$, and the gradient of QR is $-\frac{3}{4}$.
Find the coordinates of R.

Activity   Rates

In real life, gradients occur in many situations, and can be interpreted in a variety of ways. Most generally, they represent the **rate** at which one quantity varies compared with another.

For example, the sign alongside indicates to drivers that there is an uphill climb ahead. The gradient of the road indicates how fast it climbs compared with horizontal distance travelled.

In this Activity, we consider some examples where the gradients of line segments can be interpreted as rates. We will continue this study in **Chapter 15** when we consider **speed** and travel graphs.

What to do:

1

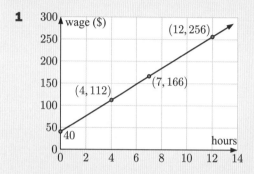

The graph alongside indicates the wages paid to security guards.

a What does the intercept on the vertical axis mean?

b Find the gradient of the line. What does this gradient mean?

c Determine the wage for a security guard working:
  i 6 hours   **ii** 15 hours.

2 This graph shows the fuel consumption and distance travelled for a vehicle at speeds 60 km/h (graph A) and 90 km/h (graph B).

a Find the gradient of each line.

b What do these gradients mean?

c At which speed would you say the vehicle is more efficient?

d Suppose fuel costs $1.40 per litre. Compare the cost of travelling 1000 km at 90 km/h with the cost at 60 km/h.

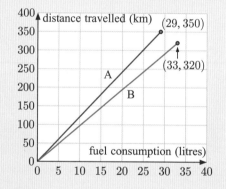

3 This graph shows the amount charged by a plumber according to the time he takes to do a job.

a What does the value at A indicate?

b Find the gradients of the line segments AB and BC. What do these gradients indicate?

c Find the gradient of AC. What does this gradient mean?

d Find the gradient of OC. What does this gradient mean?

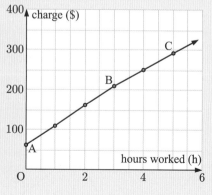

E   PARALLEL AND PERPENDICULAR LINES [E4.5]

PARALLEL LINES

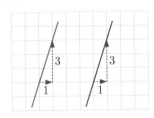

The given lines are parallel, and both of them have a gradient of 3.

- If two lines are **parallel**, then they have **equal gradient**.
- If two lines have **equal gradient**, then they are **parallel**.

PERPENDICULAR LINES

Discovery   Perpendicular lines

In this Discovery you should find the relationship between the gradients of perpendicular lines.

Consider two lines l_1 and l_2 which are neither horizontal nor vertical.

Suppose l_1 has positive gradient $\dfrac{b}{a}$ and l_2 has negative gradient $-\dfrac{a}{b}$ where $a, b > 0$.

What to do:

1 Suppose the lines intersect at A. For the points B and C marked, use the distance between points formula to write an expression for: **a** AB   **b** AC   **c** BC

2 Hence show that $AB^2 + AC^2 = BC^2$.

3 Explain the significance of your result in **2**.

4 Copy and complete:
   For lines which are not horizontal or vertical, if their gradients are .... then the lines are ......

For two lines which have gradients m_1 and m_2:

- If the lines are **perpendicular**, then their gradients are **negative reciprocals**, $m_1 \times m_2 = -1$.
- If the gradients are **negative reciprocals**, then the lines are **perpendicular**.

Example 12   ◄⁣)) Self Tutor

Find the gradient of all lines perpendicular to a line with a gradient of:

a $\dfrac{2}{7}$ **b** -5

The negative reciprocal of $\dfrac{a}{b}$ is $-\dfrac{b}{a}$.

a The negative reciprocal of $\dfrac{2}{7}$ is $-\dfrac{7}{2}$.

∴   the gradient of any perpendicular line is $-\dfrac{7}{2}$.

b The negative reciprocal of $-5 = \dfrac{-5}{1}$ is $\dfrac{1}{5}$.

∴   the gradient of any perpendicular line is $\dfrac{1}{5}$.

EXERCISE 14E

1 Find the gradient of all lines perpendicular to a line with gradient:

    a $\frac{1}{2}$ **b** $\frac{2}{5}$ **c** 3 **d** 7

    e $-\frac{2}{5}$ **f** $-\frac{7}{2}$ **g** $-1\frac{1}{3}$ **h** -1

2 If two lines have these gradients, are they perpendicular?

    a $\frac{1}{3}, 3$ **b** $5, -5$ **c** $\frac{3}{7}, -2\frac{1}{3}$ **d** $4, -\frac{1}{4}$

    e $6, -\frac{5}{6}$ **f** $\frac{2}{3}, -\frac{3}{2}$ **g** $\frac{p}{q}, \frac{q}{p}$ **h** $\frac{a}{b}, -\frac{b}{a}$

3 Consider the hexagon alongside.

    a Calculate the gradient of each side of the hexagon.

    b Which sides are:

        i parallel   **ii** perpendicular?

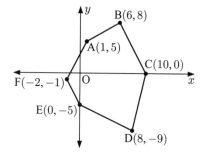

Example 13   ◄⁕ **Self Tutor**

Find t given that the line joining $D(-1, -3)$ to $C(1, t)$ is perpendicular to a line with gradient 2.

gradient of DC $= -\frac{1}{2}$ {perpendicular to line with gradient 2}

$\therefore \ \dfrac{t - (-3)}{1 - (-1)} = -\frac{1}{2}$

$\therefore \ \dfrac{t + 3}{2} = \dfrac{-1}{2}$ {simplifying}

$\therefore \ t + 3 = -1$ {equating numerators}

$\therefore \ t = -4$

---

4 Find a given that the line joining:

    a $A(1, 3)$ to $B(3, a)$ is parallel to a line with gradient 3

    b $P(a, -3)$ to $Q(4, -2)$ is parallel to a line with gradient $\frac{1}{3}$

    c $M(3, a)$ to $N(a, 5)$ is parallel to a line with gradient $-\frac{2}{5}$.

5 Find t given that the line joining:

    a $A(2, -3)$ to $B(-2, t)$ is perpendicular to a line with gradient $1\frac{1}{4}$

    b $C(t, -2)$ to $D(1, 4)$ is perpendicular to a line with gradient $\frac{2}{3}$

    c $P(t, -2)$ to $Q(5, t)$ is perpendicular to a line with gradient $-\frac{1}{4}$.

6 Consider the points $A(1, 4)$, $B(-1, 0)$, $C(6, 3)$, and $D(t, -1)$. Find t such that:

    a AB is parallel to CD   **b** AC is parallel to DB

    c AB is perpendicular to CD   **d** AD is perpendicular to BC.

7 Find the value of k:

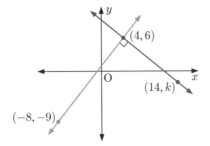

F   COLLINEAR POINTS   [E4.5]

> Three or more points are **collinear** if they lie on the same straight line.

Consider the three collinear points A, B, and C, which all lie on the line l.

$$\text{gradient of AB} = \text{gradient of BC} = \text{gradient of } l$$

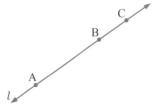

> Three points A, B, and C are **collinear** if gradient of AB = gradient of BC.

Example 14   ◀) Self Tutor

Show that the points A(1, −1), B(6, 9), and C(3, 3) are collinear.

Gradient of AB $= \dfrac{9-(-1)}{6-1} = \dfrac{10}{5} = 2.$ Gradient of BC $= \dfrac{3-9}{3-6} = \dfrac{-6}{-3} = 2.$

$\therefore$ AB is parallel to BC, and point B is common to both line segments.

$\therefore$ A, B, and C are collinear.

EXERCISE 14F

1 Determine whether the following sets of points are collinear:

  a A(1, 2), B(4, 6), and C(−4, −4)   **b** P(−6, −6), Q(−1, 0), and R(4, 6)

  c R(5, 2), S(−6, 5), and T(0, −4)   **d** A(0, −2), B(−1, −5), and C(3, 7).

2 Find c given that these three points are collinear:

  a A(−4, −2), B(0, 2), and C(c, 5)   **b** P(3, −2), Q(4, c), and R(−1, 10).

G   USING COORDINATE GEOMETRY [E4.2 - E4.5]

Coordinate geometry is a powerful tool which can be used to:

• **check** the truth of a geometrical fact   • **prove** geometrical facts using general cases.

Example 15
◀) **Self Tutor**

P(3, −1), Q(1, 7), and R(−1, 5) are the vertices of triangle PQR.
M is the midpoint of PQ, and N is the midpoint of PR.
 a Find the coordinates of M and N.   b Find the gradients of MN and QR.
 c Find distances MN and QR exactly.   d Explain the significance of your results.

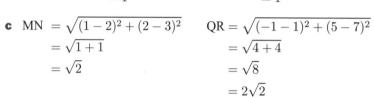

 a M is $\left(\dfrac{3+1}{2}, \dfrac{-1+7}{2}\right)$ which is (2, 3). N is $\left(\dfrac{3+(-1)}{2}, \dfrac{-1+5}{2}\right)$ which is (1, 2).

 b gradient of MN $= \dfrac{2-3}{1-2}$ gradient of QR $= \dfrac{5-7}{-1-1}$

   $= 1$ $= 1$

 c MN $= \sqrt{(1-2)^2 + (2-3)^2}$ QR $= \sqrt{(-1-1)^2 + (5-7)^2}$

   $= \sqrt{1+1}$ $= \sqrt{4+4}$

   $= \sqrt{2}$ $= \sqrt{8}$

                      $= 2\sqrt{2}$

 d The line segment between the midpoints of two sides of this triangle
   is parallel to the third side and half its length.

EXERCISE 14G

1 Consider the points P(1, 5), Q(5, 7), and R(3, 1).
 a Show that triangle PQR is isosceles.   b Find the midpoint M of QR.
 c Show that PM is perpendicular to QR.   d Illustrate what you have found.

2 Consider the points A(−1, 1), B(1, 5), and C(5, 1). M is the midpoint of AB, and N is the midpoint of BC.
 a Show that MN is parallel to AC.   b Show that MN is half the length of AC.

3 Consider the points A(1, 3), B(6, 3), C(3, −1), and D(−2, −1).
 a Use the distance formula to show that ABCD is a rhombus.
 b Find the midpoints of AC and BD.
 c Show that AC and BD are perpendicular.
 d Illustrate what you have found.

4 The points A(−2, −7), B(0, −3), C(6, 1), and D(2, −5)
form a kite.
 a Find the midpoint M of BD.
 b Show that A, M, and C are collinear.
 c Show that AC is perpendicular to BD.

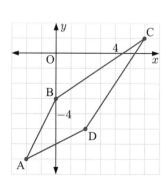

5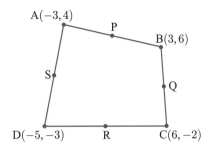

The sketch of quadrilateral ABCD is not drawn to scale. P, Q, R, and S are the midpoints of AB, BC, CD, and DA respectively.

a Find the coordinates of:
  i P   **ii** Q   **iii** R   **iv** S.

b Find the gradient of:
  i PQ   **ii** QR   **iii** RS   **iv** SP.

c What can be deduced about quadrilateral PQRS?

6 $S(s, 8)$ lies on the semi-circle shown.

  a Find s.

  b Find the gradient of:
    i PS   **ii** SQ.

  c Hence show that $P\widehat{S}Q$ is a right angle.

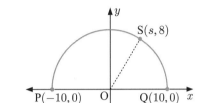

7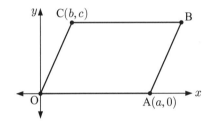

OABC is a parallelogram. You may assume that the opposite sides of the parallelogram are equal in length.

  a Find the coordinates of B.

  b Find the midpoints of AC and OB.

  c What property of parallelograms has been deduced in **b**?

Review set 14A

1 Plot the following points on the Cartesian plane: A(1, 3), B(−2, 0), C(−2, −3), D(2, −1).

2 Find the distance between:
  a P(4, 0) and Q(0, −3)   **b** R(2, −5) and S(−1, −3).

3 Find the midpoint of the line segment joining A(8, −3) and B(2, 1).

4 Find the gradients of these lines:

  a   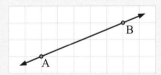   **b**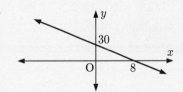

5 Given A(2, −1), B(−5, 3), C(3, 4):
  a Classify triangle ABC as equilateral, isosceles, or scalene.
  b Determine whether triangle ABC is right angled.

6 Find k given that the line joining X(2, −3) and Y(−1, k) is:
  a parallel to a line with gradient $\frac{1}{2}$ **b** perpendicular to a line with gradient $-\frac{1}{4}$.

7 Show that A(1, −2), B(4, 4), and C(5, 6) are collinear.

8 Find the gradient of all lines perpendicular to a line with gradient $\frac{2}{3}$.

9 K$(-3, 2)$ and L$(3, m)$ are $\sqrt{52}$ units apart. Find m.

10 Find the value of a:

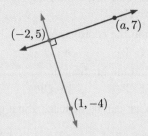

11 Consider the points A$(-3, 1)$, B$(1, 4)$, and C$(4, 0)$.

  a Show that triangle ABC is right angled and isosceles.

  b Find the midpoint X of AC.   **c** Show that BX is perpendicular to AC.

Review set 14B

1 On different sets of axes, show all points with:

  a x-coordinates equal to -3 **b** y-coordinates equal to 5

  c positive x-coordinates and negative y-coordinates.

2 If M$(1, -1)$ is the midpoint of AB, and A is $(-3, 2)$, find the coordinates of B.

3 Find the gradient of the line segment joining:

  a $(5, -1)$ and $(-2, 6)$ **b** $(5, 0)$ and $(5, -2)$.

4 Consider the points S$(7, -2)$ and T$(-1, 1)$.

  a Find the distance ST.   **b** Determine the midpoint of ST.

5 Find the gradient of all lines perpendicular to a line with gradient $-\frac{1}{2}$.

6 X$(-2, 3)$ and Y$(a, -1)$ are $\sqrt{17}$ units apart. Find the value of a.

7 Find b given that A$(-6, 2)$, B$(b, 0)$, and C$(3, -4)$ are collinear.

8 AB and CD are both diameters of the circle. Find:

  a the coordinates of D

  b the radius of the circle.

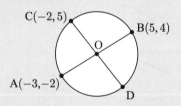

9 Find c if the line joining A$(5, 3)$ to B$(c, -2)$ is perpendicular to a line with gradient 3.

10 A$(-3, 2)$, B$(2, 3)$, C$(4, -1)$, and D$(-1, -2)$ are the vertices of quadrilateral ABCD.

  a Find the gradient of each side of the quadrilateral.

  b Find the midpoints of the diagonals AC and BD.

  c Find the gradients of the diagonals AC and BD.

  d Explain the significance of your results.

Speed, distance, and time

15

Contents:

A Speed, distance, and time   [E1.13]
B Travel graphs   [E1.13]

Opening problem

This graph shows the progress of a freight train as it travels from New Delhi to Lahore.

Things to think about:

a How *far* did the train travel?

b How *long* did the journey take?

c Did the train travel at a constant *speed*? How can you tell?

d How fast did the train travel?

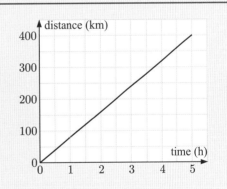

A   SPEED, DISTANCE, AND TIME   *[E1.13]*

We are all familiar with the concept of speed, or how fast something is moving.

> The **average speed** of an object is calculated by dividing the total *distance travelled* by the total *time taken*.
>
> $$\text{average speed} = \frac{\text{distance travelled}}{\text{time taken}}$$

For example, if I cycle 60 km in 3 hours then my average speed is $\dfrac{60 \text{ km}}{3 \text{ h}} = 20$ km/h.

Notice that this formula can be rearranged as   distance = speed × time

$$\text{or} \quad \text{time} = \frac{\text{distance}}{\text{speed}}.$$

The triangle alongside may help you with these rearrangements. By covering the variable you are trying to find, you can see how it is expressed in terms of the other two variables.

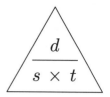

Example 1   ◆) Self Tutor

Clark ran a 42.2 km marathon in 3 h 5 min 17 s.
Find his average speed in km/h.

$$3 \text{ h } 5 \text{ min } 17 \text{ s} = 3 + \frac{5}{60} + \frac{17}{3600} \text{ hours}$$

$$\approx 3.088 \text{ hours}$$

$$\text{average speed} = \frac{\text{distance travelled}}{\text{time taken}}$$

$$\approx \frac{42.2 \text{ km}}{3.088 \text{ h}}$$

$$\approx 13.7 \text{ km/h}$$

Clark's average speed is about 13.7 km/h.

Example 2   ◆) Self Tutor

In a training session, Jo cycles 60 km at 30 km/h, then runs another 15 km at 10 km/h.

a How long did Jo train for?

b Find the average speed for Jo's training session.

a Jo's time cycling $= \dfrac{\text{distance}}{\text{speed}}$ Jo's time running $= \dfrac{\text{distance}}{\text{speed}}$

$$= \frac{60 \text{ km}}{30 \text{ km/h}} \qquad\qquad\qquad = \frac{15 \text{ km}}{10 \text{ km/h}}$$

$$= 2 \text{ hours} \qquad\qquad\qquad\quad = 1.5 \text{ hours}$$

∴ total time = 2 hours + 1.5 hours = 3.5 hours.

b Total distance travelled = 60 km + 15 km = 75 km

∴ Jo's average speed $= \dfrac{\text{total distance travelled}}{\text{total time taken}}$

$$= \frac{75 \text{ km}}{3.5 \text{ h}}$$

$$\approx 21.4 \text{ km/h}$$

EXERCISE 15A

1 An aeroplane travels 2800 km in 3 hours 40 minutes. Find the average speed of the aeroplane.

2 An Olympic sprinter runs 100 m in 10.05 seconds. Calculate his average speed in:

   a m/s   **b** km/h.

3 A boat travels for $1\frac{1}{4}$ hours at an average speed of 30 km/h. How far does the boat travel in this time?

4 A car travels for 2 h 20 min at an average speed of 65 km/h. Calculate the distance travelled.

5 Jane can run 11.4 km in 49 min 37 s. Calculate her average speed in km/h.

6 How long will it take to drive 325 km at a constant speed of 75 km/h? Give your answer in hours and minutes.

7 Find the time taken, to the nearest second, to run 10 000 m at an average speed of 11 km/h.

8 Find the distance travelled when walking at an average speed of 3.5 km/h for 2 h 15 min.

9 A student hikes for 2 hours at 3.5 km/h and then for 1 hour at 2 km/h. Find:

   a the total distance travelled   **b** the overall average speed.

10 A truck driver travels 60 km at 80 km/h, and then another 45 km at 90 km/h.

   a How long did the journey take?

   b Find the average speed for the whole journey.

11 In a 42.2 km marathon, Kuan runs the first 35 km at an average speed of 11 km/h. He walks the next 6 km at 4.5 km/h, and staggers the final 1.2 km at 1.5 km/h. Find Kuan's average speed for the marathon.

12 A family drives 775 km to their holiday destination. The first part of the journey is 52 km and takes 1 h 10 min. The remainder is covered at an average speed of 100 km/h. Find the average speed for the whole journey.

13 Two cyclists are travelling side by side along a long, straight cycle track, one at 30 km/h and the other at 31 km/h. The faster cyclist wishes to overtake the slower one, and will need to gain 4 m relative to the slower cyclist in order to do this safely. Find:

   a the time taken for the faster cyclist to overtake the slower cyclist

   b the distance travelled by the faster cyclist in this time.

14 Two cars are travelling along a straight stretch of road at the speed limit of 60 km/h. One car is 150 m ahead of the other. At a particular point on the road, the speed limit changes to 80 km/h. Assuming each car accelerates to the new speed limit at the same rate, how far apart will the cars be once they are both travelling at 80 km/h?

B   TRAVEL GRAPHS   [E1.13]

A **travel graph** or **distance-time graph** for a journey shows the relationship between *distance travelled* and the *time taken*.

We will see how distance-time graphs can be used to calculate the speeds of travel at different stages of a journey.

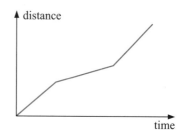

Discovery   Travel graphs

Brian is riding his bicycle along a flat stretch of road. He travels 100 metres every 10 seconds.

What to do:

1 Copy and complete the table alongside, showing the total distance Brian has travelled over the first 50 seconds.

Time (seconds)	Distance (metres)
0	0
10	100
20	200
30	
40	
50	

2 Plot these points on a graph, and join the points with a line. What feature of the graph indicates that Brian is travelling at a constant speed?

3 For Brian's journey so far, find:

   a   the total distance travelled

   b   the time taken

   c   the average speed, in metres per second.

4 Brian then encounters a steep downhill section. He travels 200 metres in the next 10 seconds.

   a   Extend your table to record the total distance travelled after 60 seconds.

   b   Extend the graph to include this new point. What feature of the graph indicates that Brian's speed has changed?

5 For the period when Brian was travelling downhill, find:

   a   the distance travelled   b   the time taken

   c   the average speed, in metres per second.

6 For the *whole journey*, find:

   a   the total distance travelled   b   the total time taken

   c   the average speed, in metres per second.

From the **Discovery** you should have observed that when the speed is constant, the travel graph will be a straight line. The speed is given by the **gradient** of the straight line.

If the travel graph is not a straight line, we can still find the **average speed** between any two points on the graph.

Example 3   🔊 *Self Tutor*

The graph shows the progress of a train travelling between cities.

a How far does the train travel in the first 3 hours?

b Find the speed of the train for the first 3 hours.

c Find the speed of the train during the final hour of the journey.

d Find the average speed of the train for the entire journey.

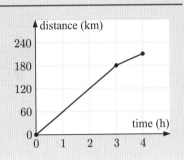

a The train travels 180 km in the first 3 hours.

b Speed $= \dfrac{\text{distance travelled}}{\text{time taken}} = \dfrac{180 \text{ km}}{3 \text{ hours}} = 60$ km/h.

c The speed of the train was 30 km/h.

d Average speed $= \dfrac{\text{total distance travelled}}{\text{total time taken}}$

$= \dfrac{210 \text{ km}}{4 \text{ hours}}$

$= 52.5$ km/h

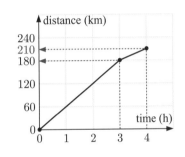

EXERCISE 15B

1 This travel graph shows Chloe's journey as she walks to school, collecting her friend Dillon from his house along the way.

   a Describe Chloe's journey.

   b Find the total distance from Chloe's house to her school.

   c How fast did Chloe walk before she reached Dillon's house?

   d Did Chloe walk faster or slower once Dillon joined her? Explain your answer.

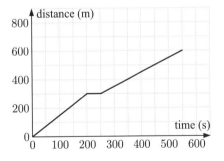

2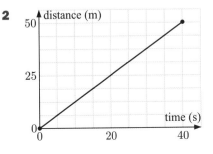

The graph alongside shows Tan's progress as he walks a distance of 50 metres.

   a Find the gradient of the line and interpret this value.

   b Is the speed of the walker constant or variable? Justify your answer.

3 Every 2 hours, a cyclist travels 40 km.

   a Copy and complete the travel graph opposite.

   b How far will the cyclist travel in 3 hours?

   c How long will it take the cyclist to travel 100 km?

   d Find the speed of the cyclist.

PRINTABLE
GRAPH

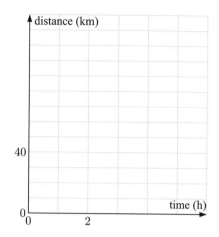

4

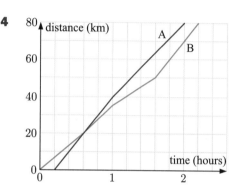

Two cyclists took part in a handicap time trial. The travel graph indicates how far each travels over time.

   a Find the difference in starting times between A and B.

   b Find the distance travelled by each cyclist.

   c How far had the cyclists travelled when A caught B?

   d How long did it take for each cyclist to travel 80 km?

   e Find the average speed of each cyclist.

5 The Reynolds and Smith families live next door to each other in San Francisco. They are taking a vacation to their favourite beach, 150 km from where they live.

   a Which family left home first?

   b Who arrived first?

   c Who travelled faster?

   d How long had the second family been driving when they passed the first family?

   e Approximately how far from San Francisco did they pass?

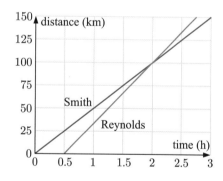

6

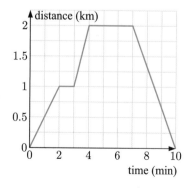

Patricia drives from home to pick up her children from school. She draws a graph to illustrate her journey. The vertical axis shows her distance from home in kilometres. The horizontal axis measures the time from when she left home in minutes. Her first stop is at traffic lights.

   a When did she stop for the red traffic light?

   b How long did the light take to change?

   c How long did she spend at the school?

   d How far away is the school from her home?

   e When was Patricia's speed greatest?

Review set 15A

1 A train travels 770 km in 8 hours, while a truck on the highway travels 120 km in 85 minutes. Which mode of transport is faster?

2 Find the time taken to drive 305 km at an average speed of 70 km/h.

3 A motorist drives for 30 minutes at 90 km/h, and then for 1 hour at 60 km/h. Find:

    a the total distance travelled   **b** the average speed for the whole trip.

4 A motorcyclist is travelling at a constant speed of 55 km/h.

    a How far will the motorcyclist travel in 3 hours?

    b How long will it take the motorcyclist to travel 100 km? Give your answer to the nearest minute.

5 This travel graph shows the progress of a truck travelling between two cities.

    a Is the truck travelling at constant speed? Explain your answer.

    b How far does the truck travel in the first 2 hours?

    c Find the speed of the truck.

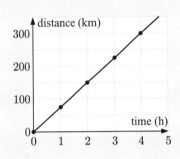

6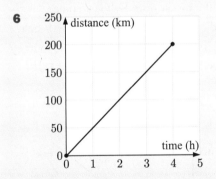

The graph shows the progress of a car as it travels between cities.

    a How far does the car travel in 3 hours?

    b How long does it take for the car to travel 100 km?

    c Find the speed of the car.

7 This travel graph shows the progress of a car travelling from town A to B to C.

    a How far is it from A to B?

    b How long does the car take to get from A to B?

    c Find the speed of the car while travelling from:

        i A to B   **ii** B to C?

    d Find the average speed of the car from A to C.

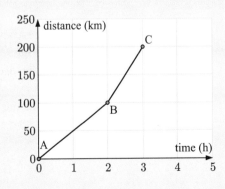

Review set 15B

1 A runner travels 32.5 km in 2 hours and 30 minutes. Find his speed in:

    a km/h   **b** m/s.

2 Alex drove 200 km in 4 hours.

    a Find his average speed.

    b Driving at this speed, how long would it take Alex to drive 325 km?

    c Write Alex's average speed in metres per second.

3 Find the distance travelled when flying at an average speed of 780 km/h for 1 hour 40 minutes.

4 Yiren walks 60 metres in 22.5 seconds, while Sean walks 150 metres in 1 minute.

    a Find the average speed of each person.

    b Yiren and Sean each walk 2000 m at their normal speed. Who will finish first, and by how much?

5 Answer the **Opening Problem** on page **237**.

6

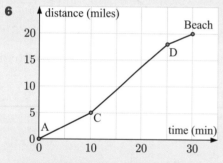

The travel graph shows Sylvie's progress when driving her car from home to the beach.

    a How far is the beach from Sylvie's home?

    b How long did it take Sylvie to get to the beach?

    c Find Sylvie's average speed for the whole journey.

    d What was Sylvie's speed between C and D?

    e At which points did the car change its speed?

7 The graph shows the journeys of two families from New York to Washington DC.

    a Find the distance between New York and Washington DC.

    b How much quicker did the Maple family complete the journey than the Johnson family?

    c Find the average speed for each family over the first two hours.

    d Find the average speed for the Johnsons over the whole journey.

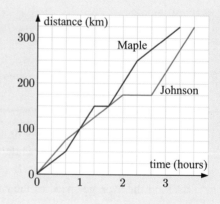

Straight lines

16

Contents:

A   Vertical and horizontal lines   [E4.6]
B   Properties of a straight line   [E4.6]
C   Gradient-intercept form   [E4.6]
D   General form   [E4.6]
E   Finding the equation of a line   [E4.6]
F   Lines of symmetry   [E4.8]

Opening problem

A(1, −3), B(6, −3), C(6, 2), and D(1, 2) are the vertices of a polygon.

Things to think about:

a Can you identify what type of polygon ABCD is by drawing it on a number plane?

b How many lines of symmetry does polygon ABCD have?

c Can you write down the *equations* of the lines of symmetry?

In **Chapter 14** we studied coordinate geometry, including the gradient of a line. In this Chapter we will see how knowledge of the gradient and a point on a line can be used to find its **equation**.

A VERTICAL AND HORIZONTAL LINES   [E4.6]

Vertical and horizontal lines are defined by specifying a constant value for one coordinate. The other coordinate can take any value.

VERTICAL LINES

For all points on a vertical line, the x-coordinate is constant regardless of the value of the y-coordinate.

The graph alongside shows the vertical lines $x = -1$ and $x = 3$.

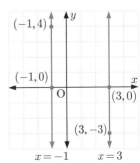

> All **vertical** lines have equations of the form $x = a$.
>
> The gradient of a vertical line is **undefined**.

HORIZONTAL LINES

For all points on a horizontal line, the y-coordinate is constant regardless of the value of the x-coordinate.

The graph alongside shows the horizontal lines $y = 1$ and $y = -2$.

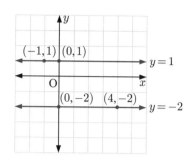

> All **horizontal** lines have equations of the form $y = c$.
>
> The gradient of a horizontal line is **zero**.

EXERCISE 16A

1 Draw the graph of each line and state its gradient:

   a $x = 2$ **b** $y = -4$ **c** $x = -3$ **d** $y = 1.5$ **e** $y = 0$

2 Find the equation of:

   a the x-axis   **b** the y-axis

   c a line parallel to the x-axis and three units below it

   d a line parallel to the y-axis and 4 units to the right of it.

3 Find the equation of:

   a the line with zero gradient that passes through $(-1, 3)$

   b the line with undefined gradient that passes through $(4, -2)$.

4 Suppose l_1 is the line with equation $x = 5$, and l_2 is the line with equation $y = -3$.

   a Graph l_1 and l_2 on the same set of axes.

   b Suppose l_1 cuts the x-axis at A, and l_2 cuts the y-axis at B. Find:

      i the coordinates of A and B   **ii** the gradient of the line segment AB.

5 **a** On the same set of axes, graph the lines $x = -2$, $x = 6$, $y = 5$, and $y = -6$.

   b Consider the quadrilateral formed by the intersection points of these lines.

      i What type of quadrilateral is it?

      ii Find the area of the quadrilateral.

      iii Find the gradients of the diagonals of the quadrilateral.

B   PROPERTIES OF A STRAIGHT LINE   [E4.6]

THE EQUATION OF A LINE

We have seen previously that a linear equation is an equation which can be written in the form $ax + b = 0$ where $a \neq 0$.

> The **equation of a line** is a rule which connects the x and y coordinates of *all* points on the line.
>
> For any non-vertical line, the equation can be written in the form $y = ax + b$.

GRAPHING FROM A TABLE OF VALUES

Consider the equation $y = 2x + 1$. We can choose any value we like for x and use our equation to find the corresponding value for y.

We can hence construct a **table of values** for points on the line.

x	-3	-2	-1	0	1	2	3
y	-5	-3	-1	1	3	5	7

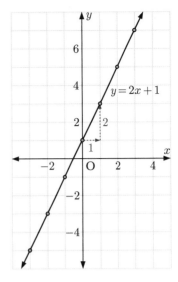

For example:
$$y = 2 \times -3 + 1 \qquad\qquad y = 2 \times 2 + 1$$
$$= -6 + 1 \qquad\qquad\qquad\quad = 4 + 1$$
$$= -5 \qquad\qquad\qquad\qquad = 5$$

From this table we plot the points $(-3, -5)$, $(-2, -3)$, $(-1, -1)$, $(0, 1)$, and so on.

The tabled points are collinear and we can connect them with a straight line.

The gradient of the line is $\dfrac{y\text{-step}}{x\text{-step}} = \dfrac{2}{1} = 2.$

AXES INTERCEPTS

> The **x-intercept** of a line is the value of x where the line cuts the x-axis.
>
> The **y-intercept** of a line is the value of y where the line cuts the y-axis.

We can see that for the graph above, the x-intercept is $-\frac{1}{2}$ and the y-intercept is 1.

Example 1   ◀ *Self Tutor*

Consider the equation $y = x - 2$.

  a Construct a table of values using $x = -3, -2, -1, 0, 1, 2$ and 3.

  b Hence draw the graph of $y = x - 2$.

  c Find the gradient and axes intercepts of the line.

a

x	-3	-2	-1	0	1	2	3
y	-5	-4	-3	-2	-1	0	1

b
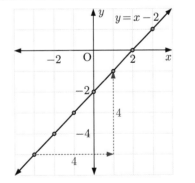

c Using $(-3, -5)$ and $(1, -1)$,

the gradient $= \dfrac{y\text{-step}}{x\text{-step}} = \dfrac{4}{4} = 1.$

The x-intercept is 2.

The y-intercept is -2.

POINTS ON A LINE

> A point lies on a line if its coordinates satisfy the equation of the line.

Example 2

◀)) **Self Tutor**

Determine whether:

a $(3, 7)$ lies on the line with equation $y = 2x + 1$

b $(4, -2)$ lies on the line with equation $5x + 3y = 16$.

a When $x = 3$, we have
$$y = 2(3) + 1$$
$$= 6 + 1$$
$$= 7 \;\checkmark$$
So, $(3, 7)$ does lie on the line.

b Substituting $x = 4$ and $y = -2$ into the LHS gives
$$5(4) + 3(-2)$$
$$= 20 - 6$$
$$= 14 \;\textbf{✗}$$
Since LHS $\neq$ RHS, $(4, -2)$ does *not* lie on the line.

EXERCISE 16B

1 For each of the following equations:

     i Construct a table of values using $x = -3, -2, -1, 0, 1, 2$, and 3.

     ii Draw the graph of the straight line.

     iii Find the gradient and axes intercepts of the line.

a $y = x$ **b** $y = -x$ **c** $y = 2x$

d $y = -2x$ **e** $y = 2x - 1$ **f** $y = \frac{1}{2}x + 2$

g $y = -\frac{1}{2}x + 2$ **h** $y = 2 - x$ **i** $y = -\frac{3}{2}x - 1$

GRAPHING
PACKAGE

2 Determine whether the point:

a $(3, 4)$ lies on the line $y = 2x - 2$ **b** $(-1, 4)$ lies on the line $y = x + 6$

c $(-2, 10)$ lies on the line $y = -3x + 4$ **d** $\left(\frac{1}{2}, -6\right)$ lies on the line $y = 2x - 8$

e $(2, -1)$ lies on the line $3x + y = 5$ **f** $(-3, 4)$ lies on the line $2x - 5y = -14$.

3 Find a given that:

a $(3, a)$ lies on $y = \frac{1}{2}x + \frac{1}{2}$ **b** $(-2, a)$ lies on $y = -3x + 7$

c $(a, 4)$ lies on $y = 2x - 6$ **d** $(a, -1)$ lies on $y = -x + 3$

e $(2, a)$ lies on $2x + y = 7$ **f** $(3, a)$ lies on $x + 2y = -1$

g $(a, 1)$ lies on $3x + 2y = 8$ **h** $(a, -3)$ lies on $2x - 3y = 5$.

4 For each of the following equations:

     i Construct a table of values using $x = -3, -2, -1, 0, 1, 2$, and 3.

     ii Draw the graph of the straight line.

     iii Determine whether the point $(-6, -3)$ lies on the graph.

a $y = x + 3$ **b** $y = -\frac{1}{3}x - 4$ **c** $y = \frac{1}{3}x - 1$

5 Find the x-intercept of each straight line by letting $y = 0$:

a $y = x - 4$ **b** $y = x + 2$ **c** $y = -x + 1$

d $y = -2x - 6$ **e** $y = 3x - 12$ **f** $y = -3x + 9$

g $x + 2y = 6$ **h** $2x - 3y = -8$ **i** $-x + y = 5$

6   Consider the straight line $y = mx + c$ where m and c are constants.

    a   Copy and complete this table of values:

x	-2	0	2	$-\dfrac{c}{m}$
y				

    b   State the axes intercepts of the straight line.

    c   Use the points with x-coordinates -2 and 2 to find the gradient of the line.

    d   Copy and complete:

       A straight line with equation $y = mx + c$ has gradient ...... and y-intercept ......

C   GRADIENT-INTERCEPT FORM   [E4.6]

> The **gradient-intercept form** of the equation of a straight line
> with gradient m and y-intercept c is $\boldsymbol{y = mx + c}$.

Example 3   ◀)) Self Tutor

State the gradient and y-intercept of the line with equation:

    a $y = 3x - 2$ **b** $y = 7 - 2x$

    a $y = 3x - 2$ has $m = 3$ and $c = -2$
       ∴   the gradient is 3 and the y-intercept is -2.

    b $y = 7 - 2x$ can be written as $y = -2x + 7$, with $m = -2$ and $c = 7$
       ∴   the gradient is -2 and the y-intercept is 7.

DRAWING THE GRAPH OF A LINE IN GRADIENT-INTERCEPT FORM

To draw the graph of a line in the form $y = mx + c$:

- Use the y-intercept c to plot the point $(0,\ c)$.
- Starting from $(0,\ c)$, use horizontal and vertical steps from
  the gradient m to locate another point on the line.
- Join the two points and extend the line in either direction.

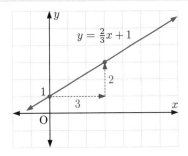

Always let the
horizontal step
be positive.

Example 4   ◀)) Self Tutor

Draw the graph of: **a** $y = \frac{2}{3}x + 1$ **b** $y = -2x - 3$.

    a   For $y = \frac{2}{3}x + 1$:

       - the y-intercept is $c = 1$
       - the gradient is

         $m = \frac{2}{3}$ ←— vertical step
              ←— horizontal step

b For $y = -2x - 3$:

  • the y-intercept is $c = -3$

  • the gradient is

$$m = \dfrac{-2}{1} \begin{array}{l} \longleftarrow \text{vertical step} \\ \longleftarrow \text{horizontal step} \end{array}$$

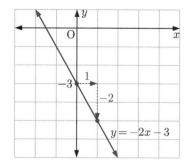

EXERCISE 16C

1 State the gradient and y-intercept of the line with equation:

  a $y = 4x + 8$ **b** $y = -3x + 2$ **c** $y = 6 - x$ **d** $y = -2x + 3$

  e $y = -2$ **f** $y = 11 - 3x$ **g** $y = \frac{1}{2}x - 5$ **h** $y = 3 - \frac{3}{2}x$

  i $y = \frac{2}{5}x + \frac{4}{5}$ **j** $y = \dfrac{x+1}{2}$ **k** $y = \dfrac{2x - 10}{5}$ **l** $y = \dfrac{11 - 3x}{2}$

2 Draw the graph of:

  a $y = x + 3$ **b** $y = -x + 4$ **c** $y = 2x + 2$ **d** $y = -3x - 2$

  e $y = \frac{1}{2}x - 1$ **f** $y = \frac{2}{3}x + 4$ **g** $y = 3x$ **h** $y = -\frac{1}{2}x$

  i $y = -2x + 1$ **j** $y = 3 - \frac{1}{3}x$ **k** $y = \frac{3}{4}x - 2$ **l** $y = -\frac{1}{4}x - 3$

3 Consider the line with equation $y = -\frac{2}{3}x + 2$.

  a Find the:

  i gradient   **ii** y-intercept   **iii** x-intercept.

  b Draw the graph of the line.   **c** Does the point $\left(4, -\frac{2}{3}\right)$ lie on the line?

D GENERAL FORM   [E4.6]

The **general form** of the equation of a straight line is $ax + by = d$ where a, b, and d are constants.

For example, the equations $4x + 5y = 3$ and $x - 3y = -4$ are in general form.

Equations in general form are usually written with a positive coefficient of x.

We can rearrange equations to convert between gradient-intercept form and general form.

Example 5   ◀)) Self Tutor

Write the equation:

  a $y = -\frac{1}{4}x + \frac{3}{4}$ in general form

  b $2x + 5y = 7$ in gradient-intercept form.

a
$$y = -\tfrac{1}{4}x + \tfrac{3}{4}$$
$$\therefore \ 4y = -x + 3 \qquad \{\text{multiplying both sides by 4}\}$$
$$\therefore \ x + 4y = 3 \qquad \{\text{adding } x \text{ to both sides}\}$$

b
$$2x + 5y = 7$$
$$\therefore \ 5y = -2x + 7 \qquad \{\text{subtracting } 2x \text{ from both sides}\}$$
$$\therefore \ y = -\tfrac{2}{5}x + \tfrac{7}{5} \qquad \{\text{dividing both sides by 5}\}$$

The general form of an equation is useful because:

- it allows us to write many equations without fractions
- it can be used for *all* straight lines, including vertical lines
- it allows to quickly calculate both axes intercepts.

DRAWING THE GRAPH OF A LINE IN GENERAL FORM

To draw the graph of a line in the form $ax + by = d$, we:

- Find the y-intercept by letting $x = 0$.
- Find the x-intercept by letting $y = 0$.
- Join the points where the line cuts the axes and extend the line in either direction.

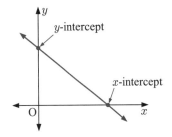

Example 6   ◀)) **Self Tutor**

Draw the graph of $4x - 3y = 12$.

When $x = 0$, $-3y = 12$
$$\therefore\ y = -4$$
So, the y-intercept is -4.

When $y = 0$, $4x = 12$
$$\therefore\ x = 3$$
So, the x-intercept is 3.

EXERCISE 16D

1 Write in general form:

   a $y = -2x + 11$
   b $y = 3x - 4$
   c $y = -\frac{1}{5}x + \frac{6}{5}$

   d $y = -\frac{6}{7}x + \frac{5}{7}$
   e $y = \frac{5}{8}x - \frac{1}{8}$
   f $y = \frac{4}{9}x + 2$

2 For each of the following lines:

   i write the equation in gradient-intercept form
   ii state the gradient of the line.

   a $3x + y = 5$
   b $2x + 5y = 10$
   c $7x + 4y = -9$

   d $6x - y = 1$
   e $5x - 11y = 2$
   f $9x - 2y = -5$

3 Draw the graph of:

   a $x + 3y = 6$
   b $3x - 2y = 12$
   c $2x + 5y = 10$

   d $4x + 3y = 6$
   e $x + y = 5$
   f $x - y = -3$

   g $3x - y = -6$
   h $7x + 2y = 14$
   i $4x + 9y = -18$

4 Consider the line with equation $3x - 5y = 15$.

   a Find the axes intercepts.

   b Determine whether the following points lie on the line: **i** $(-5, -6)$ **ii** $(1, -2)$

   c Draw the graph of the line, showing the information you have found.

5   **a**   Draw the graph of $3x + 4y = 24$.

    b   Which of these lines is parallel to $3x + 4y = 24$?

        A $y = \frac{4}{3}x + 1$ **B** $y = -\frac{4}{3}x - 5$ **C** $y = \frac{3}{4}x + 6$ **D** $y = -\frac{3}{4}x + 7$

6   By rearranging the equation into gradient-intercept form, show that the line with equation $ax - by = d$
has gradient $\dfrac{a}{b}$.

E   FINDING THE EQUATION OF A LINE   [E4.6]

> To determine the equation of a line, we need to know either:
> - its gradient and at least one point which lies on the line, *or*
> - two points which lie on the line.

GIVEN THE GRADIENT AND y-INTERCEPT

If we know the gradient m and y-intercept c of a line, we can write down the equation of the line immediately
as $y = mx + c$.

Example 7   ◄)) *Self Tutor*

Find the equation of the line with gradient 5 and y-intercept -3.

> The line has gradient $m = 5$ and y-intercept $c = -3$.
> So, the equation of the line is $y = 5x - 3$.

EXERCISE 16E.1

1   Write down the equation of the line with:

    a   gradient 3 and y-intercept 4   **b**   gradient 7 and y-intercept -1

    c   gradient -1 and y-intercept $\frac{1}{3}$ **d**   gradient $\frac{1}{2}$ and y-intercept 0

    e   gradient 0 and y-intercept 5   **f**   gradient $-\frac{5}{2}$ and y-intercept $-\frac{2}{3}$.

2   Find, in general form, the equation of a line with:

    a   gradient 2 and y-intercept 4   **b**   gradient -3 and y-intercept -2

    c   gradient $\frac{1}{2}$ and y-intercept $\frac{1}{4}$ **d**   gradient $-\frac{1}{3}$ and y-intercept 0

    e   gradient $-\frac{3}{4}$ and y-intercept 2   **f**   gradient $\frac{2}{5}$ and y-intercept -1.

GIVEN THE GRADIENT AND A POINT

If we know the gradient and one point which lies on the line, we can substitute the coordinates of the point
into the equation to find c.

Example 8

🔊 *Self Tutor*

A line has gradient $\frac{2}{3}$ and passes through the point $(3, 1)$. Find the equation of the line.

The gradient $m = \frac{2}{3}$, so the equation has the form $y = \frac{2}{3}x + c$.

Since $(3, 1)$ lies on the line, $1 = \frac{2}{3}(3) + c$

$$\therefore \ 1 = 2 + c$$
$$\therefore \ c = -1$$

So, the equation is $y = \frac{2}{3}x - 1$.

In **Exercise 16D** question **6** you should have found that:

A line with gradient $\dfrac{a}{b}$ has an equation with the general form $ax - by = d$.

We can use this fact to quickly write down the equation of a line in general form. The constant d is found by substituting the coordinates of the known point.

Example 9

🔊 *Self Tutor*

Find, in general form, the equation of the line:

a with gradient $\frac{3}{4}$ which passes through $(5, -2)$

b with gradient $-\frac{3}{4}$ which passes through $(1, 7)$.

With practice you can write down the equation very quickly.

a The equation is $3x - 4y = 3(5) - 4(-2)$
$$\therefore \ 3x - 4y = 23$$

b The equation is $3x + 4y = 3(1) + 4(7)$
$$\therefore \ 3x + 4y = 31$$

EXERCISE 16E.2

1 Find, in gradient-intercept form, the equation of the line which has gradient:

a 2 and which passes through $(1, 8)$ **b** -3 and which passes through $(4, -16)$

c 5 and which passes through $(-3, -1)$ **d** $\frac{3}{4}$ and which passes through $(8, 12)$

e 0 and which passes through $(-2, 4)$ **f** $-\frac{1}{2}$ and which passes through $(5, -9)$

g $-\frac{1}{3}$ and which passes through $(1, 4)$ **h** $\frac{2}{3}$ and which passes through $(-2, 5)$.

2 Find, in gradient-intercept form, the equation of the line:

a parallel to $y = 3x + 4$, and which passes through $(2, 4)$

b parallel to $y = -\frac{1}{4}x - 2$, and which passes through $(8, -3)$

c parallel to $2x - 5y = 6$, and which passes through $(-5, 1)$

d which is perpendicular to a line with gradient $\frac{3}{4}$, and cuts the x-axis at 5

e which is perpendicular to a line with gradient -2, and passes through $(-2, 3)$.

3 Find, in general form, the equation of the line:

   a through $(4, 1)$ with gradient $\frac{1}{2}$ **b** through $(5, 0)$ with gradient $\frac{3}{4}$

   c through $(3, -2)$ with gradient 3 **d** through $(2, -3)$ with gradient $-\frac{3}{4}$

   e through $(3, -2)$ with gradient -2 **f** through $(0, 4)$ with gradient -3.

4 Explain why:

   a any line parallel to $3x + 5y = 2$ has the form $3x + 5y = d$

   b any line perpendicular to $3x + 5y = 2$ has the form $5x - 3y = d$.

5 Find the equation of a line which is:

   a parallel to the line $3x + 4y = 6$ and passes through $(2, 1)$

   b perpendicular to the line $5x + 2y = 10$ and passes through $(-1, -1)$

   c perpendicular to the line $x - 3y + 6 = 0$ and passes through $(-4, 0)$

   d parallel to the line $x - 3y = 11$ and passes through $(0, 0)$.

6 $2x - 3y = 6$ and $6x + ky = 4$ are two straight lines.

   a Write down the gradient of each line.

   b Find the value of k such that the lines are:

      i parallel   **ii** perpendicular.

GIVEN TWO POINTS ON THE LINE

If we are given two points on a straight line, we use them to find the gradient. We can then use the gradient and either point to find the equation of the line.

Example 10   ◀ˢ Self Tutor

Find the equation of the illustrated line:

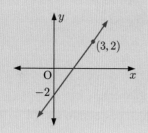

The line passes through $(0, -2)$ and $(3, 2)$.

$\therefore$ the gradient $m = \dfrac{2 - (-2)}{3 - 0} = \dfrac{4}{3}$

and the y-intercept $c = -2$

$\therefore$ the equation is $y = \frac{4}{3}x - 2$.

EXERCISE 16E.3

1 Find the equation of the illustrated line:

  a

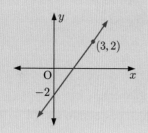

  b

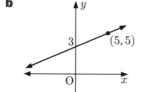

  c

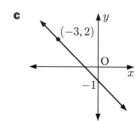

d 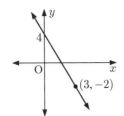   **e** 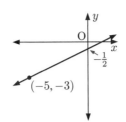   **f**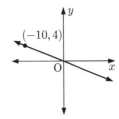

2 Find the equation of the line which has y-intercept:

    a -5, and which passes through $(3, 7)$ **b** 7, and which passes through $(5, -8)$

    c -1, and which passes through $(-8, -4)$.

3 Find the equation of the illustrated line:

a 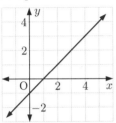   **b** 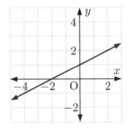   **c**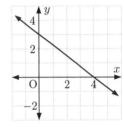

d 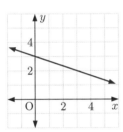   **e** 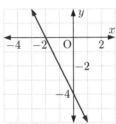   **f**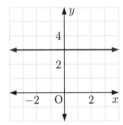

Example 11   ◀) *Self Tutor*

Find the equation of the line which passes through $(-2, 1)$ and $(3, 16)$.

The line has gradient $m = \dfrac{16 - 1}{3 - (-2)} = \dfrac{15}{5} = 3$.

$\therefore$ the equation of the line has the form $y = 3x + c$.

Since $(-2, 1)$ lies on the line, $1 = 3(-2) + c$

$\therefore$ $1 = -6 + c$

$\therefore$ $c = 7$

So, the equation of the line is $y = 3x + 7$.

> You can substitute the coordinates of *either* point into the equation.

---

4 Find the equation of the line which passes through:

    a $(2, 7)$ and $(5, 13)$ **b** $(3, 6)$ and $(6, 0)$

    c $(-3, -4)$ and $(6, 2)$ **d** $(-4, -3)$ and $(3, -3)$

    e $(-6, -14)$ and $(2, -2)$ **f** $(-8, 11)$ and $(-2, 3)$.

> Check your answer by making sure *both* points satisfy the equation of the line.

5 Find the equation of a line:

   a which cuts the x-axis at 5 and the y-axis at -2

   b which cuts the x axis at -1, and passes through $(-3,\ 4)$.

6 Find the equation of the illustrated line:

   a
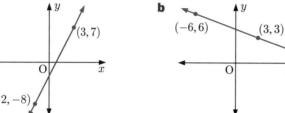
   b
   c
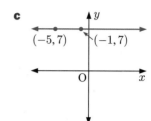

   d
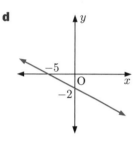
   e
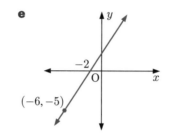
   f
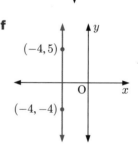

7 Find, in general form, the equation of the line passing through:

   a $(-1,\ 7)$ and $(2,\ -2)$ **b** $(5,\ 2)$ and $(-1,\ 2)$ **c** $(3,\ -1)$ and $(3,\ 4)$

   d $(3,\ -1)$ and $(0,\ 4)$ **e** $(2,\ 6)$ and $(-2,\ 1)$ **f** $(4,\ -1)$ and $(-1,\ -2)$.

8 Find the rule connecting the variables:

   a
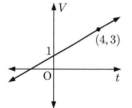
   b
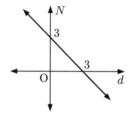
   c
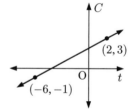

   d
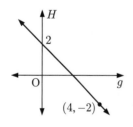
   e
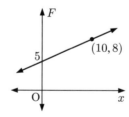
   f
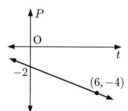

9 Lines 1 and 2 are parallel. Find the equation of:

   a line 1   **b** line 2.

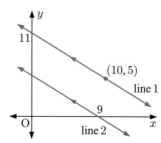

10

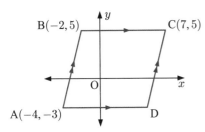

ABCD is a parallelogram. Find the equation of line:

   a AB   **b** BC   **c** CD   **d** AD

F   LINES OF SYMMETRY   [E4.8]

Many geometrical shapes have **lines of symmetry**. If the shape is drawn on the Cartesian plane, we can use the information learnt in this Chapter to find the equations of the lines of symmetry.

Example 12   ◀) *Self Tutor*

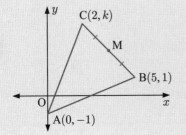

ABC is an isosceles triangle with AB = AC.

  a Find k given that $k > 0$.

  b Find the coordinates of M, the midpoint of line segment BC.

  c Show that line segments AM and BC are perpendicular.

  d Find the equation of the line of symmetry of triangle ABC.

---

a Since AB = AC, $\sqrt{(5-0)^2 + (1--1)^2} = \sqrt{(2-0)^2 + (k--1)^2}$

$$\therefore \ \sqrt{25+4} = \sqrt{4+(k+1)^2}$$

$$\therefore \ (k+1)^2 = 25$$

$$\therefore \ k+1 = \pm 5$$

$$\therefore \ k = 4 \ \text{or} \ -6$$

But $k > 0$, so $k = 4$.

b The midpoint of BC is $\left(\dfrac{5+2}{2}, \dfrac{1+4}{2}\right)$.

So, M is $\left(\frac{7}{2}, \frac{5}{2}\right)$.

c gradient of AM $= \dfrac{\frac{5}{2} - -1}{\frac{7}{2} - 0}$ gradient of BC $= \dfrac{4-1}{2-5}$ These gradients are the negative reciprocals of each other, so AM $\perp$ BC.

$\qquad\qquad\qquad = \dfrac{\frac{7}{2}}{\frac{7}{2}}$ $= \dfrac{3}{-3}$

$\qquad\qquad\qquad = 1$ $= -1$

d The line of symmetry is AM.

Its gradient $m = 1$ and its y-intercept $c = -1$.

$\therefore$ its equation is $y = x - 1$.

EXERCISE 16F

1   a   Plot the points A(1, 0), B(9, 0), C(8, 3), and D(2, 3).

    b   Classify the figure ABCD.

    c   Find the equations of any lines of symmetry of ABCD.

2   Answer the **Opening Problem** on page **245**.

3   P, Q, R, and S are the vertices of a rectangle.

    a   Given P(1, 3), Q(7, 3), and S(1, −2), find:

       i   the coordinates of R   **ii**   the midpoints of line segments PR and QS

      iii   the equations of the lines of symmetry.

    b   What geometrical fact was verified by **a ii**?

4

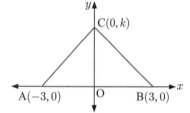

    a   Find the gradient of line segments AC and BC.

    b   If $\widehat{ACB}$ is a right angle, find the value of k.

    c   Classify triangle ABC.

    d   State the equation of the line of symmetry of triangle ABC.

5   Plot the points O(0, 0), A(1, 4), B(9, 2), and C(8, −2).

    a   Prove that line segments OA and BC are parallel, and that OA = BC.

    b   Prove that line segments OA and AB are perpendicular.

    c   What have you established about OABC from **a** and **b**?

    d   Find the midpoints of OA and AB.

    e   Find the equations of any lines of symmetry of OABC.

6   OABC is a quadrilateral with A(5, 0), B(8, 4), and C(3, 4).

    a   Plot the points A, B, and C and complete the figure OABC.

    b   Find the equation of line segment BC.

    c   By finding lengths only, show that OABC is a rhombus.

    d   Find the midpoints of line segments OB and AC. Explain the significance of this result.

    e   Find the equations of any lines of symmetry. Comment on your answer.

7   ABC is an equilateral triangle.

    a   Find the coordinates of C.

    b   Find the coordinates of M and N, the midpoints of line segments BC and AC respectively.

    c   Find the equations of all lines of symmetry of triangle ABC.

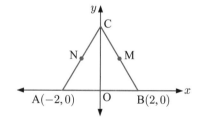

Review set 16A

1   On the same set of axes, draw graphs of the lines with equations $x = -2\tfrac{1}{2}$ and $y = -4$.

2 State the gradient and y-intercept of the line with equation:

    a $y = 4x - 3$ **b** $y = 2 - x$ **c** $y = \dfrac{3x - 1}{2}$

3 Draw the graph of:

    a $y = \frac{3}{2}x - 2$ **b** $2x - 3y = 30$ **c** $y = -\frac{1}{4}x + 5$ **d** $4x + 3y = -36$

4 Find the axes intercepts and gradient of the line with equation $2x + 3y = 6$.

5 Find the equation of the line:

    a with gradient -2 and y-intercept 3

    b with zero gradient and which passes through $(5, -4)$

    c with gradient $\frac{2}{3}$ and which passes through $(-3, 4)$

    d which passes through $(1, -2)$ and $(3, 4)$.

6 Find k given that $(-3, -1)$ lies on the line $4x - y = k$.

7 Find, in general form, the equation of the line:

    a which passes through $(-2, -3)$ and $(1, 5)$

    b parallel to $2x - 3y = 10$ and which passes through $(3, -4)$.

8 Find the equation of each line:

    a
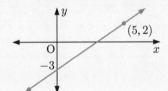
    b
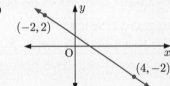

    c
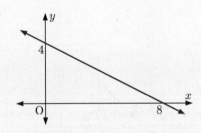
    d
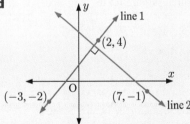

9 Given $A(-3, 1)$, $B(1, 4)$, and $C(4, 0)$:

    a Show that triangle ABC is isosceles.

    b Find the midpoint X of line segment AC.

    c Use gradients to verify that line segments BX and AC are perpendicular.

    d Find the equations of any lines of symmetry of triangle ABC.

10 Consider the points $A(3, -2)$, $B(8, 0)$, $C(6, 5)$, and $D(1, 3)$.

    a Prove that line segments AB and DC are parallel and equal in length.

    b Prove that line segments AB and BC are perpendicular and equal in length.

    c Classify the quadrilateral ABCD.

    d Find the equations of all lines of symmetry of ABCD.

Review set 16B

1 Determine whether the point:

   a $(-2, 5)$ lies on the line with equation $y = -2x + 1$

   b $(3, -2)$ lies on the line with equation $4x - 3y = 18$.

2 Write down the gradient and y-intercept of a line with equation $y = 5 - 2x$.

3 Consider the line with equation $2x - 5y = 10$.

   a Find the axes intercepts.   **b** Find the gradient of the line.

   c Draw a graph of this line.

4 Find the equation of each line:

   a   **b**   **c**

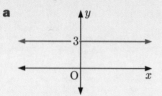 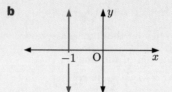 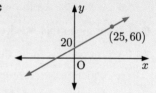

5 Draw the graph of: **a** $y = -\frac{1}{3}x + 2$ **b** $y = \frac{3}{4}x - 3$ **c** $x - 4y = 12$

6 Find k, given that $(k, 5)$ lies on the line with equation $3x - y = -8$.

7 Find the equation of the line:

   a with gradient 2 and y-intercept -3

   b with gradient $-\frac{1}{2}$ and which passes through $(-6, 5)$

   c which passes through $(-4, 6)$ and $(5, -3)$

   d which is parallel to $y = \frac{3}{2}x - 1$ and passes through $(-2, -8)$.

8 Find the equation of each line:

   a   **b**

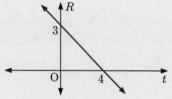 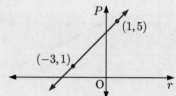

9 Find, in general form, the equation of the line:

   a with gradient $-\frac{4}{7}$ and which passes through $(-2, 2)$

   b perpendicular to $y = 2x - 3$ and which passes through $(4, 1)$.

10 Consider the points A$(-11, 2)$, B$(-5, -6)$, C$(3, 0)$, and D$(-3, 8)$.

   a Plot the points on a set of axes.

   b Show that all the sides of quadrilateral ABCD are equal in length.

   c Show that line segment AB is perpendicular to line segment BC. Hence classify ABCD.

   d ABCD has four lines of symmetry. Find their equations in general form.

   e Find the midpoint of line segment AC.

   f Check that each of the lines of symmetry passes through the point found in **e**.

Simultaneous equations

17

Contents:

A	Graphical solution	[E2.6]
B	Solution by equating values of y	[E2.6]
C	Solution by substitution	[E2.6]
D	Solution by elimination	[E2.6]
E	Problem solving with simultaneous equations	[E2.6]

Opening problem

At the summer sales, Cassandra buys a dress and a skirt. Together they cost \$30. The dress cost \$8 more than the skirt.

Suppose the dress cost \$$x$, and the skirt cost \$$y$.

Things to think about:

a Can you explain why:

  i $x + y = 30$ ii $x - y = 8$?

b How many solutions are there to the equation:

  i $x + y = 30$ ii $x - y = 8$?

c Which solution satisfies *both* equations at the same time?

We have previously studied equations involving one variable.

For example, the linear equation $3x + 5 = 14$ has exactly one solution, $x = 3$.

Some equations have more than one variable, and more than one solution.

Consider the equations in the **Opening Problem**:

- $x + y = 30$ has infinitely many solutions. They lie in a straight line on the Cartesian plane.
  $x = 1$, $y = 29$ is one solution, and $x = 2$, $y = 28$ is another.
- $x - y = 8$ also has infinitely many solutions which lie in a straight line.
  They include $x = 9$, $y = 1$, and $x = 10$, $y = 2$.

To find a solution which satisfies *both* equations at the same time, we need to solve the equations *simultaneously*. We say they are **simultaneous equations**.

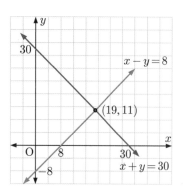

There is in fact only *one* solution to the simultaneous equations $\begin{cases} x + y = 30 \\ x - y = 8 \end{cases}$.

The solution occurs at the point where the two lines intersect.

The solution $x = 19$, $y = 11$ satisfies both equations at the same time, since $19 + 11 = 30$
and $19 - 11 = 8$.

So, Cassandra paid \$19 for the dress and \$11 for the skirt.

A   GRAPHICAL SOLUTION   [E2.6]

Suppose we are given two linear equations involving x and y. The solutions to each equation will form a straight line. If we graph the two equations on the same set of axes, any **point of intersection** corresponds to a **simultaneous solution** of the equations.

- If the lines are not parallel, the lines will meet at exactly one point. The simultaneous equations have *exactly one solution*.

- If the lines are parallel but not identical, the lines will never meet. The simultaneous equations have *no solutions*.

- If the lines are identical, there will be infinitely many points of intersection. The simultaneous equations have *infinitely many solutions*.

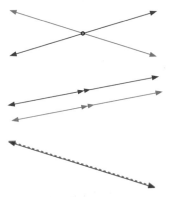

Example 1   ◀)) Self Tutor

Solve the following simultaneous equations graphically: $\begin{cases} y = 2x - 4 \\ 2x + 3y = 12 \end{cases}$

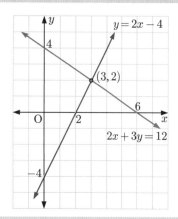

We draw the graphs of $y = 2x - 4$ and $2x + 3y = 12$ on the same set of axes.

The graphs meet at the point $(3, 2)$.

∴   the solution is $x = 3$, $y = 2$.

Check:

Substituting these values into:

- $y = 2x - 4$ gives $2 = 2(3) - 4$ ✓
- $2x + 3y = 12$ gives $2(3) + 3(2) = 12$ ✓

EXERCISE 17A

1 Solve the following simultaneous equations graphically:

a $\begin{cases} y = 4x - 1 \\ y = 2x - 3 \end{cases}$
b $\begin{cases} y = 3x \\ y = -2x + 5 \end{cases}$
c $\begin{cases} y = x + 2 \\ y = -3x - 6 \end{cases}$

2 Solve the following simultaneous equations graphically:

a $\begin{cases} y = 2x - 8 \\ 2x + 5y = 20 \end{cases}$
b $\begin{cases} 4x + y = 8 \\ 2x - 3y = 18 \end{cases}$
c $\begin{cases} 3x - y = -6 \\ 3x + 4y = -36 \end{cases}$

3 Try to solve the following simultaneous equations graphically. State the number of solutions in each case.

a $\begin{cases} y = 4x + 1 \\ y = 4x - 3 \end{cases}$
b $\begin{cases} 4x - 2y = -8 \\ y = 2x + 4 \end{cases}$

Discussion

Discuss the advantages and disadvantages of solving simultaneous equations by graphical methods.

B SOLUTION BY EQUATING VALUES OF y [E2.6]

We will now consider some **algebraic** methods for solving linear simultaneous equations. Algebraic methods are often quicker than trial and error or graphing. They are also more accurate if the solutions are not integers.

If y is the subject of *both* equations, we equate the y values and solve for x.

Example 2
 ◀) **Self Tutor**

Solve the simultaneous equations: $\begin{cases} y = 2x - 1 \\ y = x + 3 \end{cases}$

If $y = 2x - 1$ and $y = x + 3$, then

$\qquad 2x - 1 = x + 3 \qquad$ {equating ys}

$\therefore \ 2x - 1 - x = x + 3 - x \qquad$ {subtracting x from both sides}

$\therefore \quad x - 1 = 3$

$\therefore \quad x = 4 \qquad$ {adding 1 to both sides}

Now $y = x + 3$

$\therefore \ y = 4 + 3$

$\therefore \ y = 7$

The solution is $x = 4, \ y = 7$.

Check: In $y = 2x - 1$, $y = 2 \times 4 - 1 = 8 - 1 = 7$ ✓

Always check your solution in *both* equations.

EXERCISE 17B

1 Solve these simultaneous equations by equating values of y:

a $\begin{cases} y = x + 1 \\ y = 2x - 3 \end{cases}$
b $\begin{cases} y = x + 4 \\ y = -x + 2 \end{cases}$
c $\begin{cases} y = x + 2 \\ y = -2x + 5 \end{cases}$

2 Solve by equating values of y:

a $\begin{cases} y = -2x - 4 \\ y = x - 4 \end{cases}$
  b $\begin{cases} y = -x + 4 \\ y = 2x - 8 \end{cases}$
  c $\begin{cases} y = -2 - x \\ y = 2x + 13 \end{cases}$

d $\begin{cases} y = 3x + 7 \\ y = -x - 6 \end{cases}$
  e $\begin{cases} y = 2x - 10 \\ y = 3x - 18 \end{cases}$
  f $\begin{cases} y = 5 - 3x \\ y = 10 - 6x \end{cases}$

3 Try to solve by equating values of y. Comment on your results. $\begin{cases} y = 2x + 3 \\ y = 2x - 2 \end{cases}$

C | *SOLUTION BY SUBSTITUTION*   *[E2.6]*

The method of **substitution** is used when a variable is given as the subject of *one* of the equations.

For example, in the equations $\begin{cases} y = 2x + 3 \\ 3x - 4y = 8 \end{cases}$ we see that y is the subject of the first equation.

We substitute the expression for y on the RHS into the second equation.

Example 3   ◀) *Self Tutor*

Solve simultaneously by substitution: $\begin{cases} y = 2x + 3 \\ 3x - 4y = 8 \end{cases}$

$y = 2x + 3$ .... (1)
$3x - 4y = 8$ .... (2)

Substituting (1) into (2) gives $3x - 4(2x + 3) = 8$
$\therefore\ 3x - 8x - 12 = 8$
$\therefore\ -5x - 12 = 8$
$\therefore\ -5x = 20$
$\therefore\ x = -4$

Substituting $x = -4$ into (1) gives $y = 2(-4) + 3$
$\therefore\ y = -8 + 3$
$\therefore\ y = -5$

The solution is $x = -4$, $y = -5$.
Check: $3x - 4y = 3(-4) - 4(-5) = -12 + 20 = 8$ ✓

In equation (2), we replace y with $2x + 3$.

EXERCISE 17C

1 Use the method of substitution to solve:

a $\begin{cases} y = x + 2 \\ 3x + 2y = 19 \end{cases}$
  b $\begin{cases} y = 2x + 1 \\ 5x - 4y = 2 \end{cases}$
  c $\begin{cases} 4x + 3y = -14 \\ y = -3x - 3 \end{cases}$

d $\begin{cases} x = 3y + 2 \\ 2x - 5y = 1 \end{cases}$
  e $\begin{cases} 7x - 2y = -6 \\ x = y - 3 \end{cases}$
  f $\begin{cases} y = 3x + 2 \\ 4x + 2y = -1 \end{cases}$

2 Use the method of substitution to solve:

a $\begin{cases} 3x - 7y = 11 \\ x = 4y + 6 \end{cases}$
  b $\begin{cases} y = 8 - 4x \\ 12x - y = 12 \end{cases}$
  c $\begin{cases} 2x - 5y = 0 \\ y = 5 - 3x \end{cases}$

3 Find the point of intersection of the two lines:

    a $y = 3 + x$ and $5x - 2y = 0$ **b** $x + 3y = 6$ and $y = x - 2$

    c $x = 5 - y$ and $4x + y = 5$ **d** $2x + 3y = 12$ and $x = \frac{1}{3}(y - 4)$

4 Try to solve using substitution:
Comment on your results.
  a $\begin{cases} y = 3x - 5 \\ 12x - 4y = 7 \end{cases}$ **b** $\begin{cases} 6x + 3y = 15 \\ y = 5 - 2x \end{cases}$

D   SOLUTION BY ELIMINATION   [E2.6]

Solution by **elimination** is used to solve simultaneous equations such as $\begin{cases} 3x + 4y = 10 \\ 5x - 4y = 6 \end{cases}$
where neither variable is given as the subject of an equation.

In this method, we make the coefficients of x (or y) the **same size** but **opposite in sign**.

We then **add** the equations, which has the effect of **eliminating** one of the variables.

> We can add equations together without changing their solutions.

The method of elimination uses the fact that:

$$\text{If } a = b \text{ and } c = d \text{ then } a + c = b + d.$$

This allows us to add the equations together without changing their solutions.

Example 4   ◀)) Self Tutor

What equation results when $3x - y = 1$ and $-3x + 4y = 4$ are added vertically?

> Add the LHSs together and the RHSs together.

$$3x - y = 1$$
$$\underline{-3x + 4y = 4}$$
Adding, $\qquad\quad 3y = 5$

Example 5   ◀)) Self Tutor

Solve simultaneously, by elimination: $\begin{cases} 3x + 2y = 5 \\ x - 2y = 3 \end{cases}$

The coefficients of y are the same size but opposite in sign.

We **add** the LHSs and the RHSs to get an equation which contains x only.

$$3x + 2y = 5 \quad .... (1)$$
$$\underline{x - 2y = 3} \quad .... (2)$$
Adding, $\ 4x \quad\ \ = 8$
$$\therefore\ x = 2$$

Substituting $x = 2$ into (1) gives $\ 3(2) + 2y = 5$
$$\therefore\ 6 + 2y = 5$$
$$\therefore\ 2y = -1$$
$$\therefore\ y = -\tfrac{1}{2}$$

The solution is $x = 2$, $y = -\frac{1}{2}$.

Check: In (2), $(2) - 2\left(-\frac{1}{2}\right) = 2 + 1 = 3$ ✓

EXERCISE 17D.1

1 What equation results when the following are added vertically?

a $\begin{cases} 5x + 3y = 12 \\ x - 3y = -6 \end{cases}$ **b** $\begin{cases} 2x + 5y = -4 \\ -2x - 6y = 12 \end{cases}$ **c** $\begin{cases} 4x - 6y = 9 \\ x + 6y = -2 \end{cases}$

d $\begin{cases} 12x + 15y = 33 \\ -18x - 15y = -63 \end{cases}$ **e** $\begin{cases} 5x + 6y = 12 \\ -5x + 2y = -8 \end{cases}$ **f** $\begin{cases} -7x + y = -5 \\ 7x - 3y = -11 \end{cases}$

2 Solve using the method of elimination:

a $\begin{cases} 2x + y = 3 \\ 3x - y = 7 \end{cases}$ **b** $\begin{cases} 4x + 3y = 7 \\ 6x - 3y = -27 \end{cases}$

c $\begin{cases} 2x + 5y = 16 \\ -2x - 7y = -20 \end{cases}$ **d** $\begin{cases} 3x + 5y = -11 \\ -3x - 2y = 8 \end{cases}$

e $\begin{cases} 4x - 7y = 41 \\ 3x + 7y = -6 \end{cases}$ **f** $\begin{cases} -4x + 3y = -25 \\ 4x - 5y = 31 \end{cases}$

You can choose to eliminate either x or y, depending on which is easier.

MULTIPLYING EQUATIONS BY A CONSTANT

In problems where the coefficients of x (or y) are *not* the same size and opposite in sign, we first need to **multiply** an equation by a constant. This will not change the solutions to the equations.

Example 6   ◀) Self Tutor

Solve $\begin{cases} 3x + 2y = -2 \\ 5x - y = 27 \end{cases}$ using the method of elimination.

$3x + 2y = -2$ .... (1)
$5x - y = 27$ .... (2)

We have $+2y$ in (1), so we obtain $-2y$ from (2) by multiplying both sides of (2) by 2.

$$
\begin{aligned}
3x + 2y &= -2 \qquad \{(1)\} \\
10x - 2y &= 54 \qquad \{(2) \times 2\}
\end{aligned}
$$

Adding, $\overline{\quad 13x \qquad = 52}$

$\therefore \; x = 4$

It is easier to eliminate y in this case.

Substituting $x = 4$ into (1), $3(4) + 2y = -2$

$\therefore \; 12 + 2y = -2$

$\therefore \; 2y = -14$

$\therefore \; y = -7$

The solution is $x = 4$, $y = -7$.

Check: In (2), $5(4) - (-7) = 20 + 7 = 27$ ✓

Example 7

◀)) *Self Tutor*

Solve simultaneously, by elimination: $\begin{cases} 5x + 3y = 12 \\ 7x + 2y = 19 \end{cases}$

$5x + 3y = 12$ .... (1)
$7x + 2y = 19$ .... (2)

We can multiply (1) by 2 and (2) by -3:

$$10x + 6y = 24 \qquad \{(1) \times 2\}$$
$$\underline{-21x - 6y = -57} \qquad \{(2) \times -3\}$$
Adding, $\quad -11x \qquad = -33$
$$\therefore \ x = 3$$

Substituting $x = 3$ into (1), $5(3) + 3y = 12$
$$\therefore \ 15 + 3y = 12$$
$$\therefore \ 3y = -3$$
$$\therefore \ y = -1$$

Sometimes it helps to multiply *both* equations by constants.

The solution is $x = 3$, $y = -1$.
Check: In (2), $7(3) + 2(-1) = 21 - 2 = 19$ ✓

EXERCISE 17D.2

1 Give the equation that results when both sides of the equation:

  a $3x + 4y = 2$ are multiplied by 3
  b $x - 4y = 7$ are multiplied by -2
  c $5x - y = -3$ are multiplied by 5
  d $7x + 3y = -4$ are multiplied by -3
  e $-2x - 5y = 1$ are multiplied by -4
  f $3x - y = -1$ are multiplied by -1.

2 Solve using the method of elimination:

  a $\begin{cases} 4x - 3y = 6 \\ -2x + 5y = 4 \end{cases}$
  b $\begin{cases} 2x - y = 9 \\ x + 4y = 36 \end{cases}$
  c $\begin{cases} 3x + 4y = 6 \\ x - 3y = -11 \end{cases}$

  d $\begin{cases} 4x + 3y = 17 \\ 5x - 9y = 34 \end{cases}$
  e $\begin{cases} 2x - 7y = -5 \\ 6x + 5y = -15 \end{cases}$
  f $\begin{cases} 5x + 8y = 8 \\ 9x + 2y = 33 \end{cases}$

3 Solve using the method of elimination:

  a $\begin{cases} x - 2y = -5 \\ 2x + y = -5 \end{cases}$
  b $\begin{cases} 2x + 3y = 7 \\ 3x - 2y = 4 \end{cases}$
  c $\begin{cases} 3x + 2y = 11 \\ 9x - 5y = 22 \end{cases}$

  d $\begin{cases} 4x - 3y = 6 \\ 6x + 7y = 32 \end{cases}$
  e $\begin{cases} 2x + 5y = 20 \\ 3x + 2y = 19 \end{cases}$
  f $\begin{cases} 3x - 2y = 10 \\ 4x + 3y = 19 \end{cases}$

  g $\begin{cases} -4x + 3y = -5 \\ 3x + 2y = -9 \end{cases}$
  h $\begin{cases} 7x - 3y = 29 \\ 3x + 4y = -14 \end{cases}$
  i $\begin{cases} 3x + 4y + 11 = 0 \\ 5x + 6y + 7 = 0 \end{cases}$

4 Consider the simultaneous equations $\begin{cases} 2x + 2y = 12 \\ 5x - 10y = 15 \end{cases}$.

  a Can you *divide* an equation by a non-zero constant without changing its solution? Explain your answer.

  b Divide *one* equation by a non-zero constant so you will be able to eliminate y.

  c Hence solve the simultaneous equations.

5 Use the method of elimination to attempt to solve: **a** $\begin{cases} 3x + y = 8 \\ 6x + 2y = 16 \end{cases}$ **b** $\begin{cases} 2x + 5y = 8 \\ 4x + 10y = -1 \end{cases}$
    Comment on your results.

E | PROBLEM SOLVING WITH SIMULTANEOUS EQUATIONS   [E2.6]

In this Section we deal with problems given in sentences. We need to interpret the information and use it to write two equations in two unknowns. We use the techniques we have learnt during the Chapter to solve the equations simultaneously, and hence answer the original problem.

Example 8   ◄) Self Tutor

Two numbers have a difference of 7 and an average of 4. Find the numbers.

Let x be the larger number and y be the smaller number.

The difference between x and y is $x - y = 7$ .... (1)

    The average of x and y is $\dfrac{x + y}{2} = 4$ .... (2)

$$x - y = 7 \qquad \{(1)\}$$
$$x + y = 8 \qquad \{(2) \times 2\}$$

Adding, $2x \quad = 15$

    $\therefore \ x = \frac{15}{2}$

Substituting $x = \frac{15}{2}$ into (1) gives $\frac{15}{2} - y = 7$

    $\therefore \ y = \frac{15}{2} - 7$

    $\therefore \ y = \frac{1}{2}$

The numbers are $\frac{1}{2}$ and $\frac{15}{2}$.

Check: (1) $\frac{15}{2} - \frac{1}{2} = 7$ ✓   (2) $\dfrac{\frac{15}{2} + \frac{1}{2}}{2} = 4$ ✓

When solving problems with simultaneous equations we must find two equations containing two unknowns.

Example 9   ◄) Self Tutor

At a clearance sale, all CDs are sold for one price and all DVDs are sold for another price. Marisa bought 3 CDs and 2 DVDs for a total of $34.50. Nico bought 2 CDs and 5 DVDs for a total of $56. Find the cost of each item.

Let x cents be the cost of one CD, and y cents be the cost of one DVD.

3 CDs and 2 DVDs cost $34.50,   so $3x + 2y = 3450$ .... (1)

2 CDs and 5 DVDs cost $56,   so $2x + 5y = 5600$ .... (2)

We will eliminate x by multiplying equation (1) by 2 and equation (2) by -3.

$$\therefore \ 6x + 4y = 6900 \qquad \{(1) \times 2\}$$
$$-6x - 15y = -16\,800 \qquad \{(2) \times -3\}$$

Adding, $-11y = -9900$

    $\therefore \ y = 900$

Substituting $y = 900$ into (1) gives $3x + 2(900) = 3450$

$\therefore \ 3x + 1800 = 3450$

$\therefore \ \ 3x = 1650$

$\therefore \ \ x = 550$

The cost of one CD is \$5.50, and the cost of one DVD is \$9.

EXERCISE 17E

1 The difference between two numbers is 84, and their sum is 278. What are the numbers?

2 Two numbers have a sum of 200 and a difference of 37. Find the numbers.

3 Find two numbers whose difference is 8 and whose average is 13.

4 Two hammers and a screwdriver cost a total of \$34. A hammer and 3 screwdrivers cost a total of \$32. Find the price of each type of tool.

5 Four adults and three children go to a theatre for \$148. Two adults and five children are charged \$116 for the same performance. Find the price of an adult's ticket and a child's ticket.

6 Four nectarines and three peaches cost \$2.90. Three nectarines and a peach cost \$1.90. Find the cost of each fruit.

7 A purse contains \$3.75 in 5 cent and 20 cent coins. There are 33 coins altogether. How many of each type of coin are in the purse?

8 A yard contains rabbits and pheasants only. There are 35 heads and 98 feet in the yard. How many rabbits and pheasants does the yard contain?

9 Milk is sold in one litre and two litre cartons. A shop owner orders 120 litres of milk, and receives 97 cartons. How many of each type did she receive?

10 The figure alongside is a rectangle.

    a Find x and y.

    b Hence, find the area of the rectangle.

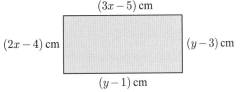

11 KLM is an equilateral triangle.

    a Find x and y.

    b Hence, find the perimeter of the triangle.

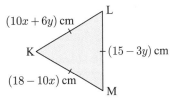

12 On the Celsius temperature scale, ice melts at $0°C$ and water boils at $100°C$.

On the Fahrenheit temperature scale, ice melts at $32°F$ and water boils at $212°F$.

There is a linear relationship between temperatures in Celsius (C) and Fahrenheit (F). It has the form $C = aF + b$ where a and b are constants.

    a Find the values of a and b as fractions in simplest form.

    b Convert $77°F$ to degrees Celsius.

Review set 17A

1 Solve graphically: $\begin{cases} y = 2x - 1 \\ y = x - 2 \end{cases}$

2 Solve by substitution: $\begin{cases} y = 11 - 3x \\ 4x + 3y = -7 \end{cases}$

3 Solve by equating values of y: **a** $\begin{cases} y = 2x + 3 \\ y = x - 2 \end{cases}$ **b** $\begin{cases} y = -5x + 1 \\ y = -5x - 1 \end{cases}$

4 Solve simultaneously: **a** $\begin{cases} 3x - 2y = 16 \\ y = 2x - 10 \end{cases}$ **b** $\begin{cases} 3x - 5y = 11 \\ 4x + 3y = 5 \end{cases}$

5 Two pencils and a ruler cost 98 cents in total. One pencil and two rulers cost $1.24 in total. Find the cost of each item.

6 **a** Rearrange $4x + y = 29$ to make y the subject of the formula.

b Hence, use the method of substitution to solve simultaneously: $\begin{cases} 4x + y = 29 \\ 2x - 3y = 25 \end{cases}$

7 Solve by elimination: $\begin{cases} 2x - 3y = 18 \\ 4x + 5y = -8 \end{cases}$

8 The figure alongside is a rectangle.

a Find x and y.

b Hence, find the area of the rectangle.

$(x + 2y)$ cm

$(3y - 11)$ cm $(x - y)$ cm

$(2x + 3)$ cm

Review set 17B

1 **a** By drawing their graphs on the same set of axes, find the point of intersection of $y = 3x - 2$ and $y = 2x + 1$.

b Hence, solve the simultaneous equations: $\begin{cases} y = 3x - 2 \\ y = 2x + 1 \end{cases}$

2 Solve by equating values of y:

$\begin{cases} y = 16 - 3x \\ y = 2x - 4 \end{cases}$

3 Solve by substitution:

$\begin{cases} y = 2x - 3 \\ 3x - 2y = 4 \end{cases}$

4 Solve simultaneously: **a** $\begin{cases} y = 2x - 5 \\ 3x - 2y = 11 \end{cases}$ **b** $\begin{cases} 3x + 5y = 1 \\ 4x - 3y = 11 \end{cases}$

5 The difference between two numbers is 11, and their sum is 85. Find the numbers.

6 Sally has only 10 cent and 50 cent coins in her purse. She has 21 coins altogether with a total value of $5.30. How many of each coin type does she have?

7 Solve simultaneously: **a** $\begin{cases} 3x + y = -4 \\ y = -2x + 5 \end{cases}$ **b** $\begin{cases} y = 3x + 2 \\ y = 3x - 5 \end{cases}$

8

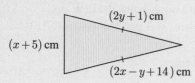

$(2y + 1)$ cm

$(x + 5)$ cm

$(2x - y + 14)$ cm

The perimeter of this triangle is 29 cm.

a Find x and y.

b Hence, find the length of the equal sides of the triangle.

One-variable statistics

18

Contents:

A	Variables used in statistics	[E11.2]
B	Organising data	[E11.2, E11.3]
C	Measuring the centre of discrete data	[E11.4, E11.7]
D	Measuring the spread of discrete data	[E11.4, E11.7]
E	Estimating the centre of data in class intervals	[E11.4, E11.5]
F	Cumulative frequency	[E11.6]

Opening problem

Roland owns two hotels, one in Leeds and one in Manchester. He wants to find out whether there is a difference in the number of nights guests stay at the hotels.

He therefore inspects the last 40 reservations placed for each hotel, and records the number of nights the guests stayed.

Leeds

```
2  3  1  2  4  2  6  3  4  5
8  3  1  3  4  2  1  2  4  5
3  6  2  3  2  1  3  6  2  4
8  1  5  7  2  1  8  5  3  2
```

Manchester

```
2  4  4  5  3  6  2  3  1  7
2  3  4  3  5  6  5  2  4  7
3  2  8  1  7  3  1  2  5  6
4  5  6  4  5  4  8  1  3  7
```

Things to think about:

a What is the best way to organise this data?

b How can the data be displayed?

c What is the *most common* length of stay at each hotel?

d How can Roland best measure:
  i the *average* length of stay for each hotel
  ii the *spread* of each data set?

e Can a reliable conclusion be drawn from the data? What factors could affect the reliability of the conclusion?

f How could Roland improve the accuracy of his investigation?

STATISTICS

Statistics is the study of data collection and analysis.

In a **statistical investigation** we collect information about a group of individuals, then analyse this information to draw conclusions about those individuals.

The facts or pieces of information we collect are called **data**. Data is the plural of the word *datum*, which means a single piece of information.

A list of information is called a **data set** and because it is not in an organised form it is called **raw data**.

A statistical investigation involves the following steps:

Step 1: **Stating the problem**

Step 2: **Collecting data**

Data for a statistical investigation can be collected from records, from surveys (face-to-face, online, telephone, or postal), by direct observation, or by measuring or counting.

Step 3: **Organising and displaying data**

Data can be organised into tables and displayed on graphs. This allows us to identify features of the data more easily.

Step 4: **Calculating descriptive statistics**

Descriptive statistics allow us to measure the **centre** and the **spread** of the data.

Step 5: **Interpreting statistics**

This process involves explaining the meaning of the table, graph, or descriptive statistics in terms of the problem being investigated.

POPULATIONS AND SAMPLES

A **population** is a collection of individuals or objects about which we want to draw conclusions.

The population might be the people living in a certain suburb, the trees in a forest, or the bottles from a production line.

A **census** is the process of collecting data from the whole population.

A census is the most accurate way to investigate a population of interest. It involves collecting data from *every* member of the population. However, in most situations, it is impractical or impossible to to this. Instead, we can collect data from *some* members of the population.

A **sample** is a group of individuals from the population.

A **survey** is the process of collecting data from a sample.

Conclusions based on a sample will never be as accurate as conclusions based on the entire population. However, if the sample is chosen carefully, we can use it to draw reliable conclusions about the whole population.

For a sample to truly reflect the characteristics of the whole population, it must be **unbiased** and **sufficiently large**.

A **biased sample** is one in which the data has been unfairly influenced by the collection process, and is therefore not truly representative of the whole population.

Historical note

Florence Nightingale (1820 - 1910) was a British nurse in Turkey during the Crimean War. She worked in very difficult conditions, with overcrowding, poor sanitation, little food, and few basic supplies. Nightingale provided a statistical argument for the British government to provide improved facilities. By the time the war ended in 1856, the hospitals were well-run and efficient, with mortality rates no greater than civilian hospitals in England. Nightingale had earned an extraordinary reputation, along with the label "the lady with the lamp".

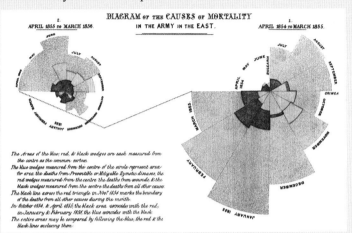

Florence Nightingale

Nightingale's best-known chart was a variation of a pie graph called the **polar area diagram**. It showed the number of deaths each month and their causes. Each month is represented as a twelfth of a circle. Months with more deaths were shown with longer wedges, and the area of each wedge represented the number of deaths in that month from wounds, disease, or other causes. Nightingale used blue wedges to represent disease, red wedges for wounds, and black wedges for other causes. Using this diagram, Nightingale illustrated the dramatic effect of the Sanitary Commission's work in 1855, as the wedges were far smaller in the following months.

A | VARIABLES USED IN STATISTICS   [E11.2]

When we collect data, we measure or observe a particular feature or **variable** associated with the population. The variables we observe are described as either **categorical** or **quantitative**.

CATEGORICAL VARIABLES

A **categorical variable** describes a particular quality or characteristic.

The data is divided into **categories**, and the information collected is called **categorical data**.

Some examples of categorical variables are:

- *continent of birth*:   the variable could take the values Europe, Asia, Africa, and so on.

- *occupation of worker at a hospital*:   the variable could take the values doctor, nurse, secretary, cleaner, and so on.

We studied graphs and charts involving categorical variables in **Chapter 4**.

QUANTITATIVE VARIABLES

> A **quantitative variable** is one where data is given in number form. It is often called a **numerical variable**. The information collected is called **numerical data**.

Quantitative variables can either be **discrete** or **continuous**.

> A **discrete quantitative variable** takes exact number values. It is usually a result of **counting**.

Some examples of discrete quantitative variables are:
- *the number of goals scored*:   the variable could take the values 0, 1, 2, 3, ...
- *the number rolled on a die*:   the variable could take the values 1, 2, 3, 4, 5, or 6.

> A **continuous quantitative variable** can take any numerical value within a certain range. It is usually a result of **measuring**.

Some examples of continuous quantitative variables are:
- *the weight of pumpkins*:   the variable would likely be between 1 kg and 15 kg.
- *the width of a child's hand*:   the variable could take values from 2 cm to 10 cm.

EXERCISE 18A

1 Classify each variable as either categorical or quantitative:
- **a** the brand of shoes a person wears
- **b** the number of cousins a person has
- **c** voting intention at the next election
- **d** the number of cars in a household
- **e** the temperature of coffee in a mug
- **f** favourite type of apple
- **g** the town or city where a person was born
- **h** the cost of houses on a street

2 Write down the possible categories for the following categorical variables:
- **a** gender
- **b** hair colour
- **c** favourite section of the orchestra

3 State whether a census or a sample would be used for these investigations, giving a brief reason for each answer:
- **a** the reasons for people using taxis
- **b** the heights of the basketballers at a particular school
- **c** the percentage of people in a city who suffer from asthma
- **d** the resting pulse rates of members of your favourite sporting team
- **e** the number of pets in Canadian households
- **f** the amount of daylight each month where you live

4 Classify these variables as quantitative discrete or quantitative continuous:
- **a** the number of clocks in each house
- **b** the weights of the members of a basketball team
- **c** the number of kittens in each litter
- **d** the number of bread rolls baked each week in a bakery
- **e** the number of leaves on a rose plant stem
- **f** the amount of soup in each can
- **g** the number of people who die from heart attacks each year
- **h** the amount of rainfall in each month of the year
- **i** the stopping distances of cars from 80 km/h
- **j** the number of cars passing through an intersection each hour

5 Discuss any possible bias in the following situations:

   a Only Year 12 students are interviewed about changes to the school uniform.

   b Motorists stopped in peak hour are interviewed about traffic problems.

   c A phone poll is conducted in which participants must vote by text message.

   d A "who will you vote for" survey is conducted at an expensive city restaurant.

B   ORGANISING DATA   [E11.2, E11.3]

DISCRETE DATA

Discrete quantitative data with not many different data values can be arranged in a **tally-frequency table**, and displayed in a **vertical bar chart**.

In the tally-frequency table we count the data systematically using | to indicate each data value, or ||||| to represent five.

For example, consider the data set:

         5 4 5 7 4 5 3 6 5 4
         4 5 6 4 6 5 5 6 4 5
         5 4 5 5 3 4 6 5 5 4

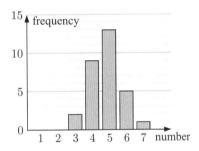

Number	Tally	Frequency
3	||	2
4	|||| ||||	9
5	|||| |||| |||	13
6	||||	5
7	|	1

Tally-frequency table   **Vertical bar chart**

If the data has many different data values, we can sort the data using a **stem-and-leaf diagram** or **stem plot**. Data values with the same first digit are placed on the same stem, but the actual data values are retained using the leaves.

     28 47 39 23 17 33
     35 26 49 35 9 36
     43 44 38 27 32 51
     31 11 26 42 24 30

For the data shown, we can construct an unordered or an ordered stem plot.

Unordered stem plot

Stem	Leaf
0	9
1	7 1
2	8 3 6 7 6 4
3	9 3 5 5 6 8 2 1 0
4	7 9 3 4 2
5	1

Key: 5 | 1 = 51

Ordered stem plot

Stem	Leaf
0	9
1	1 7
2	3 4 6 6 7 8
3	0 1 2 3 5 5 6 8 9
4	2 3 4 7 9
5	1

Key: 5 | 1 = 51

In the ordered stem plot, the data are given in ascending order.

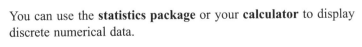

You can use the **statistics package** or your **calculator** to display discrete numerical data.

STATISTICS
PACKAGE

GRAPHICS
CALCULATOR
INSTRUCTIONS

Example 1
◀) *Self Tutor*

The scores for a test out of 50 were recorded for 36 students.

25, 36, 38, 49, 23, 46, 47, 15, 28, 38, 34, 9, 30, 24, 27, 27, 42, 16, 28, 31, 24, 46, 25, 31, 37, 35, 32, 39, 43, 40, 50, 47, 29, 36, 35, 33

a Display the data using a stem plot.

b What percentage of students scored 40 or more marks?

a The stems will be 0, 1, 2, 3, 4, 5 to account for scores from 9 to 50.

Unordered stem plot

Stem	Leaf
0	9
1	5 6
2	5 3 8 4 7 7 8 4 5 9
3	6 8 8 4 0 1 1 7 5 2 9 6 5 3
4	9 6 7 2 6 3 0 7
5	0

Key: 2 | 4 = 24 marks

Ordered stem plot

Stem	Leaf
0	9
1	5 6
2	3 4 4 5 5 7 7 8 8 9
3	0 1 1 2 3 4 5 5 6 6 7 8 8 9
4	0 2 3 6 6 7 7 9
5	0

b 9 students scored 40 or more marks.

∴ the percentage of students scoring 40 or more marks = $\frac{9}{36} \times 100\% = 25\%$.

DESCRIBING THE DISTRIBUTION OF THE DATA SET

The most commonly occuring value in a data set is called the **mode**.

Many data sets show **symmetry** or **partial symmetry** about the centre of the distribution. We can see this by drawing a curve over the graph of the data. For example, if we place a curve over the column graph opposite, we see that the curve is symmetric. We say we have a **symmetrical distribution** of data.

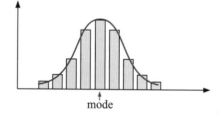

The distribution alongside is said to be **positively skewed** since it is "stretched" on the right or positive side of the centre.

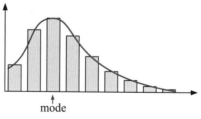

So we have:

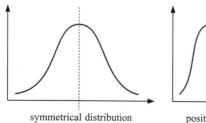

symmetrical distribution

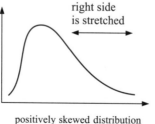

positively skewed distribution

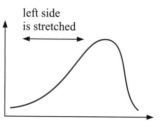

negatively skewed distribution

Example 2

◆⑨ Self Tutor

45 people were asked how many times they had visited the doctor this year. The results are given in the frequency table alongside.

a Display this information on a vertical bar chart.

b Identify the mode of the data.

c Describe the distribution of the data.

d What percentage of people had visited the doctor more than 4 times?

Number of visits	Frequency
0	6
1	8
2	9
3	7
4	6
5	4
6	2
7	2
8	1

a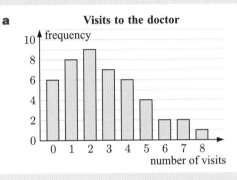

b The mode is 2 visits.

c The right side of the graph is stretched out, so the data is positively skewed.

d $4 + 2 + 2 + 1 = 9$ people had seen the doctor more than 4 times.

This is $\frac{9}{45} \times 100\% = 20\%$ of the people.

EXERCISE 18B.1

1 A random sample of shoppers was asked, "How many times did you shop at a supermarket in the past week?" A vertical bar chart was constructed to display the results.

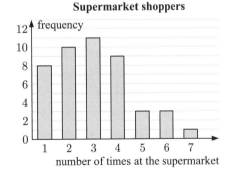

a How many shoppers gave data in the survey?

b How many of the shoppers shopped once or twice?

c What percentage of the shoppers shopped more than four times?

d What is the mode for this data? Explain what this number means.

e Describe the distribution of the data.

2 When 20 students were asked "How many pets do you have in your household?" the following data was collected: 2 1 0 3 1 2 1 3 4 0 0 2 2 0 1 1 0 1 0 1

a What is the variable in this investigation?   b Explain why the data is discrete.

c Construct a tally-frequency table to organise the data.

d Construct a vertical bar chart to display the data. Include a heading for the graph, and add an appropriate scale and label to each axis.

e State the mode of the data.   f Describe the distribution of the data.

g What percentage of the households had no pets?

h What percentage of the households had three or more pets?

3 The stem-and-leaf diagram alongside shows the ten pin bowling scores Ron has obtained this year.

Stem	Leaf
7	6 8
8	2 5 8
9	1 1 2 5 9
10	1 2 4
11	0
12	6
13	2 7

Key: $8 \mid 2 = 82$

  a How many games has Ron played?

  b Find Ron's: **i** lowest score   **ii** highest score.

  c Describe the distribution of the data.

  d How many times has Ron scored less than 100?

  e What percentage of Ron's scores have been 130 or higher?

4 An ice hockey player scored the following numbers of goals in his last 30 matches:

    1   1   3   2   0   0   4   2   2   4   3   1   0   1   0
    2   2   5   1   3   7   2   3   1   1   2   1   4   0   3

  a Organise the data in a tally-frequency table.

  b Construct a vertical bar chart to display the data.

  c Describe the distribution of the data.

  d What was the highest number of goals scored in any game?

  e In what fraction of games did the player score at least 3 goals?

5 The following marks were scored for a test out of 50 marks:

    47   32   32   29   36   39   40   46   43   39   44   18   38   45   35   46   7   44   27   48

  a Construct a stem-and-leaf diagram to display the data.

  b How many students scored 40 or more marks?

  c What percentage of the students scored less than 30 marks?

  d A score of 25 or more is required to pass the test. What percentage of the students passed?

  e Describe the distribution of the data.

6 The number of toothpicks in a box is stated as 50, but the actual number of toothpicks has been found to vary. To investigate this, the number of toothpicks in a box was counted for a sample of 60 boxes. The results were:

        50 52 51 50 50 51 52 49 50 48 51 50 47 50 52 48 50 49 51 50
        49 50 52 51 50 50 52 50 53 48 50 51 50 50 49 48 51 49 52 50
        49 49 50 52 50 51 49 52 52 50 49 50 49 51 50 50 51 50 53 48

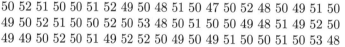

  a Use a tally-frequency table to organise this data.

  b Display the data using a vertical bar chart.

  c Describe the distribution of the data.

  d What percentage of the boxes contained exactly 50 toothpicks?

7 This *back-to-back* stem-and-leaf diagram shows the cricket scores for a batsman in the 2017 and 2018 seasons.

Season 2017	Stem	Season 2018
4 3 0	0	
8 8 6 1	1	4
9 6 5 5	2	0 6
9 7 6 2 0	3	1 3 3 6 9
7 4	4	2 2 4 5 8 9
7	5	2 3 6 7
2	6	1 1

Key: $2 \mid 0$ means 20 runs

  a Find the highest score for the batsman in 2017.

  b Find the lowest score for the batsman in 2018.

  c In which season was the batsman more consistent?

  d In which season did the batsman score more runs?

Example 3
◀)) *Self Tutor*

15 students were examined in Geography and Mathematics. The results were:

Geography	65	70	56	67	49	82	79	88	47	76	69	58	90	45	82
Mathematics	75	67	81	88	84	66	77	72	60	58	67	71	74	82	89

Use an ordered back-to-back stem-and-leaf diagram to compare the results.

Before ordering:

Geography		Mathematics
5 7 9	4	
8 6	5	8
9 7 5	6	7 6 0 7
6 9 0	7	5 7 2 1 4
2 8 2	8	1 8 4 2 9
0	9	**Key:** 8 | 2 means 82

After ordering:

Geography		Mathematics
9 7 5	4	
8 6	5	8
9 7 5	6	0 6 7 7
9 6 0	7	1 2 4 5 7
8 2 2	8	1 2 4 8 9
0	9	**Key:** 8 | 2 means 82

From the stem-and-leaf diagram, we observe that:
- the Geography marks are more spread than those for Mathematics
- the Mathematics marks are generally higher than those for Geography.

8 Two brothers living together travel by different means to university; Alex travels by train and Stan travels by bus. Over a three week period, their travel times in minutes were:

Alex	17	22	34	60	41	15	55	30	36	23	27	48	34	25	45
Stan	31	19	28	42	24	18	30	36	34	25	38	31	22	29	32

a Construct a back-to-back stem-and-leaf diagram of the data.

b Who had the fastest journey to university?

c Which mode of transport is more reliable? Explain your answer.

9 Consider the data in the **Opening Problem** on page **271**.

a Organise the data sets using tally-frequency tables.

b Draw a multiple bar chart to display each set of data.

c Describe the distribution of each data set.

d At which hotel do guests generally stay longer?

10 The sets of data below show the weights, in kilograms, of 32 adults before and after a lengthy diet and exercise program.

Before program									After program							
95	82	96	87	102	78	76	86		94	78	91	80	95	76	71	79
108	94	96	88	72	111	105	89		97	87	98	81	67	104	94	90
76	80	106	115	92	94	90	103		72	77	101	107	83	89	91	96
95	78	83	124	106	83	96	84		97	72	79	111	102	78	91	78

a Display the data using a back-to-back stem plot.

b What was the highest weight in the group before the program started?

c Do you think the diet and exercise program was effective in reducing the participants' weights? Explain your answer.

GROUPED DISCRETE DATA

In situations where there are lots of different numerical values recorded, it may not be practical to use an ordinary tally-frequency table, or to display the data using a vertical bar chart. Instead, we group the data into **class intervals**.

For example, a local hardware store is studying the number of people visiting the store at lunch time.   Over 30 consecutive weekdays they recorded the data:

37, 30, 17, 13, 46, 23, 40, 28, 38, 24, 23, 22, 18, 29, 16,
35, 24, 18, 24, 44, 32, 54, 31, 39, 32, 38, 41, 38, 24, 32.

In this case, we group the data into class intervals of length 10. The tally-frequency table is shown below.

We can also use this table to draw a vertical bar chart for the data. However, we must remember that the individual data values are no longer seen.

The most commonly occuring class interval is called the **modal class**.

Number of people	Tally	Frequency
10 to 19	||||	5
20 to 29	|||| ||||	9
30 to 39	|||| |||| |	11
40 to 49	||||	4
50 to 59	|	1
	Total	30

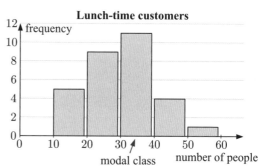

EXERCISE 18B.2

1 The data gives the number of chairs completed each day by a furniture production company over 26 days:

38 27 29 33 18 22 42 27 36 30 16 23 34
22 19 37 28 44 37 25 33 40 22 16 39 25

   a Construct a tally-frequency table for this data.

   b Draw a vertical bar chart to display the data.

   c On what percentage of days were less than 40 chairs made?

   d On how many days were at least 30 chairs made?

   e Find the modal class for the data.

2 Over a 6 week period, a museum keeps a record of the number of visitors it receives each day. The results are:

515 432 674 237 445 510 585 411 605 332 196
432 537 421 318 570 640 298 554 611 458 322
584 232 674 519 174 377 543 630 490 501
139 549 322 612 222 625 582 381 459 609

   a Construct a tally-frequency table for this data using class intervals 0 - 99, 100 - 199, 200 - 299, ..., 600 - 699.

   b Draw a vertical bar chart to display the data.

   c On how many days did the museum receive at least 500 visitors?

   d What is the modal class for the data?

   e Describe the distribution of the data.

3 The data below are the test scores (out of 100) for a Science test for 50 students.

92	29	78	67	68	58	80	89	92
69	66	56	88	81	70	73	63	55
67	64	62	74	56	75	90	56	47
59	64	89	39	51	87	89	76	59
72	80	95	68	80	64	53	43	61
71	38	44	88	62				

a Construct a tally-frequency table for this data using class intervals 20 - 29, 30 - 39, ..., 90 - 100.

b Display the data on a vertical bar chart.

c What percentage of the students scored 80 or more for the test?

d What percentage of students scored less than 50 for the test?

e Copy and complete the following:
More students had a test score in the interval ...... than in any other interval.

f Describe the distribution of the data.

4 A test score out of 60 marks is recorded for a group of 45 students:

34	37	44	51	53	39	33	58	40	42	43	43	47	37	35
41	43	48	50	55	44	44	52	54	59	39	31	29	44	57
45	34	29	27	18	49	41	42	37	42	43	43	45	34	51

a Organise the data in a tally-frequency table, using the test score ranges 15 - 19, 20 - 24, and so on.

b Draw a vertical bar chart to display the data.

c Describe the distribution of the data.

d An A is awarded to students who scored 50 or more in the test. What percentage of students scored an A?

CONTINUOUS DATA

When data is recorded for a continuous variable, there will be many different values. The data is therefore organised using class intervals.

We commonly use a **frequency histogram** to display continuous data. A frequency histogram is similar to a vertical bar chart, but because the data is continuous, the bars are joined together.

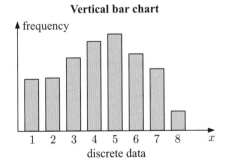
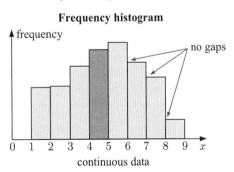

The *sides* of the bars are labelled on the horizontal axis to show the end points of each class interval. For example, in the frequency histogram above, the red shaded bar corresponds to data values in the class interval $4 \leqslant x < 5$.

The **modal class** is the class of values that appears most often. On a frequency histogram, the modal class has the highest bar.

In this course you are not required to draw histograms, but you should know how to interpret them.

Example 4

◀⦿ *Self Tutor*

The weights of parcels (w kg), sent on a given day from a post office are shown in the frequency histogram alongside.

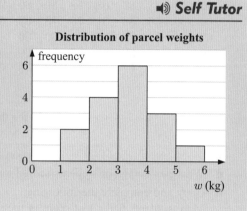

Distribution of parcel weights

a Describe the distribution of the data.

b State the modal class.

c How many parcels were sent in total on this particular day?

d Over the next month, 564 parcels are sent from the post office. Estimate the number which weigh more than 4 kg.

---

a The distribution is approximately symmetrical.

b The modal class is $3 \leqslant w < 4$ kg.

c $2 + 4 + 6 + 3 + 1 = 16$ parcels were sent in total.

d Of the 16 parcels sent on the one day, $\frac{4}{16} = \frac{1}{4}$ of them weighed more than 4 kg.

∴ for the next month we expect $\frac{1}{4} \times 564 = 141$ parcels to weigh more than 4 kg.

EXERCISE 18B.3

1

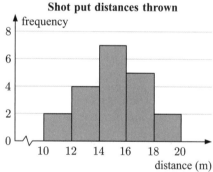

Shot put distances thrown

During a training session, Daniel performed 20 throws of the shot put. The results are shown in the frequency histogram alongside.

a Describe the distribution of the data.

b State the modal class.

c Calculate the percentage of times Daniel threw the shot put further than 16 m.

2 A frequency histogram of the weights w of players in a volleyball squad is given alongside.

a Explain why *weight* is a continuous variable.

b Describe the distribution of the data.

c State and interpret the modal class.

d How many players are in this squad?

e Calculate the proportion of players who weighed more than 95 kg.

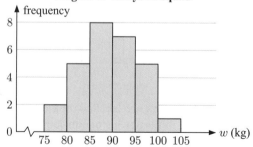

Weights of volleyball squad

3 A botanist took a random sample of seedlings from a nursery, and measured their height h in millimetres. He drew the frequency histogram alongside to display his results.

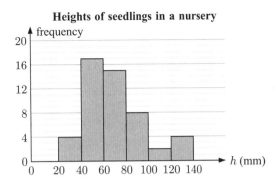

Heights of seedlings in a nursery

  a Describe the distribution of the data.

  b **i** Write down the class intervals the botanist used to organise the data.

  ii Hence copy and complete the table.

  c Use your table to answer the following:

  i How many of the seedlings are at least 100 mm tall?

  ii What percentage of the seedlings are between 60 and 80 mm tall?

Height (h mm)	Frequency
$20 \leqslant h < 40$	

  d There are 857 seedlings in the nursery. Estimate the number of seedlings which measure:

  i less than 100 mm   **ii** between 40 and 100 mm.

4 Lewis is a physical education teacher. He recorded the times each of his students took to sprint 100 m. He drew two histograms to display his results, one for each gender.

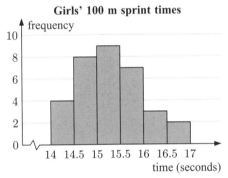

Girls' 100 m sprint times

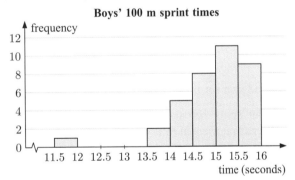

Boys' 100 m sprint times

  a For each data set:

  i describe its distribution   **ii** state the modal class.

  b Which gender had more students with times in the interval $15 \leqslant t < 16$ seconds?

  c Which gender generally had faster times for the 100 m sprint?

  d Which of Lewis' data sets contains an outlier? Explain your answer.

C MEASURING THE CENTRE OF DISCRETE DATA   *[E11.4, E11.7]*

We can get a better understanding of a data set if we can locate the **middle** or **centre** of the data, and also get an indication of its **spread** or dispersion. Knowing one of these without the other is often of little use.

There are *three statistics* that are used to measure the **centre** of a data set. These are the **mode**, the **mean**, and the **median**.

THE MODE

For discrete quantitative data, the **mode** is the most frequently occurring value in the data set.

For grouped data and for continuous quantitative data, we talk about a **modal class**, which is the class or group that occurs most frequently.

If a data set has two values which occur most frequently, we say it is **bimodal**.

If a data set has three or more values which occur most frequently, we do not use the mode as a measure of centre.

THE MEAN

The **mean** of a data set is the statistical name for the arithmetic average.

If the data values are $x_1, x_2, x_3, ..., x_n$, then

$$\text{mean } \overline{x} = \frac{\textbf{sum of all data values}}{\textbf{the number of data values}}$$

$$= \frac{x_1 + x_2 + x_3 + ... + x_n}{n} \quad \text{or} \quad \frac{\sum x}{n}$$

$\overline{x}$ is read "x bar".

$\sum x$ is short for $\sum_{i=1}^{n} x_i$, and means the sum of the values $x_1 + x_2 + ... + x_n$.

THE MEDIAN

The **median** is the *middle value* of an ordered data set.

An ordered data set is obtained by listing the data from smallest to largest value.

The median splits the data in halves. Half of the data values are less than or equal to the median, and half are greater than or equal to it.

For example, if the median mark for a test is 68% then you know that half the class scored less than or equal to 68% and half scored greater than or equal to 68%.

For an **odd number** of data values, the median is one of the original data values.

For an **even number** of data values, the median is the average of the two middle values, and hence may not be in the original data set.

If there are n data values listed in order from smallest to largest, the median is the $\left(\dfrac{n+1}{2}\right)$th data value.

For example:

If $n = 13$, $\dfrac{n+1}{2} = 7$, so the median is the 7th ordered data value.

If $n = 14$, $\dfrac{n+1}{2} = 7.5$, so the median is the average of the 7th and 8th ordered data values.

DEMO

Example 5   ◀) *Self Tutor*

The number of peas in a randomly selected sample of pods were:

3   6   5   7   7   4   6   5   6   7   6   8   10   7   8

a For this data set, find:

    i the mean   **ii** the median   **iii** the mode.

b A 16th pod is randomly selected, and it is found to contain 9 peas. How does this affect:

    i the mean   **ii** the median?

---

a **i** mean $= \dfrac{3+6+5+....+10+7+8}{15}$ ◀—— sum of the data

                                 15 ◀———— 15 data values

                $= \frac{95}{15} \approx 6.33$ peas

  ii As $n = 15$, $\dfrac{n+1}{2} = 8$

     The ordered data set is: $\cancel{3}$ $\cancel{4}$ $\cancel{5}$ $\cancel{5}$ $\cancel{6}$ $\cancel{6}$ $\cancel{6}$ 6 $\cancel{7}$ $\cancel{7}$ $\cancel{7}$ $\cancel{7}$ $\cancel{8}$ $\cancel{8}$ $\cancel{10}$

                                           8th value

     $\therefore$ median $= 6$ peas

  iii 6 and 7 are the data values which occur the most often, so the data is bimodal with modes
     6 and 7.

b **i** We expect the mean to rise since the new data value is greater than the old mean.

     In fact, the new mean $= \dfrac{95+9}{16} = \dfrac{104}{16} = 6.5$ peas.

  ii Since $n = 16$, $\dfrac{n+1}{2} = 8.5$

     The new ordered data set is: $\cancel{3}$ $\cancel{4}$ $\cancel{5}$ $\cancel{5}$ $\cancel{6}$ $\cancel{6}$ $\cancel{6}$ 6 7 $\cancel{7}$ $\cancel{7}$ $\cancel{7}$ $\cancel{8}$ $\cancel{8}$ $\cancel{9}$ $\cancel{10}$

                                       two middle scores

     $\therefore$ the new median $= \dfrac{6+7}{2} = 6.5$ peas.

EXERCISE 18C

1 For each of the following data sets, find the:

    i mean   **ii** median   **iii** mode.

    Use technology to check your answers.

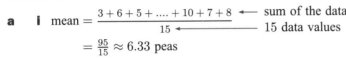

STATISTICS
PACKAGE

GRAPHICS
CALCULATOR
INSTRUCTIONS

  a 12, 17, 20, 24, 30, 30, 42

  b 8, 8, 8, 10, 11, 11, 12, 12, 16, 20, 20, 24

  c 7.9, 8.5, 9.1, 9.2, 9.9, 10.0, 11.1, 11.2, 11.2, 12.6, 12.9

  d 427, 423, 415, 405, 445, 433, 442, 415, 435, 448, 429,

     427, 403, 430, 446, 440, 425, 424, 419, 428, 441

2 Consider the following two data sets:

     Data set A: 5, 6, 6, 7, 7, 7, 8, 8, 9, 10, 12

     Data set B: 5, 6, 6, 7, 7, 7, 8, 8, 9, 10, 20

  a Find the mean for both *data set A* and *data set B*.

  b Find the median for both *data set A* and *data set B*.

  c Explain why the mean of *data set A* is less than the mean of *data set B*.

  d Explain why the median of *data set A* is the same as the median of *data set B*.

3 The selling price of ten houses in a particular suburb are:

$234 000, $240 000, $240 000, $255 000, $258 000,
$267 000, $291 000, $304 000, $365 000, $505 000

a Find the mean, median, and modal selling prices.

b Explain why the mode is an unsatisfactory measure of the middle in this case.

c A young couple wants to buy a house in this suburb. They want to determine the price of a typical house in the suburb based on this data set. Which measure of centre do you recommend that they use? Explain your answer.

4 The following raw data is the daily rainfall (to the nearest millimetre) of a city for the month of February 2014:

0, 4, 1, 0, 0, 0, 2, 9, 3, 0, 0, 0, 8, 27, 5, 0, 0, 0, 0, 8, 1, 3, 0, 0, 15, 1, 0, 0

a Find the mean, median, and mode for the data.

b **i** Identify any outliers in the data set.

   ii Should the outliers be removed before finding the measures of centre? Explain your answer.

5 A basketball team scored 38, 52, 43, 54, 41, and 36 points in their first six matches.

a Find the mean number of points scored for the first six matches.

b What score does the team need in their next match to maintain the same mean score?

c The team scores only 20 points in their seventh match. Find the mean number of points scored for the seven matches.

d The team scores 42 points in their eighth and final match.

   i Will their previous mean score increase or decrease? Explain your answer.

   ii Find the mean score for all eight matches.

Example 6   **Self Tutor**

Each student in a class of 20 is assigned a number between 1 and 10 to indicate his or her fitness. The results are: 7, 9, 8, 8, 10, 9, 8, 7, 8, 6, 9, 5, 6, 8, 9, 7, 7, 8, 10, 8

Organise the data into a frequency table, and hence calculate the:

a mean   **b** median   **c** mode.

a

Score	Tally	Number of students	Product
5	|	1	$1 \times 5 = 5$
6	||	2	$2 \times 6 = 12$
7	||||	4	$4 \times 7 = 28$
8	|||| ||	7	$7 \times 8 = 56$
9	||||	4	$4 \times 9 = 36$
10	||	2	$2 \times 10 = 20$
	Total	20	157

The mean score

$= \dfrac{\text{total of scores}}{\text{number of scores}}$

$= \dfrac{157}{20}$

$= 7.85$

b There are 20 scores, so the median is the average of the 10th and 11th ordered scores.

Score	Number of students	
5	1 ←	──── 1st student
6	2 ←	──── 2nd and 3rd student
7	4 ←	──── 4th, 5th, 6th, and 7th student
8	7 ←	──── 8th, 9th, **10th**, **11th**, 12th,
9	4	13th, 14th student
10	2	

GRAPHICS
CALCULATOR
INSTRUCTIONS

The 10th and 11th students both scored 8, so the median = 8.

c Looking down the *number of students* column, the highest frequency is 7. This corresponds to a score of 8, so the mode = 8.

STATISTICS
PACKAGE

---

6 3 coins were tossed simultaneously 40 times, and the number of heads for each toss was recorded.

Calculate the:

  a mode   **b** median

  c mean.

Number of heads	Frequency
0	6
1	16
2	14
3	4
Total	40

7 The bar chart alongside gives the value of donations for an overseas aid organisation, collected in a particular street.

  a Construct a frequency table from the bar chart.

  b Determine the total number of donations.

  c Find the:

   i mean   **ii** median   **iii** mode.

  d Which of the measures of centre can be found easily from the bar chart only?

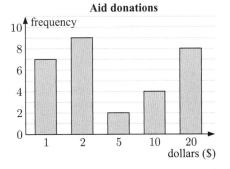

8 Hui breeds ducks. The number of ducklings surviving for each pair after one month is recorded in the table.

  a Calculate the:

   i mean   **ii** mode   **iii** median.

  b Is the data skewed?

  c How does the skewness of the data affect the measures of the centre of the distribution?

Number of survivors	Frequency
0	1
1	2
2	5
3	9
4	20
5	30
6	9
Total	76

9 Consider the **Opening Problem** on page **271**.

  a For each data set, find the:

   i mean   **ii** mode   **iii** median.

  b At which hotel do guests generally stay longer?

10 Chiara planted 19 seedlings, which she divided into groups A and B. Plants in group A were fertilised and plants in group B were not.

The heights of Chiara's plants in centimetres after one month were:

   Group A: 18.8, 21.2, 17.6, 22.8, 20.0, 15.7, 19.7, 24.1, 21.0, 18.2
   Group B: 11.8, 14.3, 17.6, 20.6, 15.4, 18.5, 27.9, 18.4, 16.2

  a Calculate the mean and median for each data set.

  b Do you think the fertiliser is effective? Explain your answer.

Example 7   ◀) Self Tutor

Linda has taken four Mathematics tests so far this year. Each test has been out of 20 marks, and her average mark has been 15.

What mark does Linda need in the 5th test to raise her average to 16?

Average mark $= \dfrac{\text{sum of marks}}{4} = 15$

$\therefore$ sum of marks $= 15 \times 4 = 60$

Let Linda's mark for the 5th test be x.

$\therefore$ we require $\dfrac{60 + x}{5} = 16$

$\therefore$ $60 + x = 80$

$\therefore$ $x = 20$

So, Linda needs a mark of 20 in the 5th test.

---

11 The mean of 12 scores is 8.8. Find the sum of the scores.

12 While on a camping holiday, Lachlan hiked an average of 12.4 km per day for 8 days. How far did Lachlan hike in total?

13 The mean monthly sales for a department store were $216 000. Calculate the total sales for the store for the year.

14 Find x given that 7, 15, 6, 10, 4, and x have a mean of 9.

15 Find a given that 10, a, 15, 20, a, a, 17, 7, and 15 have a mean of 12.

16 Over a semester, Jamie did 8 science tests. Each was marked out of 30, and Jamie averaged 25. However, when checking his files, he could only find 7 of the 8 tests. For these he scored 29, 26, 18, 20, 27, 24, and 29. How many marks did he score for the eighth test?

17 A sample of 12 measurements has a mean of 8.5, and a sample of 20 measurements has a mean of 7.5. Find the mean of all 32 measurements.

18 In the United Kingdom, the months of autumn are September, October, and November. If the mean temperature was $S°C$ for September, $O°C$ for October, and $N°C$ for November, find an expression for the mean temperature $A°C$ for the whole of autumn.

19 The mean, median, and mode of seven numbers are 8, 7, and 6 respectively. Two of the numbers are 8 and 10. If the smallest of the seven numbers is 4, find the largest of the seven numbers.

Activity　　　　　　　　　　　　　　　　　A mean game

Use the bridges to move from the Start circle to the Finish circle. The mean of the numbers you have landed on must never drop below 5 or rise above 10. You cannot land on the same island more than once.

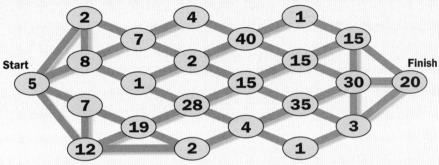

D

MEASURING THE SPREAD
OF DISCRETE DATA　　　　[E11.4, E11.7]

Knowing the middle of a data set can be quite useful, but for a more accurate picture of the data set we also need to know its spread.

For example, these two data sets both have mean 6.

>　　*Data set A*:　2, 3, 4, 5, 6, 7, 8, 9, 10
>　　*Data set B*:　4, 5, 5, 6, 6, 6, 7, 7, 8

However, the *data set A* is more widely spread than the *data set B*.

THE RANGE

> The **range** is the difference between the maximum (largest) and the minimum (smallest) data value.
>
> $$\textbf{range} = \textbf{maximum} - \textbf{minimum}$$

Example 8　　　　　　　　　　　　　　　◀) Self Tutor

The number of bedrooms in the houses on a street are listed below:

>　　2　3　1　3　2　2　4　3　2　2　5　1　2　1　3　1

Find the range of this data set.

The minimum value is 1, and the maximum value is 5.

∴　the range $= 5 - 1 = 4$.

The **range** is not considered to be a particularly reliable measure of spread because it uses only two data values. It may be influenced by data values which are extremely low or extremely high compared with the rest of the data.

THE QUARTILES AND THE INTERQUARTILE RANGE

The median divides the ordered data set into two halves, and these halves are divided in half again by the **quartiles**.

The middle value of the *lower* half is called the **lower quartile** or **25th percentile**. One quarter or 25% of the data have values less than or equal to the lower quartile. 75% of the data have values greater than or equal to the lower quartile.

The middle value of the *upper* half is called the **upper quartile** or **75th percentile**. One quarter or 25% of the data have values greater than or equal to the upper quartile. 75% of the data have values less than or equal to the upper quartile.

The data set is thus divided into quarters by the lower quartile (Q_1), the median (Q_2), and the upper quartile (Q_3).

The **interquartile range (IQR)** is the range of the middle half or 50% of the data.

$$\text{interquartile range} = \textbf{upper quartile} - \textbf{lower quartile}$$
$$= \mathbf{Q_3 - Q_1}$$

The interquartile range is not affected by extremely low or extremely high data values, as these lie outside the middle 50% of data values.

Example 9   ◀ᴼ) Self Tutor

For the data set   7, 3, 4, 2, 5, 6, 7, 5, 5, 9, 3, 8, 3, 5, 6,   find the:
  a median
               b lower and upper quartiles
               c interquartile range.

The ordered data set is: 2 3 3 3 4 5 5 5 5 6 6 7 7 8 9   (15 of them)

a Since $n = 15$, $\dfrac{n+1}{2} = 8$ $\therefore$ the median = 8th score = 5

b As the median is a data value, we now ignore it and split the remaining data into two:

$$\underbrace{2\ 3\ 3\ \underset{Q_1}{3}\ 4\ 5\ 5\ 5}_{\text{lower}}\ \underbrace{5\ 6\ 6\ \underset{Q_3}{7}\ 7\ 8\ 9}_{\text{upper}}$$

         Q_1 = median of lower half = 3
         Q_3 = median of upper half = 7

c IQR = $Q_3 - Q_1 = 7 - 3 = 4$

Example 10   ◀ᴼ) Self Tutor

For the data set   6, 10, 7, 8, 13, 7, 10, 8, 1, 7, 5, 4, 9, 4, 2, 5, 9, 6, 3, 2,   find the:
  a median
               b lower and upper quartiles
               c interquartile range.

The ordered data set is:

1 2 2 3 4 4 5 5 6 6 7 7 7 8 8 9 9 10 10 13   (20 of them)

a Since $n = 20$, $\dfrac{n+1}{2} = 10.5$

    $\therefore$ the median = $\dfrac{\text{10th value + 11th value}}{2} = \dfrac{6+7}{2} = 6.5$

b As the median is not a data value, we split the data into two halves:

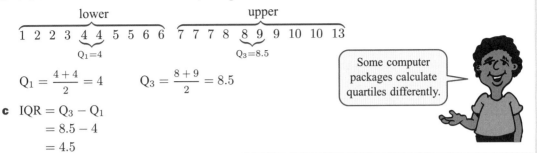

$$Q_1 = \frac{4+4}{2} = 4 \qquad Q_3 = \frac{8+9}{2} = 8.5$$

Some computer packages calculate quartiles differently.

c IQR = $Q_3 - Q_1$
$= 8.5 - 4$
$= 4.5$

EXERCISE 18D

1 For each of the following data sets, make sure the data is ordered and then find:

    i the median   **ii** the upper and lower quartiles

    iii the range   **iv** the interquartile range.

GRAPHICS CALCULATOR INSTRUCTIONS

  a 5, 6, 6, 6, 7, 7, 7, 8, 8, 8, 8, 9, 9, 9, 9, 9, 10, 10, 11, 11, 11, 12, 12

  b 11, 13, 16, 13, 25, 19, 20, 19, 19, 16, 17, 21, 22, 18, 19, 17, 23, 15

  c 23.8, 24.4, 25.5, 25.5, 26.6, 26.9, 27, 27.3, 28.1, 28.4, 31.5

2 The following amounts of money were withdrawn from an ATM on a particular day:

$100 $60 $120 $90 $130 $150 $200 $120 $180
$70 $140 $100 $50 $200 $120 $80 $100 $150

Find the:

  a median   **b** lower quartile   **c** upper quartile   **d** interquartile range of the data.

3 The times spent (in minutes) by 24 people in a queue at a supermarket were:

1.4 5.2 2.4 2.8 3.4 3.8 2.2 1.5
0.8 0.8 3.9 2.3 4.5 1.4 0.5 0.1
1.6 4.8 1.9 0.2 3.6 5.2 2.7 3.0

  a Find the:

      i median   **ii** lower quartile

      iii upper quartile of the data.

  b Find the range and interquartile range of the waiting time.

  c Copy and complete the following statements:

      i "50% of the waiting times were greater than ...... minutes."

      ii "75% of the waiting times were less than ...... minutes."

      iii "The minimum waiting time was ...... minutes and the maximum waiting time was ......
         minutes. The waiting times were spread over ...... minutes."

4 This stem plot shows the heights of bean seedlings two weeks after the seeds germinated. Find the:

  a minimum value   **b** maximum value

  c median   **d** lower quartile

  e upper quartile   **f** range

  g interquartile range.

Stem	Leaf
6	0 3 8
7	0 1 5 6 7
8	1 1 2 4 4 8 9 9
9	0 4 7 9
10	1

Key: $7 \mid 5 = 7.5$ cm

5 The intelligence quotient (IQ) of members of a book club are given below:

118 115 123 108 119 98 111 120 104 109 125 116 101 119 121

   a Find the range and interquartile range of the data.

   b A person with an IQ of 136 joins the club. Find the new range and interquartile range of the data.

   c A person with an IQ of 89 also joins the club. Find the new range and interquartile range of the data.

   d Which of the measures of spread is most affected by the introduction of outliers?

E ESTIMATING THE CENTRE OF DATA IN CLASS INTERVALS [E11.4, E11.5]

When data is presented in **class intervals**, either for grouped discrete data or for continuous data, the actual data values are not known. This makes it impossible to calculate the exact mean of the data set.

To *estimate* the mean of the data, we use the **midpoint** of an interval to represent all of the scores within the interval.

Example 11   ◀) Self Tutor

The table summarises the marks received by students for a Physics examination out of 50.

   a Estimate the mean mark.

   b What is the modal class?

   c Can the range of the data be found?

Class interval	Frequency
0 - 9	2
10 - 19	31
20 - 29	73
30 - 39	85
40 - 49	26

Class interval	Frequency	Interval midpoint	Product
0 - 9	2	4.5	9.0
10 - 19	31	14.5	449.5
20 - 29	73	24.5	1788.5
30 - 39	85	34.5	2932.5
40 - 49	26	44.5	1157.0
Total	217		6336.5

a Mean $= \dfrac{\text{sum of the data values}}{\text{number of data values}}$

$\phantom{\text{Mean }} = \dfrac{6336.5}{217} \approx 29.2$

b The modal class is 30 - 39 marks.

c No, as we do not know the smallest and largest score.

Example 12   ◀) Self Tutor

The speeds of 129 cars were measured at a particular point on a country road. They are shown in the table alongside.

Estimate the mean speed of the drivers.

Speed (v km/h)	Frequency
$40 \leqslant v < 50$	1
$50 \leqslant v < 60$	3
$60 \leqslant v < 70$	17
$70 \leqslant v < 80$	39
$80 \leqslant v < 90$	48
$90 \leqslant v < 100$	17
$100 \leqslant v < 110$	4

Speed (v km/h)	Frequency	Interval midpoint	Product
$40 \leqslant v < 50$	1	45	45
$50 \leqslant v < 60$	3	55	165
$60 \leqslant v < 70$	17	65	1105
$70 \leqslant v < 80$	39	75	2925
$80 \leqslant v < 90$	48	85	4080
$90 \leqslant v < 100$	17	95	1615
$100 \leqslant v < 110$	4	105	420
Total	129		10 355

We assume that each score in an interval takes the value of the interval midpoint.

$$\therefore \quad \text{mean} = \frac{\text{sum of the data values}}{\text{number of data values}}$$

$$\approx \frac{10\,355}{129} \approx 80.3 \text{ km/h}$$

EXERCISE 18E

1 Sixty people were asked: "How many times have you been to the cinema in the last twelve months?".   The results are given in the table.

Number of times	Frequency
0 - 4	19
5 - 9	24
10 - 14	10
15 - 19	5
20 - 24	2

   a Extend the table to include an *interval midpoint* and a *product* column.

   b Estimate the mean of the data.

2 50 adults each kicked a football. The table alongside shows the distances the ball travelled in the air before it bounced.

Distance (d m)	Frequency
$20 \leqslant d < 30$	10
$30 \leqslant d < 40$	19
$40 \leqslant d < 50$	14
$50 \leqslant d < 60$	7

   a Explain why the distance of a kick is a continuous variable.

   b Is it possible to determine the furthest distance the ball was kicked?

   c Extend the table alongside to include an *interval midpoint* and *product* column.

   d Estimate the mean distance the ball was kicked.

3

Area (A m^2)	Frequency
$400 \leqslant A < 500$	5
$500 \leqslant A < 600$	11
$600 \leqslant A < 700$	12
$700 \leqslant A < 800$	10
$800 \leqslant A < 900$	8

The table alongside shows the areas of the blocks of land along a street.

   a Find the modal class.

   b Estimate the mean land block size.

4 The frequency histogram shows the weights of cats at a cat show.

   a Describe the distribution of the data.

   b Construct a frequency table for the data.

   c Estimate the mean weight of the cats at the show.

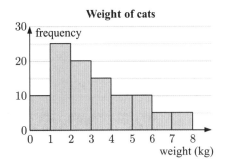

Weight of cats

5 Nick served a tennis ball 200 times. The speeds of the serves are summarised in the table alongside.

    a Find the modal class of the data.

    b If possible, find the:

        i number of serves faster than 170 km/h

        ii number of serves slower than 162 km/h

        iii percentage of serves between 155 km/h and 175 km/h.

    c Estimate the mean speed of the serves.

Speed (s km/h)	Frequency
$150 \leqslant s < 155$	18
$155 \leqslant s < 160$	28
$160 \leqslant s < 165$	35
$165 \leqslant s < 170$	43
$170 \leqslant s < 175$	41
$175 \leqslant s < 180$	35

6 40 students receive marks out of 100 for an examination in Chemistry. Their results were:

    70 65 50 40 58 72 39 85 90 65 53 75 83 92 66 78 82 88 56 68

    43 90 80 85 78 72 59 83 71 75 54 68 75 89 92 81 77 59 63 80

    a Find the exact mean and median of the data.

    b Group the data into the classes 0 - 9, 10 - 19, 20 - 29, ..., 90 - 99.

    c Use your grouped data to estimate the mean of the data. Compare your answer with the exact mean.

7 A plant inspector takes a random sample of ten week old plants from a nursery, and measures their heights in millimetres. The results are shown in the table.

    a State the modal class.

    b Estimate the mean height of the plants.

    c How many of the plants are 80 mm or more?

    d What percentage of the plants are between 65 and 75 mm?

    e The total number of plants in the nursery is 579. Estimate the number which measure:

        i less than 80 mm   **ii** between 70 and 85 mm.

Height (h mm)	Frequency
$60 \leqslant h < 65$	1
$65 \leqslant h < 70$	2
$70 \leqslant h < 75$	10
$75 \leqslant h < 80$	24
$80 \leqslant h < 85$	20
$85 \leqslant h < 90$	2

8 The percentage marks for boys and girls in a science test are given in the table.

Estimate the mean mark for each gender, and compare your results.

Marks	Girls	Boys
21 - 30	2	0
31 - 40	6	5
41 - 50	10	8
51 - 60	8	11
61 - 70	4	5
71 - 80	5	6
81 - 90	3	4
91 - 100	1	0

9 The times taken in minutes for players to finish a computer game were:

Time (t)	$5 \leqslant t < 10$	$10 \leqslant t < 15$	$15 \leqslant t < 20$	$20 \leqslant t < 25$	$25 \leqslant t < 30$	$30 \leqslant t < 35$
Frequency	2	8	16	20	24	10

    a What percentage of the players finished the game in less than 20 minutes?

    b Estimate the mean time to finish the game.

    c If 2589 other people play the game, estimate the number who will complete it in less than 25 minutes.

F | CUMULATIVE FREQUENCY   [E11.6]

Sometimes it is useful to know the number or proportion of scores that lie above or below a particular value. In such situations we construct a **cumulative frequency table** and a **cumulative frequency graph** to represent the data.

> The **cumulative frequency** gives a *running total* of the scores up to a particular value. It is the total frequency up to that value.

In a cumulative frequency graph, we plot cumulative frequencies on the vertical axis.

We can use the cumulative frequency graph to find percentiles, including the quartiles and the median.

> The **nth percentile** P_n is the score value $n\%$ of the data lies at or below.

So, the lower quartile $Q_1 = P_{25}$
   the median $Q_2 = P_{50}$
   the upper quartile $Q_3 = P_{75}$

Example 13   ◀)) *Self Tutor*

The table summarises the weights of 80 male basketball players.

a Construct a cumulative frequency table.

b Represent the data on a cumulative frequency graph.

c Use your graph to estimate the:

  i   median weight

  ii number of men weighing less than 83 kg

  iii number of men weighing more than 92 kg

  iv 85th percentile.

Weight (w kg)	Frequency
$65 \leqslant w < 70$	1
$70 \leqslant w < 75$	2
$75 \leqslant w < 80$	8
$80 \leqslant w < 85$	16
$85 \leqslant w < 90$	21
$90 \leqslant w < 95$	19
$95 \leqslant w < 100$	8
$100 \leqslant w < 105$	3
$105 \leqslant w < 110$	1
$110 \leqslant w < 115$	1

a

Weight (w kg)	Frequency	Cumulative frequency
$65 \leqslant w < 70$	1	1
$70 \leqslant w < 75$	2	3 ← this is $1 + 2$
$75 \leqslant w < 80$	8	11 ← this is $1 + 2 + 8$
$80 \leqslant w < 85$	16	27
$85 \leqslant w < 90$	21	48 ← 48 players weigh less than 90 kg.
$90 \leqslant w < 95$	19	67
$95 \leqslant w < 100$	8	75
$100 \leqslant w < 105$	3	78
$105 \leqslant w < 110$	1	79
$110 \leqslant w < 115$	1	80

b

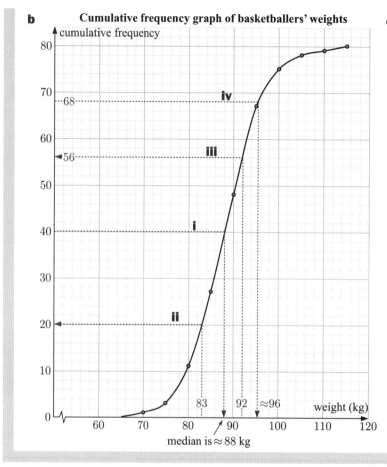

Cumulative frequency graph of basketballers' weights

median is ≈ 88 kg

c **i** 50% of 80 = 40,
∴   median ≈ 88 kg

ii There are 20 men who weigh less than 83 kg.

iii There are $80 - 56 = 24$ men who weigh more than 92 kg.

iv 85% of 80 = 68, so the 85th percentile ≈ 96 kg.

COMPARING DISTRIBUTIONS OF UNEQUAL SIZE

If we wish to *compare* distributions of unequal size, we can construct our cumulative frequency graph using percentiles rather than cumulative frequency on the vertical axis. This effectively scales the graph for each data set so they both range from 0 to 100.

$$\text{percentile} = \frac{\text{cumulative frequency}}{\text{number of data}} \times 100\%$$

Example 14   ◀ﻌ)) Self Tutor

The heights of 100 14-year-old girls and 200 14-year-old boys were measured and the results tabled.

a Draw a cumulative frequency curve for both data sets on the same set of axes.

b Estimate for each data set:
  i the median
  ii the interquartile range (IQR).

c Compare the two distributions.

Height	Frequency	
(h cm)	Girls	Boys
$140 \leqslant h < 145$	5	4
$145 \leqslant h < 150$	10	10
$150 \leqslant h < 155$	15	20
$155 \leqslant h < 160$	30	26
$160 \leqslant h < 165$	20	40
$165 \leqslant h < 170$	10	60
$170 \leqslant h < 175$	8	30
$175 \leqslant h < 180$	2	10

a

Height	Frequency		Cumulative frequency		Percentile	
(h cm)	Girls	Boys	Girls	Boys	Girls	Boys
$140 \leqslant h < 145$	5	4	5	4	5	2
$145 \leqslant h < 150$	10	10	15	14	15	7
$150 \leqslant h < 155$	15	20	30	34	30	17
$155 \leqslant h < 160$	30	26	60	60	60	30
$160 \leqslant h < 165$	20	40	80	100	80	50
$165 \leqslant h < 170$	10	60	90	160	90	80
$170 \leqslant h < 175$	8	30	98	190	98	95
$175 \leqslant h < 180$	2	10	100	200	100	100

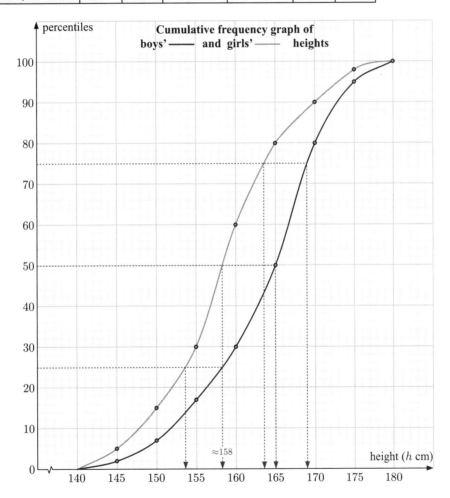

b For girls: **i** median ≈ 158 cm   **ii** IQR $\approx 163.5 - 153.7 \approx 10$ cm

 For boys: **i** median ≈ 165 cm   **ii** IQR $\approx 169 - 158 \approx 11$ cm

c The two distributions are similar in shape, but the boys' heights are further right than the girls'. The median height for the boys is 7 cm more than for the girls, so they are considerably taller. However, the IQRs are nearly the same, so the spread of heights is similar for each gender.

EXERCISE 18F

1

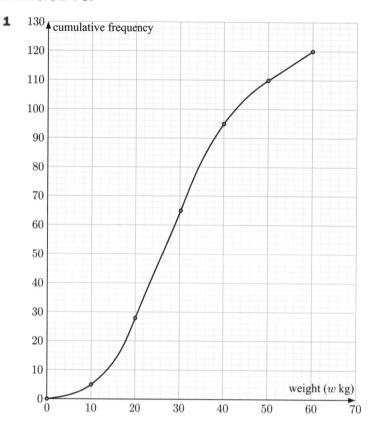

This cumulative frequency curve shows the weights of Sam's goat herd in kilograms.

a How many goats does Sam have?

b Estimate the median goat weight.

c Goats heavier than the 60th percentile will go to market on Tuesday. How many goats will go to market on Tuesday?

d Find the IQR for the weights of Sam's herd.

2 The times (in minutes) of 160 competitors in a cross-country race were recorded in the table alongside.

   a Draw a cumulative frequency graph to display the data.

   b Estimate:

    i the median time

    ii the number of runners whose time was less than 32 minutes

    iii the time in which the fastest 40 runners completed the course

    iv the interquartile range.

Times (min)	Frequency
$20 \leqslant t < 25$	18
$25 \leqslant t < 30$	45
$30 \leqslant t < 35$	37
$35 \leqslant t < 40$	33
$40 \leqslant t < 45$	19
$45 \leqslant t < 50$	8

3 The lengths of 30 trout (l cm) were measured and the results summarised in the table.

   a Construct a cumulative frequency curve for the data.

   b Estimate:

    i the percentage of trout with length less than 39 cm

    ii the median length of trout caught

    iii the IQR and explain what this represents

    iv the 35th percentile and explain what this represents.

   c Use a calculator to estimate the mean of the data.

   d Comment on the shape of the distribution of trout lengths.

Length (l cm)	Frequency
$30 \leqslant l < 32$	1
$32 \leqslant l < 34$	1
$34 \leqslant l < 36$	3
$36 \leqslant l < 38$	7
$38 \leqslant l < 40$	11
$40 \leqslant l < 42$	5
$42 \leqslant l < 44$	2

4

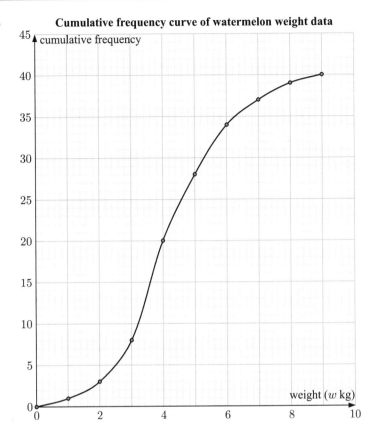

Cumulative frequency curve of watermelon weight data

The given graph describes the weight of 40 watermelons.

a Estimate the:

   i median weight

   ii IQR.

b Construct a cumulative frequency table for the data, including a frequency column.

c Estimate the mean weight of the watermelons.

---

5 The times taken for trampers to climb Ben Nevis were recorded in the table below:

Time (t min)	$175 \leqslant t < 200$	$200 \leqslant t < 225$	$225 \leqslant t < 250$	$250 \leqslant t < 275$	$275 \leqslant t < 300$
Frequency	11	35	74	32	8

a Construct a cumulative frequency curve for the walking times.

b Estimate the median time for the walk.

c Estimate the IQR and explain what it means.

d Guides on the walk say that anyone who completes the walk in 3 hours 15 min or less is extremely fit. Estimate the proportion of extremely fit trampers.

e Comment on the shape of the distribution of walking times.

---

6 The weights of cabbages grown by two brothers on separate properties were measured for comparison. The results are shown in the table:

a Draw a cumulative frequency curve for both cabbage samples on the same set of axes.

b Estimate for each data set:

   i the median weight   **ii** the IQR.

c Compare the 60th percentile weights for the data sets.

d Compare the two distributions.

Weight	Frequency	
(w grams)	Alan	John
$400 \leqslant w < 550$	4	5
$550 \leqslant w < 700$	32	60
$700 \leqslant w < 850$	44	70
$850 \leqslant w < 1000$	52	60
$1000 \leqslant w < 1150$	44	35
$1150 \leqslant w < 1300$	24	20
Total	200	250

Review set 18A

1 Classify these quantitative variables as either discrete or continuous:

   a the number of oranges on each orange tree

   b the heights of seedlings after two weeks

   c the scores of team members in a darts competition.

2 A randomly selected sample of small businesses were asked "How many full-time employees are there in your business?" A vertical bar chart has been constructed for the results.

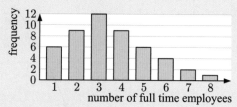

   a How many small businesses gave data in the survey?

   b How many of the businesses had only one or two full-time employees?

   c What percentage of the businesses had five or more full-time employees?

   d Describe the distribution of the data.   **e** Find the mean of the data.

3 The test score out of 40 marks was recorded for a group of 30 students:

   a Construct a tally-frequency table for this data.

   b Draw a vertical bar chart to display the data.

   c How many students scored less than 20 for the test?

   d If an "A" was awarded to students who scored 30 or more for the test, what percentage of students scored an "A"?

```
25  18  35  32  34  28  24  39  29  33
22  34  39  31  36  35  36  33  35  27
26  25  20  18   9  19  32  23  28  27
```

4 For the given data on calf weights:

   a Explain what 5 | 1 means.

   b Find the minimum calf weight.

   c Find the range of the calf weights.

   d Which weight occurs most frequently?

   e What fraction of calves weigh less than 45 kg?

Weight of calves (kg)

2	8
3	1 4 9
4	0 3 3 6 7
5	1 4 4 4 5 5 8
6	3 5

Key: 6 | 3 means 63 kg

5 The data alongside are the number of call-outs each day for a city fire department over a period of 25 days:

```
29  14  23  32  28  30   9  24  31
30  18  22  27  15  32  26  22  19
16  23  38  12   8  22  31
```

   a Construct a tally-frequency table for the data using class intervals 0 - 9, 10 - 19, 20 - 29, and 30 - 39.

   b Display the data on a vertical bar chart.

   c On how many days were there at least 20 call-outs?

   d On what percentage of days were there less than 10 call-outs?

   e Find the modal class for the data.

6 The following data are the number of points scored by a rugby team in each game of a season:

   28, 24, 16, 6, 46, 34, 43, 16, 36, 49, 30, 28, 4, 31, 47, 41, 26, 25, 20, 29, 42

   Find:

   a the mean   **b** the mode   **c** the median   **d** the range

   e the upper and lower quartiles   **f** the interquartile range.

7 Eight scores have an average of six. Scores of 15 and x increase the average to 7. Find x.

8 For the data set given, find the:

    a minimum value   **b** maximum value

    c median   **d** lower quartile

    e upper quartile   **f** range

    g interquartile range.

Stem	Leaf
1	2 4 4 6 8
2	2 3 7 7 7 9 9
3	0 0 2 4 5 8
4	0 2 3

Key: $4 \mid 0 = 40$

9 Consider the bar chart shown.

    a Construct a frequency table for the data.

    b Find the total number of:

        i games played   **ii** goals scored.

    c Find the:

        i mean   **ii** median

        iii mode   **iv** range.

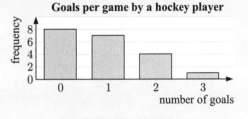

Goals per game by a hockey player

10 The data below shows the number of pages contained in a random selection of books from a library:

295 612 452 182 335 410 256 715 221 375
508 310 197 245 411 162 95 416 372 777
411 236 606 192 487

    a Use technology to find the:

        i mean   **ii** median

        iii lower quartile   **iv** upper quartile.

    b Find the range and interquartile range for the data.

11 The numbers of potatoes growing on each of 100 potato plants were recorded and summarised in the table below:

Number of potatoes	0 - 2	3 - 5	6 - 8	9 - 11	12 - 14	15 - 17
Frequency	7	11	25	40	15	2

Estimate the mean number of potatoes per plant.

12 The speeds of vehicles (v km/h) travelling along a stretch of road are recorded over a 60 minute period. The results are given in the table alongside.

    a Estimate the mean speed of the vehicles.

    b Find the modal class.

    c What percentage of drivers exceeded the speed limit of 60 km/h?

    d Describe the distribution of the data.

Speed (v km/h)	Frequency
$40 \leqslant v < 45$	14
$45 \leqslant v < 50$	22
$50 \leqslant v < 55$	35
$55 \leqslant v < 60$	38
$60 \leqslant v < 65$	25
$65 \leqslant v < 70$	10

13 The weekly wages of employees in a factory are recorded in the table below.

Weekly wage ($\$w$)	$0 \leqslant w < 400$	$400 \leqslant w < 800$	$800 \leqslant w < 1200$	$1200 \leqslant w < 1600$	$1600 \leqslant w < 2000$
Frequency	20	60	120	40	10

    a Draw a cumulative frequency graph to illustrate this information.

    b Use the graph to estimate:

        i the median wage   **ii** the wage that is exceeded by 20% of the employees.

14 The cumulative frequency curve shows the time spent by people in a supermarket on a given day.

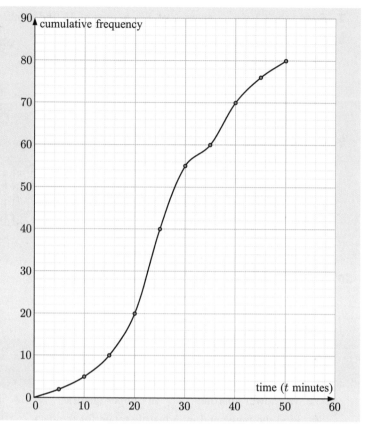

  a Construct a cumulative frequency table for the data, using the intervals $0 \leqslant t < 5$, $5 \leqslant t < 10$, and so on.

  b Use the graph to estimate:

   i the median time

   ii the IQR

   iii the 80th percentile.

  c Copy and complete:

   i 60% of the people spent less than ...... minutes in the supermarket.

   ii 80% of the people spent at least ...... minutes in the supermarket.

Review set 18B

1 A survey is conducted in Beijing airport to find out the most popular holiday destinations for Chinese people.

  a What type of variable is *favourite holiday destination*?

  b Discuss ways in which this sample may be biased.

2 A class of 20 students was asked "How many children are there in your household?" and the following data was collected:

    1 2 3 3 2 4 5 4 2 3 8 1 2 1 3 2 1 2 1 2

  a What is the variable in the investigation?

  b Is the data discrete or continuous? Explain your answer.

  c Construct a tally-frequency table and vertical bar chart for the data.

  d Describe the distribution of the data.   **e** What is the mode of the data?

3 A class of thirty students were asked how many emails they had sent in the last week.

  The results were: 12   6   21   15   18   4   28   32   17   44   9   32   26   18   11
                        24   31   17   52   7   42   37   19   6   20   15   27   8   36   28

  a Construct a tally-frequency table for this data, using intervals 0 - 9, 10 - 19, ..., 50 - 59.

  b Draw a vertical bar chart to display the data.   **c** Find the modal class.

  d What percentage of students sent at least 30 emails?

  e Describe the distribution of the data.

4 To test whether a training program is effective, a group of 200 m sprinters compared their best times from last season with those from this season. The results (in seconds) are shown below:

Last season						This season				
20.6	21.3	21.7	21.1	23.4		20.4	20.8	21.8	20.9	22.6
21.4	22.1	21.0	22.6	21.9		21.2	22.2	20.8	22.5	21.4
22.8	21.6	21.3	21.4	21.0		22.9	21.1	20.7	21.0	20.8
23.1	22.3	23.5	22.1	21.7		22.9	22.4	23.3	21.8	21.5

   a Construct a back-to-back stem-and-leaf diagram to display the data.

   b Would you say the training program is effective? Explain your answer.

5 Sixty people were asked: "How many times have you been to the cinema in the last twelve months?". The results are given in the table alongside.

Number of times	Frequency
0 - 2	19
3 - 5	24
6 - 8	10
9 - 11	5
12 - 15	2

   a Draw a vertical bar chart to display the data.

   b Can you tell how many people did not go to the cinema at all? Explain your answer.

   c What percentage of people went to the cinema between 3 and 8 times?

   d Describe the distribution of the data.

6 The lengths of newborn babies at a hospital were recorded over a one month period. The results are shown in the frequency histogram.

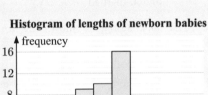

Histogram of lengths of newborn babies

   a Describe the distribution of the data.

   b How many babies were 52 cm or more?

   c What percentage of babies had lengths in the interval 50 cm $\leqslant l < 53$ cm?

   d In the following month, 67 babies were born at the same hospital.
   Estimate the number of babies that measured less than 51 cm in length.

7 A sample of 15 measurements has a mean of 14.2, and a sample of 10 measurements has a mean of 12.6. Find the mean of the total sample of 25 measurements.

8 Consider the numbers 7, 5, 7, 2, 8, and 7. If two new numbers, 2 and x, are added to the data, the mean is reduced by 1. Find x.

9 Jenny's golf scores for her last 20 rounds were:

90 106 84 103 112 100 105 81 104 98
107 95 104 108 99 101 106 102 98 101

   a Find the median, lower quartile, and upper quartile of the data set.

   b Find the interquartile range of the data set and explain its meaning.

10 For the data displayed in the stem-and-leaf diagram, find the:

Stem	Leaf
3	8 9
4	2 2 5
5	0 1 1 7 9
6	1 3 4
7	0

   a mean   **b** median

   c lower quartile   **d** upper quartile

   e range   **f** interquartile range.

Key: 7 | 0 represents 70

11 The given table shows the distribution of scores for a Year 10 spelling test in Austria.

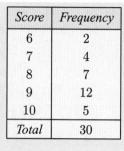

Score	Frequency
6	2
7	4
8	7
9	12
10	5
Total	30

   a Calculate the: **i** mean   **ii** mode
                    iii median   **iv** range of the scores.

   b The average score for all Year 10 students across Austria in this spelling test was 6.2. How does this class compare with the national average?

   c Describe the distribution of the data.

12 A transport authority recorded the number of vehicles travelling along a stretch of road each day for 40 days. The data is displayed in the bar chart alongside:

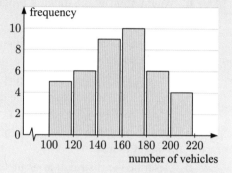

   a On how many days were there at least 180 vehicles?

   b On what percentage of days were there less than 160 vehicles?

   c What is the modal class?

   d Estimate the mean number of vehicles on the stretch of road each day.

13 The table alongside shows the weights of competitors in a boxing tournament.

   a Identify the modal class.

   b Estimate the mean weight of the boxers.

   c Draw a cumulative frequency graph of the data.

   d Boxers weighing between 79 kg and 91 kg are in the cruiserweight class. Estimate the number of boxers in this class.

   e Estimate the median weight of the boxers.

Weight (w kg)	Frequency
$50 \leqslant w < 60$	14
$60 \leqslant w < 70$	19
$70 \leqslant w < 80$	28
$80 \leqslant w < 90$	23
$90 \leqslant w < 100$	16

14 The percentage scores in a test were recorded, and the results categorised by gender.

   a Draw cumulative frequency graphs for boys and girls on the same set of axes. Use percentiles on the vertical axis.

   b Estimate the median and interquartile range of each data set.

   c Compare the distributions.

Percentage	Frequency	
score (s)	Boys	Girls
$0 \leqslant s < 10$	5	0
$10 \leqslant s < 20$	8	4
$20 \leqslant s < 30$	12	8
$30 \leqslant s < 40$	10	10
$40 \leqslant s < 50$	30	15
$50 \leqslant s < 60$	50	25
$60 \leqslant s < 70$	20	40
$70 \leqslant s < 80$	10	10
$80 \leqslant s < 90$	5	5
$90 \leqslant s < 100$	0	3

Two-variable analysis

19

Contents:

A	Correlation	[E11.8]
B	Line of best fit by eye	[E11.8]
C	Linear regression	[E11.8]

Opening problem

The relationship between the *height* and *weight* of members of a football team is to be investigated. Data for each player is given below.

Player	1	2	3	4	5	6	7	8	9
Height (cm)	203	189	193	187	186	197	180	186	188
Weight (kg)	106	93	95	86	85	92	78	84	93

Player	10	11	12	13	14	15	16	17	18
Height (cm)	181	179	191	178	178	186	190	189	193
Weight (kg)	84	86	92	80	77	90	86	95	89

Things to think about:

a Are the variables categorical or quantitative?

b Which is the *dependent* variable?

c What would the scatter diagram for this data look like?

d Does an increase in the *height* of a player generally correspond to an increase or a decrease in their *weight*?

e How can we indicate the strength of the linear relationship between the variables?

f How can we use this data to estimate the weight of a player who is 200 cm tall? How reliable will this estimate be?

We often want to know how two variables are **associated** or **related**, and whether an increase in one variable results in an increase or a decrease in the other. We call this **bivariate statistics** because we are dealing with *two* variables.

To analyse the relationship between two variables, we first need to decide which is the **dependent** variable and which is the **independent** variable. The value of the dependent variable *depends* on the value of the independent variable.

For example:

- the height of a girl *depends* on her age
- Jonathon's pay rate *depends* on the number of years he has worked for the company.

Having made this decision, we can then draw a **scatter diagram** to display the data. The independent variable is placed on the horizontal axis, and the dependent variable is placed on the vertical axis.

Consider the scatter diagrams opposite.

In the first scatter diagram the points are quite random. It is hard to tell how they could be related.

In the second diagram the points are all close to the red line shown. We say that there is a strong **linear correlation** between these two variables. The red line is called the **line of best fit** because it best represents the data.

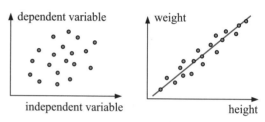

A   *CORRELATION*   *[E11.8]*

Correlation is a measure of the strength of the relationship or association between two variables.

We can use a scatter diagram to describe the correlation between two variables.

Step 1:   Look at the scatter diagram for any **pattern**.

For a generally *upward* shape, we say that the correlation is **positive**.

As the independent variable increases, the dependent variable generally increases.

For a generally *downward* shape, we say that the correlation is **negative**.

As the independent variable increases, the dependent variable generally decreases.

For *randomly scattered* points with no upward or downward trend, we say there is **no correlation**.

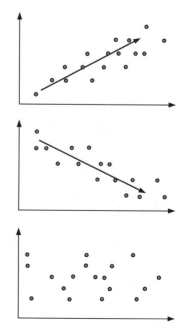

Step 2:   Look at the pattern of points to see if the relationship is **linear**.

The relationship is approximately linear.   The relationship is not linear.

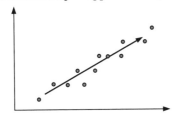 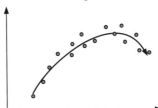

Step 3:   Look at the spread of points to judge the **strength** of the correlation.

These scatter diagrams show strength classifications for positive relationships:

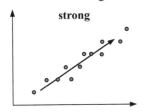 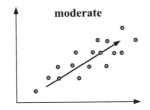 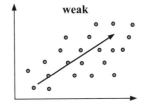

These scatter diagrams show strength classifications for negative relationships:

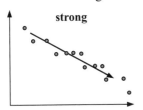 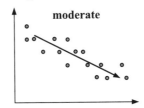 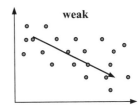

Example 1   ◀ᵈⁱ) *Self Tutor*

Alexander researched the elevation above sea level and mean annual temperature of 12 cities around the world. The results are given in this table.

Elevation (m)	600	850	150	300	100	200	500	450	750	30	300	50
Mean annual temperature (°C)	15	10	16	15	25	20	21	19	9	27	22	28

a   Draw a scatter diagram of the data.

b   Describe the relationship between *elevation* and *mean temperature*.

a

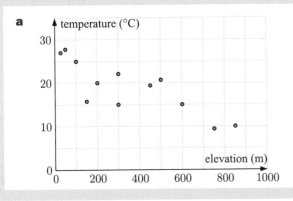

b   There is a moderate negative linear correlation between *elevation* and *mean temperature*.

What factors other than elevation affect the mean annual temperature of a city?

EXERCISE 19A

1 For each scatter diagram:
  i State whether there is positive, negative, or no association between the variables.
  ii Decide whether the relationship between the variables is linear.
  iii Describe the strength of the association (zero, weak, moderate, or strong).

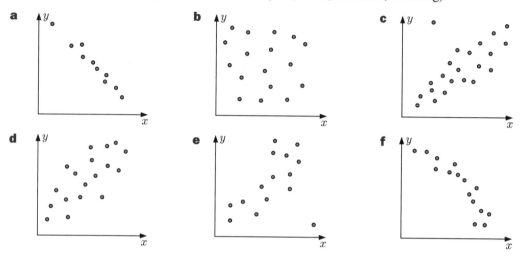

2 a There is a positive association between x and y. What happens to y as x increases?
  b There is a negative correlation between T and d. What happens to d as T increases?
  c Copy and complete: If there is no association between two variables then the points on the scatter diagram are ....

3 A class of 15 students was asked how many text messages they had sent and received in the last week. The results are shown below:

Student	A	B	C	D	E	F	G	H	I	J	K	L	M	N	O
Messages sent	5	0	12	9	17	15	10	4	8	18	25	17	0	6	13
Messages received	8	0	15	7	19	11	8	7	12	15	21	16	4	6	16

  a Draw a scatter diagram to display the data.
  b Describe the relationship between *messages sent* and *messages received*.

4 a 10 students were asked for their exam marks in Physics and Mathematics. Their percentages are given in the table below.

Student	A	B	C	D	E	F	G	H	I	J
Physics	75	83	45	90	70	78	88	50	55	95
Mathematics	68	70	50	65	60	72	75	40	45	80

  i Draw a scatter diagram of the data, with the Physics marks on the horizontal axis.
  ii Comment on the relationship between the Physics and Mathematics marks.

  b The same students were asked for their Art exam results. Their percentages were:

Student	A	B	C	D	E	F	G	H	I	J
Art	75	70	80	85	82	70	60	75	78	65

Draw a scatter diagram to see if there is any relationship between the Physics marks and the Art marks of each student.

5 The following table shows the sales of hot drinks in a popular café each month, along with the average daily temperature for the month.

Month	Jan	Feb	Mar	Apr	May	Jun	Jul	Aug	Sep	Oct	Nov	Dec
Temperature (°C)	5	12	13	18	20	21	22	17	14	10	7	6
Sales ($ × 1000)	22	25	20	15	16	12	12	8	10	15	16	18

a Draw a scatter diagram of the data with the independent variable *temperature* along the horizontal axis.

b Comment on the relationship between the sales and the temperature.

6 A group of shoe store customers were asked to record their height in centimetres, and their shoe size. The results are shown in the table below:

Height (cm)	165	155	140	145	158	148	160	164	160	155	150	160
Shoe size	6.5	4.5	4	5.5	6	5.5	6	6.5	5.5	5	5	5.5

a Draw a scatter diagram to display the data.

b Comment on the relationship between height and shoe size.

B *LINE OF BEST FIT BY EYE*   *[E11.8]*

A scatter diagram for the data in the **Opening Problem** is shown alongside. We can see there is a moderate positive linear correlation between the variables, so it is reasonable to use a line of best fit to model the data.

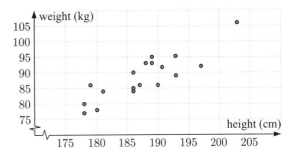

For a bivariate data set involving x and y, we use these steps to find the **line of best fit by eye**:

Step 1:   Find the means $\overline{x}$ and $\overline{y}$ of the x and y values respectively.

Step 2:   Plot the **mean point** $(\overline{x}, \overline{y})$ on a scatter diagram of the data.

Step 3:   Draw a line through the mean point which fits the trend of the data and which has about as many points above the line as below it.

For the **Opening Problem**, the mean point is approximately $(187, 88)$.

We have added the mean point and the line of best fit by eye on the scatter diagram.

As this line is an estimate only, lines drawn by eye will vary from person to person.

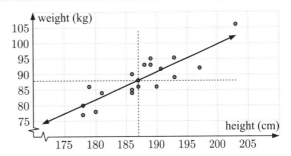

The line of best fit is a **linear model** for the relationship between the variables. We can use it to estimate the value of one variable for any given value of the other.

INTERPOLATION AND EXTRAPOLATION

Given a bivariate data set, the data values with the lowest and highest values of x are called the **poles**.

If we use values of x **in between** the poles to estimate y, we say we are **interpolating** between the poles.

If we use values of x **outside** the poles to estimate y, we say we are **extrapolating** outside the poles.

As a general rule, it is reasonable to interpolate between the poles, but unreliable to extrapolate outside them.

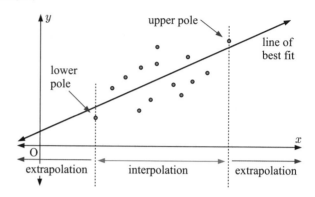

Example 2   ◀)) *Self Tutor*

On a hot day, six cars were left in the sun in a car park. The length of time each car was left in the sun was recorded, as well as the temperature inside the car at the end of the period.

Car	A	B	C	D	E	F
Time (x minutes)	50	5	25	40	15	45
Temperature (y °C)	47	28	36	42	34	41

a Calculate $\overline{x}$ and $\overline{y}$.

b Draw a scatter diagram of the data. Plot the mean point $(\overline{x}, \overline{y})$ on the scatter diagram, and draw a line of best fit through this point.

c Predict the temperature of a car which has been left in the sun for:

    i 35 minutes   **ii** 75 minutes.

    Comment on the reliability of your estimates.

a $\quad \overline{x} = \dfrac{50 + 5 + 25 + 40 + 15 + 45}{6} = 30, \qquad \overline{y} = \dfrac{47 + 28 + 36 + 42 + 34 + 41}{6} = 38$

b

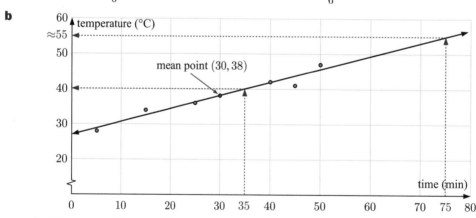

c   **i** When $x = 35$, $y \approx 40$.

      The temperature of a car left in the sun for 35 minutes will be approximately 40°C.

      This estimate is an interpolation, so we expect it to be reliable.

  ii When $x = 75$, $y \approx 55$.

      The temperature of a car left in the sun for 75 minutes will be approximately 55°C.

      This estimate is an extrapolation, and therefore may not be reliable. We cannot assume that the linear trend observed in the data will continue up to a time of 75 minutes.

EXERCISE 19B

1 Consider the bivariate data alongside.

x	5	10	2	13	6
y	11	3	18	5	13

    a Find $\overline{x}$ and $\overline{y}$.

    b Draw a scatter diagram of the data.

    c Does the data appear to be positively correlated or negatively correlated?

    d Plot the mean point $(\overline{x},\ \overline{y})$ on the scatter diagram, and draw a line of best fit through this point.

    e Estimate the value of y when $x = 8$.

2 The table alongside shows the *percentage of unemployed adults* and the *number of major thefts per day* in eight large cities.

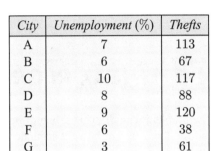

City	Unemployment (%)	Thefts
A	7	113
B	6	67
C	10	117
D	8	88
E	9	120
F	6	38
G	3	61
H	7	76

    a Find the mean unemployment percentage $\overline{x}$ and the mean number of thefts $\overline{y}$.

    b Draw a scatter diagram of the data.

    c Plot $(\overline{x},\ \overline{y})$ on the scatter diagram.

    d Draw the line of best fit on the scatter diagram.

    e Another city has 15% unemployment.

      i   Estimate the number of major thefts per day for that city.

      ii Comment on the reliability of your estimate.

3 Each month, an opinion poll shows the approval rating of the Prime Minister and the Opposition leader. The approval ratings for the last 10 polls are shown below:

Prime Minister (x%)	55	59	68	61	46	42	38	45	42	44
Opposition (y%)	37	35	31	35	43	40	42	37	41	39

    a Calculate $\overline{x}$ and $\overline{y}$.

    b Draw a scatter diagram of the data. Plot the mean point $(\overline{x},\ \overline{y})$ on the scatter diagram, and draw a line of best fit through this point.

    c In a new opinion poll, the Prime Minister's approval rating is 47%. Estimate the approval rating of the Opposition leader.

4 A café manager believes that during April the *number of people wanting dinner* is related to the *temperature at noon*. Over a 13 day period, the number of diners and the noon temperature were recorded.

Temperature (x °C)	8	10	13	15	15	12	10	13	17	16	18	14	12
Number of diners (y)	63	70	74	81	77	65	75	87	91	75	96	82	88

    a Find the mean point $(\overline{x},\ \overline{y})$.

    b Draw a scatter diagram of the data. Plot $(\overline{x},\ \overline{y})$ on the scatter diagram, and draw a line of best fit through this point.

    c Estimate the number of diners at the café when the temperature is:

      i   11°C   **ii** 4°C.

    d Comment on the reliability of your estimates in **c**.

5 Consider the data in the table alongside:

x	2	8	4	3	9	6	1	5	10	7
y	21.0	9.1	18.1	50.0	8.3	12.3	21.9	14.3	5.3	11.2

  a Draw a scatter diagram for the data and circle the outlier.

  b Find the mean point $(\overline{x},\ \overline{y})$ and plot it on your scatter diagram. Draw a line of best fit through the mean point.

  c Recalculate $\overline{x}$ and $\overline{y}$ without the outlier and repeat **b**.

  d Compare your two lines of best fit. Which line of best fit better describes the trend seen in the *main body* of data?

C   LINEAR REGRESSION   [E11.8]

The problem with drawing a line of best fit by eye is that the answer will vary from one person to another, and the line may not be very accurate. Instead, we can use a method called **linear regression**.

> **Linear regression** is a formal method of fitting a line which best fits a set of data.

This line of best fit is called the **least squares regression line**. It is the line which makes the sum of the squares of the distances $d_1^2 + d_2^2 + d_3^2 + ...$ as small as possible.

We use a **graphics calculator** or the **statistics package** to find the equation of the least squares regression line.

STATISTICS PACKAGE

GRAPHICS CALCULATOR INSTRUCTIONS

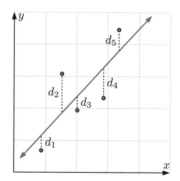

For example, consider the following data which was collected by a milkbar owner over ten consecutive days:

Maximum daily temperature (t °C)	29	40	35	30	34	34	27	27	19	37
Number of ice creams sold (N)	119	164	131	152	206	169	122	143	63	208

The screenshots alongside show the scatter diagram and information about the regression line from a graphics calculator.

So, the linear regression model is $y \approx 5.64x - 28.4$ or $N \approx 5.64t - 28.4$.

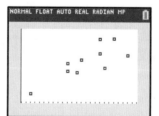

PEARSON'S CORRELATION COEFFICIENT r

In the information screen from the calculator above, there is a value $r \approx 0.795$.

This value is called **Pearson's correlation coefficient**. Knowledge of this statistic is not required for this course, but it is very useful when studying correlation, as it tells us the *strength* and *direction* of the linear correlation between the variables.

- The values of r range from -1 to $+1$.
- The **sign** of r indicates the **direction** of the correlation.
  - ▸ A positive value for r indicates the variables are **positively correlated**.
    An increase in one variable results in an increase in the other.
  - ▸ A negative value for r indicates the variables are **negatively correlated**.
    An increase in one variable results in a decrease in the other.
- The **size** of r indicates the **strength** of the correlation.
  - ▸ A value of r close to $+1$ or -1 indicates strong correlation between the variables.
  - ▸ A value of r close to zero indicates weak correlation between the variables.

Some examples of scatter diagrams with their corresponding values of r are given below.

POSITIVE CORRELATION

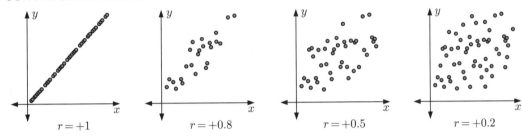

NEGATIVE CORRELATION

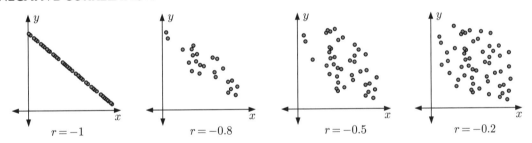

COEFFICIENT OF DETERMINATION r^2

The square of Pearson's correlation coefficient r is called the **coefficient of determination**.
Since $-1 \leqslant r \leqslant 1$, $0 \leqslant r^2 \leqslant 1$.

The following table is a guide for describing the **strength** of linear correlation using the coefficient of determination:

Value	Strength of correlation
$r^2 = 0$	no correlation
$0 < r^2 < 0.25$	very weak correlation
$0.25 \leqslant r^2 < 0.50$	weak correlation
$0.50 \leqslant r^2 < 0.75$	moderate correlation
$0.75 \leqslant r^2 < 0.90$	strong correlation
$0.90 \leqslant r^2 < 1$	very strong correlation
$r^2 = 1$	perfect correlation

Since $r^2 \geqslant 0$, it does not show the *direction* of correlation.

Example 3   ◀) Self Tutor

The annual income and average weekly grocery bill for a selection of families is shown below:

Income (x thousand dollars)	55	36	25	47	60	64	42	50
Grocery bill (y dollars)	120	90	60	160	190	250	110	150

a Construct a scatter diagram to illustrate the data.

b Use technology to find the least squares regression line.

c Discuss the strength and direction of the linear relationship between the variables.

d Estimate the weekly grocery bill for a family with an annual income of $95 000. Comment on whether this estimate is likely to be reliable.

a
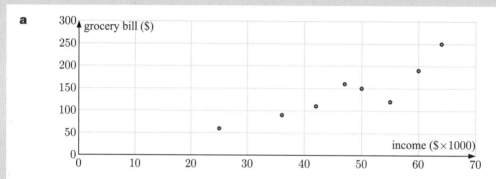

b
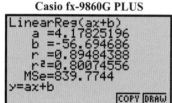

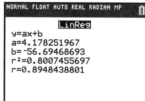

Using technology, the least squares regression line is $y \approx 4.18x - 56.7$

c Since $r > 0$ and $r^2 \approx 0.801$, there is a strong positive correlation between the variables.

d When $x = 95$, $y \approx 4.18(95) - 56.7 \approx 340$

So, we expect a family with an income of $95 000 to have a weekly grocery bill of about $340. This is an extrapolation, however, so the estimate may not be reliable.

EXERCISE 19C

1 For each data set:

    i Draw a scatter diagram of the data.

    ii Find the equation of the least squares regression line.

    iii Comment on the strength and direction of the linear relationship between the variables.

a

x	3	5	6	9	13	15	18	20
y	4	8	11	17	15	19	25	24

b

x	16	6	11	8	14	24	2	14	19	6
y	15	30	20	26	17	9	35	10	7	27

2 Tomatoes are sprayed with a pesticide-fertiliser mix. The table below gives the yield of tomatoes per row of bushes for various spray concentrations.

Spray concentration (x ml per 2 litres)	2	4	6	8	10	12
Yield of tomatoes per row (y)	45	76	93	105	119	124

a Draw a scatter diagram of the data.

b Find the equation of the least squares regression line.

c Interpret the y-intercept of this line.

d Comment on the strength and direction of the linear relationship between the variables.

e Use the equation of the line to predict the yield if the spray concentration was 7 ml.
Comment on whether this prediction is reasonable.

3 A group of friends competed in a fun-run. The table below shows how long each friend spent training, and the time they recorded for the fun-run.

Training time (x hours)	7	2	11	3	7	15	3	0	5	9	0
Fun-run time (y minutes)	60	75	47	70	52	37	72	75	60	62	80

a Draw a scatter diagram of the data.

b Find r and r^2. Discuss the significance of these values.

c Find the equation of the least squares regression line.

d Interpret the gradient of this line.

e Another friend of the group trained for 30 hours.

    i Use the least squares regression line to estimate his fun-run time.

    ii Comment on the reliability of your estimate.

4 The yield of cherries from an orchard each year depends on the number of frosty mornings.

The table alongside shows the yield of cherries from an orchard over several years with different numbers of frosty mornings.

Frosty mornings (n)	18	29	23	38	35	27
Yield (Y tonnes)	29.4	34.6	32.1	36.9	36.1	32.5

a Produce a scatter diagram of Y against n.

b Find the linear model which best fits the data. Discuss its suitability.

c Estimate the yield from the orchard if there are 31 frosty mornings in the year.

d Copy and complete: "The greater the number of frosty mornings, the ...... the yield of cherries."

5 Carbon dioxide (CO_2) is a chemical linked to acid rain and global warming. The concentration of CO_2 in the atmosphere has been recorded over a 40 year period. It is measured in parts per million or ppm found in Law Dome Ice Cores in Antarctica.

Year	1960	1970	1980	1990	2000
CO_2 concentration (ppm)	313	321	329	337	345

Let t be the number of years since 1960 and C be the CO_2 concentration.

a Draw a scatter diagram of C against t.   **b** Describe the correlation between C and t.

c Obtain the linear model which best fits the data.

d Estimate the CO_2 concentration for 1987.

e If CO_2 emission continues at the same rate, estimate the concentration in 2020.

6 Answer the **Opening Problem** on page **305**.

7 Safety authorities advise drivers to travel 3 seconds behind the car in front of them. This provides the driver with a greater chance of avoiding a collision if the car in front has to brake quickly or is itself involved in an accident. A test was carried out to find out how long it would take a driver to bring a car to rest from the time a red light was flashed. This *stopping time* includes both the reaction time of the driver and the braking time for the car. The following results are for one driver in the same car under the same test conditions:

Speed (v km/h)	10	20	30	40	50	60	70	80	90
Stopping time (t s)	1.23	1.54	1.88	2.20	2.52	2.83	3.15	3.45	3.83

a Produce a scatter diagram for the data.

b Find the linear model which best fits the data.

c Describe the correlation between the variables.

d Use the model to estimate the stopping time for a speed of: **i** 55 km/h   **ii** 110 km/h

e Comment on the reliability of your results in **d**.

f Interpret the vertical intercept of the line of best fit.

g Explain why the 3 second rule applies at all speeds, with a good safety margin.

Review set 19A

1 The scatter diagram shows the number of defective items made by each employee of a factory, plotted against the employee's number of weeks of experience.

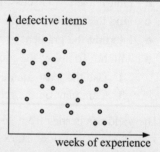

   a State the independent and dependent variables.

   b Describe the correlation between the variables.

2 The maximum speed of a Chinese dragonboat with different numbers of paddlers is recorded in the table alongside:

Number of paddlers (x)	4	6	10	14	18	20
Maximum speed (y km/h)	8	10	12	14	16	17

   a Draw a scatter diagram for the data.   **b** Find $\bar{x}$ and $\bar{y}$.

   c Draw the line of best fit by eye on your scatter diagram.

   d Predict the maximum speed of a dragonboat with:

   i 12 paddlers   **ii** 24 paddlers.

3 Following an outbreak of a deadly virus, medical authorities begin taking records of the number of cases. Their records are shown below.

Days after outbreak (n)	2	3	4	5	6	7	8	9	10	11
Diagnosed cases (d)	8	14	33	47	80	97	118	123	139	153

   a Produce a scatter diagram of d against n.

   b Plot the point $(\bar{n}, \bar{d})$ on the scatter diagram, and draw the line of best fit by eye.

   c Estimate the number of diagnosed cases on day 14. Comment on the reliability of your estimate.

4 The whorls on a cone shell get wider as you go from the top of the shell towards the bottom. Measurements from a shell are summarised in the following table:

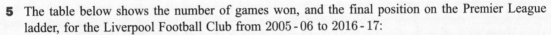

Position of whorl (p)	1	2	3	4	5	6	7	8
Width of whorl (w cm)	0.7	1.2	1.4	2.0	2.0	2.7	2.9	3.5

a Draw a scatter diagram for this data.

b Find r and r^2. Discuss the significance of these values.

c Find the linear regression model which best fits the data.

d **i** If a cone shell has 14 whorls, what width do you expect the 14th whorl to have?

   ii How reliable is this prediction?

5 The table below shows the number of games won, and the final position on the Premier League ladder, for the Liverpool Football Club from 2005-06 to 2016-17:

Games won (x)	25	20	21	25	18	17	14	16	26	18	16	22
Position (y)	3	3	4	2	7	6	8	7	2	6	8	4

a Would you expect x and y to be positively or negatively correlated? Explain your answer.

b Draw a scatter diagram of the data.

c Describe the correlation between the variables.

d Use technology to find the line of best fit.

e Suppose Liverpool wins 22 games next season. Predict their position on the ladder.

Review set 19B

1 Traffic analysts want to find the association between the *average speed* of cars in a city and the *age of drivers*. Devices for measuring average speed were fitted to the cars of drivers participating in a survey. The results are shown in the scatter diagram.

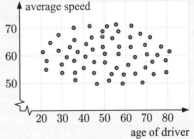

a What is the independent variable?

b Describe the association between the variables.

c Is it sensible to find the linear regression line for this data? Explain your answer.

2 Consider the bivariate data alongside.

x	11	7	13	3	12	8
y	17	14	20	5	26	8

a Find $\overline{x}$ and $\overline{y}$.

b Draw a scatter diagram of the data.

c Does the data appear to be positively correlated or negatively correlated?

d Plot the mean point $(\overline{x}, \overline{y})$ on the scatter diagram, and draw a line of best fit through this point.

e Estimate the value of y when $x = 5$. How reliable is this estimate?

3 Consider the relationship between a *number* and the *number of factors* it has.

   a Would you expect the correlation between these variables to be:

     i positive or negative   **ii** strong, moderate, or weak?

     Explain your answers.

   b Copy and complete this table:

Number (x)	1	2	3	4	5	....	16	17	18	19	20
Number of factors (y)	1	2	2	3		....				2	6

   c Draw a scatter diagram of the data.

   d Find r and r^2. Discuss the significance of these values.

4 In a Los Angeles shopping mall, David asked 10 people how many coins they had in their wallet or purse, and the total value of those coins.

Number of coins	5	8	11	7	5	10	2	10	1	12
Value of coins	$1.10	$0.82	$1.56	$0.90	$0.51	$1.54	$0.30	$1.02	$0.10	$1.23

Let n be the number of coins, and v be the value of the coins.

   a Draw a scatter diagram for the data.

   b Describe the correlation between the variables.

   c Find the equation of the least squares regression line.

   d Interpret the gradient of this line.

   e Terese has 20 coins in her purse.

     i Estimate the total value of these coins.

     ii How reliable is your prediction?

5 The following table gives peptic ulcer rates per 1000 people for differing family incomes.

Income (I thousand dollars)	20	25	30	35	40	50	60	80	100
Peptic ulcer rate (R)	8.3	7.7	6.9	7.3	5.9	4.7	3.6	2.6	1.2

   a Draw a scatter diagram for the data.

   b Find the equation of the line of best fit for the data.

   c Describe the correlation between the variables.

   d Estimate the peptic ulcer rate in families with an income of $55 000.

   e Explain why the model is inadequate for families with an income in excess of $120 000.

   f It is later realised that one of the values was recorded incorrectly.

     i Which is it likely to be? Explain your answer.

     ii Repeat **b** to **d** with the incorrect data value removed.

Algebraic fractions

20

Contents:

A	Evaluating algebraic fractions	[E2.9]
B	Simplifying algebraic fractions	[E2.9]
C	Multiplying and dividing algebraic fractions	[E2.9]
D	Adding and subtracting algebraic fractions	[E2.9]

Opening problem

To participate in a tennis league, each team must pay $150 in court fees, and a $60 team registration fee. The court fees are shared equally between the players in the team, and the registration fee is shared equally between the players and the team coach.

Suppose a team has x players.

Things to think about:

a Can you write the amount that each player must pay as a single fraction involving x?

b How much must each player pay if the team has:
   i 4 players   **ii** 5 players?

Algebraic fractions are fractions which contain at least one variable or unknown.

The variable may be in the numerator, the denominator, or both the numerator and denominator.

For example, $\dfrac{x}{7}$, $\dfrac{-2}{5-y}$, and $\dfrac{x+2y}{1-y}$ are all algebraic fractions.

Algebraic fractions are sometimes called **rational expressions**.

In this Chapter we will see how we can simplify, add, subtract, multiply, and divide algebraic fractions in the same way as we do ordinary fractions.

For example:

- $\dfrac{2}{7} + \dfrac{4}{7} = \dfrac{2+4}{7}$ leads to $\dfrac{a}{c} + \dfrac{b}{c} = \dfrac{a+b}{c}$

- $\dfrac{5}{7} - \dfrac{2}{7} = \dfrac{5-2}{7}$ leads to $\dfrac{a}{c} - \dfrac{b}{c} = \dfrac{a-b}{c}$

- $\dfrac{2}{3} \times \dfrac{5}{7} = \dfrac{2 \times 5}{3 \times 7}$ leads to $\dfrac{a}{b} \times \dfrac{c}{d} = \dfrac{ac}{bd}$

A   *EVALUATING ALGEBRAIC FRACTIONS*   *[E2.9]*

To **evaluate** an algebraic expression, we replace the variables with their known values. We then give our answer in simplest form.

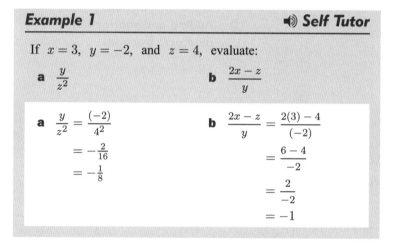

Example 1   ◀) *Self Tutor*

If $x = 3$, $y = -2$, and $z = 4$, evaluate:

a $\dfrac{y}{z^2}$ **b** $\dfrac{2x - z}{y}$

a $\dfrac{y}{z^2} = \dfrac{(-2)}{4^2}$ **b** $\dfrac{2x - z}{y} = \dfrac{2(3) - 4}{(-2)}$

$\qquad = -\dfrac{2}{16}$ $= \dfrac{6 - 4}{-2}$

$\qquad = -\dfrac{1}{8}$ $= \dfrac{2}{-2}$

$\qquad\qquad\qquad\qquad\qquad\qquad\qquad\qquad = -1$

EXERCISE 20A

1 If $a = 2$, $b = 3$, $c = 5$, evaluate:

a $\dfrac{a}{2}$ **b** $\dfrac{b}{6}$ **c** $\dfrac{b+1}{a}$ **d** $\dfrac{a+2b}{c}$

e $\dfrac{c-b}{a}$ **f** $\dfrac{3c-a}{b}$ **g** $\dfrac{a^2}{b-1}$ **h** $\dfrac{ab}{-1-c}$

i $\dfrac{2a^2}{b+1}$ **j** $\dfrac{ac}{b^2+1}$ **k** $\dfrac{b}{\sqrt{2a+c}}$ **l** $\dfrac{\sqrt{a^2-b}}{c-b}$

2 If $x = -1$, $y = 2$, $z = -3$, evaluate:

a $\dfrac{y}{x}$ **b** $\dfrac{z}{x}$ **c** $-\dfrac{z}{y+1}$ **d** $\dfrac{y^2}{-4}$

e $\dfrac{z-y}{x}$ **f** $\dfrac{x-y}{z}$ **g** $\dfrac{y}{x+z}$ **h** $\dfrac{x+y}{x-y}$

i $\dfrac{x+z}{y^2}$ **j** $\dfrac{x^2y}{z-1}$ **k** $\dfrac{x^2+y^2}{10}$ **l** $\dfrac{x^2+z^2}{y}$

m $\dfrac{x-z^2}{y}$ **n** $\dfrac{y^2-z^2}{-2y}$ **o** $\dfrac{3x-2y}{z^2}$ **p** $\dfrac{z-xy}{\sqrt{4y+x^2}}$

B   SIMPLIFYING ALGEBRAIC FRACTIONS   [E2.9]

We have observed previously that number fractions can be simplified by cancelling common factors.

For example, $\dfrac{15}{35} = \dfrac{3 \times \cancel{5}^{1}}{7 \times \cancel{5}_{1}} = \dfrac{3}{7}$ where the common factor 5 is cancelled.

The same principle can be applied to algebraic fractions.

> If the numerator and denominator of an algebraic fraction are both written in factored form and common factors are found, we can simplify by **cancelling the common factors**.

For example: $\dfrac{2xy}{4x} = \dfrac{{}^{1}\cancel{2} \times \cancel{x}^{1} \times y}{{}_{1}\cancel{2} \times 2 \times \cancel{x}_{1}}$ {cancelling the common factor $2x$}

$\qquad\qquad = \dfrac{y}{2}$

Fractions such as $\dfrac{3xy}{7z}$ cannot be simplified since the numerator and denominator do not have any common factors.

ERRORS IN CANCELLING

A common **error** in cancelling is to cancel terms, rather than common factors.

For example, this cancelling is **incorrect**:

$$\dfrac{x + \cancel{2}^{1}}{\cancel{6}_{3}} = \dfrac{x + 1}{3}$$

Only common factors can be cancelled, not terms.

The numerator $x + 2$ cannot be written as the product of factors other than $1 \times (x + 2)$. x and 2 are *terms* of the expression, not factors.

Example 2   ◀) Self Tutor

Simplify: **a** $\dfrac{a^2}{2a}$ **b** $\dfrac{6a^2b}{3b}$ **c** $\dfrac{a+b}{a}$

a $\dfrac{a^2}{2a} = \dfrac{a \times \cancel{a}^{1}}{2 \times \cancel{a}_{1}}$

$\qquad = \dfrac{a}{2}$

b $\dfrac{6a^2b}{3b} = \dfrac{{}^{2}\cancel{6} \times a \times a \times \cancel{b}^{1}}{{}_{1}\cancel{3} \times \cancel{b}_{1}}$

$\qquad = \dfrac{2 \times a \times a}{1}$

$\qquad = 2a^2$

c $\dfrac{a+b}{a}$ cannot be simplified as $a+b$ is a sum, not a product.

EXERCISE 20B.1

1 Simplify:

a $\dfrac{2a}{4}$ **b** $\dfrac{4m}{2}$ **c** $\dfrac{6a}{a}$ **d** $\dfrac{6a}{2a}$ **e** $\dfrac{2a^2}{a}$

f $\dfrac{2x^3}{2x}$ **g** $\dfrac{2x^3}{x^2}$ **h** $\dfrac{2x^3}{x^3}$ **i** $\dfrac{2a^2}{4a^3}$ **j** $\dfrac{8m^2}{4m}$

k $\dfrac{4a^2}{a^2}$ **l** $\dfrac{6t}{3t^2}$ **m** $\dfrac{4d^2}{2d}$ **n** $\dfrac{ab^2}{2ab}$ **o** $\dfrac{4ab^2}{6a^2b}$

2   Simplify if possible:

    a $\dfrac{2t}{2}$ **b** $\dfrac{2+t}{2}$ **c** $\dfrac{xy}{x}$

    d $\dfrac{x+y}{x}$ **e** $\dfrac{ac}{bc}$ **f** $\dfrac{a+c}{b+c}$

    g $\dfrac{2a^2}{4a}$ **h** $\dfrac{5a}{9b}$ **i** $\dfrac{14c}{8d}$

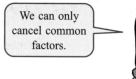

We can only cancel common factors.

Example 3   ◀» *Self Tutor*

Simplify: **a** $\dfrac{(-4b)^2}{2b}$ **b** $\dfrac{18}{3(c-1)}$

    a $\dfrac{(-4b)^2}{2b} = \dfrac{(-4b)\times(-4b)}{2\times b}$ **b** $\dfrac{18}{3(c-1)} = \dfrac{\overset{6}{\cancel{18}}}{\underset{1}{\cancel{3}}(c-1)}$

               $= \dfrac{\overset{8}{\cancel{16}}\times b \times \overset{1}{\cancel{b}}}{\underset{1}{\cancel{2}}\times \cancel{b}_1}$ $= \dfrac{6}{c-1}$

               $= 8b$

---

3   Simplify:

    a $\dfrac{(2a)^2}{a^2}$ **b** $\dfrac{(4n)^2}{8n}$ **c** $\dfrac{(-a)^2}{a}$ **d** $\dfrac{a^2}{(-a)^2}$

    e $\dfrac{(-2a)^2}{4}$ **f** $\dfrac{(-3n)^2}{6n}$ **g** $\dfrac{2b}{(2b^2)^2}$ **h** $\dfrac{(3k^2)^2}{18a^3}$

4   Simplify:

    a $\dfrac{4(x+5)}{2}$ **b** $\dfrac{2(n+5)}{12}$ **c** $\dfrac{7(b+2)}{14}$ **d** $\dfrac{6(k-2)}{8}$

    e $\dfrac{15}{3(t-1)}$ **f** $\dfrac{10}{25(k+4)}$ **g** $\dfrac{4}{12(x-3)}$ **h** $\dfrac{20(p+4)}{12}$

Example 4   ◀» *Self Tutor*

Simplify: **a** $\dfrac{(2x+3)(x+4)}{5(2x+3)}$ **b** $\dfrac{12(x+4)^2}{3(x+4)}$

    a $\dfrac{^1\cancel{(2x+3)}(x+4)}{5\cancel{(2x+3)}_1} = \dfrac{(x+4)}{5}$ **b** $\dfrac{12(x+4)^2}{3(x+4)} = \dfrac{^4\cancel{12}(x+4)\cancel{(x+4)}^1}{_1\cancel{3}\cancel{(x+4)}_1}$

                        $= \dfrac{x+4}{5}$ $= 4(x+4)$

---

5   Simplify:

    a $\dfrac{(x+4)(x+2)}{9(x+4)}$ **b** $\dfrac{12(a-3)}{(a-3)(a+1)}$ **c** $\dfrac{(x+y)(x-y)}{3(x-y)}$ **d** $\dfrac{(x+y)^2}{x+y}$

    e $\dfrac{2(x+2)}{(x+2)^2}$ **f** $\dfrac{(a+5)^2}{3(a+5)}$ **g** $\dfrac{2xy(x-y)}{6x(x-y)}$ **h** $\dfrac{5(y+2)(y-3)}{15(y+2)}$

    i $\dfrac{x(x+1)(x+2)}{3x(x+2)}$ **j** $\dfrac{3(b-4)}{6(b-4)^2}$ **k** $\dfrac{8(p+q)^2}{12(p+q)}$ **l** $\dfrac{24(r-2)}{15(r-2)^2}$

$$\text{m} \quad \frac{x^2(x+2)}{x(x+2)(x-1)} \qquad \text{n} \quad \frac{(x+2)^2(x+1)}{4(x+2)} \qquad \text{o} \quad \frac{2(x+2)^2(x-1)^2}{8x(x+2)}$$

FACTORISATION AND SIMPLIFICATION

It is often necessary to **factorise** either the numerator or denominator before simplification can take place. To do this we use the rules for factorisation that we have seen previously.

Example 5   ◀) **Self Tutor**

Simplify: **a** $\dfrac{3a+9}{3}$ **b** $\dfrac{4a+12}{8}$

a $\dfrac{3a+9}{3} = \dfrac{^1\cancel{3}(a+3)}{\cancel{3}_1}$ **b** $\dfrac{4a+12}{8} = \dfrac{^1\cancel{4}(a+3)}{2\cancel{8}}$

$\phantom{\dfrac{3a+9}{3}} = a+3$ $\phantom{\dfrac{4a+12}{8}} = \dfrac{a+3}{2}$

EXERCISE 20B.2

1 Simplify by factorising:

a $\dfrac{2x+4}{2}$ **b** $\dfrac{3x-6}{3}$ **c** $\dfrac{3x+6}{6}$ **d** $\dfrac{4x-20}{8}$

e $\dfrac{4y+12}{12}$ **f** $\dfrac{6x-30}{4}$ **g** $\dfrac{ax+bx}{x}$ **h** $\dfrac{ax+bx}{cx+dx}$

2 Simplify, if possible:

a $\dfrac{4x+6}{6}$ **b** $\dfrac{4x+6}{5}$ **c** $\dfrac{6a-3}{2}$ **d** $\dfrac{6a-3}{3}$

e $\dfrac{6a+2}{4}$ **f** $\dfrac{3b+9}{2}$ **g** $\dfrac{3b+9}{6}$ **h** $\dfrac{8b-12}{6}$

Example 6   ◀) **Self Tutor**

Simplify by factorising:

a $\dfrac{ab+ac}{b+c}$ **b** $\dfrac{6x^2-6xy}{3x-3y}$

a $\dfrac{ab+ac}{b+c} = \dfrac{a(b+c)}{b+c}$ ◀—— HCF is a

$\phantom{\dfrac{ab+ac}{b+c}} = \dfrac{a\cancel{(b+c)}^1}{\cancel{(b+c)}_1}$

$\phantom{\dfrac{ab+ac}{b+c}} = a$

b $\dfrac{6x^2-6xy}{3x-3y} = \dfrac{6x(x-y)}{3(x-y)}$ ◀—— HCF is $6x$
 ◀—— HCF is 3

$\phantom{\dfrac{6x^2-6xy}{3x-3y}} = \dfrac{^2\cancel{6} \times x \times \cancel{(x-y)}^1}{1\cancel{3} \times \cancel{(x-y)}_1}$

$\phantom{\dfrac{6x^2-6xy}{3x-3y}} = 2x$

---

3 Simplify by factorising:

a $\dfrac{3x+6}{4x+8}$ **b** $\dfrac{5x-15}{3x-9}$ **c** $\dfrac{ax+bx}{a+b}$ **d** $\dfrac{16x-8}{20x-10}$

e $\dfrac{a+b}{ay+by}$ **f** $\dfrac{ax+bx}{ay+by}$ **g** $\dfrac{4x^2+8x}{x+2}$ **h** $\dfrac{3x^2+9x}{x+3}$

i $\dfrac{5x^2-5xy}{7x-7y}$ **j** $\dfrac{9b^2-9ab}{12b-12a}$ **k** $\dfrac{6x^2-18x}{9x-27}$ **l** $\dfrac{6a+6b}{8a^3+4a^2b}$

Example 7
◄》 Self Tutor

Simplify: **a** $\dfrac{6a - 6b}{b - a}$ **b** $\dfrac{xy^2 - xy}{1 - y}$

$b - a = -1(a - b)$
is a useful rule.

a $\dfrac{6a - 6b}{b - a}$

$= \dfrac{6\cancel{(a - b)}^1}{-1\cancel{(a - b)}_1}$

$= -6$

b $\dfrac{xy^2 - xy}{1 - y}$

$= \dfrac{xy\cancel{(y - 1)}^1}{-1\cancel{(y - 1)}_1}$

$= -xy$

4 Simplify:

a $\dfrac{2x - 2y}{y - x}$ **b** $\dfrac{3x - 3y}{2y - 2x}$ **c** $\dfrac{m - n}{n - m}$ **d** $\dfrac{r - 2s}{4s - 2r}$

e $\dfrac{3r - 6s}{2s - r}$ **f** $\dfrac{2x - 2}{x - x^2}$ **g** $\dfrac{ab^2 - ab}{2 - 2b}$ **h** $\dfrac{4x^2 - 4x}{2 - 2x}$

Example 8
◄》 Self Tutor

Simplify: **a** $\dfrac{x^2 - 1}{x^2 + 3x + 2}$ **b** $\dfrac{6x^2 + 10x - 4}{18x^2 + 3x - 3}$

a $\dfrac{x^2 - 1}{x^2 + 3x + 2} = \dfrac{(x - 1)\cancel{(x + 1)}^1}{(x + 2)\cancel{(x + 1)}_1}$

$= \dfrac{x - 1}{x + 2}$

b $\dfrac{6x^2 + 10x - 4}{18x^2 + 3x - 3} = \dfrac{2(3x^2 + 5x - 2)}{3(6x^2 + x - 1)}$

$= \dfrac{2\cancel{(3x - 1)}^1(x + 2)}{3\cancel{(3x - 1)}_1(2x + 1)}$

$= \dfrac{2(x + 2)}{3(2x + 1)}$

5 Simplify:

a $\dfrac{x^2 - 1}{x - 1}$ **b** $\dfrac{x^2 - 1}{x + 1}$ **c** $\dfrac{x^2 - 1}{1 - x}$ **d** $\dfrac{x + 2}{x^2 - 4}$

e $\dfrac{a^2 - b^2}{a + b}$ **f** $\dfrac{a^2 - b^2}{b - a}$ **g** $\dfrac{2x + 2}{x^2 - 1}$ **h** $\dfrac{9 - x^2}{3x - x^2}$

i $\dfrac{3x^2 - 3y^2}{2xy - 2y^2}$ **j** $\dfrac{2b^2 - 2a^2}{a^2 - ab}$ **k** $\dfrac{4xy - y^2}{16x^2 - y^2}$ **l** $\dfrac{4x(x - 4)}{16 - x^2}$

6 Simplify:

a $\dfrac{x^2 - x - 2}{x - 2}$ **b** $\dfrac{a + 3}{a^2 - 2a - 15}$ **c** $\dfrac{2x^2 + 2x}{x^2 - 4x - 5}$

d $\dfrac{x^2 - 4}{x^2 + 4x + 4}$ **e** $\dfrac{x^2 - x - 12}{x^2 - 5x + 4}$ **f** $\dfrac{x^2 + 2x + 1}{1 - x^2}$

g $\dfrac{n^2 - n - 20}{n^2 + 7n + 12}$ **h** $\dfrac{2x^2 + 5x + 2}{2x^2 + 7x + 3}$ **i** $\dfrac{3x^2 + 7x + 2}{6x^2 - x - 1}$

j $\dfrac{8x^2 + 2x - 1}{4x^2 - 5x + 1}$ **k** $\dfrac{12x^2 - 5x - 3}{6x^2 + 5x + 1}$ **l** $\dfrac{15x^2 + 17x - 4}{5x^2 + 9x - 2}$

7 Given that $k \in \mathbb{Z}$ and $k \neq 5$, show that $\dfrac{2k^2 - 7k - 15}{k - 5}$ is an odd integer.

LEARNING
ALGEBRA

C   MULTIPLYING AND DIVIDING ALGEBRAIC FRACTIONS   [E2.9]

Variables are used in algebraic fractions to represent unknown numbers. We can treat algebraic fractions in the same way that we treat numerical fractions, since they are in fact *representing* numerical fractions.

The rules for multiplying and dividing algebraic fractions are identical to those used with numerical fractions.

MULTIPLICATION

To **multiply** two or more fractions, we multiply the numerators to form the new numerator, and we multiply the denominators to form the new denominator.

$$\frac{a}{b} \times \frac{c}{d} = \frac{a \times c}{b \times d} = \frac{ac}{bd}$$

We can then cancel any common factors, and write our answer in simplest form.

Example 9   🔊 *Self Tutor*

Simplify: **a** $\dfrac{3}{m} \times \dfrac{m}{6}$ **b** $\dfrac{3}{m} \times m^2$

a $\dfrac{3}{m} \times \dfrac{m}{6} = \dfrac{{}^1\cancel{3} \times \cancel{m}^1}{{}_1\cancel{m} \times \cancel{6}_2}$

$= \dfrac{1}{2}$

b $\dfrac{3}{m} \times m^2 = \dfrac{3}{m} \times \dfrac{m^2}{1}$

$= \dfrac{3 \times m \times \cancel{m}^1}{{}_1\cancel{m} \times 1}$

$= 3m$

DIVISION

To **divide** by a fraction, we multiply by its **reciprocal**. The reciprocal is obtained by swapping the numerator and denominator.

$$\frac{a}{b} \div \frac{c}{d} = \frac{a}{b} \times \frac{d}{c} = \frac{ad}{bc}$$

Example 10   🔊 *Self Tutor*

Simplify: **a** $\dfrac{4}{n} \div \dfrac{2}{n^2}$ **b** $\dfrac{3}{a} \div 2$

a $\dfrac{4}{n} \div \dfrac{2}{n^2} = \dfrac{4}{n} \times \dfrac{n^2}{2}$

$= \dfrac{{}^2\cancel{4} \times n \times \cancel{n}^1}{{}_1\cancel{n} \times \cancel{2}_1}$

$= 2n$

b $\dfrac{3}{a} \div 2 = \dfrac{3}{a} \times \dfrac{1}{2}$

$= \dfrac{3 \times 1}{a \times 2}$

$= \dfrac{3}{2a}$

The reciprocal of $2 = \dfrac{2}{1}$ is $\dfrac{1}{2}$.

EXERCISE 20C

1 Simplify:

a $\dfrac{x}{2} \times \dfrac{y}{5}$

b $\dfrac{a}{2} \times \dfrac{3}{a}$

c $\dfrac{a}{2} \times a$

d $\dfrac{a}{4} \times \dfrac{2}{3a}$

e $\dfrac{c}{5} \times \dfrac{1}{c}$

f $\dfrac{c}{5} \times \dfrac{c}{2}$

g $\dfrac{a}{b} \times \dfrac{c}{d}$

h $\dfrac{a}{b} \times \dfrac{b}{a}$

i $\dfrac{1}{m^2} \times \dfrac{m}{2}$

j $\dfrac{m}{2} \times \dfrac{4}{m}$

k $\dfrac{a}{x} \times \dfrac{x}{b}$

l $m \times \dfrac{4}{m}$

m $\dfrac{3}{m^2} \times m$

n $\left(\dfrac{a}{b}\right)^2$

o $\left(\dfrac{2}{x}\right)^2$

p $\dfrac{1}{a} \times \dfrac{a}{b} \times \dfrac{b}{c}$

2 Simplify:

a $\dfrac{a}{2} \div \dfrac{a}{3}$

b $\dfrac{2}{a} \div \dfrac{2}{3}$

c $\dfrac{3}{4} \div \dfrac{4}{x}$

d $\dfrac{3}{x} \div \dfrac{4}{x}$

e $\dfrac{2}{n} \div \dfrac{1}{n}$

f $\dfrac{c}{5} \div 5$

g $\dfrac{c}{5} \div c$

h $m \div \dfrac{2}{m}$

i $m \div \dfrac{m}{2}$

j $1 \div \dfrac{m}{n}$

k $\dfrac{3}{g} \div 4$

l $\dfrac{3}{g} \div \dfrac{9}{g^2}$

m $\dfrac{4}{x} \div \dfrac{x^2}{2}$

n $\dfrac{2}{x} \div \dfrac{6}{x^3}$

o $\dfrac{a}{b} \div \dfrac{a^2}{b}$

p $\dfrac{a^2}{5} \div \dfrac{a}{3}$

Example 11

◀) **Self Tutor**

Simplify:

a $\dfrac{y^2 - y}{y - 2} \times \dfrac{3y - 6}{4y - 4}$

b $\dfrac{5m - 20}{4} \div \dfrac{2m - 8}{3}$

a $\dfrac{y^2 - y}{y - 2} \times \dfrac{3y - 6}{4y - 4}$

$= \dfrac{y(y - 1)^1}{y - 2_{\,1}} \times \dfrac{3(y - 2)^1}{4(y - 1)_{\,1}}$

$= \dfrac{3y}{4}$

b $\dfrac{5m - 20}{4} \div \dfrac{2m - 8}{3}$

$= \dfrac{5m - 20}{4} \times \dfrac{3}{2m - 8}$

$= \dfrac{5(m - 4)^1}{4} \times \dfrac{3}{2(m - 4)_{\,1}}$

$= \dfrac{15}{8}$

---

3 Simplify:

a $\dfrac{x^2 + 3x}{x - 2} \times \dfrac{5}{2x + 6}$

b $\dfrac{t - 5}{t^2 + t} \times \dfrac{4t + 4}{3t - 15}$

c $\dfrac{4a - 28}{a} \div \dfrac{a - 7}{5}$

d $\dfrac{6k - 2}{k + 2} \times \dfrac{2k^2 + 4k}{9k - 3}$

e $\dfrac{x^2 - 2x}{x + 5} \div \dfrac{8 - 4x}{2x + 10}$

f $\dfrac{m^2 - 4m}{10m - 2} \div \dfrac{m^2 - 16}{3m + 12}$

D | ADDING AND SUBTRACTING ALGEBRAIC FRACTIONS   [E2.9]

The rules for addition and subtraction of algebraic fractions are identical to those used with numerical fractions.

To **add** two or more fractions, we obtain the *lowest common denominator* and then add the resulting numerators.	$\dfrac{a}{c} + \dfrac{b}{c} = \dfrac{a+b}{c}$
To **subtract** two or more fractions, we obtain the *lowest common denominator* and then subtract the resulting numerators.	$\dfrac{a}{c} - \dfrac{d}{c} = \dfrac{a-d}{c}$

To find the lowest common denominator of numerical fractions, we look for the **lowest common multiple of the denominators**.

For example:
- when finding $\frac{3}{2} + \frac{5}{3}$, the lowest common denominator is 6
- when finding $\frac{5}{6} + \frac{4}{9}$, the lowest common denominator is 18.

The same method is used when there are variables in the denominator.

For example:
- when finding $\dfrac{2}{a} + \dfrac{3}{b}$, the lowest common denominator is ab
- when finding $\dfrac{2}{x} + \dfrac{4}{5x}$, the lowest common denominator is $5x$
- when finding $\dfrac{5}{6x} + \dfrac{4}{9y}$, the lowest common denominator is $18xy$.

Example 12
◀)) *Self Tutor*

Simplify: **a** $\dfrac{x}{2} + \dfrac{3x}{4}$ **b** $\dfrac{a}{3} - \dfrac{2a}{5}$

a $\dfrac{x}{2} + \dfrac{3x}{4}$ $\{\text{LCD} = 4\}$

$= \dfrac{x \times 2}{2 \times 2} + \dfrac{3x}{4}$

$= \dfrac{2x}{4} + \dfrac{3x}{4}$

$= \dfrac{2x + 3x}{4}$

$= \dfrac{5x}{4}$

b $\dfrac{a}{3} - \dfrac{2a}{5}$ $\{\text{LCD} = 15\}$

$= \dfrac{a \times 5}{3 \times 5} - \dfrac{2a \times 3}{5 \times 3}$

$= \dfrac{5a}{15} - \dfrac{6a}{15}$

$= \dfrac{5a - 6a}{15}$

$= -\dfrac{a}{15}$

EXERCISE 20D

1 Simplify by writing as a single fraction:

a $\dfrac{a}{2} + \dfrac{a}{3}$

b $\dfrac{b}{5} - \dfrac{b}{10}$

c $\dfrac{c}{4} + \dfrac{3c}{2}$

d $\dfrac{d}{2} - \dfrac{3}{5}$

e $\dfrac{5}{8} + \dfrac{x}{12}$

f $\dfrac{x}{7} - \dfrac{x}{2}$

g $\dfrac{a}{3} + \dfrac{b}{4}$

h $\dfrac{t}{3} - \dfrac{5t}{9}$

i $\dfrac{m}{7} + \dfrac{2m}{21}$ **j** $\dfrac{5d}{6} - \dfrac{d}{3}$ **k** $\dfrac{3p}{5} - \dfrac{2p}{7}$ **l** $\dfrac{2t}{9} + \dfrac{4t}{15}$

m $\dfrac{7k}{8} - \dfrac{11k}{18}$ **n** $\dfrac{m}{2} + \dfrac{m}{3} + \dfrac{m}{6}$ **o** $\dfrac{a}{2} - \dfrac{a}{3} + \dfrac{a}{4}$ **p** $\dfrac{x}{4} - \dfrac{x}{3} + \dfrac{x}{6}$

q $\dfrac{z}{2} - \dfrac{z}{5} + \dfrac{z}{4}$ **r** $2q - \dfrac{q}{3} + \dfrac{2q}{7}$

Example 13   ◀) Self Tutor

Simplify: **a** $\dfrac{4}{a} + \dfrac{3}{b}$ **b** $\dfrac{5}{x} - \dfrac{4}{3x}$

a $\dfrac{4}{a} + \dfrac{3}{b}$ $\{$LCD $= ab\}$

$= \dfrac{4 \times b}{a \times b} + \dfrac{3 \times a}{b \times a}$

$= \dfrac{4b}{ab} + \dfrac{3a}{ab}$

$= \dfrac{4b + 3a}{ab}$

b $\dfrac{5}{x} - \dfrac{4}{3x}$ $\{$LCD $= 3x\}$

$= \dfrac{5 \times 3}{x \times 3} - \dfrac{4}{3x}$

$= \dfrac{15}{3x} - \dfrac{4}{3x}$

$= \dfrac{15 - 4}{3x}$

$= \dfrac{11}{3x}$

---

2 Simplify:

a $\dfrac{7}{a} + \dfrac{3}{b}$ **b** $\dfrac{3}{a} + \dfrac{2}{c}$ **c** $\dfrac{4}{a} + \dfrac{5}{d}$ **d** $\dfrac{2a}{m} - \dfrac{a}{n}$ **e** $\dfrac{a}{x} + \dfrac{b}{2x}$

f $\dfrac{3}{a} - \dfrac{1}{2a}$ **g** $\dfrac{4}{x} - \dfrac{1}{xy}$ **h** $\dfrac{5}{x} + \dfrac{6}{5x}$ **i** $\dfrac{11}{3z} - \dfrac{3}{4z}$ **j** $\dfrac{a}{b} + \dfrac{c}{d}$

k $\dfrac{3}{a} + \dfrac{a}{2}$ **l** $\dfrac{x}{y} + \dfrac{2}{3}$ **m** $\dfrac{8}{p} - \dfrac{2}{5}$ **n** $\dfrac{x}{6y} + \dfrac{2x}{9y}$ **o** $\dfrac{1}{8t} - \dfrac{3}{5t}$

p $\dfrac{1}{x} + \dfrac{1}{x^2}$ **q** $\dfrac{1}{x} - \dfrac{2}{x^2}$ **r** $\dfrac{5}{2x} + \dfrac{3}{x^2}$ **s** $\dfrac{1}{x^2 y} + \dfrac{2}{xy}$ **t** $\dfrac{2}{x} - \dfrac{1}{xy^2}$

u $\dfrac{3}{2x^2} - \dfrac{4}{x}$ **v** $\dfrac{q}{p^2} - \dfrac{1}{pq}$ **w** $\dfrac{3}{rs} + \dfrac{2r}{s^2}$ **x** $\dfrac{3}{x^2 y} - \dfrac{1}{2y^2}$

Example 14   ◀) Self Tutor

Simplify: **a** $\dfrac{b}{3} + 1$ **b** $\dfrac{a}{4} - a$

a $\dfrac{b}{3} + 1 = \dfrac{b}{3} + \dfrac{3}{3}$

$= \dfrac{b + 3}{3}$

b $\dfrac{a}{4} - a = \dfrac{a}{4} - \dfrac{a \times 4}{1 \times 4}$

$= \dfrac{a}{4} - \dfrac{4a}{4}$

$= \dfrac{-3a}{4}$

$= -\dfrac{3a}{4}$

3 Simplify by writing as a single fraction:

a $\dfrac{x}{2} + 1$ **b** $\dfrac{y}{3} - 1$ **c** $\dfrac{a}{2} + a$ **d** $\dfrac{b}{4} - 3$

e $\dfrac{x}{2} - 4$ **f** $2 + \dfrac{a}{3}$ **g** $x - \dfrac{x}{5}$ **h** $2 + \dfrac{1}{x}$

i $5 - \dfrac{2}{x}$ **j** $a + \dfrac{2}{a}$ **k** $\dfrac{3}{b} + b$ **l** $\dfrac{1}{x^2} - 2x$

Example 15   ◀)) *Self Tutor*

Write as a single fraction: **a** $\dfrac{x}{6} + \dfrac{x-2}{3}$ **b** $\dfrac{x+1}{2} - \dfrac{x-2}{3}$

a $\dfrac{x}{6} + \dfrac{x-2}{3}$ $\{\text{LCD} = 6\}$

$= \dfrac{x}{6} + \dfrac{2}{2}\left(\dfrac{x-2}{3}\right)$

$= \dfrac{x}{6} + \dfrac{2(x-2)}{6}$

$= \dfrac{x + 2(x-2)}{6}$

$= \dfrac{x + 2x - 4}{6} = \dfrac{3x - 4}{6}$

b $\dfrac{x+1}{2} - \dfrac{x-2}{3}$ $\{\text{LCD} = 6\}$

$= \dfrac{3}{3}\left(\dfrac{x+1}{2}\right) - \dfrac{2}{2}\left(\dfrac{x-2}{3}\right)$

$= \dfrac{3(x+1)}{6} - \dfrac{2(x-2)}{6}$

$= \dfrac{3(x+1) - 2(x-2)}{6}$

$= \dfrac{3x + 3 - 2x + 4}{6} = \dfrac{x+7}{6}$

---

4 Write as a single fraction, and hence simplify:

a $\dfrac{x}{2} + \dfrac{x+1}{3}$ **b** $\dfrac{x-1}{4} - \dfrac{x}{2}$ **c** $\dfrac{2x}{3} + \dfrac{x+3}{4}$ **d** $\dfrac{x+1}{2} - \dfrac{x-1}{3}$

e $\dfrac{x-1}{3} + \dfrac{1-2x}{4}$ **f** $\dfrac{2x+3}{2} + \dfrac{2x-3}{3}$ **g** $\dfrac{x}{3} - \dfrac{x+1}{4}$ **h** $\dfrac{x}{6} + \dfrac{3x-1}{5}$

i $\dfrac{a+b}{3} - \dfrac{b-a}{2}$ **j** $\dfrac{x+1}{5} + \dfrac{2x-1}{4}$ **k** $\dfrac{x}{6} - \dfrac{2-x}{5}$ **l** $\dfrac{2x-1}{5} - \dfrac{x}{4}$

m $\dfrac{x}{8} - \dfrac{1-x}{4}$ **n** $\dfrac{x-1}{5} + \dfrac{2x-7}{3}$ **o** $\dfrac{1-3x}{4} - \dfrac{2x+1}{3}$

Example 16   ◀)) *Self Tutor*

Write as a single fraction: **a** $\dfrac{1}{x} + \dfrac{2}{x-1}$ **b** $\dfrac{2}{x-1} - \dfrac{3}{x+1}$

a $\dfrac{1}{x} + \dfrac{2}{x-1}$ $\{\text{LCD} = x(x-1)\}$

$= \dfrac{1}{x}\left(\dfrac{x-1}{x-1}\right) + \left(\dfrac{2}{x-1}\right)\dfrac{x}{x}$

$= \dfrac{1(x-1) + 2x}{x(x-1)}$

$= \dfrac{x - 1 + 2x}{x(x-1)}$

$= \dfrac{3x - 1}{x(x-1)}$

b $\dfrac{2}{x-1} - \dfrac{3}{x+1}$ $\{\text{LCD} = (x-1)(x+1)\}$

$= \left(\dfrac{2}{x-1}\right)\left(\dfrac{x+1}{x+1}\right) - \left(\dfrac{3}{x+1}\right)\left(\dfrac{x-1}{x-1}\right)$

$= \dfrac{2(x+1) - 3(x-1)}{(x-1)(x+1)}$

$= \dfrac{2x + 2 - 3x + 3}{(x-1)(x+1)}$

$= \dfrac{-x + 5}{(x-1)(x+1)}$ or $\dfrac{5-x}{(x-1)(x+1)}$

5 Simplify:

a $\dfrac{3}{x} + \dfrac{4}{x+1}$

b $\dfrac{5}{x+2} - \dfrac{3}{x}$

c $\dfrac{4}{x+1} - \dfrac{3}{x-1}$

d $3 + \dfrac{1}{x+2}$

e $\dfrac{1}{x} + \dfrac{4}{x-4}$

f $\dfrac{2}{x+3} - 4$

g $\dfrac{x+1}{x-1} + \dfrac{x}{x+1}$

h $\dfrac{5}{x} + \dfrac{6}{x-2}$

i $\dfrac{2}{x+2} - \dfrac{4}{x+1}$

j $\dfrac{x}{x-1} + \dfrac{4}{2x+1}$

k $\dfrac{5}{x-1} + \dfrac{x-2}{x+3}$

l $\dfrac{x}{x+5} - \dfrac{x}{x-3}$

m $\dfrac{1}{x} + \dfrac{1}{x+1} + \dfrac{1}{x+2}$

n $\dfrac{2}{x} - \dfrac{5}{x+3} + \dfrac{3}{x-4}$

o $\dfrac{x}{x-1} - \dfrac{1}{x} + \dfrac{x}{x+1}$

6 Answer the **Opening Problem** on page **319**.

7 Write as a single fraction:

a $\dfrac{2}{x(x+1)} + \dfrac{1}{x+1}$

b $\dfrac{2x}{x-3} + \dfrac{4}{(x+2)(x-3)}$

c $\dfrac{3}{(x-2)(x+3)} + \dfrac{x}{x+3}$

d $\dfrac{x+5}{x-2} - \dfrac{63}{(x-2)(x+7)}$

e $\dfrac{3}{x^2+2x} + \dfrac{5}{x+2}$

f $\dfrac{7}{x} - \dfrac{4}{x^2-3x}$

g $\dfrac{1}{x^2-2x-8} + \dfrac{6}{x-4}$

h $\dfrac{x^2+5x}{x^2+4x-5} - \dfrac{3x}{x-1}$

8 **a** Write $\dfrac{a+2}{a+1} - \dfrac{a+1}{a}$ as a single fraction.

   b Hence show that if a is positive, then $\dfrac{a+2}{a+1} - \dfrac{a+1}{a}$ is negative.

9 A *unit fraction* is a fraction with numerator 1, for example $\frac{1}{4}$ or $\frac{1}{7}$.

   a Show that $\dfrac{1}{n} = \dfrac{1}{n+1} + \dfrac{1}{n(n+1)}$.

   b Hence write the following unit fractions as the sum of two other unit fractions:

   i $\frac{1}{2}$ **ii** $\frac{1}{5}$ **iii** $\frac{1}{9}$

10 Simplify:

a $\dfrac{\frac{x}{x-2}-3}{x-3}$

b $\dfrac{\frac{3x}{x+4}-1}{x-2}$

c $\dfrac{\frac{x^2}{x+2}-1}{x+1}$

d $\dfrac{\frac{x^2}{2-x}+9}{x-3}$

e $\dfrac{\frac{1}{x^2}-\frac{1}{4}}{x-2}$

f $\dfrac{\frac{x-3}{x^2}-\frac{1}{16}}{x-4}$

11 For each of the following expressions:

   i Write the expression as a single fraction.

   ii Hence find a value of x for which the expression is zero.

   iii Find the values of x for which the expression is undefined.

a $\dfrac{2x}{x+1} - \dfrac{4}{(x-1)(x+1)}$

b $\dfrac{6}{(x+2)(x+5)} + \dfrac{x}{x+2}$

Review set 20A

1 If $p = 5$, $q = -3$, and $r = 6$, evaluate:

a $\dfrac{r}{q}$

b $\dfrac{p-q}{p+q}$

c $\dfrac{\sqrt{p^2-16}}{r-q}$

d $\dfrac{3q-2}{r^2-p^2}$

2 Evaluate $\dfrac{x^2 + y}{x - y}$ given: **a** $x = 4, \ y = 2$ **b** $x = -1, \ y = 5$

3 Simplify:

    a $\dfrac{(2t)^2}{6t}$ **b** $\dfrac{16a + 8b}{6a + 3b}$ **c** $\dfrac{x(x - 4)}{3(x - 4)}$ **d** $\dfrac{8}{4x + 8}$

4 Simplify:

    a $\dfrac{2x + 6}{x^2 - 9}$ **b** $\dfrac{x^2 + 4x + 4}{x^2 + 2x}$ **c** $\dfrac{3x^2 - 6x}{3x^2 - 5x - 2}$

5 Simplify:

    a $\dfrac{2a - 2b}{b - a}$ **b** $\dfrac{5x - 15}{3x - x^2}$ **c** $\dfrac{16 - x^2}{2x - 8}$

6 Simplify:

    a $\dfrac{a}{b} \times \dfrac{b}{3}$ **b** $\dfrac{a}{b} \div \dfrac{b}{3}$ **c** $\dfrac{a}{b} + \dfrac{b}{3}$ **d** $\dfrac{a}{b} - \dfrac{b}{3}$

7 Simplify:

    a $\dfrac{7x - 14}{x} \times \dfrac{3}{x - 2}$ **b** $\dfrac{t^2 - 3t}{6t + 6} \times \dfrac{t + 1}{4t - 12}$

8 Simplify:

    a $\dfrac{9}{n} \div 6$ **b** $\dfrac{7}{3x - 6} \div \dfrac{x + 5}{x^2 - 2x}$

9 Write as a single fraction:

    a $\dfrac{2x}{3} + \dfrac{x}{4}$ **b** $2 + \dfrac{x}{7}$ **c** $\dfrac{x}{4} - 1$ **d** $\dfrac{x}{2} + \dfrac{x}{4} - \dfrac{x}{3}$

10 Simplify:

    a $\dfrac{x}{3} + \dfrac{x - 1}{4}$ **b** $\dfrac{x + 2}{3} - \dfrac{2 - x}{6}$ **c** $\dfrac{2x + 1}{5} - \dfrac{x - 1}{10}$

11 Simplify:

    a $\dfrac{1}{x + 1} + \dfrac{2}{x - 2}$ **b** $\dfrac{5}{x - 1} - \dfrac{4}{x + 1}$ **c** $\dfrac{1}{x^2} + \dfrac{1}{x + 1}$

12 **a** Write as a single fraction: **i** $a - \dfrac{9}{a}$ **ii** $1 - \dfrac{a}{3}$

    b Hence simplify $\left(a - \dfrac{9}{a}\right) \div \left(1 - \dfrac{a}{3}\right)$.

    c Evaluate $\left(a - \dfrac{9}{a}\right) \div \left(1 - \dfrac{a}{3}\right)$ for:

      i $a = 1$ **ii** $a = 3$ **iii** $a = 5$

Review set 20B

1 If $m = -4, \ n = 3,$ and $p = 6,$ evaluate:

    a $\dfrac{p}{m + n}$ **b** $\dfrac{p - 2n}{m + n}$ **c** $\dfrac{p - m}{\sqrt{m^2 + n^2}}$

2 Simplify:

   a $\dfrac{(3x)^2}{6x^3}$ **b** $\dfrac{3a+6b}{3}$ **c** $\dfrac{(x+2)^2}{x^2+2x}$

3 Simplify:

   a $\dfrac{a+b}{3b+3a}$ **b** $\dfrac{2x^2-8}{x+2}$ **c** $\dfrac{x^2-6x+9}{4x-12}$

4 Simplify:

   a $\dfrac{m}{n}\times\dfrac{2}{n}$ **b** $\dfrac{m}{n}\div\dfrac{2}{n}$ **c** $m^2\div\dfrac{n}{m}$

5 Simplify:

   a $\dfrac{3}{x}+\dfrac{5}{2x}$ **b** $\dfrac{6}{y}-\dfrac{a}{b}$ **c** $\dfrac{8}{3x}+\dfrac{1}{4x}$

6 Simplify:

   a $\dfrac{3x}{7}-\dfrac{x}{14}$ **b** $\dfrac{4}{3x}+\dfrac{3}{x^2}$

7 Write as a single fraction:

   a $5+\dfrac{x}{2}$ **b** $3-\dfrac{y}{x}$ **c** $1+\dfrac{x}{2}+\dfrac{y}{3}$

8 Simplify:

   a $\dfrac{y^2-5y}{y+2}\times\dfrac{3}{2y-10}$ **b** $\dfrac{9-3x}{4x+16}\div\dfrac{x^2-3x}{x+4}$

9 Simplify:

   a $\dfrac{x}{4}-\dfrac{2-x}{8}$ **b** $\dfrac{x+5}{2}+\dfrac{2x+1}{5}$ **c** $\dfrac{3-x}{6}-\dfrac{2x}{9}$

10 Simplify:

   a $\dfrac{2}{x-1}-\dfrac{3}{x+2}$ **b** $\dfrac{1}{x-1}-\dfrac{2}{x^2}$ **c** $\dfrac{x}{x+2}-\dfrac{2}{x}+\dfrac{x}{x+3}$

11 If m is an even integer and $m\neq-10$, show that $\dfrac{70-m^2-3m}{m+10}$ is an odd integer.

12 **a** Evaluate $(x+y)\div\left(\dfrac{1}{x}+\dfrac{1}{y}\right)$ for: **i** $x=3,\ y=4$ **ii** $x=5,\ y=10$

   b In terms of x and y, what do you suspect $(x+y)\div\left(\dfrac{1}{x}+\dfrac{1}{y}\right)$ simplifies to?

   c Prove your answer to **b** is correct by first writing $\dfrac{1}{x}+\dfrac{1}{y}$ as a single fraction.

   d Hence, state the value of $\dfrac{41}{\frac{1}{21}+\frac{1}{20}}$.

13 Consider the expression $\dfrac{24}{x^2-4}-\dfrac{3x}{x+2}$.

   a Write the expression as a single fraction.

   b Hence find the value of x for which the expression is zero.

   c For what values of x is the expression undefined?

Similarity

21

Contents:

A Similar figures   [E5.5]
B Similar triangles   [E5.5]
C Problem solving   [E5.5]
D Areas of similar objects [E5.5]
E Volumes of similar objects [E5.5]

Opening problem

Nanna's Treat is a start-up company manufacturing homestyle jams and marmalade. They will sell their products in cylindrical glass jars in three sizes: 300 g, 500 g, and 750 g.

The dimensions of the jars will be *in proportion*.

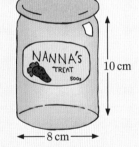

Things to think about:

a What does it mean that the dimensions are *in proportion*?

b Can you write down the ratio of the jars':
    i capacities   **ii** heights   **iii** surface areas?

c Can you find:
    i the height of the 300 g jar   **ii** the base radius of the 750 g jar
    iii the surface area of the 300 g jar, excluding the lid?

In previous courses you should have seen that **congruent figures** are identical in every respect apart from position. In this Chapter we will study **similar figures** which have the same *shape* but are not necessarily the same *size*.

A   SIMILAR FIGURES   [E5.5]

The word *similar* suggests a comparison between objects which have some, but not all, properties in common. In mathematics, similar figures have the same **shape**, but not necessarily the same **size**.

Two figures are **similar** if one is an enlargement of the other.

Common examples of similar figures include television images, photo enlargements, house plans, maps, and model cars.

A'B'C'D' is an enlargement of ABCD. The two figures are therefore similar.

Notice that

$$\frac{A'B'}{AB} = \frac{B'C'}{BC} = \frac{C'D'}{CD} = \frac{D'A'}{DA} = 3,$$

so the corresponding side lengths are in the **same ratio**.

We say that $k = 3$ is the **scale factor** for the enlargement.

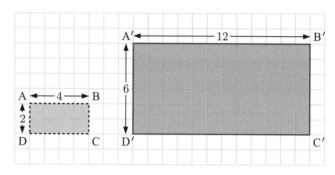

When a figure is enlarged or reduced, the sizes of its angles do not change. The figures are therefore **equiangular**.

> Two figures are **similar** if:
> - the figures are **equiangular** *and*
> - the corresponding side lengths are in the **same ratio**.
>
> We say that the figures are *in proportion*.

Example 1   ◀⅃) *Self Tutor*

Determine whether the following pairs of figures are similar:

a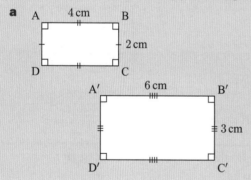

b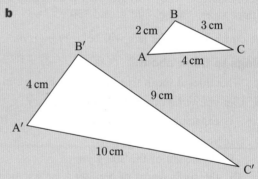

a $\dfrac{A'B'}{AB} = \dfrac{6}{4} = \dfrac{3}{2}$ and $\dfrac{B'C'}{BC} = \dfrac{3}{2}$

∴ the corresponding side lengths are in the same ratio.

The figures are also equiangular, so the figures are similar.

b $\dfrac{A'B'}{AB} = \dfrac{4}{2} = 2$ and $\dfrac{B'C'}{BC} = \dfrac{9}{3} = 3$

∴ the corresponding side lengths are *not* in the same ratio.

∴ the figures are not similar.

EXERCISE 21A

1 Determine whether the following pairs of figures are similar:

a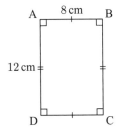

b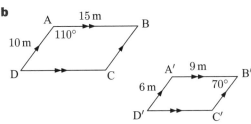

2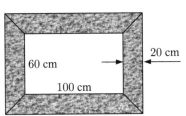

A 20 cm wide picture frame surrounds a painting which is 100 cm by 60 cm.

Are the two rectangles shown here similar?

3 Comment on the truth of the following statements. For any statement which is false, you should justify your answer with an illustration.

   a All circles are similar.
                                                 b All parallelograms are similar.

   c All squares are similar.
                                                 d All rectangles are similar.

Example 2
                                                             ◀)) *Self Tutor*

These figures are similar.
Find x, rounded to 2 decimal places.

Since the figures are similar, their corresponding sides are in the same ratio.

$$\therefore \quad \frac{x}{4} = \frac{5}{3}$$
$$\therefore \quad x = \frac{5}{3} \times 4$$
$$\therefore \quad x = \frac{20}{3}$$
$$\therefore \quad x \approx 6.67$$

4 These figures are similar. Find x exactly:

a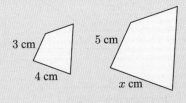

b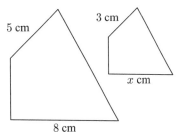

c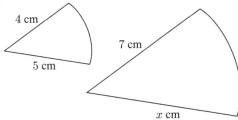

d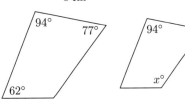

5 Narelle is drawing a scale diagram of her bedroom, which is a rectangle 4.2 m long by 3.6 m wide. On her diagram she draws her room 7 cm long.

    a How wide will her bedroom be on her diagram?

    b What is the scale factor for the diagram?

6   **a** If a line of length 2 cm is enlarged with scale factor 3, find its new length.

    b A 3 cm length has been enlarged to 4.5 cm. Find the scale factor k.

7 Rectangles ABCD and FGHE are similar. Find the length of FG.

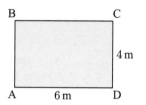 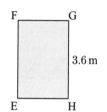

8 Find x given that triangle ABC is similar to triangle A′B′C′:

a

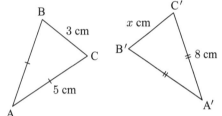

b

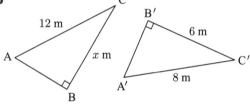

c

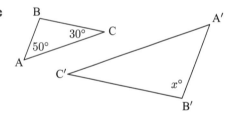

d

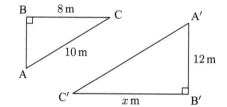

9 Sketch two quadrilaterals that:

    a are equiangular, but not similar

    b have sides in proportion, but are not similar.

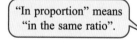

"In proportion" means "in the same ratio".

10 Can you draw two triangles which are equiangular but not similar?

Discussion

- Are these figures similar? Justify your answer using the definition of similar figures.
- What else can you say about these figures?

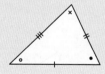 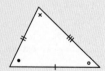

B   SIMILAR TRIANGLES   [E5.5]

In the previous Exercise we saw that quadrilaterals that are equiangular are not necessarily similar, and quadrilaterals that have sides in proportion are not necessarily similar.

However, if *triangles* are equiangular, then their corresponding sides *must* be in the same ratio, and vice versa. So, to show that two triangles are similar, we only need to show that **one** of these properties is true.

TESTS FOR TRIANGLE SIMILARITY

Two triangles are similar if either:
- they are equiangular   *or*   • their side lengths are in the same ratio.

Notice that:
- either of these properties is sufficient to prove that two triangles are similar
- since the angles of any triangle add up to $180°$, if two angles of one triangle are equal to two angles of another triangle, then the remaining angles of the triangles must also be equal.

Example 3   ◀ᴗ Self Tutor

Show that the following figures possess similar triangles:

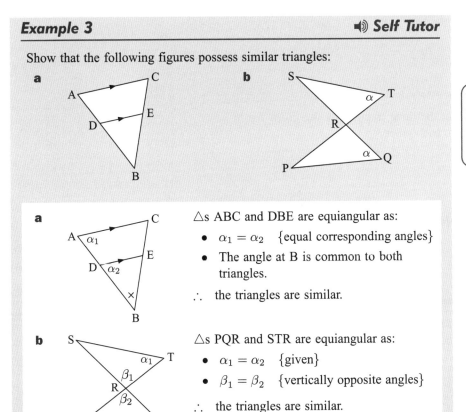

If two triangles are similar, we list corresponding vertices in the same order.

a $\triangle$s ABC and DBE are equiangular as:
- $\alpha_1 = \alpha_2$ {equal corresponding angles}
- The angle at B is common to both triangles.

∴   the triangles are similar.

b $\triangle$s PQR and STR are equiangular as:
- $\alpha_1 = \alpha_2$ {given}
- $\beta_1 = \beta_2$ {vertically opposite angles}

∴   the triangles are similar.

EXERCISE 21B.1

1 Show that the following figures possess similar triangles:

a
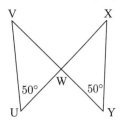

b
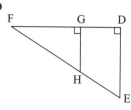

> If two angles of one triangle are equal in size to two angles of another triangle, then the remaining angles of the triangles must also be equal.

c
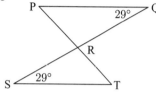

d
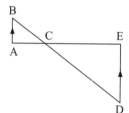

e
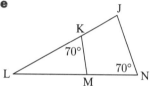

f
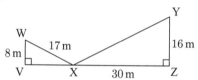

2 **a** Show that $\widehat{ACB} = \alpha$.

    b Hence show that the three triangles in the given figure are all similar to each other.

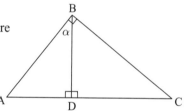

FINDING SIDE LENGTHS

Once we have established that two triangles are similar, we may use the fact that corresponding sides are in the same ratio to find unknown lengths.

Example 4   ◀) Self Tutor

Establish that a pair of triangles is similar, and find x:

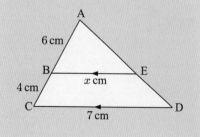
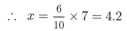

$\triangle$s ABE and ACD are equiangular as:

- $\alpha_1 = \alpha_2$ {equal corresponding angles}
- $\beta_1 = \beta_2$ {equal corresponding angles}

$\therefore$ the triangles are similar.

$\therefore \dfrac{BE}{CD} = \dfrac{AB}{AC}$ {same ratio}

$\therefore \dfrac{x}{7} = \dfrac{6}{6+4}$

$\therefore x = \dfrac{6}{10} \times 7 = 4.2$

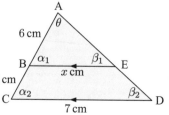

When solving similar triangle problems, it may be useful to use a table. Consider the following method, written in the context of the Example on the previous page:

Step 1:   Label equal angles.

Step 2:   Show that the triangles are equiangular, and hence similar.

Step 3:   Put the information in a table, showing the equal angles and the side lengths *opposite* these angles.

Step 4:   Use the columns to write down the equation for the ratio of the corresponding sides.

Step 5:   Solve the equation.

α	β	θ	
-	6	x	small $\triangle$
-	10	7	large $\triangle$

from which $\dfrac{6}{10} = \dfrac{x}{7}$

$\therefore\ x = 4.2$

Example 5   ◀) Self Tutor

Establish that a pair of triangles is similar, and hence find x.

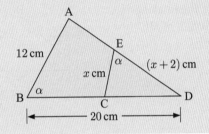

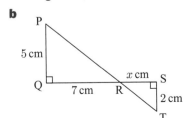

$\triangle$s ABD and CED are equiangular since:

- $\widehat{ABD} = \widehat{CED}$ {given}
- $\widehat{D}$ is common

$\therefore$ the triangles are similar.

$\therefore\ \widehat{BAD} = \widehat{ECD}$, and we call this angle β.

Using the table, $\dfrac{x+2}{20} = \dfrac{x}{12}$ {same ratio}

$\therefore\ \dfrac{3(x+2)}{60} = \dfrac{5x}{60}$

$\therefore\ 3x+6 = 5x$

$\therefore\ 2x = 6$

$\therefore\ x = 3$

α	β	θ	
-	$x+2$	x	small $\triangle$
-	20	12	large $\triangle$

EXERCISE 21B.2

1 In each figure, establish that a pair of triangles is similar. Hence find x.

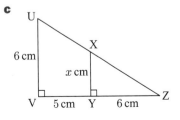

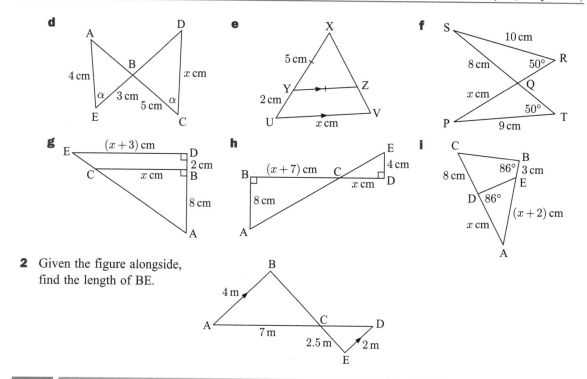

2 Given the figure alongside, find the length of BE.

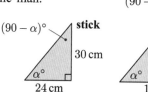

<table>
<tr><td>**C**</td><td># PROBLEM SOLVING</td><td>**[E5.5]**</td></tr>
</table>

The properties of similar triangles have been known since ancient times.   However, even with the technologically advanced measuring instruments available today, similar triangles are still important for finding heights and distances which would otherwise be difficult to measure.

Step 1: Read the question carefully. Draw a diagram showing all of the given information.	Diagrams are very useful. Make sure your diagrams are neat and large enough.
Step 2: Introduce a variable such as x, for the unknown quantity to be found.	
Step 3: Establish that a pair of triangles are similar, and hence write an equation involving the variable.	
Step 4: Solve the equation.	
Step 5: Answer the question in a sentence.	

Example 6   ◀》 *Self Tutor*

When a 30 cm stick is stood vertically on the ground, it casts a 24 cm shadow.
At the same time a man casts a shadow of length 152 cm. How tall is the man?

The sun shines at the same angle on both the stick and the man.
We suppose this is angle $\alpha°$ to the horizontal.
Let the man be h cm tall.

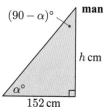

The triangles are equiangular and therefore similar.

$\therefore \dfrac{h}{30} = \dfrac{152}{24}$ {same ratio}

$\therefore h = \dfrac{152}{24} \times 30$

$\therefore h = 190$

The man is 190 cm tall.

$\alpha°$	$(90-\alpha)°$	$90°$	
h cm	152 cm	-	large $\triangle$
30 cm	24 cm	-	small $\triangle$

EXERCISE 21C

1 Find the height of the pine tree:

a
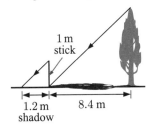

b
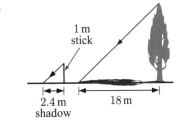

2
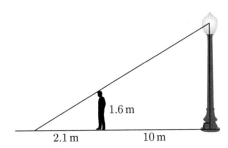

When a 1.6 m tall person stands 10 m from the base of an electric light pole, the shadow of the person is 2.1 m long.
Find the height of the globe above ground level.

3 A ramp is built to enable wheelchair access to a building that is 24 cm above ground level. The ramp has a constant slope of 2 in 15, which means that for every 15 cm horizontally it rises 2 cm. Calculate the length of the base of the ramp.

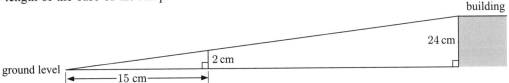

4 A piece of timber rests against both the top of a fence and the wall behind it, as shown.
   a Find how far up the wall the timber reaches.
   b Find the length of the timber.

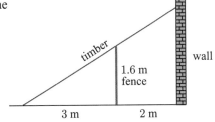

5

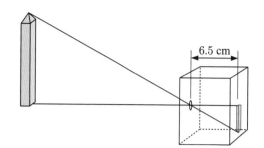

A pinhole camera displays an image on a screen as shown alongside. The monument shown is 21 m tall, and its image is 3.5 cm high. The distance from the pinhole to the image is 6.5 cm.

How far is the pinhole from the monument?

6

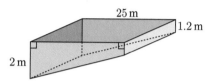

A swimming pool is 1.2 m deep at one end, and 2 m deep at the other end. The pool is 25 m long. Isaac jumps into the pool 10 metres from the shallow end. How deep is the pool at this point?

7 A, B, C, and D are pegs on the bank of a canal which has parallel straight sides. C and D are directly opposite each other. AB = 30 m and BC = 140 m.

When I walk from A directly away from the bank, I reach a point E, 25 m from A, where E, B, and D line up.

How wide is the canal?

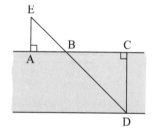

8

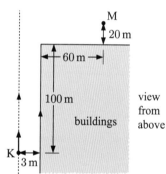

Kalev is currently at K, driving with speed 10 m/s along a street parallel to a line of buildings. A monument is located at M.

How long will it be before Kalev will be able to see the monument?

9 The dimensions of a tennis court are given alongside.

Samantha hits a shot from the base line corner at S. The ball passes over her service line at T such that UT = 1.92 m.

The ball then travels over the net and lands on the opposite base line AD.

a Find the length of:

  i SU   **ii** BC

b A ball landing on the base line is "in" if it lands between points B and C.

Assuming the ball continues along the same trajectory, will it land "in"?

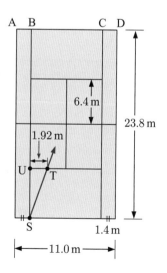

10 Squash player Kenny is about to play a shot at K. He wants to rebound the ball off the wall at P so that it hits the corner at Q. Locate the position of P by finding the length PR.

You may assume that the ball leaves the wall at the same angle with which it entered, so $\widehat{KPR} = \widehat{QPS}$.

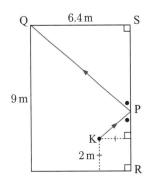

11 Alison and Brianna are in the basement of a department store.

Alison steps onto an escalator to the ground floor, and Brianna steps onto an escalator to the first floor. The escalators' paths cross at P. When Alison reaches P, she has completed $\frac{11}{20}$ of her escalator trip.

   a What fraction of Brianna's escalator trip has been completed at P?

   b Find the ratio of the height from the basement to the ground floor, compared with the height from the ground floor to the first floor.

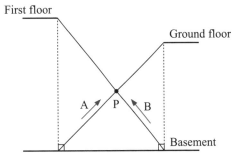

D | AREAS OF SIMILAR OBJECTS   [E5.5]

We have seen that if two objects are similar, then there is a relationship between the lengths of their sides. The sides are *in proportion*.

For objects which are 2-dimensional, there is also a relationship between the **areas** of the figures.

For example:

- The two circles shown are similar.   Circle **B** is an enlargement of circle **A** with scale factor k.

  Area of **B** $= \pi(kr)^2$
  $\quad\quad\quad\quad = k^2 \times \pi r^2$
  $\quad\quad\quad\quad = k^2 \times$ area of **A**

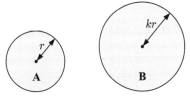

- The two rectangles shown are also similar. Rectangle **B** is an enlargement of rectangle **A** with scale factor k.

  Area of **B** $= ka \times kb$
  $\quad\quad\quad\quad = k^2 \times ab$
  $\quad\quad\quad\quad = k^2 \times$ area of **A**

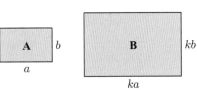

Using examples like this we can conclude that:

> If a figure is enlarged with scale factor k to produce a similar figure, then the new area $= k^2 \times$ the old area.

Example 7

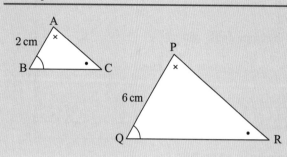

Triangles ABC and PQR are equiangular and therefore similar.

AB = 2 cm and PQ = 6 cm.

The area of $\triangle$ABC is 5 cm^2.

Find the area of $\triangle$PQR.

Suppose we enlarge $\triangle$ABC with scale factor k to give $\triangle$PQR.

$\therefore\ k = \frac{6}{2} = 3$

Area $\triangle$PQR $= k^2 \times$ area $\triangle$ABC

$\qquad\qquad = 9 \times 5$ cm^2

$\qquad\qquad = 45$ cm^2

EXERCISE 21D

1   For each pair of *similar* shapes, find the unknown area:

a

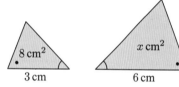

b

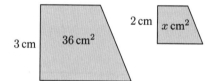

Example 8

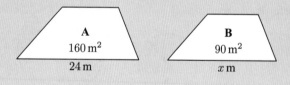

Given that figures **A** and **B** are similar, find x.

Figure **A** is reduced with scale factor k to give figure **B**.

$\qquad$ Area of **B** $= k^2 \times$ area of **A**

$\qquad\quad \therefore\ 90 = k^2 \times 160$

$\qquad\quad \therefore\ \frac{9}{16} = k^2$

$\qquad\quad \therefore\ k = \frac{3}{4} \qquad\qquad \{k > 0\}$

$\qquad$ Now $\ x = \frac{3}{4} \times 24 \qquad$ {sides in the same ratio}

$\qquad\quad \therefore\ x = 18$

2 For each pair of *similar* shapes, find the unknown length:

a

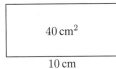

b

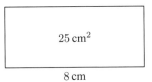

3 The side lengths of triangle A are 5 cm, 6 cm, and 7 cm. The longest side of a similar triangle B is 28 cm.

    a Find the scale factor when enlarging triangle A to give triangle B.

    b Find the lengths of the other two sides of triangle B.

    c How many times larger is the area of triangle B than the area of triangle A?

4

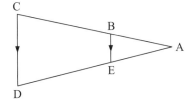

In the given figure, $DE = 6$ cm, $AE = 4$ cm, and $\triangle ABE$ has area 16 cm².

    a Show that $\triangle ABE$ and $\triangle ACD$ are similar.

    b Find the scale factor to enlarge $\triangle ABE$ into $\triangle ACD$.

    c Find the area of:

        i $\triangle ACD$ **ii** trapezium BCDE.

5 In the given figure, $AE = 3$ cm, $\triangle ABE$ has area 5 cm², and BEDC has area 6 cm².

Find the length of ED, rounding your answer to 3 significant figures.

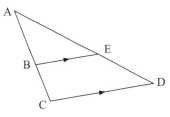

6 Figures **A** and **B** are similar. The dots shown are equally spaced at intervals of 1 unit.

If figure **A** has area 1.6 units², find the area of figure **B**.

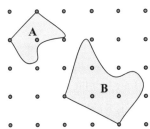

E   VOLUMES OF SIMILAR OBJECTS   [E5.5]

For 3-dimensional objects which are similar, there is also a relationship between the **volumes** of the figures.

For example:

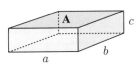 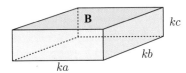

Volume of box **B**
$= ka \times kb \times kc$
$= k^3 \times abc$
$= k^3 \times$ volume of box **A**

If a 3-dimensional object is enlarged with scale factor k to produce a similar object, then the new volume $= k^3 \times$ the old volume.

Example 9
🔊 *Self Tutor*

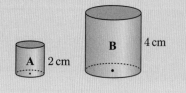

Cylinders **A** and **B** are similar with heights 2 cm and 4 cm respectively. Cylinder **A** has volume 10 cm³.

Find the volume of cylinder **B**.

Suppose cylinder **A** is enlarged with scale factor k to give cylinder **B**.

$$\therefore \ k = \tfrac{4}{2} = 2$$

Volume of **B** $= k^3 \times$ volume of **A**
$$= 8 \times 10 \text{ cm}^3$$
$$= 80 \text{ cm}^3$$

EXERCISE 21E

1 Consider the following *similar* solids. Find the unknown volume:

a

b

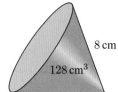

Example 10
🔊 *Self Tutor*

A and **B** are similar cones with volumes 54 cm³ and 250 cm³ respectively.

If cone **A** is 6 cm high, find the height of cone **B**.

Suppose cone **A** is enlarged with scale factor k to give cone **B**.

Volume of cone **B** $= k^3 \times$ volume of cone **A**
$$\therefore \ 250 = k^3 \times 54$$
$$\therefore \ \tfrac{125}{27} = k^3$$
$$\therefore \ k = \tfrac{5}{3}$$

So, the height of cone **B** $= \tfrac{5}{3} \times$ the height of cone **A**
$$= \tfrac{5}{3} \times 6 \text{ cm}$$
$$= 10 \text{ cm}$$

2 For each pair of *similar* solids, find the unknown length:

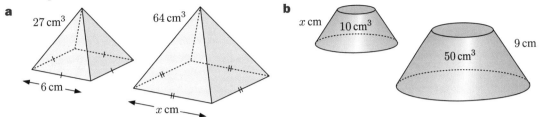

a 27 cm³ 64 cm³ 6 cm x cm

b x cm 10 cm³ 50 cm³ 9 cm

3 Two solid wooden spheres have radii a cm and $3a$ cm respectively. If the smaller one has volume 250 cm³, find the volume of the larger one.

4 Two similar pyramids have volumes 7500 cm³ and 480 cm³. If the larger pyramid is 30 cm high, find the height of the smaller pyramid.

5 A pet store sells small and large fish tanks. The small fish tank is 30 cm by 60 cm by 50 cm high. The large fish tank is similar to the small tank, and has capacity 150 litres. Find, to 3 significant figures, the scale factor for the enlargement.

6 Two similar statues have heights 3.5 m and 4.9 m.

   a If the volume of the smaller statue is 1.5 m³, find the volume of the larger statue.

   b If the surface area of the larger statue is 7.35 m², find the surface area of the smaller statue.

7 Two cylindrical containers have capacities 875 ml and 2240 ml respectively.

Thin straws are placed in the cylinders as shown. They have length 15 cm and 24 cm respectively.

Are the cylinders similar? Give evidence to support your answer.

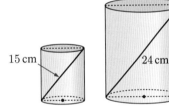

15 cm   24 cm

8 The surface areas of two similar cylinders are 6 cm² and 54 cm² respectively.

   a If the larger cylinder has height 12 cm, find the height of the smaller cylinder.

   b If the volume of the smaller cylinder is 24 cm³, find the volume of the larger cylinder.

9

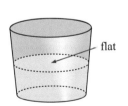

flat

Two buckets are similar in shape. The smaller one is 30 cm tall and the larger one is 45 cm tall. Both buckets contain water to a depth equal to half of their heights. The volume of water in the small bucket is 4400 cm³.

   a What is the scale factor in comparing the smaller bucket to the larger one?

   b Find the volume of water in the larger bucket.

   c The surface area of the water in the larger bucket is 630 cm². Find the surface area of the water in the smaller bucket.

10 Answer the **Opening Problem** on page **333**.

Review set 21A

1 Determine whether these rectangles are similar.

A   15 cm   B

10 cm

D   C

A′ 8 cm D′

12 cm

B′   C′

2   Draw two equiangular quadrilaterals which are not similar.

3   Find x, given that the figures are similar:

 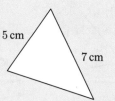

4   Show that the following figures possess similar triangles.

a 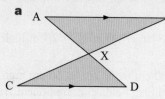   **b** 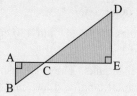   **c**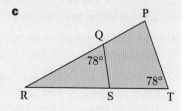

5   Are all rhombuses similar? Explain your answer.

6   Find the value of x:

a 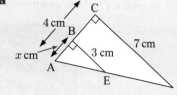   **b**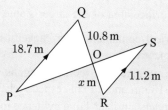

c 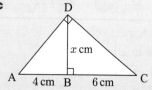   **d**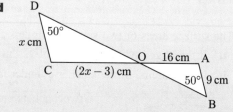

7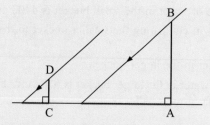

AB is a vertical flagpole of unknown height.

CD is a vertical stick 1.4 m long.

When the shadow of the flagpole is 12.3 m long, the shadow of the stick is 1.65 m long.

Find, rounded to 3 significant figures, the height of the flagpole.

8   Find the unknowns for each pair of similar figures:

a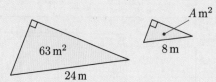

b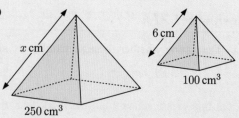

c

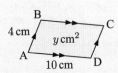 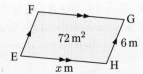

9 P and Q are markers on the banks of a canal which has parallel sides. R and S are telegraph poles which are directly opposite each other. PQ = 30 m and QR = 100 m. When I walk 20 m from P directly away from the bank, I reach the point T such that T, Q, and S line up. How wide is the canal?

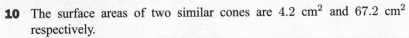

10 The surface areas of two similar cones are 4.2 cm² and 67.2 cm² respectively.

a Find the scale factor k to enlarge the smaller cone into the larger cone.

b If the height of the larger cone is 3.96 cm, find the height of the smaller cone.

c If the volume of the larger cone is 32 cm³, find the volume of the smaller cone.

Review set 21B

1 Draw two quadrilaterals which have sides in proportion but are not similar.

2 Find the value of x:

a

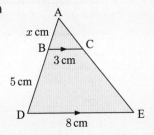

b

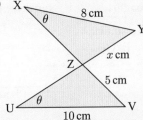

c

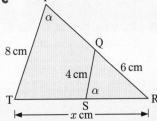

3

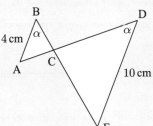

a Show that △ABC is similar to △EDC.

b Given that CD = 8 cm, find the length of CB.

4

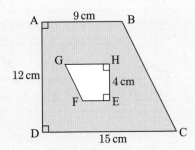

The trapeziums in the diagram alongside are similar.

a Find the length of:

i EF   **ii** GH

b Find the blue shaded area.

5

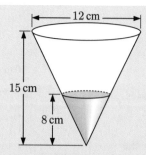

A conical flask has height 15 cm and base diameter 12 cm. Water is poured into the flask to a depth of 8 cm.

Find the diameter of the surface of the water.

6 Find the unknowns given that each pair of figures is similar:

a

12 cm²   27 cm²

x cm   6 cm

b

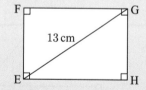

8 cm   30 cm³   9 cm x cm³

c

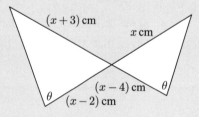

A   3 cm   3.6 cm²   C   B   2.7 cm

P   4 cm y cm²   R   Q x cm

7 Two solids are similar and the ratio of their volumes is 343 : 125.
Find the ratio of their: **a** lengths   **b** surface areas.

8 Rectangles ABCD and EFGH are similar.
Find the dimensions of rectangle EFGH.

B   C   2 cm   A   3 cm   D

F   G   13 cm   E   H

9 Find the value of x:

$(x+3)$ cm x cm θ $(x-4)$ cm θ $(x-2)$ cm

10 Triangle ABE has area 10 cm². Find:

a the length of CD

b the area of quadrilateral BEDC.

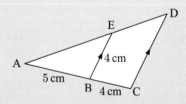

D   E   4 cm   A   5 cm   B   4 cm   C

11 Two similar cylinders have surface areas of 250 cm² and 360 cm². The volume of the smaller cylinder is 375 cm³. Find the volume of the larger cylinder.

Trigonometry

22

Contents:

A Labelling right angled triangles   [E8.1]
B The trigonometric ratios   [E8.1, 8.2]
C Finding side lengths   [E8.1]
D Finding angles   [E8.1]
E Problem solving   [E8.1, E8.7]
F True bearings   [E8.7]
G The angle between a line and a plane   [E8.7]
H The angle between two planes   [E8.7]

Opening problem

A group of students is asked to measure the height of the school gymnasium. It is a symmetric building 24 m wide, as shown.

From a point 32 m from the side wall, the students measure the angles of elevation to the top of the side wall, and to the top of the roof.

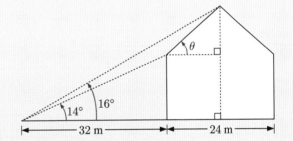

Things to think about:

a How high is:
    i the side wall of the gymnasium   **ii** the top of the roof?

b Can you find the angle θ which is the pitch of the roof?

Trigonometry is the study of the relationships between the side lengths and angles of triangles.

We can apply trigonometry in engineering, astronomy, architecture, navigation, surveying, the building industry, and in many other branches of applied science.

Historical note   *Astronomy and trigonometry*

The Greek astronomer **Hipparchus** (140 BC) is credited with being the founder of trigonometry. To aid his astronomical calculations, he produced a table of numbers in which the lengths of chords of a circle were related to the length of the radius.

Ptolemy, another great Greek astronomer of the time, extended this table in his major published work *Almagest*, which was used by astronomers for the next 1000 years. In fact, much of Hipparchus' work is known through the writings of Ptolemy. These writings found their way to Hindu and Arab scholars.

Aryabhata, a Hindu mathematician in the 5th and 6th Century AD, constructed a table of the lengths of half-chords of a circle with radius one unit. This was the first table of **sine** values.

In the late 16th century, **Georg Joachim de Porris**, also known as **Rheticus**, produced comprehensive and remarkably accurate tables of all six trigonometric ratios, three of which you will learn about in this Chapter. These involved a tremendous number of tedious calculations, all without the aid of calculators or computers.

Rheticus was the only student of **Nicolaus Copernicus**, and helped his tutor publish his work *De revolutionibus orbium coelestium*, which means "On the Revolutions of the Heavenly Spheres".

Nicolaus Copernicus

A LABELLING RIGHT ANGLED TRIANGLES [E8.1]

In trigonometry, there is a convention for labelling the sides of a right angled triangle.

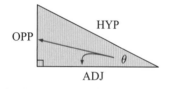

For the right angled triangle with angle θ:
• the **hypotenuse (HYP)** is the longest side
• the **opposite (OPP)** side is opposite θ
• the **adjacent (ADJ)** side is adjacent to θ.

Example 1   ◀) *Self Tutor*

For the triangle alongside, name the:
 a hypotenuse
 b side opposite θ
 c side adjacent to θ.

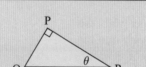

 a The hypotenuse is QR.
 b The side opposite θ is PQ.
 c The side adjacent to θ is PR.

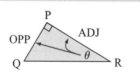

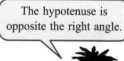

The hypotenuse is opposite the right angle.

EXERCISE 22A

1 For the triangles given, name the:

    i hypotenuse   **ii** side opposite angle θ **iii** side adjacent to θ.

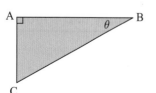

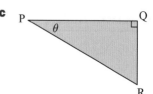

2 For the triangles given, name the:

>   **i** hypotenuse   **ii** side opposite α **iii** side adjacent to α
>   **iv** side opposite β **v** side adjacent to β.

a 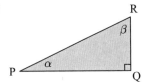   **b** 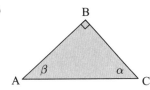   **c**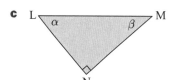

Discovery 1   *Ratio of sides of right angled triangles*

In this Discovery we consider the ratios $\dfrac{\text{OPP}}{\text{HYP}}$, $\dfrac{\text{ADJ}}{\text{HYP}}$, and $\dfrac{\text{OPP}}{\text{ADJ}}$ in a series of *similar* right angled triangles.

What to do:

1 For each set of four similar triangles below, complete a table like the one shown. Measure each side length to the nearest millimetre, and round each of the ratios to 2 decimal places.

Triangle	HYP	OPP	ADJ	$\dfrac{\text{OPP}}{\text{HYP}}$	$\dfrac{\text{ADJ}}{\text{HYP}}$	$\dfrac{\text{OPP}}{\text{ADJ}}$
1						
2						
3						
4						

PRINTABLE
WORKSHEET

a 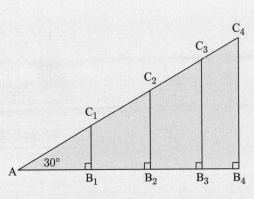   **b**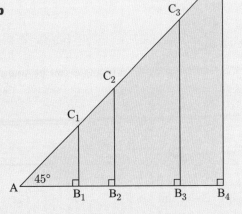

2 Use your calculator to evaluate $\dfrac{\sqrt{3}}{2}$, $\dfrac{1}{\sqrt{3}}$, and $\dfrac{1}{\sqrt{2}}$.

3 Summarise your results from **1** and **2**.

B   *THE TRIGONOMETRIC RATIOS*   *[E8.1, 8.2]*

We have seen previously that similar triangles are equiangular, and that the lengths of their sides are in the same ratio. This means there is a special relationship between the ratios of side lengths, and the angles in the triangle.

In **Discovery 1** you should have found that for any set of *similar* right angled triangles, the ratios $\frac{\text{OPP}}{\text{HYP}}$, $\frac{\text{ADJ}}{\text{HYP}}$, and $\frac{\text{OPP}}{\text{ADJ}}$ are constant.

These ratios have the traditional names **sine**, **cosine**, and **tangent** respectively. We abbreviate them to **sin**, **cos**, and **tan**.

> In any right angled triangle with one angle θ:
>
> $$\sin \theta = \frac{\text{OPP}}{\text{HYP}}, \quad \cos \theta = \frac{\text{ADJ}}{\text{HYP}}, \quad \tan \theta = \frac{\text{OPP}}{\text{ADJ}}$$

Notice that $\dfrac{\sin \theta}{\cos \theta} = \dfrac{\frac{\text{OPP}}{\text{HYP}}}{\frac{\text{ADJ}}{\text{HYP}}} = \dfrac{\text{OPP}}{\text{ADJ}} = \tan \theta.$

So, $\tan \theta = \dfrac{\sin \theta}{\cos \theta}$

In **Discovery 1** you should also have found some particular values of the trigonometric ratios:

$\sin 30° = 0.5$ $\sin 45° = \dfrac{1}{\sqrt{2}} \approx 0.71$

$\cos 30° = \dfrac{\sqrt{3}}{2} \approx 0.87$ $\cos 45° = \dfrac{1}{\sqrt{2}} \approx 0.71$

$\tan 30° = \dfrac{1}{\sqrt{3}} \approx 0.58$ $\tan 45° = 1$

Trigonometric ratios for any angle can be found using a calculator. You should first check that your calculator is in "degree" mode.

GRAPHICS
CALCULATOR
INSTRUCTIONS

Example 2   ◀) *Self Tutor*

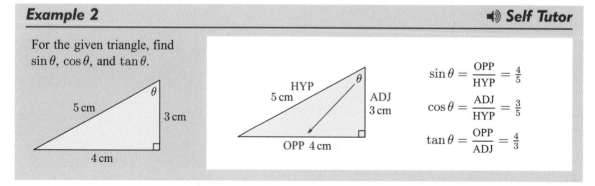

For the given triangle, find $\sin \theta$, $\cos \theta$, and $\tan \theta$.

$\sin \theta = \dfrac{\text{OPP}}{\text{HYP}} = \dfrac{4}{5}$

$\cos \theta = \dfrac{\text{ADJ}}{\text{HYP}} = \dfrac{3}{5}$

$\tan \theta = \dfrac{\text{OPP}}{\text{ADJ}} = \dfrac{4}{3}$

EXERCISE 22B

1 For the given triangles, find: **i** $\sin\theta$ **ii** $\cos\theta$ **iii** $\tan\theta$.

a
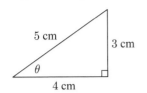

b
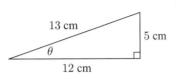

c
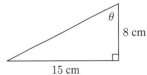

d
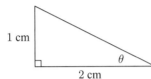

e
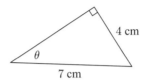

f
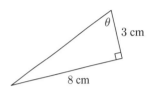

2
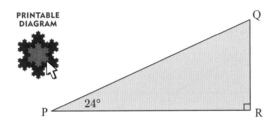

    a Use a ruler to find the length of each side of the triangle, to the nearest millimetre.

    b Hence, estimate the value of:
       i $\sin 24°$ **ii** $\cos 24°$
       iii $\tan 24°$

    c Check your answers using a calculator.

3 The side lengths in the figure alongside have been rounded to the nearest millimetre.

    a Use the diagram to estimate the value of:
       i $\sin 36°$ **ii** $\cos 51°$
      iii $\tan 54°$ **iv** $\cos 39°$

    b Check your answers using a calculator.

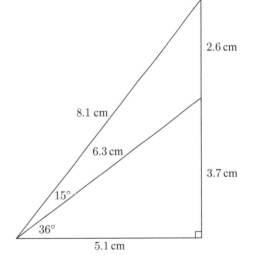

4 $\cos^2\theta$ is shorthand notation for $\cos\theta \times \cos\theta$.

    a Use your calculator to find, correct to 4 decimal places:

       i $\cos^2 16°$ **ii** $\sin^2 16°$ **iii** $\cos^2 16° + \sin^2 16°$
      iv $\cos^2 65°$ **v** $\sin^2 65°$ **vi** $\cos^2 65° + \sin^2 65°$

    b For any value of θ, what do you suspect is the value of $\cos^2\theta + \sin^2\theta$?

    c Use the figure alongside to prove your answer to **b**.

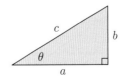

5 **a** Use your calculator to find:

     i $\tan 70° \times \tan 20°$ **ii** $\tan 63° \times \tan 27°$ **iii** $\tan 49° \times \tan 41°$

  b What do you suspect is the relationship between $\tan \theta$
     and $\tan(90° - \theta)$?

  c Use the figure alongside to prove your answer to **b**.

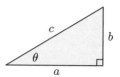

6

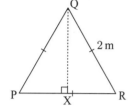

Suppose PQR is an equilateral triangle with side lengths 2 m.
Use the diagram to prove that:

  a $\cos 60° = \frac{1}{2}$ **b** $\sin 60° = \frac{\sqrt{3}}{2}$ **c** $\tan 60° = \sqrt{3}$

  d $\cos 30° = \frac{\sqrt{3}}{2}$ **e** $\sin 30° = \frac{1}{2}$ **f** $\tan 30° = \frac{1}{\sqrt{3}}$

7 **a** Find the size of $P\hat{Y}X$.

  b Hence show that:

     i $\tan 75° = 2 + \sqrt{3}$

     ii $\tan 15° = 2 - \sqrt{3}$

     iii $\cos^2 75° = \frac{2 - \sqrt{3}}{4}$

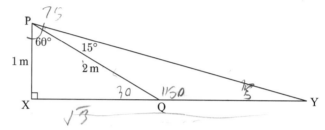

C *FINDING SIDE LENGTHS*   *[E8.1]*

Suppose we are given the angles of a right angled triangle, and the length of a side. We can use the trigonometric ratios to find the other side lengths.

> *Step 1*: Redraw the figure and mark on it HYP, OPP, and ADJ relative to a given angle.
> *Step 2*: Choose an appropriate trigonometric ratio, and construct an equation.
> *Step 3*: Solve the equation to find the unknown side length.

Example 3   ◆) *Self Tutor*

Find x, rounding your answer to 2 decimal places:

a

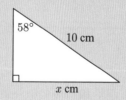

b

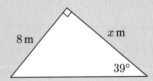

  a The relevant sides are OPP and HYP, so we use the *sine* ratio.

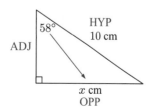

     $\sin 58° = \frac{x}{10}$ $\{\sin \theta = \frac{\text{OPP}}{\text{HYP}}\}$

     $\therefore \ \sin 58° \times 10 = x$ {multiplying both sides by 10}

     $\therefore \ \ x \approx 8.48$ {calculator}

b The relevant sides are OPP and ADJ, so we use the *tangent* ratio.

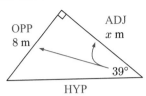

$$\tan 39° = \frac{8}{x} \qquad \{\tan \theta = \frac{\text{OPP}}{\text{ADJ}}\}$$

$$\therefore \quad x \times \tan 39° = 8 \qquad \{\text{multiplying both sides by } x\}$$

$$\therefore \quad x = \frac{8}{\tan 39°} \qquad \{\text{dividing both sides by } \tan 39°\}$$

$$\therefore \quad x \approx 9.88 \qquad \{\text{calculator}\}$$

EXERCISE 22C

1 Write down a trigonometric equation connecting the angle and the sides given:

a
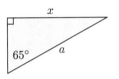

b
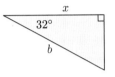

c
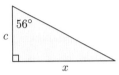

d
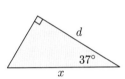

e
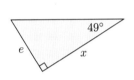

f
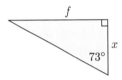

2 Find x, rounding your answer to 2 decimal places:

a
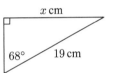

b
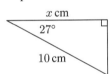

c
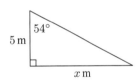

d
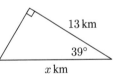

e
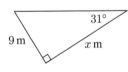

f
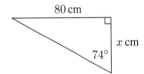

g
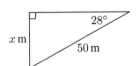

h
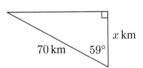

i
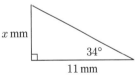

j
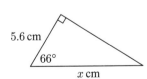

k
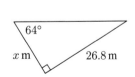

l
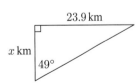

3 Find, to 1 decimal place, *all* unknown angles and sides:

a
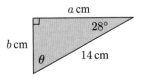

b
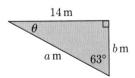

c
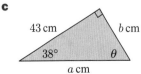

4 Find the perimeter of triangle ABC.

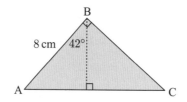

D ***FINDING ANGLES***   **[E8.1]**

If we know two side lengths of a right angled triangle, we can use trigonometry to find the angles.

In the right angled triangle shown, $\cos\theta = \frac{3}{5}$.

To find θ, we need an angle whose cosine is $\frac{3}{5}$.

We say that θ is the **inverse cosine** of $\frac{3}{5}$, and write

$\theta = \cos^{-1}\left(\frac{3}{5}\right)$.

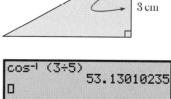

We can use a calculator to evaluate inverse cosines. Click on the icon for instructions.

GRAPHICS CALCULATOR INSTRUCTIONS

For the right angled triangle with hypotenuse 5 cm and adjacent side 3 cm, $\theta \approx 53.1°$.

We define **inverse sine** and **inverse tangent** in a similar way.

Example 4   ◀)) *Self Tutor*

Find, to 1 decimal place, the measure of the angle marked θ.

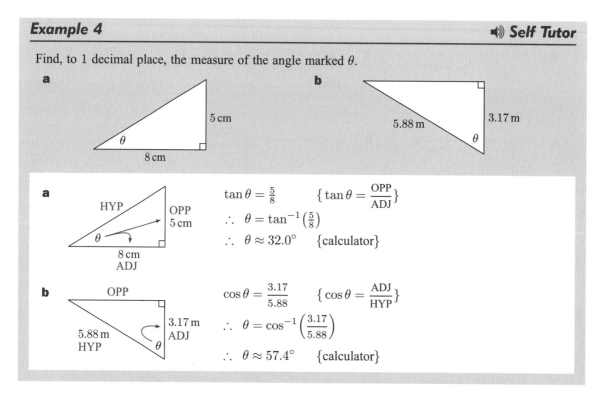

a
$$\tan\theta = \frac{5}{8} \qquad \left\{\tan\theta = \frac{\text{OPP}}{\text{ADJ}}\right\}$$
$$\therefore \ \theta = \tan^{-1}\left(\frac{5}{8}\right)$$
$$\therefore \ \theta \approx 32.0° \quad \{\text{calculator}\}$$

b
$$\cos\theta = \frac{3.17}{5.88} \qquad \left\{\cos\theta = \frac{\text{ADJ}}{\text{HYP}}\right\}$$
$$\therefore \ \theta = \cos^{-1}\left(\frac{3.17}{5.88}\right)$$
$$\therefore \ \theta \approx 57.4° \quad \{\text{calculator}\}$$

EXERCISE 22D

1 Find, to 1 decimal place, the measure of the angle marked θ.

a

5 cm

4 cm

θ

b

θ

6 cm

4 cm

c

4.8 cm

3.7 cm

θ

d

3.2 m

5.2 m

θ

e

θ

3.1 km

2.1 km

f

3.1 m

4.2 m

θ

g

5.1 km

θ

4.1 km

h

4.4 m

6.1 m

θ

i

7.5 mm

θ

1.25 cm

2 Find, to 1 decimal place, all unknown sides and angles in the following triangles. Check your answers for x using Pythagoras' theorem.

a
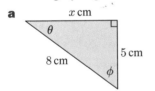

x cm

θ

5 cm

8 cm

ϕ

b
α

3.5 m

x m

β

6.1 m

c
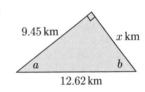

9.45 km

x km

a

b

12.62 km

3 Try to find θ in the following diagrams. What conclusions can you draw?

a
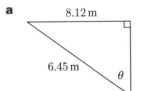

8.12 m

6.45 m

θ

b

17.9 mm

θ

15.6 mm

c
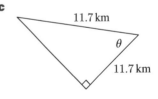

11.7 km

θ

11.7 km

E   **PROBLEM SOLVING**   **[E8.1, E8.7]**

The trigonometric ratios can be used to solve a wide variety of problems involving right angled triangles. When solving these problems it is important to follow the steps below:

Step 1:   Draw a **diagram** to illustrate the situation.

Step 2:   Mark on the diagram the **unknown** angle or side that needs to be calculated. We often use x for a length and θ for an angle.

Step 3:   Locate a **right angled triangle** in your diagram.

Step 4:   Write an **equation** connecting an angle and two sides of the triangle using an appropriate trigonometric ratio.

Step 5:   **Solve** the equation to find the unknown.

Step 6:   **Write** your answer in sentence form.

We can use right angled triangle trigonometry to solve problems involving:

- isosceles triangles   - rectangles   - rhombuses

  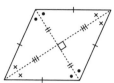

- kites   - tangents

 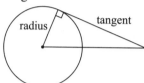

We will see more right angles associated with circles later, when we study **circle geometry**.

ANGLES OF ELEVATION AND DEPRESSION

When an object is **higher** than an observer, the **angle of elevation** is the angle from the horizontal **up** to the object.

When an object is **lower** than an observer, the **angle of depression** is the angle from the horizontal **down** to the object.

If the angle of elevation from A to B is θ, then the angle of depression from B to A is also θ.

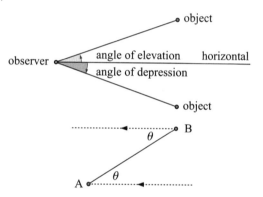

Example 5   ◀)) *Self Tutor*

The roof alongside has a pitch of $16°$. Find the length of the horizontal beam.

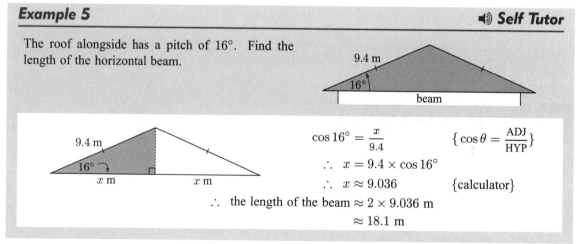

$$\cos 16° = \frac{x}{9.4} \qquad \left\{ \cos \theta = \frac{\text{ADJ}}{\text{HYP}} \right\}$$

$$\therefore \; x = 9.4 \times \cos 16°$$

$$\therefore \; x \approx 9.036 \qquad \{\text{calculator}\}$$

$$\therefore \; \text{the length of the beam} \approx 2 \times 9.036 \text{ m}$$

$$\approx 18.1 \text{ m}$$

EXERCISE 22E

1 From a point 235 m from the base of a cliff, the angle of elevation to the cliff top is $25°$. Find the height of the cliff.

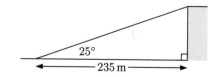

2 A 5 m ladder reaches 4.2 m up a wall. What angle does the ladder make with the wall?

3 The angle of elevation from a row boat to the top of a lighthouse 25 m above sea-level is $6°$. Calculate the horizontal distance from the boat to the lighthouse.

4 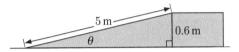 From a vertical cliff 80 m above sea level, a whale is observed at an angle of depression of $6°$.

Find the distance between the observer at the top of the cliff, and the whale.

5 A train travelling up an incline of $4°$ travels a horizontal distance of 4 km. How much altitude has the train gained?

6 At the entrance to a building there is a ramp for wheelchair access. The length of the ramp is 5 metres, and it rises to a height of 0.6 metres. Find the angle θ that the ramp makes with the ground.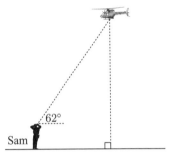

7 A rectangular gate has a diagonal strut of length 3 m. The angle between the diagonal and a side is $28°$. Find the length of the longer side of the gate.

8 A model helicopter takes off from the horizontal ground with a constant vertical speed of 5 m/s. After 10 seconds the angle of elevation from Sam to the helicopter is $62°$. Given that Sam is 1.8 m tall, how far is Sam's head from the helicopter at this time?

9 A kite is attached to a 50 m long string. The other end of the string is secured to the ground. If the kite is flying 35 m above ground level, find the angle that the string makes with the ground.

10 A goal post was hit by lightning and snapped in two. The top of the post is now resting 15 m from its base, at an angle of $25°$. Find the height of the goal post before it snapped.

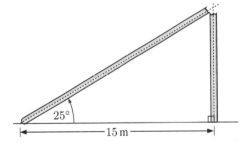

11 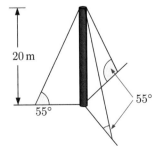 Three strong cables are used to brace a 20 m tall pole against movement due to the wind. Each cable is attached so that the angle of elevation to the top of the pole is $55°$. Find the total length of the cables.

12 A rectangle has length 6 m and width 4 m. Find the acute angle formed where the diagonals intersect.

Example 6   ◀)) **Self Tutor**

A point P is 9.5 cm from the centre C of a circle with radius 2 cm.
Find the angle between PC and the tangent to the circle from P.

$\sin \theta = \dfrac{2}{9.5}$ $\left\{ \sin \theta = \dfrac{\text{OPP}}{\text{HYP}} \right\}$

$\therefore \quad \theta = \sin^{-1} \left(\dfrac{2}{9.5} \right)$

$\therefore \quad \theta \approx 12.2°$ {calculator}

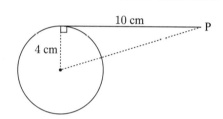

The angle between PC and the tangent is approximately 12.2°.

13 A tangent from point P to a circle of radius 4 cm is 10 cm
long. Find the angle between the tangent and the line
joining P to the centre of the circle.

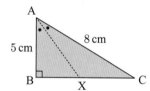

14 A rhombus has sides of length 10 cm, and the angle between two adjacent sides is 76°. Find the length
of the longer diagonal of the rhombus.

15 Point P is 32 mm from the centre C of a circle. The length of a tangent from P to the circle is 26 mm.
Find:
    a the radius of the circle   **b** the angle between the tangent and CP.

16 Find the area of the parallelogram:

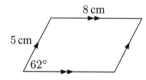

17 In triangle ABC, the angle bisector at A meets BC at X.
Is X the midpoint of BC? If not, what is the distance between X
and the midpoint?

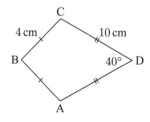

18 Find the size of A$\hat{\text{B}}$C.

19 In an isosceles triangle, the equal sides are $\frac{2}{3}$ of the length of the base. Determine the measure of the
base angles.

20 An isosceles triangle is drawn with base angles 24° and base 28 cm. Find the base angles of the
isosceles triangle with the same base length but with treble the area.

21   Answer the **Opening Problem** on page **351**.

22   From a point A which is 30 m from the base of a building B, the angle
of elevation to the top of the building C is 56°, and to the top of the
flagpole CD is 60°.
Find the length of the flagpole.

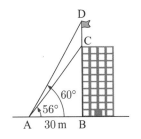

23   The angle of elevation from a marker on level ground to the top of a building 100 m high is 22°. Find
the distance:

    a   from the marker to the base of the building

    b   the marker must be moved towards the building so that the angle of elevation becomes 40°.

24   An observer notices an aeroplane flying directly overhead. Two minutes later the aeroplane is at an
angle of elevation of 27°. Assuming the aeroplane is travelling with constant speed and altitude, what
will be its angle of elevation after another two minutes?

25   A surveyor standing on a horizontal plain can see a volcano in the distance. The angle of elevation to
the top of the volcano is 23°. If the surveyor moves 750 m closer, the angle of elevation is now 37°.
Determine the height of the volcano above the plain.

26   Find the shortest distance between the two parallel lines using:

    a   trigonometry   **b**   areas.

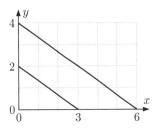

27

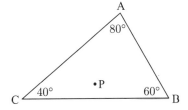

In the triangle alongside, P is 5 m from each of the vertices. Find
the length of each side of the triangle.

Example 7   ◀) *Self Tutor*

A cube has sides of length 10 cm. Find the angle between
the diagonal AB and the edge BC.

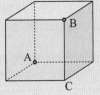

Let AC = x cm.

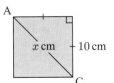

Using Pythagoras, $x^2 = 10^2 + 10^2$

                $\therefore\ x^2 = 200$

                $\therefore\ x = \sqrt{200}$

The required angle is $A\widehat{B}C$. We let this angle be θ.

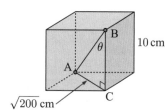
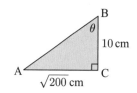

$\tan\theta = \frac{\sqrt{200}}{10}$ $\{\tan\theta = \frac{\text{OPP}}{\text{ADJ}}\}$

$\therefore\ \theta = \tan^{-1}\left(\frac{\sqrt{200}}{10}\right)$

$\therefore\ \theta \approx 54.7°$

The angle between the diagonal AB and the edge BC is about $54.7°$.

---

28 The figure alongside is a cube with sides of length 15 cm. Find:

   a EG

   b $A\widehat{G}E$.

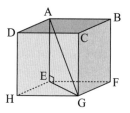

29

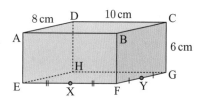

The figure alongside is a rectangular prism. X and Y are the midpoints of EF and FG respectively. Find:

   a HX

   c HY

   b $D\widehat{X}H$

   d $D\widehat{Y}H$.

30 In the triangular prism below, find:

   a DF   **b** $A\widehat{F}D$.

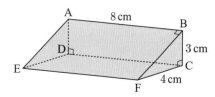

31 AB and BC are wooden support struts on a crate. Find the total length of wood required to make the two struts.

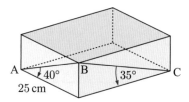

32 All edges of a square-based pyramid are 12 m in length.

   a Find the angle between a slant edge and a base diagonal.

   b Show that this angle is the same for any square-based pyramid with all edge lengths equal.

33 Each side of a tent is fixed to the ground by ropes as shown. The peg is 1.5 m from the side of the tent. Find the angle θ between the ropes.

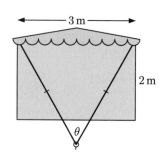

34

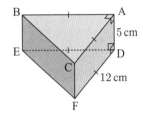

A man M observed two poles on the other side of a river. He knows they are 100 m apart and have the same height.

From the point directly opposite pole A, the angle of elevation to its top is 22°. The angle of elevation from the same point to the top of pole B is 19°.

Find the width of the river.

35 Consider the triangular prism shown.

  a Find the length of AE.

  b Find the angle between AC and CE.

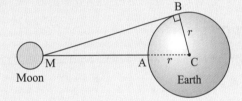

Discovery 2   *Hipparchus and the universe*

Hipparchus was a Greek astronomer and mathematician born in Nicaea in the 2nd century BC. He is considered among the greatest astronomers of all time.

Part 1: How Hipparchus measured the distance to the moon

Consider two points A and B on the Earth's equator. The moon is directly overhead A. From B the moon is just visible, since MB is a tangent to the Earth and is therefore perpendicular to BC. Angle BCM is the difference in longitude between A and B, which Hipparchus calculated to be approximately 89°.

What to do:

 1 Given $r = 6378$ km and $\widehat{BCM} = 89°$, estimate the distance from the centre of the Earth C to the moon.

 2 Now calculate the distance AM *between* the Earth and the moon.

 3 In calculating just one distance between the Earth and the moon, Hipparchus was assuming that the orbit of the moon was circular. In fact it is not. Research the shortest and longest distances to the moon. How were these distances determined? How do they compare with the distance obtained using Hipparchus' method?

Part 2: How Hipparchus measured the radius of the moon

From point A on the Earth's surface, the angle between an imaginary line to the centre of the moon and a tangent to the moon is about 0.25°.

The average distance from the Earth to the moon is about 384 403 km.

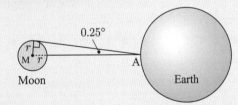

What to do:

 1 Confirm from the diagram that $\sin 0.25° = \dfrac{r}{r + 384\,403}$.

 2 Solve this equation to find r, the radius of the moon.

 3 Research the actual radius of the moon, and if possible, find out how it was calculated. Compare your answer in **2** to the actual radius.

F   TRUE BEARINGS   [E8.7]

We can describe a direction by comparing it with the **true north direction**. We call this a **true bearing**.

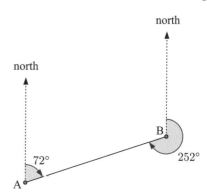

Imagine you are standing at point A, facing north. You turn **clockwise** through an angle until you face B. The **bearing of B from A** is the angle through which you have turned.

So, the bearing of B from A is the clockwise measure of the angle between the "north" line through A, and AB.

In the diagram alongside, the bearing of B from A is 72° from true north. We write this as 72°T or 072°.

To find the **bearing of A from B**, we place ourselves at point B, face north, then turn clockwise until we face A. The true bearing of A from B is 252°.

Note that:

• A true bearing is always written using three digits. For example, we write 072° rather than 72°.

• The bearing of A from B always differs from the bearing of B from A by 180°.
  You should be able to explain this using angle pair properties for parallel lines.

EXERCISE 22F

1 Draw diagrams to represent bearings from O of:

    a 136°   **b** 240°   **c** 051°   **d** 327°

2 Find the bearing of Q from P if the bearing of P from Q is:

    a 054°   **b** 113°   **c** 263°   **d** 304°

3 Write the bearing of Q from P in each diagram:

    a   **b**   **c**

4 A, B, and C are the checkpoints of a triangular orienteering course. Find the bearing of:

    a B from A   **b** C from B   **c** B from C

    d C from A   **e** A from B   **f** A from C.

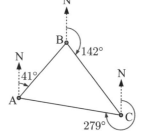

5 Find the bearing of:

    a B from A   **b** A from B

    c C from A   **d** A from C

    e C from B   **f** B from C.

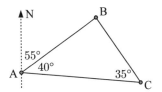

6 A bushwalker hikes to a hilltop which is 5.4 km east and 2.8 km north of her starting point. Find the bearing of:

    a the hilltop from the starting point   **b** the starting point from the hilltop.

7 A kayaker paddles to a point 3.1 km south and 1.6 km west of his starting point.

    a How far is he from his starting point?

    b On what bearing must he paddle to return directly to his starting point?

Example 8   ◄ Self Tutor

A rally driver travels on a bearing of 145° for 2.85 km. How far east of the starting position is the rally driver?

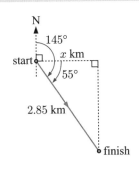

$$\cos 55° = \frac{x}{2.85} \qquad \left\{ \cos\theta = \frac{\text{ADJ}}{\text{HYP}} \right\}$$

$$\therefore \quad x = 2.85 \times \cos 55°$$

$$\therefore \quad x \approx 1.63$$

The driver is about 1.63 km east of his starting position.

---

8 A ship sails for 60 km on the bearing 040°. How far north of its starting point is the ship?

9 An athlete ran for 12 minutes in the direction 164° at a speed of 14 km/h.

    a Draw a fully labelled diagram of the situation.

    b Find the distance travelled by the athlete.

    c How far **i** east **ii** south of his starting point is the athlete?

10 According to her GPS, a runner is on the bearing 215° from her starting point, and she is 2 km south of it. How far is she from her starting point?

Example 9

🔊 *Self Tutor*

A small aeroplane departs A and flies on a 143° course for 368 km to B. Having landed and delivered cargo, it departs on a 233° course and flies a further 472 km to C. Find:

   a the distance of C from A   **b** the bearing of C from A.

$A\widehat{B}N = 180° - 143° = 37°$ {cointerior angles}

$\therefore\ \ A\widehat{B}C = 360° - 37° - 233°$

            $= 90°$ {angles at a point}

a $AC^2 = 368^2 + 472^2$ {Pythagoras}

   $\therefore\ \ AC = \sqrt{368^2 + 472^2}$ {as $AC > 0$}

         ≈ 599

So, C is about 599 km from A.

b To find the bearing of C from A, we first need to find θ.

Now $\tan\theta = \dfrac{472}{368}$ $\{\tan\theta = \dfrac{\text{OPP}}{\text{ADJ}}\}$

    $\therefore\ \ \theta = \tan^{-1}\left(\frac{472}{368}\right)$

    $\therefore\ \ \theta \approx 52.1°$

The bearing of C from A is
$143° + 52.1° \approx 195°$.

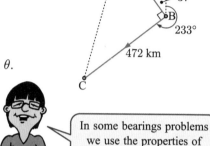

In some bearings problems we use the properties of parallel lines to find angles.

11 A cyclist departs point R and rides on a straight road for 2.3 km in the direction 197°. She then turns and rides for 1.8 km in the direction 107° to point S.

    a Draw a fully labelled sketch of this situation.   **b** Find the distance between R and S.

    c Find the bearing of S from R.

12 A fishing trawler sails from port P in the direction 313° for 10 km, and then in the direction 043° for 32 km. Find the distance and bearing of the trawler from P.

13 An orienteerer runs 2.16 km in the direction 024°, and then 1.48 km in the direction 114°. Find the distance and bearing of the finishing point from the starting point.

G | THE ANGLE BETWEEN A LINE AND A PLANE
[E8.7]

Suppose Jonathon holds his pen at an angle to a piece of paper. If we shine a light from directly above the pen, a shadow will be cast on the paper. This shadow is called the **projection** of the pen onto the paper.

The angle that the pen makes with the paper is the angle between the pen and its projection.

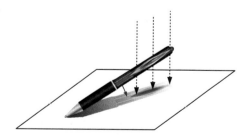

The **angle between a line and a plane** is the angle between the line and its **projection** on the plane.

Example 10   ◀⁾ Self Tutor

Name the angle between the following line segments and the
base plane EFGH:

   a AH   **b** AG

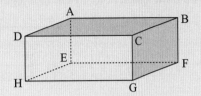

a The projection of AH onto the base plane EFGH is EH.

    ∴ the required angle is $\widehat{\text{AHE}}$.

b The projection of AG onto the base plane EFGH is EG.

    ∴ the required angle is $\widehat{\text{AGE}}$.

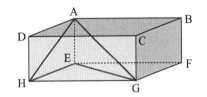

Example 11   ◀⁾ Self Tutor

Find the angle between the following line segments
and the base plane EFGH:

   a DG   **b** BH

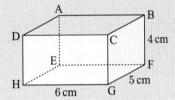

a The required angle is $\widehat{\text{DGH}}$.

$$\tan \theta = \frac{\text{OPP}}{\text{ADJ}} = \frac{4}{6}$$

∴ $\theta = \tan^{-1}\left(\frac{4}{6}\right)$

∴ $\theta \approx 33.69°$

The angle is about $33.7°$.

b The required angle is $\widehat{\text{BHF}}$.

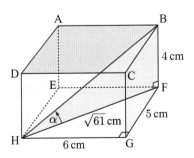

Let HF $= x$ cm.

Using Pythagoras,

$$x^2 = 6^2 + 5^2$$

∴ $x^2 = 61$

∴ $x = \sqrt{61}$

$$\tan \alpha = \frac{\text{OPP}}{\text{ADJ}} = \frac{4}{\sqrt{61}}$$

∴ $\alpha = \tan^{-1}\left(\frac{4}{\sqrt{61}}\right)$

∴ $\alpha \approx 27.12°$

The angle is about $27.1°$.

EXERCISE 22G

1 Find the projection of each line segment onto the base plane of the given figure:

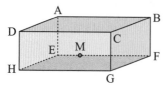

   a **i** CF
       ii DG
       iii DF
       iv CM

   b **i** BD
       ii AE
       iii AF
       iv AX

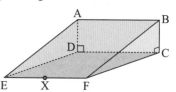

2 Name the angle between the given line segment and the base plane of the figure:

   a **i** BG
       ii BH
       iii DF
       iv AX

   b **i** PZ
       ii QY
       iii PW
       iv QW

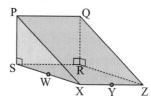

   c **i** AS
       ii AY

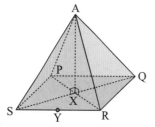

3 Find the angle between the line segment and the base plane of the figure:

   a **i** DG
       ii AG
       iii CX
       iv BX

   b **i** SV
       ii SU
       iii PX

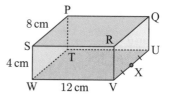

   c **i** JN
       ii JO
       iii KX

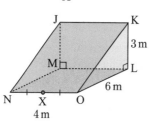

   d **i** XB
       ii XY

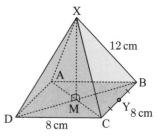

H   THE ANGLE BETWEEN TWO PLANES   [E8.7]

Whenever the plane faces of a solid meet to form an edge of the
solid, we have an example of two planes meeting in a line.

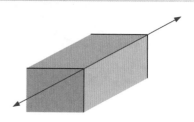

To find the acute angle between two planes, we follow
these steps:

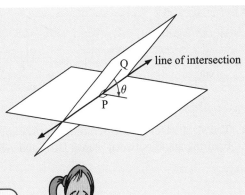

Step 1:   Identify the line of intersection of the planes.

Step 2:   Choose a point P on the line of intersection.

Step 3:   Locate a point Q on one plane such that PQ
          is perpendicular to the line of intersection.

Step 4:   Find the angle θ between PQ and the other
          plane.

Find the angle between
PQ and its projection
onto the other plane.

Example 12   ◀)) Self Tutor

A square-based pyramid has base lengths 6 cm and height 8 cm.
Find the angle between a triangular face and the base.

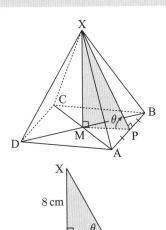

The line of intersection between the triangular face ABX and
the base is AB.

PX is perpendicular to AB, and MP is the projection of XP onto
the base plane.

$\therefore$ $M\widehat{P}X$ is the required angle.

Now   MX = height of pyramid = 8 cm

$MP = \frac{1}{2}$ of side length of base = 3 cm.

$\tan \theta = \dfrac{\text{OPP}}{\text{ADJ}} = \dfrac{8}{3}$

$\therefore$ $\theta = \tan^{-1}\left(\frac{8}{3}\right) \approx 69.4°$

The angle is about $69.4°$.

EXERCISE 22H

1 A cube has sides of length 10 cm. Find the angle between
   plane BGD and plane ABCD.

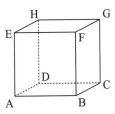

2

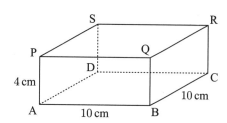

Find the angle that plane ASC makes with plane ABCD.

3 The slant edges of the pyramid opposite are 5 cm long.
Find the angle between planes BCE and ABCD.

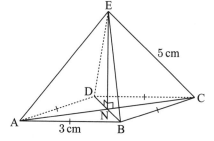

4 The pyramid of Cheops in Egypt has a height of 145 m and has base lengths 230 m. Find the angle
between a sloping face and the base.

Review set 22A

1 Find $\sin\theta$, $\cos\theta$, and $\tan\theta$ for this triangle:

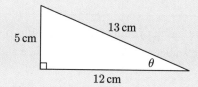

2 Find the value of x:

a

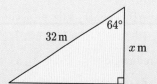

b

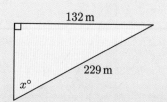

3 Find the measure of all unknown sides and angles
in triangle CDE:

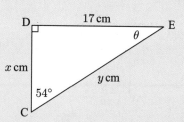

4

The shadow of a cathedral is 85 m in length. The angle
of elevation from the end of the shadow to the top of
the steeple is 33°. Find the height of the cathedral.

5 Find the bearing of Q from P in the following diagrams:

a

b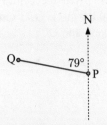

6 A taxi journey takes the passenger to a destination 8 km south and 3 km west of its starting point. Find the distance and bearing of the destination from its starting point.

7 Find the diameter of this circle.

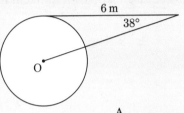

8 Find the angle that:

a BG makes with FG

b AG makes with the base plane EFGH.

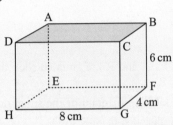

9 Two aeroplanes leave from an airport at the same time. Aeroplane A flies on a bearing of 124° at 450 km/h. Aeroplane B flies on a bearing of 214° at 380 km/h. Find the distance and bearing of B from A after 30 minutes.

Review set 22B

1 Find the measure of the angle marked θ:

a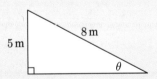

b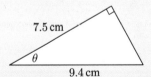

2 Find the value of x, rounding your answer to 2 decimal places:

a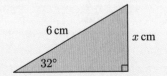

b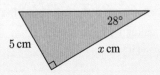

3 Find the measure of all unknown sides and angles in triangle KLM.

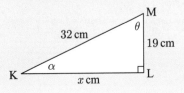

4 Point P is 13 cm from the centre O of a circle. The
tangent from P to the circle is 11 cm long. Find the angle
between the tangent and OP.

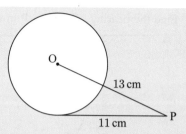

5 The angle of elevation from a point 2 km from the base of the vertical cliff to the top of the cliff
is 17.7°. Find the height of the cliff in metres.

6 A ship sails 40 km on the bearing 056°. How far north is it from its starting point?

7 Find the bearing of:

    a P from Q   **b** R from Q

    c R from P.

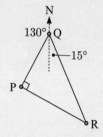

8 Three towns P, Q, and R are situated such that Q lies 10.8 km southeast of P, and R lies 15.4 km
southwest of P.

    a Draw a labelled diagram of the situation.

    b Find the distance from R to Q.

    c Find the bearing of Q from R.

9

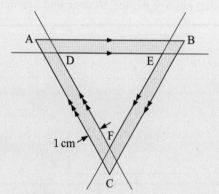

Triangle ABC is equilateral with sides 10 cm long.
Triangle DEF is formed by drawing lines parallel to, and
1 cm away from, the sides of triangle ABC as illustrated.
Find the perimeter of triangle DEF.

10 The figure alongside is a square-based pyramid in which
all edges are 20 cm in length. Find the angle that:

    a AD makes with plane EBCD

    b plane ADC makes with plane EBCD.

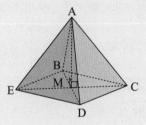

Quadratic equations 23

Contents:

A	Equations of the form $x^2 = k$	[E2.10]
B	Solving equations by factorisation	[E2.10]
C	The quadratic formula	[E2.10]
D	Problem solving	[E2.10]

Opening problem

A square garden gazebo is surrounded by 4 semi-circles of lawn as shown.

For a wedding, quarter circles of flowers are placed in each corner of the gazebo. The lawn covers 4 times as much area as the flower beds.

Suppose the flower beds are x metres apart as shown.

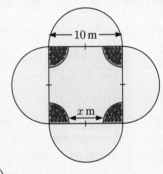

Things to think about:

a Can you explain why the radius of each flower bed is $\left(5 - \dfrac{x}{2}\right)$ metres?

b Can you use this radius to show that $x^2 - 20x + 50 = 0$?

c Can you *solve* this equation to find the distance between the flower beds?

In the past we have solved many equations of the form $ax + b = 0$, $a \neq 0$. These are called **linear equations**, and have *only one* solution.

For example, $3x - 2 = 0$ is a linear equation which has the solution $x = \frac{2}{3}$.

> A **quadratic equation** is an equation which can be written in the form $ax^2 + bx + c = 0$, where a, b, and c are constants, $a \neq 0$.
>
> A quadratic equation may have *two*, *one*, or *zero* real solutions.

For example: $x^2 + 3x - 10 = 0$ is a quadratic equation.

If $x = 2,$ $x^2 + 3x - 10$ If $x = -5,$ $x^2 + 3x - 10$
                $= 2^2 + 3 \times 2 - 10$ $= (-5)^2 + 3 \times (-5) - 10$
                $= 4 + 6 - 10$ $= 25 - 15 - 10$
                $= 0$ $= 0$

$x = 2$ and $x = -5$ both satisfy the equation $x^2 + 3x - 10 = 0,$ so we say that they are both **solutions** or **roots** of the equation.

In contrast, the quadratic equation $x^2 + 2x + 1 = 0$ has only the one solution $x = -1,$
and the quadratic equation $x^2 + 1 = 0$ has no real solutions.

A │ EQUATIONS OF THE FORM $x^2 = k$ [E2.10]

Consider the equation $x^2 = 7.$

If $x = \sqrt{7},$ then $x^2 = (\sqrt{7})^2$
                               $= 7$

$\pm\sqrt{7}$ is read as "plus or minus the square root of 7".

If $x = -\sqrt{7},$ then $x^2 = (-\sqrt{7})^2$
                               $= (-\sqrt{7}) \times (-\sqrt{7})$
                               $= 7$

So, the solutions of $x^2 = 7$ are $x = \pm\sqrt{7}.$

$$\text{If} \quad x^2 = k \quad \text{then} \quad \begin{cases} x = \pm\sqrt{k} & \text{if } k > 0 \\ x = 0 & \text{if } k = 0 \\ \text{there are \textbf{no real solutions}} & \text{if } k < 0. \end{cases}$$

Example 1   ◀ⁱⁱ) *Self Tutor*

Solve for x:

a $2x^2 + 1 = 15$ **b** $2 - 3x^2 = 8$

a $2x^2 + 1 = 15$
   $\therefore \ 2x^2 = 14$ {subtracting 1 from both sides}
   $\therefore \ x^2 = 7$ {dividing both sides by 2}
   $\therefore \ x = \pm\sqrt{7}$

b $2 - 3x^2 = 8$
   $\therefore \ -3x^2 = 6$ {subtracting 2 from both sides}
   $\therefore \ x^2 = -2$ {dividing both sides by -3}
   which has no real solutions as x^2 cannot be $< 0.$

Example 2 ◀) **Self Tutor**

Solve for x:

a $(x-3)^2 = 16$

b $(x+2)^2 = 11$

For equations of the form $(x \pm a)^2 = k$ we do not expand the LHS.

a $(x-3)^2 = 16$

$\therefore \ x - 3 = \pm\sqrt{16}$

$\therefore \ x - 3 = \pm 4$

$\therefore \ x = 3 \pm 4$

$\therefore \ x = 7 \text{ or } -1$

b $(x+2)^2 = 11$

$\therefore \ x + 2 = \pm\sqrt{11}$

$\therefore \ x = -2 \pm \sqrt{11}$

EXERCISE 23A

1 Solve for x:

a $x^2 - 10 = 90$

b $2x^2 = 50$

c $5x^2 = 20$

d $6x^2 = 54$

e $5x^2 = -45$

f $7x^2 = 0$

g $3x^2 - 2 = 25$

h $4 - 2x^2 = 12$

i $4x^2 + 2 = 10$

2 Solve for x:

a $(x-1)^2 = 9$

b $(x+4)^2 = 16$

c $(x+2)^2 = -1$

d $(x-4)^2 = 5$

e $(x-6)^2 = -4$

f $(x+2)^2 = 0$

g $(2x-5)^2 = 0$

h $(3x+2)^2 = 4$

i $(3x+1)^2 = 81$

j $(2x+1)^2 = 48$

k $(3-2x)^2 = 7$

l $\frac{1}{3}(2x+3)^2 = 2$

3 Solve for x by first eliminating the algebraic fractions:

a $\frac{x}{4} = \frac{1}{x}$

b $\frac{5}{x} = \frac{x}{2}$

c $\frac{x}{8} = \frac{2}{x}$

4 Solve for x:

a $(x+1)^2 = (3-x)^2$

b $(2x-1)^2 = (2-3x)^2$

B SOLVING EQUATIONS BY FACTORISATION   [E2.10]

For quadratic equations which are not of the form $x^2 = k$, we need an alternative method of solution. One method is to **factorise** the quadratic and then apply the **null factor law**.

The **null factor law** states that:

When the product of two or more numbers is zero, then *at least one* of them must be zero.

So, if $ab = 0$ then $a = 0$ or $b = 0$.

To solve quadratic equations by factorisation, we follow these steps:

Step 1:   If necessary, rearrange the equation so one side is **zero**.

Step 2:   **Fully factorise** the other side (usually the LHS).

Step 3:   Apply the **null factor law**.

Step 4:   **Solve** the resulting linear equations.

Example 3
🔊 **Self Tutor**

Solve for x: $x^2 = 3x$

$$x^2 = 3x$$
$$\therefore \quad x^2 - 3x = 0 \qquad \{\text{making the RHS} = 0\}$$
$$\therefore \quad x(x - 3) = 0 \qquad \{\text{factorising the LHS}\}$$
$$\therefore \quad x = 0 \ \text{ or } \ x - 3 = 0 \qquad \{\text{null factor law}\}$$
$$\therefore \quad x = 0 \ \text{ or } \ 3$$

If $a \times b = 0$ then either $a = 0$ or $b = 0$.

WARNING ON INCORRECT CANCELLING

In the equation $x^2 = 3x$ from **Example 3**, notice that there is a common factor of x on both sides.

If we cancel x from both sides, we will have $\dfrac{x^2}{x} = \dfrac{3x}{x}$ and thus $x = 3$.

Consequently, we will "lose" the solution $x = 0$.

From this example we conclude that:

> We must never cancel a variable that is a common factor from both sides of an equation unless we know that the factor cannot be zero.

Example 4
🔊 **Self Tutor**

Solve for x: $x^2 + 3x = 28$

$$x^2 + 3x = 28$$
$$\therefore \quad x^2 + 3x - 28 = 0 \qquad \{\text{making the RHS} = 0\}$$
$$\therefore \quad (x + 7)(x - 4) = 0 \qquad \{\text{the numbers } +7 \text{ and } -4 \text{ have sum 3 and product } -28\}$$
$$\therefore \quad x + 7 = 0 \ \text{ or } \ x - 4 = 0 \qquad \{\text{null factor law}\}$$
$$\therefore \quad x = -7 \ \text{ or } \ 4$$

Check: If $x = -7$, then $x^2 + 3x = (-7)^2 + 3(-7) = 49 - 21 = 28$ ✓
   If $x = 4$,   then $x^2 + 3x = 4^2 + 3(4) = 16 + 12 = 28$ ✓

EXERCISE 23B

1 Solve using the null factor law:

    a $mn = 0$
    b $pq = 0$
    c $2xy = 0$

2 Solve for x using the null factor law:

    a $x(x - 5) = 0$
    b $2x(x + 3) = 0$
    c $(x + 1)(x - 3) = 0$

    d $3x(7 - x) = 0$
    e $-2x(x + 1) = 0$
    f $4(x + 6)(2x - 3) = 0$

    g $(2x + 1)(2x - 1) = 0$
    h $11(x + 2)(x - 7) = 0$
    i $-6(x - 5)(3x + 2) = 0$

3 Solve for x:

    a $x^2 - 7x = 0$
    b $x^2 - 5x = 0$
    c $x^2 = 8x$

    d $x^2 = 4x$
    e $3x^2 + 6x = 0$
    f $2x^2 + 5x = 0$

    g $4x^2 - 3x = 0$
    h $4x^2 = 5x$
    i $3x^2 = 9x$

4 Solve for x:

  a $x^2 + 3x + 2 = 0$ **b** $x^2 - 3x + 2 = 0$ **c** $x^2 - 10x + 25 = 0$ **d** $x^2 + 5x + 6 = 0$

  e $x^2 + 6 = 5x$ **f** $x^2 + 7x = -6$ **g** $x^2 + 14 = -9x$ **h** $x^2 + 11x = -30$

  i $x^2 = 15 - 2x$ **j** $x^2 + 4x = 12$ **k** $x^2 = 11x - 24$ **l** $x^2 = 14x - 49$

5 Solve for x:

  a $2x^2 + 18x + 36 = 0$ **b** $-x^2 - 11x - 28 = 0$ **c** $3x^2 + 6x = 24$

  d $2x^2 + 2x = 24$ **e** $4x^2 + 24 = 20x$ **f** $5x^2 + 20 = 20x$

  g $3x^2 = 3x + 18$ **h** $-x^2 = 7x - 60$ **i** $140 + 6x = 2x^2$

Example 5   ◄)) *Self Tutor*

Solve for x:
$5x^2 = 3x + 2$

$$5x^2 = 3x + 2$$
$$\therefore\ 5x^2 - 3x - 2 = 0 \qquad \{\text{making the RHS} = 0\}$$
We need two numbers with sum -3 and product -10. These are -5 and $+2$.
$$\therefore\ 5x^2 - 5x + 2x - 2 = 0 \qquad \{\text{"splitting" the middle term}\}$$
$$\therefore\ 5x(x - 1) + 2(x - 1) = 0$$
$$\therefore\ (x - 1)(5x + 2) = 0$$
$$\therefore\ x - 1 = 0 \ \text{ or } \ 5x + 2 = 0 \qquad \{\text{null factor law}\}$$
$$\therefore\ x = 1 \ \text{ or } \ -\tfrac{2}{5}$$

6 Solve for x:

  a $2x^2 - 5x + 2 = 0$ **b** $3x^2 + 8x - 3 = 0$ **c** $3x^2 + 17x + 20 = 0$ **d** $2x^2 + 5x = 3$

  e $2x^2 + 5 = 11x$ **f** $2x^2 + 7x + 5 = 0$ **g** $3x^2 + 13x + 4 = 0$ **h** $5x^2 - 6 = 13x$

  i $2x^2 + 17x = 9$ **j** $2x^2 = 3x + 5$ **k** $3x^2 = 8 - 2x$ **l** $2x^2 = 18 - 9x$

  m $-6x^2 + 17x + 3 = 0$ **n** $-2x^2 - 5x + 12 = 0$ **o** $12x^2 - 22x + 6 = 0$

  p $9x^2 + 6x - 48 = 0$ **q** $28x^2 - 8 = 2x$ **r** $36x^2 + 39x = 12$

7 Solve for x:

  a $x(x + 5) + 2(x + 6) = 0$ **b** $x(1 + x) + x = 3$ **c** $(x - 1)(x + 9) = 8x$

  d $3x(x + 2) - 5(x - 3) = 17$ **e** $4x(x + 1) = -1$ **f** $2x(x - 6) = x - 20$

  g $x(8 - x) + 20 = -13$ **h** $(8x + 1)(x - 2) = 13 - x$

Example 6   ◄)) *Self Tutor*

Solve for x:
$\dfrac{x - 2}{x} = \dfrac{6 + x}{2}$

$$\frac{x - 2}{x} = \frac{6 + x}{2} \qquad \{\text{LCD} = 2x\}$$
$$\therefore\ \left(\frac{x - 2}{x}\right) \times \frac{2}{2} = \left(\frac{6 + x}{2}\right) \times \frac{x}{x} \qquad \{\text{to achieve a common denominator}\}$$
$$\therefore\ 2(x - 2) = x(6 + x) \qquad \{\text{equating numerators}\}$$
$$\therefore\ 2x - 4 = 6x + x^2$$
$$\therefore\ x^2 + 4x + 4 = 0$$
$$\therefore\ (x + 2)^2 = 0$$
$$\therefore\ x + 2 = 0$$
$$\therefore\ x = -2$$

Check: If $x = -2$ then
$$\text{LHS} = \frac{(-2) - 2}{(-2)} = \frac{-4}{-2} = 2$$
and $\text{RHS} = \dfrac{6 + (-2)}{2} = \dfrac{4}{2} = 2$ ✓

8 Solve for x:

  a $\dfrac{x+1}{4} = \dfrac{1}{2x}$ **b** $\dfrac{x+4}{2} = \dfrac{6}{x}$ **c** $\dfrac{x+2}{x} = x$

  d $\dfrac{x-1}{x+2} = \dfrac{2}{x}$ **e** $\dfrac{x}{1+2x} = \dfrac{1}{3x}$ **f** $\dfrac{3x+1}{2x} = x+2$

Example 7   ◀) **Self Tutor**

Solve for x: $\dfrac{1}{x} + \dfrac{4}{x+6} = 1$

$$\dfrac{1}{x} + \dfrac{4}{x+6} = 1 \qquad \{\text{LCD} = x(x+6)\}$$

$$\therefore \dfrac{1}{x} \times \dfrac{(x+6)}{(x+6)} + \left(\dfrac{4}{x+6}\right) \times \dfrac{x}{x} = 1 \times \dfrac{x(x+6)}{x(x+6)} \qquad \{\text{to achieve a common denominator}\}$$

$$\therefore \ x + 6 + 4x = x(x+6) \qquad \{\text{equating numerators}\}$$

$$\therefore \ 5x + 6 = x^2 + 6x$$

$$\therefore \ 0 = x^2 + x - 6$$

$$\therefore \ (x+3)(x-2) = 0$$

$$\therefore \ x = -3 \ \text{ or } \ 2$$

---

9 Solve for x:

  a $\dfrac{2}{x} + \dfrac{3}{x+2} = 1$ **b** $\dfrac{5}{x} + \dfrac{x}{x-6} = 2$ **c** $\dfrac{4}{x+1} + \dfrac{3}{x+3} = -1$

  d $\dfrac{5}{x+2} - \dfrac{6}{x-1} = -2$ **e** $\dfrac{4}{x-2} + \dfrac{3}{x-1} = 3$ **f** $\dfrac{x}{x-2} - \dfrac{x+3}{x} = -5$

  g $\dfrac{1}{x+3} + \dfrac{1}{x-3} = x$ **h** $\dfrac{4}{x+2} - \dfrac{2}{x+1} = x$

10 Solve for x:

  a $x^4 - 5x^2 + 4 = 0$ **b** $x^4 - 7x^2 + 12 = 0$ **c** $x^4 = 4x^2 + 5$

  Hint: Treat these as quadratics in the variable x^2.

Historical note   *Babylonian algebra*

The mathematics used by the **Babylonians** was recorded on clay tablets in cuneiform. One such tablet which has been preserved is called *Plimpton 322*, written around 1600 BC.

The Ancient Babylonians were able to solve difficult equations using the rules we use today, such as transposing terms, multiplying both sides by like quantities to remove fractions, and factorisation.

They could, for example, add $4xy$ to $(x-y)^2$ to obtain $(x+y)^2$.

Plimpton 322

This was all achieved without the use of letters for unknown quantities. Instead, they often used words for the unknown.

Consider the following example from about 4000 years ago:

Problem: *"I have subtracted the side of my square from the area and the result is 870. What is the side of the square?"*

Solution: Take half of 1, which is $\frac{1}{2}$, and multiply $\frac{1}{2}$ by $\frac{1}{2}$ which is $\frac{1}{4}$.

Add this to 870 to get $870\frac{1}{4}$.   This is the square of $29\frac{1}{2}$.

Now add $\frac{1}{2}$ to $29\frac{1}{2}$ and the result is 30, the side of the square.

Using our modern symbols, the equation is $x^2 - x = 870$, and one of the solutions is $x = \sqrt{(\frac{1}{2})^2 + 870} + \frac{1}{2} = 30$.

C   THE QUADRATIC FORMULA   [E2.10]

Many quadratic equations cannot be solved easily by factorisation. Consequently, the **quadratic formula** has been developed.

$$\text{If} \quad ax^2 + bx + c = 0 \quad \text{where} \quad a \neq 0, \quad \text{then} \quad x = \frac{-b \pm \sqrt{b^2 - 4ac}}{2a}.$$

Proof:

If $\quad ax^2 + bx + c = 0$

then $\quad x^2 + \dfrac{b}{a}x + \dfrac{c}{a} = 0 \qquad$ {dividing each term by a, as $a \neq 0$}

$\therefore \quad x^2 + \dfrac{b}{a}x \quad = -\dfrac{c}{a}$

$\therefore \quad x^2 + \dfrac{b}{a}x + \left(\dfrac{b}{2a}\right)^2 = -\dfrac{c}{a} + \left(\dfrac{b}{2a}\right)^2 \qquad$ {adding $\left(\dfrac{b}{2a}\right)^2$ to both sides}

$\therefore \quad \left(x + \dfrac{b}{2a}\right)^2 = -\dfrac{c}{a}\left(\dfrac{4a}{4a}\right) + \dfrac{b^2}{4a^2}$

$\therefore \quad \left(x + \dfrac{b}{2a}\right)^2 = \dfrac{b^2 - 4ac}{4a^2}$

$\therefore \quad x + \dfrac{b}{2a} = \pm\sqrt{\dfrac{b^2 - 4ac}{4a^2}}$

$\therefore \quad x = -\dfrac{b}{2a} \pm \dfrac{\sqrt{b^2 - 4ac}}{2a}$

$\therefore \quad x = \dfrac{-b \pm \sqrt{b^2 - 4ac}}{2a}$

The quantity $b^2 - 4ac$ under the square root sign is called the **discriminant**.

The symbol **delta** Δ is used to represent the discriminant, so $\Delta = b^2 - 4ac$.

If $\Delta > 0$, the quadratic equation has two distinct real solutions.

If $\Delta = 0$, the quadratic equation has one real solution, which is $x = -\dfrac{b}{2a}$.

If $\Delta < 0$, there are no real solutions.

Example 8

◂⟩ *Self Tutor*

Solve for x:

a $x^2 - 2x - 2 = 0$

b $2x^2 + 3x - 4 = 0$

a $x^2 - 2x - 2 = 0$ has
$a = 1, \ b = -2, \ c = -2$

$$\therefore \ x = \frac{-(-2) \pm \sqrt{(-2)^2 - 4(1)(-2)}}{2(1)}$$

$$\therefore \ x = \frac{2 \pm \sqrt{4 + 8}}{2}$$

$$\therefore \ x = \frac{2 \pm \sqrt{12}}{2}$$

$$\therefore \ x = \frac{2 \pm 2\sqrt{3}}{2}$$

$$\therefore \ x = 1 \pm \sqrt{3}$$

b $2x^2 + 3x - 4 = 0$ has
$a = 2, \ b = 3, \ c = -4$

$$\therefore \ x = \frac{-3 \pm \sqrt{3^2 - 4(2)(-4)}}{2(2)}$$

$$\therefore \ x = \frac{-3 \pm \sqrt{9 + 32}}{4}$$

$$\therefore \ x = \frac{-3 \pm \sqrt{41}}{4}$$

EXERCISE 23C

1 Solve the following equations using:

    i factorisation   **ii** the quadratic formula.

  a $x^2 + 6x + 8 = 0$ **b** $x^2 - 10x + 25 = 0$ **c** $3x^2 - 7x - 6 = 0$

2 Use the quadratic formula to solve for x, giving exact answers:

  a $x^2 + x - 5 = 0$ **b** $x^2 - 5x + 5 = 0$ **c** $x^2 - 4x - 1 = 0$

  d $x^2 + 1 = 3x$ **e** $2x^2 = 2x + 3$ **f** $9x^2 = 6x + 1$

3 Use the quadratic formula to solve for x, rounding your answers to 2 decimal places:

  a $3x^2 + 5x - 1 = 0$ **b** $-2x^2 + x + 7 = 0$ **c** $5x^2 - 8x + 1 = 0$

  d $7x^2 = 5x + 1$ **e** $3x^2 + 2x = 2$ **f** $25x^2 + 1 = 20x$

4 Show that the following quadratic equations have no real solutions:

  a $x^2 - 3x + 12 = 0$ **b** $x^2 + 2x + 4 = 0$ **c** $-2x^2 + x - 1 = 0$

5 Solve for x, where possible:

  a $x^2 - 25 = 0$ **b** $x^2 + 25 = 0$ **c** $x^2 - 7 = 0$

  d $x^2 + 7 = 0$ **e** $4x^2 - 9 = 0$ **f** $4x^2 + 9 = 0$

  g $x^2 - 4x + 5 = 0$ **h** $x^2 - 4x - 5 = 0$ **i** $x^2 - 10x + 29 = 0$

  j $x^2 + 6x + 25 = 0$ **k** $2x^2 - 6x - 5 = 0$ **l** $2x^2 + x - 2 = 0$

6 Use the quadratic formula to solve for x:

  a $(x + 2)(x - 1) = 5$ **b** $(x + 1)^2 = 3 - x^2$ **c** $\frac{x - 1}{x} = \frac{x}{3}$

  d $x + \frac{1}{x + 2} = 4$ **e** $3x - \frac{4}{x + 1} = 10$ **f** $\frac{x + 2}{x - 1} = \frac{3x}{x + 1}$

D   *PROBLEM SOLVING*   *[E2.10]*

When practical problems are converted into algebraic form, a quadratic equation may result. To solve these problems, follow these steps:

Step 1:   Carefully **read the question** until you understand the problem. A **sketch** may be useful.
Step 2:   Decide on the **unknown** quantity and label it x, say.
Step 3:   Use the information given to write an **equation**.
Step 4:   **Solve** the equation.
Step 5:   **Check** that any solutions satisfy the equation and are reasonable.
Step 6:   Write your answer to the question in **sentence form**.

Example 9   ◀) *Self Tutor*

The sum of a number and its square is 42. Find the number.

Let the number be x.   Therefore its square is x^2.

$$x + x^2 = 42$$
$$\therefore \ x^2 + x - 42 = 0 \qquad \{\text{rearranging}\}$$
$$\therefore \ (x+7)(x-6) = 0 \qquad \{\text{factorising}\}$$
$$\therefore \ x = -7 \ \text{ or } \ x = 6$$

So, the number is -7 or 6.

Check: The sum of -7 and its square is $-7 + (-7)^2 = -7 + 49 = 42$ ✓
The sum of 6 and its square is $6 + 6^2 = 6 + 36 = 42$ ✓

EXERCISE 23D

1 The sum of a number and its square is 110. Find the number.

2 When 24 is subtracted from the square of a number, the result is five times the original number. Find the number.

3 The sum of two numbers is 6, and the sum of their squares is 28. Find these numbers exactly.

4 Two numbers differ by 7, and the sum of their squares is 29. Find the numbers.

Example 10   ◀) *Self Tutor*

A rectangle has length 5 cm greater than its width. Its area is 84 cm². Find the rectangle's dimensions.

Let the width of the rectangle be x cm.
$\therefore$ the length of the rectangle is $(x+5)$ cm.

Now   area $= 84$ cm²
$$\therefore \ x(x+5) = 84$$
$$\therefore \ x^2 + 5x = 84$$
$$\therefore \ x^2 + 5x - 84 = 0$$
$$\therefore \ (x+12)(x-7) = 0$$
$$\therefore \ x = -12 \ \text{ or } \ 7$$

$(x+5)$ cm

x cm

But $x > 0$ as lengths must be positive, so $x = 7$.
$\therefore$ the rectangle is 7 cm by 12 cm.

5 A rectangle has length 4 cm greater than its width, and its area is 96 cm². Find the width of the rectangle.

6 The base of a triangle is 4 m longer than its altitude. The area of the triangle is 70 m². Find the triangle's altitude.

7 A rectangular enclosure is made from 60 m of fencing. The area enclosed is 216 m². Find the dimensions of the enclosure.

8 A rectangular garden bed was built against an existing brick wall. 24 m of edging was used to enclose 60 m². Find the dimensions of the garden bed to the nearest centimetre.

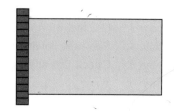

9 A right angled triangle has sides 3 cm and 8 cm respectively less than its hypotenuse. Find the length of the hypotenuse to the nearest millimetre.

10 ABCD is a rectangle in which AB = 21 cm.
The square AXYD is removed and the remaining rectangle has area 80 cm².
Find the length of BC.

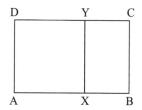

Example 11

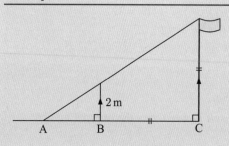

Given that AB is 3 m shorter than BC, find the height of the flagpole.

Let the height of the flagpole be x m.

$\therefore$ BC $= x$ m and AB $= (x - 3)$ m

The triangles are equiangular, so they are similar.

$$\therefore \quad \frac{x}{2} = \frac{(x-3)+x}{x-3}$$

$$\therefore \quad x(x-3) = 2(2x-3)$$

$$\therefore \quad x^2 - 3x = 4x - 6$$

$$\therefore \quad x^2 - 7x + 6 = 0$$

$$\therefore \quad (x-1)(x-6) = 0$$

$$\therefore \quad x = 1 \text{ or } 6$$

But $x - 3 > 0$ as lengths must be positive.

$\therefore \quad x = 6$

So, the flagpole is 6 m high.

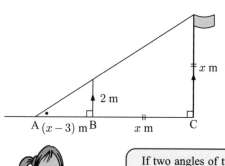

If two angles of two triangles are equal, then the third angles must also be equal.

11 Find x in:

a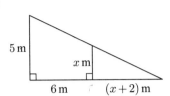

b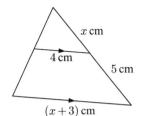

c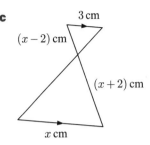

d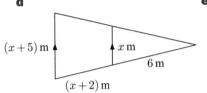

e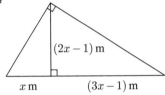

f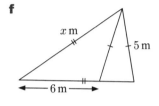

12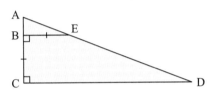

In the figure alongside, AC = 10 cm, BC is the same length as BE, and CD is 3 cm more than twice the length of BE.

Find the length of BE.

13 A, B, C, and D are posts on the banks of a 20 m wide canal. A and B are 2 m apart, and OA = CD.

Find the exact distance between C and D.

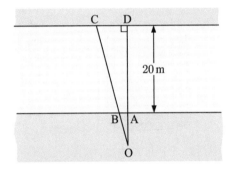

14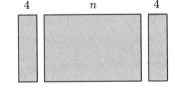

A theatre contains a central block of seats with n seats per row. Blocks on either side contain 4 seats per row. The number of rows is 5 less than the total number of seats per row. In total there are 126 seats in the theatre. Find the value of n.

15 The numerator of a fraction is 3 less than the denominator. If the numerator is increased by 6 and the denominator is increased by 5, the fraction is doubled in value. Find the original fraction.

16 At a fruit market, John bought some oranges for a total of $20. When Jenny visited a different stall, she bought 10 more oranges than John for the same total amount. Given that the difference in price per orange was 10 cents, how many oranges did John purchase?

17 The sum of a number and its reciprocal is $2\frac{1}{12}$. Find the number.

18 Two numbers have a sum of 4, and the sum of their reciprocals is 8. Find the numbers.

19 A sheet of cardboard is 15 cm long and 10 cm wide. It is to be made into an open box with base area 66 cm², by cutting out equal squares from the four corners and then bending the edges upwards.

Find the size of the squares to be cut out.

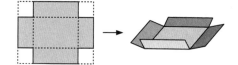

20 Answer the **Opening Problem** on page **375**.

21 A circular magnet has an inner radius of x cm, an outer radius 2 cm larger, and its depth is the same as the inner radius. The total volume of the magnet is 120π cm³. Find x.

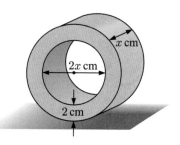

22 A rectangular swimming pool is 12 m long by 6 m wide. It is surrounded by a pavement of uniform width. The area of the pavement is $\frac{7}{8}$ of the area of the pool.

   a If the pavement is x m wide, show that the area of the pavement is $(4x^2 + 36x)$ m².

   b Hence, show that $4x^2 + 36x - 63 = 0$.

   c How wide is the pavement?

23

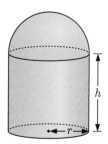

A takeaway milkshake container is cylindrical, with a hemispherical lid on top.

The height h of the container is 7 cm greater than its base radius r.

The surface area of the container and lid is 96π cm².

Find the base radius of the container.

Review set 23A

1 Solve for x:

   a $2x^2 = 4$

   b $3x^2 + 18 = 0$

   c $5x(x - 3) = 0$

   d $x^2 + 24 = 11x$

   e $10x^2 - 11x - 6 = 0$

   f $3x^2 = 2x + 21$

2 Solve for x, if possible:

   a $x^2 = x$

   b $(x + 3)^2 = -1$

   c $3(x - 2)^2 = 15$

   d $\dfrac{x}{x - 3} = \dfrac{18}{x + 15}$

   e $\dfrac{x + 3}{2} = \dfrac{x + 5}{3x}$

   f $\dfrac{7}{x - 2} - \dfrac{2}{x + 1} = 2$

3 Solve for x:

   a $x^2 - 4x - 21 = 0$

   b $4x^2 - 25 = 0$

   c $6x^2 - x - 2 = 0$

   d $3x^2 - 6x - 72 = 0$

   e $5x^2 + 30x + 45 = 0$

   f $4x^2 - 18x + 8 = 0$

4 The sum of a number and its reciprocal is $2\frac{1}{6}$. Find the number.

5 Solve for x:

  a $x^2 + 24x = 11$ **b** $(x+6)(x-3) = 10x$ **c** $10x^2 - 6 = 11x$

6 Use the quadratic formula to solve for x:

  a $2x^2 - 3x - 2 = 0$ **b** $3x^2 + 4x - 5 = 0$ **c** $\dfrac{x+4}{x-2} = \dfrac{5x}{x-1}$

7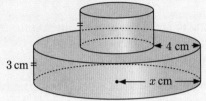

The volume of the solid alongside is 174π cm^3.
Find x.

8 In a right angled triangle, the second longest side is 5 cm longer than the shortest side, and the hypotenuse is three times the length of the shortest side. Find the exact length of the hypotenuse.

9 Find the value of x, rounding your answer to 2 decimal places:

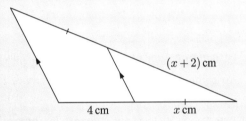

10 A straight length of wire is 20 cm long. It is bent at right angles to form the two shorter sides of a right angled triangle.

  a If the triangle's area is 30 cm^2, find:

    i the length of each side

    ii the triangle's perimeter.

  b Is it possible for a right angled triangle with its two shorter sides made from a 20 cm length of wire to have an area of 51 cm^2? Explain your answer.

11 Solve for x: $\dfrac{1}{x-3} + \dfrac{3}{x+1} = 1$

Review set 23B

1 Solve for x:

  a $-2(x-3)^2 = 0$ **b** $(x+5)(x-4) = 0$ **c** $(2-x)^2 = -1$

  d $x^2 - 5x = 24$ **e** $2x^2 = 8$ **f** $6x^2 - x - 2 = 0$

2 Use the quadratic formula to solve:

  a $x^2 - 4x = 10$ **b** $x^2 + x - 9 = 0$

3 Solve for x:

  a $\dfrac{x}{x+3} = \dfrac{5}{x+7}$ **b** $\dfrac{2x-3}{10} = \dfrac{x-2}{x}$ **c** $\dfrac{1}{x+1} + \dfrac{3}{3x-5} = 1$

4   Solve for x:

   a $8 - 3x^2 = -10$ **b** $2x^2 - 5 = -3$ **c** $(3x - 1)^2 = 17$

   d $x^2 - 8x - 33 = 0$ **e** $8x^2 + 2x - 3 = 0$ **f** $6x^2 + 26x = 20$

5   The hypotenuse of a right angled triangle is one centimetre more than twice the length of the shortest side. The other side is 7 cm longer than the shortest side. Find the length of each side of the triangle.

6   A group of friends hires a bus for a day for $480, agreeing to share the cost equally. At the last minute, two more people decide to go on the trip, and as a result each person pays $8 less. How many people go on the trip and how much does each person pay?

7   In the flag alongside, the area of the red stripes is 700 cm². Find the width of the red stripes.

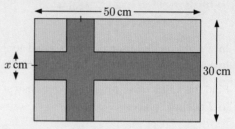

8   The sum of a number and five times its square, is equal to four. Find the number.

9   Two numbers differ by 3 and the difference between their reciprocals is 4. Find the exact values of the numbers, given that they are both positive.

10   Kuan has $180 to share amongst his grandchildren. However, three of his grandchildren have misbehaved recently, so they will not receive any money. As a result, the remaining grandchildren receive an extra $5 each. How many grandchildren does Kuan have?

11   A 90 m × 90 m block of land is to be divided into three paddocks using two straight fences as shown.

   The three paddocks must have the same area. Determine where the fencing needs to be placed. To do this, specify the lengths of CX and AY, rounding your answers to 2 decimal places if necessary.

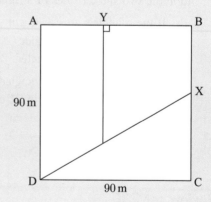

Transformation geometry

24

Contents:

A	Translations	[E6.4]
B	Reflections	[E6.4, E6.6]
C	Rotations	[E6.4, E6.6]
D	Enlargements and reductions	[E6.4]
E	Stretches	[E6.4]
F	The inverse of a transformation	[E6.5]
G	Combinations of transformations	[E6.6]

Opening problem

Consider the grey triangle on the illustrated plane.

a What transformation would map the triangle onto:

   i triangle A   **ii** triangle B

   iii triangle C   **iv** triangle D?

b What single transformation would map triangle A onto triangle C?

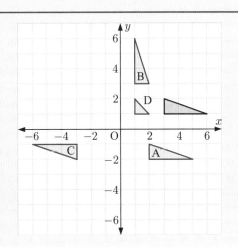

TRANSFORMATIONS

A change in the size, shape, orientation, or position of a figure is called a **transformation**.

Many trees, plants, flowers, animals, and insects are **symmetrical** in some way. Such symmetry results from a reflection, so we can describe symmetry using transformations.

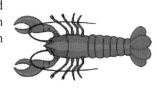

Reflections, rotations, translations, and dilations are all examples of transformations. We can describe these transformations mathematically using **transformation geometry**.

The original figure is called the **object** and the new figure is called the **image**.

We will consider the following **transformations**:

- **Translations**, where every point moves a fixed distance in a given direction
- **Reflections** or mirror images
- **Rotations** about a point through a given angle
- **Enlargements** and **reductions** of three kinds:
  - ▸ with centre the origin
  - ▸ horizontal stretch with y-axis fixed.
  - ▸ vertical stretch with x-axis fixed

Here are some examples:

- **a translation**

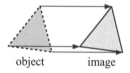

- **reflection**

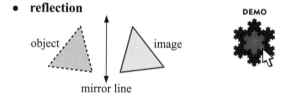

- **rotation about** O
  through angle θ

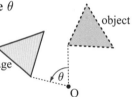

- **enlargement**

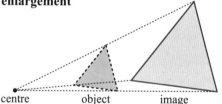

- **reduction**

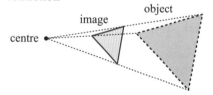

- **stretch**

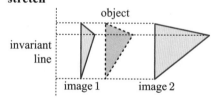

A   *TRANSLATIONS*   *[E6.4]*

A **translation** moves a figure from one place to another. Every point on the figure moves the same distance in the same direction.

If $P(x, y)$ is **translated** h units in the x-direction and k units in the y-direction, then the image point P' has coordinates $(x + h, y + k)$.

We write $P(x, y) \ \xrightarrow{\binom{h}{k}} \ P'(x + h, y + k)$

where P' is called the **image** of the object P, and

$\begin{pmatrix} h \\ k \end{pmatrix}$ is called the **translation vector**.

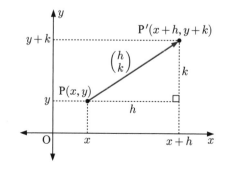

Example 1
🔊 **Self Tutor**

Triangle OAB with vertices O(0, 0), A(2, 3), and B(−1, 2) is translated $\begin{pmatrix} 3 \\ 2 \end{pmatrix}$.

Find the image vertices and illustrate the object and image.

> When we translate point A, we label its image A′.

O(0, 0) $\xrightarrow{\begin{pmatrix} 3 \\ 2 \end{pmatrix}}$ O′(3, 2)

A(2, 3) $\xrightarrow{\begin{pmatrix} 3 \\ 2 \end{pmatrix}}$ A′(5, 5)

B(−1, 2) $\xrightarrow{\begin{pmatrix} 3 \\ 2 \end{pmatrix}}$ B′(2, 4)

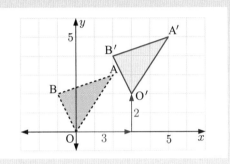

EXERCISE 24A

1 Find the image point when:

    a (2, −1) is translated $\begin{pmatrix} 3 \\ 4 \end{pmatrix}$
    b (5, 2) is translated $\begin{pmatrix} -1 \\ 4 \end{pmatrix}$.

2 Find the translation vector which translates the point:

    a (3, −2) to (3, 1)
    b (−1, 7) to (4, 2).

3 What point has image (−3, 2) under the translation $\begin{pmatrix} -3 \\ 1 \end{pmatrix}$?

4 Find the translation vector which maps:

    a A onto E   **b** E onto A

    c A onto C   **d** C onto A

    e B onto E   **f** D onto E

    g E onto C   **h** E onto D

    i D onto B   **j** A onto D.

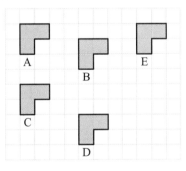

5

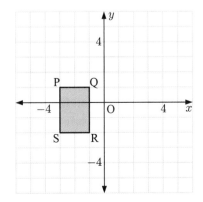

PQRS is a rectangle.

    a State the coordinates of P, Q, R, and S.

    b Copy the rectangle, and translate it $\begin{pmatrix} 5 \\ 1 \end{pmatrix}$.

    c State the coordinates of the image vertices P′, Q′, R′, and S′.

6 Triangle ABC has vertices A$(-1, 3)$, B$(4, 1)$, and C$(0, -2)$.

    a Draw triangle ABC on a set of axes.   **b** Translate the figure $\begin{pmatrix} 4 \\ -2 \end{pmatrix}$.

    c State the coordinates of the image vertices A$'$, B$'$, and C$'$.

    d Find the distance each point has moved.

7 What single transformation is equivalent to a translation of $\begin{pmatrix} 2 \\ 1 \end{pmatrix}$ followed by a translation of $\begin{pmatrix} 3 \\ 4 \end{pmatrix}$?

Example 2
◀ッ Self Tutor

Find the equation of the image line when $2x - 3y = 6$ is translated $\begin{pmatrix} -1 \\ 2 \end{pmatrix}$.

For the line $2x - 3y = 6$:

When $x = 0$, $y = -2$

When $y = 0$, $x = 3$

$\therefore$ $(0, -2)$ and $(3, 0)$ lie on the line.

Under the translation,

$(0, -2)\ \xrightarrow{\begin{pmatrix} -1 \\ 2 \end{pmatrix}}\ (-1, 0)$

$(3, 0)\ \xrightarrow{\begin{pmatrix} -1 \\ 2 \end{pmatrix}}\ (2, 2)$

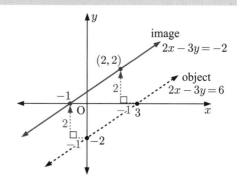

The image line is parallel to the original line, so its equation has the form $2x - 3y = k$.

Substituting the coordinates $(-1, 0)$, we find $k = -2$.

$\therefore$ the image line is $2x - 3y = -2$.

---

8 Find the equation of the image line when:

    a $y = 2x + 3$ is translated $\begin{pmatrix} -1 \\ 2 \end{pmatrix}$

    b $y = \frac{1}{3}x + 2$ is translated $\begin{pmatrix} 3 \\ 0 \end{pmatrix}$

    c $y = -x + 2$ is translated $\begin{pmatrix} 2 \\ 3 \end{pmatrix}$

    d $y = -\frac{1}{2}x$ is translated $\begin{pmatrix} -2 \\ -5 \end{pmatrix}$

    e $3x + 2y = 8$ is translated $\begin{pmatrix} -1 \\ 3 \end{pmatrix}$

    f $x = 4$ is translated $\begin{pmatrix} 2 \\ 1 \end{pmatrix}$

    g $2x - y = 6$ is translated $\begin{pmatrix} -3 \\ 0 \end{pmatrix}$

    h $y = 5$ is translated $\begin{pmatrix} 2 \\ -5 \end{pmatrix}$.

B REFLECTIONS   [E6.4, E6.6]

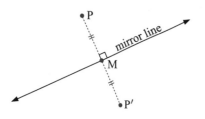

When P(x, y) is **reflected** in the **mirror line** to become P$'(x', y')$, the mirror line perpendicularly bisects PP$'$. This means that PM $=$ P$'$M.

> In a reflection, the mirror line perpendicularly bisects the line segment joining each point on an object with its image.

We will concentrate on the following reflections:

- reflection in horizontal lines
- reflection in the line $y = x$
- reflection in vertical lines
- reflection in the line $y = -x$.

Example 3   ◀)) *Self Tutor*

Find the image of the point $(3, 1)$ under a reflection in:

a   the x-axis   **b**   the y-axis   **c** $y = x$ **d** $y = -x$.

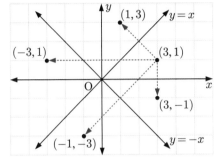

a $(3, 1) \xrightarrow{\text{reflection } x\text{-axis}} (3, -1)$

b $(3, 1) \xrightarrow{\text{reflection } y\text{-axis}} (-3, 1)$

c $(3, 1) \xrightarrow{\text{reflection } y = x} (1, 3)$

d $(3, 1) \xrightarrow{\text{reflection } y = -x} (-1, -3)$

From the Example above, you may observe the following general properties for reflecting a point (x, y):

Object	Reflection	Image
(x, y)	reflection in x-axis	$(x, -y)$
(x, y)	reflection in y-axis	$(-x, y)$
(x, y)	reflection in $y = x$	(y, x)
(x, y)	reflection in $y = -x$	$(-y, -x)$

Example 4   ◀)) *Self Tutor*

Find the image of the line $y = 2x + 2$ when it is reflected in the line $x = 1$.

Using the axes intercepts, two points which lie on the line $y = 2x + 2$ are $(0, 2)$ and $(-1, 0)$.

When reflected in the line $x = 1$, these points are mapped to $(2, 2)$ and $(3, 0)$ respectively.

$\therefore$ $(2, 2)$ and $(3, 0)$ lie on the image line.

$\therefore$ the image line has gradient $\dfrac{0 - 2}{3 - 2} = -2$

so its equation is $2x + y = 2(3) + (0)$ {using $(3, 0)$}

or $2x + y = 6$.

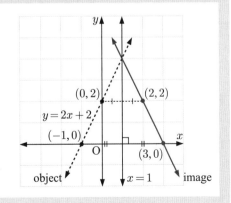

EXERCISE 24B

1 Copy and reflect in the given line:

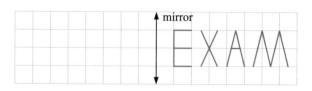

2 Find, by graphical means, the image of the point $(4, -1)$ under a reflection in:

   a the x-axis   **b** the y-axis   **c** $y = x$ **d** $y = -x$.

3 Find, by graphical means, the image of the point $(-1, -3)$ under a reflection in:

   a the y-axis   **b** the line $y = -x$ **c** the line $x = 2$ **d** the line $y = -1$

   e the x-axis   **f** the line $x = -3$ **g** the line $y = x$ **h** the line $y = 2$.

4 Copy the graph given. Reflect T in:

   a the x-axis and label it U

   b the y-axis and label it V

   c the line $y = -x$ and label it W.

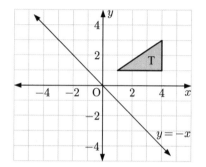

5 Find the image of:

   a $(2, 3)$ under a reflection in the x-axis followed by a translation of $\begin{pmatrix} -1 \\ 2 \end{pmatrix}$

   b $(4, -1)$ under a reflection in $y = -x$ followed by a translation of $\begin{pmatrix} 4 \\ 3 \end{pmatrix}$

   c $(-1, 5)$ under a reflection in the y-axis followed by a reflection in the x-axis followed by a
translation of $\begin{pmatrix} 2 \\ -4 \end{pmatrix}$

   d $(3, -2)$ under a reflection in $y = x$ followed by a translation of $\begin{pmatrix} 3 \\ 4 \end{pmatrix}$

   e $(4, 3)$ under a translation of $\begin{pmatrix} 1 \\ -4 \end{pmatrix}$ followed by a reflection in the x-axis

   f $(-2, 5)$ under a reflection in $y = -x$ followed by a translation of $\begin{pmatrix} -3 \\ 1 \end{pmatrix}$.

6 Find the equation of the image of $y = 2x$ when it is reflected in:

   a the x-axis   **b** the line $y = x$ **c** the line $x = 1$ **d** the line $y = 3$.

7 Find the image of the line:

   a $y = \frac{1}{2}x$ when it is reflected in the x-axis

   b $3x + 2y = 12$ when it is reflected in the y-axis

   c $2x + 3y = 4$ when it is reflected in the line $y = -x$

   d $y = -x + 3$ when it is reflected in the line $y = -1$.

8 Consider the line $y = 2x + 3$.

    a Find the equation of the image when the line is translated $\begin{pmatrix} 3 \\ -2 \end{pmatrix}$.

    b If the result is reflected in the x-axis, find the equation of the reflected image.

    c Draw the three lines on the same set of axes, clearly labelling each line.

    d Describe the single transformation which maps $y = 2x + 3$ onto the final image.

C ROTATIONS   [E6.4, E6.6]

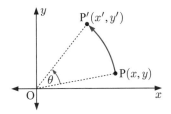

If $P(x, y)$ is moved under a **rotation** about O through an angle of θ to a new position $P'(x', y')$, then $OP = OP'$ and $\widehat{POP'} = \theta$.

Positive θ is measured anticlockwise.

O is the only point which does not move under such a rotation.

In this course we concentrate on rotations of:

- $90°$, which means $90°$ anticlockwise
- $180°$
- $-90°$, which means $90°$ clockwise.

Example 5   ◀) Self Tutor

Find the image of the point $(3, 1)$ under a rotation about O of:

    a $90°$ anticlockwise   **b** $90°$ clockwise   **c** $180°$

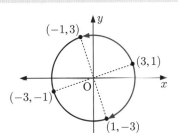

    a $(3, 1) \xrightarrow{90° \text{ about O}} (-1, 3)$ {anticlockwise}

    b $(3, 1) \xrightarrow{-90° \text{ about O}} (1, -3)$ {clockwise}

    c $(3, 1) \xrightarrow{180° \text{ about O}} (-3, -1)$

EXERCISE 24C

1 Find the image of the point $(-2, 3)$ under a rotation about O of:

    a $90°$ anticlockwise   **b** $90°$ clockwise   **c** $180°$

2 Find the image of the point $(4, -1)$ under a rotation about $(0, 2)$ of:

    a $90°$ anticlockwise   **b** $90°$ clockwise   **c** $180°$

Example 6

🔊 *Self Tutor*

Triangle ABC has vertices A(−1, 2), B(−1, 5), and C(−3, 5). It is rotated clockwise through 90° about (−2, 0). Draw the image of triangle ABC and label it A′B′C′.

A(−1, 2) $\xrightarrow{\text{−90° about }(-2,\,0)}$ A′(0, −1)

B(−1, 5) $\xrightarrow{\text{−90° about }(-2,\,0)}$ B′(3, −1)

C(−3, 5) $\xrightarrow{\text{−90° about }(-2,\,0)}$ C′(3, 1)

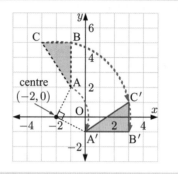

3 Triangle ABC has vertices A(2, 4), B(4, 1), and C(2, 1). It is rotated anticlockwise through 90° about O.

  a Draw triangle ABC and its image A′B′C′.

  b Write down the coordinates of A′, B′, and C′.

4 Triangle PQR with P(3, −2), Q(1, 4), and R(−1, 1) is rotated about R through 180°.

  a Draw triangle PQR and its image P′Q′R′.

  b Write down the coordinates of P′, Q′, and R′.

5 Find the image of:

  a (2, 3) under an anticlockwise rotation of 90° about O followed by a reflection in the x-axis

  b (−2, 5) under a reflection in $y = -x$ followed by a rotation of −90° about O

  c (−3, −1) under a reflection in $y = x$ followed by a rotation of 180°

  d (4, −2) under a rotation of 90° about O followed by a translation of $\begin{pmatrix} -2 \\ -3 \end{pmatrix}$.

> **Positive θ is** measured **anticlockwise.**

6 **a** Draw triangle T with vertices (1, 1), (3, 1), and (2, 2) on a grid with x and y values ranging from −5 to 5.
Reflect T in the x-axis and label its image U.
Reflect U in the line $y = x$ and label its image V.

  b Describe the single transformation which maps T directly onto V.

7 **a** Draw triangle F with vertices (1, 2), (4, 0), and (3, 4) on a grid with x and y values ranging from −5 to 5.
Reflect F in the line $y = x$ and label its image G.
Reflect G in the line $y = -x$ and label its image H.

  b Describe the single transformation which maps F directly onto H.

Example 7

◀) *Self Tutor*

Find the image equation of the line $2x - 3y = -6$ under a clockwise rotation about O through $90°$.

For the line $2x - 3y = -6$:

When $x = 0$, $y = 2$

When $y = 0$, $x = -3$

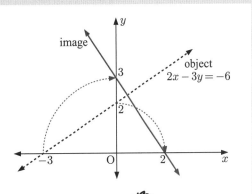

We plot the line using these axes intercepts, then rotate the axes intercepts clockwise through $90°$.

The gradient of the object was $\frac{2}{3}$ so the gradient of the image is $-\frac{3}{2}$.

Using the gradient and y-intercept, the image has equation $y = -\frac{3}{2}x + 3$.

Under a rotation of $90°$, the object and image are perpendicular.

8 Find the image equation when:

    a $2x + 3y = 12$ is rotated $90°$ about O   **b** $y = -3$ is rotated $90°$ about O

    c $x = 7$ is rotated $180°$ about O   **d** $3x - 4y = 7$ is rotated $-90°$ about O.

9 Find the single transformation equivalent to a rotation about $O(0, 0)$ through $\theta°$ followed by a rotation about $O(0, 0)$ through $\phi°$.

10 Find the image of:

    a $x + 2y = -4$ under a rotation of $-90°$ about O, followed by a translation of $\begin{pmatrix} 2 \\ -5 \end{pmatrix}$

    b $x + y = 1$ under a clockwise rotation of $90°$ about O, followed by a reflection in $y = x$, followed by a translation of $\begin{pmatrix} 3 \\ 1 \end{pmatrix}$.

D   ENLARGEMENTS AND REDUCTIONS   *[E6.4]*

When an object is enlarged or reduced, we create an image which is mathematically *similar* to the original. Enlargements and reductions are defined in terms of a **scale factor** and a **centre**.

The **scale factor** k of an enlargement or reduction is the ratio of lengths in the image to those in the object.

If $k > 1$, the image is an **enlargement** of the object.

If $0 < k < 1$, the image is a **reduction** of the object.

To construct an enlargement or reduction with centre C and scale factor k, we draw lines from C through important points on the object. The image P′ of a point P lies on the line through C and P, such that $CP' = k \times CP$.

For example:

- The diagram alongside shows the **enlargement** of triangle PQR with centre C and scale factor $k = 3$. The image vertices P′, Q′, and R′ are located such that $CP' = 3 \times CP$, $CQ' = 3 \times CQ$, and $CR' = 3 \times CR$. The sides of P′Q′R′ are 3 times longer than those of the object PQR.

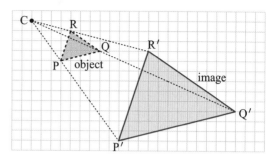

- The diagram alongside shows a **reduction** of triangle KLM with centre C and scale factor $k = \frac{1}{2}$.
  To obtain the image, the distance from C to each point on the object is halved.
  Note that it is acceptable to refer to all transformations of this type as "enlargements", regardless of the scale factor. So, the reduction alongside may be presented as an enlargement with scale factor $\frac{1}{2}$.

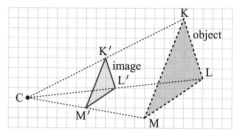

Example 8   ◀ゆ *Self Tutor*

Consider the triangle ABC with vertices A(1, 1), B(4, 1), and C(1, 4).

Draw the image of triangle ABC under:

a an enlargement with centre O and $k = 2$ **b** a reduction with centre (9, 6) and $k = \frac{1}{2}$.

a
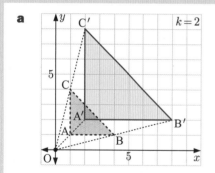

b
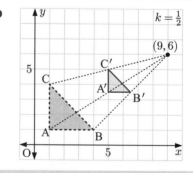

EXERCISE 24D

1 Copy each diagram onto squared paper. Enlarge or reduce it with centre C and the scale factor k given.

a
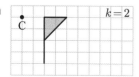

b
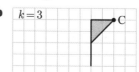

c
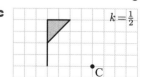

2 Copy triangle T onto squared paper.

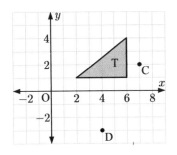

   a Enlarge T with centre $C(7, 2)$ and scale factor $k = 2$.

   b Reduce T with centre $D(4, -3)$ and scale factor $k = \frac{1}{2}$.

3 Find the image of the point:

   a $(3, 4)$ under an enlargement with centre $O(0, 0)$ and scale factor $k = 1\frac{1}{2}$

   b $(-1, 4)$ under a reduction with centre $C(2, -2)$ and scale factor $k = \frac{2}{3}$

   c (x, y) under an enlargement with centre $O(0, 0)$ and scale factor k.

4 Find the image equation of $y = 2x + 3$ under an enlargement with centre O and scale factor 2.

5

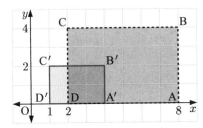

ABCD is mapped onto A′B′C′D′. Describe the single transformation which has occurred.

Discussion   *Invariant points*

Invariant points are points which do not move under a transformation.

What points would be invariant under:

- a translation
- a reflection
- a rotation
- an enlargement or reduction?

E   STRETCHES   *[E6.4]*

In a **stretch** we enlarge or reduce an object in one direction only.

Stretches are defined in terms of a **scale factor** and an **invariant line**.

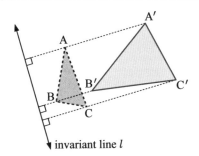

invariant line l

In the diagram alongside, triangle A′B′C′ is a stretch of triangle ABC with scale factor $k = 3$ and invariant line l.

Every point on the image triangle A′B′C′ is 3 times as far from the invariant line as the corresponding point on the object.

Points on the invariant line will not move under a stretch.

Example 9

Consider the triangle ABC with A(1, 1), B(5, 1), and C(1, 4).

Draw the image of triangle ABC under:

a a stretch with invariant x-axis and scale factor $k = 2$

b a stretch with invariant line $x = -1$ and scale factor $k = \frac{1}{2}$.

a
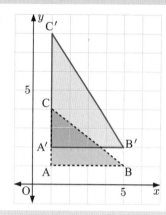

b
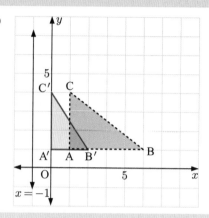

EXERCISE 24E

1 Copy each diagram, then perform the stretch with the given invariant line l and scale factor k:

a
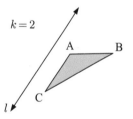

b
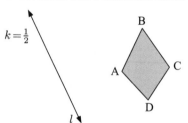

c
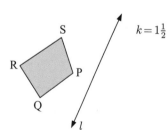

d
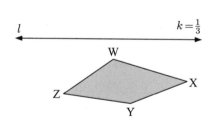

2 Copy each diagram, then perform the stretch with the given invariant line l and scale factor k:

a
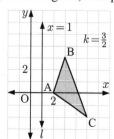

b
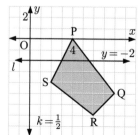

3 Find the image of:

  a $(3, -1)$ under a stretch with invariant x-axis and scale factor 4

  b $(4, 5)$ under a stretch with invariant x-axis and scale factor 2

  c $(-2, 1)$ under a stretch with invariant y-axis and scale factor $\frac{1}{2}$

  d $(3, -4)$ under a stretch with invariant y-axis and scale factor $\frac{3}{2}$

  e $(2, 3)$ under a stretch with invariant line $y = -x$ and scale factor $\frac{1}{2}$

  f (x, y) under a stretch with invariant x-axis and scale factor k

  g (x, y) under a stretch with invariant y-axis and scale factor k.

4 Consider triangle ABC given A(1, 2), B(4, 1), and C(2, 5). Find the image when the triangle is stretched with:

  a invariant line $y = 1$ and scale factor $k = 2$

  b invariant line $x = -1$ and scale factor $k = \frac{1}{2}$.

5 a Describe the single transformation which maps the object rectangle OABC onto the image rectangle OA′B′C′.

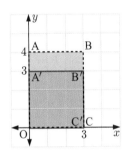

  b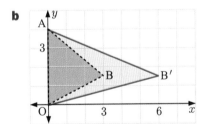

  Describe the single transformation which maps the object triangle OAB onto the image triangle OAB′.

  c ABCD is mapped onto A′B′C′D′. Describe the single transformation which has occurred.

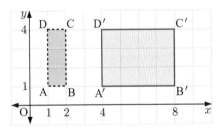

  d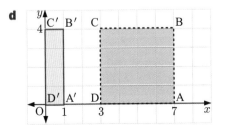

  ABCD is mapped onto A′B′C′D′. Describe fully the single transformation which has occurred.

6 Find the image equation when:

    a $y = 2x$ is subjected to a stretch with invariant x-axis and scale factor $k = 3$

    b $y = \frac{3}{2}x$ is subjected to a stretch with invariant y-axis and scale factor $k = \frac{2}{3}$

    c $y = \frac{1}{2}x + 2$ is subjected to a stretch with invariant line $x = 1$ and scale factor $k = 2$.

F │ THE INVERSE OF A TRANSFORMATION [E6.5]

> The **inverse** of a transformation maps the image back onto the object.

Example 10
◀ᴺ **Self Tutor**

Find the inverse of an enlargement with centre $(1, 2)$ and scale factor $k = 3$.

Consider the triangle ABC shown under this transformation.

The inverse transformation is a reduction with centre $(1, 2)$
and scale factor $k = \frac{1}{3}$.

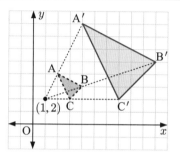

EXERCISE 24F

1 Describe the inverse transformation for each of the following, using a triangle to help you if needed:

    a a reflection in the y-axis
        b a rotation about $O(0, 0)$ through $180°$

    c a translation of $\begin{pmatrix} 3 \\ 0 \end{pmatrix}$
        d a translation of $\begin{pmatrix} 0 \\ -2 \end{pmatrix}$

    e a translation of $\begin{pmatrix} 3 \\ -1 \end{pmatrix}$
        f a 90° clockwise rotation about $O(0, 0)$

    g an enlargement with centre $O(0, 0)$ and scale factor 4

    h a reduction with centre $C(6, 3)$ and scale factor $\frac{1}{2}$ **i** a reflection in $y = -x$

    j a stretch with invariant x-axis and scale factor $\frac{3}{2}$ **k** a reflection in $y = -2$

    l a stretch with invariant y-axis and scale factor $\frac{1}{2}$

2 Describe the inverse transformation for:

    a a translation of $\begin{pmatrix} h \\ k \end{pmatrix}$ **b** a reflection in line M **c** a rotation with centre C through $\theta°$

    d an enlargement with centre C and scale factor k

    e a stretch with invariant line l and scale factor k.

G | COMBINATIONS OF TRANSFORMATIONS   [E6.6]

In previous Exercises we have already looked at the single transformation equivalent to one transformation followed by another.

We now take a more formal approach to combining transformations.

We refer to a particular transformation using a capital letter, and we define:

> HG means "transformation G followed by transformation H".

Notice the order here. While it may not seem immediately intuitive, it is consistent with how we will combine functions in the next Chapter, and it is the order needed to perform transformations with matrices in later courses.

Example 11   ◀)) *Self Tutor*

Consider triangle ABC with vertices A(2, 1), B(4, 1), and C(4, 2).

Suppose R is a reflection in the line $y = -x$, and S is a rotation of 90° clockwise about O(0, 0).

Use triangle ABC to help find the single transformation equivalent to:

a RS   **b** SR.

a For RS, we perform the rotation S first, and then the reflection R.
The single transformation equivalent to RS is a reflection in the x-axis.

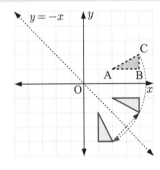

b For SR, we perform the reflection R first, and then the rotation S.
The single transformation equivalent to SR is a reflection in the y-axis.

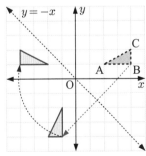

EXERCISE 24G

1 Consider triangle ABC with A(2, 1), B(4, 1), and C(4, 2).

   a Let R be a 90° anticlockwise rotation about O(0, 0), and S be a stretch with invariant y-axis and scale factor $k = 2$. Draw the image of:

      i RS   **ii** SR.

   b Let M be a reflection in the line $y = x$, and E be an enlargement with centre O(0, 0) and scale factor 2. Draw the image of:

      i ME   **ii** EM.

   c Let R be a reflection in the x-axis, and M be a reflection in the line $y = -x$. Find the single transformation equivalent to:

      i RM   **ii** MR.

   d Let T_1 be a clockwise rotation about O(0, 0) through 180°, and T_2 be a reflection in the y-axis. Find the single transformation equivalent to:

      i $T_2 T_1$ **ii** $T_1 T_2$.

2 Let the blue triangle (0) be the object. Consider the following transformations:

   T_0:   leave unchanged

   T_1:   reflect in the line $y = x$

   T_2:   rotate 90° anticlockwise about O(0, 0)

   T_3:   reflect in the y-axis

   T_4:   rotate 180° about O(0, 0)

   T_5:   reflect in the line $y = -x$

   T_6:   rotate 90° clockwise about O(0, 0)

   T_7:   reflect in the x-axis.

   a Find the single transformation equivalent to:

      i $T_1 T_2$ **ii** $T_2 T_1$ **iii** $T_4 T_2$ **iv** $T_7 T_7$ **v** $T_5 T_4$

   b Copy and complete the table to indicate the result of combining the first transformation with the second transformation.

second transformation

		T_0	T_1	T_2	T_3	T_4	T_5	T_6	T_7
	T_0	T_0		T_2	T_3				
	T_1			T_3					
	T_2								
first	T_3								
transformation	T_4			T_6					
	T_5								
	T_6								
	T_7	T_7							

The combination $T_2 T_4$ is equivalent to T_6.

Review set 24A

1 Find the image of (2, −5) under a reflection in:

   a the x-axis   **b** the line $y = x$ **c** the line $x = 3$.

2 Find the image of (−1, 4) under a clockwise rotation of 90° about:

   a O(0, 0)   **b** A(2, 1).

3 Find the image of $(3, -1)$ under:

    a a translation of $\begin{pmatrix} -3 \\ 4 \end{pmatrix}$ **b** an enlargement with centre $O(0, 0)$ and scale factor 2

    c a stretch with invariant x-axis and scale factor $2\frac{1}{2}$

    d a stretch with invariant line $x = 2$ and scale factor $\frac{1}{2}$.

4 Find the image of $(6, 2)$ under a $180°$ rotation about $O(0, 0)$ followed by a translation of $\begin{pmatrix} -2 \\ 3 \end{pmatrix}$.

5 Find the equation of the image when $y = 2x - 1$ is:

    a translated $\begin{pmatrix} 2 \\ -4 \end{pmatrix}$ **b** reflected in the x-axis

    c rotated $90°$ clockwise about $O(0, 0)$

    d stretched with invariant y-axis and scale factor 2.

6 Consider the line $2x + y = 6$.

    a Rotate the line anticlockwise $90°$ about O.   **b** Translate the resulting image $\begin{pmatrix} 3 \\ -1 \end{pmatrix}$.

    c Draw the three lines on the same set of axes, clearly labelling each.

7

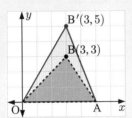

The triangle OAB is mapped onto OAB′.

Describe the transformation which has occurred.

8 Find the image equation of:

    a $y = 3x + 2$ under an enlargement with centre O and scale factor 3

    b $2x - 5y = 10$ under a stretch with invariant x-axis and scale factor 2

    c $y = -2x + 1$ under a stretch with invariant y-axis and scale factor $\frac{1}{2}$.

9 Find the *inverse* transformation of:

    a a translation of $\begin{pmatrix} 2 \\ -3 \end{pmatrix}$ **b** a reflection in the line $y = -x$

    c a stretch with invariant y-axis and scale factor 2.

10 Suppose R is a clockwise rotation of $90°$ about $O(0, 0)$, and M is a reflection in the line $y = -x$.

Use a triangle on a set of axes like the one given to find the single transformation equivalent to:

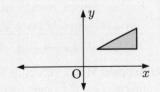

    a RM   **b** MR.

Review set 24B

1 Find the image of $(3, -2)$ under a reflection in:

    a the x-axis   **b** the line $y = -x$ **c** the line $y = 4$.

2 Find the image of $(3, -7)$ under:

    a a translation of $\begin{pmatrix} 2 \\ -4 \end{pmatrix}$ followed by a reflection in the y-axis

    b a reflection in the x-axis followed by a reflection in the line $y = -x$.

3 Find the image of:

    a $(3, 5)$ under an enlargement with centre $O(0, 0)$ and scale factor 3

    b $(-2, 3)$ under a stretch with invariant y-axis and scale factor 2

    c $(-5, -3)$ under a stretch with invariant x-axis and scale factor $\frac{1}{2}$.

4 Find the equation of the image of $y = -2x + 1$ under:

    a a translation of $\begin{pmatrix} 3 \\ -1 \end{pmatrix}$ **b** a reflection in the line $y = x$

    c a $90°$ anticlockwise rotation about $O(0, 0)$

    d a stretch with invariant x-axis and scale factor $\frac{1}{2}$.

5 Find the image of:

    a $5x - 2y = 8$ under the translation $\begin{pmatrix} 3 \\ -2 \end{pmatrix}$

    b $3x - 4y = 8$ under a reflection in $y = x$

    c $2x + 3y = 9$ under a $90°$ rotation about O.

6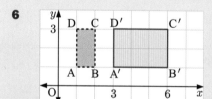

The object ABCD is mapped onto the image A'B'C'D'. Describe the single transformation which has occurred.

7 Consider the line $5x - y = 2$.

    a Reflect the line in the y-axis.   **b** Rotate the resulting image $-90°$ about O.

    c Draw all three lines on the same set of axes, clearly labelling each.

8 Answer the **Opening Problem** on page **389**.

9 Find the *inverse* transformation of:

    a a reflection in the x-axis   **b** a $180°$ rotation about $O(0, 0)$

    c an enlargement with centre $O(0, 0)$ and scale factor $k = 3$.

10 Suppose M is a reflection in the y-axis and R is an anticlockwise rotation through $90°$ about the origin. Find the single transformation which is equivalent to:

    a MR   **b** RM.

Functions

25

Contents:

A Mapping diagrams   [E3.1]
B Functions   [E3.1, E3.2, E3.6]
C Function notation   [E3.1]
D Composite functions   [E3.7]
E The absolute value function   [E1.6, E3.2]
F Reciprocal functions   [E3.2, E3.5]
G Graphs of functions   [E2.11, E3.6]
H Transforming functions   [E3.8]
I Inverse functions   [E3.9]

Opening problem

A dot is placed at the 20 cm mark of a ruler as illustrated.

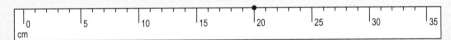

Things to think about:

a How far from the dot is the:

     i 5 cm mark   **ii** 16 cm mark   **iii** 20 cm mark   **iv** 24 cm mark   **v** 30 cm mark?

b Can you write a formula for the distance d cm between the dot and the x cm mark?

A   MAPPING DIAGRAMS   *[E3.1]*

Consider the family of Mr and Mrs Schwarz. Their sons are Hans and Gert, and their daughter is Alex.

The set of parents is $P = \{$Mr Schwarz, Mrs Schwarz$\}$. The set of children is $C = \{$Hans, Gert, Alex$\}$.

Each member of C is a child of each member of P. We can illustrate these connections using a **mapping diagram** which maps C onto P.

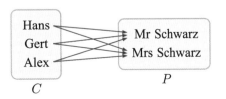

A **mapping** is used to map the members or **elements** of one set called the **domain**, onto the members of another set called the **range**.

Mappings can be further categorised as:

- **one-to-one** if every element in the domain and range corresponds to a unique element in the other
- **many-to-one** if every element in the domain maps to a unique element in the range, but at least two elements of the domain map to one particular element in the range
- **one-to-many** if every element in the range is mapped from a unique element in the domain, but an element of the domain maps to more than one element in the range
- **many-to-many** if more than one element in the domain maps to the same element in the range, and an element in the domain maps to more than one element in the range.

For example, consider these mappings:

- $y = x + 3$ is one-to-one

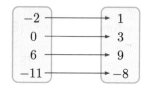

x (domain) y (range)

- $y = x^2 + 1$ is many-to-one

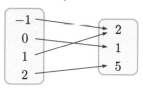

x (domain) y (range)

- $y = \pm\sqrt{x}$ is one-to-many

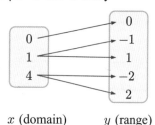

x (domain) y (range)

- $y = \pm\sqrt{x^2}$ is many-to-many

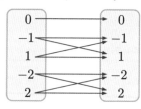

x (domain) y (range)

EXERCISE 25A

1 Copy and complete each mapping diagram. State whether the mapping is one-to-one, many-to-one, one-to-many, or many-to-many.

a mapping "$y = 2x - 5$"

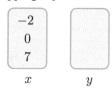

x y

b mapping "is not equal to"

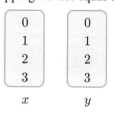

x y

c mapping "$x = y^2$"

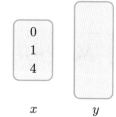

x y

d mapping "is greater than"

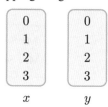

x y

e mapping "add 1"

2 For each domain and mapping, describe the corresponding range:

    a domain {real numbers}   mapping: "subtract 20"

    b domain {odd numbers}   mapping: "double"

    c domain {positive real numbers}   mapping: "find the square root"

    d domain {real numbers $\geqslant 0$}   mapping: "add 10"

    e domain {even numbers}   mapping: "divide by 2"

Example 1 ◀) *Self Tutor*

For each of the following graphs, state the domain and range:

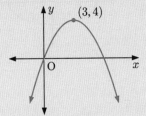 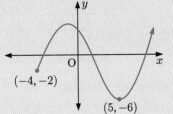 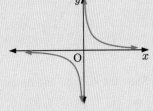

a Domain is $\{x \mid x \in \mathbb{R}\}$.	**b** Domain is $\{x \mid x \geqslant -4\}$.	**c** Domain is $\{x \mid x \neq 0\}$.
Range is $\{y \mid y \leqslant 4\}$.	Range is $\{y \mid y \geqslant -6\}$.	Range is $\{y \mid y \neq 0\}$.

---

3 For each of the following graphs, state the domain and range:

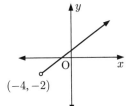 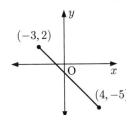 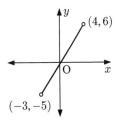

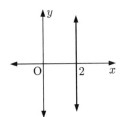 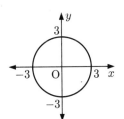 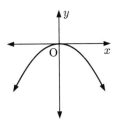

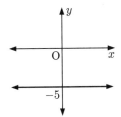 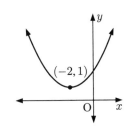 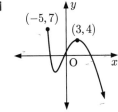

j	k	l
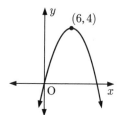	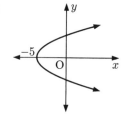	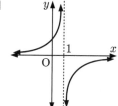

4 State the domain and range of:

a	b	c
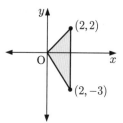	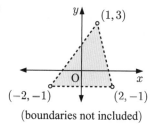	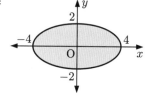
	(boundaries not included)	

5 State the domain and range for these sets of points:

   a $\{(-1, 5), (-2, 3), (0, 4), (-3, 8), (6, -1), (-2, 3)\}$

   b $\{(5, 4), (-3, 4), (4, 3), (2, 4), (-1, 3), (0, 3), (7, 4)\}$.

6 Find the range if each element of:

   a $D = \{-1, 0, 2, 7, 9\}$ has 3 added to it

   b $D = \{-2, -1, 0, 1, 2\}$ is squared and the result divided by 2

   c $D = \{x \mid -2 < x < 2\}$ is doubled and the result increased by 1

   d $D = \{x \mid -3 \leqslant x \leqslant 4\}$ is cubed.

B FUNCTIONS   [E3.1, E3.2, E3.6]

A **function** is a mapping in which no two different ordered pairs have the same first member.
A function may either be one-to-one or many-to-one.

For example, the grid alongside shows the set of points:
$\{(-1, 3), (2, 2), (-1, -2), (3, 2), (4, -1)\}$.

The two circled points $(-1, -2)$ and $(-1, 3)$ have the same first
member, so the set of points is not a function.

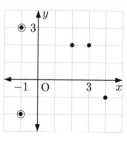

GEOMETRIC TEST FOR FUNCTIONS: "VERTICAL LINE TEST"

Suppose we draw all possible vertical lines on a graph.
- If each line cuts the graph at most once, then the graph is a function.
- If *any* line cuts the graph more than once, then the graph is *not* a function.

Example 2

Which of these graphs are functions?

a
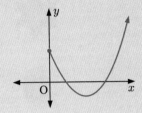

b
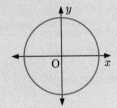

a Every vertical line we could draw cuts
  the graph only once.
  ∴ the graph is a function.

b This vertical line
  cuts the graph twice.
  ∴ the graph is not
  a function.

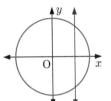

EXERCISE 25B

1 Which of the following sets of ordered pairs are functions? Give reasons for your answers.

  a $\{(1, 1), (2, 2), (3, 3), (4, 4)\}$
  b $\{(-1, 2), (-3, 2), (3, 2), (1, 2)\}$
  c $\{(2, 5), (-1, 4), (-3, 7), (2, -3)\}$
  d $\{(3, -2), (3, 0), (3, 2), (3, 4)\}$
  e $\{(-7, 0), (-5, 0), (-3, 0), (-1, 0)\}$
  f $\{(0, 5), (0, 1), (2, 1), (2, -5)\}$

2 Use the vertical line test to determine which of the following graphs are functions:

a
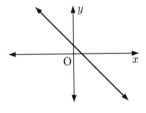

b
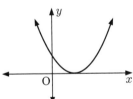

c
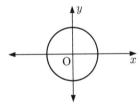

d
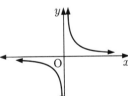

e
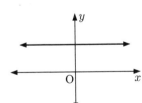

f
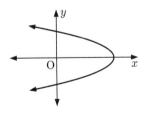

g
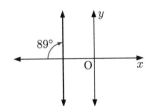

h
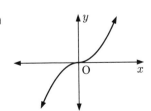

i
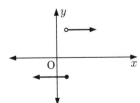

3 Will the graph of a straight line always be a function? Explain your answer.

4 For each of these functions:

    i Sketch the graph of the function with the help of technology.

    ii Find the range of the function on the given domain.

GRAPHING
PACKAGE

a $y = 3x + 1$ on the domain $\{x \mid -2 \leqslant x \leqslant 2\}$

b $y = x^2$ on the domain $\{x \mid -3 \leqslant x \leqslant 4\}$

c $y = 4x - 1$ on the domain $\{x \mid -2 \leqslant x \leqslant 3\}$

d $y = \dfrac{1}{x - 1}$ on the domain $\{x \mid 0 \leqslant x \leqslant 3, \ x \neq 1\}$

e $y = x + \dfrac{1}{x}$ on the domain $\{x \mid -4 \leqslant x \leqslant 4, \ x \neq 0\}$

f $y = x^2 + 1$ on the domain $\{x \mid x \in \mathbb{R}\}$

g $y = x^3$ on the domain $\{x \mid x \in \mathbb{R}\}$

GRAPHICS
CALCULATOR
INSTRUCTIONS

C   FUNCTION NOTATION   [E3.1]

We sometimes use a *function machine* to illustrate how functions behave.

For example, the machine alongside has been programmed to perform a particular function: "double the number and then subtract 1".

If 3 is fed into the machine, $2 \times 3 - 1 = 5$ comes out.

If f is used to represent this particular function, we can write:

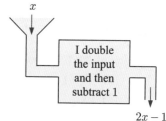

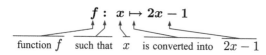

$$f : \ x \mapsto 2x - 1$$

function f such that x is converted into $2x - 1$

We can also write this function as $f(x) = 2x - 1$.

> $f(x)$ is read as "f of x". It is sometimes called the *image* of x.

> If f is the function which converts x into $f(x)$, then $f : x \mapsto f(x)$.
>
> For any function f, the value of the function when $x = a$ is $f(a)$.

For $f(x) = 2x - 1$, we find
$$f(2) = 2(2) - 1 = 3 \ \text{ and}$$
$$f(-4) = 2(-4) - 1 = -9.$$

These calculations tell us that the points $(2, 3)$ and $(-4, -9)$ lie on the graph $y = f(x)$.

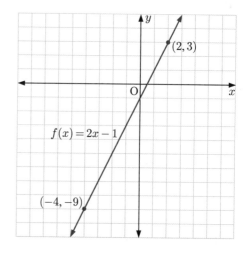

Example 3

◄ﻪ) **Self Tutor**

For $f(x) = 4 - 3x - x^2$, find:

  a $f(2)$ **b** $f(-3)$ **c** $f(-x)$ **d** $f(x+2)$

a $f(2) = 4 - 3(2) - (2)^2$
$\qquad = 4 - 6 - 4$
$\qquad = -6$

b $f(-3) = 4 - 3(-3) - (-3)^2$
$\qquad = 4 + 9 - 9$
$\qquad = 4$

c $f(-x) = 4 - 3(-x) - (-x)^2$
$\qquad = 4 + 3x - x^2$

d $f(x+2) = 4 - 3(x+2) - (x+2)^2$
$\qquad = 4 - 3x - 6 - (x^2 + 4x + 4)$
$\qquad = -x^2 - 7x - 6$

EXERCISE 25C

1 For $f : x \mapsto 2x + 3$, find:

  a $f(0)$ **b** $f(2)$ **c** $f(-1)$ **d** $f(-5)$ **e** $f(-\frac{1}{2})$

2 For $E(x) = 2(x-3)$, find:

  a $E(0)$ **b** $E(1)$ **c** $E(5)$ **d** $E(-2)$ **e** $E(\frac{7}{2})$

3 For $h(x) = \dfrac{x}{x-3}$, find:

  a $h(2)$ **b** $h(5)$ **c** $h(10)$ **d** $h(0)$ **e** $h(-7)$

4 For $g(x) = -5x + 3$, find:

  a $g(1)$ **b** $g(4)$ **c** $g(-2)$ **d** $g(-x)$ **e** $g(x+4)$

5 For $f(x) = 2x^2 - 3x + 2$, find:

  a $f(0)$ **b** $f(3)$ **c** $f(-4)$ **d** $f(-x)$ **e** $f(x+1)$

6 For $P : x \mapsto 4x^2 + 4x - 3$, find:

  a $P(3)$ **b** $P(-1)$ **c** $P(\frac{1}{2})$ **d** $P(x-3)$ **e** $P(2x)$

7 Suppose $m(x) = \dfrac{x+1}{3}$. Find the value of a for which:

  a $m(a) = 2$ **b** $m(a) = -1$ **c** $m(a) = -\frac{7}{6}$

8 Consider the function $R(x) = \dfrac{2x-3}{x+2}$.

  a Evaluate: **i** $R(0)$ **ii** $R(1)$ **iii** $R(-\frac{1}{2})$

  b Find a value of x such that $R(x)$ does not exist.

  c Find $R(x-2)$ in simplest form.

  d Find x such that $R(x) = -5$.

9 The value of a car t years after purchase is given by $V(t) = 28\,000 - 4000t$ dollars.

  a Find $V(4)$ and state what this value means.

  b Find t when $V(t) = 8000$ and explain what this represents.

  c Find the original purchase price of the car.

10 The graph of $y = f(x)$ is shown alongside.

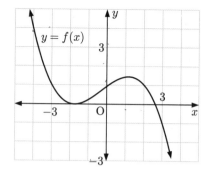

   a Find:

      i $f(2)$ **ii** $f(3)$

   b Find the value of x such that $f(x) = 4$.

11

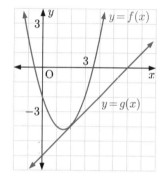

Consider the graphs of $y = f(x)$ and $y = g(x)$ shown.

   a Find:

      i $f(4)$ **ii** $g(0)$ **iii** $g(5)$

   b Find the *two* values of x such that $f(x) = -2$.

   c Find the value of x such that $f(x) = g(x)$.

   d Show that $g(x) = x - 6$.

12 Draw a graph of $y = f(x)$ such that $f(-2) = 5$, $f(1) = 0$, and $f(4) = 3$.

13 The graph of $y = f(x)$ is a straight line passing through $(-3, -5)$ and $(1, 7)$.

   a Draw the graph of $y = f(x)$.   **b** Find $f(-3)$ and $f(1)$.   **c** Find $f(x)$.

D   COMPOSITE FUNCTIONS   *[E3.7]*

Sometimes functions are built up in two or more stages.

For example, consider $f(x) = 2\sqrt{x}$

      $\therefore \ f(x+3) = 2\sqrt{x+3}$ {replacing x by $(x+3)$}

If we let $g(x) = x + 3$, then $f(g(x)) = 2\sqrt{x+3}$.

We say the function $f(g(x)) = 2\sqrt{x+3}$ is *composed* of $f(x) = 2\sqrt{x}$ and $g(x) = x + 3$.

Given $f : x \mapsto f(x)$ and $g : x \mapsto g(x)$, the **composite function** of f and g will convert x into $f(g(x))$.

Example 4   ◀》 *Self Tutor*

If $f(x) = 3x + 2$ and $g(x) = x^2 + 4$, find in simplest form:

  a $f(g(x))$ **b** $g(f(x))$

To find $f(g(x))$ we look at the f function. Whenever we see x we replace it by $g(x)$ within brackets.

a $f(g(x))$
$= f(x^2 + 4)$
$= 3(x^2 + 4) + 2$
$= 3x^2 + 12 + 2$
$= 3x^2 + 14$

b $g(f(x))$
$= g(3x + 2)$
$= (3x + 2)^2 + 4$
$= 9x^2 + 12x + 4 + 4$
$= 9x^2 + 12x + 8$

From the previous Example, we can see that in general, $f(g(x)) \neq g(f(x))$.

Example 5
◀)) Self Tutor

If $f(x) = 2x - 1$, find:

a $f(f(x))$

b $f(f(5))$

a $f(f(x)) = f(2x - 1)$
$ = 2(2x - 1) - 1$
$ = 4x - 2 - 1$
$ = 4x - 3$

b $f(f(5)) = 4(5) - 3$ {using **a**}
$ = 17$

EXERCISE 25D

1 If $f(x) = 3x - 4$ and $g(x) = 2 - x$, find in simplest form:

a $f(g(x))$ **b** $g(f(x))$ **c** $f(f(x))$ **d** $g(g(x))$

2 If $f(x) = \sqrt{x}$ and $g(x) = 4x - 3$, find in simplest form:

a $f(g(x))$ **b** $g(f(x))$ **c** $f(g(7))$ **d** $g(f(4))$

3 Find two functions f and g such that:

a $f(g(x)) = \sqrt{x - 3}$ **b** $f(g(x)) = (x + 5)^3$ **c** $f(g(x)) = \dfrac{5}{x + 7}$

d $g(f(x)) = \dfrac{1}{\sqrt{3 - 4x}}$ **e** $g(f(x)) = 3^{x^2}$ **f** $g(f(x)) = \left(\dfrac{x + 1}{x - 1}\right)^2$

4 Suppose $f(x) = 3x + 1$ and $g(x) = x^2 + 2x$.

a Find $f(g(x))$.

b Find x such that $f(g(x)) = 10$.

5 Suppose $f(x) = \dfrac{1}{x + 2}$ and $g(x) = 4x + 1$.

a Find $f(g(x))$.

b Find $f(g(-1))$.

c Find x such that $f(g(x)) = 3$.

6 Suppose $f(x) = 2x + 5$ and $g(x) = \dfrac{x - 5}{2}$.

a Find: **i** $f(4)$ **ii** $g(13)$ **iii** $g(17)$ **iv** $f(6)$.

b Find $f(g(x))$ and $g(f(x))$.

c Find: **i** $f(g(3))$ **ii** $g(f(-7))$.

E   THE ABSOLUTE VALUE FUNCTION [E1.6, E3.2]

The **absolute value** or **modulus** of a real number is its size, ignoring its sign.

We denote the absolute value of x by $|x|$.

Geometrically, $|x|$ is the distance of x from O on the number line. Since $|x|$ is a distance, it cannot be negative.

For example:

- The absolute value of 7 is 7, so we write $|7| = 7$.
- The absolute value of -7 is also 7, so we write $|-7| = 7$.

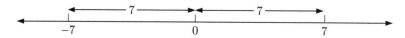

Example 6   ◀) Self Tutor

If $a = -7$ and $b = 3$, find:

a $|a + b|$ **b** $|ab|$

| **a** | $\begin{aligned} &\quad\lvert a+b\rvert \\ &= \lvert -7+3\rvert \\ &= \lvert -4\rvert \\ &= 4 \end{aligned}$ | **b** | $\begin{aligned} &\quad\lvert ab\rvert \\ &= \lvert -7\times 3\rvert \\ &- \lvert -21\rvert \\ &= 21 \end{aligned}$ |

Absolute value signs are grouping symbols like brackets. Perform all operations within the absolute value signs first.

If $x > 0$, its distance from 0 is just x.

$\therefore \ |x| = x$

If $x = 0$, its distance from 0 is 0.

$\therefore \ |x| = x$

If $x < 0$, its distance from 0 is $-x$.

$\therefore \ |x| = -x$

We conclude that:

$$|x| = \begin{cases} x & \text{if } x \geqslant 0 \\ -x & \text{if } x < 0 \end{cases}$$

Discovery 1   *The absolute value function*

What to do:

1 Suppose $y = \begin{cases} x & \text{if } x \geqslant 0 \\ -x & \text{if } x < 0. \end{cases}$

a Copy and complete the table of values:

x	-10	-8	-2	0	$\frac{1}{2}$	3	5	7
y								

b Plot the points from the table and hence graph $y = \begin{cases} x & \text{if } x \geqslant 0 \\ -x & \text{if } x < 0. \end{cases}$

2 Copy and complete:

x	-10	-8	-2	0	$\frac{1}{2}$	3	5	7
$\sqrt{x^2}$								

3 What can you conclude from **1** and **2**?

From the **Discovery**, you should have found that:

- The absolute value function $|x| = \sqrt{x^2}$ for all x.

- The graph of $y = |x|$ is:

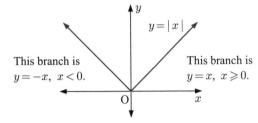

This branch is
$y = -x, \; x < 0$.

This branch is
$y = x, \; x \geqslant 0$.

To draw graphs involving $|x|$, we consider the cases $x \geqslant 0$ and $x < 0$ separately. This allows us to write the function without the absolute value signs.

Example 7   🔊 *Self Tutor*

Draw the graph of $f(x) = x + 2|x|$.

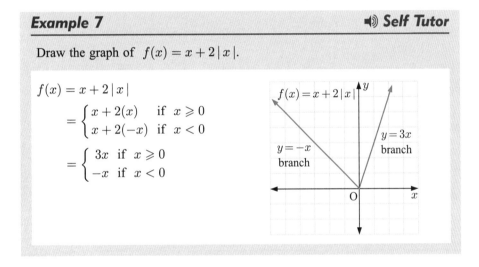

$$f(x) = x + 2|x|$$
$$= \begin{cases} x + 2(x) & \text{if } x \geqslant 0 \\ x + 2(-x) & \text{if } x < 0 \end{cases}$$
$$= \begin{cases} 3x & \text{if } x \geqslant 0 \\ -x & \text{if } x < 0 \end{cases}$$

EXERCISE 25E

1 Write down the value of:

   a $|7|$ **b** $|-7|$ **c** $|0.93|$ **d** $\left| \, 2\frac{1}{4} \, \right|$ **e** $|-0.0932|$

2 If $x = -4$, find the value of:

   a $|x+6|$ **b** $|x-6|$ **c** $|2x+3|$ **d** $|7-x|$

   e $|x-7|$ **f** $|x^2 - 6x|$ **g** $|6x - x^2|$ **h** $\dfrac{|x|}{x+2}$

3 If $a = 5$ and $b = -2$, find the value of:

   a $|a+b|$ **b** $|ab|$ **c** $|b-a|$ **d** $|a|+b$

   e $|3a+b|$ **f** $\dfrac{|b-8|}{a}$ **g** $\left| \dfrac{a}{b} \right|$ **h** $\dfrac{|b^2|}{|a|}$

4 **a** Copy and complete the table:

    b Summarise your observations.

x	9	3	0	-3	-9
x^2					
$|x|^2$					

5   **a**   Copy and complete the table:

    b   Summarise your observations.

a	b	$\lvert ab \rvert$	$\lvert a \rvert \lvert b \rvert$	$\left\lvert \dfrac{a}{b} \right\rvert$	$\dfrac{\lvert a \rvert}{\lvert b \rvert}$
12	3				
12	−3				
−12	3				
−12	−3				

6   **a**   Copy and complete the table:

    b   Summarise your observations.

a	b	$\lvert a+b \rvert$	$\lvert a \rvert + \lvert b \rvert$	$\lvert a-b \rvert$	$\lvert a \rvert - \lvert b \rvert$
2	5				
2	−5				
−2	5				
−2	−5				

7   Use the definition $\lvert x \rvert = \begin{cases} x & \text{for } x \geqslant 0 \\ -x & \text{for } x < 0 \end{cases}$ to help graph each function:

    a $f(x) = -\lvert x \rvert$
        b $f(x) = \lvert x \rvert + x$
        c $f(x) = \lvert x \rvert + 2$

    d $f(x) = 5 - \lvert x \rvert$
        e $f(x) = x - 2\lvert x \rvert$
        f $f(x) = \dfrac{\lvert x \rvert}{x}$

8   Solve for x using the definition $\lvert x \rvert = \sqrt{x^2}$:

    a $\lvert x \rvert = 4$
      b $\lvert x \rvert = 1.4$
      c $\lvert x \rvert = -2$
      d $\lvert x \rvert + 1 = 7$

    e $\lvert x+1 \rvert = 3$
      f $\lvert 2-x \rvert = 5$
      g $5 - \lvert x \rvert = 1$
      h $\lvert 5-x \rvert = 1$

9   Answer the **Opening Problem** on page **407**.

Example 8   ◀)) *Self Tutor*

Graph $y = \lvert 2x - 3 \rvert$. Comment on any symmetry in the graph.

$y = 2x - 3$ has gradient 2 and
y-intercept -3.

The x-intercept is $\frac{3}{2}$.

To obtain the graph of $y = \lvert 2x - 3 \rvert$,
the part below the x-axis is reflected
in the x-axis.

$x = \frac{3}{2}$ is a vertical line of symmetry.

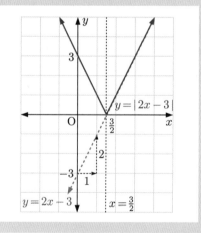

To draw the graph
of $y = \lvert f(x) \rvert$,
start with $y = f(x)$
then reflect any part
below the x-axis in
the x-axis.

---

10   Sketch the graph of:

    a $f(x) = \lvert x+1 \rvert$
        b $f(x) = \lvert x-1 \rvert$
        c $f(x) = \lvert 2x-1 \rvert$

    d $f(x) = \lvert 4-x \rvert$
        e $f(x) = \lvert 2-3x \rvert$
        f $f(x) = -\lvert 3x+2 \rvert$

11 Find the equation of the line of symmetry of $f(x) = |ax + b|$.

12 Find the function $f(x) = |ax + b|$ which has the graph:

a
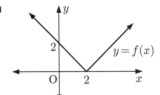

b
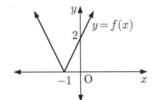

c
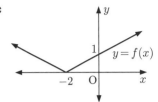

F   RECIPROCAL FUNCTIONS   [E3.2, E3.5]

Discovery 2   The family of curves $y = \frac{k}{x}$, $k \neq 0$

In this Discovery we will look at curves of the form $y = \frac{k}{x}$, where $k \neq 0$. You can use the **graphing package** or **graphics calculator** to help you.

What to do:

1 On the same set of axes, draw the graphs of $y = \frac{1}{x}$, $y = \frac{4}{x}$, and $y = \frac{8}{x}$.   **GRAPHING PACKAGE**

2 Describe the effect of the value of k on the graph for $k > 0$.

3 On the same set of axes, draw the graphs of $y = \frac{-1}{x}$, $y = \frac{-4}{x}$, and $y = \frac{-8}{x}$.

4 Describe the effect of the sign of k.

5 Explain why there is no point on the graph when $x = 0$.

6 Explain why there is no point on the graph when $y = 0$.

A **reciprocal function** has an equation of the form $y = \frac{k}{x}$ where k is a constant, $k \neq 0$.

The graph of a reciprocal function is called a **rectangular hyperbola**.

We see many examples of hyperbolae in the world around us.

- When an aeroplane flies faster than the speed of sound (about 1200 km/h) we say it breaks the sound barrier. It sets up a conic shock wave which intersects the ground in a hyperbola.

- When two quantities vary inversely, their relationship is described using a reciprocal function.

  For example, the pressure and volume of a gas at room temperature vary inversely according to the equation

  $P = \dfrac{77.4}{V}$.

  If P is graphed against V, the curve is one branch of a hyperbola.

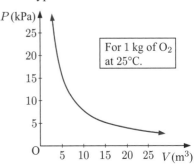

- When a lamp is placed close to a wall, the light and shadow form part of a hyperbola.

ASYMPTOTES

You should have noticed in the **Discovery** that functions of the form $y = \dfrac{k}{x}$ have no points corresponding to $x = 0$ or $y = 0$.

On the graph we see that the function is defined for values of x getting closer and closer to $x = 0$, but the function never reaches the line $x = 0$. We say that $x = 0$ is a **vertical asymptote**.

Likewise, as the values of x get larger, the values of y get closer to 0, but never quite reach 0. We say that $y = 0$ is a **horizontal asymptote**.

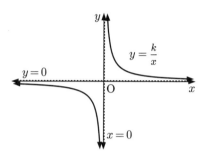

EXERCISE 25F

1 Consider the function $y = \dfrac{5}{x}$, which can be written as $xy = 5$.

   a Explain why both x and y can take all real values except 0.

   b State the asymptotes of the function $y = \dfrac{5}{x}$.

   c Find the value of y when: **i** $x = 500$ **ii** $x = -500$

   d Find the value of x when: **i** $y = 500$ **ii** $y = -500$

   e By plotting points or by using technology, graph $y = \dfrac{5}{x}$.

   f Without calculating new values, sketch the graph of $y = -\dfrac{5}{x}$.

2 Kate has to make 40 invitations for her birthday party. The number of invitations she can make each hour will affect the total time it will take her to do the job.

Suppose Kate can make n invitations per hour and the job takes her t hours.

   a Copy and complete the table of values:

Invitations per hour (n)	4	8	12	20
Time taken (t)				

   b Draw a graph of n versus t, with n on the horizontal axis.

   c What shape do the points form?

   d Write a formula for the relationship between n and t.

3 Determine the equation of each reciprocal graph:

   a   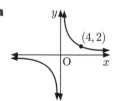   **b**   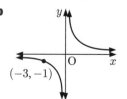   **c**   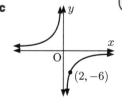

For a reciprocal function $y = \dfrac{k}{x}$, notice that $xy = k$.

GRAPHS OF FUNCTIONS   *[E2.11, E3.6]*

In our study of linear functions, we used a **table of values** to help graph straight lines. We then considered properties of the graph including its **axes intercepts**.

In our study of simultaneous equations, we saw how their solution could be found using the points where graphs intersect.

In this Section we consider how to graph and study unfamiliar functions using technology. This will help in our investigation of particular function types later, since we will know what important properties to look for.

GRAPHING PACKAGE

We can use a graphics calculator to obtain:

- a **table of values** for a function
- a **sketch** of the function
- the *x*-intercepts of a graph, which we call the **zeros** of the function
- the *y*-intercept of a graph
- any **asymptotes** of a graph

GRAPHICS CALCULATOR INSTRUCTIONS

- **turning points** of a graph, which are points where the sign of the gradient of the curve changes
    - At a **local maximum**, the gradient changes from positive to negative.
    - At a **local minimum**, the gradient changes from negative to positive.

- the coordinates of points where graphs intersect.

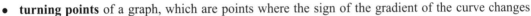

Example 9   ◀)) *Self Tutor*

Consider $f(x) = \dfrac{3x - 9}{x^2 - x - 2}$.

- **a** Use technology to help graph the function.
- **b** State the equations of the *asymptotes* of the function.
- **c** State the *axes intercepts* of the function.   **d** Describe the *turning points* of the function.

a
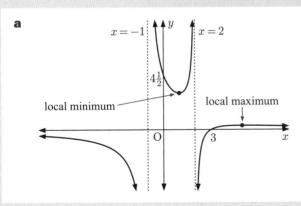

b The horizontal asymptote is $y = 0$.
    The vertical asymptotes are $x = -1$ and $x = 2$.

c The *x*-intercept is 3. The *y*-intercept is $4\frac{1}{2}$.

d There is a local maximum at $(5, \frac{1}{3})$ and a local minimum at $(1, 3)$.

SOLVING EQUATIONS

If we are given any equation involving a single variable x, we can think of it as the intersection of two functions.

The solutions to $f(x) = g(x)$ are the x-coordinates of the points where $y = f(x)$ and $y = g(x)$ meet.

Example 10
◀) **Self Tutor**

Solve the equation $2x^2 = 3x + 2$ using:

a algebra   **b** technology.

a
$$2x^2 = 3x + 2$$
$$\therefore \ 2x^2 - 3x - 2 = 0$$
$$\therefore \ (2x + 1)(x - 2) = 0$$
$$\therefore \ x = -\tfrac{1}{2} \text{ or } 2$$

b We graph $y = 2x^2$ and $y = 3x + 2$ on the same set of axes.

The graphs intersect at $(-\tfrac{1}{2}, \tfrac{1}{2})$ and $(2, 8)$.

$\therefore$ the solutions are $x = -\tfrac{1}{2}$ or 2.

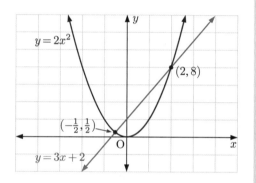

EXERCISE 25G

1 For each of the following:

    i Use technology to graph the function.   **ii** Find the equations of any asymptotes.

    a $y = \dfrac{3}{x - 2}$ **b** $y = \dfrac{2}{x + 1}$ **c** $y = \dfrac{1}{x - 3} + 1$

2 For each of the following:

    i Use technology to help graph the function.   **ii** State the axes intercepts.
    iii Describe the turning point.

    a $y = x^2 - 3$ **b** $f(x) = -2x^2 + 2x + 1$ **c** $f(x) = 9x^2 + 6x - 4$

3 Use technology to sketch the graph of each function:

    a $y = |2x - 1| + 2$ **b** $y = |x(x - 3)|$ **c** $y = |(x - 2)(x - 4)|$

    d $y = |x| + |x - 2|$ **e** $y = |x| - |x + 2|$ **f** $y = |9 - x^2|$

    If the graph possesses a line of symmetry, state its equation.

4 Consider $f(x) = x^3 - 4x^2 + 5x - 3$ for $-1 \leqslant x \leqslant 4$.

    a Sketch the graph with the help of technology.   **b** Find the axes intercepts of the graph.

    c Find and classify any turning points.   **d** State the range of the function.

    e Create a table of values for $f(x)$ with x-steps of 0.5.

5 Consider $f(x) = x^4 - 3x^3 - 10x^2 - 7x + 3$ for $-4 \leqslant x \leqslant 6$.

You may need to adjust your viewing window to see all the necessary detail.

  a Use technology to sketch the graph of $y = f(x)$.

  b Find the largest zero of $f(x)$.

  c Find the turning point of the function with x-coordinate ≈ 4.

  d Sketch the function for $-2 \leqslant x \leqslant 1$.

  e Find the other two turning points, and classify them.

  f Create a table of values for $f(x)$ on $0 \leqslant x \leqslant 1$ with x-steps of 0.1.

6 Solve each of the following equations using: **i** algebra   **ii** technology.

  a $5x - 1 = 2x + 5$

  b $\dfrac{1}{x} = \dfrac{2}{x + 5}$

  c $x^2 = 6 - x$

  d $\dfrac{2}{x} = x - 1$

  e $5x = 4 + \dfrac{1}{x}$

  f $x^2 - 3x - 4 = 3x^2 + 4x - 1$

7 For each of the following:

    i Use technology to help graph the function.   **ii** State the equations of any asymptotes.

    iii Find the axes intercepts.   **iv** Find and classify any turning points.

  a $f(x) = \dfrac{4}{x - 2}$

  b $f(x) = 2 - \dfrac{3}{x + 1}$

  c $f(x) = 2^x - 3$

  d $f(x) = 2x + \dfrac{1}{x}$

  e $f(x) = \dfrac{4x}{x^2 - 4x - 5}$

  f $f(x) = 3^{-x} + 2$

  g $f(x) = \dfrac{x^2 - 1}{x^2 + 1}$

  h $f(x) = \dfrac{x^2 + 1}{x^2 - 1}$

  i $f(x) = \dfrac{2^x + 3}{2^x + 1}$

8 Use technology to find the coordinates, correct to 2 decimal places, of the points of intersection of each pair of graphs:

  a $y = x^2 + 3x + 1$ and $y = 2x + 2$

  b $y = x^2 - 5x + 2$ and $y = \dfrac{3}{x}$

  c $y = -x^2 - 2x + 5$ and $y = x^2 + 7$

  d $y = x^2 - 1$ and $y = x^3$

9 For what values of k does $\dfrac{x^2 + 4}{x^2 + 1} = k$ have exactly two solutions?

10 Solve using technology, giving answers to 3 significant figures where necessary:

  a $-2x^2 = x - 3$

  b $\frac{1}{2}x^2 = x + 2$

  c $(x + 2)(x - 1) = 2 - 3x$

  d $(2x + 1)^2 = 3 - x$

  e $2^x = 3x$

  f $\sqrt{x} = 3 - x$

  g $x^2 = \sqrt{x + 2}$

  h $3^x = x^2$

  i $x^3 + 2 = 3x - x^2$

  j $x^3 - x + 3 = 0$

  k $3^x = x^3 + 1$

  l $x^2 - 3 = \sqrt[3]{x}$

  m $\dfrac{x + 7}{x - 3} = 2^{-x}$

  n $\dfrac{5}{x} = \dfrac{1}{\sqrt{x}} + 1$

  o $2^x - 1 = \dfrac{1}{x^3}$

H TRANSFORMING FUNCTIONS   [E3.8]

In this Section we consider transformations which map the graph of $y = f(x)$ onto the graphs of $y = f(x) + k$, $y = f(x - h)$, $y = f(x - h) + k$, $y = k\, f(x)$ where $k > 0$, and $y = -f(x)$.

Discovery 3   *Transforming functions*

What to do:

1 **a** On the same set of axes, graph $y = \dfrac{1}{x}$, $y = \dfrac{1}{x} + 2$, and $y = \dfrac{1}{x} - 3$.

      GRAPHING PACKAGE

  b What transformation maps $y = \dfrac{1}{x}$ onto $y = \dfrac{1}{x} + k$?

2 **a** On the same set of axes, graph $y = \dfrac{1}{x}$, $y = \dfrac{1}{x+2}$, and $y = \dfrac{1}{x-3}$.

  b What transformation maps $y = \dfrac{1}{x}$ onto $y = \dfrac{1}{x-h}$?

3 **a** On the same set of axes, graph $y = \dfrac{1}{x}$, $y = \dfrac{1}{x-4} + 2$, and $y = \dfrac{1}{x+3} - 4$.

  b What transformation maps $y = \dfrac{1}{x}$ onto $y = \dfrac{1}{x-h} + k$?

4 **a** On the same set of axes, graph $y = \dfrac{1}{x}$, $y = \dfrac{2}{x}$, and $y = \dfrac{4}{x}$.

  b What transformation maps $y = \dfrac{1}{x}$ onto $y = \dfrac{k}{x}$ where $k > 0$?

5 **a** On the same set of axes, graph $y = \dfrac{1}{x}$ and $y = -\dfrac{1}{x}$.

  b What transformation maps $y = \dfrac{1}{x}$ onto $y = -\dfrac{1}{x}$?

6 What *combination* of transformations map $y = \dfrac{1}{x}$ onto $y = -\dfrac{k}{x}$?

You should have discovered that:

- $y = f(x)$ maps onto $y = f(x) + k$ under a **vertical translation** of $\begin{pmatrix} 0 \\ k \end{pmatrix}$.

- $y = f(x)$ maps onto $y = f(x - h)$ under a **horizontal translation** of $\begin{pmatrix} h \\ 0 \end{pmatrix}$.

- $y = f(x)$ maps onto $y = f(x - h) + k$ under a translation of $\begin{pmatrix} h \\ k \end{pmatrix}$.

- $y = f(x)$ maps onto $y = k\,f(x)$, $k > 0$ under a stretch with invariant x-axis and scale factor k.

- $y = f(x)$ maps onto $y = -f(x)$ under a reflection in the x-axis.

- $y = f(x)$ maps onto $y = -k\,f(x)$ under a reflection in the x-axis followed by a stretch with invariant x-axis and scale factor k.

Example 11   ◀) **Self Tutor**

Consider $f(x) = \frac{1}{2}x + 1$. On separate sets of axes, graph:

  a $y = f(x)$ and $y = f(x + 2)$ **b** $y = f(x)$ and $y = f(x) + 2$

  c $y = f(x)$ and $y = 2\,f(x)$ **d** $y = f(x)$ and $y = -f(x)$.

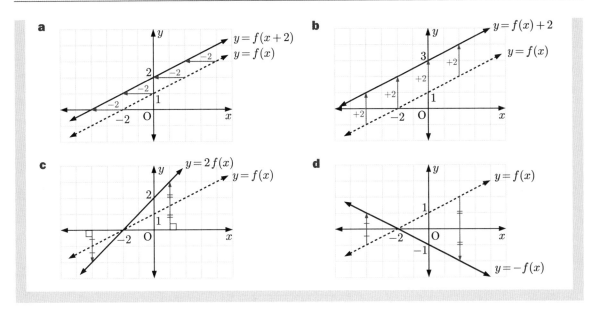

To help draw the graphs in the following Exercise, you may wish to use the **graphing package** or your **graphics calculator**.

GRAPHING PACKAGE

EXERCISE 25H

1 Consider $f(x) = 3x - 2$.

   a Describe the transformation which maps $y = f(x)$ onto:

      i $y = f(x) + 4$ **ii** $y = f(x + 4)$

   b On the same grid, graph $y = f(x)$, $y = f(x) + 4$, and $y = f(x + 4)$. Label each graph.

2 Consider $f(x) = 2^x$.

   a Describe the transformation which maps $y = f(x)$ onto:

      i $y = f(x) - 1$ **ii** $y = f(x - 3)$

   b On the same grid, graph $y = f(x)$, $y = f(x) - 1$, and $y = f(x - 3)$. Label each graph.

   c Describe the single transformation which maps the graph of $y = f(x) - 1$ onto $y = f(x - 3)$.

3 Consider $g(x) = \left(\frac{1}{2}\right)^x$.

   a On the same set of axes, graph $y = g(x)$, $y = g(x) - 1$, and $g(x - 1)$.

   b Write down the equation of the asymptote of $y = g(x) - 1$.

4 Consider $f(x) = 2x - 1$.

   a Graph $y = f(x)$ and $y = 3f(x)$ on the same set of axes.

   b What point(s) are invariant under this transformation?

5 Consider $h(x) = x^3$.

   a On the same set of axes, graph $y = h(x)$, $y = 2h(x)$, and $y = \frac{1}{2}h(x)$.

   b Describe fully the single transformation which maps the graph of $y = 2h(x)$ onto $y = \frac{1}{2}h(x)$.

6 Consider $f(x) = x^2 - 1$.

  a Graph $y = f(x)$ and state its axes intercepts.

  b Without using technology, sketch the graph of:

   i $y = f(x) + 3$ **ii** $y = f(x - 1)$ **iii** $y = 2f(x)$ **iv** $y = -f(x)$

  c Describe the combination of transformations which map $y = f(x)$ onto $y = -2f(x)$.

  d Hence graph $y = f(x)$ and $y = -2f(x)$ on the same set of axes.

  e What points on $y = f(x)$ are invariant when it is transformed into $y = -2f(x)$?

7 On each graph, $f(x)$ is mapped onto $g(x)$ using a single transformation.

   i Describe the transformation fully.   **ii** Write $g(x)$ in terms of $f(x)$.

a 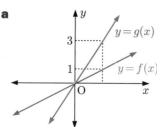   **b** 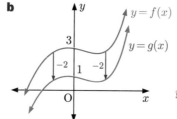   **c**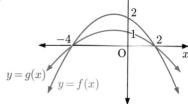

8 Copy each graph and draw the required function:

a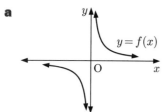
sketch $y = f(x - 2)$

b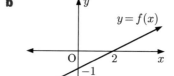
sketch $y = f(x) + 2$

c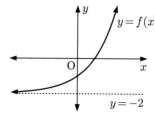
sketch $y = \frac{1}{2}f(x)$

d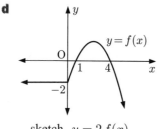
sketch $y = 2f(x)$

e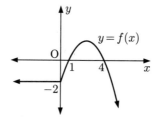
sketch $y = -2f(x)$

f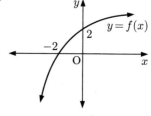
sketch $y = \frac{1}{2}f(x)$

9 Copy the graph of $y = f(x)$, and on the same set of axes graph $y = -f(x)$, $y = \frac{3}{2}f(x)$, $y = f(x) + 2$, and $y = f(x - 2)$.

Label each graph clearly.

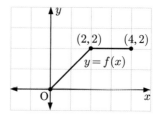

10 Consider $f(x) = x^2 - 4$, $g(x) = 2f(x)$, and $h(x) = f(2x)$.

  a Write $g(x)$ and $h(x)$ in terms of x.

  b Use technology to graph $y = f(x)$. On the same set of axes, sketch $y = g(x)$ and $y = h(x)$.

  c State the zeros of: **i** $f(x)$ **ii** $g(x)$ **iii** $h(x)$.

I   INVERSE FUNCTIONS   [E3.9]

Consider the mapping "add 5":

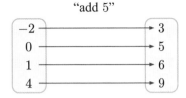

If we want to *reverse* this mapping, we need to apply the *inverse* operation, which is "subtract 5":

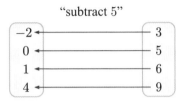

For a function f which converts x to $f(x)$, the **inverse function** f^{-1} converts $f(x)$ back to x.

Since the inverse function must convert every value of $f(x)$ back to a particular value of x, the original function must be one-to-one.

A function f has an inverse if and only if it is one-to-one.

Consider a one-to-one function $f : x \mapsto f(x)$, and that $f(a) = b$. The inverse function f^{-1} converts b back to a, so $f^{-1}(b) = a$.

From this we notice two things:

- (a, b) lies on the graph of $y = f(x)$, and (b, a) lies on the graph of $y = f^{-1}(x)$.
- Since $f(a) = b$ and $f^{-1}(b) = a$:
  - $f^{-1}(f(a)) = f^{-1}(b) = a$
  - $f(f^{-1}(b)) = f(a) = b$

These observations lead us to the following properties of inverse functions:

> If a function f has an inverse function f^{-1}, then:
> - f^{-1} can be found by interchanging x and y in the formula for f
> - $y = f^{-1}(x)$ is the reflection of $y = f(x)$ in the line $y = x$
> - $f^{-1}(f(x)) = x$ and $f(f^{-1}(x)) = x$.

Example 12   ◀)) *Self Tutor*

Consider $f(x) = \frac{1}{2}x - 1$.

a Find $f^{-1}(x)$.   **b** Check that $f(f^{-1}(x)) = f^{-1}(f(x)) = x$.

c Sketch $y = f(x)$, $y = f^{-1}(x)$, and $y = x$ on the same set of axes.

a $y = \frac{1}{2}x - 1$ has inverse function $x = \frac{1}{2}y - 1$ {interchanging x and y}

$$\therefore \ 2x = y - 2$$
$$\therefore \ y = 2x + 2$$
$$\therefore \ f^{-1}(x) = 2x + 2$$

b $f(f^{-1}(x)) = f(2x+2)$
$\qquad\qquad = \frac{1}{2}(2x+2) - 1$
$\qquad\qquad = x + 1 - 1$
$\qquad\qquad = x$

$f^{-1}(f(x)) = f^{-1}(\frac{1}{2}x - 1)$
$\qquad\qquad = 2(\frac{1}{2}x - 1) + 2$
$\qquad\qquad = x - 2 + 2$
$\qquad\qquad = x$

c

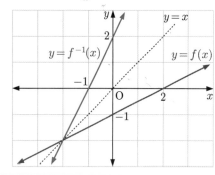

$y = f^{-1}(x)$ is a reflection of $y = f(x)$ in the line $y = x$.

EXERCISE 25I

1 For each of the following functions:

    i Find $f^{-1}(x)$.   **ii** Sketch $y = f(x)$, $y = f^{-1}(x)$, and $y = x$ on the same set of axes.

  a $f(x) = x + 3$ **b** $f(x) = 2x + 5$ **c** $f(x) = \dfrac{3 - 2x}{4}$

2 Copy the following graphs and draw the graph of each inverse function:

  a   **b**   **c**

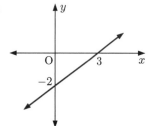 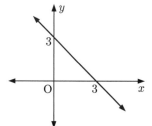 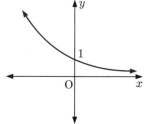

3 Consider $f(x) = 2x + 7$.

  a Find $f^{-1}(x)$.   **b** Check that $f(f^{-1}(x)) = f^{-1}(f(x)) = x$.

4 Consider $f(x) = \dfrac{2x+1}{x+3}$.

  a Find $f^{-1}(x)$.   **b** Check that $f(f^{-1}(x)) = f^{-1}(f(x)) = x$.

5 Consider $g(x) = \dfrac{x}{x-5}$.

  a Find $g^{-1}(x)$.   **b** Check that $g(g^{-1}(x)) = x$ and $g^{-1}(g(x)) = x$.

  c Find $g(6)$ and $g^{-1}(1)$.

6 **a** Sketch the graph of $y = x^2$ and reflect it in the line $y = x$.

  b Does $f(x) = x^2$ have an inverse function? Explain your answer.

  c Does $f(x) = x^2$, $x \geqslant 0$ have an inverse function? Explain your answer.

GRAPHING PACKAGE

7 The **horizontal line test** says that *"for a function to have an inverse function, no horizontal line can cut it more than once".*

    a Explain why this is a valid test for the existence of an inverse function.

    b Which of the following functions have an inverse function?

      i 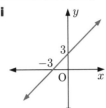   **ii** 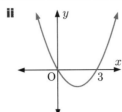   **iii** 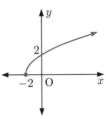   **iv**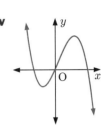

8 **a** Find the inverse function of: **i** $f(x) = 8 - x$ **ii** $f(x) = \dfrac{9}{x}$

    b Comment on your answers.

    c If $y = f(x)$ has the vertical asymptote $x = k$, explain why $y = f^{-1}(x)$ will have the horizontal asymptote $y = k$.

9 **a** Find the inverse function of $f(x) = mx + c$.

    b Hence find the inverse of: **i** $f(x) = 3x - 2$ **ii** $f(x) = -\tfrac{1}{2}x + 2$

10 For each of the following functions:

    i Find $f^{-1}(x)$.   **ii** Graph $y = f(x)$ and $y = f^{-1}(x)$ on the same set of axes.

  a $f(x) = \dfrac{2}{x - 3}$ **b** $f(x) = -\dfrac{3}{x + 1}$ **c** $f(x) = \dfrac{x}{x - 2}$ **d** $f(x) = \dfrac{x + 1}{x - 1}$

11 **a** Use technology to sketch the graph of $y = x^2 - 2x + 5$.

    b Explain why $f(x) = x^2 - 2x + 5$ is a function but does not have an inverse function.

    c Explain why $g(x) = x^2 - 2x + 5$, $x \geqslant 1$ *does* have an inverse function, and that $g^{-1}(x) = 1 + \sqrt{x - 4}$.

    d Sketch $g(x)$ and $g^{-1}(x)$ on the same set of axes.

Review set 25A

1 **a** Copy and complete the mapping diagram.   mapping *"$y = x^2 - 2$"*

    b State whether the mapping is one-to-one, many-to-one, one-to-many, or many-to-many.

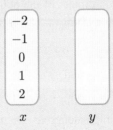

2 For $f(x) = 3x - x^2$, find:

  a $f(2)$ **b** $f(-1)$ **c** $f(x - 3)$

3 Determine whether the following sets of ordered pairs are functions:

  a $\{(-3, 5), (1, 7), (-1, 7), (2, 5)\}$ **b** $\{(-4, -5), (-1, 3), (5, 4), (0, 3), (-1, 2)\}$

4 Consider the function $g(x) = x^2 + 2x$. Find:

    a $g(2)$ **b** $g(3x)$ **c** the value of x such that $g(x) = 15$.

5 If $f(x) = \sqrt{x}$ and $g(x) = 5x - 3$, find in simplest form:

    a $f(g(x))$ **b** $g(f(x))$ **c** $g(g(x))$

6 If $x = -3$, find the value of:

    a $|x - 4|$ **b** $|x| - 4$ **c** $|x^2 + 3x|$

7 Draw the graph of $y = f(x)$ for:

    a $f(x) = |x| + 3x$ **b** $f(x) = 2|x| - 4$

8 Determine the equation of each reciprocal graph:

    a 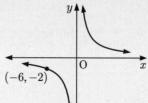   **b** 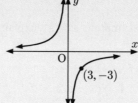   **c**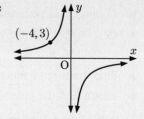

9 Consider the function $f(x) = \dfrac{4}{x + 3} - 1$.

    a Use technology to graph $y = f(x)$.

    b Find the equations of any vertical or horizontal asymptotes.

10 Suppose $f(x) = \dfrac{x^2 + 4}{x^2 - 9}$.

    a Use technology to sketch the graph of $y = f(x)$.

    b Find the equations of the asymptotes.   **c** Find the domain and range of $f(x)$.

    d For what values of k does $\dfrac{x^2 + 4}{x^2 - 9} = k$ have 2 solutions?

11 Solve for x, correct to 3 significant figures:

    a $7^x = 50$ **b** $5x^3 - \sqrt{x} = 12$ **c** $3x^2 - 5 = 2^{-x}$

12 Find the coordinates of the points of intersection of:

    a $y = (1.5)^{-x}$ and $y = 2x^2 - 7$ **b** $y = 6 - 2^x$ and $y = (x - 3)^2 - \dfrac{1}{\sqrt{x}}$

13 Consider $f(x) = 2x - 1$. On separate axes, graph:

    a $y = f(x)$ and $y = f(x - 2)$ **b** $y = f(x)$ and $y = f(x) - 2$

    c $y = f(x)$ and $y = 2f(x)$ **d** $y = f(x)$ and $y = -f(x)$.

14 Copy the graph alongside. On the same axes, draw the graphs of $y = f(x) + 3$ and $y = -2f(x)$.

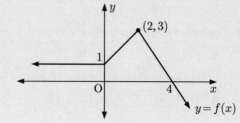

15 Consider the function $f(x) = \dfrac{x+2}{7}$.

     a Find $f^{-1}(x)$.   **b** Show that $f(f^{-1}(x)) = f^{-1}(f(x)) = x$.

     c Sketch $y = f(x)$, $y = f^{-1}(x)$, and $y = x$ on the same set of axes.

16 Find $f^{-1}(x)$ for:

     a $f(x) = 8x$ **b** $f(x) = \dfrac{2}{x-1}$ **c** $f(x) = \sqrt{x+3}$

Review set 25B

1 For each graph:

     i Find the domain and range.   **ii** Determine whether the graph is a function.

     a 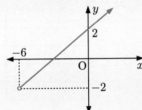   **b** 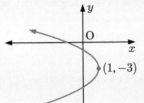   **c**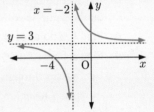

2 For $f(x) = 5x^2 + x$, find:

     a $f(-3)$ **b** $f(-x)$ **c** $f(x+1)$

3 The graph of $y = f(x)$ is a straight line passing through $(-1, 5)$ and $(3, -3)$.

     a Draw the graph of $y = f(x)$.   **b** Find $f(-1)$ and $f(3)$.

     c Find $f(x)$.   **d** Find $f^{-1}(x)$.

4 If $f(x) = 2x + 1$ and $g(x) = 7 - x$, find in simplest form:

     a $f(g(x))$ **b** $g(f(x))$ **c** $f(g(-2))$

5 If $a = -4$ and $b = 9$, find the value of:

     a $|ab|$ **b** $|2a - b| + a$ **c** $\dfrac{|a^2 - b|}{|a|}$

6 Suppose $f(x) = \dfrac{1}{x-4}$ and $g(x) = 3x - 1$.

     a Find $f(g(x))$.   **b** Find $f(g(5))$.

     c Find x such that $f(g(x)) = -\frac{1}{2}$.

7 Sketch the graphs of:

     a $f(x) = |x - 4|$ **b** $f(x) = |3x + 4|$

8 For each of the following:

     i Use technology to help graph the function.

     ii State the axes intercepts.

     iii State the equations of any asymptotes.

     a $y = 4 \times 3^{-x} - 3$ **b** $y = \dfrac{8 - 2^x}{x}$

9 For the function $f(x) = \dfrac{x-3}{x^2+3x-4}$:

    a Use technology to help graph the function.   **b** State the equations of any asymptotes.

    c Find the axes intercepts.   **d** Find and classify any turning points.

10 Solve for x, correct to 3 significant figures:

    a $3^x = 11$ **b** $x^3 - 6x = 5 + x^2$ **c** $5^x = x^2 + 2$

11 Find the coordinates of the points of intersection of:

    a $y = x^3$ and $y = \dfrac{5}{x} - 2$ **b** $y = 3^x + 2$ and $y = \dfrac{1}{x^2}$

12 Suppose $f(x) = (1.2)^{\frac{x}{10}}$ and $g(x) = (0.8)^{\frac{x}{10}}$.

    a Copy and complete the table of values alongside.

    b Use technology and your table to sketch $y = f(x)$ and $y = g(x)$ on the same set of axes.

    c Find the point of intersection of $f(x)$ and $g(x)$.

    d Find a linear function which:

x	$f(x)$	$g(x)$
-10	0.833	1.25
-5		
0		
5		
10		
15		
20		

        • passes through the point of intersection of $f(x)$ and $g(x)$

        • has a negative gradient

        • does not meet either graph again on the domain $-10 \leqslant x \leqslant 20$.

13 Consider $f(x) = \frac{1}{2}x + 3$. On separate axes, graph:

    a $y = f(x)$ and $y = f(x+1)$ **b** $y = f(x)$ and $y = f(x) + 1$

    c $y = f(x)$ and $y = -f(x)$ **d** $y = f(x)$ and $y = \frac{1}{2}f(x)$

14 $y = f(x)$ is mapped onto $y = g(x)$ by a single transformation.

    a Describe the transformation fully.

    b Write $g(x)$ in terms of $f(x)$.

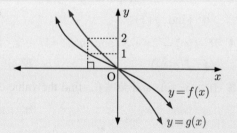

15 Copy the following graphs, and draw the graph of each function's inverse on the same set of axes:

    a

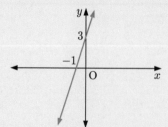

    b

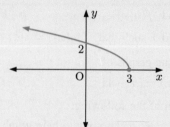

16 Consider $f(x) = \dfrac{x+1}{x-2}$.

    a Find $f^{-1}(x)$.   **b** Show that $f(f^{-1}(x)) = f^{-1}(f(x)) = x$.   **c** Find $f^{-1}(4)$.

Polynomial functions

26

Contents:

A	Quadratic functions	[E3.2]
B	Graphs of quadratic functions	[E3.2, E3.8]
C	Axes intercepts	[E3.2]
D	Axis of symmetry of a quadratic	[E3.2]
E	Vertex of a quadratic	[E3.2]
F	Finding a quadratic function	[E3.3, E3.4]
G	Problem solving with quadratic functions	[E3.2]
H	Cubic functions	[E3.2, E3.3]

Opening problem

Tennis player Bradley tosses the ball in the air before he serves it. The ball's height above the ground t seconds after it is tossed is given by the function $H(t) = -5t^2 + 6t + 2$ metres.

Things to think about:

a How high was the ball when it was released?

b What was the maximum height reached by the ball?

c Bradley hits the ball when it is 3 metres above the ground, and on its way down. How long after Bradley releases the ball does he hit it?

The *linear* functions we have studied already are the first members of a family of functions called **polynomials**. In this Chapter we study the next members of the family, **quadratics** and **cubics**.

Polynomial	Form
linear	$ax + b, \ a \neq 0$
quadratic	$ax^2 + bx + c, \ a \neq 0$
cubic	$ax^3 + bx^2 + cx + d, \ a \neq 0$

A QUADRATIC FUNCTIONS   [E3.2]

A **quadratic function** is a relationship between two variables which can be written in the form $y = ax^2 + bx + c$ where x and y are the variables, and a, b, and c are constants, $a \neq 0$.

Using function notation, we can write $f(x) = ax^2 + bx + c$.

FINDING y GIVEN x

For any value of x, the corresponding value of y can be found by substitution into the function equation.

Example 1   ◀ Self Tutor

Suppose $y = 2x^2 + 4x - 5$. Find the value of y when:
a $x = 0$ **b** $x = 3$

a When $x = 0$,
$$y = 2(0)^2 + 4(0) - 5$$
$$= 0 + 0 - 5$$
$$= -5$$

b When $x = 3$,
$$y = 2(3)^2 + 4(3) - 5$$
$$= 18 + 12 - 5$$
$$= 25$$

FINDING x GIVEN y

When we substitute a value for y, we are left with a quadratic equation which we need to solve for x. Since the equation is quadratic, there may be 0, 1, or 2 possible values for x.

Example 2   ◀ Self Tutor

Suppose $y = x^2 - 6x + 8$. Find the value(s) of x for which:
a $y = 15$ **b** $y = -1$

a When $y = 15$,
$$x^2 - 6x + 8 = 15$$
$$\therefore x^2 - 6x - 7 = 0$$
$$\therefore (x+1)(x-7) = 0$$
$$\therefore x = -1 \text{ or } x = 7$$

b When $y = -1$,
$$x^2 - 6x + 8 = -1$$
$$\therefore x^2 - 6x + 9 = 0$$
$$\therefore (x-3)^2 = 0$$
$$\therefore x = 3$$

EXERCISE 26A

1 Which of the following are quadratic functions?
   a $y = 15x - 8$ **b** $y = \frac{1}{3}x^2 + 6$ **c** $3y + 2x^2 - 7 = 0$ **d** $y = 15x^3 + 2x - 16$

2 For each of the following functions, find the value of y for the given value of x:
   a $y = x^2 + 5x - 14$ when $x = 2$ **b** $y = 2x^2 + 9x$ when $x = -5$
   c $y = -2x^2 + 3x - 6$ when $x = 3$ **d** $y = 4x^2 + 7x + 10$ when $x = -2$

3 State whether the following quadratic functions are satisfied by the given ordered pairs:

   a $f(x) = 6x^2 - 10$ $(0, 4)$ **b** $y = 2x^2 - 5x - 3$ $(4, 9)$

   c $y = -4x^2 + 6x$ $\left(-\frac{1}{2}, -4\right)$ **d** $f(x) = -7x^2 + 9x + 11$ $(-1, -6)$

   e $f(x) = 3x^2 - 11x + 20$ $(2, -10)$ **f** $y = -3x^2 + x + 6$ $\left(\frac{1}{3}, 4\right)$

4 For each of the following quadratic functions, find the value(s) of x for the given value of y:

   a $y = x^2 + 6x + 10$ when $y = 1$ **b** $y = x^2 + 5x + 8$ when $y = 2$

   c $y = x^2 - 5x + 1$ when $y = -3$ **d** $y = 3x^2$ when $y = -3$

5 Find the value(s) of x for which:

   a $f(x) = 3x^2 - 3x + 6$ has the value 6   **b** $f(x) = x^2 - 2x - 7$ has the value -4

   c $f(x) = -2x^2 - 13x + 3$ has the value -4 **d** $f(x) = 2x^2 - 10x + 1$ has the value -11

6 An object is projected into the air with a velocity of 80 m/s. Its height after t seconds is given by the function $h(t) = 80t - 5t^2$ metres.

   a Calculate the height of the object after: **i** 1 second   **ii** 3 seconds   **iii** 5 seconds.

   b Calculate the time(s) at which the height of the object is: **i** 140 m   **ii** 0 m.

   c Explain your answers to part **b**.

7 A cake manufacturer finds that the profit from making x cakes per day is given by the function $P(x) = -\frac{1}{2}x^2 + 36x - 40$ dollars.

   a Calculate the profit if   **i** 0 cakes   **ii** 20 cakes   are made per day.

   b How many cakes need to be made per day to achieve a profit of $270?

B   GRAPHS OF QUADRATIC FUNCTIONS   *[E3.2, E3.8]*

The graphs of all quadratic functions are **parabolas**. The parabola is one of the **conic sections**.

Historical note   *Conic sections*

Conic sections are curves which can be obtained by cutting a cone with a plane. The Ancient Greek mathematicians were fascinated by conic sections.

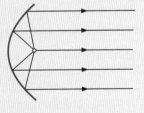

The name parabola comes from the Greek word for **thrown** because when an object is thrown, its path makes a parabolic arc.

There are many other examples of parabolas in everyday life. For example, parabolic mirrors are used in car headlights, heaters, satellite dishes, and radio telescopes, because of their special geometric properties.

You may like to explore the conic sections for yourself using the software.

CONIC SECTIONS

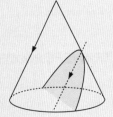

The simplest quadratic function is $y = x^2$. Its graph can be drawn from
a table of values.

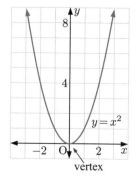

x	-3	-2	-1	0	1	2	3
y	9	4	1	0	1	4	9

We can see that the graph:

- is symmetrical about the x-axis

- has a minimum turning point at $(0, 0)$ which we call the **vertex** of
  the parabola.

Example 3   ◁》 Self Tutor

a Draw the graph of $y = x^2 + 2x - 3$ using a table of values from $x = -3$ to $x = 3$.
b State the coordinates of the vertex.

a Consider $f(x) = x^2 + 2x - 3$

Now $f(-3) = (-3)^2 + 2(-3) - 3$
$$= 9 - 6 - 3$$
$$= 0$$

We complete the table by performing the same
calculations for the other values of x:

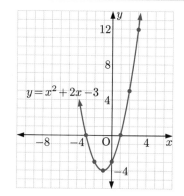

x	-3	-2	-1	0	1	2	3
y	0	-3	-4	-3	0	5	12

b The vertex is $(-1, -4)$.

EXERCISE 26B.1

1 Using a table of values from $x = -3$ to $x = 3$, draw the graph of:

GRAPHING
PACKAGE

a $y = x^2 - 2x + 8$ **b** $f(x) = -x^2 + 2x + 1$

c $y = 2x^2 + 3x$ **d** $y = -2x^2 + 4$

e $y = x^2 + x + 4$ **f** $f(x) = -x^2 + 4x - 9$

Check your graphs using technology.

2 **a** Use tables of values to graph $y = 2x^2 - x - 3$ and $y = -x^2 + 2x + 3$ on the same set of axes.
  b *Hence* find the values of x for which $2x^2 - x - 3 = -x^2 + 2x + 3$.
  c Solve algebraically: $2x^2 - x - 3 = -x^2 + 2x + 3$

USING TRANSFORMATIONS TO GRAPH QUADRATICS

By observing how a quadratic function is related to $f(x) = x^2$, we can transform the graph of $y = x^2$ to
produce the graph of the function.

From the transformations of functions we studied in **Chapter 25**, you should recognise that:

- Graphs of the form $y = (x - h)^2 + k$ have the same shape as the graph of $y = x^2$.

  The graph of $y = x^2$ is translated by $\begin{pmatrix} h \\ k \end{pmatrix}$ to give the graph of $y = (x - h)^2 + k$.

  The vertex is shifted to $(h,\ k)$.
- $y = -x^2$ is a reflection of $y = x^2$ in the x-axis.

  $y = x^2$ opens upwards.

  $y = -x^2$ opens downwards.

Discovery 1   *Graphs of quadratic functions*

What to do:

1 On the same set of axes, graph:

GRAPHING
PACKAGE

   a $y = x^2$, $y = 2x^2$, $y = 4x^2$, $y = \frac{1}{2}x^2$

   b $y = -x^2$, $y = -2x^2$, $y = -4x^2$, $y = -\frac{1}{2}x^2$

2 For a function of the form $y = ax^2$, what effect does a have on:

   a the position of the graph   **b** the shape of the graph

   c the direction in which the graph opens?

3 Graph each pair of functions on the same set of axes, and observe the coordinates of the vertex of each function.

   a $y = 2x^2$ and $y = 2(x - 1)^2 + 3$ **b** $y = -x^2$ and $y = -(x + 2)^2 - 1$

   c $y = \frac{1}{2}x^2$ and $y = \frac{1}{2}(x - 3)^2 - 2$ **d** $y = -3x^2$ and $y = -3(x + 1)^2 + 4$

4 Copy and complete:

   The graph of $y = a(x - h)^2 + k$ is found by translating $y = ax^2$ by $\begin{pmatrix} ...... \\ ...... \end{pmatrix}$.

In the **Discovery** you should have found that:

- If $|a| > 1$, $y = ax^2$ is "thinner" than $y = x^2$.

  If $|a| < 1$, $y = ax^2$ is "wider" than $y = x^2$.
- If $a > 0$, $y = ax^2$ opens upwards.

  If $a < 0$, $y = ax^2$ opens downwards.
- The graph of $y = a(x - h)^2 + k$ has the same shape and opens in the same direction as the graph

  of $y = ax^2$. It is found by translating $y = ax^2$ by $\begin{pmatrix} h \\ k \end{pmatrix}$.

Example 4   ◀》 Self Tutor

Sketch each of the following functions on the same set of axes as $y = x^2$. In each case state the coordinates of the vertex.

a $y = x^2 + 3$ **b** $y = (x + 3)^2$

a We draw $y = x^2$, then translate it
3 units upwards.

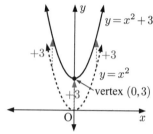

The vertex is at $(0, 3)$.

b We draw $y = x^2$, then translate it
3 units to the left.

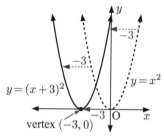

The vertex is at $(-3, 0)$.

Use transformations to draw the graphs in this Exercise. Check your answers using technology.

EXERCISE 26B.2

1 Sketch each function on the same set of axes as $y = x^2$. Use a separate set of axes for each part, and in each case state the coordinates of the vertex.

a $y = x^2 - 3$ **b** $y = x^2 - 1$ **c** $y = x^2 + 2$
d $y = x^2 - 5$ **e** $y = x^2 + 5$ **f** $y = x^2 - \frac{1}{2}$

2 Sketch each function on the same set of axes as $y = x^2$. Use a separate set of axes for each part, and in each case state the coordinates of the vertex.

a $y = (x - 3)^2$ **b** $y = (x + 1)^2$ **c** $y = (x - 2)^2$
d $y = (x - 5)^2$ **e** $y = (x + 5)^2$ **f** $y = (x - \frac{3}{2})^2$

Example 5   ◀》 Self Tutor

Sketch each of the following functions on the same set of axes as $y = x^2$. In each case state the coordinates of the vertex.

a $y = (x - 2)^2 + 3$ **b** $y = (x + 2)^2 - 5$

a We draw $y = x^2$, then translate it 2 units
to the right and 3 units upwards.

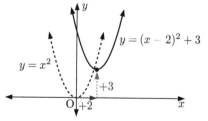

The vertex is at $(2, 3)$.

b We draw $y = x^2$, then translate it 2 units
to the left and 5 units downwards.

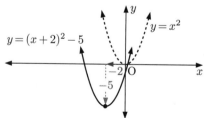

The vertex is at $(-2, -5)$.

3 Sketch each function on the same set of axes as $y = x^2$. Use a separate set of axes for each part, and in each case state the coordinates of the vertex.

    a $y = (x-1)^2 + 3$ **b** $y = (x-2)^2 - 1$ **c** $y = (x+1)^2 + 4$

    d $y = (x+2)^2 - 3$ **e** $y = (x+3)^2 - 2$ **f** $y = (x-3)^2 + 3$

Example 6   ◀⑴ *Self Tutor*

Sketch $y = x^2$ on a set of axes and hence sketch:

    a $y = 3x^2$ **b** $y = -3x^2$

    a $y = 3x^2$ is "thinner" than $y = x^2$.

    b $y = -3x^2$ has the same shape as $y = 3x^2$, but opens downwards.

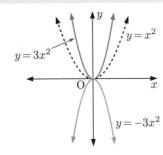

---

4 Sketch each function on the same set of axes as $y = x^2$. Comment on the shape of the graph, and the direction in which the graph opens.

    a $y = 5x^2$ **b** $y = -5x^2$ **c** $y = \frac{1}{3}x^2$

    d $y = -\frac{1}{3}x^2$ **e** $y = -4x^2$ **f** $y = \frac{1}{4}x^2$

Example 7   ◀⑴ *Self Tutor*

Sketch the graph of $y = -(x-2)^2 - 3$ from the graph of $y = x^2$, and hence state the coordinates of its vertex.

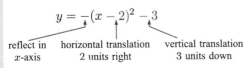

reflect in   horizontal translation   vertical translation
x-axis   2 units right   3 units down

We start with $y = x^2$, then reflect it in the x-axis to give $y = -x^2$.

We then translate $y = -x^2$ 2 units to the right and 3 units down.

The vertex of $y = -(x-2)^2 - 3$ is $(2, -3)$.

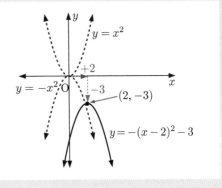

---

5 Sketch each function on the same set of axes as $y = x^2$. In each case, state the coordinates of the vertex.

    a $y = -(x-1)^2 + 3$ **b** $y = 2x^2 + 4$ **c** $y = -(x-2)^2 + 4$

    d $y = 3(x+1)^2 - 4$ **e** $y = \frac{1}{2}(x+3)^2$ **f** $y = -\frac{1}{2}(x+3)^2 + 1$

    g $y = -2(x+4)^2 + 3$ **h** $y = 2(x-3)^2 + 5$ **i** $y = \frac{1}{2}(x-2)^2 - 1$

6 Match the following quadratic functions
with their graphs:

a $y = -(x+2)^2 - 3$

b $y = (x-3)^2 + 2$

c $y = 2(x+3)^2 + 2$

d $y = -(x-3)^2 + 2$

e $y = -\frac{1}{2}(x+2)^2 - 3$

f $y = (x+3)^2 + 2$

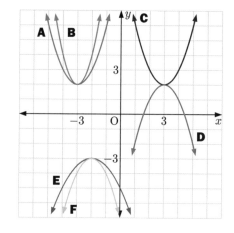

7 **a** Show that $(x-2)^2 - 3 = x^2 - 4x + 1$.

b Graph $y = x^2$ and $y = x^2 - 4x + 1$ on the same set of axes.

8 **a** Show that $3(x-1)^2 + 2 = 3x^2 - 6x + 5$.

b Graph $y = 3x^2$ and $y = 3x^2 - 6x + 5$ on the same set of axes.

9 **a** Show that $-(x+3)^2 + 13 = -x^2 - 6x + 4$.

b Graph $y = -x^2$ and $y = -x^2 - 6x + 4$ on the same set of axes.

10 **a** Show that $-2(x - \frac{3}{2})^2 + \frac{9}{2} = -2x^2 + 6x$.

b Graph $y = -2x^2$ and $y = -2x^2 + 6x$ on the same set of axes.

11 **a** Expand $a\left(x + \dfrac{b}{2a}\right)^2 + \left(c - \dfrac{b^2}{4a}\right)$ and simplify.

b Explain why any graph of the form $y = ax^2 + bx + c$ has the same shape as the graph of $y = ax^2$.

C   AXES INTERCEPTS   [E3.2]

- An **x-intercept** of a function is a value of x
  where its graph meets the x-axis.
  x-intercepts are found by letting y be 0 in the
  equation of the function.

- A **y-intercept** of a function is a value of y where
  its graph meets the y-axis.
  y-intercepts are found by letting x be 0 in the
  equation of the function.

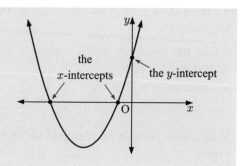

Discovery 2   *Axes intercepts*

What to do:

1   Use technology to draw graphs of the following quadratic functions. Make sure
    you find and label the axes intercepts.

GRAPHING
PACKAGE

   a $y = x^2 - 3x - 4$ **b** $y = -x^2 + 2x + 8$ **c** $y = 2x^2 - 3x$

   d $y = -2x^2 + 2x - 3$ **e** $y = (x-1)(x-3)$ **f** $y = -(x+2)(x-3)$

   g $y = 3(x+1)(x+4)$ **h** $y = 2(x-2)^2$ **i** $y = -3(x+1)^2$

2   **a** State the y-intercept of a quadratic function in the form $y = ax^2 + bx + c$.

   b State the x-intercepts of a quadratic function in the form:

     i $y = a(x - \alpha)(x - \beta)$ **ii** $y = a(x - \alpha)^2$

From the **Discovery** you should have found:

- For a quadratic function in the form $y = ax^2 + bx + c$,
  the y-intercept is the constant term c.

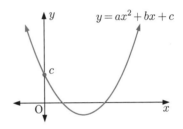

- A quadratic function with factored form
  $y = a(x - \alpha)(x - \beta)$ has x-intercepts α and β.

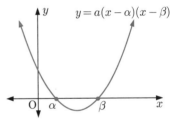

- A quadratic function with factored form $y = a(x - \alpha)^2$
  touches the x-axis at $x = \alpha$. The only x-intercept is α.

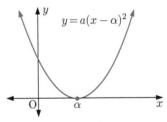

Example 8   ◀) *Self Tutor*

Find the x-intercepts of:

   a $y = 2(x-3)(x+2)$ **b** $y = -(x-4)^2$

a When $y = 0$,	**b** When $y = 0$,
$2(x-3)(x+2) = 0$	$-(x-4)^2 = 0$
$\therefore$ $x = 3$ or $x = -2$	$\therefore$ $x = 4$
$\therefore$ the x-intercepts are 3 and -2.	$\therefore$ the x-intercept is 4.

FACTORISING TO FIND x-INTERCEPTS

> For any quadratic function of the form $y = ax^2 + bx + c$, the x-intercepts can be found by solving the equation $ax^2 + bx + c = 0$.

In **Chapter 23** we saw that quadratic equations may have two, one, or no real solutions. These solutions correspond to the two, one, or no x-intercepts of the graph of the corresponding quadratic function.

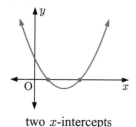

two x-intercepts

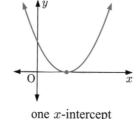

one x-intercept

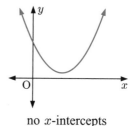

no x-intercepts

Example 9   ◀)) Self Tutor

Find the x-intercept(s) of the quadratic function:

a $y = x^2 - 6x + 9$ **b** $y = -x^2 - x + 6$

> If a quadratic function has only one x-intercept then its graph must **touch** the x-axis.

a When $y = 0$,
$x^2 - 6x + 9 = 0$
$\therefore \ (x - 3)^2 = 0$
$\therefore \quad x = 3$
$\therefore$ the x-intercept is 3.

b When $y = 0$,
$-x^2 - x + 6 = 0$
$\therefore \ x^2 + x - 6 = 0$
$\therefore \ (x + 3)(x - 2) = 0$
$\therefore \quad x = -3$ or 2
$\therefore$ the x-intercepts are -3 and 2.

EXERCISE 26C

1 State the y-intercept of:

a $y = x^2 + 3x + 3$ **b** $y = x^2 - 5x + 2$ **c** $f(x) = 2x^2 + 7x - 8$

d $y = 3x^2 - x + 1$ **e** $f(x) = -x^2 + 3x + 6$ **f** $y = -2x^2 + 5 - x$

g $y = 6 - x - x^2$ **h** $f(x) = 8 + 2x - 3x^2$ **i** $y = 5x - x^2 - 2$

2 State the x-intercepts of:

a $y = (x - 3)(x + 1)$ **b** $f(x) = -(x - 2)(x - 4)$ **c** $y = 2(x + 3)(x + 2)$

d $y = -3(x - 4)(x - 5)$ **e** $y = 2(x + 3)^2$ **f** $f(x) = -5(x - 1)^2$

3 Find the x-intercepts of:

a $y = x^2 - 9$ **b** $y = 25 - x^2$ **c** $y = x^2 - 6x$

d $f(x) = x^2 + 7x + 10$ **e** $y = x^2 + x - 12$ **f** $y = 4x - x^2$

g $y = -x^2 - 6x - 8$ **h** $f(x) = -2x^2 - 4x - 2$ **i** $y = 4x^2 - 24x + 36$

4 Use the quadratic formula to find the x-intercepts of each function:

a $y = x^2 - 4x + 1$ **b** $y = x^2 + 4x - 3$ **c** $y = -x^2 + 6x - 4$

d $f(x) = 3x^2 - 7x - 2$ **e** $f(x) = 2x^2 - x - 5$ **f** $f(x) = -4x^2 + 9x - 3$

Example 10

◄ Self Tutor

Sketch the graph of each function by considering:

    i the value of a **ii** the y-intercept   **iii** the x-intercepts.

a $y = x^2 - 2x - 3$ **b** $y = -2(x+1)(x-2)$ **c** $y = 2(x-3)^2$

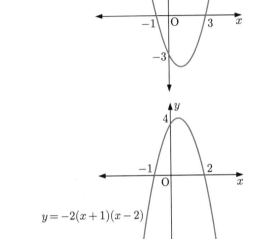

a $y = x^2 - 2x - 3$

  i $a = 1$ which is > 0, so the parabola opens upwards.

  ii When $x = 0$, $y = -3$

    $\therefore$ the y-intercept is -3.

  iii When $y = 0$, $x^2 - 2x - 3 = 0$

    $\therefore$ $(x-3)(x+1) = 0$

    $\therefore$ $x = 3$ or $x = -1$

    $\therefore$ the x-intercepts are 3 and -1.

b $y = -2(x+1)(x-2)$

  i $a = -2$ which is < 0, so the parabola opens downwards.

  ii When $x = 0$, $y = -2(0+1)(0-2)$

    $= 4$

    $\therefore$ the y-intercept is 4.

  iii When $y = 0$, $-2(x+1)(x-2) = 0$

    $\therefore$ $x = -1$ or $x = 2$

    $\therefore$ the x-intercepts are -1 and 2.

c $y = 2(x-3)^2$

  i $a = 2$ which is > 0, so the parabola opens upwards.

  ii When $x = 0$, $y = 2(0-3)^2 = 18$

    $\therefore$ the y-intercept is 18.

  iii When $y = 0$, $2(x-3)^2 = 0$

    $\therefore$ $x = 3$

    $\therefore$ the x-intercept is 3.

    There is only one x-intercept, which means the graph *touches* the x-axis.

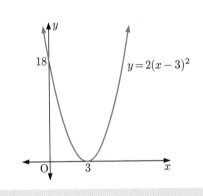

5 Sketch the graph of the quadratic function which has:

  a x-intercepts -1 and 1, and y-intercept -1 **b** x-intercepts -3 and 1, and y-intercept 2

  c x-intercepts 2 and 5, and y-intercept -4 **d** x-intercept 2 and y-intercept 4.

6 Sketch the graph of each quadratic function by considering:

    i the value of a **ii** the y-intercept   **iii** the x-intercepts.

  a $y = x^2 - 4x + 4$ **b** $f(x) = (x-1)(x+3)$ **c** $y = 2(x+2)^2$

  d $f(x) = -(x-2)(x+1)$ **e** $y = -3(x+1)^2$ **f** $y = -3(x-4)(x-1)$

  g $y = 2(x+3)(x+1)$ **h** $y = -2x^2 - 3x + 5$ **i** $f(x) = -x^2 + 8x - 10$

D AXIS OF SYMMETRY OF A QUADRATIC [E3.2]

The graphs of all quadratic functions are symmetrical about a vertical line passing through the vertex. This line is called the **axis of symmetry**.

If the graph has two x-intercepts, then the axis of symmetry is midway between them.

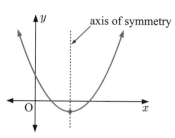

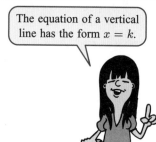

The equation of a vertical line has the form $x = k$.

Example 11
◀⑨ *Self Tutor*

Find the equation of the axis of symmetry for the quadratic graph below.

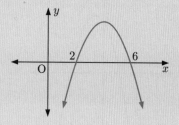

The x-intercepts are 2 and 6, and 4 is midway between 2 and 6.

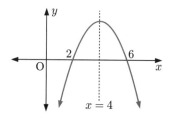

The axis of symmetry is $x = 4$.

If the quadratic does not have any x-intercepts, or if we do not know the x-intercepts, we can still use the knowledge that the axis of symmetry passes through the vertex.

We know the equation $y = a(x - h)^2 + k$ has vertex (h, k), so its line of symmetry is $x = h$.

Expanding, $y = a(x - h)^2 + k$
$= a(x^2 - 2hx + h^2) + k$
$= ax^2 - 2ahx + [ah^2 + k]$.

Comparing the coefficient of x with that from $y = ax^2 + bx + c$, we find $-2ah = b$

$$\therefore \ h = \frac{-b}{2a}$$

So, the line of symmetry is $x = \frac{-b}{2a}$.

The equation of the axis of symmetry of $y = ax^2 + bx + c$ is $x = \frac{-b}{2a}$.

Example 12
◀⑨ *Self Tutor*

Find the equation of the axis of symmetry of $y = 2x^2 + 3x + 1$.

$y = 2x^2 + 3x + 1$ has $a = 2$, $b = 3$, $c = 1$.

Now $\frac{-b}{2a} = \frac{-3}{2 \times 2} = -\frac{3}{4}$

$\therefore$ the axis of symmetry has equation $x = -\frac{3}{4}$.

EXERCISE 26D

1   For each graph, find the equation of the axis of symmetry:

a 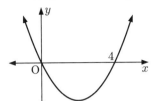   **b** 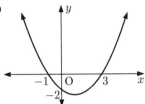   **c**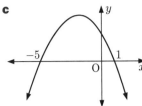

d 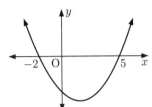   **e** 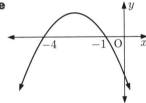   **f**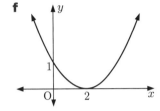

2   Find the equation of the axis of symmetry of each function:

   a $y = (x - 2)(x - 4)$ **b** $y = -(x + 1)(x - 5)$ **c** $y = 2(x + 3)(x - 3)$

   d $y = x(x + 5)$ **e** $y = -3(x + 4)^2$ **f** $y = 4(x + 6)(x - 9)$

3   Find the equation of the axis of symmetry of each function:

   a $y = x^2 + 4x + 1$ **b** $y = 2x^2 - 6x + 3$ **c** $f(x) = 3x^2 + 4x - 1$

   d $y = -x^2 - 4x + 5$ **e** $y = -2x^2 + 5x + 1$ **f** $f(x) = \frac{1}{2}x^2 - 10x + 2$

   g $y = \frac{1}{3}x^2 + 4x$ **h** $f(x) = 100x - 4x^2$ **i** $y = -\frac{1}{10}x^2 + 30x$

4   Find all x-intercepts of the quadratic function which:

   a   cuts the x-axis at 1 and has axis of symmetry $x = 2$

   b   cuts the x-axis at -1 and has axis of symmetry $x = -\frac{3}{2}$.

5   Sketch the graph, including the axis of symmetry, of the parabola with:

   a x-intercepts -3 and 3, and y-intercept 6   **b** x-intercepts -1 and 2, and y-intercept -3

   c   only x-intercept -2, and y-intercept 4.

E   VERTEX OF A QUADRATIC   [E3.2]

The **vertex** or **turning point** of the quadratic function $y = ax^2 + bx + c$ is the point at which the function has:

- a **maximum value** for $a < 0$,   or

- a **minimum value** for $a > 0$.

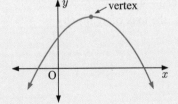

Since the vertex lies on the axis of symmetry, its x-coordinate will be $\dfrac{-b}{2a}$.

The y-coordinate is found by substituting this x-coordinate into the function.

Example 13
◀) **Self Tutor**

Consider the quadratic function $y = -x^2 + 2x + 3$.

a Find the axes intercepts.   **b** Find the equation of the axis of symmetry.

c Find the coordinates of the vertex.

d Sketch the function, showing all important features.

a When $x = 0$, $y = 3$

   $\therefore$ the y-intercept is 3.

   When $y = 0$, $-x^2 + 2x + 3 = 0$

   $\therefore$ $x^2 - 2x - 3 = 0$

   $\therefore$ $(x - 3)(x + 1) = 0$

   $\therefore$ $x = 3$ or -1

   $\therefore$ the x-intercepts are 3 and -1.

b $a = -1$, $b = 2$, $c = 3$

   $\therefore$ $\dfrac{-b}{2a} = \dfrac{-2}{-2} = 1$

   $\therefore$ the axis of symmetry is $x = 1$.

c When $x = 1$,

   $y = -(1)^2 + 2(1) + 3$

   $\quad = -1 + 2 + 3$

   $\quad = 4$

   $\therefore$ the vertex is $(1, 4)$.

d
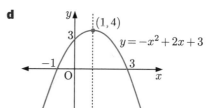

Example 14
◀) **Self Tutor**

Consider the quadratic function $y = 2(x - 2)(x + 4)$.

a Find the axes intercepts.   **b** Find the equation of the axis of symmetry.

c Find the coordinates of the vertex.   **d** Sketch the function, showing all important features.

a When $x = 0$, $y = 2 \times -2 \times 4 = -16$

   $\therefore$ the y-intercept is -16.

   When $y = 0$, $2(x - 2)(x + 4) = 0$

   $\therefore$ $x = 2$ or $x = -4$

   $\therefore$ the x-intercepts are 2 and -4.

b The axis of symmetry is halfway between the x-intercepts, and -1 is halfway between 2 and -4.

   $\therefore$ the axis of symmetry is $x = -1$.

c When $x = -1$,

   $y = 2(-1 - 2)(-1 + 4)$

   $\quad = 2 \times -3 \times 3$

   $\quad = -18$

   $\therefore$ the vertex is $(-1, -18)$.

d
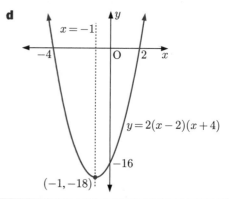

EXERCISE 26E

1 For each of the following quadratic functions:

   i Find the coordinates of the vertex.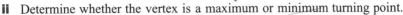

   ii Determine whether the vertex is a maximum or minimum turning point.

   iii Find the range of the function.

   a $y = x^2 - 4x + 2$

   b $y = x^2 + 2x - 3$

   c $f(x) = 2x^2 + 4$

   d $y = -3x^2 + 1$

   e $y = -x^2 - 4x - 4$

   f $y = 2x^2 - 10x + 3$

2 For each of the following quadratic functions:

   i Find the axes intercepts.

   ii Find the equation of the axis of symmetry.

   iii Find the coordinates of the vertex.

   iv Hence, sketch the graph of the function.

   a $y = x^2 - 2x - 8$

   b $y = 4x - x^2$

   c $y = x^2 + 3x$

   d $f(x) = x^2 + 4x + 4$

   e $y = x^2 + 3x - 4$

   f $y = -x^2 + 2x - 1$

   g $y = 2x^2 + 5x - 3$

   h $f(x) = -3x^2 - 4x + 4$

   i $y = x^2 - 6x + 3$

3 For each of the following quadratic functions:

   i Find the axes intercepts.

   ii Find the equation of the axis of symmetry.

   iii Find the coordinates of the vertex.

   iv Hence, sketch the graph of the function.

   a $f(x) = x(x - 2)$

   b $y = 2(x - 3)^2$

   c $y = -(x - 1)(x + 3)$

   d $y = -2(x - 1)^2$

   e $f(x) = -5(x + 2)(x - 2)$

   f $y = 2(x + 1)(x + 4)$

F | FINDING A QUADRATIC FUNCTION   [E3.3, E3.4]

We can use information about axes intercepts, the vertex, and other points on a graph to establish the equation of a quadratic function.

In particular, notice that:

- If a quadratic has vertex (h, k), its equation has the form $f(x) = a(x - h)^2 + k$.
- If a quadratic has x-intercepts α and β, its equation has the form $f(x) = a(x - \alpha)(x - \beta)$.
- If a quadratic touches the x-axis at α, its equation has the form $f(x) = a(x - \alpha)^2$.

Example 15   ◀⦂) Self Tutor

Find the quadratic function with:

   a vertex $(1, 2)$ and y-intercept 3

   b vertex $(2, 11)$ and which passes through $(-1, -7)$.

a Using the vertex, $f(x) = a(x - 1)^2 + 2$
for some value of a.

But $f(0) = 3$, so $\quad a + 2 = 3$

$\therefore \quad a = 1$

$\therefore \quad f(x) = (x - 1)^2 + 2$

b Using the vertex, $f(x) = a(x - 2)^2 + 11$
for some value of a.

But $f(-1) = -7$, so $\quad a(-3)^2 + 11 = -7$

$\therefore \quad 9a = -18$

$\therefore \quad a = -2$

$\therefore \quad f(x) = -2(x - 2)^2 + 11$

EXERCISE 26F

1 Find the quadratic function with:

   a vertex $(2, -5)$ and y-intercept 3   **b** vertex $(-4, 19)$ and y-intercept 3

   c vertex $(1, 8)$ and y-intercept 7   **d** vertex $(-2, 11)$ and y-intercept 3.

   Give your answers in the form $f(x) = a(x - h)^2 + k$.

2 Find the quadratic function represented in each graph. Give your answers in the form $y = a(x - h)^2 + k$.

a 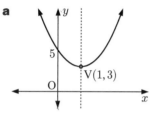   **b** 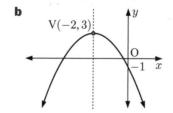   **c**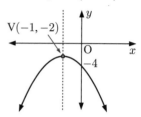

3 Find the quadratic function which has:

   a vertex $(-2, -5)$ and which passes through $(1, 13)$

   b vertex $(3, -19)$ and which passes through $(-2, 31)$.

   Give your answers in the form $f(x) = a(x - h)^2 + k$.

4 Suppose $f(x) = x^2 + bx + c$. Find the values of b and c given $y = f(x)$ has vertex:

   a $(1, 3)$ **b** $(0, 2)$ **c** $(3, 0)$ **d** $(-3, -2)$ **e** $(\frac{1}{2}, 1)$

5 Find the quadratic function with:

   a vertex $(1, -4)$ and y-intercept -7 **b** vertex $(-2, 3)$ and y-intercept 15

   c vertex $(-3, -5)$ and y-intercept 7   **d** vertex $(3, 8)$ and y-intercept -10

   e vertex $(2, -3)$, and which passes through $(-1, 15)$

   f vertex $(-1, 5)$, and which passes through $(3, -3)$.

   Give your answers in the form $f(x) = ax^2 + bx + c$.

Example 16   ◀) Self Tutor

The graph of a quadratic function has x-intercepts $-\frac{5}{2}$ and $\frac{1}{3}$, and it passes through $(1, 42)$. Find the function.

Using the x-intercepts, $f(x) = a(x + \frac{5}{2})(x - \frac{1}{3})$

$\qquad\qquad\qquad\qquad \equiv a(2x + 5)(3x - 1)$ for some value of a.

But $f(1) = 42$, so $a(7)(2) = 42$

$\qquad\qquad \therefore \; 14a = 42$

$\qquad\qquad \therefore \; a = 3$

$\therefore \; f(x) = 3(2x + 5)(3x - 1)$

6 Suppose $f(x) = x^2 + bx + c$. Find the values of b and c given $y = f(x)$ has x-intercepts:

   a 0 and 2   **b** -4 and 1   **c** -5 and 2   **d** -7 and 0.

7 Find the quadratic function which has x-intercepts:

    a -2 and 2, and which passes through $(0, 8)$ **b** 1 and 4, and which passes through $(0, -12)$

    c -2 and 3, and which passes through $(4, 18)$ **d** -4 and 5, and which passes through $(-1, 36)$

    e $1\frac{1}{2}$ and 3, and which passes through $(1, 2)$ **f** $-\frac{3}{4}$ and $\frac{5}{4}$, and which passes through $(2, 33)$.

 G   ## PROBLEM SOLVING WITH QUADRATIC FUNCTIONS   **[E3.2]**

Example 17   Self Tutor

The height of a rocket t seconds after it is fired upwards is given by
$H(t) = 100t - 5t^2$ metres, $t \geqslant 0$.

    a How long does the rocket take to reach its maximum height?

    b Find the maximum height reached by the rocket.

    c How long does it take for the rocket to fall back to Earth?

a $H(t) = 100t - 5t^2$

     $\therefore\ H(t) = -5t^2 + 100t$

     Now $a = -5$ which is < 0, so the shape of the graph is 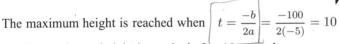.

     The maximum height is reached when $t = \dfrac{-b}{2a} = \dfrac{-100}{2(-5)} = 10$

     $\therefore$ the maximum height is reached after 10 seconds.

b $H(10) = 100(10) - 5(10)^2 = 500$

     $\therefore$ the maximum height reached is 500 m.

c The rocket falls back to Earth when $H(t) = 0$

                     $\therefore\ -5t^2 + 100t = 0$

                     $\therefore\ -5t(t - 20) = 0$

                         $\therefore\ t = 0$ or 20

     $\therefore$ the rocket falls back to Earth after 20 seconds.

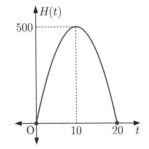

EXERCISE 26G

1 The height of a ball t seconds after it is kicked upwards is given by $H(t) = 20t - 5t^2$ metres.

    a How long does the ball take to reach its maximum height?

    b Find the maximum height reached by the ball.

    c How long does it take for the ball to hit the ground?

2 A manufacturer finds that the profit $\$P$ from assembling x bicycles per day is given by
$P(x) = -x^2 + 50x - 200$.

    a How many bicycles should be assembled per day to maximise the profit?

    b Find the maximum profit.

    c What is the loss made if no bicycles are assembled in a day? Suggest why this loss would be made.

3 The driver of a car travelling downhill applied the brakes. The speed of the car, t seconds after the brakes were applied, is given by $s(t) = -6t^2 + 12t + 60$ km/h.

   a How fast was the car travelling when the driver applied the brakes?

   b After how many seconds did the car reach its maximum speed?

   c Find the maximum speed reached.

4 The hourly profit obtained from operating a fleet of n taxis is given by $P(n) = 120n - 200 - 2n^2$ dollars.

   a What number of taxis gives the maximum hourly profit?

   b Find the maximum hourly profit.

   c How much money is lost per hour if no taxis are on the road?

5 The temperature $T°C$ in a greenhouse t hours after 7:00 pm is given by $T(t) = \frac{1}{4}t^2 - 6t + 25$ for $t \leqslant 20$.

   a Find the temperature in the greenhouse at 7:00 pm.

   b At what time is the temperature at a minimum?

   c Find the minimum temperature in the greenhouse for $0 \leqslant t \leqslant 20$.

6 Answer the **Opening Problem** on page **433**.

7 Infinitely many rectangles may be inscribed within the triangle ACE shown. One of them is illustrated.

Suppose $EF = x$ cm.

   a Show that triangles ABF and ACE are similar.

   b Show that $BF = 2(1 - x)$ cm.

   c Show that the area of rectangle BDEF is given by $A = -2x^2 + 2x$ cm^2.

   d   **i** Find x such that the area of the rectangle is maximised.

       ii What is the maximum area?

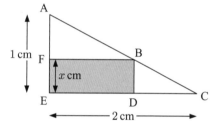

H   CUBIC FUNCTIONS   *[E3.2, E3.3]*

> A **cubic function** is a function which can be written in the form
> $f(x) = ax^3 + bx^2 + cx + d$ where a, b, c, d are constants, $a \neq 0$.

Discovery 3   *Cubic functions*

To discover the shape of different cubic functions, you can either use the graphing package or your graphics calculator.

GRAPHING
PACKAGE

What to do:

1   **a**   Use technology to help sketch, on the same set of axes:

     i $y = x^3$, $y = 2x^3$, $y = 3x^3$, $y = \frac{1}{2}x^3$

     ii $y = x^3$ and $y = -x^3$

     iii $y = -x^3$, $y = -2x^3$, $y = -3x^3$, $y = -\frac{1}{2}x^3$

   b   Discuss the geometrical significance of a in $y = ax^3$. Comment on both the sign and the size of a.

2   **a**   Use technology to help sketch, on the same set of axes:
$$y = x^3, \quad y = (x-2)^3 + 3, \quad y = (x-4)^3 - 2, \quad y = (x+3)^3 + 1$$

   b   Discuss the family of cubic functions with the form $y = (x-h)^3 + k$.

3   **a**   Use technology to help sketch, on the same set of axes:
$$y = (x-4)(x-2)(x+1), \quad y = 2x(x-3)(x+2),$$
$$y = -x(x-2)(x+3), \qquad y = -2(x-5)(x-1)(x+2).$$

   b   Discuss the geometrical significance of α, β, and γ for the cubic $y = a(x-\alpha)(x-\beta)(x-\gamma)$.

4   **a**   Use technology to help sketch, on the same set of axes:
$$y = (x-2)(x+1)(x+4), \qquad y = 2(x-2)(x+1)(x+4),$$
$$y = \tfrac{1}{2}(x-2)(x+1)(x+4), \quad y = -2(x-2)(x+1)(x+4).$$

   b   Discuss the geometrical significance of a in $y = a(x-\alpha)(x-\beta)(x-\gamma)$.

5   **a**   Use technology to help sketch, on the same set of axes:
$$y = x(x+2)^2, \qquad y = (x+3)^2(x-1), \qquad y = 2(x-1)^2(x+2),$$
$$y = \tfrac{1}{2}x^2(x+4), \quad y = -2(x+2)(x-1)^2.$$

   b   Discuss the geometrical significance of α and β for the cubic $y = a(x-\alpha)^2(x-\beta)$.

6   **a**   Predict the geometrical significance of a and α for the cubic $y = a(x-\alpha)^3$.

   b   Check your prediction is correct by sketching:
$$y = (x-2)^3, \quad y = -(x+1)^3, \quad y = 2(x+3)^3, \quad y = -3(x+2)^3.$$

You should have discovered that:

- If $a > 0$, the graph's shape is   or   , if $a < 0$ it is   or   .

- $y = (x-h)^3 + k$ is the translation of $y = x^3$ by $\begin{pmatrix} h \\ k \end{pmatrix}$.

- For a cubic function of the form $y = a(x-\alpha)(x-\beta)(x-\gamma)$, the graph has x-intercepts α, β, and γ, and the graph crosses over or **cuts** the x-axis at these points.

- For a cubic function of the form $y = a(x-\alpha)^2(x-\beta)$, the graph **touches** the x-axis at α and **cuts** it at β.

- For a cubic function of the form $y = a(x-\alpha)^3$, the graph cuts the x-axis at α. The curve changes shape at that point.

Example 18   ◀) *Self Tutor*

Use axes intercepts to sketch the graph of:

a $f(x) = (x + 3)(x + 1)(x - 2)$ **b** $f(x) = -x(x + 3)^2$

a $f(x) = (x + 3)(x + 1)(x - 2)$ has
  x-intercepts -3, -1, and 2.
  $f(0) = (3)(1)(-2) = -6$
  ∴ the y-intercept is -6.
  $a > 0$ so the graph has shape

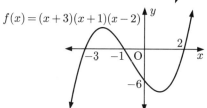

b $f(x) = -x(x + 3)^2$ cuts the x-axis when
  $x = 0$ and touches the x-axis when $x = -3$.
  $f(0) = -0(3)^2 = 0$
  ∴ the y-intercept is 0.
  $a < 0$ so the graph has shape

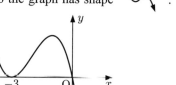

Example 19   ◀) *Self Tutor*

Find the cubic function with graph:

a

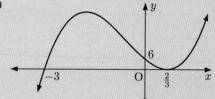

b

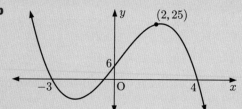

a The graph *cuts* the x-axis at -3 and *touches* it at $\frac{2}{3}$.
  ∴   the function has the form $f(x) = a(x + 3)(3x - 2)^2$.
  But $f(0) = 6$,   so $a(3)(-2)^2 = 6$
  $$\therefore \quad 12a = 6$$
  $$\therefore \quad a = \tfrac{1}{2}$$
  ∴ $f(x) = \tfrac{1}{2}(x + 3)(3x - 2)^2$

b The graph *cuts* the x-axis at -3 and 4.
  We suppose the third linear factor is $(ax + b)$, so the function has the form
  $f(x) = (x + 3)(x - 4)(ax + b)$.
  But $f(0) = 6$,   so $(3)(-4)b = 6$ And $f(2) = 25$,   so $(5)(-2)(2a - \tfrac{1}{2}) = 25$
  $$\therefore \quad -12b = 6 \qquad\qquad\qquad\qquad\qquad\qquad \therefore \quad 2a - \tfrac{1}{2} = -\tfrac{5}{2}$$
  $$\therefore \quad b = -\tfrac{1}{2} \qquad\qquad\qquad\qquad\qquad\qquad\qquad \therefore \quad 2a = -2$$
  $$\qquad\qquad\qquad\qquad\qquad\qquad\qquad\qquad\qquad\qquad\qquad \therefore \quad a = -1$$
  ∴ $f(x) = (x + 3)(x - 4)(-x - \tfrac{1}{2}) = -(x + 3)(x - 4)(x + \tfrac{1}{2})$

EXERCISE 26H

1 By expanding out the following, show that they are cubic functions.

    a $f(x) = (x+3)(x-2)(x-1)$ **b** $f(x) = (x+4)(x-1)(2x+3)$

    c $f(x) = (x+2)^2(2x-5)$ **d** $f(x) = (x+1)^3 + 2$

2 Use axes intercepts to sketch the graph of:

    a $f(x) = x(x-3)(x+2)$ **b** $y = (x-1)(x-4)(x+2)$

    c $f(x) = -(x+3)(x-2)(x-4)$ **d** $y = 2x(x-1)(x+1)$

    e $f(x) = -\frac{1}{2}(x+3)(x+1)(x-1)$ **f** $y = -3x(x+2)(x-1)$

3 Use axes intercepts to sketch the graph of:

    a $f(x) = (x-1)^2(x+1)$ **b** $y = -x(x+2)^2$

    c $f(x) = -\frac{1}{2}(x-2)(x+2)^2$ **d** $y = \frac{1}{4}x^2(x+4)$

    e $y = \frac{1}{3}(x-3)^3$ **f** $f(x) = -2(x+1)^3$

4 Find the cubic function with graph:

    a
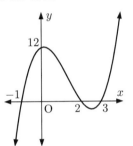
    b
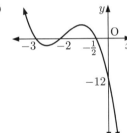
    c
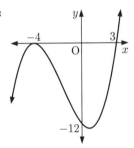

    d
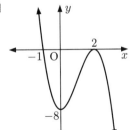
    e
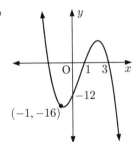
    f
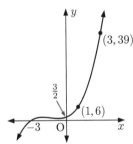

5 Find the equation of the cubic function which:

    a has x-intercepts 1 and 3, y-intercept 9, and passes through $(-1, 8)$

    b touches the x-axis at 3, has y-intercept 18, and passes through $(1, 20)$.

6 The graph alongside has the form $y = 2x^3 + bx^2 + cx - 12$.
Find the values of b and c.

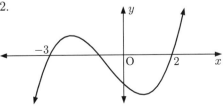

7 The graph alongside has the form
$y = -x^3 + bx^2 + 4x + d$.
Find the values of b and d.

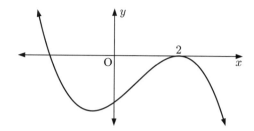

Review set 26A

1 For the quadratic function $y = x^2 - 3x - 15$, find:

    a the value of y when $x = 4$ **b** the values of x when $y = 3$.

2 Sketch each of the following functions on the same set of axes as $y = x^2$:

    a $y = 3x^2$ **b** $y = (x - 2)^2 + 1$ **c** $y = -(x + 3)^2 - 2$

3 **a** Show that $(x - 2)^2 + 6 = x^2 - 4x + 10$.

    b Hence sketch the graph of $y = x^2 - 4x + 10$, stating the coordinates of the vertex.

4 Find the x-intercepts of:

    a $y = 5x(x + 4)$ **b** $y = 2x^2 + 6x - 56$

5 Find the equation of the axis of symmetry for:

    a

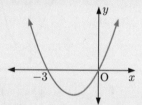

    b

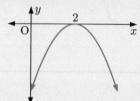

6 Consider the quadratic function $y = -2(x - 1)(x + 3)$.

    a Find the:

        i direction the parabola opens   **ii** y-intercept

        iii x-intercepts   **iv** equation of the axis of symmetry.

    b Sketch the function, showing all of the above features.

7 Find the vertex of each of the following quadratic functions:

    a $y = x^2 - 8x - 3$ **b** $y = -4x^2 + 4x - 3$

8 Consider the function $y = x^2 - 2x - 15$.

    a Find the:

        i y-intercept   **ii** x-intercepts

        iii equation of the axis of symmetry   **iv** coordinates of the vertex.

    b Sketch the function, showing all of the above features.

9 The graph of $f(x) = x^2 + bx + c$ has its vertex at $(-3, -11)$. Find the values of b and c.

10 Consider the function $f(x) = \frac{1}{2}(x + 1)^2 - 2$:

    a Find the coordinates of the vertex.   **b** Find the y-intercept.   **c** Sketch $y = f(x)$.

11 Find the quadratic function with vertex $(-1, -5)$ and y-intercept -3. Give your answer in the form $f(x) = a(x - h)^2 + k$.

12 A vegetable gardener has 40 m of fencing to enclose a rectangular garden plot where one side is an existing brick wall. Suppose the plot is x m wide as shown.

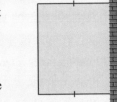

 a Show that the area enclosed is given by
 $A = -2x^2 + 40x$ m².

 b Find x such that the vegetable garden has the maximum possible area.

 c Find the maximum possible area.

13 The graph of a quadratic function has x-intercepts -4 and $-\frac{1}{3}$, and passes through the point $(-1, -18)$. Find the quadratic function in the form $f(x) = ax^2 + bx + c$.

14 Find the quadratic function with vertex $(6, -2)$ which passes through the point $(4, 16)$. Give your answer in the form $f(x) = ax^2 + bx + c$.

15 Sketch the graphs of the following cubics, showing all axes intercepts:

 a $y = x(x - 2)(x + 3)$ **b** $y = -2(x + 1)^2(x - 3)$

16 Find the cubic function which has x-intercepts -1, 0, and 2, and which passes through $(1, 6)$.

17 Find the equation of the cubic function with the graph alongside.
Give your answer in factored form.

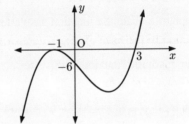

Review set 26B

1 Find the values of x for which $f(x) = x^2 + x - 12$ takes the value 30.

2 Determine whether the ordered pair $(2, 5)$ satisfies the quadratic function $f(x) = x^2 - 3x + 8$.

3 Draw the graphs of $y = x^2$ and $y = (x + 2)^2 + 5$ on the same set of axes.

4 Use the quadratic formula to find the x-intercepts of:

 a $y = 3x^2 - x - 5$ **b** $y = -x^2 + 2x + 6$

5 Draw the graph of $y = 3(x - 2)^2$, showing the axes intercepts and the coordinates of the vertex.

6 Determine the equation of the axis of symmetry for the following quadratic functions:

 a $f(x) = (x + 3)(x - 5)$ **b** $f(x) = 3x^2 - 5x + 2$

7 **a** Find the vertex of the quadratic function $f(x) = -x^2 + 4x - 7$.

 b Hence, find the range of the function.

8 Consider the quadratic function $f(x) = (x-1)(x-4)$.

   a Find $f(-1)$.   **b** Find the axes intercepts.

   c Find the equation of the axis of symmetry.   **d** Find the coordinates of the vertex.

   e Sketch the graph of $y = f(x)$, showing all of the above features.

9 Suppose $f(x) = (x+2)(x+6)$ and $g(x) = -x^2 - 8x - 20$.

   a Find the axes intercepts of each function.

   b Show that the two functions have the same vertex.

   c State the range of each function.

   d Sketch the functions on the same set of axes.

10 The quadratic function $f(x) = x^2 + bx + c$ has x-intercepts -5 and 3. Find the values of b and c.

11 Consider the function $y = -x^2 + 7x - 10$.

   a Find the:

      i y-intercept   **ii** x-intercepts

      iii equation of the axis of symmetry   **iv** coordinates of the vertex.

   b Sketch the function, showing all of the above features.

12 Use axes intercepts to sketch the graph of:

   a $f(x) = 2(x-3)(x+1)$ **b** $g(x) = -x(x+4)$

13 The graph of a quadratic function has vertex $(2, 2)$, and passes through the point $(-1, -7)$. Find the function in the form $f(x) = a(x-h)^2 + k$.

14 Find the quadratic function with vertex $(-4, 15)$ and y-intercept -17. Give your answer in the form $f(x) = ax^2 + bx + c$.

15 The graph of $y = a(x-h)^2 + k$ is shown alongside.

   a Find the value of h.

   b Find the values of a and k by solving simultaneous equations.

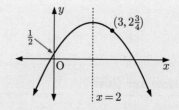

16 Use axes intercepts to sketch the graph of:

   a $y = (x+3)(x-4)(x-2)$ **b** $y = 3x^2(x+2)$

17 The graph alongside has the form $y = x^3 + 6x^2 + cx + d$. Find the values of c and d.

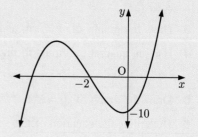

Sequences

27

Contents:

A Number sequences [E2.12]
B Formulae for sequences [E2.12]
C Geometric sequences [E2.12]
D The difference method for sequences [E2.12]

Opening problem

contains 1 square

contains $1 + 4 = 5$ squares
one 2×2
four 1×1

contains $1 + 4 + 9 = 14$ squares
one 3×3
four 2×2
nine 1×1

Things to think about:

a How many squares are contained in each diagram?

i
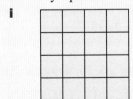

ii
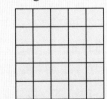

iii
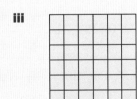

b Can you find a *formula* for the total number of squares in an $n \times n$ grid?
c How many squares are contained in a 100×100 grid?

A   NUMBER SEQUENCES   [E2.12]

A **number sequence** is an ordered list of numbers defined by a rule.

The numbers in the sequence are called the **terms** of the sequence.

The **nth term** or **general term** is written as u_n, so the sequence is $u_1, u_2, u_3, u_4, ...$

We often use words to describe a number sequence, giving a starting term and a rule which connects one term with the next.

For example: Consider the sequence 15, 11, 7, 3, -1, ...

The sequence can be described by the rule

"Start with 15, then subtract 4 each time to get the next term".

The next two terms are $u_6 = -1 - 4 = -5$ and $u_7 = -5 - 4 = -9$.

Example 1   ◀) Self Tutor

Write a rule to describe the sequence, and hence find its next two terms:

a   3, 7, 11, 15, 19, ...   **b**   2, 6, 18, 54, ...   **c**   1, 1, 2, 3, 5, 8, ...

a   Start with 3, then add 4 each time to get the next term.
$u_6 = 23$ and $u_7 = 27$.

b   Start with 2, then multiply by 3 each time to get the next term.
$u_5 = 54 \times 3 = 162$ and $u_6 = 162 \times 3 = 486$.

c   The first two terms are 1 and 1, and each term thereafter is the sum of the previous two terms.
$u_7 = 5 + 8 = 13$ and $u_8 = 8 + 13 = 21$.

EXERCISE 27A

1 Consider the sequence 8, 5, 2, -1, ...

> The line of dots tells us to assume the pattern continues.

   a Write a rule to describe the sequence.

   b State the values of u_2 and u_4.

   c Find the values of u_5 and u_6.

2 Write a rule to describe the sequence, and hence find its next *two* terms:

   a 2, 6, 10, 14, 18, ...   **b** 2, 9, 16, 23, 30, ...   **c** 8, 19, 30, 41, 52, ...

   d 20, 16, 12, 8, 4, ...   **e** 3, -2, -7, -12, -17, ...   **f** 10, $8\frac{1}{2}$, 7, $5\frac{1}{2}$, ...

3 Write a rule to describe the sequence, and hence find its next *two* terms:

   a 1, 2, 4, 8, 16, ...   **b** 1, -2, 4, -8, 16, ...   **c** 36, 18, 9, $4\frac{1}{2}$, ...

   d $\frac{1}{81}, \frac{1}{27}, \frac{1}{9}, \frac{1}{3}$, ...   **e** 405, 135, 45, 15, ...   **f** 1, 1.1, 1.21, 1.331, ...

4 Write a rule to describe the sequence, and hence find its next *two* terms:

   a 1, 4, 9, 16, 25, ...   **b** 1, 8, 27, 64, ...   **c** 1, $\frac{1}{4}, \frac{1}{9}, \frac{1}{16}$, ...

   d 2, 3, 5, 9, 17, ...   **e** 2, 3, 5, 8, 12, ...   **f** 2, 3, 5, 7, 11, ...

   g 0, 1, 1, 2, 3, 5, ...   **h** 1, 1, 2, 6, 24, ...   **i** 3, 3, 5, 4, 4, 3, ...

Example 2   ◆ Self Tutor

Draw the next two matchstick figures in the sequence, and write the number of matchsticks used as a number sequence:

a   **b**

□, □□, □□□, □□□□, ...

a   **b**

□□□□□, □□□□□□

4, 7, 10, 13, 16, 19, ...   10, 15, 20, 25, 30, ...

---

5 Draw the next *two* matchstick figures in the sequence, and write the number of matchsticks used as a number sequence:

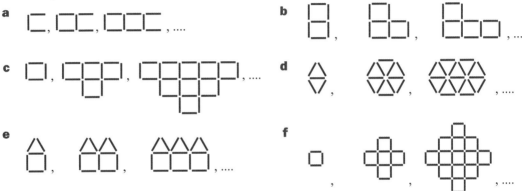

6 Draw the next *two* figures in these sequences and write the number of dots used as a number sequence:

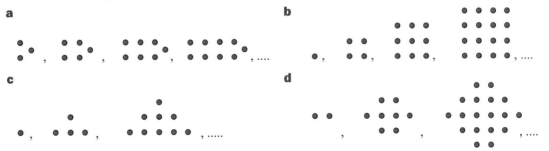

B **FORMULAE FOR SEQUENCES**   **[E2.12]**

An alternative way to describe a sequence is to write an algebraic formula for its general term u_n in terms of n.

For example: $u_n = 3n + 2$, $u_n = n^2 + n$, $u_n = \dfrac{1}{n}$

An explicit formula for the general term u_n allows us to quickly calculate the value of any term in the sequence. We can substitute any value of $n \in \mathbb{Z}^+$.

Example 3
◀)) **Self Tutor**

Find the first 5 terms of the sequence with the rule:
  a $u_n = 5n - 3$ **b** $u_n = n(n+2)$ **c** $u_n = 3 \times 2^n$

a $u_1 = 5(1) - 3 = 2$ **b** $u_1 = 1(3) = 3$ **c** $u_1 = 3(2)^1 = 6$
  $u_2 = 5(2) - 3 = 7$ $u_2 = 2(4) = 8$ $u_2 = 3(2)^2 = 12$
  $u_3 = 5(3) - 3 = 12$ $u_3 = 3(5) = 15$ $u_3 = 3(2)^3 = 24$
  $u_4 = 5(4) - 3 = 17$ $u_4 = 4(6) = 24$ $u_4 = 3(2)^4 = 48$
  $u_5 = 5(5) - 3 = 22$ $u_5 = 5(7) = 35$ $u_5 = 3(2)^5 = 96$

EXERCISE 27B

1 Find the first *four* terms of the sequence with nth term:
  a $u_n = 2n + 3$ **b** $u_n = 3n + 5$ **c** $u_n = -2n + 1$
  d $u_n = -2n + 3$ **e** $u_n = 17 - 4n$ **f** $u_n = 76 - 7n$

2 Find the first *four* terms of the sequence with nth term:
  a $u_n = n^2 - 1$ **b** $u_n = n^2 + n$ **c** $u_n = -n^2$
  d $u_n = n(n+3)$ **e** $u_n = n^3 - 1$ **f** $u_n = n^3 + 2n^2 - 1$

3 List the first *five* terms of the sequence with nth term:
  a $u_n = 5 \times 2^n$ **b** $u_n = 5 \times 2^{n-1}$ **c** $u_n = 5 \times 2^{n+1}$
  d $u_n = 4 \times 3^{n-1}$ **e** $u_n = 24 \times \left(\frac{1}{2}\right)^{n-1}$ **f** $u_n = 36 \times \left(\frac{1}{3}\right)^{n-1}$
  g $u_n = 24 \times (-2)^n$ **h** $u_n = 8(-1)^{n-1}$ **i** $u_n = 8\left(-\frac{1}{2}\right)^n$

4 The **triangular numbers** are numbers which can be represented by a triangular arrangement of dots.

1 dot   3 dots   6 dots

  a Find the first five numbers in the sequence of triangular numbers.
  b The general term formula for the sequence of triangular numbers is $u_n = \frac{1}{2}n(n+1)$.
    i Verify this rule for the first five triangular numbers.
    ii Use the rule to find the 10th triangular number.

Example 4
◀)) **Self Tutor**

A sequence has nth term $5n - 3$.
  a Show that 42 is a term of the sequence.   **b** Is 63 a term of the sequence?

a Suppose the nth term is 42.   **b** Suppose the nth term is 63.
  $\therefore \ 5n - 3 = 42$ $\therefore \ 5n - 3 = 63$
  $\therefore \ \ 5n = 45$ $\therefore \ \ 5n = 66$
  $\therefore \ \ n = 9$ $\therefore \ \ n = 13\frac{1}{5}$
  So, 42 is the 9th term of the sequence.   But n must be an integer, so 63 is *not* a
                                                   term of the sequence.

5 A sequence has nth term $88 - 7n$.

    a Show that 39 is a term of the sequence.   **b** Is 8 a term of the sequence?

    c Is -52 a term of the sequence?

6 A sequence has nth term $n^2 + 5$.

    a Find the 4th term of the sequence.   **b** Is 41 a term of the sequence?

    c Is 80 a term of the sequence?

Example 5   ◀)) *Self Tutor*

  a Write a formula for the general term u_n of the sequence 3, 6, 9, 12, 15, ...

  b Hence find a formula for the general term u_n of:

    i 4, 7, 10, 13, 16, ...   **ii** 1, 4, 7, 10, 13, ...   **iii** $\frac{1}{5}, \frac{1}{8}, \frac{1}{11}, \frac{1}{14}, ...$

  a $u_1 = 3 \times 1, \quad u_2 = 3 \times 2, \quad u_3 = 3 \times 3, \quad u_4 = 3 \times 4, \quad u_5 = 3 \times 5$

    $\therefore \quad u_n = 3 \times n = 3n$

  b **i** $u_1 = 3 + 1, \quad u_2 = 6 + 1, \quad u_3 = 9 + 1, \quad u_4 = 12 + 1, \quad u_5 = 15 + 1$

      Each term is 1 more than in the sequence in **a**.

      $\therefore \quad u_n = 3n + 1$

   ii $u_1 = 3 - 2, \quad u_2 = 6 - 2, \quad u_3 = 9 - 2, \quad u_4 = 12 - 2, \quad u_5 = 15 - 2$

      Each term is 2 less than in the sequence in **a**.

      $\therefore \quad u_n = 3n - 2$

   iii $u_1 = \dfrac{1}{3+2}, \quad u_2 = \dfrac{1}{6+2}, \quad u_3 = \dfrac{1}{9+2}, \quad u_4 = \dfrac{1}{12+2}, \quad u_5 = \dfrac{1}{15+2}$

      By comparison with the sequence in **a**, $u_n = \dfrac{1}{3n+2}$

---

7 **a** Write a formula for the general term u_n of the sequence: 2, 4, 6, 8, 10, ...

   b Hence find a formula for the general term u_n of:

    i 4, 6, 8, 10, 12, ...   **ii** 1, 3, 5, 7, 9, ...   **iii** $\frac{1}{2}, \frac{1}{4}, \frac{1}{6}, \frac{1}{8}, \frac{1}{10}, ...$

8 **a** Write a formula for the general term u_n of the sequence: 5, 10, 15, 20, 25, ...

   b Hence find a formula for the general term u_n of:

    i 6, 11, 16, 21, 26, ...   **ii** 3, 8, 13, 18, 23, ...   **iii** $\frac{1}{5}, \frac{1}{10}, \frac{1}{15}, \frac{1}{20}, \frac{1}{25}, ...$

9 **a** Write a formula for the general term u_n of the sequence: 2, 4, 8, 16, 32, ...

   b Hence find a formula for the general term u_n of:

    i 6, 12, 24, 48, 96, ...   **ii** $\frac{1}{2}, \frac{1}{4}, \frac{1}{8}, \frac{1}{16}, \frac{1}{32}, ...$

10 Write a formula for the general term u_n of the sequence:

    a 1, 2, 3, 4, 5, 6, ...   **b** 2, 3, 4, 5, 6, 7, ...   **c** 3, 4, 5, 6, 7, 8, ...

    d $\frac{1}{1}, \frac{1}{2}, \frac{1}{3}, \frac{1}{4}, \frac{1}{5}, ...$ **e** $\frac{1}{2}, \frac{1}{3}, \frac{1}{4}, \frac{1}{5}, \frac{1}{6}, ...$ **f** $\frac{1}{2}, \frac{2}{3}, \frac{3}{4}, \frac{4}{5}, \frac{5}{6}, ...$

    g $\frac{3}{1}, \frac{4}{2}, \frac{5}{3}, \frac{6}{4}, \frac{7}{5}, \frac{8}{6}, ...$ **h** $1 \times 2, \; 2 \times 3, \; 3 \times 4, \; 4 \times 5, \; ....$

    i $2 \times 3, \; 3 \times 4, \; 4 \times 5, \; 5 \times 6, \; ....$ **j** $1 \times 3, \; 2 \times 4, \; 3 \times 5, \; 4 \times 6, \; ....$ **k** $\frac{1}{3}, \frac{4}{6}, \frac{7}{9}, \frac{10}{12}, ...$

11 Write a formula for the general term u_n of:

    a 1, 4, 9, 16, 25, ...   **b** 0, 1, 4, 9, 16, ...   **c** 2, 5, 10, 17, 26, ...

12 Write a formula for the general term u_n of:

    a   1, 8, 27, 64, 125, ...   **b**   0, 7, 26, 63, 124, ...

13 An **arithmetic sequence** is a sequence in which each term differs from the previous term by the same fixed number. The difference between successive terms is called the **common difference** d.

    a Find the first *five* terms of a sequence with the *linear* general term $u_n = an + b$.

    b Explain why the sequence generated is an arithmetic sequence, and how we can find the common difference directly from the formula.

    c Write a formula for the general term of the arithmetic sequence:

        i   3, 7, 11, 15, ...   **ii**   5, 11, 17, 23, ...   **iii**   13, 6, -1, -8, ...

C   GEOMETRIC SEQUENCES   *[E2.12]*

In a **geometric sequence**, each term is found by multiplying the previous one by the same non-zero constant.

The number we multiply by to get from one term to the next is called the **common ratio** r.

Discovery 1   *Geometric sequences*

What to do:

1 Consider the sequence: "Start with 2, then multiply by 3 each time to get the next term."

    a Find the first *five* terms of the sequence.

    b Copy and complete:

$$u_1 = 2 \qquad\qquad\qquad\qquad = 2 \times 3^{....}$$
$$u_2 = 2 \times 3 \qquad\qquad\qquad = 2 \times 3^{....}$$
$$u_3 = 2 \times 3 \times 3 \qquad\qquad = 2 \times 3^{....}$$
$$u_4 = 2 \times 3 \times 3 \times 3 \qquad = 2 \times 3^{....}$$
$$u_5 = 2 \times 3 \times 3 \times 3 \times 3 = 2 \times 3^{....}$$
$$\therefore \; u_n \qquad\qquad\qquad\qquad\quad = 2 \times 3^{....}$$

    c Copy and complete:

        The common ratio $r = \dfrac{u_2}{u_1} = \dfrac{u_3}{u_2} = \dfrac{u_4}{u_3} = \dfrac{u_5}{u_4} = \; ....$

2 Consider the sequence with general term $u_n = A \times r^{n-1}$.

    a Find the first term u_1.

    b Find the $(n+1)$th term u_{n+1}.

    c Find the common ratio $\dfrac{u_{n+1}}{u_n}$. Hence explain why this sequence is geometric.

From the **Discovery** you should have found that:

For a geometric series:

- the ratio $\dfrac{u_{n+1}}{u_n}$ is a **constant**

- the general term can be written in the form $u_n = u_1 \times r^{n-1}$.

EXERCISE 27C

1 For the sequence 3, 6, 12, 24, 48, ... :

  a Show that the ratio of consecutive terms is a constant.

  b Hence write a formula for the general term of the sequence.

2 For each sequence below:

  i Find the next *two* terms.

  ii Write a formula for the nth term of the sequence.

  a 1, −1, 1, −1, 1, ...

  b −1, 1, −1, 1, −1, ...

  c 2, 4, 8, 16, 32, ...

  d 2, −4, 8, −16, 32, ...

  e 6, 18, 54, 162, ...

  f 6, −18, 54, −162, ...

3 Write a formula for the general term of the sequence:

  a 4, 12, 36, 108, ...

  b 2, −14, 98, −686, ...

  c 3, −6, 12, −24, ...

  d −16, 8, −4, 2, ...

  e 12, 6, 3, $\frac{3}{2}$, ...

  f 12, −8, $\frac{16}{3}$, −$\frac{32}{9}$, ...

4 Show that the sequence with general term $u_n = 5 \times 2^n$ is geometric by:

  a listing the first four terms and showing the ratio of consecutive terms is constant

  b using the exponent laws to write u_n in the form $u_1 \times r^{n-1}$.

D THE DIFFERENCE METHOD FOR SEQUENCES [E2.12]

We have seen that a **linear** or **arithmetic** sequence is one in which each term differs from the previous term by the same constant. The general term has the linear form $u_n = an + b$ where a and b are constants.

In the same way, a **quadratic** sequence has general term $u_n = an^2 + bn + c$, and a **cubic** sequence has general term $u_n = an^3 + bn^2 + cn + d$.

To find the formula for one of these sequences, we use a technique called the **difference method**.

Discovery 2   *The difference method*

Part 1: Linear sequences

Consider the linear sequence $u_n = 3n + 2$ where $u_1 = 5$, $u_2 = 8$, $u_3 = 11$, $u_4 = 14$, and $u_5 = 17$.

We construct a **difference table** to display the sequence. We include a row for the **first difference** $\Delta 1$ which is the difference between successive terms of the sequence. Notice that this difference is constant.

n	1	2	3	4	5
u_n	5	8	11	14	17
$\Delta 1$		3	3	3	3

What to do:

1 Construct a difference table for the sequence defined by:

  a $u_n = 4n + 3$

  b $u_n = -3n + 7$

2 Copy and complete:

For the linear sequence $u_n = an + b$, the values of $\Delta 1$ are ......

3 Copy and complete the difference table for the general linear sequence $u_n = an + b$:

n	1	2	3	4	5
u_n	$(a + b)$	$2a + b$	$3a + b$	......	......
$\Delta 1$		(a)	......	......	......

4 The circled entries of the difference table above can be used to find u_n.

For example, in the original example on the previous page, $a = 3$ and $a + b = 5$.

$\therefore$ $u_n = 3n + 2$.

Use the difference method to find the general term $u_n = an + b$ for the sequence:

a 4, 11, 18, 25, 32, 39, ...   **b** 41, 37, 33, 29, 25, 21, ...

Part 2:   Quadratic sequences

Now consider the quadratic sequence $u_n = 2n^2 - n + 3$.

Its terms are: $u_1 = 4$, $u_2 = 9$, $u_3 = 18$, $u_4 = 31$, $u_5 = 48$, $u_6 = 69$, ...

We again construct a difference table, and this time we include an extra row for the **second difference** $\Delta 2$. This is the difference between consecutive terms of the first difference row.

n	1	2	3	4	5	6
u_n	4	9	18	31	48	69
$\Delta 1$		5	9	13	17	21
$\Delta 2$			4	4	4	4

What to do:

1 Construct a difference table for the quadratic sequence defined by:

a $u_n = n^2 + 2n + 3$ **b** $u_n = -n^2 + 5n + 4$

2 Copy and complete:

For the quadratic sequence $u_n = an^2 + bn + c$, the values of $\Delta 2$ are ......

3 Copy and complete the difference table for the general quadratic sequence $u_n = an^2 + bn + c$:

n	1	2	3	4	5	6
u_n	$(a + b + c)$	$4a + 2b + c$	$9a + 3b + c$	......	......	......
$\Delta 1$	$(3a + b)$	$5a + b$	......	......	......	
$\Delta 2$	$(2a)$	......	......	......		

4 Describe how the circled entries in the difference table above can be used to find the formula for u_n.

5 Use the difference method to find the general term $u_n = an^2 + bn + c$ for the sequence:

a 2, 0, 0, 2, 6, ...   **b** −5, 4, 19, 40, 67, ...

Part 3:   Cubic sequences

What to do:

1 Consider the general cubic sequence $u_n = an^3 + bn^2 + cn + d$.
Construct a difference table for $n = 1, 2, 3, 4, 5$.
Include rows for $\Delta 1$, $\Delta 2$, and $\Delta 3$. Record your observations.

2 Describe how your difference table can be used to find the formula for u_n.

3 Use the difference method to find the general term $u_n = an^3 + bn^2 + cn + d$ for the sequence
15, 27, 35, 33, 15, ...

You should have discovered that:

- For the **linear sequence** $u_n = an + b$, the **first differences** are constant
  and equal to a.
  The general difference table is:

We use the circled terms to find the unknowns in u_n.

n	1	2	3	4	5
u_n	$a+b$	$2a+b$	$3a+b$	$4a+b$	$5a+b$
$\Delta 1$		a	a	a	a

- For the **quadratic sequence** $u_n = an^2 + bn + c$, the **second differences** are constant and equal to $2a$.
  The general difference table is:

n	1	2	3	4
u_n	$a+b+c$	$4a+2b+c$	$9a+3b+c$	$16a+4b+c$
$\Delta 1$		$3a+b$	$5a+b$	$7a+b$
$\Delta 2$			$2a$	$2a$

- For the **cubic sequence** $u_n = an^3 + bn^2 + cn + d$, the **third differences** are constant and equal to $6a$.
  The general difference table is:

n	1	2	3	4
u_n	$a+b+c+d$	$8a+4b+2c+d$	$27a+9b+3c+d$	$64a+16b+4c+d$
$\Delta 1$		$7a+3b+c$	$19a+5b+c$	$37a+7b+c$
$\Delta 2$			$12a+2b$	$18a+2b$
$\Delta 3$				$6a$

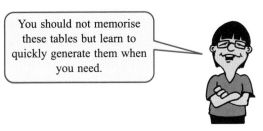

You should not memorise these tables but learn to quickly generate them when you need.

Example 6

Consider the sequence of triangular numbers:

a   How many dots are in the next *two* figures?

b   Use the difference method to find a formula for u_n, the number of dots in the nth figure.

a

15 dots   21 dots

b $u_1 = 1$, $u_2 = 3$, $u_3 = 6$, $u_4 = 10$, $u_5 = 15$, $u_6 = 21$

The difference table is:

n	1	2	3	4	5	6
u_n	①	3	6	10	15	21
$\Delta 1$	②	3	4	5	6	
$\Delta 2$		①	1	1	1	

The $\Delta 2$ values are constant, so the sequence is quadratic with general term $u_n = an^2 + bn + c$.

Using the general difference table: $2a = 1$, so $a = \frac{1}{2}$

$3a + b = 2$, so $\frac{3}{2} + b = 2$ and $\therefore$ $b = \frac{1}{2}$

$a + b + c = 1$, so $\frac{1}{2} + \frac{1}{2} + c = 1$ and $\therefore$ $c = 0$

$\therefore$ the general term is $u_n = \frac{1}{2}n^2 + \frac{1}{2}n$

Example 7

Use the difference method to find a formula for the general term u_n of the sequence:
-6, -4, 10, 42, 98, 184, ...

The difference table is:

n	1	2	3	4	5	6
u_n	−6	−4	10	42	98	184
$\Delta 1$	②	14	32	56	86	
$\Delta 2$		⑫	18	24	30	
$\Delta 3$			⑥	6	6	

The $\Delta 3$ values are constant, so the sequence is cubic with general term $u_n = an^3 + bn^2 + cn + d$.

Using the general difference table: $6a = 6$, so $a = 1$

$12a + 2b = 12$, so $12 + 2b = 12$ and $\therefore$ $b = 0$

$7a + 3b + c = 2$, so $7 + c = 2$ and $\therefore$ $c = -5$

$a + b + c + d = -6$, so $1 - 5 + d = -6$ and $\therefore$ $d = -2$

$\therefore$ the general term is $u_n = n^3 - 5n - 2$

To save remembering or writing out the general difference tables, it is often more practical to only use the difference table to identify the *form* of the sequence.

You can then use the **quadratic** or **cubic regression** functions on your graphics calculator to find the coefficients.

GRAPHICS
CALCULATOR
INSTRUCTIONS

EXERCISE 27D

1 Use the difference method to find the general term u_n of each sequence:

    a 1, 5, 9, 13, 17, 21, ...

    b 17, 14, 11, 8, 5, 2, ...

    c 2, 6, 12, 20, 30, 42, ...

    d 0, 6, 14, 24, 36, 50, ...

    e 6, 13, 32, 69, 130, 221, 348, ...

    f 2, 7, 18, 38, 70, 117, 182, ...

2 Consider the sequence: 2, 12, 30, 56, 90, 132, ...

    a Use the difference method to find the general term u_n.

    b Suggest an alternative formula for u_n by considering $u_1 = 1 \times 2$, $u_2 = \ldots\ldots \times \ldots\ldots$, $u_3 = \ldots\ldots \times \ldots\ldots$, and so on.

3 Consider the dot pattern:

 , , , , ...

    Let u_n be the number of dots in the nth figure of the pattern.

    a Find u_n for $n = 1, 2, 3, 4, 5, 6$, and 7.

    b Find a formula for the general term u_n.

    c How many dots are needed to make up the 30th figure in the pattern?

4 These diagrams represent the handshakes between two people (A and B), three people (A, B, and C), four people (A, B, C, and D), and so on.

A —— B

1 handshake

   3 handshakes

   6 handshakes

   10 handshakes

    a Draw diagrams showing handshakes for 6 and 7 people.

    b When you are sure that you have counted them correctly, find the formula for the general term u_n of the sequence 1, 3, 6, 10, ...

    c Suppose 179 delegates attend a conference. If every person shakes hands with every other person, how many handshakes take place?

5 Consider the sequence u_n where:
$$u_1 = 1 \times 3$$
$$u_2 = 1 \times 3 + 2 \times 5$$
$$u_3 = 1 \times 3 + 2 \times 5 + 3 \times 7$$
$$u_4 = 1 \times 3 + 2 \times 5 + 3 \times 7 + 4 \times 9 \quad \text{and so on.}$$

    a Find the values of u_1, u_2, u_3, u_4, u_5, and u_6.

    b Use the difference method to find a formula for u_n.

    c Hence, find the value of u_{50}.

6 Consider the **Opening Problem** on page **457**.

Notice that: $u_1 = 1^2$

$u_2 = 1^2 + 2^2$

$u_3 = 1^2 + 2^2 + 3^2$

$u_4 = 1^2 + 2^2 + 3^2 + 4^2$

a Find u_n for $n = 1, 2, 3, 4, 5, 6$, and 7.

b Use the difference method to find a formula for u_n.

c How many squares are contained in a 100×100 grid?

7 Consider the pattern: , , , , ...

Suppose u_n is the number of squares contained in the nth figure, so $u_1 = 2$ and $u_2 = 6 + 2 = 8$.

a Find the values of u_3, u_4, u_5, and u_6.   **b** Find a formula for u_n.

c How many squares are contained in the 15th figure?

Activity   *The Fibonacci sequence*

Click on the icon to obtain this Activity.

THE FIBONACCI
SEQUENCE

Review set 27A

1 Write down a rule for the sequence, and find its next two terms:

a 6, 10, 14, 18, 22, ...   **b** 810, 270, 90, 30, ...

2 Draw the next two matchstick figures in the pattern, and write down the number of matchsticks used as a number sequence:

a

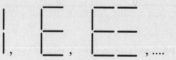

b

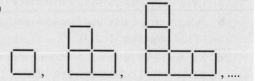

3 Find the first four terms of the sequence with nth term:

a $u_n = 6n - 1$ **b** $u_n = n^2 + 5n - 2$

4 **a** Write a formula for the general term u_n of the sequence: 4, 8, 12, 16, ...

b Hence find the general term u_n for the sequence:

i 1, 5, 9, 13, ...   **ii** $\frac{1}{3}, \frac{1}{7}, \frac{1}{11}, \frac{1}{15}$, ...

c Find the 20th term for each of the sequences in **b**.

5 List the first four terms of the geometric sequence defined by:

   a $u_n = 27 \times \left(\frac{2}{3}\right)^n$ **b** $u_n = 5 \times (-2)^{n-1}$

6 Write a formula for the general term u_n of the sequence:

   a 3, 12, 48, 192, ...   **b** 88, −44, 22, −11, ...

7 Use the difference method to find the general term u_n of:

   a 5, 12, 19, 26, 33, ...   **b** −1, 6, 15, 26, 39, 54, ...

8 Consider the sequence of figures:

 , , , ...

   Suppose u_n is the number of triangles in the nth figure, so $u_1 = 1$ and $u_2 = 5$.

   a Find u_n for $n = 3, 4, 5$.

   b Use the difference method to find a formula for u_n.

   c How many triangles are in the 50th figure?

9 Consider the sequence 6, 24, 60, 120, 210, 336, ...

   a Use the difference method to find a formula for the general term u_n.

   b Suggest an alternative formula for u_n by considering $u_1 = 1 \times 2 \times 3$, $u_2 = \ldots\ldots \times \ldots\ldots \times \ldots\ldots$,
       $u_3 = \ldots\ldots \times \ldots\ldots \times \ldots\ldots$, and so on.

10 Sarah has baked a cake, and wishes to divide it into pieces using straight line cuts.

                   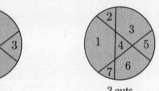

         1 cut   2 cuts   3 cuts

   Suppose u_n is the maximum number of pieces which can be made from n cuts, so $u_1 = 2$, $u_2 = 4$,
   and $u_3 = 7$.

   a Find u_4 and u_5.

   b Use the difference method to find a formula for u_n.

   c What is the maximum number of pieces Sarah can make from 10 cuts?

Review set 27B

1 Write down a rule for the sequence, and find its next two terms:

   a 17, 12, 7, 2, ...   **b** −2, 4, −8, 16, ...

2 Draw the next two figures, and write down the number of dots used as a number sequence:

   a   **b**

3 Find the first four terms of the sequence with nth term:

    a $u_n = -4n + 5$ **b** $u_n = (n + 2)(n - 1)$

4 **a** Write a formula for the general term u_n of the sequence: 16, 22, 28, 34, ...

    b Hence find the general term u_n for the sequence:

        i 10, 16, 22, 28, ...   **ii** $\frac{5}{7}, \frac{11}{13}, \frac{17}{19}, \frac{23}{25}$, ...

    c Find the 15th term for each of the sequences in **b**.

5 Write a formula for the general term u_n of the sequence:

    a 2, 5, 10, 17, 26, ...   **b** $\frac{1}{1}, \frac{1}{8}, \frac{1}{27}, \frac{1}{64}$, ...

6 List the first *four* terms of the general sequence defined by:

    a $u_n = 5 \times 3^{n-1}$ **b** $u_n = 48 \times \left(-\frac{1}{4}\right)^n$

7 Find a formula for the nth term of the sequence:

    a 4, -12, 36, -108, ...   **b** 224, 56, 14, $3\frac{1}{2}$, ...

8 Use the difference method to find the general term u_n of:

    a 43, 34, 25, 16, 7, ...   **b** 4, 12, 22, 34, 48, ...

9 Consider the sequence of figures:

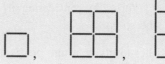

Suppose u_n is the number of matchsticks required to make the nth figure, so $u_1 = 4$ and $u_2 = 12$.

    a Find u_n for $n = 3, 4, 5, 6$.

    b Use the difference method to find a formula for u_n.

    c How many matches are in the 10th figure?

10 Consider the sequence of figures:

  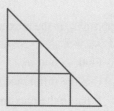

Suppose u_n is the number of rectangles present in the nth figure, so, $u_1 = 0$, $u_2 = 1$, and $u_3 = 5$.

    a Show that $u_4 = 15$, $u_5 = 35$, and $u_6 = 70$.

    b Use the difference method to show that the number of rectangles forms a *quartic* sequence of the form $u_n = an^4 + bn^3 + cn^2 + dn + e$.

    c Use technology to find the quartic model that fits the data. Give the quartic in the form $an^4 + bn^3 + cn^2 + dn + e$, where $a, b, c, d, e \in \mathbb{Q}$.

Exponentials

28

Contents:

A	Rational exponents	[E1.9, E2.4]
B	Exponential functions	[E3.2]
C	Graphs of exponential functions	[E3.2, E3.3, E3.5, E3.8]
D	Exponential equations	[E2.11]
E	Problem solving with exponential functions	[E3.2]
F	Exponential modelling	[E3.3]

Opening problem

A lotus plant initially covers an area of 40 cm^2. The area it covers increases by 20% each week.

Things to think about:

a Does the area covered by the plant increase by a constant amount each week?

b Can you explain why the area covered by the lotus plant after n weeks is given by the function $A(n) = 40 \times 1.2^n$ cm^2?

c What does the graph of $A(n)$ look like?

d What area is covered by the lotus plant after 3 weeks?

e How long will it take for the plant to cover an area of 100 cm^2?

A   RATIONAL EXPONENTS   [E1.9, E2.4]

In **Chapter 1** we studied **exponent laws**:

For all bases a, b and integers m, n:

- $a^m \times a^n = a^{m+n}$

- $\dfrac{a^m}{a^n} = a^{m-n}, \ a \neq 0$

- $(a^m)^n = a^{mn}$

- $(ab)^n = a^n b^n$

- $\left(\dfrac{a}{b}\right)^n = \dfrac{a^n}{b^n}, \ b \neq 0$

- $a^0 = 1, \ a \neq 0$

- $a^{-n} = \dfrac{1}{a^n}, \ a \neq 0$

- $\dfrac{1}{a^{-n}} = a^n, \ a \neq 0$

For *positive* bases, these laws can also be applied to rational exponents. This helps give meaning to values such as $5^{\frac{1}{2}}$ and $7^{\frac{1}{3}}$.

For $a > 0$, notice that $\quad a^{\frac{1}{2}} \times a^{\frac{1}{2}} = a^{\frac{1}{2}+\frac{1}{2}} = a^1 = a \quad$ {exponent laws}

and $\quad \sqrt{a} \times \sqrt{a} = a \quad$ also.

So, $\qquad a^{\frac{1}{2}} = \sqrt{a}$ $\qquad\qquad$ {by direct comparison}

Likewise $\quad a^{\frac{1}{3}} \times a^{\frac{1}{3}} \times a^{\frac{1}{3}} = a^1 = a$

and $\quad \sqrt[3]{a} \times \sqrt[3]{a} \times \sqrt[3]{a} = a$

suggests $\qquad a^{\frac{1}{3}} = \sqrt[3]{a}$

In general, $\qquad a^{\frac{1}{n}} = \sqrt[n]{a} \quad$ where $\sqrt[n]{a}$ reads "the nth root of a", for $n \in \mathbb{Z}^+$.

We can now determine that $\quad \sqrt[n]{a^m} = (a^m)^{\frac{1}{n}} = a^{\frac{m}{n}}$

$\therefore \qquad a^{\frac{m}{n}} = \sqrt[n]{a^m} \quad$ for $a > 0$, $n \in \mathbb{Z}^+$, $m \in \mathbb{Z}$.

Example 1 ◀) *Self Tutor*

Evaluate without using a calculator:

a $49^{\frac{1}{2}}$ $\qquad$ **b** $27^{-\frac{1}{3}}$ $\qquad$ **c** $8^{\frac{2}{3}}$ $\qquad$ **d** $32^{-\frac{2}{5}}$

a $49^{\frac{1}{2}} = \sqrt{49}$
$\quad\quad = 7$

b $27^{-\frac{1}{3}} = \dfrac{1}{27^{\frac{1}{3}}}$
$\quad\quad\quad = \dfrac{1}{\sqrt[3]{27}}$
$\quad\quad\quad = \frac{1}{3}$

c $8^{\frac{2}{3}} = (2^3)^{\frac{2}{3}}$
$\quad\quad = 2^{3 \times \frac{2}{3}}$
$\quad\quad = 2^2$
$\quad\quad = 4$

d $32^{-\frac{2}{5}} = (2^5)^{-\frac{2}{5}}$
$\quad\quad\quad = 2^{5 \times -\frac{2}{5}}$
$\quad\quad\quad = 2^{-2}$
$\quad\quad\quad = \frac{1}{4}$

In addition, the exponent laws can be applied for *negative* bases and rational exponents *provided* the denominator of the exponent is *odd*.

For example: $\quad (-8)^{\frac{1}{2}}$ has no real value.

$\qquad\qquad (-8)^{\frac{1}{3}} = \sqrt[3]{-8} = \sqrt[3]{(-2)^3} = -2.$

EXERCISE 28A

1 Evaluate without using your calculator:

a $16^{\frac{1}{2}}$ $\qquad$ **b** $16^{-\frac{1}{2}}$ $\qquad$ **c** $25^{\frac{1}{2}}$ $\qquad$ **d** $25^{-\frac{1}{2}}$

e $8^{\frac{1}{3}}$ $\qquad$ **f** $8^{-\frac{1}{3}}$ $\qquad$ **g** $27^{\frac{1}{3}}$ $\qquad$ **h** $27^{-\frac{1}{3}}$

i $81^{\frac{1}{4}}$ $\qquad$ **j** $81^{-\frac{1}{4}}$ $\qquad$ **k** $32^{\frac{1}{5}}$ $\qquad$ **l** $32^{-\frac{1}{5}}$

2 Evaluate, if possible:

    a $(-1)^{\frac{1}{2}}$
    b $(-1)^{\frac{1}{3}}$
    c $(-27)^{-\frac{1}{3}}$
    d $(-64)^{-\frac{1}{2}}$

3 Write in exponent form:

    a $\sqrt{10}$
    b $\dfrac{1}{\sqrt{10}}$
    c $\sqrt[3]{15}$
    d $\dfrac{1}{\sqrt[3]{15}}$

    e $\sqrt[4]{19}$
    f $\dfrac{1}{\sqrt[4]{19}}$
    g $\sqrt[5]{13}$
    h $\dfrac{1}{\sqrt[5]{13}}$

4 Evaluate without using a calculator:

    a $9^{\frac{3}{2}}$
    b $16^{\frac{3}{2}}$
    c $9^{\frac{5}{2}}$
    d $32^{\frac{2}{5}}$

    e $32^{\frac{3}{5}}$
    f $16^{-\frac{3}{2}}$
    g $16^{-\frac{3}{4}}$
    h $8^{-\frac{2}{3}}$

    i $25^{-\frac{3}{2}}$
    j $81^{\frac{3}{4}}$
    k $81^{-\frac{3}{4}}$
    l $125^{\frac{2}{3}}$

5 Evaluate to 3 significant figures:

    a $9^{\frac{2}{3}}$
    b $11^{\frac{3}{2}}$
    c $15^{\frac{5}{3}}$
    d $4^{-\frac{2}{3}}$
    e $27^{-\frac{5}{2}}$

B   EXPONENTIAL FUNCTIONS   [E3.2]

> An **exponential function** is a function in which the variable occurs as part of the exponent or index.

Examples of exponential functions are $f(x) = 3^x$, $g(x) = 2^{x-4}$, and $h(x) = 6 + 5^{-x}$.

Example 2   ◀)) *Self Tutor*

For the function $f(x) = 3 - 2^{-x}$, find:

    a $f(0)$
    b $f(3)$
    c $f(-x)$

    a $f(0) = 3 - 2^0$
      b $f(3) = 3 - 2^{-3}$
      c $f(-x) = 3 - 2^{-(-x)}$

          $= 3 - 1$
               $= 3 - \frac{1}{8}$
               $= 3 - 2^x$

          $= 2$
               $= 2\frac{7}{8}$

EXERCISE 28B

1 Determine whether the following are exponential functions:

    a $f(x) = 7^x$
    b $f(x) = x^4$
    c $f(x) = 5 - 3^{x-2}$

    d $f(x) = 10 \times 2^{\frac{x}{2}}$
    e $f(x) = 9x - x^6$
    f $f(x) = -2 - 5^{3x}$

2 For the function $f(x) = 3^x + 2$, find:

    a $f(0)$
    b $f(2)$
    c $f(-1)$
    d $f(2x)$

3 For the function $f(x) = 5^{-x} - 3$, find:

    a $f(0)$
    b $f(1)$
    c $f(-2)$
    d $f(-x)$

4 For the function $g(x) = 3^{x-2}$, find:

     a $g(0)$ **b** $g(4)$ **c** $g(-1)$ **d** $g(x+5)$

C | GRAPHS OF EXPONENTIAL FUNCTIONS
[E3.2, E3.3, E3.5, E3.8]

We can draw graphs of exponential functions using a table of values.

For example, the graph of $f(x) = 2^x$ is shown alongside.

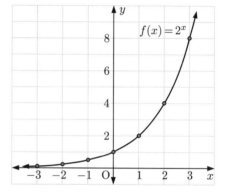

x	-3	-2	-1	0	1	2	3
y	$\frac{1}{8}$	$\frac{1}{4}$	$\frac{1}{2}$	1	2	4	8

Notice that:

- the y-intercept of the function is 1
- the graph lies entirely above the y-axis
- as the values of x get smaller, the values of y get closer and closer to zero, but never actually reach zero. We say that the line $y = 0$ is a **horizontal asymptote** of the function.

Discovery 1   *Simple exponential functions*

In this Discovery you will study simple exponential functions of the form $f(x) = a^x$ where $a > 0$, $a \neq 1$.

What to do:

1 Use technology to draw the graph of:

     a $f(x) = 1.3^x$ **b** $f(x) = 2^x$ **c** $f(x) = 3^x$ **d** $f(x) = 5^x$

     e $f(x) = 0.8^x$ **f** $f(x) = \left(\frac{1}{2}\right)^x$ **g** $f(x) = 0.3^x$ **h** $f(x) = 0.1^x$

GRAPHING
PACKAGE

2 What do you notice about:

     a the y-intercept of each graph   **b** the horizontal asymptote of each graph?

     Explain why this is the case.

3 For the graph of $f(x) = a^x$, what effect does a have on:

     a whether the graph is increasing or decreasing   **b** the steepness of the graph?

In the **Discovery** you should have found that:

> For all exponential functions of the form $f(x) = a^x$, $a > 0$, $a \neq 1$:
> - The y-intercept is 1, since $f(0) = a^0 = 1$.
> - The graph has the horizontal asymptote $y = 0$.

- If $a > 1$, the graph is **increasing**.

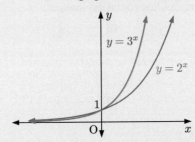

The rise towards infinity is steeper as a increases.

- If $0 < a < 1$, the graph is **decreasing**.

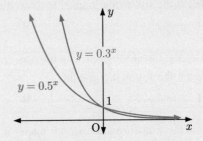

The fall from infinity is steeper as $\dfrac{1}{a}$ increases.

EXERCISE 28C

1 Use a table of values from $x = -3$ to $x = 3$ to help sketch these exponential functions:

   a $f(x) = 3^x$ **b** $f(x) = 4^x$ **c** $f(x) = \left(\frac{1}{2}\right)^x$ **d** $f(x) = \left(\frac{1}{3}\right)^x$

2 Use technology to graph the following functions on the same set of axes:

   $y = 5^x$, $y = 1.8^x$, $y = 0.7^x$, and $y = \left(\frac{2}{5}\right)^x$.

3 Match each function with the correct graph:

   a $y = 3.6^x$

   b $y = 0.9^x$

   c $y = 1.5^x$

   d $y = \left(\frac{1}{4}\right)^x$

   e $y = \left(\frac{2}{3}\right)^x$

   f $y = \left(\frac{5}{2}\right)^x$

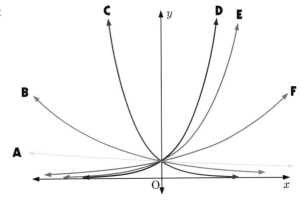

Example 3   ◀)) *Self Tutor*

Sketch the graph of: **a** $y = 2^x + 3$ **b** $y = 2 \times 3^{-x}$

a We translate $y = 2^x$ by $\begin{pmatrix} 0 \\ 3 \end{pmatrix}$.

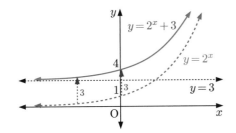

b We reflect $y = 3^x$ in the y-axis to give $y = 3^{-x}$, then stretch the result vertically with invariant x-axis and scale factor 2.

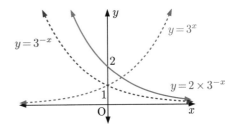

4 **a** State the transformation which maps $y = f(x)$ onto $y = f(x) + k$.

  b Sketch the following graphs, including the y-intercept and horizontal asymptote:

    i $y = 2^x - 1$ **ii** $y = 3^x + 2$ **iii** $y = \left(\frac{1}{2}\right)^x - 3$

5 **a** State the transformation which maps $y = f(x)$ onto $y = a\,f(x),\ a > 0$.

  b Sketch the following graphs:

    i $y = 3 \times 2^x$ **ii** $y = \frac{1}{2} \times 5^x$ **iii** $y = 4 \times \left(\frac{1}{2}\right)^x$

6 **a** State the transformation which maps $y = f(x)$ onto $y = f(x - h)$.

  b Sketch the following graphs:

    i $y = 2^{x-3}$ **ii** $y = 5^{x+2}$ **iii** $y = \left(\frac{1}{3}\right)^{x-1}$

7 **a** State the transformation which maps $y = f(x)$ onto: **i** $y = -f(x)$ **ii** $y = f(-x)$

  b Sketch the following graphs:

    i $y = -2^x$ **ii** $y = 2^{-x}$ **iii** $y = -\left(\frac{1}{3}\right)^x$

8 Translate $y = 2^x$ by $\begin{pmatrix} -1 \\ 3 \end{pmatrix}$ and graph its image.

9 Find and draw the image of $y = 2^{-x}$ under:

  a a reflection in the x-axis   **b** a reflection in the y-axis.

10 Find and draw the image of $y = 3^x$ under:

  a a stretch with invariant x-axis and scale factor 2

  b a stretch with invariant y-axis and scale factor $\frac{1}{3}$.

11 Consider $f(x) = 2^x$.

  a Find, in the form a^x:

    i $f(2x)$ **ii** $f(3x)$ **iii** $f(\frac{1}{2}x)$

  b Graph all four functions on the same set of axes.

12 For each function:

    i State the transformations which have been applied to $y = 2^x$.

    ii Sketch the graph including the y-intercept and horizontal asymptote.

  a $f(x) = 2 - 2^x$ **b** $f(x) = \dfrac{2^{-x} + 1}{3}$ **c** $f(x) = 2(2^{-x}) + 1$

13 Consider the functions $y = 3^{x-1}$ and $y = \frac{1}{3} \times 3^x$.

  a Draw $y = 3^{x-1}$ as a translation of $y = 3^x$.

  b Draw $y = \frac{1}{3} \times 3^x$ as a stretch with invariant x-axis and scale factor $\frac{1}{3}$.

  c Use the exponent laws to explain why the functions are the same.

  d Explain why a horizontal translation of $y = a^x,\ a > 0$, is always indistinguishable from a stretch with invariant x-axis.

14 Explain why $(-2)^x$ is undefined for some real numbers x.

Example 4   ◀》 *Self Tutor*

Find the values of a and k given this graph of $y = ka^x$.

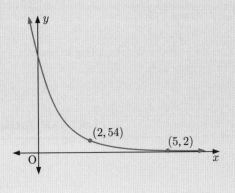

Substituting the given points,

$$ka^2 = 54 \quad \text{and} \quad ka^5 = 2$$

$$\therefore \ k = \frac{54}{a^2} \quad \text{and} \quad k = \frac{2}{a^5}$$

$$\therefore \ \frac{54}{a^2} = \frac{2}{a^5} \qquad \{\text{equating values of } k\}$$

$$\therefore \ 54a^5 = 2a^2$$

$$\therefore \ a^3 = \frac{1}{27}$$

$$\therefore \ a = \frac{1}{3}$$

Using $k = \frac{54}{a^2}$, $\quad k = 54 \times 9 = 486$

So, $a = \frac{1}{3}$ and $k = 486$.

15 The following graphs show functions of the form $y = ka^x$. Find the values of a and k for each graph.

a

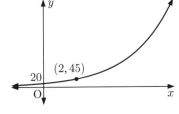

b

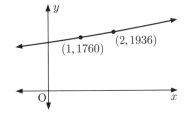

c

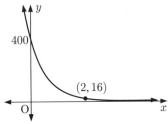

d

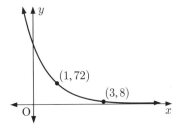

D EXPONENTIAL EQUATIONS   [E2.11]

An **exponential equation** is an equation in which the unknown occurs as part of the exponent or index.

For example: $2^x = 8$ and $30 \times 3^x = 7$ are both exponential equations.

To solve exponential equations, we try to write both sides of the equation with the **same base**. We can then **equate exponents**.

$$\text{If } a^x = a^k, \text{ then } x = k.$$

Example 5   ◀) *Self Tutor*

Solve for x: **a** $2^x = 32$ **b** $3^{x-2} = \frac{1}{9}$

a $2^x = 32$
$\therefore \ 2^x = 2^5$
$\therefore \ x = 5$ {equating exponents}

b $3^{x-2} = \frac{1}{9}$
$\therefore \ 3^{x-2} = 3^{-2}$
$\therefore \ x - 2 = -2$ {equating exponents}
$\therefore \ x = 0$

Example 6   ◀) *Self Tutor*

Solve for x: **a** $6 \times 3^x = 54$ **b** $4^{x-1} = \left(\frac{1}{2}\right)^{1-3x}$

a $6 \times 3^x = 54$
$\therefore \ 3^x = 9$
$\therefore \ 3^x = 3^2$
$\therefore \ x = 2$ {equating exponents}

b $4^{x-1} = \left(\frac{1}{2}\right)^{1-3x}$
$\therefore \ (2^2)^{x-1} = (2^{-1})^{1-3x}$
$\therefore \ 2^{2x-2} = 2^{3x-1}$
$\therefore \ 2x - 2 = 3x - 1$ {equating exponents}
$\therefore \ -2 + 1 = 3x - 2x$
$\therefore \ x = -1$

EXERCISE 28D

1 Solve for x:

a $3^x = 3$ **b** $3^x = 9$ **c** $2^x = 8$ **d** $5^x = 1$

e $3^x = \frac{1}{3}$ **f** $5^x = \frac{1}{5}$ **g** $2^x = \frac{1}{16}$ **h** $5^{x+2} = 25$

i $2^{x+2} = \frac{1}{4}$ **j** $3^{x-1} = \frac{1}{27}$ **k** $2^{x-1} = 32$ **l** $3^{1-2x} = \frac{1}{27}$

m $4^{2x+1} = \frac{1}{2}$ **n** $9^{x-3} = 3$ **o** $\left(\frac{1}{2}\right)^{x-1} = 2$ **p** $\left(\frac{1}{3}\right)^{2-x} = 9$

2 Solve for x:

a $5 \times 2^x = 40$ **b** $6 \times 2^{x+2} = 24$ **c** $3 \times \left(\frac{1}{2}\right)^x = 12$ **d** $4 \times 5^x = 500$

e $54 \times 3^{x+2} = 2$ **f** $7 \times \left(\frac{1}{3}\right)^x = 63$ **g** $2^{2-5x} = 4^x$ **h** $5^{x-1} = \left(\frac{1}{25}\right)^x$

i $9^{x-2} = \left(\frac{1}{3}\right)^{3x-1}$ **j** $2^x \times 4^{2-x} = 8$ **k** $3^{x+1} \times 9^{-x} = \left(\frac{1}{3}\right)^{x+1}$ **l** $2^{x^2-2x} = 8$

3 Suppose $a \times 5^n = 150$ and $a \times 10^n = 600$. Find a and n.

4 Suppose $b \times 2^t = 8$ and $b \times 6^t = 1944$. Find b and t.

5 Suppose $2^{x+3y} = 32$ and $3^{2x-y} = \frac{1}{81}$. Find x and y.

6 Use technology to solve for x, giving answers correct to 3 decimal places:

a $2^x = 100$ **b** $2^x = 0.271$ **c** $2^x = -3$ **d** $5^x = 8$

e $7^{-x} = 23$ **f** $9^x = 10\,000$ **g** $3^x = 0.006\,51$ **h** $5 \times 2^{-x} = 18$

i $200 \times 2^x = 5800$ **j** $300 \times 2^{-3x} = 4.1$ **k** $25 \times 3^{-2x} = 0.035$ **l** $4 \times 2^{-0.02x} = 0.07$

m $3^{x+1} = 4$ **n** $2^{3x-2} = 5$ **o** $3(2^{x-2}) = 1$

E   PROBLEM SOLVING WITH EXPONENTIAL FUNCTIONS   [E3.2]

Exponential functions model real life situations in many branches of science and commerce. Common applications include compound interest, population modelling, and radioactive decay.

Example 7

◀)) **Self Tutor**

The population of rabbits on a farm is given by the function $R = 50 \times (1.07)^n$ where n is the number of weeks after the rabbit farm was established.

a What was the original rabbit population?

b How many rabbits were present after 15 weeks?

c Sketch the graph of R against n for $n \geqslant 0$.

d How long will it take for the population to reach 500?

a When $n = 0$, $R = 50 \times (1.07)^0$
$$= 50 \times 1$$
$$= 50 \qquad \therefore \text{ there were 50 rabbits originally.}$$

b When $n = 15$, $R = 50 \times (1.07)^{15}$
$$\approx 137.95 \qquad \therefore \text{ there were 138 rabbits after 15 weeks.}$$

c

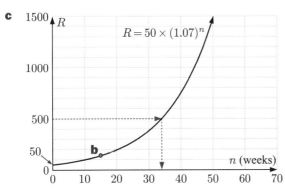

d We use technology to solve $50 \times (1.07)^n = 500$.

We find $n \approx 34.03$

∴ it will take about 34 weeks.

EXERCISE 28E

1 A local zoo starts a breeding program to ensure the survival of a species of mongoose. Using results from a previous program, the expected population in n years' time is given by $P = 40 \times 1.15^n$.

a What is the initial population purchased by the zoo?

b Find the expected population after:

    i 3 years   **ii** 10 years   **iii** 30 years.

c Sketch the graph of P against n for $n \geqslant 0$.

d How long will it take for the population to reach 100?

2 In Tasmania, a reserve is set aside for the breeding of echidnas. The expected population after t years is given by $P = 50 \times 1.26^t$.

    a What is the initial breeding colony size?

    b Find the expected colony size after: **i** 3 years   **ii** 9 years   **iii** 20 years.

    c Graph P against t for $t \geqslant 0$.

    d How long will it take for the population to reach 150?

3 In Uganda, the number of breeding females in an endangered population of gorillas is G_0. Biologists predict that the number of breeding females G in n years' time will grow according to $G = G_0 \times 1.01^n$.

    a There are currently 28 breeding females in the colony. Find G_0.

    b Predict the number of breeding females after: **i** 5 years   **ii** 10 years   **iii** 20 years.

    c Sketch the graph of G against n for $n \geqslant 0$.

    d Estimate the time it will take for the number of breeding females in the population to reach 200.

4 Boiling water is left in a pot to cool. After t minutes, its temperature is given by $T = 100 \times 0.84^t$ °C.

    a Find the initial temperature of the water.

    b Find the water temperature after: **i** 2 minutes   **ii** 10 minutes   **iii** 20 minutes.

    c Graph T against t for $t \geqslant 0$.

    d How long will it take for the temperature to fall to 48°C?

5 The weight of radioactive material in an ore sample after t years is given by $W = 2.3 \times 0.96^t$ grams.

    a Find the initial weight.

    b Find the weight after: **i** 20 years   **ii** 40 years   **iii** 60 years.

    c Sketch the graph of W against t for $t \geqslant 0$.

    d Find the percentage weight loss in the first 20 years.

6 The value of an investment in n years' time at 8.3% p.a. compound interest is given by $F = 5800 \times (1.083)^n$ dollars.

    a What was the original investment?

    b Find the value of the investment after: **i** 3 years   **ii** 10 years.

    c Find the time taken for the value of the investment to double.

7 After m months, the value of a washing machine is given by $V = 500(0.981)^m$ dollars.

    a What was the washing machine's original value?

    b How much is it worth after: **i** 6 months   **ii** 4 years?

    c How long will it take for the washing machine's value to reduce to \$150?

8 Answer the **Opening Problem** on page **471**.

9 A colony of bacteria is grown on an agar plate. Initially there are 5000 bacteria in the colony, and the population doubles every 8 hours.

The formula for the population of bacteria in the colony over time has the form $B = b \times 2^{mt}$ where B is the population, t is the time in days, and b, m are constants.

    a Find the value of b.   **b** Find the population after 8 hours.

    c Hence find the value of m.   **d** Sketch the graph of B against t for the first 2 days.

    e Use your formula to find the population of bacteria after 4 days.

    f Use technology to estimate how long it will take for the population to reach 500 000 bacteria.

Activity

Carbon dating

Click on the icon to obtain this Activity.

CARBON
DATING

F EXPONENTIAL MODELLING [E3.3]

In **Chapter 19** we saw how **linear regression** could be used to find a linear model connecting two related variables x and y. We used technology to find a **line of best fit** in the form $y = ax + b$.

In this Section we use technology to connect variables x and y related by an **exponential model** of the form $y = a \times b^x$.

For example, consider the relationship between two variables H and t given in the table of values below, and the scatter diagram alongside.

t	2	5	8	12
H	40	113	320	1280

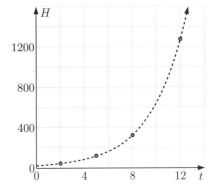

The relationship between H and t is clearly not linear. If a smooth curve is drawn through the points, we see it has the shape of an exponential function. We therefore perform **exponential regression** using technology.

For this data we find that $H \approx 20.0 \times (1.414)^t$.

In this case the **coefficient of determination** $r^2 \approx 1$, which indicates that the exponential model is an excellent fit for the data.

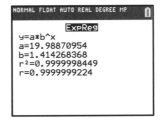

GRAPHICS
CALCULATOR
INSTRUCTIONS

To test whether two variables x and y are related by an exponential model of the form $y = a \times b^x$:

- Draw a scatter diagram of y against x.
  The trend of the data should look like: 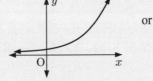 or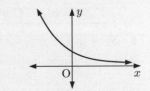

- Perform exponential regression using technology. The closer r^2 is to 1, the better the exponential model fits the data.

Example 8

◀》 *Self Tutor*

The weight W grams of bacteria in a culture was measured regularly. The results were:

Time (t days)	1	2	3	4	5
Weight (W grams)	11	20	35	62	118

a Use technology to show that an exponential model fits the data well.

b Find the exponential relationship between the variables.

c Use the model to estimate the original weight of the culture.

a The scatter diagram and $r^2 \approx 1$ suggest an exponential function is an appropriate model.

b $W \approx 6.09 \times 1.80^t$ grams

c When $t = 0$, $W \approx 6.09 \times 1.80^0$
$$\approx 6.09$$

So, the original weight was about 6.09 grams.

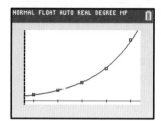

EXERCISE 28F

1 Show that an exponential function is appropriate for the following data, and state the equation of the exponential model.

a

x	2	5	10	20
P	44	100	401	6448

b

t	1	3	6	8	11
N	4.6	3.1	1.7	1.1	0.6

2 Over the last 8 years, Jane and Pierre have had their house valued four times.

Let t be the number of years since the year 2010.

Year	2010	2012	2015	2018
Value ($\$V$)	216 000	226 000	242 000	260 000

a Show that there is an exponential relationship between V and t, and find a formula for the relationship.

b Hence estimate the value of their house in the years: **i** 2014 **ii** 2022.

c Which of your estimates do you think is more reliable? Explain your answer.

3 The table below shows the concentration of a drug in the bloodstream of a patient at various times after an intravenous injection was administered.

Time (t minutes)	1	2	3	4	5	6	7
Concentration (C micrograms/ml)	104.6	36.5	12.7	4.43	1.55	0.539	0.188

a Show that an exponential model fits the data well, and find the model.

b Estimate how long it will be before the concentration falls to 2×10^{-4} micrograms/ml.

Review set 28A

1 Write in exponent form:

a $\sqrt{5}$ **b** $\dfrac{1}{\sqrt[3]{7}}$ **c** $\sqrt[4]{51}$ **d** $\dfrac{1}{\sqrt[5]{47}}$

2 Evaluate without using a calculator:

a $16^{\frac{3}{4}}$ **b** $125^{-\frac{1}{3}}$ **c** $9^{-\frac{3}{2}}$ **d** $32^{-\frac{3}{5}}$

3 Let $f(x) = 5^x$.

  a Express in the form $k \times a^x$:

    i $f(-x)$ **ii** $-f(x)$ **iii** $2 \times f(x)$ **iv** $f(2x)$

  b Sketch all five graphs on the same set of axes.

4 If $f(x) = 3^x - 1$, find the value of:

  a $f(0)$ **b** $f(3)$ **c** $f(-1)$ **d** $f(-2)$

5 Sketch the following graphs, including the y-intercept and horizontal asymptote:

  a $y = 2^x + 2$ **b** $y = 3^{-x} - 1$ **c** $y = 4 - 2^x$

6 Translate $y = 5^x$ by $\begin{pmatrix} -2 \\ -5 \end{pmatrix}$ and graph its image.

7 Find the values of a and k:

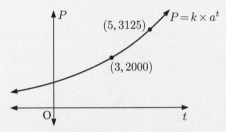

8 Solve for x:

  a $3^x = \frac{1}{81}$ **b** $2^{x-2} = \frac{1}{8}$ **c** $25^{4-x} = 1$

  d $4 \times 5^x = 100$ **e** $5 \times \left(\frac{1}{2}\right)^{x+1} = 80$ **f** $4^{x+1} \times 8^x = \frac{1}{4}$

9 Find k and n given that $k \times 2^n = 144$ and $k \times 8^n = 9$.

10 Solve for x, correct to 2 decimal places:

  a $5^x = 90$ **b** $3^{-2x} = 0.05$ **c** $20 \times 2^{0.2x} = 50$

11 Danielle writes an online blog. The number of people following her blog after t weeks is given by $N(t) = 10 \times 1.3^t$.

  a How many people are following Danielle's blog:

    i initially   **ii** after 4 weeks   **iii** after 8 weeks?

  b Sketch the graph of N against t for $t \geqslant 0$.

  c How long will it take for Danielle's blog to have 200 followers?

12 A conservationist is concerned that a local population of sea birds is declining. He carefully counts the number of chicks which successfully hatch every three years.

Year (t)	0	3	6	9	12
Number of chicks (N)	530	513	499	484	472

  a Fit a *linear* model to the data. Discuss whether you think this model is suitable.

  b Fit an *exponential* model to the data. Discuss the advantages of this model over the linear model.

  c Use your exponential model to estimate the number of chicks the conservationist will count in year 18.

Review set 28B

1 Evaluate, correct to 3 decimal places: **a** $\sqrt[3]{25}$ **b** $\sqrt[5]{100}$ **c** $\sqrt[4]{15.1}$

2 Evaluate without using a calculator: **a** $64^{-\frac{1}{3}}$ **b** $4^{\frac{5}{2}}$ **c** $64^{\frac{2}{3}}$ **d** $81^{-\frac{5}{4}}$

3 If $P(x) = 2 \times 3^{-x}$, find the value of:

  a $P(0)$ **b** $P(1)$ **c** $P(2)$ **d** $P(-1)$ **e** $P(-2)$

4 Suppose $f(x) = 2^x$.

  a Express in the form $k \times a^x$:

   i $f(-x)$ **ii** $f(2x)$ **iii** $f(x+1)$ **iv** $f(x-1)$

  b Sketch all five graphs on the same set of axes.

5 Sketch the following graphs:

  a $y = 5^{x-2}$ **b** $y = 3 \times 2^{-x}$ **c** $y = 2 - 2 \times 3^x$

6 **a** Sketch $y = 2^{-x}$ and its reflection in the line $y = x$.

  b Is the reflection the inverse function of $y = 2^{-x}$? Explain your answer.

7 Find the values of a and k:

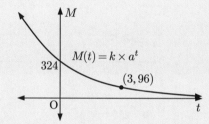

8 Solve for x:

  a $5^{x+1} = \frac{1}{25}$ **b** $27^{2x} = \frac{1}{3}$ **c** $8^x = 4^{5-x}$

  d $14 \times 9^{3-2x} = 14$ **e** $3 \times \left(\frac{1}{4}\right)^{x+1} = 96$ **f** $7^{x^2-x} = 49$

9 Suppose $3^{x-2y} = 27$ and $2^{2x+y} = \frac{1}{16}$. Find x and y.

10 Solve for x, correct to 2 decimal places:

  a $3^x = 20$ **b** $7^{2x} = -1$ **c** $12 \times 5^{-0.01x} = 10$

11 At the zoo, Terry the giant turtle is overweight. It is decided to put him on a diet. His weight t weeks after starting the diet is given by $W = 130 \times 3^{-0.01t}$ kilograms.

  a How much did Terry weigh before he was started on the diet?

  b How much weight will Terry have lost after:

   i 2 weeks   **ii** 6 weeks?

  c The keepers would like Terry to lose 20 kg. How long will it take to achieve this?

12 The value of an investment n years after it begins, is given by $P = 3500 \times (1.0375)^n$ dollars.

  a Find the initial investment.

  b Explain why this formula corresponds to a *compound* interest investment.

  c How many years will it take for the investment to reach $5000?

Logarithms

29

Contents:

A	Logarithms	[E3.10]
B	The logarithmic function	[E3.10]
C	Laws of logarithms	[E3.10]
D	Logarithms in base 10	[E3.10]
E	Logarithmic equations	[E3.10]
F	Solving exponential equations	[E3.10]

Opening problem

Tony invests \$8500 at 3.8% p.a. compounding annually. The interest rate is fixed for the duration of the investment. The value of the investment after n years is given by $V = 8500 \times (1.038)^n$ dollars.

Things to think about:

a How long will it take for Tony's investment to:

   i amount to \$12 000   **ii** double in value?

b Is there a way to solve this problem *other than* by drawing a graph?

In this Chapter we consider **logarithms** and how they are related to the exponentials we have just studied.

A   LOGARITHMS   [E3.10]

Given the exponential function $y = a^x$, we want a way to write x in terms of y. To do this, we define a function called a **logarithm**.

> If $y = a^x$ then we say "x is the **logarithm** of y in base a", and write this as $x = \log_a y$.

For example, since $8 = 2^3$ we can write $3 = \log_2 8$. These two statements are **equivalent**, and we can indicate this using the symbol $\Leftrightarrow$. We write: $2^3 = 8 \Leftrightarrow \log_2 8 = 3$.

In general, $y = a^x$ and $x = \log_a y$ are **equivalent** statements and we write: $\boxed{y = a^x \Leftrightarrow x = \log_a y}$

Example 1   ◀ッ **Self Tutor**

Write an equivalent:

a logarithmic statement for $4^{\frac{1}{2}} = 2$ **b** exponential statement for $\log_4 64 = 3$.

a $4^{\frac{1}{2}} = 2 \Leftrightarrow \log_4 2 = \frac{1}{2}$ **b** $\log_4 64 = 3 \Leftrightarrow 4^3 = 64$

EXERCISE 29A

1 Write an equivalent logarithmic statement for:

   a $3^2 = 9$ **b** $4^2 = 16$ **c** $5^2 = 25$ **d** $5^3 = 125$

   e $10^4 = 10\,000$ **f** $7^{-1} = \frac{1}{7}$ **g** $3^{-3} = \frac{1}{27}$ **h** $27^{\frac{1}{3}} = 3$

   i $5^{-2} = \frac{1}{25}$ **j** $2^{-\frac{1}{2}} = \frac{1}{\sqrt{2}}$ **k** $4\sqrt{2} = 2^{2.5}$ **l** $0.001 = 10^{-3}$

2 Write an equivalent exponential statement for:

   a $\log_2 8 = 3$ **b** $\log_2 1 = 0$ **c** $\log_5 625 = 4$ **d** $\log_2 \left(\frac{1}{2}\right) = -1$

   e $\log_2 \sqrt{2} = \frac{1}{2}$ **f** $\log_2 \left(\frac{1}{\sqrt{2}}\right) = -\frac{1}{2}$ **g** $\log_{\sqrt{2}} 2 = 2$ **h** $\log_9 3 = \frac{1}{2}$

Example 2   ◀ッ **Self Tutor**

Find the value of:

   a $\log_3 81$ **b** $\log_3(9\sqrt{3})$

a $\log_3 81$ **b** $\log_3(9\sqrt{3}) = \log_3(3^2 \times 3^{\frac{1}{2}})$

     $= \log_3(3^4)$ $= \log_3(3^{\frac{5}{2}})$

     $= 4$ $= \frac{5}{2}$

> The logarithm of 81 in base 3 is the exponent or power of 3 which gives 81.

---

3 Without using a calculator, find the value of:

   a $\log_{10} 100$ **b** $\log_2 8$ **c** $\log_3 3$ **d** $\log_4 1$

   e $\log_5 125$ **f** $\log_5(0.2)$ **g** $\log_{10} 0.001$ **h** $\log_2 128$

   i $\log_2 \left(\frac{1}{2}\right)$ **j** $\log_3 \left(\frac{1}{9}\right)$ **k** $\log_2(\sqrt{2})$ **l** $\log_2(\sqrt{8})$

   m $\log_7(\sqrt[3]{7})$ **n** $\log_2(4\sqrt{2})$ **o** $\log_{\sqrt{2}} 2$ **p** $\log_2 \left(\frac{1}{4\sqrt{2}}\right)$

   q $\log_{10}(0.01)$ **r** $\log_{\sqrt{2}} 4$ **s** $\log_{\sqrt{3}} \left(\frac{1}{3}\right)$ **t** $\log_3 \left(\frac{1}{9\sqrt{3}}\right)$

4 Rewrite as logarithmic equations:

   a $y = 4^x$ **b** $y = 9^x$ **c** $y = a^x$ **d** $y = (\sqrt{3})^x$

   e $y = 2^{x+1}$ **f** $y = 3^{2n}$ **g** $y = 2^{-x}$ **h** $y = 2 \times 3^a$

5 Rewrite as exponential equations:

    a $y = \log_2 x$ **b** $y = \log_3 x$ **c** $y = \log_a x$ **d** $y = \log_m b$

    e $T = \log_5 \left(\dfrac{a}{2} \right)$ **f** $M = \frac{1}{2} \log_3 p$ **g** $G = 5 \log_b m$ **h** $P = \log_{\sqrt{b}} n$

6 For each equation, make x the subject:

    a $y = \log_7 x$ **b** $y = 3^x$ **c** $y = (0.5)^x$ **d** $z = 5^x$

    e $t = \log_2 x$ **f** $y = 2^{3x}$ **g** $y = 5^{\frac{x}{2}}$ **h** $w = \log_3(2x)$

    i $z = \frac{1}{2} \times 3^x$ **j** $y = \frac{1}{5} \times 4^x$ **k** $D = \frac{1}{10} \times 2^{-x}$ **l** $G = 3^{x+1}$

7 Explain why, for all $a > 0$, $a \neq 1$:

    a $\log_a 1 = 0$ **b** $\log_a a = 1$

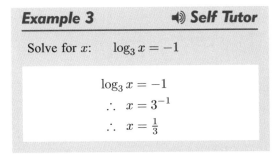

Example 3   ◀ⁱ) *Self Tutor*

Solve for x: $\log_3 x = -1$

$$\log_3 x = -1$$
$$\therefore x = 3^{-1}$$
$$\therefore x = \tfrac{1}{3}$$

8 Solve for x:

    a $\log_2 x = 2$ **b** $\log_5 x = -2$ **c** $\log_2(x + 2) = 2$ **d** $\log_5(2x) = -1$

B   THE LOGARITHMIC FUNCTION   [E3.10]

The exponential function $y = a^x$ is one-to-one, so it has an inverse.

The inverse function is a reflection of $y = a^x$ in the line $y = x$, and it is found by swapping the variables.

So, for the inverse function, $x = a^y$
$$\therefore y = \log_a x$$

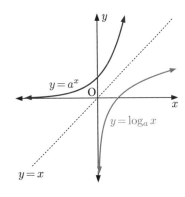

> The **logarithmic function** is $y = \log_a x$ where $a > 0$, $a \neq 1$.

Notice that:

- The domain of $y = a^x$ is $x \in \mathbb{R}$, so the range of $y = \log_a x$ is $y \in \mathbb{R}$.

- The range of $y = a^x$ is $y > 0$, so the domain of $y = \log_a x$ is $x > 0$.

- $y = a^x$ has horizontal asymptote $y = 0$, so $y = \log_a x$ has vertical asymptote $x = 0$.

- If $f(x) = a^x$ and $f^{-1}(x) = \log_a x$ then $f(f^{-1}(x)) = f(\log_a x) = a^{\log_a x} = x$
      and $f^{-1}(f(x)) = f^{-1}(a^x) = \log_a(a^x) = x$.

Example 4   ◀⑨ *Self Tutor*

Given $f(x) = 5^{-x}$:

a Find the inverse function $f^{-1}(x)$.

b Graph $y = f(x)$ and $y = f^{-1}(x)$ on the same set of axes.

a $y = 5^{-x}$ has inverse function $x = 5^{-y}$ **b**

$\quad\quad\quad \therefore \;\; -y = \log_5 x$

$\quad\quad\quad \therefore \;\; y = -\log_5 x$

$\quad\quad$ So, $f^{-1}(x) = -\log_5 x$

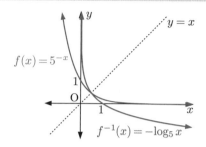

EXERCISE 29B

1 **a** Copy and complete this table of values for $f(x) = 2^x$.

x	-3	-2	-1	0	1	2	3
y							

  b *Hence* copy and complete this table of values for the inverse function $f^{-1}(x) = \log_2 x$.

y	-3	-2	-1	0	1	2	3
x							

  c Graph $f(x) = 2^x$ and $f^{-1}(x) = \log_2 x$ on the same set of axes.

  d State the equation of the asymptote of $f^{-1}(x)$.   **e** State the domain and range of $f^{-1}(x)$.

2 For each function $f(x)$:

  i   Find the inverse function $f^{-1}(x)$.

  ii Graph $y = f(x)$ and $y = f^{-1}(x)$ on the same set of axes.

  iii Describe the asymptotes of $y = f(x)$ and $y = f^{-1}(x)$.

  iv State the domain and range of $f(x)$ and $f^{-1}(x)$.

  a $f(x) = 4^x$ **b** $f(x) = 3^{-x}$

3 Find the inverse function $f^{-1}(x)$ for:

  a $f(x) = 10^x$ **b** $f(x) = 2 \times 3^x$ **c** $f(x) = \frac{1}{2}(3^{-x})$

  d $f(x) = \log_7 x$ **e** $f(x) = 3\log_2 x$ **f** $f(x) = 5\log_3 x$

C   LAWS OF LOGARITHMS   *[E3.10]*

Consider the following logarithms in base a where $a \neq 1$, $a > 0$:

- $\log_a(xy)$
  $= \log_a\left(a^{\log_a x} \times a^{\log_a y}\right)$
  $= \log_a\left(a^{\log_a x + \log_a y}\right)$
  $= \log_a x + \log_a y$

- $\log_a\left(\dfrac{x}{y}\right) = \log_a\left(\dfrac{a^{\log_a x}}{a^{\log_a y}}\right)$
  $= \log_a\left(a^{\log_a x - \log_a y}\right)$
  $= \log_a x - \log_a y$

- $\log_a(x^n)$
  $= \log_a\left((a^{\log_a x})^n\right)$
  $= \log_a\left(a^{n \log_a x}\right)$
  $= n\log_a x$

We summarise these observations as the **laws of logarithms**:

These rules correspond closely to the **exponent laws**.

For any base $a \neq 1$, $a > 0$:

$$\log_a(xy) = \log_a x + \log_a y \quad \text{for } x, y > 0$$

$$\log_a\left(\frac{x}{y}\right) = \log_a x - \log_a y \quad \text{for } x, y > 0$$

$$\log_a(x^n) = n \log_a x \qquad\qquad \text{for } x > 0$$

Example 5
◀)) **Self Tutor**

Write as a single logarithm:

a $\log_2 7 + \log_2 5 - \frac{1}{2} \log_2 3$ **b** $3 - \log_2 5$

a $\quad \log_2 7 + \log_2 5 - \frac{1}{2} \log_2 3$

$= \log_2 7 + \log_2 5 - \log_2 3^{\frac{1}{2}}$

$= \log_2(7 \times 5) - \log_2 \sqrt{3}$

$= \log_2\left(\frac{35}{\sqrt{3}}\right)$

b $\quad 3 - \log_2 5$

$= \log_2 2^3 - \log_2 5$

$= \log_2\left(\frac{8}{5}\right)$

$= \log_2(1.6)$

EXERCISE 29C

1 Write as a single logarithm:

a $\log_3 2 + \log_3 8$ **b** $\log_2 9 - \log_2 3$ **c** $3 \log_5 2 + 2 \log_5 3$

d $\log_3 8 + \log_3 7 - \log_3 4$ **e** $1 + \log_3 4$ **f** $2 + \log_3 5$

g $1 + \log_7 3$ **h** $1 + 2 \log_4 3 - 3 \log_4 5$ **i** $2 \log_3 m + 7 \log_3 n$

j $5 \log_2 k - 3 \log_2 n$

2 Suppose $\log_2 7 = p$ and $\log_2 3 = q$. Write, in terms of p and q:

a $\log_2 21$ **b** $\log_2\left(\frac{3}{7}\right)$ **c** $\log_2 49$ **d** $\log_2 27$

e $\log_2\left(\frac{7}{9}\right)$ **f** $\log_2 63$ **g** $\log_2\left(\frac{56}{9}\right)$ **h** $\log_2(5.25)$

3 For each equation, make y the subject:

a $\log_2 y = 3 \log_2 u$ **b** $\log_3 y = 3 \log_3 u - \log_3 v$

c $\log_5 y = 2 \log_5 u + 3 \log_5 v$ **d** $\log_2 y = u + v$

e $\log_2 y = u - \log_2 v$ **f** $\log_5 y = -\log_5 u$

g $\log_7 y = 1 + 2 \log_7 v$ **h** $\log_2 y = \frac{1}{2} \log_2 v - 2 \log_2 u$

i $\log_6 y = 2 - \frac{1}{3} \log_6 u$ **j** $\log_3 y = \frac{1}{2} \log_3 u + \log_3 v + 1$

4 Without using a calculator, simplify:

a $\dfrac{\log_2 16}{\log_2 4}$ **b** $\dfrac{\log_p 16}{\log_p 4}$ **c** $\dfrac{\log_5 25}{\log_5\left(\frac{1}{5}\right)}$ **d** $\dfrac{\log_m 25}{\log_m\left(\frac{1}{5}\right)}$

D   *LOGARITHMS IN BASE* 10   *[E3.10]*

Logarithms in base 10 are called **common logarithms** as they are used in many common scales, such as:
- the **Richter scale** for measuring the magnitude of earthquakes
- the **decibel scale** for measuring sound   • the **pH scale** for measuring acidity and alkalinity.

$\log_{10} x$ is often written as just $\log x$, and we *assume* the logarithm has base 10.

Discovery   *Calculating logarithms*

Logarithms were invented by **John Napier** (1550 - 1617) and first published in 1614.

For hundreds of years, logarithms could be found using a **slide rule** or found on tables created by people who had done huge amounts of manual calculation.

Fortunately, we can now evaluate logarithms rapidly using the [log] key on our calculator.

What to do:

1   Copy and complete, *without* using your calculator:

2   Use your calculator to find:

    a $\log 25$ **b** $\log 150$

    c $\log 1150$ **d** $\log 0.15$

x	x as a power of 10	$\log x$
10		
100		
1000		
100 000	10^5	$\log(100\,000) = 5$
0.1		
0.001		

3   Use the values you have calculated to complete:

For a number which in standard form is $a \times 10^k$, its logarithm will lie between the integers ......
and ......

4   Copy and complete, *without* using your calculator:

x	x as a power of 10	$\log x$
$\sqrt{10}$		
$\sqrt[3]{10}$		
$\sqrt{1000}$		
$\frac{1}{\sqrt{10}}$		

Now that we can calculate logarithms, we can write any positive number as a power of 10.

Example 6   ◄⑴ *Self Tutor*

Write as a power of 10:
  a 2   **b** 20

  a $2 = 10^{\log 2}$ **b** $20 = 10^{\log 20}$
        $\approx 10^{0.301}$ $\approx 10^{1.301}$

If the base for a logarithm is not given then we assume it is 10.

RULES FOR BASE 10 LOGARITHMS

$$\log(xy) = \log x + \log y$$

$$\log\left(\frac{x}{y}\right) = \log x - \log y$$

$$\log(x^n) = n \log x$$

Example 7

◄)) *Self Tutor*

Write as a single logarithm:

a $\log 2 + \log 7$ **b** $\log 6 - \log 3$ **c** $2 + \log 9$ **d** $\dfrac{\log 49}{\log\left(\frac{1}{7}\right)}$

a $\log 2 + \log 7$
$= \log(2 \times 7)$
$= \log 14$

b $\log 6 - \log 3$
$= \log\left(\frac{6}{3}\right)$
$= \log 2$

c $2 + \log 9$
$= \log 10^2 + \log 9$
$= \log(100 \times 9)$
$= \log 900$

d $\dfrac{\log 49}{\log\left(\frac{1}{7}\right)}$
$= \dfrac{\log 7^2}{\log 7^{-1}}$
$= \dfrac{2 \log 7}{-1 \log 7}$
$= -2$

EXERCISE 29D

1 Write as a power of 10:

   a 8   **b** 80   **c** 800   **d** 0.8   **e** 0.008

   f 0.3   **g** 0.03   **h** 0.000 03   **i** 50   **j** 0.0005

2 Write as a single logarithm in the form $\log k$:

   a $\log 6 + \log 5$ **b** $\log 10 - \log 2$ **c** $2 \log 2 + \log 3$

   d $\log 5 - 2 \log 2$ **e** $\frac{1}{2} \log 4 - \log 2$ **f** $\log 2 + \log 3 + \log 5$

   g $\log 20 + \log(0.2)$ **h** $-\log 2 - \log 3$ **i** $3 \log\left(\frac{1}{8}\right)$

   j $4 \log 2 + 3 \log 5$ **k** $6 \log 2 - 3 \log 5$ **l** $1 + \log 2$

   m $1 - \log 2$ **n** $2 - \log 5$ **o** $3 + \log 2 + \log 7$

3 Explain why $\log 30 = \log 3 + 1$ and $\log(0.3) = \log 3 - 1$

4 Without using a calculator, simplify:

   a $\dfrac{\log 8}{\log 2}$ **b** $\dfrac{\log 9}{\log 3}$ **c** $\dfrac{\log 4}{\log 8}$ **d** $\dfrac{\log 5}{\log\left(\frac{1}{5}\right)}$

   e $\dfrac{\log(0.5)}{\log 2}$ **f** $\dfrac{\log 8}{\log(0.25)}$ **g** $\dfrac{\log 2^b}{\log 8}$ **h** $\dfrac{\log 4}{\log 2^a}$

5 Without using a calculator, show that:

   a $\log 8 = 3 \log 2$ **b** $\log 32 = 5 \log 2$ **c** $\log\left(\frac{1}{7}\right) = -\log 7$

   d $\log\left(\frac{1}{4}\right) = -2 \log 2$ **e** $\log \sqrt{5} = \frac{1}{2} \log 5$ **f** $\log \sqrt[3]{2} = \frac{1}{3} \log 2$

   g $\log\left(\frac{1}{\sqrt{3}}\right) = -\frac{1}{2} \log 3$ **h** $\log 5 = 1 - \log 2$ **i** $\log 500 = 3 - \log 2$

E   LOGARITHMIC EQUATIONS   [E3.10]

The laws of logarithms can be used to write equations in different forms.

In particular:

- If both sides of an equation are positive, we can take the logarithm of both sides to remove powers.
- We can use exponentials to remove logarithms.

Example 8   ◀) Self Tutor

Write as a logarithmic equation in base 10:

a $y = a^3 b^2$ **b** $y = \dfrac{m}{\sqrt{n}}$

a $y = a^3 b^2$ **b** $y = \dfrac{m}{\sqrt{n}}$

$\therefore \ \log y = \log(a^3 b^2)$ $\therefore \ \log y = \log\left(\dfrac{m}{n^{\frac{1}{2}}}\right)$

$\therefore \ \log y = \log a^3 + \log b^2$

$\therefore \ \log y = 3\log a + 2\log b$ $\therefore \ \log y = \log m - \log n^{\frac{1}{2}}$

$\therefore \ \log y = \log m - \tfrac{1}{2}\log n$

EXERCISE 29E

1 Write as a logarithmic equation in base 10:

a $y = ab^2$ **b** $y = \dfrac{a^2}{b}$ **c** $y = d\sqrt{p}$

d $M = a^2 b^5$ **e** $P = \sqrt{ab}$ **f** $Q = \dfrac{\sqrt{m}}{n}$

g $R = abc^2$ **h** $T = 5\sqrt{\dfrac{d}{c}}$ **i** $M = \dfrac{ab^3}{\sqrt{c}}$

Example 9   ◀) Self Tutor

Write without logarithms:

a $\log D = 2x + 1$ **b** $\log N \approx 1.301 - 2x$

a $\log D = 2x + 1$ **b** $\log N \approx 1.301 - 2x$

$\therefore \ D = 10^{2x+1}$ $\therefore \ N \approx 10^{1.301 - 2x}$

or $D = 100^x \times 10$ $\therefore \ N \approx \dfrac{10^{1.301}}{10^{2x}} \approx \dfrac{20}{10^{2x}}$

---

2 Write without logarithms:

a $\log Q = x + 2$ **b** $\log J = 2x - 1$ **c** $\log M = 2 - x$

d $\log P \approx 0.301 + x$ **e** $\log R \approx x + 1.477$ **f** $\log K = \tfrac{1}{2}x + 1$

Example 10
◀) **Self Tutor**

Write these equations without logarithms:

a $\log C = \log a + 3 \log b$ **b** $\log G = 2 \log d - 1$

a $\log C = \log a + 3 \log b$

$\qquad = \log a + \log b^3$

$\qquad = \log(ab^3)$

$\quad \therefore \ C = ab^3$

b $\log G = 2 \log d - 1$

$\qquad = \log d^2 - \log 10^1$

$\qquad = \log\left(\dfrac{d^2}{10}\right)$

$\quad \therefore \ G = \dfrac{d^2}{10}$

3 Write without logarithms:

a $\log M = \log a + \log b$

b $\log N = \log d - \log e$

c $\log F = 2 \log x$

d $\log T = \frac{1}{2} \log p$

e $\log D = -\log g$

f $\log S = -2 \log b$

g $\log A = \log B - 2 \log C$

h $2 \log p + \log q = \log s$

i $-\log d + 3 \log m = \log n - 2 \log p$

j $\log m - \frac{1}{2} \log n = 2 \log P$

k $\log N = 1 + \log t$

l $\log P = 2 - \log x$

4 Solve for x:

a $\log x - \log 7 = 2 \log 2$

b $2 \log 5 + \log x = 3 \log 2$

c $\log_2 x + 3 = 4 \log_2 3$

d $2 \log x - 1 = \frac{1}{2} \log 36$

5 Use graphic methods on your calculator to solve the following correct to 3 significant figures:

GRAPHICS
CALCULATOR
INSTRUCTIONS

a $\log x = 3 - x$ **b** $\log(x - 2) = 2^{-x}$ **c** $\log\left(\dfrac{x}{4}\right) = x^2 - 2$

d $\log x = x - 1$ **e** $\log x = 5^{-x}$ **f** $\log x = 3^x - 3$

Example 11
◀) **Self Tutor**

Let $x = \log_2 11$.

a Write the equation without logarithms.

b Take the logarithm in base 10 of both sides of the equation from **a**.

Hence show that $\log_2 11 = \dfrac{\log 11}{\log 2}$, and evaluate this value.

a $\qquad x = \log_2 11$

$\quad \therefore \ 2^x = 11$

b $\qquad \log(2^x) = \log 11$

$\quad \therefore \ x \log 2 = \log 11$

$\quad \therefore \ \ x = \dfrac{\log 11}{\log 2}$

$\quad \therefore \ \log_2 11 = \dfrac{\log 11}{\log 2} \approx 3.46$

6 Let $x = \log_5 13$.

   a Write the equation without logarithms.

   b Take the logarithm in base 10 of both sides of the equation from **a**.

      Hence show that $\log_5 13 = \dfrac{\log 13}{\log 5}$, and evaluate this value.

7 Consider the exponential equation $a^x = b$ where $a, b > 0$.

   a Explain why $x = \log_a b$.   **b** Take the logarithm in base 10 of both sides of $a^x = b$.

   c Hence show that $x = \log_a b = \dfrac{\log b}{\log a}$.

   d Use this rule to calculate: **i** $\log_3 7$ **ii** $\log_2 40$ **iii** $\log_5 180$

F   SOLVING EXPONENTIAL EQUATIONS   [E3.10]

In question **7** of the previous Exercise, you should have shown that:

$$\text{If } a^x = b \text{ where } a, b > 0, \text{ then } x = \log_a b = \frac{\log b}{\log a}.$$

Example 12   ◀) Self Tutor

Use logarithms to solve for x, giving answers correct to 3 significant figures:

   a $2^x = 30$ **b** $(1.02)^x = 2.79$ **c** $3^x = 0.05$

   a $2^x = 30$ **b** $(1.02)^x = 2.79$ **c** $3^x = 0.05$

      $\therefore\ x = \dfrac{\log 30}{\log 2}$ $\therefore\ x = \dfrac{\log(2.79)}{\log(1.02)}$ $\therefore\ x = \dfrac{\log(0.05)}{\log 3}$

      $\therefore\ x \approx 4.91$ $\therefore\ x \approx 51.8$ $\therefore\ x \approx -2.73$

EXERCISE 29F

1 Solve for x, giving answers to 4 significant figures:

   a $10^x = 80$ **b** $10^x = 8000$ **c** $10^x = 0.025$

   d $10^x = 456.3$ **e** $10^x = 0.8764$ **f** $10^x = 0.000\,179\,2$

2 Solve for x, giving answers to 4 significant figures:

   a $2^x = 3$ **b** $2^x = 10$ **c** $2^x = 400$

   d $2^x = 0.0075$ **e** $5^x = 1000$ **f** $6^x = 0.836$

   g $(1.1)^x = 1.86$ **h** $(1.25)^x = 3$ **i** $(0.87)^x = 0.001$

   j $(0.7)^x = 0.21$ **k** $(1.085)^x = 2$ **l** $(0.997)^x = 0.5$

3 Solve for x, giving answers to 3 significant figures:

   a $2 \times 3^x = 10$ **b** $1.5 \times 2^x = 18$ **c** $4 \times 5^x = 27$

4 The weight of bacteria in a culture t hours after it has been established is $W = 2.5 \times 2^{0.04t}$ grams. After what time will the weight reach: **a** 4 grams   **b** 15 grams?

5 The population of bees in a hive t hours after it has been discovered is given by $P = 5000 \times 2^{0.09t}$.
After how many hours will the population reach:

   a $15\,000$ **b** $50\,000$?

6 Answer the **Opening Problem** on page **485**.

Review set 29A

1 Copy and complete:

   a $\log_a a^x = \boxed{}$ **b** $y = b^x \Leftrightarrow x = \boxed{}$

2 Find the value of:

   a $\log_2 16$ **b** $\log_3\left(\frac{1}{3}\right)$ **c** $\log_2 \sqrt{32}$ **d** $\log_4 8$

3 Write in terms of logarithms:

   a $y = 5^x$ **b** $y = 7^{-x}$

4 Write as exponential equations:

   a $y = \log_3 x$ **b** $T = \frac{1}{3}\log_4 n$

5 **a** On the same set of axes, sketch the graphs of $y = 2^{-x}$ and $y = -\log_2 x$.

   b What transformation maps $y = 2^{-x}$ onto $y = -\log_2 x$?

   c State the domain and range of $y = -\log_2 x$.

6 Find the inverse function $f^{-1}(x)$ of:

   a $f(x) = 4 \times 5^x$ **b** $f(x) = 2\log_3 x$

7 Write as a single logarithm:

   a $\log 12 - \log 2$ **b** $2\log 3 + \log 4$ **c** $2\log_2 3 + 3\log_2 5$

8 Let $\log_2 3 = a$ and $\log_2 5 = b$. Write in terms of a and b:

   a $\log_2 15$ **b** $\log_2\left(1\frac{2}{3}\right)$ **c** $\log_2 10$

9 Make y the subject of:

   a $\log_2 y = 4\log_2 u$ **b** $\log_5 y = -2\log_5 v$ **c** $\log_3 y = \frac{1}{2}\log_3 u + \log_3 v$

10 Write without logarithms:

   a $\log T = -x + 3$ **b** $\log N = 2\log c - \log d$

11 Use a graphics calculator to solve, correct to 4 significant figures:

   a $\log x = 3^{-x}$ **b** $\log(2x) = (x-1)(x-4)$

12 Find $\log_3 15$ correct to 4 decimal places.

13 Solve for x, giving your answers correct to 5 significant figures:

   a $4^x = 100$ **b** $4^x = 0.001$ **c** $(0.96)^x = 0.013\,74$

14 The population of a colony of wasps t days after discovery is given by $P = 400 \times 2^{0.03t}$.

   a Find the population after 10 days.

   b How long will it take for the population to reach 1200?

Review set 29B

1 Find the value of:

   a $\log_2 \sqrt{2}$ **b** $\log_2 \frac{1}{\sqrt{8}}$ **c** $\log_{\sqrt{3}} 27$ **d** $\log_9 27$

2 Write in terms of logarithms:

   a $y = 4^x$ **b** $y = a^{-n}$

3 Make x the subject of:

   a $y = \log_3 x$ **b** $T = \log_b(3x)$ **c** $3t = 5 \times 2^{x+1}$

4 Solve for x:

   a $\log_3 x = -2$ **b** $\log_7(2x) = 2$

5 **a** On the same set of axes, sketch the graphs of $y = 3^x$ and $y = \log_3 x$.

   b State the domain and range of each function.

   c Describe the asymptotes of each function.

6 Find the inverse function $f^{-1}(x)$ of:

   a $f(x) = 6^x$ **b** $f(x) = \frac{1}{2}\log_5 x$

7 Write as a single logarithm:

   a $\log_2 5 + \log_2 3$ **b** $\log_3 8 - \log_3 2$ **c** $2\log 5 - 1$ **d** $2\log_2 5 - 1$

8 Let $\log_3 7 = a$ and $\log_3 4 = b$. Write in terms of a and b:

   a $\log_3\left(\frac{4}{7}\right)$ **b** $\log_3 28$ **c** $\log_3\left(\frac{7}{3}\right)$

9 Make y the subject of:

   a $\log_2 y = 2\log_2 c$ **b** $\log_3 y = \frac{1}{3}\log_3 c - 2\log_3 d$

10 Write as a logarithmic equation in base 10:

   a $D = \dfrac{100}{n^2}$ **b** $G^2 = c^3 d$

11 Write without logarithms:

   a $\log M = 2x + 1$ **b** $\log G = \frac{1}{2}\log d - 1$

12 Solve for x:

   a $\log_3 x + 2 = -\log_3 5$ **b** $3\log x + 2\log 6 = \frac{1}{2}\log 9$

13 Find $\log_7 200$ correct to 3 decimal places.

14 The value of a rare banknote has been modelled by $V = 400 \times 2^{0.15t}$ dollars, where t is the time in years since 1970.

   a Estimate the value of the banknote in: **i** 1970   **ii** 2005.

   b How long will it take for the banknote to be worth \$100 000?

Advanced trigonometry

30

Contents:

A	The unit circle	[E8.2, E8.3]
B	The multiples of $30°$ and $45°$	[E8.2, E8.3]
C	The area of a triangle	[E8.6]
D	The sine rule	[E8.4]
E	The cosine rule	[E8.5]
F	Problem solving with the sine and cosine rules	[E8.1, E8.4, E8.5, E8.7]
G	Graphs from the unit circle	[E3.2, E8.8]
H	Trigonometric functions	[E3.2, E8.8]
I	Transformations of trigonometric functions	[E3.2, E3.3, E8.8]

Opening problem

A triangular property is bounded by two roads and a long, straight drain.

Things to think about:

a How can we define the trigonometric ratios for obtuse angles such as $120°$?

b Can you find:

i the area of the property in hectares

ii the length of the drain boundary

iii the angle that the Johns Road boundary makes with the drain boundary?

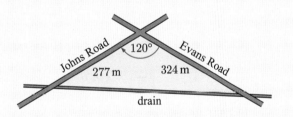

In **Chapter 22** we studied right angled triangle trigonometry, which required defining trigonometric ratios for acute angles.

We now extend our definitions to include *all* angles, and show how trigonometric ratios can be used in non-right angled triangles.

We will also see how the trigonometric ratios can be studied as functions.

A   THE UNIT CIRCLE   [E8.2, E8.3]

> The **unit circle** is the circle with radius 1 unit which is centred at the origin O. Its equation is $x^2 + y^2 = 1$.

SINE AND COSINE

Suppose P lies on the circle so that OP makes angle θ measured anticlockwise from the positive x-axis.

For any acute angle θ, notice that $\cos \theta = \dfrac{a}{1} = a$ and $\sin \theta = \dfrac{b}{1} = b$.

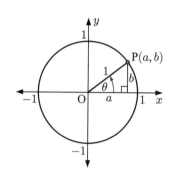

> For any point P on the unit circle which makes an angle θ measured anticlockwise from the positive x-axis:
> - The x-coordinate of P is the **cosine** of angle θ, written $\cos \theta$.
> - The y-coordinate of P is the **sine** of angle θ, written $\sin \theta$.

For example, consider the points on the unit circle alongside with coordinates defined in terms of trigonometric ratios.

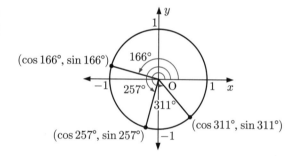

Note that:

- $-1 \leqslant x \leqslant 1$ and $-1 \leqslant y \leqslant 1$ for all points on the unit circle, so

$$-1 \leqslant \cos \theta \leqslant 1 \quad \text{and} \quad -1 \leqslant \sin \theta \leqslant 1 \quad \text{for all } \theta.$$

- θ is **positive** for anticlockwise rotations and **negative** for clockwise rotations.

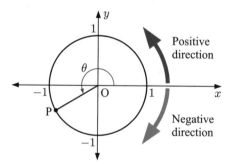

- Using the equation of the unit circle,

$$\cos^2 \theta + \sin^2 \theta = 1 \quad \text{for all } \theta.$$

Discovery 1   Supplementary angles

Supplementary angles are angles which sum to $180°$.

In this Discovery we consider the relationships between the trigonometric ratios of supplementary angles.

What to do:

1 Copy and complete the following table, giving answers correct
to four decimal places:

θ	$\cos\theta$	$\sin\theta$	$\cos(180° - \theta)$	$\sin(180° - \theta)$
$18°$				
$27°$				
$53°$				
$62°$				
$80°$				
$125°$				

Make sure your calculator is in degrees mode.

2 By considering the results in your table, suggest relationships between:

 a $\cos\theta$ and $\cos(180° - \theta)$ **b** $\sin\theta$ and $\sin(180° - \theta)$

3 To prove your suggestions in **2**, consider the diagram opposite.

State the coordinates of P' using:

 a the angle $(180° - \theta)$ from the positive x-axis

 b the reflection of P in the y-axis.

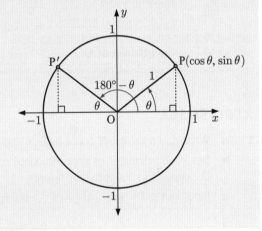

From the **Discovery**, you should have found that for any angle θ,

$$\cos(180° - \theta) = -\cos\theta$$
$$\sin(180° - \theta) = \sin\theta$$

TANGENT

If $P(\cos\theta, \sin\theta)$ is a point on the unit circle, the **tangent** of
the angle θ is the gradient of the line segment OP.

$\tan\theta = \dfrac{\sin\theta}{\cos\theta}$ for all angles θ.

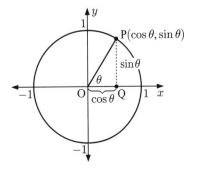

Example 1   ◀ੇ *Self Tutor*

a Find the coordinates of P and Q, rounded to
   3 decimal places.
b Find $\tan 212°$ and $\tan(-51°)$.
   Interpret their meaning.

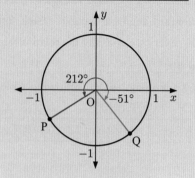

a P is $(\cos 212°, \sin 212°)$, which is
   approximately $(-0.848, -0.530)$.
   Q is $(\cos(-51°), \sin(-51°))$, which
   is approximately $(0.629, -0.777)$.

b $\tan 212° = \dfrac{\sin 212°}{\cos 212°} \approx 0.625$ is the

   gradient of OP.

   $\tan(-51°) = \dfrac{\sin(-51°)}{\cos(-51°)} \approx -1.235$ is

   the gradient of OQ.

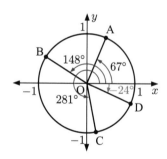

EXERCISE 30A

1 a Write down the exact coordinates of points A, B, C, and D.
    b Use your calculator to state the coordinates of A, B, C, and
       D, rounded to 3 significant figures.
    c Find $\tan 281°$ and $\tan(-24°)$. Interpret their meanings.

2 Use a unit circle to explain why:
    a $\cos 380° = \cos 20°$ b $\sin 413° = \sin 53°$ c $\sin 160° = \sin 20°$
    d $\cos 160° = -\cos 20°$ e $\cos 310° = \cos 50°$ f $\tan 25° = \tan 205°$

3 Use a unit circle diagram to find the values of:
    a $\cos 0°$ and $\sin 0°$ b $\cos 90°$ and $\sin 90°$
    c $\cos 360°$ and $\sin 360°$ d $\cos 450°$ and $\sin 450°$
    e $\cos(-90°)$ and $\sin(-90°)$ f $\cos(-180°)$ and $\sin(-180°)$

4 Find the obtuse angle which has the same sine as:
    a $26°$ b $45°$ c $69°$ d $86°$

5 Find the acute angle which has the same sine as:

   a 98°   **b** 127°   **c** 156°   **d** 168°

6 Find the obtuse angle whose cosine is the negative of:

   a $\cos 26°$ **b** $\cos 45°$ **c** $\cos 69°$ **d** $\cos 86°$

7 Find the acute angle whose cosine is the negative of:

   a $\cos 98°$ **b** $\cos 127°$ **c** $\cos 156°$ **d** $\cos 168°$

8 Determine whether $\cos\theta$, $\sin\theta$, and $\tan\theta$ are positive or negative for:

   a $\theta = 49°$ **b** $\theta = 158°$ **c** $\theta = 207°$ **d** $\theta = 296°$

   Use your calculator to check your answers.

9 The diagram alongside shows the 4 quadrants.
They are numbered anticlockwise.

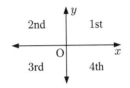

   a Copy and complete:

Quadrant	Degree measure	$\cos\theta$	$\sin\theta$	$\tan\theta$
1	$0° < \theta < 90°$	positive	positive	positive
2				
3				
4				

   b Determine the quadrants in which:

   i $\sin\theta$ is negative

   ii $\cos\theta$ is positive

   iii $\cos\theta$ and $\sin\theta$ are both negative

   iv $\cos\theta$ is positive and $\tan\theta$ is negative.

10 Show that $\tan(180° - \theta) = -\tan\theta$.

11

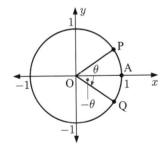

   a State the coordinates of point P.
   b Find the coordinates of Q using:

   i the unit circle

   ii symmetry in the x-axis.

   c What can be deduced from **b**?
   d Find the relationship between $\tan\theta$ and $\tan(-\theta)$.

12 Use a unit circle diagram to establish relationships between:

   a $\sin(180° + \theta)$ and $\sin\theta$ **b** $\cos(180° + \theta)$ and $\cos\theta$ **c** $\tan(180° + \theta)$ and $\tan\theta$.

13 Find the exact value of $\sin\theta$ if:

   a $\cos\theta = \frac{3}{5}$ and $0° < \theta < 90°$

   b $\cos\theta = \frac{1}{4}$ and $270° < \theta < 360°$

   c $\cos\theta = -\frac{3}{4}$ and $90° < \theta < 180°$

   d $\cos\theta = -\frac{5}{13}$ and $180° < \theta < 270°$

14 Suppose $180° < \theta < 270°$ and $\sin\theta = -\frac{3}{8}$.

   a Find the exact value of $\cos\theta$.

   b Hence, find the exact value of $\tan\theta$.

B　THE MULTIPLES OF $30°$ AND $45°$　[E8.2, E8.3]

MULTIPLES OF $45°$

Consider $\theta = 45°$.

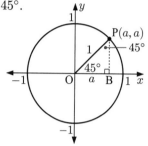

$\widehat{OPB}$ also measures $45°$, so triangle OBP is isosceles.

∴ we let $OB = BP = a$

Now $a^2 + a^2 = 1^2$ 　　{Pythagoras}

$\therefore a^2 = \frac{1}{2}$

$\therefore a = \frac{1}{\sqrt{2}}$ 　　{since $a > 0$}

∴ 　P is $(\frac{1}{\sqrt{2}}, \frac{1}{\sqrt{2}})$　where　$\frac{1}{\sqrt{2}} \approx 0.7$.

We can now find the coordinates of all points on the unit circle corresponding to multiples of $45°$ by using rotations and reflections.

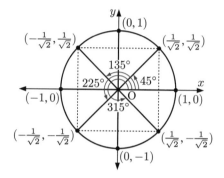

MULTIPLES OF $30°$

Consider $\theta = 60°$.

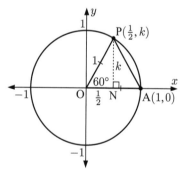

Since $OA = OP$, triangle OAP is isosceles.

Now $A\widehat{O}P = 60°$, so the remaining angles are therefore also $60°$. Triangle AOP is therefore equilateral.

The altitude PN bisects base OA, so $ON = \frac{1}{2}$.

If P is $(\frac{1}{2}, k)$, then $(\frac{1}{2})^2 + k^2 = 1$

$\therefore k^2 = \frac{3}{4}$

$\therefore k = \frac{\sqrt{3}}{2}$ 　{since $k > 0$}

∴ 　P is $(\frac{1}{2}, \frac{\sqrt{3}}{2})$　where　$\frac{\sqrt{3}}{2} \approx 0.9$.

We can now find the coordinates of all points on the unit circle corresponding to multiples of $30°$ by using rotations and reflections.

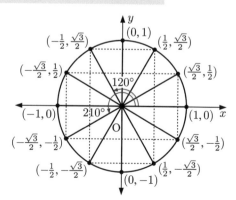

Summary:

- If θ is a **multiple of 90°**, the coordinates of the points on the unit circle involve 0 and ± 1.
- If θ is a **multiple of 45°**, but not a multiple of 90°, the coordinates involve $\pm \frac{1}{\sqrt{2}}$.
- If θ is a **multiple of 30°**, but not a multiple of 90°, the coordinates involve $\pm \frac{1}{2}$ and $\pm \frac{\sqrt{3}}{2}$.

We can calculate the **tangent** of any angle θ using $\quad \tan \theta = \dfrac{\sin \theta}{\cos \theta}$.

Example 2   ◀) Self Tutor

Use a unit circle diagram to find $\sin \theta$, $\cos \theta$, and $\tan \theta$ for:

a $\theta = 60°$ **b** $\theta = 150°$ **c** $\theta = 225°$

a
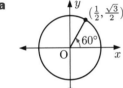

$\sin 60° = \frac{\sqrt{3}}{2}$

$\cos 60° = \frac{1}{2}$

$\tan 60° = \dfrac{\frac{\sqrt{3}}{2}}{\frac{1}{2}}$

$= \sqrt{3}$

b
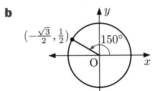

$\sin 150° = \frac{1}{2}$

$\cos 150° = -\frac{\sqrt{3}}{2}$

$\tan 150° = \dfrac{\frac{1}{2}}{-\frac{\sqrt{3}}{2}}$

$= -\dfrac{1}{\sqrt{3}}$

c
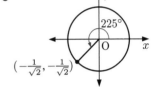

$\sin 225° = -\frac{1}{\sqrt{2}}$

$\cos 225° = -\frac{1}{\sqrt{2}}$

$\tan 225° = 1$

EXERCISE 30B

1 Use a unit circle to find $\sin \theta$, $\cos \theta$, and $\tan \theta$ for:

a $\theta = 30°$ **b** $\theta = 45°$ **c** $\theta = 135°$ **d** $\theta = 120°$

e $\theta = 210°$ **f** $\theta = 240°$ **g** $\theta = 315°$ **h** $\theta = 300°$

2 Without using a calculator, find the exact value of:

a $\sin^2 45°$ **b** $\cos^2 60°$ **c** $\tan^2 30°$

d $\cos^2(-30°)$ **e** $\sin^2 150°$ **f** $\tan^2 300°$

Check your answers using a calculator.

3 Use a unit circle diagram to find all angles between 0° and 360° which have:

a a sine of $\frac{1}{2}$ **b** a cosine of $\frac{\sqrt{3}}{2}$ **c** a sine of $\frac{1}{\sqrt{2}}$

d a sine of $-\frac{1}{2}$ **e** a sine of -1 **f** a cosine of $-\frac{\sqrt{3}}{2}$

g a tangent of 1   **h** a tangent of $\frac{1}{\sqrt{3}}$ **i** a tangent of $-\sqrt{3}$.

C   *THE AREA OF A TRIANGLE*   [E8.6]

We can use trigonometry to find the area of a triangle if we are given the lengths of **two sides**, as well as the **included angle** between the sides.

Consider triangle ABC in which the sides opposite angles A, B, and C are labelled a, b, and c respectively.

Suppose N lies on BC such that AN is perpendicular to BC.

In $\triangle$ANC, $\sin C = \dfrac{h}{b}$

$\qquad \therefore \ h = b \sin C$

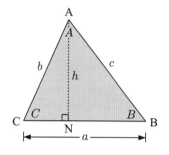

Since the area of $\triangle$ABC $= \frac{1}{2}ah$, we find: $\boxed{\textbf{Area} = \dfrac{1}{2}\textbf{\textit{ab}}\sin \textbf{\textit{C}}}$

If the altitudes from B and C were drawn, we could also show that the area is $\frac{1}{2}bc\sin A$ or $\frac{1}{2}ac\sin B$.

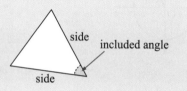

> The **area of a triangle** is:
>
> *"a half of the product of two sides and the sine of the included angle."*

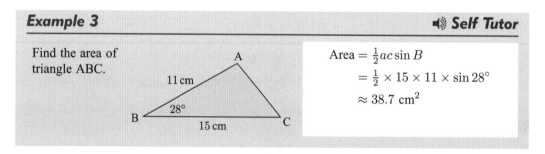

Example 3   ◄) *Self Tutor*

Find the area of triangle ABC.

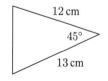

$$\text{Area} = \tfrac{1}{2}ac\sin B$$
$$\qquad = \tfrac{1}{2} \times 15 \times 11 \times \sin 28^\circ$$
$$\qquad \approx 38.7 \text{ cm}^2$$

EXERCISE 30C

1 Find the area of:

a
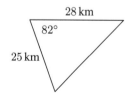

b
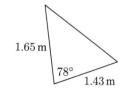

c

2 The proof of the area formula given above assumes that the included angle C is acute. Use the diagram alongside to prove that the formula is also true in the case where C is obtuse.
  Hint: $\sin(180^\circ - C) = \sin C$

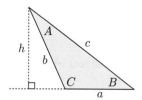

3 Find the area of:

a
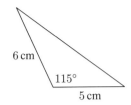

b
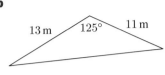

c
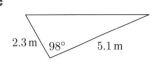

4 Find the area of:

a
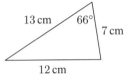

b
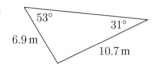

c
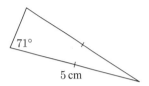

5 Find the area of a parallelogram with sides 6.4 cm and 8.7 cm, and one interior angle 64°.

6 Triangle ABC has area 150 cm².
Find the value of x.

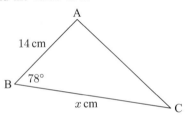

7 Triangle XYZ has area 80 cm².
Find the length of the equal sides.

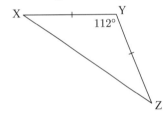

8 AB is the diameter of a circle with centre O and radius r.
Show that the shaded triangles have equal area.

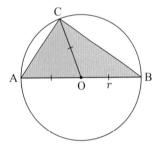

9 Triangle PQR has $\widehat{PQR} = \theta$. PQ = 10 m, QR = 12 m, and the area of the triangle is 30 m². Find the possible values of θ.

10 Triangle ABC has AB = 13 cm and BC = 17 cm, and its area is 73.4 cm². Find the measure of $\widehat{ABC}$.

11   **a**   Find the area of triangle ABC using:
  i angle A **ii** angle C

   b   Hence, show that $\dfrac{\sin A}{a} = \dfrac{\sin C}{c}$.

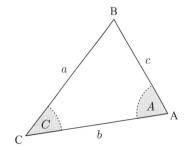

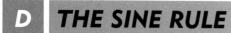

THE SINE RULE   [E8.4]

The **sine rule** is a set of equations that connects the lengths of the sides of any triangle with the sines of the opposite angles.

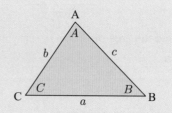

In any triangle ABC with sides a, b, and c units, and opposite angles A, B, and C respectively,

$$\frac{\sin A}{a} = \frac{\sin B}{b} = \frac{\sin C}{c} \quad \text{or} \quad \frac{a}{\sin A} = \frac{b}{\sin B} = \frac{c}{\sin C}.$$

Proof:

The area of any triangle ABC is given by $\frac{1}{2}bc\sin A = \frac{1}{2}ac\sin B = \frac{1}{2}ab\sin C$.

Dividing each expression by $\frac{1}{2}abc$ gives $\dfrac{\sin A}{a} = \dfrac{\sin B}{b} = \dfrac{\sin C}{c}$.

GEOMETRY
PACKAGE

FINDING SIDES

If we are given two angles and one side of a triangle, we can use the sine rule to find another side length.

Example 4   ◀) *Self Tutor*

Find x, rounded to 2 decimal places:

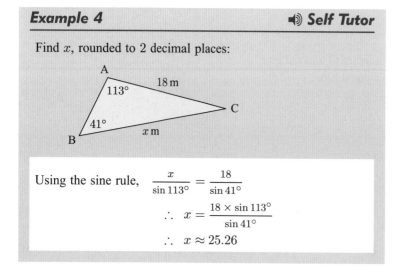

Using the sine rule, $\dfrac{x}{\sin 113°} = \dfrac{18}{\sin 41°}$

$$\therefore \quad x = \frac{18 \times \sin 113°}{\sin 41°}$$

$$\therefore \quad x \approx 25.26$$

We use the form
$$\frac{a}{\sin A} = \frac{b}{\sin B}$$
so that the unknown is in the numerator.

EXERCISE 30D.1

1 Find x, rounded to 2 decimal places:

a
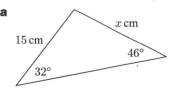

b
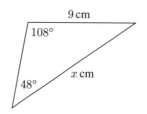

c
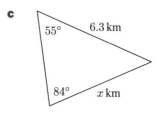

2 Find x:

a

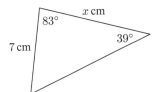

b

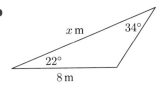

c

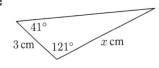

3 Find the area of this triangle.

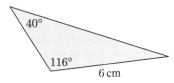

4 Consider triangle ABC.

  a If $A = 65°$, $B = 35°$, and $b = 18$ cm, find a.

  b If $A = 72°$, $C = 27°$, and $c = 24$ cm, find b.

FINDING ANGLES

Finding angles using the sine rule is more complicated than finding sides because there may be two possible answers.

In **Section A**, we saw that $\sin(180° - \theta) = \sin\theta$. This means that an equation of the form $\sin\theta = k$ has two solutions, $\theta = \sin^{-1} k$ and $\theta = 180° - \sin^{-1} k$.

We must examine both of the possible solutions to see whether each is feasible. Sometimes there is information in the question which enables us to **reject** one of the solutions.

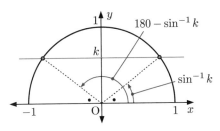

Example 5   ◀) *Self Tutor*

In triangle ABC, AB = 12 cm, AC = 8 cm, and angle B measures $28°$.
Find, rounded to 1 decimal place, the measure of angle C.

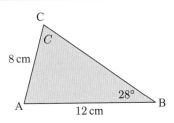

$$\frac{\sin C}{12} = \frac{\sin 28°}{8} \quad \{\text{sine rule}\}$$

$$\therefore \quad \sin C = \frac{12 \times \sin 28°}{8}$$

$$\text{Now} \quad \sin^{-1}\left(\frac{12 \times \sin 28°}{8}\right) \approx 44.8°$$

This is called the "ambiguous case".

Since the angle at C could be acute or obtuse, $C \approx 44.8°$ or $(180 - 44.8)°$

$$\therefore \quad C \approx 44.8° \text{ or } 135.2°$$

In this case there is insufficient information to determine the actual shape of the triangle.

The validity of the two answers in the previous Example can be demonstrated by a simple construction.

Step 1:   Draw AB of length 12 cm, and
construct an angle of 28° at B.

Step 2:   From A, draw an arc of radius
8 cm.

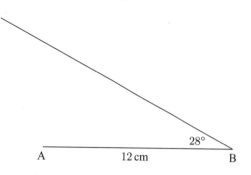

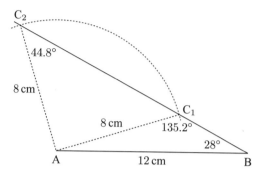

Example 6   ◀)) **Self Tutor**

In triangle KLM, LK̂M measures 52°, LM = 158 m, and KM = 128 m.
Find the measure of angle L.

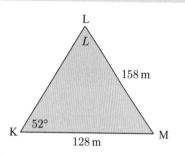

$$\frac{\sin L}{128} = \frac{\sin 52°}{158} \quad \{\text{sine rule}\}$$

$$\therefore \quad \sin L = \frac{128 \times \sin 52°}{158}$$

Now $\sin^{-1}\left(\frac{128 \times \sin 52°}{158}\right) \approx 39.7°$

$\therefore$ since L could be acute or obtuse,

$$L \approx 39.7° \quad \text{or} \quad (180 - 39.7)° \approx 140.3°$$

However, we can reject $L \approx 140.3°$ as $140.3° + 52° > 180°$ which is impossible.
$\therefore$ the angle $L \approx 39.7°$.

EXERCISE 30D.2

1 In triangle ABC, AB = 10 cm, BC = 7 cm, and CÂB measures 42°.

    a Find the two possible values for AĈB.

    b Draw a diagram to illustrate the two possible triangles.

2 In triangle PQR, PQ = 10 cm, QR = 12 cm, and RP̂Q measures 42°.

    a Show that there is only one possible value for PR̂Q, and state its measure.

    b Draw a diagram to demonstrate that only one triangle can be drawn from the information given.

3 The following diagrams are not drawn to scale, but the information on them is correct.
Find the value of θ:

    a

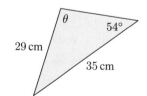

    b

There may be
two possible
solutions.

c

2.4 km   6.4 km θ 15°

d

8.2 m   6.9 m θ 51°

4 Consider triangle ABC. Find the measure of:

   a angle A if $a = 12.6$ cm, $b = 15.1$ cm, and $\widehat{ABC} = 65°$

   b angle B if $b = 38.4$ cm, $c = 27.6$ cm, and $\widehat{ACB} = 43°$

   c angle C if $a = 5.5$ km, $c = 4.1$ km, and $\widehat{BAC} = 71°$.

E | *THE COSINE RULE*   *[E8.5]*

The **cosine rule** relates the three sides of a triangle and one of its angles.

Consider triangle ABC with side lengths a, b, and c as shown.

Using Pythagoras' theorem in $\triangle$BCN,

$$a^2 = h^2 + (c - x)^2$$
$$\therefore \ \ a^2 = h^2 + c^2 - 2cx + x^2$$

In $\triangle$ACN, $b^2 = h^2 + x^2$ and so $h^2 = b^2 - x^2$

   Thus, $a^2 = (b^2 - x^2) + c^2 - 2cx + x^2$

      $\therefore \ \ a^2 = b^2 + c^2 - 2cx$

In $\triangle$ACN, $\cos A = \dfrac{x}{b}$ and so $x = b\cos A$

      $\therefore \ \ a^2 = b^2 + c^2 - 2bc\cos A$

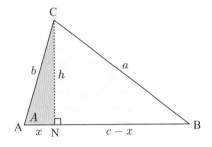

In any triangle ABC with sides a, b, and c units, and opposite angles A, B, and C respectively,

$$a^2 = b^2 + c^2 - 2bc\cos A$$
$$b^2 = a^2 + c^2 - 2ac\cos B$$
$$c^2 = a^2 + b^2 - 2ab\cos C.$$

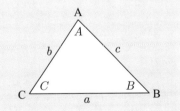

GEOMETRY
PACKAGE

Activity

Prove the **cosine rule** $a^2 = b^2 + c^2 - 2bc\cos A$
in the case where A is obtuse.

Hint: $\cos(180° - A) = -\cos A$

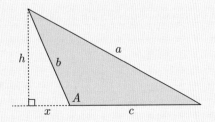

If we are given two sides of a triangle and the included angle, we can use the cosine rule to find the third side.

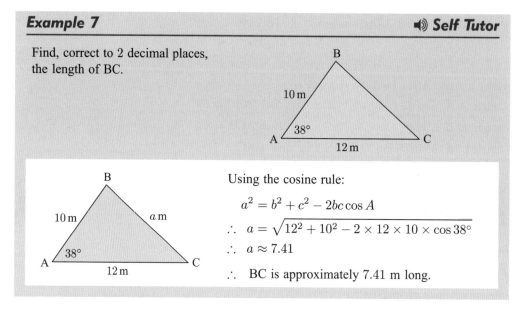

Example 7

◀)) *Self Tutor*

Find, correct to 2 decimal places, the length of BC.

Using the cosine rule:
$$a^2 = b^2 + c^2 - 2bc \cos A$$
$$\therefore \quad a = \sqrt{12^2 + 10^2 - 2 \times 12 \times 10 \times \cos 38°}$$
$$\therefore \quad a \approx 7.41$$
$$\therefore \quad \text{BC is approximately 7.41 m long.}$$

If we know all three side lengths of a triangle, we can use the cosine rule to find any of the angles. To do this, we rearrange the original cosine rule formulae:

$$\cos A = \frac{b^2 + c^2 - a^2}{2bc}, \quad \cos B = \frac{a^2 + c^2 - b^2}{2ac}, \quad \cos C = \frac{a^2 + b^2 - c^2}{2ab}$$

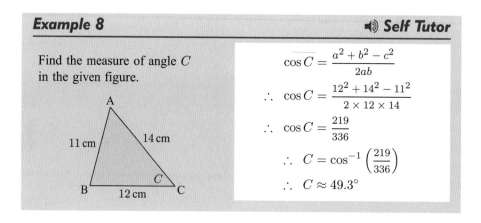

Example 8

◀)) *Self Tutor*

Find the measure of angle C in the given figure.

$$\cos C = \frac{a^2 + b^2 - c^2}{2ab}$$
$$\therefore \quad \cos C = \frac{12^2 + 14^2 - 11^2}{2 \times 12 \times 14}$$
$$\therefore \quad \cos C = \frac{219}{336}$$
$$\therefore \quad C = \cos^{-1}\left(\frac{219}{336}\right)$$
$$\therefore \quad C \approx 49.3°$$

EXERCISE 30E

1 Find the length of the remaining side in the triangle:

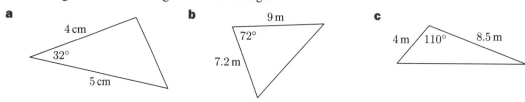

d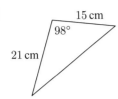

e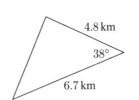

f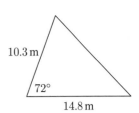

2 Find θ, rounded to 1 decimal place:

a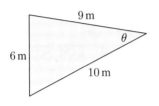

b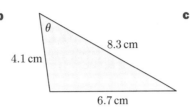

c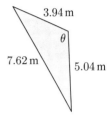

3 Find the measure of all angles of the triangle:

a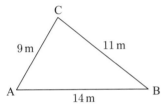

b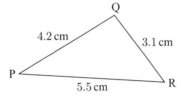

4 Find:

a the smallest angle of a triangle with sides 9 cm, 11 cm, and 13 cm

b the largest angle of a triangle with sides 3 cm, 5 cm, and 7 cm.

5 **a** Use the cosine rule in $\triangle$BCM to find $\cos\theta$ in terms of a, c, and m.

b Use the cosine rule in $\triangle$ACM to find $\cos(180° - \theta)$ in terms of b, c, and m.

c Use the fact that $\cos(180° - \theta) = -\cos\theta$ to prove **Apollonius' median theorem**:
$a^2 + b^2 = 2m^2 + 2c^2$.

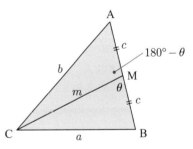

d Find x in the following:

i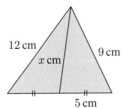

ii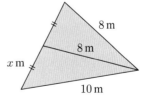

6 In triangle ABC, AB = 10 cm, AC = 9 cm, and $\widehat{ABC} = 60°$. Let BC = x cm.

a Use the cosine rule to show that x is a solution of $x^2 - 10x + 19 = 0$.

b Solve this equation for x.

c Use a scale diagram and a compass to explain why there are two possible values of x.

7 Find the area of each triangle, correct to 3 significant figures.

a

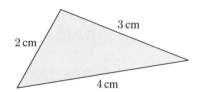

b

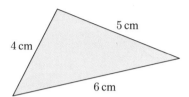

F	**PROBLEM SOLVING WITH THE SINE AND COSINE RULES** *[E8.1, E8.4, E8.5, E8.7]*

When using trigonometry to solve problems, you should draw a diagram of the situation. The diagram should be reasonably accurate, and all important information should be clearly marked on it.

Whenever you have the choice between the sine rule or cosine rule, use the *cosine* rule to avoid the ambiguous case.

Example 9   ◄)) *Self Tutor*

A ship sails 58 km on the bearing 072°. Once it has passed a reef, it turns and sails 41 km on the bearing 158°. How far is the ship from its starting point?

We suppose the ship starts at S, sails to A, then changes direction and sails to F.

$\hat{\text{SAN}} = 180° - 72° = 108°$

      {co-interior angles}

$\therefore \quad \hat{\text{SAF}} = 360° - 158° - 108°$

$\quad = 94°$ {angles at a point}

Let $SF = x$ km.

Using the cosine rule, $x^2 = 58^2 + 41^2 - 2 \times 58 \times 41 \times \cos 94°$

$\therefore \quad x = \sqrt{58^2 + 41^2 - 2 \times 58 \times 41 \times \cos 94°}$

$\therefore \quad x \approx 73.3$

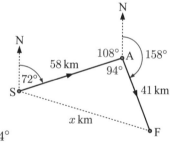

The ship is about 73.3 km from its starting point.

EXERCISE 30F

1 Two farm houses A and B are 10.3 km apart. A third farm house C is located such that $\hat{\text{BAC}} = 83°$ and $\hat{\text{ABC}} = 59°$. How far is C from A?

2 A roadway is horizontal from A to B, then rises up a 12° incline from B to C.
How far is it directly from A to C?

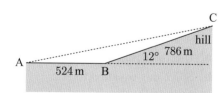

3 Sharon drives a golf ball 253 m from the tee T to point X on the fairway. X is 93 m from the flag, and $\widehat{XFT}$ is 39°.
Find the angle θ that Sharon's drive was off line.

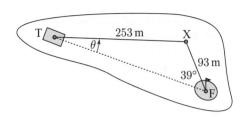

4 Towns A, B, and C are located such that $\widehat{BAC} = 50°$ and B is twice as far from C as A is from C. Find the measure of $\widehat{BCA}$.

5 Hazel's property is triangular with the dimensions shown.

 a Find the measure of the angle at A, rounded to 2 decimal places.

 b Find the area of Hazel's property, to the nearest hectare.

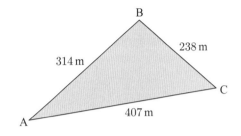

6 Fred walks 83 m in the direction 111°, and then 78 m in the direction 214°. How far is Fred from his starting point?

7 A boat travels 13 km in the direction 138°, and then a further 11 km in the direction 067°. Find the distance and bearing of the boat from its starting point.

8 Mount X is 9 km from Mount Y, on a bearing 146°. Mount Z is 14 km from Mount X, and on a bearing 072° from Mount Y. Find the bearing of X from Z.

9 A parallelogram has sides of length 8 cm and 12 cm. Given that one of its angles is 65°, find the lengths of its diagonals.

10 Calculate the length of a side of a regular pentagon whose vertices lie on a circle with radius 12 cm.

11 Answer the **Opening Problem** on page **497**.

12 X is 20 km north of Y. A mobile telephone mast M is to be placed 15 km from Y so the bearing of M from X is 140°.

 a Draw a sketch to show the two possible positions where the mast could be placed.

 b Calculate the distance of each of these positions from X.

13 The area of triangle ABD is 33.6 m². Find the length of CD.

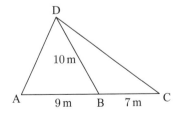

14 Find the value of x:

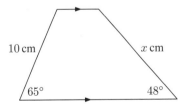

15

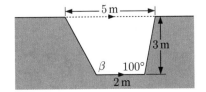

A stormwater drain is to have the shape shown. Determine the angle β which the left hand side makes with the bottom of the drain.

16 From points A and B at sea 1200 m apart, the angles of elevation to the top of the mountain T are 37° and 41° respectively.

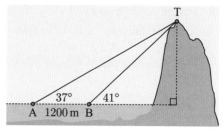

     a Find the size of AT̂B.

     b Find the distance from:

         i A to T   **ii** B to T.

     c Find the height of the mountain.

     d Use the given figure to show that

$$d = h \left(\frac{1}{\tan \theta} - \frac{1}{\tan \phi} \right).$$

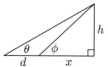

     Use this formula to check your answer to **c**.

17

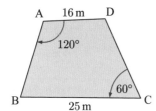

The quadrilateral ABCD represents David's garden plot.
AD = 16 m, BC = 25 m, and DC is 5 m longer than AB.
A fence runs around the entire boundary of the plot. How long is the fence?

18 In the given triangle, X is 5 m from each of the vertices. Find the length of each side of the triangle.

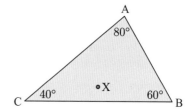

G   GRAPHS FROM THE UNIT CIRCLE [E3.2, E8.8]

Suppose we let $y = \sin \theta$. We can use our knowledge of trigonometric ratios for the multiples of 30° to construct a table of values:

θ	0	30°	60°	90°	120°	150°	180°	210°	240°	270°	300°	330°	360°
$y = \sin \theta$	0	$\frac{1}{2}$	$\frac{\sqrt{3}}{2}$	1	$\frac{\sqrt{3}}{2}$	$\frac{1}{2}$	0	$-\frac{1}{2}$	$-\frac{\sqrt{3}}{2}$	-1	$-\frac{\sqrt{3}}{2}$	$-\frac{1}{2}$	0

We can hence generate the graph of $y = \sin \theta$:

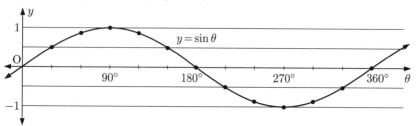

> The graph of $y = \sin \theta$ shows the y-coordinate of the point P as P moves around the unit circle.

Once we reach 360°, P has completed a full revolution of the unit circle, and so this pattern repeats itself.

DEMO

EXERCISE 30G

1 **a** Suppose $y = \cos\theta$. Use the unit circle to copy and complete this table of values:

θ	0°	30°	60°	90°	120°	150°	180°	210°	240°	270°	300°	330°	360°
$y = \cos\theta$													

  b Hence graph $y = \cos\theta$ for $0° \leqslant \theta \leqslant 360°$, making sure the graph is fully labelled.

  c State the maximum value of $\cos\theta$ and when it occurs.

  d State the minimum value of $\cos\theta$ and when it occurs.

2 **a** By using $\tan\theta = \dfrac{\sin\theta}{\cos\theta}$, copy and complete:

θ	0°	30°	60°	90°	120°	150°	180°	210°	240°	270°	300°	330°	360°
$y = \tan\theta$	0	$\frac{1}{\sqrt{3}}$	$\sqrt{3}$	und.									

  b Find the equations of the vertical asymptotes of $y = \tan\theta$ for $0° \leqslant \theta \leqslant 360°$.

  c Hence graph $y = \tan\theta$ for $0° \leqslant \theta \leqslant 360°$.

H TRIGONOMETRIC FUNCTIONS [E3.2, E8.8]

If a point P is allowed to keep rotating around the unit circle, it will return to its starting point and its coordinates will start repeating. This means the graphs of $y = \sin\theta$, $y = \cos\theta$, and $y = \tan\theta$ will also repeat themselves. They are therefore called *periodic* functions.

TERMINOLOGY FOR TRIGONOMETRIC FUNCTIONS

- A **periodic function** is one which repeats itself in a regularly occurring pattern.
- The **period** of a periodic function is the length of one repetition or cycle.
- The graph oscillates about a horizontal line called the **principal axis** or **mean line**.
- A **maximum point** occurs at the top of a crest.
- A **minimum point** occurs at the bottom of a trough.
- The **amplitude** is the vertical distance between a maximum or minimum point and the principal axis.

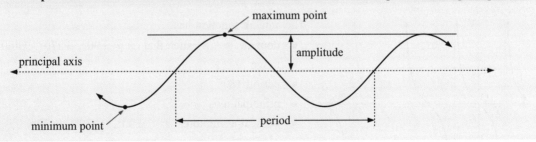

Instead of using θ, we will now use x to represent the angle variable. This is just for convenience, so we are dealing with the familiar function form $y = f(x)$.

THE SINE FUNCTION $y = \sin x$

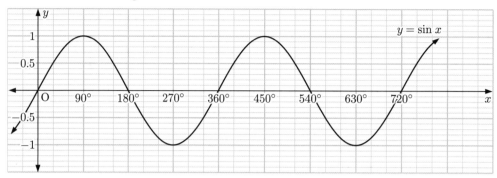

The sine function has:

- domain $x \in \mathbb{R}$
- principal axis $y = 0$
- range $-1 \leqslant y \leqslant 1$
- amplitude 1.
- period $360°$

THE COSINE FUNCTION $y = \cos x$

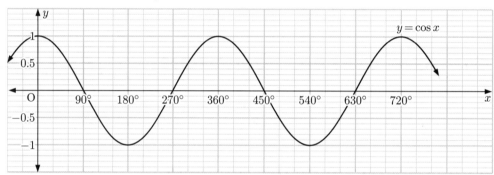

The cosine function has:

- domain $x \in \mathbb{R}$
- principal axis $y = 0$
- range $-1 \leqslant y \leqslant 1$
- amplitude 1.
- period $360°$

You may also notice that the cosine function has the same shape as the sine function, but is translated $90°$ to the left.

$$\cos x = \sin(x + 90°)$$

THE TANGENT FUNCTION $y = \tan x$

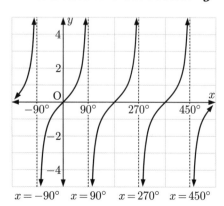

The tangent function has:

- domain $x \in \mathbb{R}$ such that $x \neq \pm 90°, \pm 270°, \pm 450°, \ldots$
- range $y \in \mathbb{R}$
- period $180°$
- principal axis $y = 0$
- vertical asymptotes $x = \pm 90°, \pm 270°, \pm 450°, \ldots$

EXERCISE 30H

1 Use the graphs of $y = \sin x$ and $y = \cos x$ to find:

    a $\sin 150°$ **b** $\sin 210°$ **c** $\cos 120°$ **d** $\cos 300°$

2 Use the graph of $y = \sin x$ to find all angles between $0°$ and $720°$ which have the same sine as:

    a $50°$ **b** $45°$ **c** $10°$

3 Use the graph of $y = \cos x$ to find all angles between $0°$ and $720°$ which have the same cosine as:

    a $25°$ **b** $90°$ **c** $70°$

4 Use the graph of $y = \tan x$ to find all angles between $0°$ and $540°$ which have the same tan as:

    a $20°$ **b** $55°$ **c** $80°$

5 Use the graph of $y = \sin x$ and your calculator to solve these equations for $0° \leqslant x \leqslant 720°$. Give your answers correct to the nearest degree.

    a $\sin x = 0$ **b** $\sin x = 0.3$ **c** $\sin x = 0.8$ **d** $\sin x = -0.4$

6 Use the graph of $y = \cos x$ and your calculator to solve these equations for $0° \leqslant x \leqslant 720°$. Give your answers correct to the nearest degree.

    a $\cos x = 1$ **b** $\cos x = 0.7$ **c** $\cos x = 0.2$ **d** $\cos x = -0.5$

7 Use the graph of $y = \tan x$ and your calculator to solve these equations for $0° \leqslant x \leqslant 540°$. Give your answers correct to the nearest degree.

    a $\tan x = 3$ **b** $\tan x = -2$ **c** $\tan x = 10$

8 **a** Draw the graphs of $y = \cos x$ and $y = \sin x$ on the same set of axes for $0° \leqslant x \leqslant 720°$.

    b Find all values of x on this domain such that $\cos x = \sin x$.

I | TRANSFORMATIONS OF TRIGONOMETRIC FUNCTIONS   *[E3.2, E3.3, E8.8]*

Discovery 2   *Transformations of $\sin x$ and $\cos x$*

In this Discovery we consider the effect that different transformations have on the amplitude, period, and principal axis of the sine and cosine functions.

What to do:

1 **a** State the transformation which maps $f(x)$ onto $-f(x)$.

    b Sketch on the same set of axes:

        i $y = \sin x$ and $y = -\sin x$ **ii** $y = \cos x$ and $y = -\cos x$

    c Does this transformation affect the amplitude, period, or principal axis?

2 **a** State the transformation which maps $f(x)$ onto $af(x)$, $a > 0$.

    b Sketch on the same set of axes:

        i $y = \sin x$, $y = 2\sin x$, and $y = \frac{1}{2}\sin x$

        ii $y = -\sin x$, $y = -\frac{1}{3}\sin x$, $y = -3\sin x$

        iii $y = \cos x$, $y = \frac{1}{2}\cos x$, $y = 3\cos x$.

    c Does this transformation affect the amplitude, period, or principal axis?

3 **a** State the transformation which maps $f(x)$ onto $f(bx)$, $b > 0$.

    b Sketch on the same set of axes:

       i $y = \sin x$, $y = \sin 2x$, $y = \sin \frac{x}{2}$, $y = \sin 3x$

       ii $y = \cos x$, $y = \cos 2x$, $y = \cos \frac{x}{2}$, $y = \cos 3x$.

    c Does this transformation affect the amplitude, period, or principal axis?

4 **a** State the transformation which maps $f(x)$ onto $f(x) + k$.

    b Sketch on the same set of axes:

       i $y = \sin x$, $y = \sin x + 2$, $y = \sin x - 3$

       ii $y = \cos x$, $y = \cos x - 1$, $y = \cos x + 2$.

    c Does this transformation affect the amplitude, period, or principal axis?

You should have observed that for $y = a \sin bx + k$ and $y = a \cos bx + k$:

- The amplitude is $|a|$.

- The period is $\dfrac{360°}{b}$.

- The principal axis is $y = k$.

Example 10   ◀) *Self Tutor*

On the same set of axes, sketch $y = \sin x$, $y = 3 \sin x$, and $y = 3 \sin 2x$ for $0° \leqslant x \leqslant 720°$.

To transform $y = \sin x$ into $y = 3 \sin x$, we triple the amplitude.

To transform $y = 3 \sin x$ into $y = 3 \sin 2x$, we halve the period.

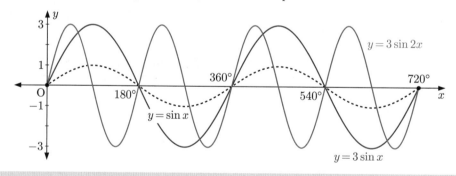

EXERCISE 30I

1 Sketch each group of functions on the same set of axes for $0° \leqslant x \leqslant 720°$:

    a $y = \sin x$ and $y = 3 \sin x$ **b** $y = \sin x$ and $y = \sin \frac{x}{3}$

    c $y = \sin x$, $y = -\sin x$, and $y = -\sin 2x$ **d** $y = \sin x$, $y = \sin 2x$, and $y = \sin 2x + 4$

2 Sketch each group of functions on the same set of axes for $0° \leqslant x \leqslant 720°$:

    a $y = \cos x$ and $y = 2 \cos x$ **b** $y = \cos x$ and $y = \cos \frac{3x}{2}$

    c $y = \cos x$, $y = \cos 2x$, and $y = \frac{1}{2} \cos 2x$ **d** $y = \cos x$, $y = 2 \cos x$, and $y = 2 \cos \frac{x}{2}$

3 Find the amplitude of:

   a $y = 4\sin x$ **b** $y = -2\cos x + 1$ **c** $y = -\frac{1}{3}\sin(x - 30°)$

4 Find the period of:

   a $y = \cos 3x$ **b** $y = 5\sin 4x + 2$ **c** $y = -\cos \frac{x}{2}$

5 Find the principal axis of:

   a $y = \sin x - 3$ **b** $y = -2\cos x + 5$ **c** $y = \frac{1}{4}\sin(x + 60°)$

6 Sketch on the same set of axes for $0° \leqslant x \leqslant 720°$:

   a $y = \sin x$ and $y = 3\sin \frac{x}{2}$ **b** $y = \cos x$ and $y = \frac{1}{2}\cos 3x$

   c $y = \sin x$ and $y = -\sin 2x$ **d** $y = \cos x$ and $y = -2\cos x$

7 Use your calculator to solve, correct to 1 decimal place, for $0° \leqslant x \leqslant 360°$:

   a $\sin x = 0.371$ **b** $\cos x = -0.673$ **c** $\sin 2x = 0.4261$

   d $\tan x = 4$ **e** $\cos 3x = \frac{1}{3}$ **f** $\sin \frac{x}{2} = 0.9384$

8 Find a and b if $y = a\sin bx$ has the graph:

   a 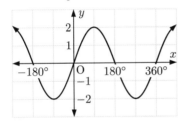   **b**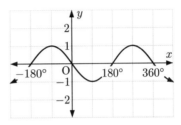

   c 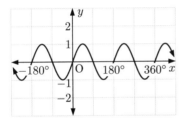   **d**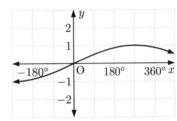

   e 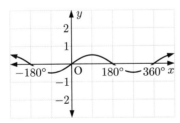   **f**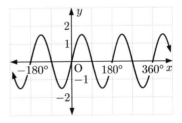

9 Find a and b if $y = a\cos bx$ has the graph:

   a 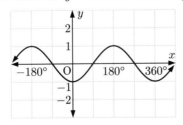   **b**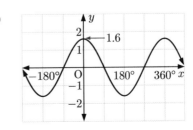

c

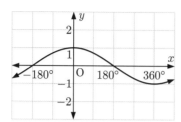

d

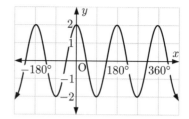

e

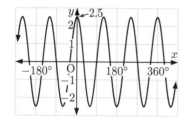

f

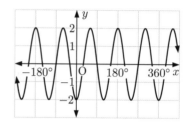

Review set 30A

1 Find:

   a the exact coordinates of point P

   b the coordinates of P correct to 3 decimal places

   c $\tan 296°$ and interpret its meaning.

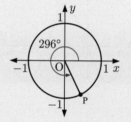

2 Use the unit circle to find the exact value of:

   a $\sin 120°$ **b** $\cos 360°$ **c** $\tan 330°$

3 **a** Find the area of triangle ABC, to the nearest m^2.

   b Find the length of side BC, rounded to 1 decimal place.

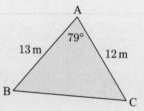

4 The area of triangle ABC is 21 m^2.
Find the value of x.

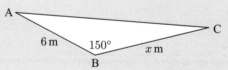

5 Write, in terms of a and b, the value of:

   a $\cos \theta$ **b** $\sin \theta$

   c $\sin(180° - \theta)$ **d** $\cos(180° - \theta)$

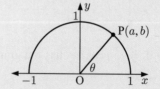

6 Stuart swam 200 m in the direction 124°, then 150 m in the direction 156°. Find the distance and bearing of Stuart from his starting point.

7 Triangle ABC has $\hat{ABC} = 48°$, AB = 10 cm, and AC = 8 cm. Show that $\hat{ACB}$ has two possible sizes. Give each answer correct to 3 significant figures.

8 Find the value of x:

a

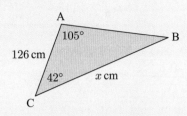

b

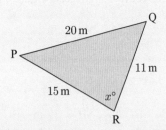

9

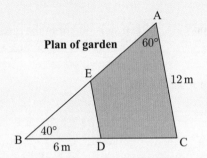

Plan of garden

In the given plan view, $AC = 12$ m, $\widehat{BAC} = 60°$, and $\widehat{ABC} = 40°$.

D is a post 6 m from corner B, E is a tap, and triangle BDE is a lawn with area 13.5 m².

a Calculate the length DC.

b Calculate the length BE.

c Find the area of quadrilateral ACDE.

10 Sketch on the same set of axes for $0° \leqslant x \leqslant 720°$:

a $y = \cos x$ and $y = -\cos 2x$

b $y = \sin x$ and $y = 2\sin \frac{3x}{2}$

11 Solve $\cos \frac{x}{2} = 0.787$ for $0° < x < 720°$.

12 This graph either has equation $y = a\cos bx$ or $y = a\sin bx$.

a Identify which of these two functions is illustrated.

b Find a and b.

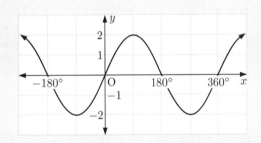

Review set 30B

1 Find:

a the exact coordinates of point Q

b the coordinates of Q correct to 4 decimal places

c $\tan 152°$ and interpret its meaning.

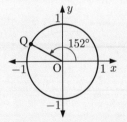

2 Find the obtuse angle:

a which has the same sine as $38°$

b whose cosine is the negative of $\cos 52°$.

3

Triangle ABC has acute angle θ at vertex A, and area 33.4 cm². Find θ.

4   Find, correct to 3 significant figures, the values of the unknowns:

    a 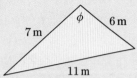   **b** 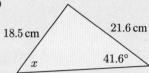   **c**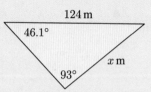

5   Triangle ABC has   AB $= 12$ m,   BC $= 10$ m,   AC $= x$ m,   and $\widehat{BAC} = 40°$.
    Show that there are two possible values for x.

6   A ship leaves port P and travels for 50 km in the direction 181°. It then sails 60 km in the direction
    274° to an island port Q.

    a   How far is Q from P?

    b   To sail directly back from Q to P, in what direction must the ship sail?

7   Find the area of this triangle.   **8**   Find the value of x:

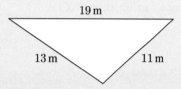   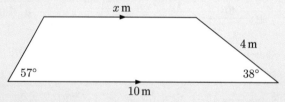

9   Jane and Peter are considering buying a block of land.
    The land agent has supplied them with the given sketch.
    Find the area of the property, giving your answer in:

    a   m^2 **b**   hectares.

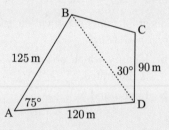

10   Sketch on the same set of axes for $0° \leqslant x \leqslant 720°$:

    a $y = \sin x$ and $y = \frac{1}{2}\sin 3x$ **b** $y = \cos x$ and $y = -3\cos x$

11   Find the principal axis of $y = \frac{3}{2} - \frac{1}{2}\cos(x - 30°)$.

12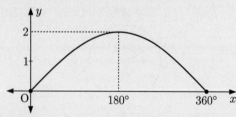

                                           The illustrated graph has equation of the form
                                             $y = a\sin bx$ for $0° \leqslant x \leqslant 360°$.
                                             Find a and b.

13   Ports P, Q, and R are equally spaced along
     the coast. A boat B is 4 km from P, and 2 km
     from Q.

     a   Show that $\cos\widehat{BQP} = \frac{13}{20}$.

     b   Hence, find $\cos\widehat{BQR}$.

     c   Show that the boat is $\sqrt{42}$ km from port R.

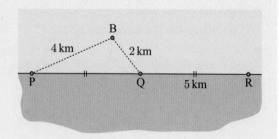

Circle geometry

31

Contents:

A	Angle in a semi-circle theorem	[E5.7]
B	Chords of a circle theorem	[E5.7]
C	Radius-tangent theorem	[E5.7]
D	Tangents from an external point theorem	[E5.7]
E	Angle between a tangent and a chord theorem	[E5.7]
F	Angle at the centre theorem	[E5.7]
G	Angles subtended by the same arc theorem	[E5.7]
H	Cyclic quadrilaterals	[E5.7]
I	Tests for cyclic quadrilaterals	[E5.7]

Opening problem

Market gardener Joe has four long straight pipes of different lengths. He places the pipes on the ground and joins them with rubber hose to form a garden bed in the shape of a quadrilateral. A sprinkler which casts water in semi-circles of diameter equal to the length of a pipe is placed at the midpoint of each pipe.

Joe draws a rough sketch of the watering system, and decides that his sprinklers will water the whole of the garden. His son Clinton is sceptical of his father's idea, and draws his own sketch which suggests that there will be an unwatered patch in the centre.

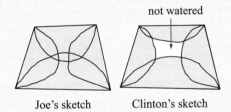

Joe's sketch   Clinton's sketch

Things to think about:

a By drawing an accurate diagram of this situation, can you determine whether Joe or Clinton is correct?

b Can you *prove* your answer using geometric theorems?

The geometry of triangles, quadrilaterals, and circles has been used for at least 3000 years in art, design, and architecture. Many amazing discoveries have been made by mathematicians and non-mathematicians who were simply drawing figures with rulers and compasses.

In this Chapter you will investigate a number of theorems for circles. You can do this with the software provided, or with a compass, ruler, and protractor.

A   ANGLE IN A SEMI-CIRCLE THEOREM   [E5.7]

Discovery 1   Angle in a semi-circle theorem

What to do:

1 Draw a circle and construct a diameter. Label it as shown.

GEOMETRY PACKAGE

2 Mark any point P not at A or B on the circle. Draw AP and PB.

3 Measure $\widehat{APB}$.

4 Repeat for different positions of P and for different circles. What do you notice?

5 Copy and complete: *The angle in a semi-circle is ......*

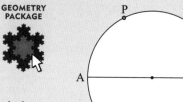

The **angle in a semi-circle theorem** states that:

    The angle in a semi-circle is a right angle.

        $\widehat{ABC} = 90°$

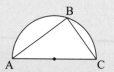

The **converse of the angle in a semi-circle theorem** states that:

    If line segment AB subtends a right angle at C, then the circle through A, B, and C has diameter AB.

Example 1   ◀ﾟ *Self Tutor*

Find x, giving brief reasons for your answer.

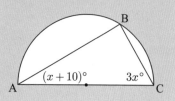

$$\widehat{ABC} \text{ measures } 90° \quad \{\text{angle in a semi-circle}\}$$
$$\therefore \ (x + 10) + 3x + 90 = 180 \quad \{\text{angles in a triangle}\}$$
$$\therefore \ 4x + 100 = 180$$
$$\therefore \ 4x = 80$$
$$\therefore \ x = 20$$

EXERCISE 31A

1 In this question we will prove the *angle in a semi-circle* theorem.
Suppose AC is the diameter of a circle with centre O, and B is any
point on the semi-circle.

Let $\widehat{OAB} = x°$ and $\widehat{OCB} = y°$.

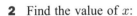

   a Find $\widehat{OBA}$ and $\widehat{OBC}$ in terms of x and y.

   b Hence, show that $\widehat{ABC} = 90°$.

2 Find the value of x:

  a

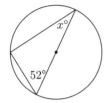

  b

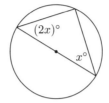

  c

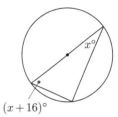

3

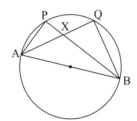

P and Q are any two points on a circle on the same side of diameter
AB.

Show that triangles APX and BQX are similar.

4 Find the value of x:

  a

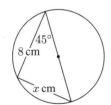

  b

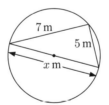

You can apply
Pythagoras' theorem in
any right angled triangle.

5

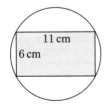

A rectangle with side lengths 11 cm and 6 cm is inscribed in a circle. Find
the radius of the circle.

6 A circle has diameter AB of length 10 cm. C is a point on the circle such that AC is 8 cm. Find the
length BC.

7

A square is inscribed in a circle of radius 6 cm. Find the length of the sides
of the square, correct to 3 significant figures.

8   AB is a diameter of the circle. AC is half the length of AB, and BC is 12 cm long. Find the radius of the circle.

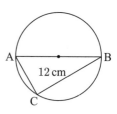

9   **a**   Find x.

     b   Hence, find the diameter of the circle.

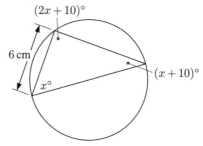

10

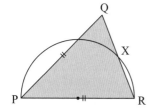

Triangle PQR is isosceles with PQ = PR.

A semi-circle with diameter PR is drawn to cut QR at X.

Prove that X is the midpoint of QR.

11   Consider the **Opening Problem** on page **523**. Consider the two semi-circles in the figure alongside.

     a   Determine the measure of $\widehat{BXA}$ and $\widehat{BXC}$.

     b   What does **a** tell us about the points A, X, and C?

     c   Do the two illustrated sprinklers water all of the area on one side of the diagonal AC?

     d   Will Joe's four sprinklers water the whole garden? Explain your answer.

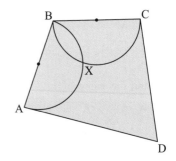

B   *CHORDS OF A CIRCLE THEOREM*   *[E5.7]*

Discovery 2   *Chords of a circle theorem*

What to do:

GEOMETRY PACKAGE

1   Draw a circle with centre O. Construct any chord AB.

2   Construct the perpendicular from O to AB which cuts the chord at M.

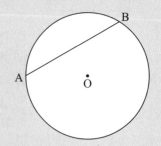

3   Measure the lengths of AM and BM. What do you notice?

4   Repeat this procedure with another circle and chord.

5   Copy and complete: *The perpendicular from the centre of a circle to a chord ......*

The **chords of a circle theorem** states that:

The perpendicular from the centre of a circle to a chord bisects the chord.

AM = BM

The **converse of the chords of a circle theorem** states that:

The perpendicular bisector of a chord of a circle passes through its centre.

Example 2   ◀)) *Self Tutor*

A circle has a chord of length 8 cm. The shortest distance from the circle's centre to the chord is 2 cm. Find, to the nearest mm, the length of the circle's radius.

Suppose the radius has length r cm.

The shortest distance from the centre to the chord is the perpendicular distance.

Let M be the foot of the perpendicular from the centre O to the chord AB.

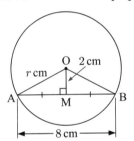

∴ M is the midpoint of AB   {chords of a circle}

∴ AM = 4 cm

In △OAM, $r^2 = 2^2 + 4^2$ {Pythagoras}

∴ $r^2 = 20$

∴ $r = \sqrt{20} \approx 4.5$ {as $r > 0$}

So, the radius is about 4.5 cm long.

EXERCISE 31B

1 In this question we will prove the *chords of a circle* theorem.
Suppose AB is a chord of a circle with centre O, and OM is perpendicular to AB.

a Show that triangles OAM and OBM are congruent.

b Hence, show that AM = BM.

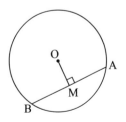

2 Find x, rounded to 2 decimal places:

a

radius $= x$ cm

b

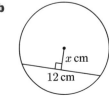

radius $= 7$ cm

c

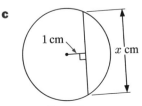

radius $= 5$ cm

3 A circle has a chord of length 12 cm. The shortest distance from the chord to the circle's centre is 2 cm. Find, to the nearest mm, the length of the circle's radius.

4 A circle has a chord of length 15 cm. The radius of the circle is 9 cm. Find, to the nearest mm, the shortest distance from the chord to the circle's centre.

5 A circle has radius 5 cm. The shortest distance from the circle's centre to a chord is 2 cm. Find, to the nearest mm, the length of this chord.

6 The chord AB is equal in length to the radius of the circle. Find the length of XY.

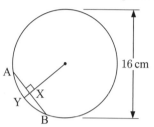

7 AB is the perpendicular bisector of the chord CD. Find the diameter of the circle.

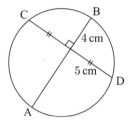

8 Find the values of a and b:

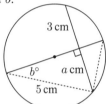

9 Find the value of m:

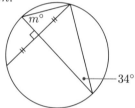

10 AB is a chord of a circle with centre O and radius 5 cm. AB has length 8 cm. Find the size of $\stackrel{\frown}{AOB}$.

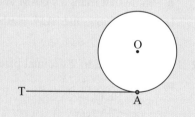

C   RADIUS-TANGENT THEOREM   [E5.7]

Discovery 3   *Radius-tangent theorem*

What to do:

1 Draw a circle with centre O, and mark on it a point A.

2 At A, draw as accurately as possible a tangent TA.

3 Draw the radius OA.

4 Measure $\stackrel{\frown}{OAT}$.

5 Repeat this procedure with another circle and tangent.

6 Copy and complete:

The tangent to a circle is ...... to the radius at the point ......

GEOMETRY
PACKAGE

The **radius-tangent theorem** states that:

The tangent to a circle is perpendicular to
the radius at the point of contact.

$$O\widehat{A}T = 90°$$

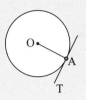

Example 3   ◀)) *Self Tutor*

A circle has radius 6 cm. At point T on the circle a tangent is drawn. The tangent is 10 cm long, and
ends at point P. Find the distance from P to the centre of the circle.

Let the distance from P to the centre of the circle be x cm.

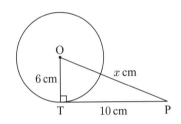

$$O\widehat{T}P = 90° \qquad \{\text{radius-tangent}\}$$
$$\therefore \ x^2 = 6^2 + 10^2 \qquad \{\text{Pythagoras}\}$$
$$\therefore \ x^2 = 136$$
$$\therefore \ x = \sqrt{136} \approx 11.7 \qquad \{\text{as } OP > 0\}$$

So, P is about 11.7 cm from the centre of the circle.

EXERCISE 31C

1 In the following diagrams, O is the centre of the circle, and TP is a tangent. Find the value of x,
rounding your answer to 1 decimal place where necessary.

a

b

c

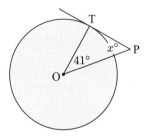

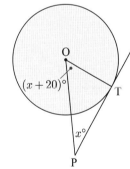

d

e

f

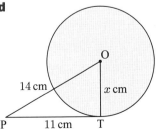

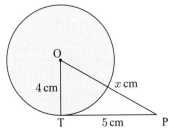

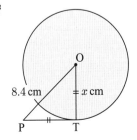

2 Point P is 9 cm from the centre of a circle. A tangent from P to the circle is 5 cm long. Find the radius
of the circle.

3 Point Q is 12 cm from the centre of a circle of radius 7 cm. A tangent is drawn from Q to touch the circle at P. Find the length of PQ.

4 In the figure alongside, the tangent TP has the same length as the radius of the circle. What proportion of triangle OTP is inside the circle?

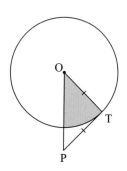

5 Find the values of the unknowns, giving reasons for your answers:

a 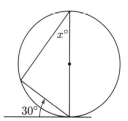 **b** 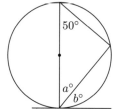 **c**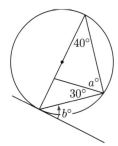

Example 4   ◀)) *Self Tutor*

Two circles have a common tangent. The points of contact A and B are 7 cm apart. The radii are 4 cm and 2 cm respectively. Find the distance between the centres.

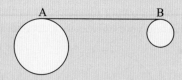

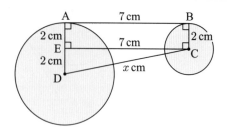

For centres C and D, we draw BC, AD, and CD.

We draw CE parallel to AB, so that ABCE is a rectangle.

$$\therefore \quad CE = 7 \text{ cm}$$

and $DE = 4 - 2 = 2$ cm

Now $x^2 = 2^2 + 7^2$ {Pythagoras in $\triangle DEC$}

$$\therefore \quad x^2 = 53$$

$$\therefore \quad x = \sqrt{53} \qquad \{\text{as } x > 0\}$$

$$\therefore \quad x \approx 7.28$$

The distance between the centres is about 7.28 cm.

6

A and B are the centres of two circles with radii 4 m and 3 m respectively. The illustrated common tangent has length 10 m. Find the distance between the centres, correct to 2 decimal places.

7 Two circles are drawn so they do not intersect. The larger circle has radius 6 cm. A common tangent is 10 cm long and the centres are 11 cm apart. Find the radius of the smaller circle, correct to 3 significant figures.

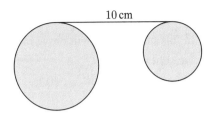

8

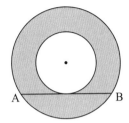

AB is a tangent to the inner circle and is a chord of the larger circle. If AB is 6 m long, find the area of the shaded annulus.

9 Chord AB of length 2 cm is drawn in a circle of radius 3 cm. Diameter BC is constructed, and the tangent from C is drawn. The chord AB is extended to meet the tangent at D. Find the length of AD.

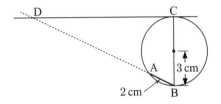

D | TANGENTS FROM AN EXTERNAL POINT THEOREM   [E5.7]

Discovery 4   Tangents from an external point theorem

What to do:

1 Draw a circle with centre O.

2 From an external point P, draw as accurately as possible the two tangents to the circle. Let the tangents meet the circle at A and B.

GEOMETRY PACKAGE

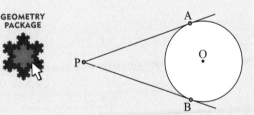

3 Measure AP and BP.

4 Repeat this procedure with a circle of a different size.

5 Copy and complete:

Tangents from an external point to a circle are ......

The **tangents from an external point theorem** states that:

Tangents from an external point are equal in length.

$$AP = BP$$

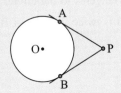

EXERCISE 31D

1 In this question we will prove the *tangents from an external point* theorem.

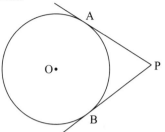

   a Show that:

     i $AP^2 = OP^2 - OA^2$

     ii $BP^2 = OP^2 - OB^2$.

   b Hence, show that $AP = BP$.

2 In the following diagrams, O is the centre of the circle, and TP and SP are tangents. Find the values of the unknowns.

   a

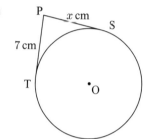

   b

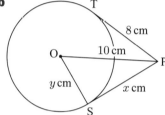

   c

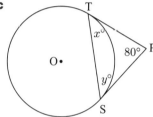

   d

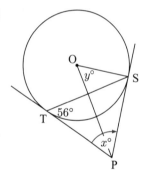

   e

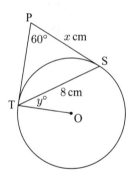

   f

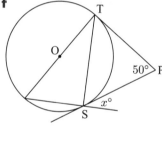

3

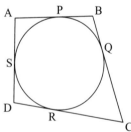

A circle is drawn, and four tangents to it are constructed as shown. Deduce that $AB + CD = BC + AD$.

4 In the figure alongside, O is the centre of the circle, and AP and BP are tangents to the circle.

Show that $A\hat{O}B$ is twice the size of $B\hat{A}P$.

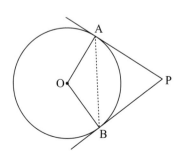

5 For the circle given, find:

   a the radius of the circle

   b the distance between A and B.

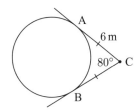

6 A circle touches the three sides of the triangle as shown. Find the radius of the circle.

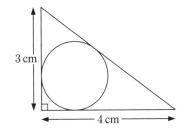

7 A circle is inscribed in a right angled triangle. The radius of the circle is 3 cm, and BC has length 8 cm.
Find the perimeter of the triangle ABC.

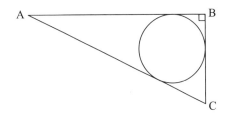

8

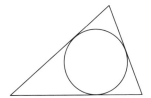

A circle is inscribed in a triangle. The triangle has area A and perimeter P. Show that:

   a the radius of the circle is given by $r = \dfrac{2A}{P}$

   b the ratio of perimeters of the circle and triangle is the same as the ratio of their areas.

E   ANGLE BETWEEN A TANGENT AND A CHORD THEOREM   [E5.7]

Discovery 5   Angle between a tangent and a chord theorem

What to do:

1 Draw a circle and mark on it points A, B, and C.

2 Draw tangent TAS at A, and join AB, BC, and CA.

3 Measure BÂS and AĈB. What do you notice?

4 Repeat the above steps with another circle.

5 Copy and complete:

    The angle between a tangent and a chord at the point of contact is ...... to the angle subtended by the chord in the alternate ......

GEOMETRY PACKAGE

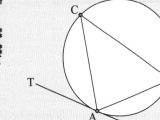

The **angle between a tangent and a chord theorem** states that:

The angle between a tangent and a chord at the point of contact is equal to the angle subtended by the chord in the alternate segment.

$$B\hat{A}S = A\hat{C}B$$

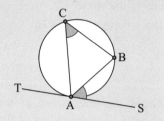

Example 5   ◀)) *Self Tutor*

AT is a tangent to the circle. Find x.

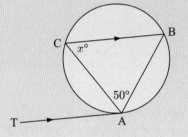

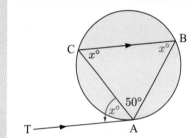

$$C\hat{A}T = x° \quad \text{\{equal alternate angles\}}$$
$$\therefore \ A\hat{B}C = C\hat{A}T = x° \quad \text{\{angle between a tangent and a chord\}}$$
$$\therefore \ x + x + 50 = 180 \quad \text{\{angles in a } \triangle\}$$
$$\therefore \ 2x = 130$$
$$\therefore \ x = 65$$

EXERCISE 31E

1 In each diagram, C is the point of contact of tangent CT. Find x, giving reasons:

a   **b**   **c**

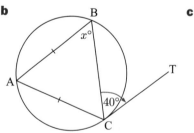
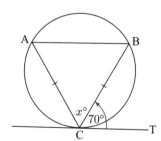

2 $\triangle$ABC is isosceles and is inscribed in a circle as shown. TC is a tangent to the circle.

Prove that AC bisects $B\hat{C}T$.

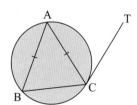

3 P is any point on a circle. QR is a chord of the circle parallel to the tangent at P. Prove that triangle PQR is isosceles.

4 B and C are the points of contact of tangents BV and CU, respectively.
Find x, giving reasons for your answer.

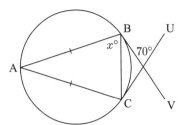

F ANGLE AT THE CENTRE THEOREM   *[E5.7]*

Discovery 6   *Angle at the centre theorem*

What to do:

1 Draw a large circle with centre O.
Mark on it points A, B, and P.

GEOMETRY PACKAGE

2 Join AO, BO, AP, and BP.

3 Measure AÔB and AP̂B.
What do you notice?

4 Repeat the above steps with another circle.

5 Copy and complete:
The angle at the centre of a circle is ...... the angle on the circle subtended by the same arc.

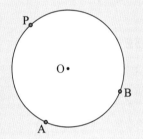

The **angle at the centre theorem** states that:

The angle at the centre of a circle is twice the angle on the circle subtended by the same arc.

$$A\widehat{O}B = 2 \times A\widehat{C}B$$

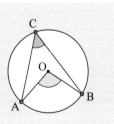

Notice that:

- The following diagrams are all cases of the *angle at the centre theorem*. They can all be explored using the **geometry package**.

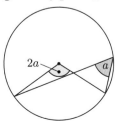 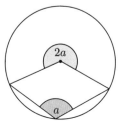 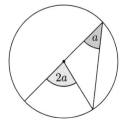

GEOMETRY PACKAGE

- The **angle in a semi-circle theorem** is a special case of the angle at the centre theorem.

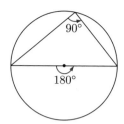

Example 6

◀) **Self Tutor**

Find the value of x:

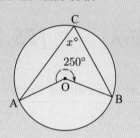

Obtuse $\widehat{AOB} = 360° - 250°$ {angles at a point}

$\therefore \quad \widehat{AOB} = 110°$

$\therefore \quad 2x = 110$ {angle at the centre}

$\therefore \quad x = 55$

EXERCISE 31F

1 Find, giving reasons, the value of x:

a
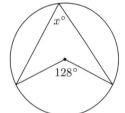

b
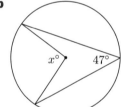

c
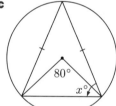

d
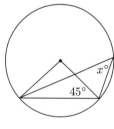

e
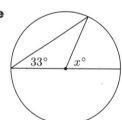

f
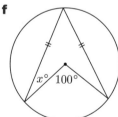

2

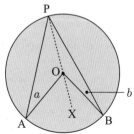

In this question we prove the *angle at the centre* theorem for the case where the centre lies within the triangle formed by the other three points.

a Explain why △s OAP and OBP are isosceles.

b Find the measures of the following angles in terms of a and b:

    i $\widehat{APO}$ **ii** $\widehat{BPO}$ **iii** $\widehat{AOX}$

    iv $\widehat{BOX}$ **v** $\widehat{APB}$ **vi** $\widehat{AOB}$

c Hence show that the angle at the centre of the circle is twice the angle on the circle subtended by the same arc.

d What other cases need to be considered, in order to formally prove the *angle at the centre* theorem?

3 AB is the diameter of a circle with centre O. X is a point on the circle, and AX is produced to Y such that $OX = XY$.

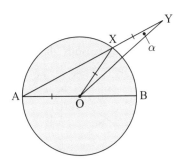

   a If $X\hat{Y}O = \alpha$, find in terms of α:

      i $X\hat{O}Y$ **ii** $A\hat{X}O$ **iii** $X\hat{A}O$

      iv $X\hat{O}B$ **v** $B\hat{O}Y$

   b What is the relationship between $B\hat{O}Y$ and $Y\hat{O}X$?

G   ANGLES SUBTENDED BY THE SAME ARC THEOREM   [E5.7]

Discovery 7   Angles subtended by the same arc theorem

What to do:

1 Draw a circle.
Mark on it points A, B, C, and D.

GEOMETRY PACKAGE

2 Join AC, BC, AD, and BD.

3 Measure $A\hat{C}B$ and $A\hat{D}B$.
What do you notice?

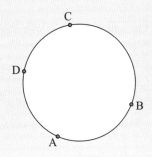

4 Repeat the above steps with another circle.

5 Copy and complete:
Angles subtended by the same arc on the circle are ...... in size.

The **angles subtended by the same arc theorem** states that:

Angles subtended by the same arc on a circle are equal in size.

$$A\hat{D}B = A\hat{C}B$$

Example 7   ◀ Self Tutor

Find the value of x:

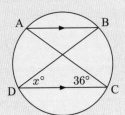

          $A\hat{B}D = 36°$ {angles subtended by the same arc}

and $B\hat{D}C = A\hat{B}D$ {equal alternate angles}

    $\therefore$ $x = 36$

EXERCISE 31G

1 Find, giving reasons, the value of each unknown:

a
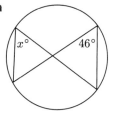

b
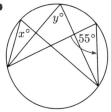

c
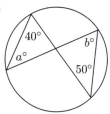

d
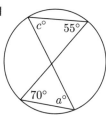

e
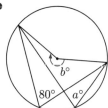

f
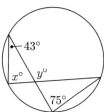

g
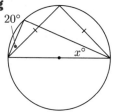

h
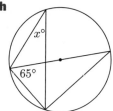

2 In this question we prove the *angles subtended by the same arc* theorem.

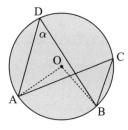

   a Use the *angle at the centre* theorem to write the size of $A\widehat{O}B$ in terms of α.

   b Hence write the size of $A\widehat{C}B$ in terms of α.

   c State the relationship between $A\widehat{D}B$ and $A\widehat{C}B$.

3

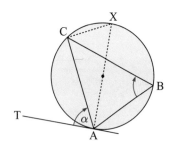

In this question we prove the *angle between a tangent and a chord* theorem for the case where the endpoints of the chord are on opposite sides of the diameter from the point of tangency.

   a We draw diameter AX and join CX.
   Find the size of:

        i $T\widehat{A}X$ **ii** $A\widehat{C}X$

   b Let $T\widehat{A}C = \alpha$. Find, in terms of α:

        i $C\widehat{A}X$ **ii** $C\widehat{X}A$ **iii** $C\widehat{B}A$

   c State the relationship between $T\widehat{A}C$ and $C\widehat{B}A$.

4 Two circles intersect at A and B.
Straight lines PQ and XY are drawn through A to meet the circles as shown.
Show that $X\widehat{B}P = Y\widehat{B}Q$.

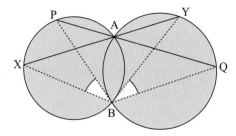

5 Brigitta notices that her angle of view of a picture on a wall depends
on how far she is standing from the wall. When she is very close to
the wall, the angle of view is small. When she moves backwards so
that she is a long way from the wall, the angle of view is also small.

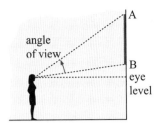

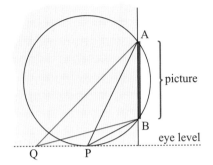

It becomes clear to Brigitta that there must be a point P in
front of the picture at which her angle of view is greatest.
The position of P can be found by drawing the circle through
A and B which touches the "eye level" line at P.

Prove this result by choosing any other point Q on the "eye
level" line, and showing that this angle must be less than $A\widehat{P}B$.

H   CYCLIC QUADRILATERALS   [E5.7]

Suppose we are given two points A and B, and we must
draw a circle passing through these points. There are
infinitely many circles that we can draw.

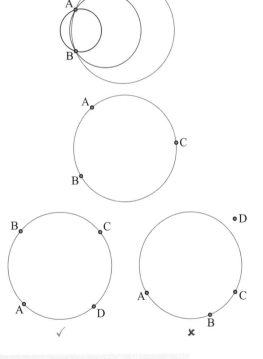

If we are given three points A, B, and C which are not
collinear, there is a unique circle which passes through
the points.

If we are given four points A, B, C, and D, no three of
which are collinear, there may or may not be a circle
which passes through the points. To see this, we draw
the unique circle which passes through A, B, and C. The
fourth point D may or may not lie on this circle.

Four points are said to be **concyclic** if a circle can
be drawn through them.

If four concyclic points are joined to form a convex
quadrilateral, then the quadrilateral is called a **cyclic
quadrilateral**.

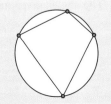

Discovery 8   *Opposite angles of a cyclic quadrilateral theorem*

What to do:

1 Draw several circles, and on each circle draw a
different cyclic quadrilateral with vertices A, B, C,
and D. Make sure the quadrilaterals are large enough
for you to measure the angles with a protractor.

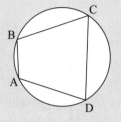

2 Measure all angles to the nearest degree, and record your results in a table like the one following.

Figure	$\widehat{A}$	$\widehat{B}$	$\widehat{C}$	$\widehat{D}$	$\widehat{A} + \widehat{C}$	$\widehat{B} + \widehat{D}$
1						
2						
⋮						

3 Write a sentence to summarise your results.

OPPOSITE ANGLES OF A CYCLIC QUADRILATERAL THEOREM

The opposite angles of a cyclic quadrilateral
are **supplementary**.

$$\alpha + \beta = 180° \quad \text{and} \quad \theta + \phi = 180°$$

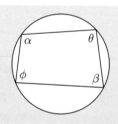

Example 8   ◀) *Self Tutor*

Find the value of x:

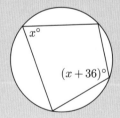

The angles given are opposite angles of a cyclic quadrilateral.

$$\therefore \quad x + (x + 36) = 180$$
$$\therefore \quad 2x + 36 = 180$$
$$\therefore \quad 2x = 144$$
$$\therefore \quad x = 72$$

EXTERIOR ANGLE OF A CYCLIC QUADRILATERAL THEOREM

The exterior angle of a cyclic quadrilateral is equal to the opposite interior angle.

$$\alpha = \beta$$

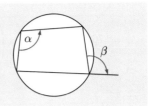

EXERCISE 31H

1 In this question we prove the *opposite angles of a cyclic quadrilateral* theorem.

   a For the given figure, find:

      i D$\widehat{O}$B in terms of a

      ii reflex D$\widehat{O}$B in terms of b.

   b Hence, show that $a + b = 180°$.

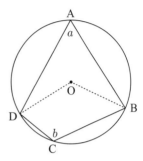

2

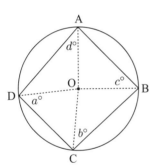

An alternative method for establishing the *opposite angles of a cyclic quadrilateral* theorem is to use the figure alongside. Show how this can be done.

3 Prove the *exterior angle of a cyclic quadrilateral* theorem.

4 Find x, giving reasons:

   a

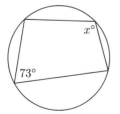

   b

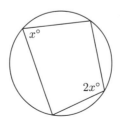

   c

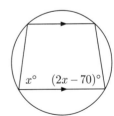

   d

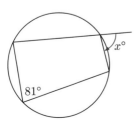

   e

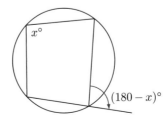

   f

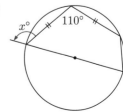

5 Find the values of the unknowns:

a

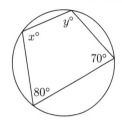

b

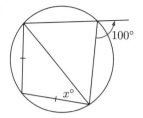

c

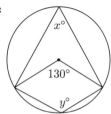

d

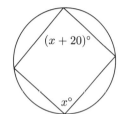

e

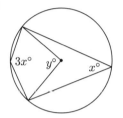

f

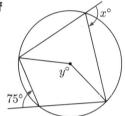

6 A parallelogram is inscribed in a circle. Prove that the parallelogram must be a rectangle.

7 ABCDE is a pentagon inscribed in a circle with centre O. BD is a diameter of the circle. AE is parallel to BD, and is extended to F. $\hat{BAC} = 45°$ and $\hat{CAE} = 70°$.

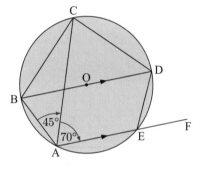

   a Find the size of: **i** $\hat{BCD}$ **ii** $\hat{BDC}$.

   b Show that BC = CD.

   c Find the size of $\hat{DEF}$.

8 ABCD is a cyclic quadrilateral. Sides AB and DC are *produced* or extended to meet at E. Sides DA and CB are produced to F.

If $\hat{AFB}$ is 30° and $\hat{BEC}$ is 20°, find all angles of quadrilateral ABCD.

I   TESTS FOR CYCLIC QUADRILATERALS   [E5.7]

The converses of the *opposite angles of a cyclic quadrilateral* theorem and the *exterior angle of a cyclic quadrilateral* theorem give us two tests for determining whether a quadrilateral is cyclic.

A third test comes from the converse of the *angles subtended by the same arc* theorem:

> A quadrilateral is a **cyclic quadrilateral** if one of the following is true:
>
> • one pair of opposite angles is supplementary
>
>
>
> If $\alpha + \beta = 180°$ then ABCD is a cyclic quadrilateral.

- an exterior angle is equal to the opposite interior angle

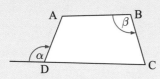

If $\alpha = \beta$ then ABCD is a cyclic quadrilateral.

- one side subtends equal angles at the other two vertices

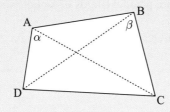

If $\alpha = \beta$ then ABCD is a cyclic quadrilateral.

Example 9   ◀) *Self Tutor*

Triangle ABC is isosceles with AB = AC. X and Y lie on AB and AC respectively such that XY is parallel to BC. Prove that XYCB is a cyclic quadrilateral.

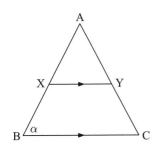

$\triangle$ABC is isosceles with AB = AC.

Let $C\widehat{B}X = \alpha$

$\therefore$ $B\widehat{C}Y = \alpha$ {equal base angles}

and $B\widehat{X}Y = 180° - \alpha$ {cointerior angles}

$\therefore$ $B\widehat{X}Y + B\widehat{C}Y = 180°$

$\therefore$ XYCB is a cyclic quadrilateral.   {opposite angles are supplementary}

EXERCISE 31I

1 Is ABCD a cyclic quadrilateral? Explain your answer.

a
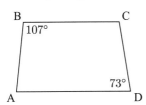

b
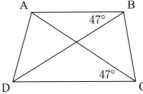

c
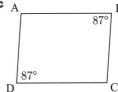

d
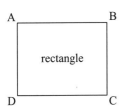

e
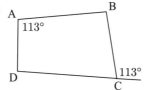

f
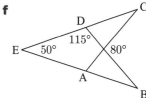

2 OABC is a parallelogram.
A circle with centre O and radius OA is drawn.
BA produced meets the circle at D.
Prove that DOCB is a cyclic quadrilateral.

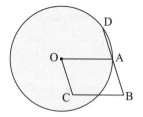

3

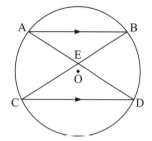

AB and CD are parallel chords of a circle with centre O. BC and AD meet at E.
Show that AEOC is a cyclic quadrilateral.

4 A circle has centre O. The tangents to the circle from an external point P meet the circle at points A and B. Show that PAOB is a cyclic quadrilateral.

5 ABCD is a cyclic quadrilateral, and X is any point on diagonal CA. XY is drawn parallel to CB to meet AB at Y. XZ is drawn parallel to CD to meet AD at Z. Prove that XYAZ is a cyclic quadrilateral.

6 ABC is an isosceles triangle with AB = AC. The angle bisectors at B and C meet the sides AC and AB at X and Y respectively. Show that BCXY is a cyclic quadrilateral.

7 The non-parallel sides of a trapezium have equal length. Prove that the trapezium is a cyclic quadrilateral.

8 RX is the bisector of $Q\widehat{R}T$.
Prove that PX bisects $Q\widehat{P}S$.

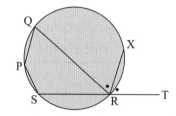

9 A, B, and C are points on a circle. P, Q, and R are any points on arcs AB, BC, and AC respectively. Prove that $A\widehat{R}C + B\widehat{Q}C + A\widehat{P}B = 360°$.

10 Two circles intersect at X and Y. A line segment AB is drawn through X to cut one circle at A and the other at B. Another line segment CD is drawn through Y to cut one circle at C and the other at D, with A and C being on the same circle. Show that AC is parallel to BD.

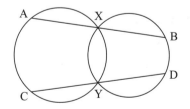

Discovery 9   *Circles and triangles*

What to do:

1 Consider three points A, B, and C. Explain how to use a ruler and geometrical compass to locate the centre of the circle passing through A, B, and C. Clearly state any geometrical theorems you have used.
Check your construction by drawing the circle.

A
∘

DEMO

B ∘   ∘ C

2 Draw any triangle PQR with sides between 6 cm and 10 cm.
Label any points X, Y, and Z on PR, PQ, and RQ respectively.

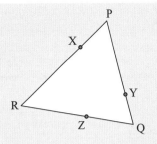

  a Use **1** to accurately construct circles through:

    i P, X, and Y   **ii** Q, Y, and Z

   iii R, X, and Z.

  b What do you notice about the three circles?

3 Repeat **2** with a different acute-angled triangle.

4 Use cyclic quadrilaterals to prove that the result you have found is always true.
Hint: Do **not** draw all three circles on your figure.

Review set 31A

1 Find the value of a:

a
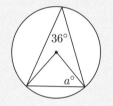

b
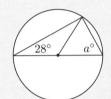

c
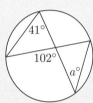

d
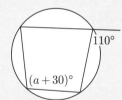

e
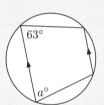

f
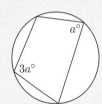

2 AB and AC are tangents to the circle.
Find an equation connecting α, β, and γ.

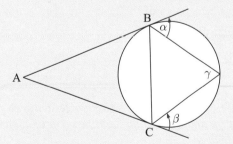

3 Find the value of x:

a
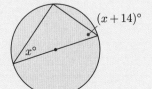

b
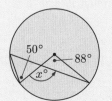

c
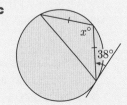

4 Find x, correct to 3 significant figures:

a

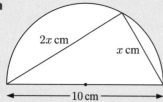

2x cm   x cm   10 cm

b

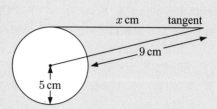

x cm   tangent
9 cm
5 cm

5 AB and CM are common tangents to two touching circles. Show that:

a M is the midpoint of AB

b $\widehat{ACB}$ is a right angle.

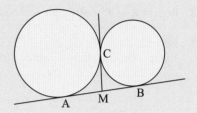

6

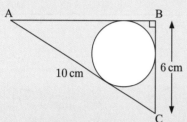

A   B   10 cm   6 cm   C

Find:

a the length of side AB

b the length of the radius of the circle.

7

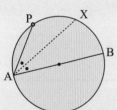

P   X   B   A

The circle alongside has diameter AB, and P is another point on the circle. The angle bisector of $\widehat{PAB}$ meets the circle at X. Show that the tangent at X is parallel to PB.

8 O is the centre of the circle alongside. The chords AC and BD are perpendicular.
Show that $\alpha + \beta = 180°$.
Hint: Join BC.

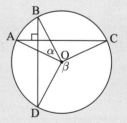

B   A   C   α   O   β   D

9 **a** Copy and complete: *"The angle between a tangent and a chord through the point of contact is equal to ......"*

b Two circles intersect at points P and Q. A line segment APB is drawn through P, and the tangents at A and B meet at C.

i Let $\widehat{ABC} = \alpha$ and $\widehat{BAC} = \beta$.
Write expressions for $\widehat{PQB}$, $\widehat{PQA}$, and $\widehat{AQB}$ in terms of α and β.

ii Hence, show that ACBQ is a cyclic quadrilateral.

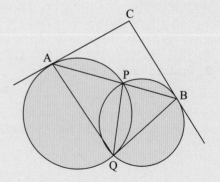

C   A   P   B   Q

10 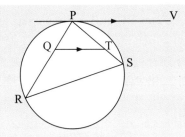 PV is a tangent to the circle, and QT is parallel to PV.
Prove that QRST is a cyclic quadrilateral.

Review set 31B

1 Find the value of x:

a

b

c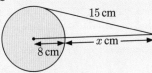

d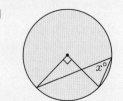

e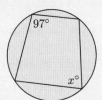

f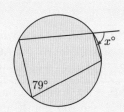

2 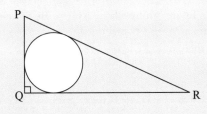 The circle inscribed in triangle PQR has radius of length 3 cm.
PQ has length 7 cm.
Find the perimeter of triangle PQR.

3 Find the value of x:

a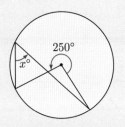

b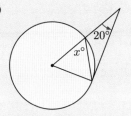

c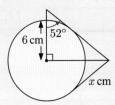

4 AB is the diameter of a circle with centre O.
AC and BD are any two chords.
Show that $B\hat{D}O = A\hat{C}D$.

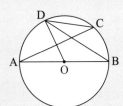

5 A, B, and C are three points on a circle. The bisector of $B\widehat{A}C$ cuts BC at P, and the circle at Q. Prove that $A\widehat{P}C = A\widehat{B}Q$.

6
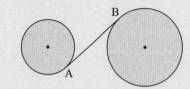
The circles illustrated have radii of length 5 cm and 7 cm respectively.

Their centres are 18 cm apart. Find the length of the common tangent AB.

7
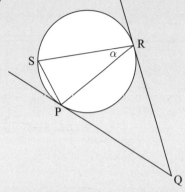
QP and QR are tangents to a circle. S is a point on the circle such that $P\widehat{S}R$ and $P\widehat{Q}R$ are equal, and both are double $P\widehat{R}S$. Let $P\widehat{R}S$ be α.

  a Find, in terms of α:

  i $P\widehat{S}R$ **ii** $P\widehat{Q}R$

  b Show that $\alpha = 30°$.

  c Find the measure of $Q\widehat{R}S$.

  d What can you conclude about RS?

8 AB and AC are any two chords which are *not* diameters of a circle with centre O. X and Y are the midpoints of AB and AC respectively.

Explain why quadrilateral OXAY is a cyclic quadrilateral.

9 AB is the diameter of a circle, and C and D are two other points on the circle. AC and BD meet at E, and AD and BC meet at F. Show that points C, D, E, and F form a cyclic quadrilateral.

10
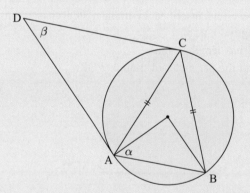
In the figure alongside, AC = BC, and the tangents at A and C meet at D.

Show that $\alpha + \beta = 90°$.

11 In the figure alongside, XT and XP are tangents.

Prove that:

  a BTXP is a cyclic quadrilateral

  b PT bisects $C\widehat{T}X$.

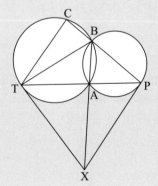

Probability

32

Contents:

A	Probability	[E10.1]
B	Experimental probability	[E10.2, E10.6]
C	Expectation	[E10.3]
D	Sample space and events	[E10.5, E10.6]
E	Theoretical probability	[E10.3, E10.6]
F	The addition law of probability	[E10.4]
G	Independent events	[E10.4, E10.5]
H	Dependent events	[E10.4, E10.5]

Opening problem

Players A, B, C, and D are the final four left in a knock-out tennis tournament. In the semi-finals, A will play B, and C will play D. The winners of these matches will play in the grand final.

The table alongside shows the probabilities of each player beating the others. For example, the yellow shaded square indicates that A has a 40% chance of beating B.

		loser		
winner	A	B	C	D
A		40%	55%	47%
B	60%		42%	54%
C	45%			35%
D	53%	46%	65%	

Things to think about:

a What is the probability that B will beat A?

b What is the sum of the probability that C will beat D and the probability that D will beat C? Can you explain why this must be true?

c Can you complete the table with the probability that C will beat B?

d How can we illustrate the possible outcomes of the finals series?

e Which player is most likely to win the grand final?

Probability deals with the **chance** or likelihood of an event occurring.

We can determine probabilities based on:

- the results of an experiment
- what we theoretically expect to happen.

The study of chance has important applications in physical and biological sciences, economics, politics, sport, life insurance, quality control, production planning, and many other areas.

Probability theory can be applied to card and dice games to try to increase our chances of success. It may therefore appear that an understanding of probability encourages gambling. However, a better knowledge of probability theory actually helps us to understand why the majority of habitual gamblers lose in the long term.

Historical note

Chevalier de Méré (1607 - 1684) was a French aristocrat and gambler in the 17th century. He wanted to know the answer to this question:

"Should I bet even money on the occurrence of at least one 'double six' when rolling a pair of dice 25 times?"

De Méré's experience of playing dice games convinced him that the answer was yes, but he did not know how to prove it. He therefore asked his friend, the French mathematician **Blaise Pascal** (1623 - 1662), for help.

Pierre de Fermat

In a series of letters between Pascal and fellow mathematician **Pierre de Fermat** (1607 - 1665), the problem was solved. In the process, they became interested in solving other questions of this kind, and together they laid the foundations of a new branch of mathematics called **theoretical probability**.

A   PROBABILITY   [E10.1]

> The **probability** of an event is a measure of the chance that it will occur.

Probabilities can be given as percentages from 0% to 100%, as proper fractions, or decimal numbers between 0 and 1.

> An **impossible** event has 0% chance of happening, and is assigned the probability 0.
>
> A **certain** event has 100% chance of happening, and is assigned the probability 1.
>
> All other events are assigned a probability between 0 and 1.

The number line below shows how we could interpret different probabilities:

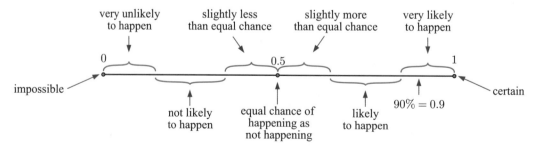

For example, suppose that the weather forecast says there is a 90% chance of rain tomorrow. We would say it is *very likely* that it will rain tomorrow.

Example 1   ◄)) *Self Tutor*

Use phrases to describe each probability:

a There is a 75% chance that Ted will be on time for school tomorrow.

b There is a 40% chance that Claire will burn her toast.

very unlikely to happen | slightly less than equal chance | slightly more than equal chance | very likely to happen

$75\% = 0.75$

0   0.5   1

impossible   certain

$40\% = 0.4$

not likely to happen | equal chance of happening as not happening | likely to happen

a It is *likely* that Ted will be on time for school tomorrow.

b There is a *slightly less than equal chance* that Claire will burn her toast.

In probability we can use capital letters such as E to represent events. The probability that event E occurs is written $P(E)$.

In **Example 1**, we could let E be the event that Ted will be on time for school tomorrow. In this case $P(E) = 0.75$.

COMPLEMENTARY EVENTS

Two events are **complementary** if exactly one of them *must* occur.

The probabilities of complementary events sum to 1.

The **complement** of event E is denoted E'. It is the event that E *does not* occur.

> For any event E with **complementary** event E',
> $$P(E) + P(E') = 1 \quad \text{or} \quad P(E') = 1 - P(E).$$

If E is the event that Ted will be on time for school tomorrow, then E' is the event that Ted will *not* be on time for school tomorrow, and $P(E') = 1 - 0.75 = 0.25$.

EXERCISE 32A

1 Use phrases to describe each probability:

a There is a 25% chance that Ella will score a goal in her next football match.

b There is a 60% chance that the restaurant will be booked out on Saturday night.

c There is a 5% chance that William will forget to take his lunch to school tomorrow.

2 Use a word or phrase to describe the probability:

a 0   **b** 0.23   **c** 0.77   **d** 1   **e** $\frac{19}{20}$ **f** $\frac{50}{100}$

3 Consider three events A, B, and C where $P(A) = \frac{1}{3}$, $P(B) = 60\%$, and $P(C) = 0.54$.
State the event which is:

   a most likely   **b** least likely.

4 Suppose a bag is filled with balls, and one ball is chosen at random. Use a phrase to describe the probability of choosing a *red* ball, if the bag contains:

   a 1 red ball and 1 blue ball   **b** 5 red balls

   c 2 blue balls and 3 green balls   **d** 1 red ball and 10 blue balls.

5 Five students are competing in a long distance race. Each student's probability of winning is given alongside.

Julie	20%
Edward	22%
Rob	7%
Tran	15%
Patricia	36%

   a Who is most likely to win the race?

   b Who is least likely to win the race?

   c Find the sum of the probabilities given. Explain your result.

   d Find the probability that either Julie *or* Tran will win the race.

   e Describe in words, the probability that Rob will win the race.

   f Let E be the event that Edward will win the race.

      i Find $P(E)$.   **ii** State the complementary event E'.   **iii** Find $P(E')$.

6 Suppose S is the event that it will snow tomorrow, and $P(S) = 0.03$.

   a State the complementary event S', in words.

   b Find $P(S')$.

   c Use a phrase to describe the probability of: **i** S occurring   **ii** S' occurring.

B   EXPERIMENTAL PROBABILITY   *[E10.2, E10.6]*

In experiments involving chance, we use the following terms to describe what we are doing and the results we are obtaining.

- The **number of trials** is the total number of times the experiment is repeated.
- The **outcomes** are the different results possible for one trial of the experiment.
- The **frequency** of a particular outcome is the number of times that this outcome is observed.
- The **relative frequency** of an outcome is the frequency of that outcome expressed as a fraction or percentage of the total number of trials.

$$\textbf{relative frequency} = \frac{\textbf{frequency}}{\textbf{number of trials}}$$

For example, when tossing a tin can in the air 250 times, it comes to rest on an end 37 times. We say:

- the number of trials is 250
- the outcomes are *end* and *side*
- the frequency of *end* is 37
- the frequency of *side* is 213
- the relative frequency of *end* $= \frac{37}{250} = 0.148$
- the relative frequency of *side* $= \frac{213}{250} = 0.852$.

                                            side   end

In the absence of any further data, the relative frequency of each outcome is our best estimate of the probability of it occurring.

The **experimental probability** is the **relative frequency** of the outcome.

Experimental probabilities are usually written as decimals.

We write $P(end) \approx 0.148$, $P(side) \approx 0.852$.

The larger the number of trials, the more accurate the estimate of the probability will be.

Example 2   ◄)) Self Tutor

A marketing company surveys 80 randomly selected people to discover what brand of shoe cleaner they use. The results are shown in the table alongside.

Brand	Frequency
Shine	27
Brite	22
Cleano	20
No Scuff	11

a Based on these results, estimate the probability that a randomly selected person uses:

   i Brite   **ii** Cleano.

b How accurate do you think your estimate in **a** will be? Explain your answer.

a We start by calculating the relative frequency for each brand.

   i $P(\text{Brite}) \approx 0.275$

   ii $P(\text{Cleano}) \approx 0.250$

b Not very accurate, as the sample size is very small.

Brand	Frequency	Relative Frequency
Shine	27	0.3375
Brite	22	0.2750
Cleano	20	0.2500
No Scuff	11	0.1375

EXERCISE 32B

1 A coin falls heads 47 times in 100 tosses. Find the experimental probability that the coin falls:

   a heads   **b** tails.

2 Clem fired 200 arrows at a target and hit the target 168 times. Estimate the probability that Clem hits the target.

3 Jackson leaves for work at the same time each day. Over a period of 227 working days he had to wait for a train at the railway crossing 58 times. Estimate the probability that Jackson has to wait for a train on his way to work.

4 Ravi has a circular spinner marked P, Q, and R on 3 sectors. Estimate the probability of getting a Q if the spinner was twirled 417 times and finished on Q on 98 occasions.

5 The tickets sold for a tennis match were recorded as people entered the stadium. The results are shown alongside.

Ticket type	Frequency	Relative frequency
Adult	3762	
Concession	1084	
Child	389	
Total		

   a How many tickets were sold in total?

   b Copy and complete the table.

   c If a person in the stadium is selected at random, estimate the probability that the person bought a Concession ticket.

6 A marketing company conducted a survey on the brands of soap people use. The results are shown alongside.

Brand	Frequency	Relative frequency
Silktouch	62	
Super	53	
Just Soap	46	
Indulgence	39	
Total		

   a How many people were selected in this survey?

   b Calculate the relative frequency for each brand of soap.

   c Estimate the probability that the soap used by a randomly selected person is:

     i Just Soap   **ii** Indulgence   **iii** Silktouch.

7 José recorded the lengths of internet commercials in seconds. His results are summarised in the table.

Estimate the probability that a randomly chosen internet commercial will last:

Length (t seconds)	Frequency
$0 \leqslant t < 20$	17
$20 \leqslant t < 40$	38
$40 \leqslant t < 60$	19
$t \geqslant 60$	4

   a between 20 and 40 seconds   **b** at least a minute

   c between 20 seconds and a minute.

8 Lauren teaches a class of 29 students. She recorded the number of students present in her class each day for 40 days. On exactly half of the days, there was no more than one student absent.

Number of students	Frequency
24	1
25	2
26	x
27	10
28	y
29	12

   a Find the values of x and y.

   b Estimate the probability that tomorrow Lauren's class will have between 25 and 27 students inclusive.

9 Ricky and Melia have 70 and 145 paper clips respectively. They each dropped their paper clips onto 6 cm by 6 cm squared paper. They then counted how many paper clips fell completely inside squares, and how many landed on a grid line:

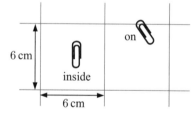

	Inside squares	On grid line
Ricky	54	16
Melia	113	32

   a Estimate the probability of a clip falling inside a square using:

     i Ricky's results   **ii** Melia's results.

   b Whose estimate is likely to be more *accurate*? Explain your answer.

Example 3   ◀) *Self Tutor*

To investigate the breakfast habits of teenagers, a survey was conducted amongst some students from a high school. The results are shown alongside.

	Male	Female
Regularly eats breakfast	87	53
Does not regularly eat breakfast	68	92

Use this table to estimate the probability that a randomly selected student from the school:

   a is male   **b** is male *and* regularly eats breakfast

   c is female *or* regularly eats breakfast.

We extend the table to include totals:

	Male	Female	*Total*
Regularly eats breakfast	87	53	140
Does not regularly eat breakfast	68	92	160
Total	155	145	300

a There are 155 males amongst the 300 students surveyed.

$\therefore$ P(male) $\approx \frac{155}{300} \approx 0.517$

b 87 of the 300 students are male and regularly eat breakfast.

$\therefore$ P(male *and* regularly eats breakfast) $\approx \frac{87}{300} \approx 0.29$

c $53 + 92 + 87 = 232$ out of the 300 are female or regularly eat breakfast.

$\therefore$ P(female *or* regularly eats breakfast) $\approx \frac{232}{300} \approx 0.773$

In probability, "*A* or *B*" means *A*, *B*, or both.

10 310 students at a high school in South Africa were surveyed on the question   "Do you like watching rugby on TV?".   The results are shown in the table.

	Like	Dislike
Junior students	87	38
Senior students	129	56

a Copy and complete the table to include totals.

b Estimate the probability that a randomly selected student:

i likes watching rugby on TV and is a junior student

ii likes watching rugby on TV and is a senior student

iii dislikes watching rugby on TV.

c Find the sum of the probabilities found in **b**. Explain your answer.

11 A random selection of students in a youth club were asked whether they wore glasses, contact lenses, or neither.   The results were further categorised by gender.

	Glasses	Contact lenses	Neither
Male	15	6	26
Female	14	8	31

a How many students were surveyed?

b Estimate the probability that a randomly chosen student in the club:

i wears glasses   **ii** is female and wears contact lenses

iii is male and wears neither   **iv** is female or wears glasses.

12 The table alongside gives the age distribution of inmates in a prison on December 31, 2017.

A new prisoner entered the prison on January 1, 2018. Estimate the probability that the new prisoner was:

a male

b aged from 17 to 19

c 19 or under *and* was female

d aged from 30 to 49 *and* was male.

Age distribution of prison inmates			
Age	*Female*	*Male*	*Total*
15	0	6	6
16	5	23	28
17 - 19	26	422	448
20 - 24	41	1124	1165
25 - 29	36	1001	1037
30 - 34	32	751	783
35 - 39	31	520	551
40 - 49	24	593	617
50 - 59	16	234	250
60+	5	148	153
Total	216	4822	5038

C   *EXPECTATION*   *[E10.3]*

The probability of an event can be used to predict the number of times the event will occur in a number of trials.

For example, from the tournaments last year, if Rory has a putt from less than 2 metres, the experimental probability that he will hit the ball in the hole is 0.861. If Rory has 62 putts from less than 2 metres in his next tournament, we would *expect* him to make $62 \times 0.861 \approx 53$ of them.

> If there are n trials of an experiment, and the probability of an event occurring in each trial is p, then the **expectation** of the occurrence of that event is np.

Example 4   *Self Tutor*

In one week, 79 out of 511 trains were late to the station at Keswick. In the next month, 2369 trains are scheduled to pass through the station. How many of these would you expect to be late?

The experimental probability of a train being late to Keswick is $p = \frac{79}{511}$.

We expect $2369 \times \frac{79}{511} \approx 366$ trains in the next month to be late.

EXERCISE 32C

1 In a particular region in Africa, the probability that it will rain on any one day is 0.177. On how many days of the year would you expect it to rain?

2 At practice, Tony kicked 53 out of 74 goals from the penalty goal spot. If he performs as well through the season and has 18 attempts to kick penalty goals, how many would you expect him to score?

3 When a drawing pin was tossed 400 times, it landed on its back 144 times. If the drawing pin is tossed 72 more times, how many "backs" would you expect?

4 When Annette throws darts at the target shown, she hits the inner circle 17% of the time and the outer circle 72% of the time.

   a Estimate the probability that Annette will miss the target completely with her next throw.

   b Suppose Annette throws a dart 100 times at the target. She receives 100 points if she hits the inner circle and 20 points if she hits the outer circle. Find:

      i the total number of points you would expect her to get

      ii the mean number of points you would expect per throw.

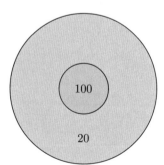

5 In a random survey of a district, people are asked whether they will vote for politician A, B, or C. The results are shown alongside.

A	B	C
165	87	48

   a How many people took part in the survey?

   b Estimate the probability that a randomly chosen voter in the district will vote for:

      i A   **ii** B   **iii** C.

   c There are 7500 people in the district. How many of these would you expect to vote for:

      i A   **ii** B   **iii** C?

6 The table alongside shows the sales for a coffee truck in one morning. In total, 80 coffees were sold.

  a Copy and complete the table.

  b The truck sold 900 coffees in total for the week. How many of these coffees would you expect to be large?

Size	Frequency	Relative frequency
Small	34	
Medium	28	
Large		

D SAMPLE SPACE AND EVENTS   [E10.5, E10.6]

The **sample space** U is the set of all possible outcomes of an experiment.

An **event** is a set of outcomes in the sample space that have a particular property.

Possible ways of representing sample spaces are:
- listing them in set notation
- using a tree diagram
- using a 2-dimensional grid
- using a Venn diagram.

Example 5   ◀) *Self Tutor*

Suppose the octahedral die alongside is rolled once. Using set notation, list:
  a the sample space U
  b the outcomes in the event A that an odd number is rolled.

  a $U = \{1, 2, 3, 4, 5, 6, 7, 8\}$ **b** $A = \{1, 3, 5, 7\}$

Example 6   ◀) *Self Tutor*

When two coins are tossed, the possible outcomes are:

  two heads   head and tail   tail and head   two tails

Represent the sample space for tossing two coins using:
  a a list in set notation   **b** a 2-dimensional grid   **c** a tree diagram.

We let H represent a "head" and T represent a "tail".
  a {HH, HT, TH, TT}

  b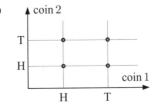

  c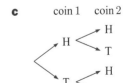

EXERCISE 32D

1 A normal six-sided die is rolled once. Using set notation, list:

   a the sample space U

   b the outcomes in the event A that a prime number is rolled.

2 Lucy randomly selects one letter from the alphabet.

   a Write down the sample space U.

   b List the outcomes in:

      i A, the event that Lucy selects a consonant

      ii B, the event that Lucy selects a letter in the word EVENT.

3 List the sample space for:

   a twirling a square spinner labelled A, B, C, D

   b the genders of a: **i** 2-child family   **ii** 3-child family.

   c the order in which 4 blocks A, B, C, and D can be lined up

   d tossing a coin: **i** twice   **ii** three times   **iii** four times.

4 Use a 2-dimensional grid to illustrate the sample space for:

   a rolling a die and tossing a coin simultaneously

   b rolling two dice

   c rolling a die and spinning a spinner with sides A, B, C, D.

5 Use a grid to illustrate the sample space for twirling two square spinners, one labelled A, B, C, D, and the other 1, 2, 3, 4. Circle the outcomes corresponding to the event "a B or an odd number".

Example 7

 Self Tutor

Illustrate, using a tree diagram, the possible outcomes when drawing two marbles from a bag containing red, green, and yellow marbles.

Highlight the outcomes corresponding to the event "drawing at least one red marble".

Let R be "drawing a red",
     G be "drawing a green", and
     Y be "drawing a yellow".

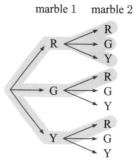

Each branch of the tree diagram represents a possible outcome.

---

6 Illustrate on a tree diagram the sample space for:

   a tossing a 5-cent and 10-cent coin simultaneously

   b tossing a coin and twirling an equilateral triangular spinner labelled A, B, and C

   c twirling two equilateral triangular spinners labelled 1, 2, 3, and X, Y, Z respectively

d   selecting bag A or bag B, then drawing a ball from that bag.

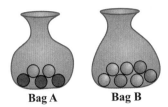

Bag A   Bag B

7   Draw a tree diagram to illustrate the sample space when drawing two tickets from a hat containing pink, blue, and white tickets. Highlight the outcomes corresponding to the event "at least one blue ticket".

8   Draw a Venn diagram to show a class of 20 students in which 7 study History and Geography, 10 study History, and 15 study Geography.

E   THEORETICAL PROBABILITY   [E10.3, E10.6]

The sample space when rolling a single die is $\{1, 2, 3, 4, 5, 6\}$.

Since the die is a cube and therefore symmetrical, we expect that each of the six outcomes will be **equally likely** to occur. We say that the **theoretical probability** of any given outcome occurring is 1 in 6, or $\frac{1}{6}$.

> If a sample space has n outcomes which are **equally likely** to occur when the experiment is performed once, then each outcome has probability $\dfrac{1}{n}$ of occurring.

Consider the event of *rolling a prime number* with an ordinary die. Of the 6 possible outcomes, the three outcomes 2, 3, and 5 all correspond to this event. So, the probability of rolling a prime number is 3 in 6, or $\frac{3}{6}$.

> When the outcomes of an experiment are equally likely, the probability that an event E occurs is:
>
> $$P(E) = \frac{\text{number of outcomes corresponding to } E}{\text{number of outcomes in the sample space}}$$

Example 8   ◀) *Self Tutor*

Suppose three coins are tossed simultaneously. Find the probability of getting:

a   three heads   **b**   at least one head.

The possible outcomes are:

$$\{HHH, HHT, HTH, THH, TTH, THT, HTT, TTT\}.$$

There are 8 possible outcomes.

a   P(three heads) $= \dfrac{1}{8}$ ◀—— three heads only occurs in the outcome HHH
         ◀—— 8 possible outcomes

b   P(at least one head) $= \dfrac{7}{8}$ ◀—— all outcomes except TTT contain at least one head
         ◀—— 8 possible outcomes

EXERCISE 32E

1 A spinner with the numbers 1 to 5 written on equal sectors is spun once. Find the probability of spinning:

    a a 4   **b** a 1 or a 2   **c** an odd number.

2 Candice has baked 6 blueberry muffins and 12 raspberry muffins. She chooses one to eat at random.

Let E be the event that the muffin is blueberry.

E' is the **complementary event** of E.

    a Explain the meaning of the event E'.

    b Find $P(E)$ and $P(E')$.

3   **a** If 2 coins are tossed, what is the chance that they both fall heads?

    b If 2 coins are tossed 300 times, how many times would you expect them to both fall heads?

4 A hat contains three yellow discs and four green discs. A disc is drawn from the hat, its colour recorded, and the disc is returned to the hat. If this procedure is performed 350 times, on how many occasions would you expect a green disc to be drawn?

5 Two dice are rolled simultaneously 180 times. How many times would you expect to get a double?

6 There are 5 different pairs of socks in Vanessa's sock drawer. The light in her room is not working, so she takes 2 socks from her drawer at random. Find the probability that Vanessa has a matching pair.

7 A die has the numbers 0, 1, 2, 2, 3, and 4 on its faces. The die is rolled 600 times. How many times would you expect the result to be:

    a 0   **b** 2   **c** 1, 2, or 3   **d** not 4?

8 The three letters E, N, and T are placed at random in a row. Find the probability of:

    a spelling NET   **b** E appearing first

    c E not appearing first   **d** spelling NET or TEN.

9 Determine the probability that a randomly selected 3-child family consists of:

    a all boys   **b** all girls   **c** boy, then girl, then girl

    d two girls and a boy   **e** a girl for the eldest   **f** at least one boy.

10 Four friends Alex, Bodi, Claire, and Daniel sit randomly in a row. Determine the probability that:

    a Alex is on one of the ends

    b Claire and Daniel are on the ends

    c Bodi is on an end, and Claire is seated next to him

    d Alex and Claire sit next to each other.

11 List the possible outcomes when four coins are tossed simultaneously. Hence determine the probability of getting:

    a all heads   **b** two heads and two tails   **c** more tails than heads

    d at least one tail   **e** exactly one head.

Example 9   ◀ﾂ) *Self Tutor*

A die has the numbers 0, 0, 1, 1, 4, and 5. It is rolled twice.
a   Illustrate the possible outcomes using a 2-dimensional grid.
b   Hence find the probability of getting:
i   a total of 5   ii   two numbers which are the same.

a   roll 2

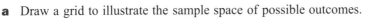

b   There are $6 \times 6 = 36$ possible outcomes.

    i   P(total of 5)

$$= \frac{8}{36} \quad \{\text{those with a } \times \}$$

$$= \frac{2}{9}$$

    ii   P(same numbers)

$$= \frac{10}{36} \quad \{\text{those circled}\}$$

$$= \frac{5}{18}$$

roll 1 axis: 0 0 1 1 4 5

12   a   Draw a grid to illustrate the sample space when a 10-cent and a 50-cent coin are tossed simultaneously.
   b   Hence, determine the probability of getting:
    i   two heads   ii   two tails   iii   exactly one head   iv   at least one head.

13   A coin and a pentagonal spinner with sectors 1, 2, 3, 4, and 5 are tossed and spun respectively.
   a   Draw a grid to illustrate the sample space of possible outcomes.
   b   Use your grid to determine the chance of getting:
    i   a head and a 4   ii   a tail and an odd number
    iii   an even number   iv   a tail or a 3.

14   a   Use a grid to display the possible outcomes when a pair of dice is rolled.

   b   Hence, determine the probability of:
    i   one die showing a 4 and the other a 5
    ii   both dice showing the same number
    iii   at least one of the dice showing a 3   iv   either a 4 or 6 being displayed
    v   both dice showing even numbers   vi   the sum of the numbers being 7.

15   The spinners shown are spun once, and the numbers spun are multiplied together.
   a   Find the probability that the result is:
    i   9   ii   6
    iii   greater than 5   iv   prime.
   b   Is the result more likely to be even or odd?
   c   If the spinners were spun 600 times, how many times would you expect the product of the numbers to be 3?

16 A 52 card pack is well shuffled, then one card is dealt from the top of the pack. Find the probability that the card is:

   a a Queen   **b** the Jack of hearts

   c a spade   **d** a picture card

   e a red 7   **f** a diamond or a club

   g a King or a heart   **h** a Queen and a 3.

Example 10   🔊 *Self Tutor*

In a library group of 50 readers, 31 like science fiction, 20 like detective stories, and 12 dislike both.

   a Draw a Venn diagram to represent this information.

   b If a reader is randomly selected, find the probability that he or she:

       i likes science fiction and detective stories

      ii likes exactly one of science fiction and detective stories.

   a Let S represent readers who like science fiction, and D represent readers who like detective stories.

      We are given that $a + b = 31$

$$b + c = 20$$
$$a + b + c = 50 - 12 = 38$$
$$\therefore \; c = 38 - 31 = 7$$
$$\therefore \; b = 13 \text{ and } a = 18$$

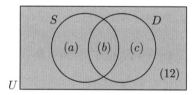

   b **i** P(likes both) $= \frac{13}{50}$

       ii P(likes exactly one) $= \dfrac{18 + 7}{50}$

$$= \tfrac{1}{2}$$

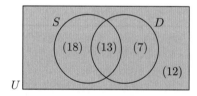

---

17 The Venn diagram shows the sports played by the students in a Year 10 class.

   a How many students are in the class?

   b A student is chosen at random. Find the probability that the student:

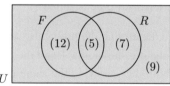

$F \equiv$ football
$R \equiv$ rugby

       i plays football   **ii** plays both sports

    iii plays football or rugby   **iv** plays exactly one of these sports.

18 In a class of 24 students, 10 study Biology, 12 study Chemistry, and 5 study neither Biology nor Chemistry. Find the probability that a student picked at random from the class studies:

   a Chemistry, but not Biology   **b** both Chemistry and Biology.

19 60 married men were asked whether they gave their wife flowers or chocolates for their last birthday. It was found that 26 gave chocolates, 21 gave flowers, and 5 gave both chocolates and flowers. If one of the married men is chosen at random, determine the probability that he gave his wife:

   a flowers but not chocolates   **b** neither chocolates nor flowers   **c** chocolates or flowers.

20 50 tourists went on a "thrill seekers" holiday. 40 went white-water rafting, 21 went paragliding, and each tourist did at least one of these activities.

Find the probability that a randomly selected tourist:

    a participated in both activities   **b** went white-water rafting but not paragliding.

21 100 people were asked the question: "Which of yesterday's meals did you make yourself?"

51 people made their breakfast, 41 people made their lunch, and 53 people made their dinner. 21 people made breakfast and lunch, 28 people made breakfast and dinner, and 26 people made lunch and dinner. 9 people made all three meals.

    a Let B represent the people who made their breakfast,
               L represent the people who made their lunch,
      and D represent the people who made their dinner.
      Copy and complete the Venn diagram alongside.

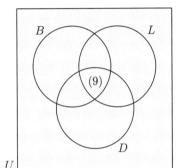

    b One of the people surveyed is chosen at random.
      Find the probability that they made:

        i   breakfast only   **ii** none of the meals

     iii lunch and dinner only

      iv breakfast or lunch, but not both

       v exactly two of the three meals.

Puzzle   *The dice problem*

Click on the icon to obtain this Puzzle.

THE DICE PROBLEM

F *THE ADDITION LAW OF PROBABILITY [E10.4]*

Discovery   *The addition law of probability*

Suppose we are conducting a probability experiment, and we are interested in the occurrence of two events, A and B.

In this Discovery, we consider how the probabilities $P(A)$, $P(B)$, $P(A \cup B)$, and $P(A \cap B)$ are related.

What to do:

  1 Suppose we randomly select an integer from 1 to 9.
     Let A be the event that a prime number is selected.
     Let B be the event that an even number is selected.

    a Draw a Venn diagram to show the sample space and the events A and B.
    b Hence find: **i** $P(A)$ **ii** $P(B)$ **iii** $P(A \cap B)$ **iv** $P(A \cup B)$
    c Show that $P(A \cup B) = P(A) + P(B) - P(A \cap B)$.

2 In a class of 26 girls, 14 play netball, 10 play tennis, and 5 play both of these sports. Let A represent girls who play netball and B represent girls who play tennis.

  a Draw a Venn diagram to show the sample space and the events A and B.

  b Hence find: **i** $P(A)$ **ii** $P(B)$ **iii** $P(A \cap B)$ **iv** $P(A \cup B)$

  c Show that $P(A \cup B) = P(A) + P(B) - P(A \cap B)$.

You should have discovered the **addition law of probability**:

> For two events A and B, $P(A \cup B) = P(A) + P(B) - P(A \cap B)$
>
> which means: P(**either** A **or** B **or** both) $= P(A) + P(B) -$ P(**both** A **and** B).

MUTUALLY EXCLUSIVE EVENTS

In a probability experiment, not all events we consider will have common outcomes.

For example, suppose we randomly select an integer from 1 to 6.

Let A be the event that a prime number is selected, so $A = \{2, 3, 5\}$.

Let B be the event that a composite number is selected, so $B = \{4, 6\}$.

The events A and B have no common outcomes, so we can draw a Venn diagram in which their circles do not overlap.

$$P(A \cap B) = 0$$

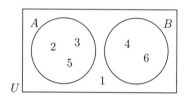

> Two events are **mutually exclusive** or **disjoint** if they have no common outcomes.
>
> If A and B are mutually exclusive events then $P(A \cap B) = 0$.
>
> For mutually exclusive events, $P(A \cup B) = P(A) + P(B)$.

Example 11
◀⟩ *Self Tutor*

Suppose $P(A) = 0.2$, $P(B) = 0.6$, and $P(A \cap B) = 0.1$.

  a Are A and B mutually exclusive events? Explain your answer.   **b** Find $P(A \cup B)$.

  a A and B are *not* mutually exclusive, since $P(A \cap B) \neq 0$.

  b $P(A \cup B) = P(A) + P(B) - P(A \cap B)$
$$= 0.2 + 0.6 - 0.1$$
$$= 0.7$$

EXERCISE 32F

1 An ordinary die with faces 1, 2, 3, 4, 5, and 6 is rolled once. Consider these events:

        A: rolling a 1 B: rolling a 3
        C: rolling an odd number D: rolling an even number
        E: rolling a prime number F: rolling a result greater than 3.

  a List the pairs of events which are mutually exclusive.

  b Find: **i** $P(B \cup D)$ **ii** $P(D \cup E)$ **iii** $P(A \cup E)$

              iv $P(B \cup E)$ **v** $P(C \cup D)$ **vi** $P(A \cup B \cup F)$.

2 A coin and an ordinary die are tossed simultaneously.

   a Draw a grid showing the 12 possible outcomes.

   b Find the probability of getting: **i** a head and a 5   **ii** a head or a 5.

   c Check that: P(H or 5) = P(H) + P(5) − P(H and 5).

3 Two ordinary dice are rolled.

   a Draw a grid showing the 36 possible outcomes.

   b Find the probability of getting: **i** a 3 and a 4   **ii** a 3 or a 4.

   c Check that: P(3 or 4) = P(3) + P(4) − P(3 and 4).

4 A playing card is selected at random from a normal 52 card deck. Identify whether the two events are mutually exclusive. If the events are *not* mutually exclusive, find the probability that they both occur.

   a a 7 *and* a 2   **b** a 7 *and* a heart

   c a spade *and* a diamond   **d** a red card *and* a King

5 Suppose $P(A) = \frac{1}{3}$, $P(B) = \frac{2}{5}$, and A and B are mutually exclusive. Find $P(A \cup B)$.

6 Suppose $P(A) = 0.7$, $P(B) = 0.2$, and $P(A \cap B) = 0.15$.

   a Are A and B mutually exclusive events? Explain your answer.

   b Find $P(A \cup B)$.

7 Suppose $P(X) = 0.3$, $P(X \cup Y) = 0.7$, and X and Y are mutually exclusive. Find $P(Y)$.

8 Suppose $P(C) = 0.6$ and $P(D) = 0.7$. Explain why C and D are not mutually exclusive.

G   INDEPENDENT EVENTS   *[E10.4, E10.5]*

We will now look more closely at **compound events** involving two operations.

> Two events are **independent** if the occurrence of each event does not affect the occurrence of the other.

Consider tossing a coin and rolling a die simultaneously.

The two events "getting a head" and "rolling a 5" are independent events, since the outcome of the coin toss has no effect on the outcome from the dice roll.

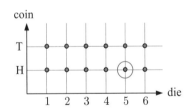

From the grid, we see there are 12 possible outcomes, only one of which is a head *and* a five.

∴   P(a head and a 5) = $\frac{1}{12}$

Also, P(a head) = $\frac{1}{2}$ and P(a 5) = $\frac{1}{6}$.

∴   P(a head) × P(a 5) = $\frac{1}{2} \times \frac{1}{6} = \frac{1}{12}$.

Notice that P(a head **and** a 5) = P(a head) × P(a 5).

> If two events A and B are **independent** then
> $P(A \cap B) = P(A) \times P(B)$.

Remember, $A \cap B$ means A *and* B.

Example 12
◀) **Self Tutor**

A coin is tossed and a square spinner labelled A, B, C, and D is spun simultaneously. Determine the probability of getting a tail and a B.

The events are independent, since the outcome from the coin does not affect the outcome from the spinner, and vice versa.

$\therefore$ P(a tail and a B) = P(a tail) $\times$ P(a B)

$$= \tfrac{1}{2} \times \tfrac{1}{4}$$

$$= \tfrac{1}{8}$$

EXERCISE 32G

1 A coin and a 6-sided die are tossed simultaneously. Find the probability of getting:
  a a tail and a number larger than 2   **b** a head and a composite number.

2 A coin and a pentagonal spinner with edges marked A, B, C, D, and E are tossed and twirled simultaneously. Find the probability of getting:
  a a head and a D   **b** a tail and either an A or a D.

3 A spinner with 6 equal sides has 3 red, 2 blue, and 1 yellow edge. A second spinner with 7 equal sides has 4 purple and 3 green edges. Both spinners are twirled simultaneously. Find the probability of getting:
  a a red and a green   **b** a blue and a purple.

4 When a nut was tossed 400 times it finished on its edge 84 times and on its side for the rest. Estimate the probability that when two of these nuts are tossed:
  a they both fall on their edges   **b** they both fall on their sides.

edge   side

Example 13
◀) **Self Tutor**

Sunil has probability $\tfrac{4}{5}$ of hitting a target and Monika has probability $\tfrac{5}{6}$.

If they both fire simultaneously at the target, determine the probability that:
  a they both hit   **b** they both miss.

Let S be the event of Sunil hitting the target and M be the event of Monika hitting it.

  a P(both hit) = P(S and M)   **b** P(both miss) = P(S' and M')

   = P(S) $\times$ P(M)   = P(S') $\times$ P(M')

   = $\tfrac{4}{5} \times \tfrac{5}{6}$ = $\tfrac{1}{5} \times \tfrac{1}{6}$

   = $\tfrac{2}{3}$ = $\tfrac{1}{30}$

5 Janice and Lee take set shots at a netball goal. From past experience, Janice throws a goal on average 2 times in every 3 shots, whereas Lee throws a goal 4 times in every 7. If they both shoot for goal, determine the probability that:
  a both score   **b** both miss   **c** Janice scores but Lee misses.

6 A school has two photocopiers. On any one day, machine A has an 8% chance of having a paper jam, and machine B has a 12% chance of having a paper jam.

Determine the probability that, on any one day, both machines will:

   a have paper jams   **b** work uninterrupted.

7 A boy and a girl were each asked what day of the week they were born. Find the probability that:

   a the boy was born on a Monday and the girl was born on a Wednesday

   b the boy was born on a weekend, but the girl was not

   c both children were born on a weekday.

8 Each day, Steve attempts the easy, medium, and hard crosswords in the newspaper. He has probability 0.84 of completing the easy crossword, probability 0.59 of completing the medium crossword, and probability 0.11 of completing the hard crossword.

Find the probability that, on any given day, Steve will:

   a complete all 3 crosswords

   b leave all 3 crosswords incomplete

   c complete the easy and medium crosswords, but not the hard crossword

   d complete the medium crossword, but not the other two crosswords.

9 A biased coin is flipped 200 times. It lands on heads 143 times, and on tails for the remainder. If the coin is flipped 3 times, estimate the probability of getting:

   a all heads   **b** all tails.

Example 14   ◀)) *Self Tutor*

A marble is selected at random from each of the bags alongside.

   a Draw a tree diagram to display the possible outcomes.

   b Find the probability of obtaining a green marble and a yellow marble.

Bag A   Bag B

   a Let G represent a green marble,
              Y represent a yellow marble, and
              O represent an orange marble.

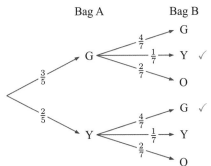

   b   P(a green and a yellow marble)

$= $ P(GY or YG)   {branches marked ✓}

$= \frac{3}{5} \times \frac{1}{7} + \frac{2}{5} \times \frac{4}{7}$

$= \frac{11}{35}$

If 2 or more branches satisfy the event, the probabilities are **added**.

10   Bag A contains 4 red jelly beans and 1 yellow jelly bean. Bag B contains 2 red and 3 yellow jelly beans. A bag is randomly selected by tossing a coin, and one jelly bean is removed from it. Determine the probability that it is yellow.

11   Suppose this spinner is spun twice.

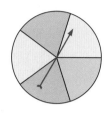

   a   Draw a tree diagram to illustrate the sample space.

   b   Determine the probability that:

   i   blue appears on both spins   **ii**   green appears on both spins

   iii   different colours appear on the two spins

   iv   blue appears on *either* spin.

12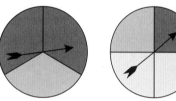

Spinner 1   **Spinner 2**

Each of the spinners alongside is spun once.

   a   Construct a tree diagram to display the possible outcomes.

   b   Find the probability that:

   i   the spinners land on the same colour

   ii   the spinners land on different colours

   iii   exactly one of the spinners lands on blue.

13   A ticket is selected at random from each of the boxes shown.

Box A   **Box B**

   a   Draw a tree diagram to display the possible outcomes.

   b   Find the probability of obtaining:

   i   a blue ticket and a green ticket

   ii   two tickets of the same colour

   iii   exactly one pink ticket.

   c   Find the sum of the probabilities in **b**. Explain your result.

14   Sharon, Christine, and Keith have agreed to meet at a restaurant for lunch. Sharon has probability 0.8 of being on time, Christine has probability 0.7 of being on time, and Keith has probability 0.4 of being on time.

   a   Draw a tree diagram to display the possible outcomes.

   b   Determine the probability that at least 2 people will arrive on time.

H   **DEPENDENT EVENTS**   **[E10.4, E10.5]**

A hat contains 5 red and 3 blue tickets. One ticket is randomly chosen, its colour is noted, and it is then thrown away. A second ticket is randomly selected.

If the first ticket was red, $P(\text{second ticket is red}) = \dfrac{4}{7}$ ◄—— 4 reds remaining

                                                                         ◄—— 7 to choose from

If the first ticket was blue, $P(\text{second ticket is red}) = \dfrac{5}{7}$ ◄—— 5 reds remaining

                                                                          ◄—— 7 to choose from

So, the probability of the second ticket being red *depends* on what colour the first ticket was.

Two events are **dependent** if they are **not independent**.

The occurrence of one of the events *does* affect the occurrence of the other event.

The rule for finding compound event probabilities for dependent events is different from the rule for independent events.

If A and B are dependent events, then $P(A \cap B) = P(A) \times P(B$ given that A has occurred$)$.

Example 15
◀)) *Self Tutor*

A bag contains 3 orange and 4 green balls. Two balls are randomly selected one after the other from the bag, the first being removed before the second ball is chosen. Find the probability that:

a both balls are orange

b the first ball is orange and the second ball is green.

a   P(both balls are orange)

= P(first ball is orange and the second ball is orange)

= P(first ball is orange) × P(second ball is orange given that the first ball is orange)

$= \dfrac{3}{7} \times \dfrac{2}{6}$ ◀── 2 orange balls remaining
    ◀── 6 balls to choose from

$= \dfrac{6}{42}$

$= \dfrac{1}{7}$

b   P(first ball is orange and the second ball is green)

= P(first ball is orange) × P(second ball is green given that the first ball is orange)

$= \dfrac{3}{7} \times \dfrac{4}{6}$ ◀── 4 green balls remaining
    ◀── 6 balls to choose from

$= \dfrac{12}{42}$

$= \dfrac{2}{7}$

EXERCISE 32H

1 A box contains 5 red and 2 purple balls. Two balls are randomly selected from the box. The first is *not* replaced in the box before the second is selected. Determine the probability that:

    a both balls are red   **b** the first ball is purple and the second is red.

2 Amelie has a bag containing 4 red apples and 6 green ones. She selects one apple at random, eats it, and then takes another, also at random.

    a Determine the probability that:

       i   both apples were red

      ii   both apples were green

     iii   the first was red and the second was green

     iv   the first was green and the second was red.

    b Find the sum of the probabilities in **a**. Explain your answer.

3 A pocket in a golf bag contains 6 white and 4 yellow golf balls. Two of them are selected at random without replacement.

  a Determine the probability that:
  > **i** both are white   **ii** the first is white and the second is yellow
  > **iii** one of each colour is selected.

  b Why do your answers in **a** not add up to 1?

4 In a class of 27 students, 13 students have brothers, 16 have sisters, and 5 have neither.

  a Illustrate this information on a Venn diagram.

  b Two students are selected at random from the class. Find the probability that both students have only sisters.

5 Balls numbered 1 to 10 are placed in a bag. Two of the balls are drawn out at random. Find the probability that the numbers on the balls are consecutive.

6 A box contains 3 red discs and 5 blue discs. Two discs are selected from the box. Find the probability that the discs have the same colour if:

  a the first disc is replaced before the second disc is selected

  b no replacement occurs.

7 A drawer contains 5 blue pens, 3 red pens, and 2 green pens. A pen is selected at random from the drawer and put to one side. A second pen is then selected at random from the drawer.

  a Draw a tree diagram to display the possible outcomes.

  b Find the probability that:
  > **i** the selected pens are the same colour   **ii** exactly one of the pens is green.

8 Matt is the best player in his lacrosse team. He has an injured knee, and has only a 60% chance of playing the next game. The team has a 70% chance of winning the next game if Matt plays, but only a 45% chance of winning if he does not play.

  a Represent this information on a tree diagram.

  b Find the probability that the team will win the next game.

9 In a netball team, the Goal Shooter takes 65% of the team's shots, and scores 70% of the time. The Goal Attack takes the remainder of the shots, and scores 60% of the time.
Find the probability that the team will score with their next shot.

10 A fair coin is tossed. If the result is heads, one marble is selected from the bag alongside. If the result is tails, two marbles are selected, without replacement. Find the probability that at least one red marble will be selected.

11 A container has 4 purple, 3 blue, and 1 gold ticket. Three tickets are selected without replacement. Find the probability that:

  a all are purple   **b** all are blue   **c** the first two are purple and the third is gold.

12 The spinner below is used to select box A, B, or C. Two discs are then randomly selected from that box, without replacement.

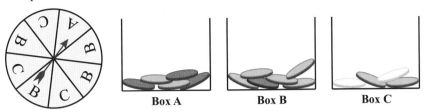

Box A   Box B   Box C

Find the probability that exactly one green disc is selected.

13 A coin is selected at random from pot A and placed in pot B. Then, a coin is selected at random from pot B and placed in pot A. Finally, a coin is selected at random from pot A. Find the probability that this coin is gold.

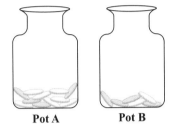

Pot A   Pot B

14 Jill and Mandy are considering whether to go to a party. If their friend Donna does *not* go, the probability that Jill will attend is 0.4, and the probability that Mandy will attend is 0.6. If Donna *does* go to the party, Jill and Mandy's probabilities will increase to 0.5 and 0.7 respectively.

The probability that Donna will go to the party is 0.8. Find the probability that exactly two of the three friends will attend.

15 A frog is in the middle of a 3×3 arrangement of squares.

Each time the frog jumps, it lands with equal probability on one of the adjacent squares (either horizontally, vertically, or diagonally).

Find the probability that, after 3 jumps, the frog is on:

  a the middle square   **b** a corner square

  c an edge square that is not a corner square.

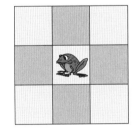

Review set 32A

1 Write a phrase to describe the probability of these events:

  a There is a 95% chance that there will be a test next week.

  b There is a 45% chance that it will snow tomorrow.

2 A survey of forty five 18 year olds was conducted. It was found that 19 enjoyed camping.

  a Estimate the probability that a randomly selected 18 year old likes camping.

  b How can the accuracy of this estimate be improved?

3 A letter of the alphabet is chosen at random. Find the probability that the letter is:

  a M or N   **b** contained in the word CHOCOLATE

  c after the letter S in the alphabet.

4 A coin is tossed, and a spinner with equal sectors numbered 1, 2, 3, 4, and 5 is spun.

  a Use a 2-dimensional grid to illustrate the sample space.

  b Find the probability of getting: **i** a head and a 5   **ii** a head or a 5.

5 A marketing company was commissioned to investigate the main reason teenagers used the internet. The results of the survey are shown alongside.

Reason	Frequency	Relative frequency
Homework	29	
Social media	43	
Playing games	15	
Streaming music	69	
Total		

   a How many teenagers were surveyed?

   b Copy and complete the table.

   c Estimate the probability that a randomly selected teenager mainly uses the internet for:

   i homework   **ii** something other than streaming music.

6 From past experience, a surfer has probability 0.83 of catching a wave. In one week she tries to catch 75 waves. How many waves do you expect her to catch?

7 A hat contains 12 tickets with the numbers 1 to 12 printed on them. If two tickets are drawn from the hat without replacement, find the probability that they are both prime numbers.

8 Each morning when Harold has a shower, there is a 90% chance that the hot water is working. The probability that Harold has a long shower is 80% if the hot water is working, and 10% if the hot water is not working.

   a Find the probability that, on any given day, Harold will have a long shower.

   b During a 365 day year, how many long showers would you expect Harold to have?

9 The table alongside shows the results from asking the question "Do you like the school uniform?".

If a student is randomly selected from these year groups, estimate the probability that the student:

	Likes	Dislikes
Year 8	129	21
Year 9	108	42
Year 10	81	69

   a likes the school uniform   **b** dislikes the school uniform

   c is in Year 8 and dislikes the uniform.

10 Matthew is taking a Mathematics test. There is a 2% chance that his calculator will not work. If his calculator works, Matthew has a 70% probability of passing the test. If his calculator does not work, Matthew has a 55% probability of passing the test.
Find the probability that Matthew passes the test.

11 A class has 25 students. 15 have blue eyes, 9 have fair hair, and 3 have both blue eyes and fair hair.

   a Represent this information on a Venn diagram.

   b Hence, find the probability that a randomly selected student from the class:

   i has neither blue eyes nor fair hair   **ii** has blue eyes, but not fair hair.

12 Let $P(A) = 0.2$ and $P(B) = 0.7$. Find $P(A \cap B)$ given that A and B are:

   a mutually exclusive   **b** independent.

13 A ball is selected from box A and placed in box B. A ball is then selected from box B, and placed in box C. A ball is then selected from box C.
Find the probability that the ball is blue.

Box A   Box B   Box C

Review set 32B

1   What is meant by saying that two events are *independent*?

2   When a box of drawing pins was dropped onto the floor, 49 pins landed on their backs and 32 landed on their sides. Estimate, to 2 decimal places, the probability of a drawing pin landing:

back   side

    a   on its back   **b**   on its side.

3   Donna kept records of the number of clients she interviewed over 38 consecutive days.

    a   Find the value of x.

    b   Estimate the probability that tomorrow Donna will interview:

        i   no clients

        ii   four or more clients

        iii   less than three clients.

Number of clients	Frequency
0	$4 - x$
1	6
2	12
3	$3x - 1$
4	6
5	x
6	0
7	2

4   Use a tree diagram to illustrate the sample spaces for the following:

    a   Bags A, B, and C contain green and yellow tickets. A bag is selected and then a ticket is taken from it.

    b   Martin and Justin play tennis. The first to win three sets wins the match.

5   Alec and Joe sit for an examination in Chemistry. Alec has a 95% chance of passing and Joe has a 25% chance of passing. Determine the probability that:

    a   both pass   **b**   both fail

    c   Joe passes *and* Alec fails

    d   Alec passes *and* Joe fails.

6   Bag X contains three white and two red marbles. Bag Y contains one white and three red marbles. A bag is randomly chosen and two marbles are drawn from it.

    a   Illustrate the information on a tree diagram.

    b   Find the probability that the two marbles drawn are different colours.

7   A water polo player has probability $\frac{1}{4}$ of scoring a goal each time she shoots. If she has 24 shots at goal, how many goals would you expect her to score?

8   A married couple own a large car and a small car. Glen uses the small car 30% of the time. When he goes to the shops, the probability that he can park in the car park is 80% if he has the small car, and 60% if he has the large car.

    Find the probability that, on a given day, Glen is able to park in the shop's car park.

9 A football team has training on Tuesdays, Wednesdays, and Fridays. Of the 40 players in the squad, 21 attended training on Tuesday, 25 attended training on Wednesday, and 24 attended training on Friday.

11 players attended on Tuesday and Wednesday, 15 attended on Wednesday and Friday, and 14 attended on Tuesday and Friday. 6 players attended all three training sessions.

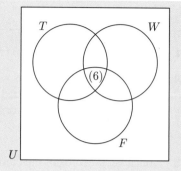

a Copy and complete the Venn diagram.

b Two players are randomly selected from the team. Find the probability that both players attended exactly one training session.

10 X and Y are independent events such that $P(X) = 0.6$ and $P(X \cap Y) = 0.3$. Find $P(X \cup Y)$.

11 Two dice are rolled simultaneously.

    a Illustrate the possible outcomes on a 2-dimensional grid.

    b Determine the probability of getting:

        i a double 5   **ii** at least one 4

        iii a sum greater than 9   **iv** a sum of 5 or 6.

    c If the dice were rolled 900 times, on how many occasions would you expect the sum of the rolls to be prime?

12 Shelley draws 3 cards without replacement from the container alongside. She will win a prize if all 3 cards are the same colour.

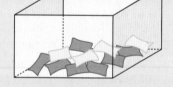

    a Find the probability that Shelley will win a prize.

    b Suppose the rules change so that Shelley now draws her cards *with* replacement.

        i Do you think this increases or decreases her probability of winning? Explain your answer.

        ii Find the probability of Shelley winning under the new rules.

13 In a weightlifting competition, 3 competitors are given one chance to lift a weight of their choosing. The table alongside shows the weights chosen by each competitor, and their probability of lifting it.

Competitor	Weight	Probability
Ihor	210 kg	0.5
Ruslan	225 kg	0.4
Behdad	240 kg	0.3

The winner is the competitor who successfully lifts the greatest weight. If nobody lifts their weight, the competition is a tie.

    a Find the probability that:

        i Ihor   **ii** Ruslan   **iii** Behdad

    will win the competition.

    b Ihor is considering increasing his weight to 230 kg, so he is lifting more than Ruslan.

    However, the probability that he can lift this weight is only 0.34.

    Would this strategy increase or decrease Ihor's probability of winning the competition?

Variation and power modelling

33

Contents:

A	Direct variation	[E2.13]
B	Powers in direct variation	[E2.13]
C	Inverse variation	[E2.13]
D	Powers in inverse variation	[E2.13]
E	Power models	[E2.13]

Opening problem

A fairground stall sells soft drink bottles for \$2 each. Suppose we buy n bottles and the total cost is \$$C$.

To study the relationship between the *number of bottles* and the *total cost*, we can use a table of values or a graph.

n	0	1	2	3	4	5
C	0	2	4	6	8	10

The total cost *depends* on the number of bottles bought.

The number of bottles is the independent variable, so it is placed on the x-axis.
The total cost is the dependent variable, so it is placed on the y-axis.

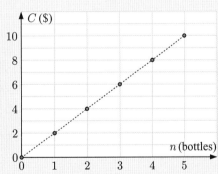

Since we can only buy a whole number of bottles, the graph of C against n consists of discrete points. However, an imagined line passing through these points would also pass through the origin.

Things to think about:

a Which of the following are true?
   i doubling the number of bottles doubles the total cost
   ii halving the number of bottles halves the total cost
   iii increasing the number of bottles by 30% increases the total cost by 30%.

b How can we describe the relationship between n and C?

A   DIRECT VARIATION   [E2.13]

The rectangles alongside are **similar**. Their sides are in the same **ratio**.

3 cm

1 cm

6 cm

2 cm

The ratios of the side lengths can be written as the *proportion* $1 : 3 = 2 : 6$

A rectangle with sides x cm and y cm will be similar to both of the rectangles above if $x : y = 1 : 3$. This occurs when $y = 3x$, for any x.

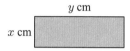

y cm

x cm

Since the sides are in proportion, we say that y is **directly proportional** to x.

Two variables are **directly proportional** or **vary directly** if multiplying one of them by a number results in the other one being multiplied by the same number.

In the **Opening Problem**, C is directly proportional to n.

- When n is tripled from 1 to 3, C is tripled from 2 to 6.
- If we plot C against n, the points lie in a straight line with gradient 2, and which passes through the origin. The variables are connected by the formula $C = 2n$.

If two quantities x and y are **directly proportional**, we write $y \propto x$.

If $y \propto x$ then $y = kx$ where k is a constant called the **proportionality constant**.

When y is graphed against x, the graph is a straight line with **gradient** k, which passes through the **origin**.

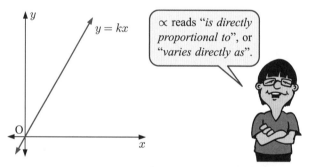

$y = kx$

$\propto$ reads "*is directly proportional to*", or "*varies directly as*".

Example 1   ◀)) *Self Tutor*

At the village bakery, fruit buns are sold for 60 cents each.

a Use a graph to show that $\$y$, the total price paid, is directly proportional to x, the number of fruit buns bought.

b Find a formula connecting x and y.

a

x	0	1	2	3	4	5
y	0	0.60	1.20	1.80	2.40	3.00

The points lie in a straight line passing through $(0, 0)$, so $y \propto x$.

b The gradient of the line $= \dfrac{0.60 - 0}{1 - 0} = 0.6$

∴ the proportionality constant k is 0.6.

∴ the formula connecting x and y is $y = 0.6x$.

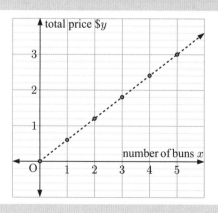

EXERCISE 33A.1

1 Which graph indicates that y is directly proportional to x?

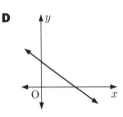

2 For each table of values:
  i Plot the graph of y against x.
  ii Determine whether y is directly proportional to x. If it is, find the proportionality constant.

a

x	0	1	2	3	4
y	0	3	6	9	12

b

x	0	1	2	3	4
y	3	5	7	9	11

c

x	0	1	3	5	6
y	0	4	8	12	16

d

x	2	3	5	6	8
y	5	7.5	12.5	15	20

3 The table alongside shows the total wages $\$W$ earned for working h hours.

h	0	1	2	3	4	5
W	0	12.50	25.00	37.50	50.00	62.50

  a Draw a graph of W against h.
  b Explain why W and h are directly proportional.
  c Find a formula connecting W and h.

4 A dripping tap leaks water at a rate of 10 ml per minute.
  a Copy and complete the table of values alongside:

Time (t minutes)	0	2	4	6	8	10
Volume of water leaked (V ml)						

  b Plot the graph of V against t.
  c Are V and t directly proportional? If so, find the proportionality constant.

5 A dry cleaner charges \$3.20 for cleaning each of the first three items, then \$2.20 for each extra item.
  a Copy and complete the table of values alongside:

Number of items (n)	0	1	2	3	4	5
Cost ($\$C$)						

  b Plot C against n.
  c Are C and n directly proportional? If so, find the proportionality constant.

6 Suppose y is directly proportional to x. State what happens to:
  a y if x is doubled
  b y if x is trebled
  c x if y is doubled
  d x if y is halved
  e y if x is increased by 20%
  f x if y is decreased by 30%
  g y if 2 is added to x
  h y if 3 is subtracted from x.

7 The law connecting the circumference C and radius r of a circle is $C = 2\pi r$.
  a Explain why $C \propto r$.
  b Find the proportionality constant.
  c State what happens to:
    i C if r is doubled
    ii r if C is increased by 50%.

PROBLEM SOLVING USING DIRECT VARIATION

If two variables are directly proportional, we can use either a formula or a multiplier to find the value of one variable given the value of the other. In general, using a multiplier is the quicker method.

Example 2
◀) **Self Tutor**

Suppose $y \propto n$ and that $y = 40$ when $n = 3$. Find n when $y = 137$.

Method 1:

Since $y \propto n$, $y = kn$ where k is the proportionality constant.

When $n = 3$, $y = 40$

$\therefore \ 40 = k \times 3$

$\therefore \ \frac{40}{3} = k$

$\therefore \ y = \frac{40}{3}n$

So, when $y = 137$,

$137 = \frac{40}{3}n$

$\therefore \ 137 \times \frac{3}{40} = n$

$\therefore \ n \approx 10.3$

Method 2:

n	3	?
y	40	137

$\times \frac{137}{40}$

To change y from 40 to 137, we multiply by $\frac{137}{40}$.

Since $y \propto n$, we must also multiply n by $\frac{137}{40}$

$\therefore \ n = 3 \times \frac{137}{40} \approx 10.3$

EXERCISE 33A.2

1 Suppose $y \propto x$ and that $y = 35$ when $x = 7$. Find:

   a y when $x = 28$ **b** x when $y = 5$.

2 Suppose $y \propto x$ and that $y = 20$ when $x = 6$. Find:

   a y when $x = 18$ **b** x when $y = 70$.

3 Complete the table alongside given that $y \propto x$:

x	5	15	
y	20		120

4 The amount of petrol Jill's car uses each day is directly proportional to the distance she travels. Yesterday she travelled 81 km, and used 6 litres of petrol.

   a If Jill travelled 54 km in one day, how much petrol would she use?

   b Jill used 9 litres of petrol in one day. How far did she travel?

5 The resistance R ohms to the flow of electricity in a wire varies in direct proportion to the length l cm of the wire. A 10 cm length of wire has resistance 0.06 ohms.

   a Find:

      i the law connecting R and l

      ii the resistance when the wire is 50 cm long

      iii the length of wire which has a resistance of 3 ohms.

   b Plot the graph of R against l.

6 A 4 litre can of paint will cover 18 m² of wall. Find:

   a the area of wall which can be covered using 10 litres of paint

   b the amount of paint required to paint a room with wall area 40.5 m².

7 Rachael eats l lollies every 5 days. Find, in terms of l:

   a the number of lollies Rachael eats in 20 days

   b the number of days it will take Rachael to eat 30 lollies.

8 The speed of a falling object is directly proportional to the time for which it falls. The speed of an object which has fallen for 5 seconds is 49 m/s.

   a Find the speed of an object which falls for 8 seconds.

   b How long will it take a falling object to reach a speed of 100 m/s?

9 The dimensions of a model car are directly proportional to the dimensions of the actual car it was designed from. The actual car is 4 m long, and the model car is 30 cm long.

   a The actual car is 1.4 m wide. Find the width of the model car.

   b The model car is 9 cm high. Find the height of the actual car.

B   POWERS IN DIRECT VARIATION   [E2.13]

The formula for finding the area A of a circle of radius r is $A = \pi r^2$.

r	0	1	2	3	4
A	0	3.14	12.57	28.27	50.27

The graph of A against r is shown alongside. The graph is not a straight line, but rather is part of a **parabola**. So, A is *not* directly proportional to r.

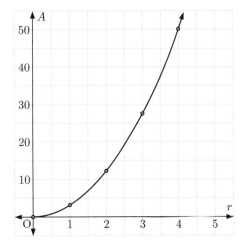

However, suppose we include a row in the table for the values of r^2:

r	0	1	2	3	4
r^2	0	1	4	9	16
A	0	3.14	12.57	28.27	50.27

The graph of A against r^2 is a straight line through the origin O. A is directly proportional to r^2, and we write $A \propto r^2$. In this case we know from the formula that the proportionality constant is $k = \pi$.

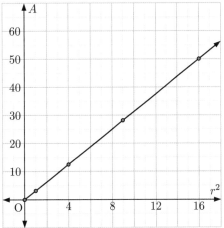

Notice from the table that if r is doubled from 1 to 2, both r^2 and A are multiplied by 4. If r is trebled from 1 to 3, both r^2 and A are multiplied by 9.

Example 3   ◀ᴖ Self Tutor

Consider $y = \dfrac{x^4}{5}$. State which two variables are directly proportional and determine the proportionality constant k.

Since $y = \frac{1}{5}x^4$, so $y \propto x^4$ and $k = \frac{1}{5}$.

y is directly proportional to the fourth power of x, and the proportionality constant $k = \frac{1}{5}$.

EXERCISE 33B

1 State which two variables are directly proportional, and determine the proportionality constant k:

   a $A = 4.9t^2$ **b** $K = 2x^3$ **c** $T = \dfrac{\sqrt{l}}{5}$ **d** $V = 500t^4$ **e** $P = 4\sqrt[3]{x}$ **f** $V = \frac{4}{3}\pi r^3$

Example 4   ◀ᴖ Self Tutor

Consider the table of values shown.

a By plotting y against x^2, establish that $y \propto x^2$.

b Hence, write down the rule connecting y and x.

x	2	4	6
y	6	24	54

a

x	2	4	6
x^2	4	16	36
y	6	24	54

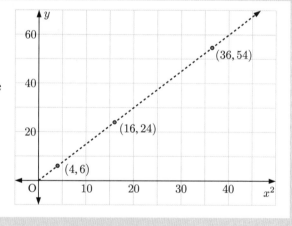

The graph of y against x^2 is a straight line through the origin, so $y \propto x^2$.

b The line has gradient $= \dfrac{24 - 6}{16 - 4}$

$= \dfrac{18}{12}$

$= 1.5$

$\therefore \quad y = 1.5x^2$

2 By plotting y against x^2, establish that $y \propto x^2$ and state the rule connecting y and x.

   a

x	2	3	5
y	16	36	100

   b

x	1	3	4	5
y	3	27	48	75

3 By plotting y against x^3, establish that $y \propto x^3$ and find the proportionality constant k.

   a

x	1	2	3
y	5	40	135

   b

x	2	3	5
y	4	13.5	62.5

Example 5   ◀ᴖ Self Tutor

Suppose T is directly proportional to d^2, and that $T = 100$ when $d = 2$. Find:

   a T when $d = 3$ **b** d when $T = 200$, given $d > 0$.

a

$\times \frac{3}{2}$

d	2	3
T	100	

d is multiplied by $\frac{3}{2}$

$\therefore$ d^2 is multiplied by $\left(\frac{3}{2}\right)^2$

$\therefore$ T is multiplied by $\left(\frac{3}{2}\right)^2$ {as $T \propto d^2$}

$\therefore$ $T = 100 \times \left(\frac{3}{2}\right)^2 = 225$

b

d	2	
T	100	200

$\times 2$

T is multiplied by 2

$\therefore$ d^2 is multiplied by 2   {as $T \propto d^2$}

$\therefore$ d is multiplied by $\sqrt{2}$ {as $d > 0$}

$\therefore$ $d = 2 \times \sqrt{2} = 2\sqrt{2}$

4 Suppose P is directly proportional to a^2, where $a > 0$. When $a = 5$, $P = 300$.   Find:
   a the value of P when $a = 2$ **b** the value of a when $P = 2700$.

5 Suppose M is directly proportional to the cube of x, and that when $x = 2$, $M = 24$. Find:
   a the value of M when $x = 3$ **b** the value of x when $M = 120$.

6 The power required to drive a motor boat is directly proportional to the cube of its speed. If an 80 hp motor drives a boat at 20 km/h, what power is required to drive a boat at 30 km/h?

7 The value of a gemstone varies in direct proportion to the square of its weight. If a 4 carat stone is valued at \$200, find the value of a 5 carat stone of the same quality.

8 The surface area of a sphere varies in direct proportion to the square of its radius. A sphere of radius 6 cm has a surface area of about 452 cm². Find, to the nearest mm, the radius of a sphere with surface area 1000 cm².

Example 6

◀ϻ **Self Tutor**

The *period* or time for one complete swing of a pendulum is directly proportional to the square root of its length. When the length is 25 cm, the period is 1.00 seconds.

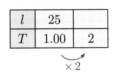

a If the length of the pendulum is 70 cm, find its period. Give your answer to 2 decimal places.

b What would the length be if the period of the pendulum was 2 seconds?

If T is the period and l is the length, then $T \propto \sqrt{l}$.

a

$\times \frac{70}{25}$

l	25	70
T	1.00	

l is multiplied by $\frac{70}{25}$

$\therefore$ $\sqrt{l}$ is multiplied by $\sqrt{\frac{70}{25}}$

$\therefore$ T is multiplied by $\sqrt{\frac{70}{25}}$ {as $T \propto \sqrt{l}$}

$\therefore$ $T = 1.00 \times \sqrt{\frac{70}{25}} \approx 1.67$

So, the period would be 1.67 seconds.

b

l	25	
T	1.00	2

$\times 2$

T is multiplied by 2

$\therefore$ $\sqrt{l}$ is multiplied by 2   {as $T \propto \sqrt{l}$}

$\therefore$ l is multiplied by 2^2

$\therefore$ $l = 25 \times 2^2 = 100$

So, the length would be 100 cm.

9 When a stone falls freely, the time taken for it to hit the ground varies in direct proportion to the square root of the distance fallen. If it takes a stone 4 seconds to fall 78.4 m, how long will it take for a stone to fall 500 m down a mine shaft?

10 At sea, the distance in km of the visible horizon is directly proportional to the square root of the height in metres of the observer's eye above sea level. So, $D \propto \sqrt{h}$.

The horizon is 9 km away when my eye is 5.4 m above sea level.

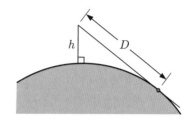

   a How far can I see from a height of 10 m?

   b From what height can I see a distance of 6 km?

11 The volume of blood flowing through a blood vessel is directly proportional to the square of the internal diameter.

   a If the diameter is multiplied by 1.1, what number is the volume multiplied by?

   b If the diameter is reduced by 20%, what percentage reduction in blood flow will occur?

12 The volume V of a sphere varies in direct proportion to the cube of its radius.

   a Find the percentage change in volume if the radius is reduced by 10%.

   b What percentage change in radius is necessary to double the volume?

13 The volume of a cone is given by $V = \frac{1}{3}\pi r^2 h$, where r is the radius and h is the height.

   a If we consider cones of fixed radius but variable height, what proportionality exists between V and h?

   b If we consider cones of fixed height but variable radius, what proportionality exists between V and r?

   c What happens to the volume of a cone if the base radius is increased by 20% and the height is decreased by 15%?

C   *INVERSE VARIATION*   *[E2.13]*

Discussion

If two painters can paint a house in three days, how long would it take four painters to paint the house, each working at the same rate?

The two variables in this example are the *number of painters* and the *time taken*.

The four painters will be able to do twice as much work in the same amount of time. So it will therefore take them a half of the time, or $1\frac{1}{2}$ days, to complete the job.

In a case like this where doubling one variable halves the other, we have an **inverse proportion**.

> Two variables are **inversely proportional** or **vary inversely** if, when one is *multiplied* by a constant, the other is *divided* by the same constant.

Dividing by k is the same as multiplying by $\frac{1}{k}$, so if one of the variables is multiplied by 2, the other must be multiplied by $\frac{1}{2}$.

Consider again the example of two painters completing a job in three days.

Suppose x is the number of painters and y is the number of days to complete the job.

The table below shows some possible combinations of x and y.

x	1	2	3	4	6
y	6	3	2	$1\frac{1}{2}$	1

When these points are plotted, they form part of a **hyperbola**.

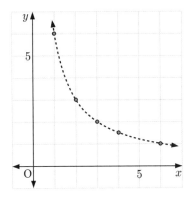

Suppose we include a row in the table for the values of $\frac{1}{x}$.

x	1	2	3	4	6
$\dfrac{1}{x}$	1	$\frac{1}{2}$	$\frac{1}{3}$	$\frac{1}{4}$	$\frac{1}{6}$
y	6	3	2	$1\frac{1}{2}$	1

The points on a graph of y against $\frac{1}{x}$ form a straight line which

passes through the origin, so y is directly proportional to $\frac{1}{x}$.

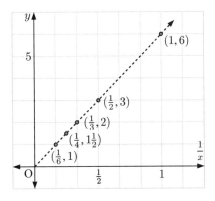

> If y is **inversely proportional** to x, then y is **directly proportional** to $\frac{1}{x}$.
>
> Consequently, $y = \dfrac{k}{x}$ or $xy = k$.

In the painters example, notice that $xy = 6$ for all points in the table. So, in this case $k = 6$.

Example 7   ◀)) *Self Tutor*

Suppose M is inversely proportional to t, and that $M = 200$ when $t = 3$. Find:

a M when $t = 5$ **b** t when $M = 746$

Since M is inversely proportional to t, $M \propto \dfrac{1}{t}$.

a

$$\times \tfrac{5}{3}$$

t	3	5
M	200	

t is multiplied by $\frac{5}{3}$

$\therefore$ M is multiplied by $\frac{3}{5}$ {as $M \propto \frac{1}{t}$}

$\therefore$ $M = 200 \times \frac{3}{5} = 120$

b

t	3	
M	200	746

$$\times \tfrac{746}{200}$$

M is multiplied by $\frac{746}{200}$

$\therefore$ t is multiplied by $\frac{200}{746}$ {as $M \propto \frac{1}{t}$}

$\therefore$ $t = 3 \times \frac{200}{746} \approx 0.80$

EXERCISE 33C

1 **a** Copy and complete the table of values:

x	1	2	4	8
$\dfrac{1}{x}$				
y	40	20	10	5

  b Plot the graph of y against $\dfrac{1}{x}$.

  c Explain why y is inversely proportional to x.

  d Calculate xy for each point in the table.

2 For each of the following tables, calculate the value of xy for each point. Hence determine whether x and y are inversely proportional. If an inverse proportionality exists, determine the law connecting the variables, and draw the graph of y against x.

a

x	1	2	3	6
y	12	6	4	2

b

x	2	3	6	9
y	12	8	4	3

c

x	7	6	12	1
y	12	14	7	84

3 Which graph(s) could indicate that y is inversely proportional to x?

A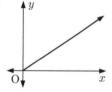

B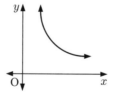

C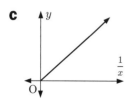

D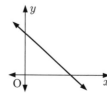

If y is inversely proportional to x, then y is directly proportional to $\dfrac{1}{x}$.

4 The formula connecting average speed s, distance travelled d, and time taken t, is $s = \dfrac{d}{t}$.

Complete the following statements by inserting "directly" or "inversely":

   a If d is fixed, s is ...... proportional to t.   **b** If t is fixed, s is ...... proportional to d.

   c If s is fixed, d is ...... proportional to t.

5 Suppose y is inversely proportional to x. Describe what happens to:

   a y if x is multiplied by 4   **b** y if x is multiplied by $\frac{7}{9}$ **c** x if y is multiplied by $\frac{8}{3}$.

6 Suppose y is inversely proportional to x, and that $y = 20$ when $x = 2$. Find:

   a the value of y when $x = 5$ **b** the value of x when $y = 100$.

7 Suppose p is inversely proportional to n, and that $p = 24$ when $n = 6$. Find:

   a the value of p when $n = 8$ **b** the value of n when $p = 12$.

8 Copy and complete this table given that $y \propto \dfrac{1}{x}$:

x	6	10	
y	25		3

9 The time taken to complete a certain job is inversely proportional to the number of workers doing the task. If 20 workers could do the job in 6 days, find how long it would take 15 workers to do the job.

10 Four people are hired to set up 5000 seats for a concert. Working together, they could complete the job in 12 hours. However, one person is unwell, and is unable to help set up the chairs.

   a How many chairs will the remaining three people be able to set up in 12 hours?

   b How long will it take them to complete the job?

11 A rectangle with dimensions x m by y m has area 60 m^2.

   a Explain why y is inversely proportional to x.

   b Copy and complete this table:

x	5		15
y		10	

   c Plot the graph of y against x.

12 The chamber of an airtight cylinder is filled with the yellow gas fluorine. For a given mass of gas kept at a constant temperature, the volume is inversely proportional to the pressure. When $V = 10$ cm^3, the pressure $P = 40$ units.

   a Find the pressure when the volume is 20 cm^3.

   b Find the volume when the pressure is 100 units.

   c Find the formula connecting P and V.

   d Plot the graph of P against V.

13 The average court time for each player in a netball team is inversely proportional to the number of players the team has. If the team has 10 players, the average court time for each player is 28 minutes.

   a If the team has 12 players, what is the average court time for each player?

   b If the average court time is 35 minutes, how many players does the team have?

   c Given that 7 players are allowed on court at one time, how long does each game last?

D   POWERS IN INVERSE VARIATION   [E2.13]

In this Section we consider the inverse variation between one variable and the power of another. We use the same techniques as for direct variation.

Example 8   ◄)) *Self Tutor*

Suppose y is inversely proportional to the square of x, and that $y = 36$ when $x = 5$.

   a   Find y when $x = 15$.   **b**   Given $x > 0$, find x when $y = 49$.

a

x	5	15
y	36	

$\times 3$

x is multiplied by 3

$\therefore \;\; x^2$ is multiplied by $3^2 = 9$

$\therefore \;\; \dfrac{1}{x^2}$ is multiplied by $\frac{1}{9}$

$\therefore \;\; y$ is multiplied by $\frac{1}{9}$ $\{$as $y \propto \dfrac{1}{x^2}\}$

$\therefore \;\; y = 36 \times \frac{1}{9} = 4$

b

x	5	
y	36	49

$\times \frac{49}{36}$

y is multiplied by $\frac{49}{36}$

$\therefore \;\; \dfrac{1}{x^2}$ is multiplied by $\frac{49}{36}$ $\{$as $y \propto \dfrac{1}{x^2}\}$

$\therefore \;\; x^2$ is multiplied by $\frac{36}{49}$

$\therefore \;\; x$ is multiplied by $\sqrt{\frac{36}{49}} = \frac{6}{7}$ $\{$as $x > 0\}$

$\therefore \;\; x = 5 \times \frac{6}{7} = \frac{30}{7}$

EXERCISE 33D

1   Suppose y is inversely proportional to the square of x, and that $y = 4$ when $x = 10$.

   a   Find y when $x = 5$.   **b**   Given $x > 0$, find x when $y = 25$.

2   Suppose F is inversely proportional to the square root of c, and that $F = 20$ when $c = 11$.

   a   Find F when $c = 33$.   **b**   Find c when $F = 30$.

3   A heavy ball is suspended from a spring, and its weight is initially supported. The ball is then dropped so it will bounce up and down. The time between successive bounces is called the *period* of the motion, and varies inversely to the square root of the stiffness of the spring. The period of a spring of stiffness 100 units is 0.2 seconds. Find:

   a   the period of a spring of stiffness 300 units

   b   the stiffness required for a 0.1 second period.

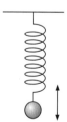

4

The amount of radiant heat received by a body varies inversely to the square of the distance of the body from the heat source. If the distance from the source is decreased by 20%, what effect does this have on the heat received?

5 The children in a class are each given the same amount of plasticine, and asked to build a solid cylinder. The radius of the cylinder produced is inversely proportional to the square root of the height. Xian's cylinder has radius 2.7 cm and height 13.1 cm.

a Beth's cylinder has radius 5.4 cm. Find its height.

b Roger's cylinder is 8 cm high. Find its radius.

c What volume of plasticine was each child given?

6 The intensity of light on a screen varies inversely to the square of the distance between the screen and the light source.

If a screen is illuminated by a light source 20 m away, the intensity is one fifth of what is required. Where should the light be placed?

E ▎ *POWER MODELS*   *[E2.13]*

Sometimes we are given data connecting two variables, but we do not know the nature of the relationship between them.

The direct and inverse variations we have studied are collectively called **power models**. They are equations of the form $y = kx^b$.

- If $b > 0$ we have **direct variation**.

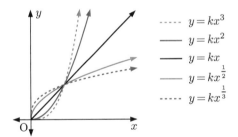

The graph passes through the origin $(0, 0)$.

- If $b < 0$ we have **inverse variation**.

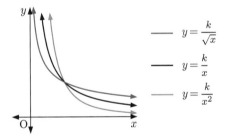

The graph is asymptotic to both the x and y axes.

Discussion

In the world around us, there are many powers which we can anticipate using our knowledge of measurements and similarity.

Suppose a souvenir shop sells scale models of the Statue of Liberty in different sizes. They are all solid and made with the same material.

1 Predict the relationship between:

- the *height* of a statue and its *volume*
- the *height* of a statue and its *mass*
- the *height* of a statue and its *surface area*.

2 If we sampled 100 statues at random from the souvenir shop and took measurements of them, will the data correlate *exactly* with the relationships you predicted in **1**? What factors might cause the correlation to be less than perfect?

3 Now suppose the statues are still scale models, but they are made with different materials. Which of the pairs of variables in **1** do you expect to now vary differently? Will there necessarily still be a power model relationship between them?

If we suspect that two variables are related by a power model, we can use the **power regression** function on our calculator to find the model of best fit.

Example 9
◀) **Self Tutor**

Gravity is the force of attraction which exists between any two objects in the universe. The force of attraction F Newtons between two masses d cm apart is given in the following table:

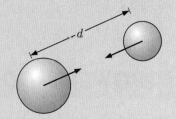

d (cm)	24	26	28	30	32	34	36	38	40
F (N)	237	202	174	152	133	118	105	95	85

a Graph F against d.

b Obtain the power model which best fits the data. Discuss whether it is reasonable.

c Estimate the force of attraction between two spheres that are:

    i 20 cm apart   **ii** 29 cm apart   **iii** 50 m apart.

a

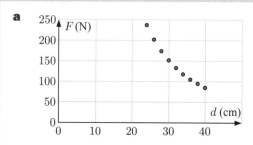

b The shape of the graph suggests that inverse variation is appropriate.

The coefficient of determination r^2 is very close to 1, so the fit is excellent. We observe that the power is extremely close to -2, so it is reasonable to conclude that F is inversely proportional to d^2.

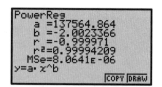

GRAPHICS
CALCULATOR
INSTRUCTIONS

The model is $F \approx 138\,000 \times d^{-2.00}$ or $F \approx \dfrac{138\,000}{d^2}$.

c   **i** When $d = 20$

$$F \approx \frac{138\,000}{20^2}$$

$\therefore$ $F \approx 345$ N

ii When $d = 29$

$$F \approx \frac{138\,000}{29^2}$$

$\therefore$ $F \approx 164$ N

iii   50 m = 5000 cm

When $d = 5000$

$$F \approx \frac{138\,000}{5000^2}$$

$\therefore$ $F \approx 0.005\,52$ N

EXERCISE 33E

1 A small glass ball is rolled down a solid ramp with constant gradient. At time t seconds it has rolled a distance d cm. The results are shown alongside:

t (s)	1	2	3	4	5
d (cm)	0.2	0.8	1.8	3.2	5.0

   a Graph d against t.

   b Obtain the power model which best fits the data. Discuss whether it is reasonable.

   c Estimate how far the ball will roll after:

      i 2.5 seconds   **ii** 6 seconds.

2 Consider the data alongside.

x	2	4	6	8	10
y	8.5	12.0	14.7	17.0	19.0

   a Graph y against x.

   b Obtain the power model which best fits the data. Discuss whether it is reasonable.

   c Estimate the value of y when: **i** $x = 16$ **ii** $x = 30$.

3 For each data set, obtain the power model which best fits the data. Discuss whether it is reasonable.

a

x	1	2	3	4	5
y	2.83	22.63	76.37	181.02	353.55

b

x	5	10	15	20	25
y	13.41	9.49	7.75	6.71	15.99

4 When a force is applied to an object, the *pressure* of the object depends on the *surface area* where the force is applied. The pressure that results when a force is applied over different areas is recorded below.

Area (a m^2)	4	7	15	20	24	30	35	40	45
Pressure (P pascals)	25	14.3	6.7	5	4.2	3.3	2.9	2.5	2.2

   a Draw a graph of P against a.

   b Obtain the power model which best fits the data. Discuss whether it is reasonable.

   c Estimate the pressure that results when the force is applied over 10 m^2.

5 A tennis ball is dropped from the top of a cliff. The distance fallen after various times is recorded alongside.

Time (t s)	1.4	2.1	2.9	3.3	3.6	4.3	4.9
Distance fallen (D m)	9.7	21.5	41.1	52.4	63.5	90.6	117.8

   a Obtain the power model which best fits the data. Discuss whether it is reasonable.

   b Estimate the distance the ball fell in the first 4 seconds.

   c Estimate how long it would take for the ball to fall 200 m.

6 Johannes Kepler is a famous figure in the history of astronomy and mathematics. He used data from observations of planetary orbits to show that these motions obey mathematical laws. He took the Earth as his "base unit", so the orbital periods are given as multiples of one Earth year, and orbital radii as multiples of one Earth orbit. Some of his observations are given in this table:

Planet	Mercury	Venus	Earth	Mars	Jupiter	Saturn
Orbital period (T)	0.241	0.615	1.000	1.881	11.862	29.457
Orbital radius (R)	0.387	0.723	1.000	1.542	5.202	9.539

   a Obtain a power model for this data. Discuss whether it is reasonable.

   b What is the result when the equation in **a** is cubed?

   c Neptune has an orbital period of 164.8 Earth years. Estimate Neptune's orbital radius.

Activity   *The pendulum*

A **pendulum** can be made by tying a small but heavy object such as a fishing sinker to a piece of inelastic string.

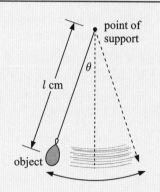

The other end of the string is fixed to a point of support which will allow the object to swing back and forth freely.

The **period** of a pendulum is the time taken for one complete oscillation, back and forth.

Our aim is to find the relationship between the *period* (T seconds) and the length (l cm) of a pendulum.

The length of the pendulum is the distance from the point of support to the object's centre of mass.

What to do:

1 Discuss an appropriate experimental procedure for measuring values of l and T. Consider whether any of the following ideas have merit when finding the period of the pendulum for a particular length:

- Several students should time one period using their stopwatches.
- Timing 8 complete swings and averaging is better than timing one complete swing.
- If several students do the timing, the highest and lowest scores should be removed and the remaining scores should be averaged.

2 List possible factors which could lead to inaccurate results.

3 After deciding on a method for determining the period, measure the period for pendulum lengths of 20 cm, 30 cm, 40 cm, ..., 100 cm. Record your results in a table like the one alongside.

4 Use technology to determine the law connecting T and l.

Length (l cm)	Period (T s)
20	
30	
40	
⋮	

Review set 33A

1 Which of the following graphs indicates that y is directly proportional to x?

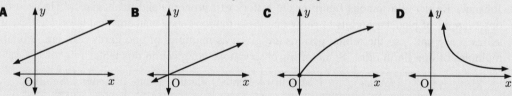

2 Consider the table of values alongside.

a Plot the graph of y against x.

b Explain why y is directly proportional to x.

c Find a formula connecting x and y.

x	2	3	6	11
y	6	9	18	33

3 Copy and complete this table given that $y \propto x$:

x	12	60	
y	3		20

4 Suppose x is inversely proportional to y, and that $y = 65$ when $x = 10$. Find:

    a the law connecting x and y **b** y when $x = 12$ **c** x when $y = 150$.

5 A school's quiz night raises money in direct proportion to the number of people attending. Last year 85 people attended the quiz night, and the event raised \$1275. This year the entry fees were the same, but the school only raised \$1080. How many people attended this year?

6 If 3 workers can build a house in 60 days, how long would it take 5 workers to build the house?

7 Suppose M is directly proportional to $\sqrt{t}$, and that $M = 20$ when $t = 4$. Find:

    a M when $t = 36$ **b** t when $M = 30$.

8 The surface area of a sphere is directly proportional to the square of its radius.

    a What happens to the surface area if the radius is trebled?

    b Find the percentage change in the radius if the surface area is increased by 20%.

9 The kinetic energy E of a solid with mass m and speed v, is given by $E = \frac{1}{2}mv^2$.

    a State the variation that exists between:

        i E and m **ii** E and v **iii** m and v.

    b Describe the change in the kinetic energy of an object if its speed is reduced by 12%.

10 The prices of various pizza sizes are given below:

Size (x inches)	6	9	12	15	18
Cost (\$$y$)	3.60	8.10	14.50	22.50	32.50

    a Sketch the graph of y against x.

    b Obtain the power model which best fits the data. Discuss whether it is reasonable.

Review set 33B

1 The variables p and q in the table are directly proportional. Find a and b.

p	4	7	a
q	12	b	42

2 If 7 litres of petrol are needed to drive 100 km, how far could you travel on 16 litres of petrol?

3 Suppose $y \propto x$ and that $y = 77.9$ when $x = 4.1$.

    a Find the proportionality constant.   **b** Find the value of y when $x = 6.3$.

4 For each table, determine whether x and y are inversely proportional. If an inverse proportionality exists, find the law connecting x and y.

    a

x	2	4	8
y	10	5	2

    b

x	3	6	9
y	12	6	4

5 Jamela thinks that if y is inversely proportional to x, then a 25% increase in y will produce a 25% decrease in x. Explain why Jamela is incorrect.

6 6 pumps can empty a lake in 45 minutes. How long would 10 pumps take to empty the lake?

7 Suppose y is inversely proportional to the square of x, and that $y = 50$ when $x = 7$. Find the value of y when $x = 5$.

8 When a train travels around a bend, the safe speed of the train is directly proportional to the square root of the radius of the curve. For a bend with radius 100 m, the safe speed is 25 m/s.

   a Find the safe speed for a bend with radius 150 m.

   b Find the bend radius for which the safe speed is 45 m/s.

9 The volume of a cylinder of fixed length is directly proportional to the square of its radius.

   a Find the change in volume produced by doubling the radius.

   b Find the change in radius needed to produce a 60% increase in volume.

10 Scale models of the Eiffel Tower are sold in different sizes all over Paris. Of those made of brass, the height and mass of several statues are given in the table below:

Height (h cm)	8	12	16	20
Mass (m g)	61.4	207.4	491.5	960

   a Obtain a power model which best fits the data. Discuss whether it is reasonable.

   b Estimate the mass of a statue that is 30 cm high.

Vectors

34

Contents:

A	Directed line segment representation	[E6.1]
B	Vector equality	[E6.2]
C	Vector addition	[E6.2]
D	Vector subtraction	[E6.2]
E	Vectors in component form	[E6.1, E6.2, E6.3]
F	Operations in component form	[E6.1, E6.2, E6.3]
G	Scalar multiplication	[E6.2]
H	Parallel vectors	[E6.2]

Opening problem

Holger can paddle in calm water at 12 km/h. However, today he needs to paddle directly across a river which is flowing at a constant speed of 5 km/h to his right.

Things to think about:

a Can you draw a diagram to illustrate the situation?

b What effect does the current in the river have on the direction in which Holger paddles?

c How can we accurately find Holger's speed and direction if he *aims* to paddle directly across the river?

d In what direction must Holger face so that he *does* paddle directly across the river?

VECTORS AND SCALARS

To solve the **Opening Problem**, we need to consider not only the *speeds* of Holger and the current, but also their *directions*.

> Quantities which have only magnitude are called **scalars**.
>
> Quantities which have both magnitude and direction are called **vectors**.

Velocity is a vector quantity which includes both **speed** *and* **direction**.

Other examples of vector quantities include acceleration, force, displacement, and momentum.

For example, when using force we consider how hard we push an object, and what direction we push it in.

DIRECTED LINE SEGMENT REPRESENTATION   *[E6.1]*

Consider a bus which is travelling at 100 km/h to the south-east. We can represent the motion of the bus using an arrow on a scale diagram.

The **length of the arrow** represents the size or magnitude of the velocity. The **arrowhead** shows the direction of travel.

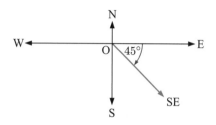

Scale: 1 cm represents 50 km/h

NOTATION

- The vector from O to A can be written as

  $\overrightarrow{OA}$ or   **a**   or $\overrightarrow{a}$.

bold used   used by

in textbooks   students

  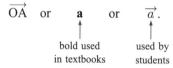

- The **magnitude** or **length** of the vector $\overrightarrow{OA}$ can be written as $|\overrightarrow{OA}|$ or   OA   or $|\mathbf{a}|$ or $|\overrightarrow{a}|$.

- $\overrightarrow{AB}$ is the vector which **emanates** from A and **terminates** at B. $\overrightarrow{AB}$ is the **position vector** of B relative to A.

  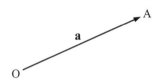

Example 1   ◀◎ *Self Tutor*

On a scale diagram, draw a vector representing a velocity of 40 m/s on the bearing 075°.

Scale: 1 cm ≡ 10 m/s

EXERCISE 34A

1 Using a scale of 1 cm represents 10 units, draw a vector which represents:
   a a velocity of 40 km/h to the south-west   **b** a velocity of 35 m/s to the north
   c a displacement of 25 m in the direction 120°
   d an aeroplane taking off at an angle of 12° to the runway, with speed 60 m/s.

2 If ———————▶ represents a force of 45 Newtons due east, draw a directed line segment to represent a force of:
   a 75 N due west   **b** 60 N south-west.

3 On a scale diagram, draw a vector representing:
   a a velocity of 60 km/h to the north-east   **b** a displacement of 25 km on the bearing 055°
   c an aeroplane taking off at an angle of 10° to the runway, with speed 90 km/h
   d a momentum of 45 kg m/s in the direction 250°.

B VECTOR EQUALITY   [E6.2]

EQUAL VECTORS

> Two vectors are **equal** if they have the same magnitude *and* direction.

Equal vectors are **parallel** and in the same direction, and are **equal in length**.

This means that arrows representing equal vectors are translations of one another.

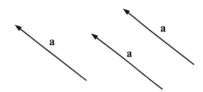

THE ZERO VECTOR

> The **zero vector**, **0**, is a vector of length 0.
> It is the only vector with no direction.

When we write the zero vector by hand, we usually write $\vec{0}$.

NEGATIVE VECTORS

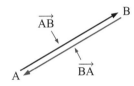

$\overrightarrow{AB}$ and $\overrightarrow{BA}$ have the same length but opposite directions.

We say that $\overrightarrow{BA}$ is the **negative** of $\overrightarrow{AB}$ and write $\overrightarrow{BA} = -\overrightarrow{AB}$.

Given the vector **a** shown, we can draw the vector $-\mathbf{a}$.

a and $-\mathbf{a}$ are parallel and equal in length, but are opposite in direction.

EXERCISE 34B

1 State the vectors which are:

   a equal in magnitude   **b** parallel
   c in the same direction   **d** equal
   e negatives of one another.

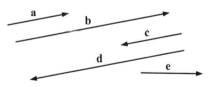

Example 2   ◀》 *Self Tutor*

ABCD is a parallelogram in which $\overrightarrow{AB} = \mathbf{a}$ and $\overrightarrow{BC} = \mathbf{b}$.

Find vector expressions for:

   a $\overrightarrow{BA}$ **b** $\overrightarrow{CB}$ **c** $\overrightarrow{AD}$ **d** $\overrightarrow{CD}$

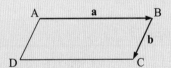

   a $\overrightarrow{BA} = -\mathbf{a}$ {the negative vector of $\overrightarrow{AB}$}   **b** $\overrightarrow{CB} = -\mathbf{b}$ {the negative vector of $\overrightarrow{BC}$}
   c $\overrightarrow{AD} = \mathbf{b}$ {parallel to and the same length as $\overrightarrow{BC}$}
   d $\overrightarrow{CD} = -\mathbf{a}$ {parallel to and the same length as $\overrightarrow{BA}$}

2 PQRS is a parallelogram in which $\overrightarrow{PQ} = \mathbf{a}$ and $\overrightarrow{PS} = \mathbf{b}$.
Find vector expressions for:

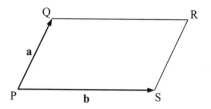

   a $\overrightarrow{QR}$ **b** $\overrightarrow{QP}$ **c** $\overrightarrow{SR}$

   d $\overrightarrow{SP}$ **e** $\overrightarrow{RS}$ **f** $\overrightarrow{RQ}$

3 ABCD is a rhombus. Let $\overrightarrow{AB} = \mathbf{a}$ and $\overrightarrow{BC} = \mathbf{b}$.
Which of the following statements are true?

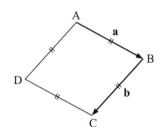

   a $\overrightarrow{AD} = \mathbf{b}$ **b** $\overrightarrow{CD} = \mathbf{a}$

   c $\overrightarrow{DC} = \mathbf{b}$ **d** $|\mathbf{a}| = |\mathbf{b}|$

   e $|\overrightarrow{DA}| = -|\mathbf{b}|$ **f** $|-\mathbf{a}| = |-\mathbf{b}|$

   g $AD - |\mathbf{a}|$ **h** $DC - |\mathbf{a}| = 0$

C   VECTOR ADDITION   [E6.2]

Suppose we have three towns A, B, and C.

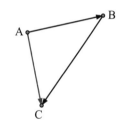

A trip from A to B, followed by a trip from B to C, is equivalent to a trip from A to C.

This can be expressed in vector form as the sum $\overrightarrow{AB} + \overrightarrow{BC} = \overrightarrow{AC}$, where the $+$ sign could mean *"followed by"*.

After considering diagrams like the one above, we can define vector addition geometrically:

> To add $\mathbf{a}$ and $\mathbf{b}$:   *Step 1*:   Draw $\mathbf{a}$.
>   *Step 2*:   At the arrowhead end of $\mathbf{a}$, draw $\mathbf{b}$.
>   *Step 3*:   Join the beginning of $\mathbf{a}$ to the arrowhead end of $\mathbf{b}$.
>   This is vector $\mathbf{a} + \mathbf{b}$.

So, given   we have

   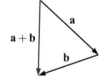

DEMO

Example 3   ◄)) *Self Tutor*

Find a single vector which is equal to:

a $\overrightarrow{AB} + \overrightarrow{BE}$

b $\overrightarrow{DC} + \overrightarrow{CA} + \overrightarrow{AE}$

c $\overrightarrow{CB} + \overrightarrow{BD} + \overrightarrow{DC}$

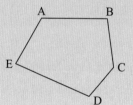

a $\overrightarrow{AB} + \overrightarrow{BE} = \overrightarrow{AE}$

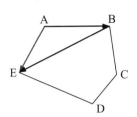

b $\overrightarrow{DC} + \overrightarrow{CA} + \overrightarrow{AE} = \overrightarrow{DE}$

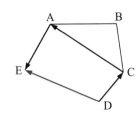

c $\overrightarrow{CB} + \overrightarrow{BD} + \overrightarrow{DC} = \overrightarrow{CC} = \mathbf{0}$
{zero vector}

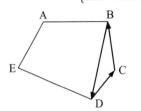

THE ZERO VECTOR

Having defined vector addition, we are now able to state that:

> The **zero vector**, **0**, is a vector of length 0.
>
> For any vector **a**: $\mathbf{a} + \mathbf{0} = \mathbf{0} + \mathbf{a} = \mathbf{a}$
> $$\mathbf{a} + (-\mathbf{a}) = (-\mathbf{a}) + \mathbf{a} = \mathbf{0}$$

Example 4   ◀) Self Tutor

Sonya can swim at 3 km/h in calm water. She swims in a river where the current is 1 km/h in an easterly direction. Find the resultant velocity if Sonya swims:

a with the current   **b** against the current   **c** northwards, across the river.

Scale: 1 cm ≡ 1 km/h

The velocity vector of the river is $\xrightarrow{\mathbf{r}}$

a Sonya's velocity vector is

$\xrightarrow{\hspace{2cm}\mathbf{s}\hspace{2cm}}$

The net result is **r** + **s**.

∴   Sonya swims at 4 km/h to the east.

b Sonya's velocity vector is

$\xleftarrow{\hspace{2cm}\mathbf{s}\hspace{2cm}}$

The net result is **r** + **s**.

∴   Sonya swims at 2 km/h to the west.

c

Sonya's velocity vector is

and the net result is **r** + **s**.

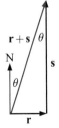

∴ $|\mathbf{r}+\mathbf{s}| = \sqrt{10} \approx 3.16$

Now $\tan\theta = \frac{1}{3}$,   so $\theta = \tan^{-1}\left(\frac{1}{3}\right)$
$\approx 18.4°$

∴   Sonya swims at about 3.16 km/h in the direction 018.4°.

EXERCISE 34C

1 Copy the given vectors **p** and **q** and show how to construct **p** + **q**:

a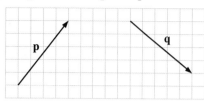

b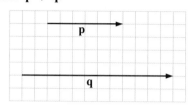

c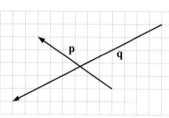

d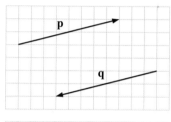

e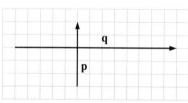

f

2 Find a single vector which is equal to:

   a $\overrightarrow{QR} + \overrightarrow{RS}$ **b** $\overrightarrow{PQ} + \overrightarrow{QR}$

   c $\overrightarrow{PS} + \overrightarrow{SR} + \overrightarrow{RQ}$ **d** $\overrightarrow{PR} + \overrightarrow{RQ} + \overrightarrow{QS}$

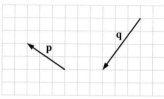

3 **a** Consider the vectors:

    Use vector diagrams to find:

     i **p** + **q**   **ii** **q** + **p**

  b For any two vectors **p** and **q**, is **p** + **q** = **q** + **p**? Explain your answer.

4 Write an expression in terms of **a**, **b**, **c**, and **d**, for:

   a $\overrightarrow{PS}$ **b** $\overrightarrow{PR}$

   c $\overrightarrow{QT}$ **d** $\overrightarrow{PT}$

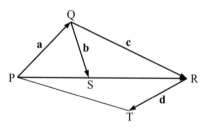

5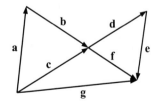

Write as a single vector:

   a **a** + **b**   **b** **d** + **e**

   c **c** + **f**   **d** **a** + **b** + **f**

   e **c** + **d** + **e**

6 Consider an aeroplane trying to fly at 500 km/h due north. Find the actual speed and direction of the aeroplane if a gale of 100 km/h is blowing:

    a from the south   **b** from the north   **c** from the west.

7 A vessel is trying to travel east at 10 km/h. Find its actual speed and direction if there is a current of 10 km/h:

    a from the east   **b** from the west   **c** from the south.

8 An aircraft flying at 400 km/h due east encounters a 60 km/h wind from the north. Find the resultant new speed and direction of the aircraft.

D | VECTOR SUBTRACTION   [E6.2]

To subtract one vector from another, we simply **add its negative**.

$$\mathbf{a} - \mathbf{b} = \mathbf{a} + (-\mathbf{b})$$

For example, given

   we have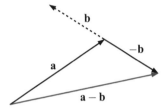

Example 5   ◀) Self Tutor

For the given vectors
s and **t**, find **s** − **t**.

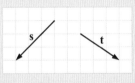   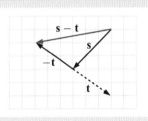

EXERCISE 34D

1 For the following vectors **p** and **q**, show how to construct **p** − **q**:

  a 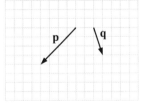   **b** 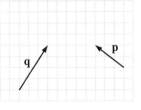   **c** 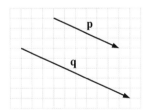

  d 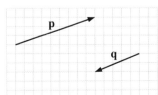   **e** 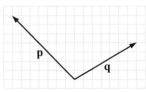   **f** 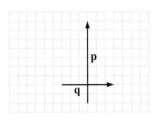

Example 6

For points P, Q, R, and S, simplify the following vector expressions:

a $\overrightarrow{QR} - \overrightarrow{SR}$ **b** $\overrightarrow{QR} - \overrightarrow{SR} - \overrightarrow{PS}$

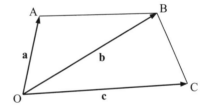

a $\overrightarrow{QR} - \overrightarrow{SR}$
$= \overrightarrow{QR} + \overrightarrow{RS}$ {as $\overrightarrow{RS} = -\overrightarrow{SR}$}
$= \overrightarrow{QS}$

b $\overrightarrow{QR} - \overrightarrow{SR} - \overrightarrow{PS}$
$= \overrightarrow{QR} + \overrightarrow{RS} + \overrightarrow{SP}$
$= \overrightarrow{QP}$

2 For points P, Q, R, and S, simplify the following vector expressions:

  a $\overrightarrow{QR} + \overrightarrow{RS}$ **b** $\overrightarrow{PS} - \overrightarrow{RS}$ **c** $\overrightarrow{RS} + \overrightarrow{SR}$

  d $\overrightarrow{RS} + \overrightarrow{SP} + \overrightarrow{PQ}$ **e** $\overrightarrow{QP} - \overrightarrow{RP} + \overrightarrow{RS}$ **f** $\overrightarrow{RS} - \overrightarrow{PS} - \overrightarrow{QP}$

3 **a** Explain why $\overrightarrow{AB} = \mathbf{b} - \mathbf{a}$.

  b Write vector expressions for:

     i $\overrightarrow{BC}$ **ii** $\overrightarrow{CA}$

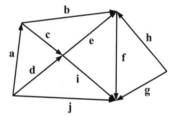

4 Use the diagram to simplify:

  a $\mathbf{a} + \mathbf{c}$ **b** $\mathbf{h} + \mathbf{f}$ **c** $\mathbf{j} - \mathbf{i}$

  d $\mathbf{d} - \mathbf{c}$ **e** $\mathbf{e} - \mathbf{b}$ **f** $-\mathbf{f} - \mathbf{h}$

Example 7

Xiang Zhu is about to fire an arrow at a target. In still conditions, the arrow would travel at 38 m/s. Today, however, there is a wind blowing at 6 m/s from the left, directly across the arrow's path.

  a In what direction should Zhu fire the arrow so that it hits the target?

  b What will its actual speed be?

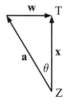

Suppose Zhu is at Z and the target is at T. Suppose Zhu fires the arrow with velocity $\mathbf{a}$, the velocity of the wind is $\mathbf{w}$, and the resulting velocity of the arrow is $\mathbf{x}$.

$$\mathbf{a} + \mathbf{w} = \mathbf{x}$$
$$\therefore \quad \mathbf{a} + \mathbf{w} - \mathbf{w} = \mathbf{x} - \mathbf{w}$$
$$\therefore \quad \mathbf{a} = \mathbf{x} - \mathbf{w}$$

a Now $|\mathbf{a}| = 38$ m/s   and $|\mathbf{w}| = 6$ m/s

$\therefore$ $\sin\theta = \frac{6}{38} = \frac{3}{19}$

$\therefore$ $\theta = \sin^{-1}\left(\frac{3}{19}\right) \approx 9.08°$

$\therefore$ Zhu should fire about $9.08°$ to the left of the target.

b By Pythagoras' theorem, $|\mathbf{x}|^2 + 6^2 = 38^2$

$\therefore$ $|\mathbf{x}| = \sqrt{38^2 - 6^2} \approx 37.52$

$\therefore$ the arrow will travel at about 37.5 m/s.

5 An aeroplane needs to fly due north with speed 500 km/h. However, it is affected by a 40 km/h wind blowing constantly from the west. In what direction should it aim, and at what speed?

6 The driver of a motorboat wishes to travel north-west to a safe haven before an electrical storm arrives. In still water the boat can travel at 30 km/h. However, a strong current is flowing at 10 km/h from the north-east.

    a In what direction must the boat head?

    b At what speed will the boat actually travel?

7 Answer the **Opening Problem** on page **593**.

E VECTORS IN COMPONENT FORM
[E6.1, E6.2, E6.3]

So far we have examined vectors in their geometric representation.

We have used arrows where:

- the **length** of the arrow represents size or magnitude
- the **arrowhead** indicates direction.

However, we can also represent vectors by describing the horizontal and vertical steps required to go from the starting point to the finishing point.

> The **component form** of a vector is $\begin{pmatrix} x\text{-step} \\ y\text{-step} \end{pmatrix}$.
>
> In this notation, it is often called a **column vector**.

The x-step is positive if we move to the right, and negative if we move to the left.

The y-step is positive if we move upwards, and negative if we move downwards.

For example:

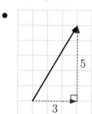
We move 3 units to the right and 5 units upwards,

so the vector is $\begin{pmatrix} 3 \\ 5 \end{pmatrix}$.

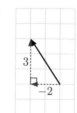
We move 2 units to the left and 3 units upwards,

so the vector is $\begin{pmatrix} -2 \\ 3 \end{pmatrix}$.

THE MAGNITUDE OF A VECTOR

By the theorem of Pythagoras,

If $\mathbf{a} = \begin{pmatrix} a_1 \\ a_2 \end{pmatrix}$, the **magnitude** or **length** of $\mathbf{a}$ is $|\mathbf{a}| = \sqrt{a_1^2 + a_2^2}$.

Example 8
◄⑴ *Self Tutor*

Find the length of:

a $\begin{pmatrix} 5 \\ 2 \end{pmatrix}$

b $\begin{pmatrix} -4 \\ 3 \end{pmatrix}$

a The length of $\begin{pmatrix} 5 \\ 2 \end{pmatrix} = \sqrt{5^2 + 2^2}$
$= \sqrt{25 + 4}$
$= \sqrt{29}$ units

b The length of $\begin{pmatrix} -4 \\ 3 \end{pmatrix} = \sqrt{(-4)^2 + 3^2}$
$= \sqrt{16 + 9}$
$= 5$ units

THE VECTOR BETWEEN TWO POINTS

The **position vector** of $A(a_1, a_2)$ is

$$\overrightarrow{OA} = \begin{pmatrix} x\text{-step} \\ y\text{-step} \end{pmatrix} = \begin{pmatrix} a_1 \\ a_2 \end{pmatrix}.$$

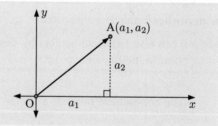

The position vector of $B(b_1, b_2)$ relative to $A(a_1, a_2)$

is $\overrightarrow{AB} = \begin{pmatrix} x\text{-step} \\ y\text{-step} \end{pmatrix} = \begin{pmatrix} b_1 - a_1 \\ b_2 - a_2 \end{pmatrix}.$

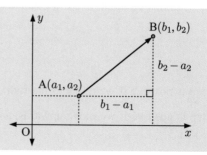

Example 9   ◀》 Self Tutor

Given the points A(2, −3) and B(4, 2), find: **a** $\overrightarrow{AB}$ **b** $\overrightarrow{BA}$

a $\overrightarrow{AB} = \begin{pmatrix} 4-2 \\ 2--3 \end{pmatrix} = \begin{pmatrix} 2 \\ 5 \end{pmatrix}$ **b** $\overrightarrow{BA} = \begin{pmatrix} 2-4 \\ -3-2 \end{pmatrix} = \begin{pmatrix} -2 \\ -5 \end{pmatrix}$

VECTOR EQUALITY

Two vectors are equal if and only if their x-components are equal *and* their y-components are equal.

$\begin{pmatrix} p \\ q \end{pmatrix} = \begin{pmatrix} r \\ s \end{pmatrix}$ if and only if $p = r$ *and* $q = s$.

Example 10   ◀》 Self Tutor

Find k given that

$\begin{pmatrix} k^2 \\ k-1 \end{pmatrix} = \begin{pmatrix} 9 \\ -4 \end{pmatrix}.$

We have $k^2 = 9$ *and* $k - 1 = -4$.

The only value of k which satisfies both equations is $k = -3$.

EXERCISE 34E

1 Draw arrow diagrams to represent the vectors:

a $\begin{pmatrix} 4 \\ 2 \end{pmatrix}$ **b** $\begin{pmatrix} 0 \\ 3 \end{pmatrix}$ **c** $\begin{pmatrix} -2 \\ 5 \end{pmatrix}$ **d** $\begin{pmatrix} 3 \\ 4 \end{pmatrix}$

2 Write the illustrated vectors in component form:

a   **b**   **c**
   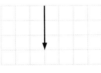

d   **e**   **f**
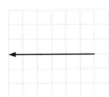   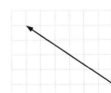   

3 Find the length of each vector:

a $\begin{pmatrix} 1 \\ 4 \end{pmatrix}$ **b** $\begin{pmatrix} 6 \\ 0 \end{pmatrix}$ **c** $\begin{pmatrix} 3 \\ -2 \end{pmatrix}$ **d** $\begin{pmatrix} -1 \\ -5 \end{pmatrix}$ **e** $\begin{pmatrix} -4 \\ 2 \end{pmatrix}$ **f** $\begin{pmatrix} -6 \\ -1 \end{pmatrix}$

4 Given the points A(3, 4), B(−1, 2), and C(2, −1), find:

a $\overrightarrow{OA}$ **b** $\overrightarrow{AB}$ **c** $\overrightarrow{CO}$ **d** $\overrightarrow{BC}$ **e** $\overrightarrow{CA}$

5 For each pair of points, find: **i** $\overrightarrow{AB}$ **ii** the distance AB.

a A(3, 5) and B(1, 2)   **b** A(−2, 1) and B(3, −1)

c A(3, 4) and B(0, 0)   **d** A(11, −5) and B(−1, 0)

6 Find k given that:

a $\begin{pmatrix} k+2 \\ k^2 \end{pmatrix} = \begin{pmatrix} -2 \\ 16 \end{pmatrix}$ **b** $\begin{pmatrix} 3 \\ k+4 \end{pmatrix} = \begin{pmatrix} k^2+2 \\ 3 \end{pmatrix}$ **c** $\begin{pmatrix} 4 \\ k^2+8 \end{pmatrix} = \begin{pmatrix} k^2-3k \\ 6k \end{pmatrix}$

7 Find values of k such that $\mathbf{v} = \begin{pmatrix} k \\ 3 \end{pmatrix}$ and $|\mathbf{v}| = 5$.

Example 11   ◀)) *Self Tutor*

A car travels at a speed of 20 m/s in the direction 125°. Write this as a vector in component form.

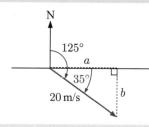

$\cos 35° = \dfrac{a}{20}$,   so $a = 20 \times \cos 35° \approx 16.4$

$\sin 35° = \dfrac{b}{20}$,   so $b = 20 \times \sin 35° \approx 11.5$

$\therefore$ the vector is $\begin{pmatrix} a \\ -b \end{pmatrix} \approx \begin{pmatrix} 16.4 \\ -11.5 \end{pmatrix}$

---

8 Write each vector in component form:

    a a velocity of 60 m/s in the direction 120°   **b** a distance of 15 km in the direction 221°

    c an aeroplane on the runway takes off at an angle of 9° and a speed of 160 km/h.

F   OPERATIONS IN COMPONENT FORM
[E6.1, E6.2, E6.3]

VECTOR ADDITION

Consider the addition of vectors $\mathbf{a} = \begin{pmatrix} a_1 \\ a_2 \end{pmatrix}$ and $\mathbf{b} = \begin{pmatrix} b_1 \\ b_2 \end{pmatrix}$.

The horizontal step for $\mathbf{a} + \mathbf{b}$ is $a_1 + b_1$,

and the vertical step for $\mathbf{a} + \mathbf{b}$ is $a_2 + b_2$.

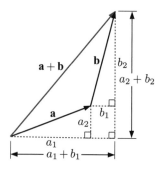

If $\mathbf{a} = \begin{pmatrix} a_1 \\ a_2 \end{pmatrix}$ and $\mathbf{b} = \begin{pmatrix} b_1 \\ b_2 \end{pmatrix}$ then $\mathbf{a} + \mathbf{b} = \begin{pmatrix} a_1+b_1 \\ a_2+b_2 \end{pmatrix}$.

Example 12   ◀)) *Self Tutor*

Given $\mathbf{a} = \begin{pmatrix} 2 \\ 5 \end{pmatrix}$ and $\mathbf{b} = \begin{pmatrix} 1 \\ -3 \end{pmatrix}$,
find $\mathbf{a} + \mathbf{b}$.

Check your answer graphically.

$\mathbf{a} + \mathbf{b} = \begin{pmatrix} 2 \\ 5 \end{pmatrix} + \begin{pmatrix} 1 \\ -3 \end{pmatrix}$

$= \begin{pmatrix} 2+1 \\ 5 + -3 \end{pmatrix}$

$= \begin{pmatrix} 3 \\ 2 \end{pmatrix}$

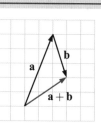

NEGATIVE VECTORS

For the vector $\mathbf{a} = \begin{pmatrix} 5 \\ 2 \end{pmatrix}$, we

notice that $-\mathbf{a} = \begin{pmatrix} -5 \\ -2 \end{pmatrix}$.

If $\mathbf{a} = \begin{pmatrix} a_1 \\ a_2 \end{pmatrix}$ then $-\mathbf{a} = \begin{pmatrix} -a_1 \\ -a_2 \end{pmatrix}$.

ZERO VECTOR

The zero vector is $\mathbf{0} = \begin{pmatrix} 0 \\ 0 \end{pmatrix}$.

For any vector $\mathbf{a}$:

$$\mathbf{a} + \mathbf{0} = \mathbf{0} + \mathbf{a} = \mathbf{a}$$

$$\mathbf{a} + (-\mathbf{a}) = (-\mathbf{a}) + \mathbf{a} = \mathbf{0}$$

The zero vector is the only vector which has no direction.

VECTOR SUBTRACTION

To subtract one vector from another, we **add its negative**.

If $\mathbf{a} = \begin{pmatrix} a_1 \\ a_2 \end{pmatrix}$ and $\mathbf{b} = \begin{pmatrix} b_1 \\ b_2 \end{pmatrix}$ then $\mathbf{a} - \mathbf{b} = \mathbf{a} + (-\mathbf{b})$

$$= \begin{pmatrix} a_1 \\ a_2 \end{pmatrix} + \begin{pmatrix} -b_1 \\ -b_2 \end{pmatrix}$$

$$= \begin{pmatrix} a_1 - b_1 \\ a_2 - b_2 \end{pmatrix}$$

If $\mathbf{a} = \begin{pmatrix} a_1 \\ a_2 \end{pmatrix}$ and $\mathbf{b} = \begin{pmatrix} b_1 \\ b_2 \end{pmatrix}$ then $\mathbf{a} - \mathbf{b} = \begin{pmatrix} a_1 - b_1 \\ a_2 - b_2 \end{pmatrix}$.

Example 13   ◀) Self Tutor

Given $\mathbf{p} = \begin{pmatrix} 3 \\ -2 \end{pmatrix}$ and $\mathbf{q} = \begin{pmatrix} 1 \\ 4 \end{pmatrix}$, find:

a $\mathbf{p} - \mathbf{q}$ **b** $\mathbf{q} - \mathbf{p}$

a $\mathbf{p} - \mathbf{q} = \begin{pmatrix} 3 \\ -2 \end{pmatrix} - \begin{pmatrix} 1 \\ 4 \end{pmatrix}$ **b** $\mathbf{q} - \mathbf{p} = \begin{pmatrix} 1 \\ 4 \end{pmatrix} - \begin{pmatrix} 3 \\ -2 \end{pmatrix}$

$= \begin{pmatrix} 3 - 1 \\ -2 - 4 \end{pmatrix}$ $= \begin{pmatrix} 1 - 3 \\ 4 - -2 \end{pmatrix}$

$= \begin{pmatrix} 2 \\ -6 \end{pmatrix}$ $= \begin{pmatrix} -2 \\ 6 \end{pmatrix}$

You do not need to write the middle step.

EXERCISE 34F

1 Find:

a $\begin{pmatrix} 2 \\ 3 \end{pmatrix} + \begin{pmatrix} 1 \\ 5 \end{pmatrix}$ **b** $\begin{pmatrix} 5 \\ 4 \end{pmatrix} + \begin{pmatrix} -1 \\ 6 \end{pmatrix}$ **c** $\begin{pmatrix} 0 \\ 3 \end{pmatrix} + \begin{pmatrix} 7 \\ -4 \end{pmatrix}$

d $\begin{pmatrix} -4 \\ -1 \end{pmatrix} + \begin{pmatrix} 2 \\ 6 \end{pmatrix}$ **e** $\begin{pmatrix} -5 \\ 0 \end{pmatrix} + \begin{pmatrix} 1 \\ -6 \end{pmatrix}$ **f** $\begin{pmatrix} -5 \\ -9 \end{pmatrix} + \begin{pmatrix} -3 \\ 7 \end{pmatrix}$

2 Given $\mathbf{a} = \begin{pmatrix} 2 \\ -3 \end{pmatrix}$, $\mathbf{b} = \begin{pmatrix} 3 \\ -1 \end{pmatrix}$, and $\mathbf{c} = \begin{pmatrix} -2 \\ -3 \end{pmatrix}$, find:

     a $\mathbf{a} + \mathbf{b}$ **b** $\mathbf{b} + \mathbf{a}$ **c** $\mathbf{b} + \mathbf{c}$ **d** $\mathbf{c} + \mathbf{b}$

     e $\mathbf{a} + \mathbf{c}$ **f** $\mathbf{c} + \mathbf{a}$ **g** $\mathbf{a} + \mathbf{a}$ **h** $\mathbf{b} + \mathbf{a} + \mathbf{c}$

3 Given $\mathbf{m} = \begin{pmatrix} 3 \\ 4 \end{pmatrix}$ and $\mathbf{n} = \begin{pmatrix} 1 \\ -2 \end{pmatrix}$, find:

     a $\mathbf{m} + \mathbf{n}$ **b** $|\mathbf{m} + \mathbf{n}|$ **c** $-\mathbf{m}$ **d** $-\mathbf{n}$

4 Find:

a $\begin{pmatrix} 7 \\ 4 \end{pmatrix} - \begin{pmatrix} 1 \\ 2 \end{pmatrix}$ **b** $\begin{pmatrix} 8 \\ 8 \end{pmatrix} - \begin{pmatrix} 3 \\ 6 \end{pmatrix}$ **c** $\begin{pmatrix} 2 \\ 5 \end{pmatrix} - \begin{pmatrix} 6 \\ 0 \end{pmatrix}$

d $\begin{pmatrix} -2 \\ 1 \end{pmatrix} - \begin{pmatrix} 4 \\ 5 \end{pmatrix}$ **e** $\begin{pmatrix} 5 \\ -2 \end{pmatrix} - \begin{pmatrix} -3 \\ 1 \end{pmatrix}$ **f** $\begin{pmatrix} 6 \\ -4 \end{pmatrix} - \begin{pmatrix} -5 \\ -1 \end{pmatrix}$

5 Given $\mathbf{p} = \begin{pmatrix} -1 \\ 3 \end{pmatrix}$, $\mathbf{q} = \begin{pmatrix} -2 \\ -3 \end{pmatrix}$, and $\mathbf{r} = \begin{pmatrix} 3 \\ -4 \end{pmatrix}$, find:

     a $\mathbf{p} - \mathbf{q}$ **b** $\mathbf{q} - \mathbf{r}$ **c** $\mathbf{p} + \mathbf{q} - \mathbf{r}$

     d $\mathbf{p} - \mathbf{q} - \mathbf{r}$ **e** $\mathbf{q} - \mathbf{r} - \mathbf{p}$ **f** $|\mathbf{r} + \mathbf{q} - \mathbf{p}|$

6 Given $\overrightarrow{AB} = \begin{pmatrix} 2 \\ 5 \end{pmatrix}$ and $\overrightarrow{BC} = \begin{pmatrix} -1 \\ 3 \end{pmatrix}$, find $\overrightarrow{AC}$.

7 Given $\overrightarrow{AB} = \begin{pmatrix} 1 \\ 4 \end{pmatrix}$ and $\overrightarrow{AC} = \begin{pmatrix} -2 \\ 1 \end{pmatrix}$, find $\overrightarrow{BC}$.

8 Given $\overrightarrow{AB} = \begin{pmatrix} -3 \\ 2 \end{pmatrix}$, $\overrightarrow{BD} = \begin{pmatrix} 0 \\ 4 \end{pmatrix}$, and $\overrightarrow{CD} = \begin{pmatrix} 1 \\ -3 \end{pmatrix}$, find $\overrightarrow{AC}$.

9 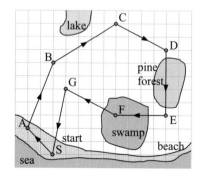 The diagram alongside shows an orienteering course run by Kahu.

     a Write a column vector to describe each leg of the course.

     b Find the sum of all of the vectors. Interpret your answer.

G | SCALAR MULTIPLICATION   [E6.2]

Numbers such as 1 and -2 are called *scalars* because they have size but no direction.

$2\mathbf{a}$ and $-2\mathbf{a}$ are examples of multiplying a vector by a scalar.

$2\mathbf{a}$ is a short way to write $\mathbf{a} + \mathbf{a}$, and similarly $-2\mathbf{a} = (-\mathbf{a}) + (-\mathbf{a})$.

For   we have   and

So, $2\mathbf{a}$ has the same direction as $\mathbf{a}$ and is twice as long as $\mathbf{a}$, and

   $-2\mathbf{a}$ is in the opposite direction to $\mathbf{a}$ and is twice as long as $\mathbf{a}$.

Example 14   ◀ Self Tutor

Given $\mathbf{r} = \begin{pmatrix} 3 \\ 2 \end{pmatrix}$ and $\mathbf{s} = \begin{pmatrix} 2 \\ -2 \end{pmatrix}$, find geometrically:

a $2\mathbf{r} + \mathbf{s}$ **b** $\mathbf{r} - 2\mathbf{s}$

a 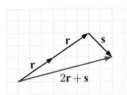 $2\mathbf{r} + \mathbf{s} = \begin{pmatrix} 8 \\ 2 \end{pmatrix}$

b 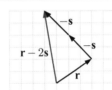 $\mathbf{r} - 2\mathbf{s} = \begin{pmatrix} -1 \\ 6 \end{pmatrix}$

To multiply a vector in component form by a scalar, we multiply each component by the scalar.

If k is a scalar then $k \begin{pmatrix} a \\ b \end{pmatrix} = \begin{pmatrix} ka \\ kb \end{pmatrix}$.

We can now check the results of **Example 14** using the component form:

In **a**, $2\mathbf{r} + \mathbf{s} = 2\begin{pmatrix} 3 \\ 2 \end{pmatrix} + \begin{pmatrix} 2 \\ -2 \end{pmatrix} = \begin{pmatrix} 6 \\ 4 \end{pmatrix} + \begin{pmatrix} 2 \\ -2 \end{pmatrix} = \begin{pmatrix} 8 \\ 2 \end{pmatrix}$

In **b**, $\mathbf{r} - 2\mathbf{s} = \begin{pmatrix} 3 \\ 2 \end{pmatrix} - 2\begin{pmatrix} 2 \\ -2 \end{pmatrix} = \begin{pmatrix} 3 \\ 2 \end{pmatrix} - \begin{pmatrix} 4 \\ -4 \end{pmatrix} = \begin{pmatrix} -1 \\ 6 \end{pmatrix}$

Example 15   ◀ Self Tutor

Sketch any two vectors $\mathbf{p}$ and $\mathbf{q}$ such that: **a** $\mathbf{p} = 2\mathbf{q}$ **b** $\mathbf{p} = -\frac{1}{2}\mathbf{q}$.

Let $\mathbf{q}$ be   **a**   **b**

EXERCISE 34G

1 Find:

a $3\begin{pmatrix} 2 \\ 5 \end{pmatrix}$

b $5\begin{pmatrix} -1 \\ 4 \end{pmatrix}$

c $-2\begin{pmatrix} 6 \\ 0 \end{pmatrix}$

d $\frac{1}{2}\begin{pmatrix} 4 \\ 14 \end{pmatrix}$

e $-4\begin{pmatrix} -2 \\ 7 \end{pmatrix}$

f $\frac{1}{3}\begin{pmatrix} -9 \\ 2 \end{pmatrix}$

g $2\begin{pmatrix} 3 \\ 8 \end{pmatrix} + \begin{pmatrix} 1 \\ -5 \end{pmatrix}$

h $\begin{pmatrix} 10 \\ 3 \end{pmatrix} - 4\begin{pmatrix} 0 \\ 4 \end{pmatrix}$

2 Suppose $\mathbf{r} = \begin{pmatrix} 2 \\ 3 \end{pmatrix}$ and $\mathbf{s} = \begin{pmatrix} 4 \\ -2 \end{pmatrix}$.

Find each vector sum using: **i** geometry   **ii** component form:

a $2\mathbf{r}$ **b** $-3\mathbf{s}$ **c** $\frac{1}{2}\mathbf{r}$ **d** $\mathbf{r} - 2\mathbf{s}$

e $3\mathbf{r} + \mathbf{s}$ **f** $2\mathbf{r} - 3\mathbf{s}$ **g** $\frac{1}{2}\mathbf{s} + \mathbf{r}$ **h** $\frac{1}{2}(2\mathbf{r} + \mathbf{s})$

3 Sketch any two vectors $\mathbf{p}$ and $\mathbf{q}$ such that:

a $\mathbf{p} = \mathbf{q}$ **b** $\mathbf{p} = -\mathbf{q}$ **c** $\mathbf{p} = 3\mathbf{q}$ **d** $\mathbf{p} = \frac{3}{4}\mathbf{q}$ **e** $\mathbf{p} = -\frac{3}{2}\mathbf{q}$

4 ABCD is a rhombus. Suppose $\overrightarrow{OA} = \mathbf{a}$ and $\overrightarrow{OB} = \mathbf{b}$.
Write, in terms of $\mathbf{a}$ and $\mathbf{b}$, a vector expression for:

a $\overrightarrow{CA}$ **b** $\overrightarrow{BD}$ **c** $\overrightarrow{CD}$

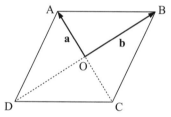

5 Let $\mathbf{p} = \begin{pmatrix} 3 \\ 1 \end{pmatrix}$ and $\mathbf{q} = \begin{pmatrix} -2 \\ 3 \end{pmatrix}$. Find $\mathbf{r} = \begin{pmatrix} x \\ y \end{pmatrix}$ such that:

a $\mathbf{r} = \mathbf{p} - 3\mathbf{q}$ **b** $\mathbf{p} + \mathbf{r} = \mathbf{q}$ **c** $\mathbf{q} - 3\mathbf{r} = 2\mathbf{p}$ **d** $\mathbf{p} + 2\mathbf{r} - \mathbf{q} = 0$

6 If $\mathbf{a}$ is any vector, prove that:

a $|k\mathbf{a}| = |k||\mathbf{a}|$ **b** $\dfrac{1}{|\mathbf{a}|}\mathbf{a}$ is a vector of length 1 in the direction of $\mathbf{a}$.

Hint: Let $\mathbf{a} = \begin{pmatrix} a_1 \\ a_2 \end{pmatrix}$.

H   PARALLEL VECTORS   [E6.2]

Two vectors are **parallel** $\Leftrightarrow$ one is a scalar multiple of the other.

$\Leftrightarrow$ means "if and only if".

This statement means both:

- if one vector is a scalar multiple of another then the two vectors are parallel
- if two vectors are parallel then one vector is a scalar multiple of the other.

If **a** is parallel to **b** then we write $\mathbf{a} \parallel \mathbf{b}$.

- If $\mathbf{a} = k\mathbf{b}$ for some non-zero scalar k, then $\mathbf{a} \parallel \mathbf{b}$.
- If $\mathbf{a} \parallel \mathbf{b}$ there exists a non-zero scalar k such that $\mathbf{a} = k\mathbf{b}$.

Example 16   ◀) Self Tutor

The vectors $\begin{pmatrix} 12 \\ t \end{pmatrix}$ and $\begin{pmatrix} 3 \\ -2 \end{pmatrix}$ are parallel. Find t.

The vectors are parallel, so $\begin{pmatrix} 12 \\ t \end{pmatrix} = k \begin{pmatrix} 3 \\ -2 \end{pmatrix}$ for some k.

$$\therefore \ 12 = 3k \quad and \quad t = -2k$$
$$\therefore \ k = 4$$
$$\therefore \ t = -2(4) = -8$$

Consider the vectors $\mathbf{a} = \begin{pmatrix} 6 \\ 3 \end{pmatrix}$ and $\mathbf{b} = \begin{pmatrix} 2 \\ 1 \end{pmatrix}$.

Notice that:
- $\begin{pmatrix} 6 \\ 3 \end{pmatrix} = 3\begin{pmatrix} 2 \\ 1 \end{pmatrix}$, so $\mathbf{a} = 3\mathbf{b}$
  $$\therefore \ \mathbf{a} \parallel \mathbf{b}$$
- $|\mathbf{a}| = \sqrt{36 + 9}$
  $$= \sqrt{45}$$
  $$= 3\sqrt{5}$$
  $$= 3|\mathbf{b}|$$

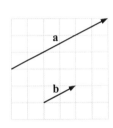

The vector $k\mathbf{a}$ is parallel to $\mathbf{a}$.
- If $k > 0$ then $k\mathbf{a}$ has the same direction as $\mathbf{a}$.
- If $k < 0$ then $k\mathbf{a}$ has the opposite direction to $\mathbf{a}$.
- The length of $k\mathbf{a}$ is the **absolute value** of k times the length of $\mathbf{a}$. $|k\mathbf{a}| = |k||\mathbf{a}|$

Example 17   ◀) Self Tutor

What two facts can be deduced about **p** and **q** if: **a** $\mathbf{p} = 5\mathbf{q}$ **b** $\mathbf{q} = -\frac{3}{4}\mathbf{p}$?

a $\mathbf{p} = 5\mathbf{q}$
  $\therefore$ **p** is parallel to **q**   and $|\mathbf{p}| = |5||\mathbf{q}| = 5|\mathbf{q}|$
  $\therefore$ **p** is 5 times longer than **q**, and they have the same direction.

b $\mathbf{q} = -\frac{3}{4}\mathbf{p}$
  $\therefore$ **q** is parallel to **p**   and $|\mathbf{q}| = |-\frac{3}{4}||\mathbf{p}| = \frac{3}{4}|\mathbf{p}|$
  $\therefore$ **q** is $\frac{3}{4}$ as long as **p**, but has the opposite direction.

EXERCISE 34H

1 Find the scalar t given the pair of parallel vectors:

a $\begin{pmatrix} 20 \\ t \end{pmatrix}$ and $\begin{pmatrix} -5 \\ 3 \end{pmatrix}$

b $\begin{pmatrix} 3 \\ 2 \end{pmatrix}$ and $\begin{pmatrix} 9 \\ t \end{pmatrix}$

c $\begin{pmatrix} -4 \\ 1 \end{pmatrix}$ and $\begin{pmatrix} t \\ -5 \end{pmatrix}$

d $\begin{pmatrix} 5 \\ 2 \end{pmatrix}$ and $\begin{pmatrix} t \\ -4 \end{pmatrix}$

2 Find a such that $\begin{pmatrix} 3 \\ a \end{pmatrix}$ and $\begin{pmatrix} 5a+2 \\ 8 \end{pmatrix}$ are parallel.

3 Consider the points A(1, 5), B(3, 8), C(5, 11), and D(−3, t). Find t such that AB ∥ DC.

4 What two facts can be deduced about **p** and **q** if:

     a $\mathbf{p} = 2\mathbf{q}$ **b** $\mathbf{p} = \frac{1}{2}\mathbf{q}$ **c** $\mathbf{p} = -3\mathbf{q}$ **d** $\mathbf{p} = -\frac{1}{3}\mathbf{q}$?

5 Using vector methods only, show that P(−2, 5), Q(3, 1), R(2, −1), and S(−3, 3) form the vertices of a parallelogram.

6 A(2, 3), B(−1, 5), C(−1, 1), and D(−7, 5) are four points in the Cartesian plane.

     a Find $\overrightarrow{AB}$ and $\overrightarrow{CD}$.   **b** Explain why $\overrightarrow{CD}$ is parallel to $\overrightarrow{AB}$.

     c Suppose E is the point $(k, 1)$ such that $\overrightarrow{AC}$ is parallel to $\overrightarrow{BE}$. Find k.

7 $\mathbf{u} = \begin{pmatrix} k \\ k \end{pmatrix}$ and $\mathbf{v} = \begin{pmatrix} k+2 \\ 1 \end{pmatrix}$ are two non parallel vectors which have equal length. Find k.

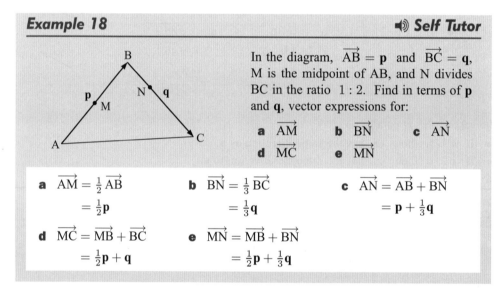

Example 18   ◀ৈ *Self Tutor*

In the diagram, $\overrightarrow{AB} = \mathbf{p}$ and $\overrightarrow{BC} = \mathbf{q}$, M is the midpoint of AB, and N divides BC in the ratio 1 : 2. Find in terms of **p** and **q**, vector expressions for:

     a $\overrightarrow{AM}$ **b** $\overrightarrow{BN}$ **c** $\overrightarrow{AN}$

     d $\overrightarrow{MC}$ **e** $\overrightarrow{MN}$

   a $\overrightarrow{AM} = \frac{1}{2}\overrightarrow{AB}$ **b** $\overrightarrow{BN} = \frac{1}{3}\overrightarrow{BC}$ **c** $\overrightarrow{AN} = \overrightarrow{AB} + \overrightarrow{BN}$

         $= \frac{1}{2}\mathbf{p}$ $= \frac{1}{3}\mathbf{q}$ $= \mathbf{p} + \frac{1}{3}\mathbf{q}$

   d $\overrightarrow{MC} = \overrightarrow{MB} + \overrightarrow{BC}$ **e** $\overrightarrow{MN} = \overrightarrow{MB} + \overrightarrow{BN}$

         $= \frac{1}{2}\mathbf{p} + \mathbf{q}$ $= \frac{1}{2}\mathbf{p} + \frac{1}{3}\mathbf{q}$

8   ABCD is a parallelogram, and side DC is extended to E such that DC = CE. Let $\overrightarrow{AD} = \mathbf{p}$ and $\overrightarrow{AB} = \mathbf{q}$. Find, in terms of **p** and **q**:

     a $\overrightarrow{DC}$ **b** $\overrightarrow{DE}$ **c** $\overrightarrow{AC}$

     d $\overrightarrow{AE}$ **e** $\overrightarrow{EA}$ **f** $\overrightarrow{BE}$

9 In triangle OAB, let $\overrightarrow{OA} = \mathbf{a}$ and $\overrightarrow{OB} = \mathbf{b}$. M and N are the midpoints of sides OB and AB respectively.

     a Find vector expressions for:

        i $\overrightarrow{BA}$ **ii** $\overrightarrow{MN}$

     b What can be deduced from **a ii**?

     c If O is the origin, find the position vector of:

        i M   **ii** N   **iii** the midpoint of MN.

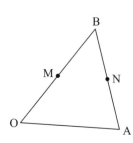

10   ABCD is a parallelogram and M is the midpoint of side DC.
P is located on line segment AM such that AP : PM = 2 : 1.

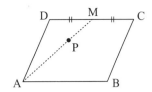

    a   If $\overrightarrow{AB} = \mathbf{p}$ and $\overrightarrow{AD} = \mathbf{q}$, find vector expressions for:

        i $\overrightarrow{DM}$ **ii** $\overrightarrow{AP}$ **iii** $\overrightarrow{DB}$ **iv** $\overrightarrow{DP}$

    b   What can be deduced about the points D, P, and B?

Review set 34A

1   Using a scale of 1 cm represents 10 units, sketch a vector to represent:

    a   an aeroplane taking off at an angle of 8° to the runway with a speed of 60 m/s

    b   a displacement of 45 m in the direction 060°.

2

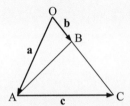

    In the figure alongside, $\overrightarrow{OA} = \mathbf{a}$, $\overrightarrow{OB} = \mathbf{b}$, and $\overrightarrow{AC} = \mathbf{c}$.
Find, in terms of **a**, **b**, and **c**:

        a $\overrightarrow{CA}$ **b** $\overrightarrow{AB}$ **c** $\overrightarrow{OC}$ **d** $\overrightarrow{BC}$

3   Given points A, B, C, and D, simplify the following vector expressions:

    a $\overrightarrow{AB} + \overrightarrow{BD}$ **b** $\overrightarrow{BC} - \overrightarrow{DC}$ **c** $\overrightarrow{AB} - \overrightarrow{CB} + \overrightarrow{CD} - \overrightarrow{AD}$

4   A yacht is moving at 10 km/h in a south-easterly direction. It encounters a 3 km/h current from
the north. Find the resultant speed and direction of the yacht.

5   What can be deduced about vectors **a** and **b** if $\mathbf{a} = \frac{1}{3}\mathbf{b}$?

6   Suppose $\mathbf{p} = \begin{pmatrix} 4 \\ 3 \end{pmatrix}$, $\mathbf{q} = \begin{pmatrix} 3 \\ -5 \end{pmatrix}$, and $\mathbf{r} = \begin{pmatrix} 0 \\ -4 \end{pmatrix}$. Find:

    a $2\mathbf{p} + \mathbf{q}$ **b** $\mathbf{p} - \mathbf{q} - \mathbf{r}$ **c**   the length of **q**.

7   Consider the vector $\mathbf{m} = \begin{pmatrix} 2 \\ -5 \end{pmatrix}$.

    a   Illustrate the vector on grid paper.   **b**   Find the length of the vector.
    c   Find the bearing of the vector.

8   If P is $(-3, 2)$ and Q is $(1, -1)$, find: **a** $\overrightarrow{PQ}$ **b** $|\overrightarrow{PQ}|$

9   Find the value of k such that $\begin{pmatrix} 2 \\ -3 \end{pmatrix}$ and $\begin{pmatrix} k \\ 6 \end{pmatrix}$ are parallel.

10   In the given figure, $\overrightarrow{AD} = \mathbf{p}$ and $\overrightarrow{AB} = 2\mathbf{q}$.
Line segment DC is parallel to line segment AB and is
$1\frac{1}{2}$ times its length. T is on line segment BC such that
BT : TC = 2 : 1. Find, in terms of **p** and **q**:

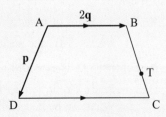

    a $\overrightarrow{DC}$ **b** $\overrightarrow{CB}$ **c** $\overrightarrow{BT}$

Review set 34B

1 What can be said about vectors **p** and **q** if:

    a $|\mathbf{p}| = |\mathbf{q}|$ **b** $\mathbf{p} = 2\mathbf{q}$?

2 A pilot wishes to fly his aeroplane due east at a speed of 200 km/h. However, his flight is affected by a wind blowing constantly at 40 km/h from the south.

    a In what direction must he face the aeroplane?

    b In order to achieve the speed of 200 km/h now, what would be his corresponding speed in still conditions?

3 Find:

    a $\begin{pmatrix} -1 \\ 2 \end{pmatrix} + \begin{pmatrix} 7 \\ -8 \end{pmatrix}$ **b** $\begin{pmatrix} 4 \\ -10 \end{pmatrix} - \begin{pmatrix} -3 \\ 6 \end{pmatrix}$ **c** $\begin{pmatrix} 3 \\ 0 \end{pmatrix} - \frac{1}{2}\begin{pmatrix} 6 \\ -4 \end{pmatrix}$

4 For $\mathbf{m} = \begin{pmatrix} 3 \\ -1 \end{pmatrix}$ and $\mathbf{n} = \begin{pmatrix} 2 \\ 4 \end{pmatrix}$, find:

    a $\mathbf{m} - 2\mathbf{n}$ **b** $|\mathbf{m} + \mathbf{n}|$

5 Suppose $\mathbf{d} = \begin{pmatrix} 3 \\ 1 \end{pmatrix}$ and $\mathbf{e} = \begin{pmatrix} -2 \\ 2 \end{pmatrix}$.

    a Draw a vector diagram to illustrate $\mathbf{d} - \mathbf{e}$.

    b Write in component form: **i** $\mathbf{d} - \mathbf{e}$ **ii** $2\mathbf{e} + 3\mathbf{d}$ **iii** $4\mathbf{d} - 3\mathbf{e}$

6 Consider the points P(4, 7), Q(8, 4), R(7, 0), and S(−1, t). Find t given that PQ ∥ SR.

7 For A(−1, 1) and B(2, −3), find:

    a $\overrightarrow{AB}$ **b** the distance AB.

8 Find k given that $\begin{pmatrix} k \\ k^2 + 3k \end{pmatrix} = \begin{pmatrix} k^2 - 2 \\ 10 \end{pmatrix}$.

9 In the given figure, $\overrightarrow{AB} = \mathbf{p}$ and $\overrightarrow{BC} = \mathbf{q}$.
$\overrightarrow{DC}$ is parallel to $\overrightarrow{AB}$ and twice its length.
Find, in terms of **p** and **q**:

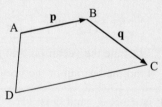

    a $\overrightarrow{DC}$ **b** $\overrightarrow{AC}$ **c** $\overrightarrow{AD}$

10 In the given figure, O is the origin and OUWV is a parallelogram. $\overrightarrow{OU} = \mathbf{u}$, $\overrightarrow{OV} = \mathbf{v}$, and X lies on UW such that UX : XW = 4 : 1.

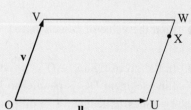

    a Find, in terms of **u** and **v**:

        i $\overrightarrow{UX}$ **ii** the position vector of X.

    b Suppose OX is extended to Y so that $\overrightarrow{OY} = \frac{5}{4}\overrightarrow{OX}$.

        i Find $\overrightarrow{VY}$ in terms of **u** and **v**.

      ii What can be deduced about V, W, and Y? Explain your answer.

Inequalities

35

Contents:

A Linear inequalities   [E2.2]
B Solving linear inequalities   [E2.2]
C Sign diagrams
D Quadratic inequalities   [E2.2]
E Solving inequalities
    using technology   [E2.2]
F Linear inequalities in
    the Cartesian plane   [E4.7]

Opening problem

The **Bermuda triangle** is an area in the Atlantic Ocean bounded by Bermuda, Puerto Rico, and Florida in which numerous ships and aeroplanes have allegedly disappeared.

Recorded incidents date back to the *Ellen Austin* in 1881, and have included both civilian and military craft.

The latitude and longitude coordinates of the vertices are, approximately: Bermuda ($32.3°$N, $64.8°$W), Puerto Rico ($18.2°$N, $66.6°$W), Melbourne, Florida ($28.1°$N, $80.6°$W).

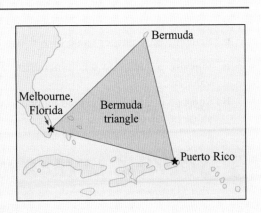

Things to think about:

How can the *region* of the Bermuda triangle be described using the coordinates of its vertices?

In this course so far, we have mostly dealt with **equations** in which two expressions are separated by the equality sign $=$.

In this Chapter we consider **inequalities** in which two expressions are separated by one of the four inequality signs $<$, $\leqslant$, $>$, or $\geqslant$.

A   LINEAR INEQUALITIES   [E2.2]

Linear inequalities take the same form as linear equations, except they contain an inequality sign instead of an "equals" sign. For example, $2x < 7$ and $3x + 5 \geqslant -10$ are linear inequalities.

We have already used linear inequalities to describe intervals on the number line. We called this **interval notation**. For example:

- $x \geqslant 2$
- $-3 < x \leqslant 1$
- $x < 1$ or $x > 5$

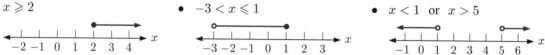

You should have already noticed that if $x \geqslant 2$ then $2 \leqslant x$.

> If we interchange the LHS and RHS of an inequality, the **inequality sign** needs to be **reversed**.

EXERCISE 35A

1   Write a mathematical sentence for:

    a   the speed S must not exceed 40 km/h   **b**   the age A must be at least 18 years

    c a is greater than 3   **d** b is less than or equal to -3

    e d is less than 5   **f** -20 is greater than or equal to x

    g   4 is less than y **h** z is greater than or equal to 0.

2   Rewrite the following inequalities with the variable on the LHS:

    a $2 < x$ **b** $5 > b$ **c** $2\frac{1}{2} \leqslant c$ **d** $-7 \geqslant d$ **e** $-19 > a$ **f** $-3 < p$

3   **a**   On the same number line, illustrate the solutions to the inequalities $x > 3$ and $x \leqslant \frac{5}{2}$.

    b   State the only integer value of x which does not satisfy either of these inequalities.

4   **a**   Suppose p and q are whole numbers, where $p > 25$ and $q \leqslant 10$. Find the *smallest* possible value of $p - q$.

    b   Suppose w and x are whole numbers, where $w \leqslant 36$ and $x < 20$. Find the *largest* possible value of $w + x$.

B   SOLVING LINEAR INEQUALITIES   [E2.2]

We have previously compared a mathematical equation to a balanced set of scales. An inequality is like an **unbalanced** set of scales.

For example, consider the inequality $3x + 2 > 7$. We let a square represent x and a circle represent 1.

To solve a linear inequality, we need to maintain the *imbalance*.

We can carry out the same operation on both sides of the inequality sign, but we need to make sure this will not change its solutions.

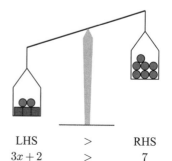

LHS	>	RHS
$3x + 2$	>	7

Discovery 1   *Operations with inequalities*

Click on the icon to discover what operations we can perform with inequalities, and which   **INEQUALITIES**
of these require reversing the inequality sign.

From the **Discovery**, you should have found that when we multiply or divide both sides of an inequality by
a *negative* number, the inequality is no longer true.

To illustrate why this occurs, consider the values 5 and 2 on
this number line. 5 is to the *right* of 2 on the number line, so
$5 > 2$.

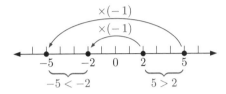

Suppose we multiply each value by -1, giving -5 and -2.
-5 is now to the *left* of -2. Therefore, to keep the inequality
correct, we must **reverse** the inequality sign, giving $-5 < -2$.

RULES FOR SOLVING INEQUALITIES

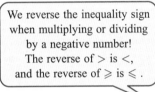

- If we **swap** the LHS and RHS, we **reverse** the inequality
  sign.
- If we **add to** or **subtract from** both sides, we **keep** the
  inequality sign.
- If we **multiply** or **divide** both sides by:
  - a **positive** number we **keep** the inequality sign
  - a **negative** number we **reverse** the inequality sign.

We reverse the inequality sign
when multiplying or dividing
by a negative number!
The reverse of $>$ is $<$,
and the reverse of $\geqslant$ is $\leqslant$.

Example 1   ◀) *Self Tutor*

Solve for x and graph the solution:

a $3x - 4 \leqslant 2$ **b** $3 - 2x < 7$

a $3x - 4 \leqslant 2$

$\therefore \ 3x \leqslant 6$ {adding 4 to both sides}

$\therefore \ x \leqslant 2$ {dividing both sides by 3}

Check: If $x = 1$ then $3x - 4 = 3 \times 1 - 4 = -1$ and $-1 \leqslant 2$ ✓

b $3 - 2x < 7$

$\therefore \ -2x < 4$ {subtracting 3 from both sides}

$\therefore \ x > -2$ {dividing both sides by -2,
                 so reverse the sign}

Notice the reversal of the
inequality sign when we
divide both sides by -2.

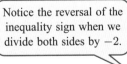

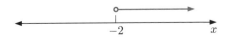

Check: If $x = 3$ then $3 - 2x = 3 - 2 \times 3 = -3$
                 and $-3 < 7$ ✓

EXERCISE 35B

1 Solve the following inequalities, and show their solutions on separate number lines:

   a $a + 4 > 6$ **b** $3b \leqslant -9$ **c** $s - 4 < 2$ **d** $\dfrac{c}{5} < 2$

   e $x - 8 \geqslant -3$ **f** $-4b > 16$ **g** $5 + t > 0$ **h** $5k < -30$

2 Solve the following inequalities, and show their solutions on separate number lines:

   a $2x + 5 > 11$ **b** $3a - 2 \geqslant 8$ **c** $4a + 9 < 1$

   d $7 - 2b < -3$ **e** $16 + 7s > 2$ **f** $3b - 1 \geqslant 0$

   g $5n + 7 < -3$ **h** $18 - x > 5$ **i** $11 - 4b \leqslant 4$

3 Solve for x and graph the solution:

   a $\dfrac{x}{3} + 1 > 4$ **b** $\dfrac{x}{5} - 2 \leqslant -3$ **c** $\dfrac{3x}{2} + 5 \geqslant -2$

   d $1 - \dfrac{x}{2} < 4$ **e** $3 - \dfrac{2x}{5} < 2$ **f** $5 - \dfrac{3x}{4} > -2$

   g $\dfrac{x - 3}{2} < 6$ **h** $\dfrac{4x + 3}{5} \leqslant -1$ **i** $\dfrac{5 - 3x}{2} \leqslant -6$

4 Solve for x and graph the solution:

   a $7 \geqslant 2x - 1$ **b** $-13 < 3x + 2$ **c** $20 > -5x$

   d $-3 \geqslant 4 - 3x$ **e** $1 < \dfrac{5 - 2x}{3}$ **f** $2 \leqslant 5(1 - x)$

Example 2   ◀)) **Self Tutor**

Solve for x and graph the solution: $3 - 5x \geqslant 2x + 7$

$\qquad 3 - 5x \geqslant 2x + 7$

$\therefore \quad 3 - 7x \geqslant 7 \qquad$ {subtracting $2x$ from both sides}

$\therefore \quad -7x \geqslant 4 \qquad$ {subtracting 3 from both sides}

$\therefore \quad x \leqslant -\tfrac{4}{7} \qquad$ {dividing both sides by -7, so reverse the sign}

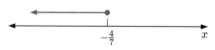

---

5 Solve for x, and show the solution on a number line:

   a $5x - 3 > 3x + 1$ **b** $2x + 1 \geqslant 4x + 7$ **c** $8x + 6 < 3x + 1$

   d $2x + 7 > 7x + 3$ **e** $6x + 2 \leqslant 3x - 7$ **f** $x - 11 \leqslant 6x - 1$

   g $3x + 1 \leqslant 7 - x$ **h** $1 - 4x > x + 5$ **i** $2 - 5x > \dfrac{1 - 3x}{4}$

6 Solve for x:

   a $3(x + 5) < -2$ **b** $2(x - 4) \geqslant x + 5$ **c** $5(2x - 3) \leqslant 4x - 8$

   d $4(x - 1) > \dfrac{5x + 1}{2}$ **e** $2(3 - x) \leqslant \dfrac{x + 4}{3}$ **f** $3(x + 2) > \dfrac{1 - 2x}{4}$

7   **a**   Find the largest integer which satisfies:

      i $2x - 5 \leqslant 15$ **ii** $\dfrac{x+2}{4} < -1$ **iii** $5 - \dfrac{2x}{3} \geqslant 2$

   b   Find the smallest integer which satisfies:

      i $3x + 4 \geqslant 30$ **ii** $\dfrac{x}{4} - 2 > 5$ **iii** $3x - 1 < 6x + 12$

8   Find the integer values of x which satisfy *both* $\dfrac{3x+5}{2} > -1$ *and* $5(x-3) \leqslant \dfrac{2-x}{2}$.

Discussion

- Try to solve the quadratic inequality $x^2 + 5x < 14$.
- Can you solve quadratic inequalities in the same way you solve quadratic equations?

C   SIGN DIAGRAMS

To solve inequalities which are *non-linear*, we do not usually need a complete graph of a function. We only need to know when the function is positive, negative, zero, or undefined.

A **sign diagram** consists of:
- a **horizontal line** which represents the x-axis
- **positive** $(+)$ and **negative** $(-)$ signs indicating where the graph is **positive** or **negative**
- **critical values**, which indicate where the function is **zero** or **undefined**.

Consider this graph of $y = f(x)$:

We use a solid line to indicate where the function is zero, and a dashed line to indicate where the function is undefined.

The corresponding sign diagram is:

Further examples are:

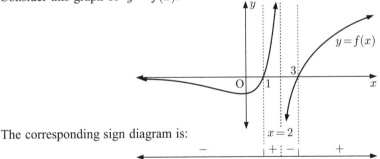

Function	$y = -(x+3)(x-2)$	$y = 3(x-1)^2$	$y = -\dfrac{1}{x}$
Graph			
Sign diagram			

Notice that:

- when a linear factor has an **odd power** there is a change of sign about that zero
- when a linear factor has an **even power** there is no sign change about that zero.

Example 3

◀ᴹ) *Self Tutor*

Draw a sign diagram for:

a $(x+5)(x-2)$

b $-x^2 - 4x - 4$

a $(x+5)(x-2)$ has critical values -5 and 2.

We try any number > 2:
When $x = 10$, we have $(15)(8) > 0$, so we put a $+$ sign here.

The factors are single, so the signs alternate.

b $-x^2 - 4x - 4 = -(x^2 + 4x + 4)$
$$= -(x+2)^2$$

$-(x+2)^2$ has critical value -2.

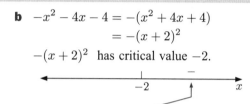

When $x = 10$, we have $-12^2 < 0$, so we put a $-$ sign here.

A squared factor indicates no change of sign about the critical value.

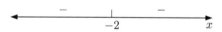

EXERCISE 35C

1 Draw a sign diagram for each graph:

a
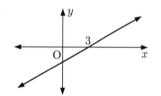

b
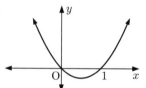

c
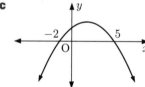

d
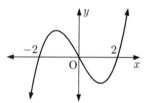

e
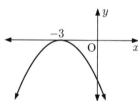

f
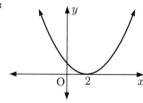

g
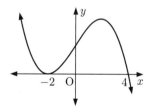

h
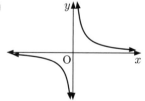

i
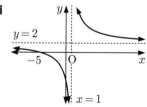

2 Draw a sign diagram for:

a $(x + 3)(x - 1)$ **b** $(x + 4)(x + 2)$ **c** $x(x + 5)$

d $-(x + 2)(x - 3)$ **e** $(2x + 1)(x - 5)$ **f** $(3x - 1)(4 - x)$

g $(3 - x)(1 - 2x)$ **h** $(x - 1)^2$ **i** $(x + 4)^2$

j $-(x + 3)^2$ **k** $-(x - 2)^2$ **l** $(3x - 1)^2$

3 Draw a sign diagram for:

a $x^2 - 16$ **b** $1 - x^2$ **c** $2x - x^2$

d $x^2 - 4x + 3$ **e** $2 - 18x^2$ **f** $-x^2 + 2x + 24$

g $3x^2 - 8x - 3$ **h** $2 - 2x - 4x^2$ **i** $-10x^2 + 9x + 9$

j $x^2 - 6x + 9$ **k** $-x^2 + 2x - 1$ **l** $-4x^2 - 4x - 1$

Example 4 ◀)) *Self Tutor*

Given the sign diagram alongside, describe where the function is:

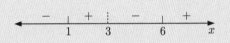

a positive   **b** non-negative.

a The function is positive where its value is > 0.
This occurs for $1 < x < 3$ or $x > 6$.

b The function is non-negative where its value is positive or zero, so the function is $\geqslant 0$.
This occurs for $1 \leqslant x < 3$ or $x \geqslant 6$.

We do not include 3 here because the
function is undefined at $x = 3$.

---

4 Describe where the functions with these sign diagrams are:

i positive   **ii** non-negative   **iii** negative   **iv** non-positive.

D QUADRATIC INEQUALITIES   [E2.2]

Quadratic inequalities take the same form as quadratic equations except they contain an inequality sign instead of an "equals" sign.

$x^2 \leqslant 4$, $x^2 + 3x + 2 < 0$, and $x^2 - 4x > 21$ are examples of quadratic inequalities.

While quadratic equations have 0, 1, or 2 solutions, quadratic inequalities may have 0, 1, or infinitely many solutions.

To solve quadratic inequalities, we follow these steps:

> *Step 1*: Make the RHS zero by shifting all terms to the LHS.
> *Step 2*: Fully factorise the LHS.
> *Step 3*: Draw a sign diagram for the LHS.
> *Step 4*: Determine the set of solutions from the sign diagram.

Example 5
🔊 *Self Tutor*

Solve for x:

a $x^2 + 5x < 14$ **b** $x^2 + 4 \geqslant -4x$

a
$$x^2 + 5x < 14$$
$$\therefore \ x^2 + 5x - 14 < 0 \qquad \text{\{making RHS zero\}}$$
$$\therefore \ (x + 7)(x - 2) < 0 \qquad \text{\{fully factorising LHS\}}$$

Sign diagram of LHS is

The inequality is true for $-7 < x < 2$.

b
$$x^2 + 4 \geqslant -4x$$
$$\therefore \ x^2 + 4x + 4 \geqslant 0 \qquad \text{\{making RHS zero\}}$$
$$\therefore \ (x + 2)^2 \geqslant 0 \qquad \text{\{fully factorising LHS\}}$$

Sign diagram of LHS is
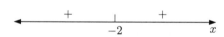

The LHS is always $\geqslant 0$, so the inequality is true for all real x.

EXERCISE 35D

1 **a** Draw a sign diagram for $x^2 + x - 6$.

   b Hence, solve for x:

   i $x^2 + x - 6 > 0$ **ii** $x^2 + x - 6 \geqslant 0$ **iii** $x^2 + x - 6 < 0$ **iv** $x^2 + x - 6 \leqslant 0$

2 Solve for x:

   a $(x - 1)(x - 3) \leqslant 0$ **b** $(x + 2)(x - 4) \geqslant 0$ **c** $(x + 1)(x - 2) > 0$

   d $(2x + 3)(4 - x) > 0$ **e** $(x - 3)^2 \geqslant 0$ **f** $(x + 5)^2 < 0$

3 Solve for x:

   a $x^2 - 2x \geqslant 0$ **b** $4x^2 + 2x < 0$ **c** $x^2 < 16$

   d $3x^2 \leqslant 12$ **e** $x^2 > \frac{9}{4}$ **f** $x^2 + 4x - 5 > 0$

   g $x^2 \leqslant x + 2$ **h** $x^2 - 4x + 4 < 0$ **i** $x^2 + 3x \leqslant 28$

   j $3x^2 - 6x + 3 > 0$ **k** $2x^2 - 5 \leqslant 3x$ **l** $3x^2 \geqslant 2(x + 4)$

   m $4 < 5x^2 + 8x$ **n** $6(x^2 + 2) < 17x$ **o** $9x^2 \leqslant 12x - 4$

4 Solve for x, and show the solutions on a number line:

    a $x^2 - 2x - 15 \leqslant 0$ **b** $x^2 + 18 > 9x$ **c** $3x^2 - 5x - 2 \geqslant 0$

    d $5x < 12 - 2x^2$ **e** $2(2x^2 - 1) > 7x$ **f** $6x(x - 1) < x + 3$

E   SOLVING INEQUALITIES USING TECHNOLOGY   [E2.2]

For inequalities which are difficult or impossible to solve algebraically, we can estimate the solutions by examining a graph.

For example, to solve $f(x) > g(x)$, we graph $y = f(x)$ and $y = g(x)$ on the same set of axes. We find the values of x for which $y = f(x)$ is *above* $y = g(x)$.

Example 6   ◀) *Self Tutor*

Solve for x:

    a $5 - 2x - x^2 < 0$ **b** $3 + x > 2^x$

a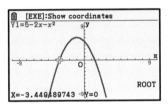

b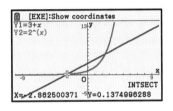

The graph is below the x-axis when $x < -3.45$ or $x > 1.45$.

$y = 3 + x$ is above $y = 2^x$ when $-2.86 < x < 2.44$.

EXERCISE 35E

1 The graph of $f(x) = x^3 - 3x - 1$ is shown alongside.

    a Use your calculator to find the coordinates of A, B, and C.

    b Solve for x:

        i $x^3 - 3x - 1 > 0$

        ii $x^3 - 3x - 1 \leqslant 0$

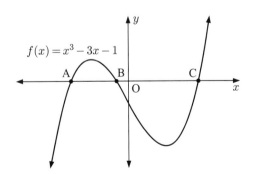

2 **a** Use your calculator to help sketch $f(x) = \sqrt{x} - \dfrac{x^2}{5} + 3$.

    b State the domain of $f(x)$.

    c Solve the inequality $\sqrt{x} - \dfrac{x^2}{5} + 3 > 0$.

3   **a** Sketch the graph of $f(x) = \dfrac{2}{x^2 + x - 6} + 1$.

    b Find the equations of the vertical asymptotes.

    c Solve $f(x) \leqslant 0$.

4 Solve for x:

    a $x^2 - 2x - 5 < 0$ **b** $2x^3 - 5x + 6 > 0$ **c** $x^3 - x^2 - 2x + 1 < 0$

    d $3^x - 5 \geqslant 0$ **e** $x^2 - \dfrac{1}{3x} > 0$ **f** $\sqrt{x+2} - 0.5^x < 0$

5   **a** Sketch the graphs of $f(x) = 2^x$ and $g(x) = 5 - x^2$ on the same set of axes.

    b Find the points of intersection of the graphs.

    c Hence solve $2^x > 5 - x^2$.

6 Solve for x:

    a $x^2 \geqslant x + 3$ **b** $3^x > 2$ **c** $x^2 > 2^x$

    d $1 - x - x^2 > \dfrac{3}{x}$ **e** $\dfrac{1}{x} \leqslant x^2 + 1$ **f** $|x^2 - 5| < 1$

7 Solve for x:

    a $\sin 2x > 0.461$ for $0° \leqslant x \leqslant 360°$ **b** $|x| + |1 - 2x| < 3$

8   **a** Sketch the graph of $f(x) = 2^x - 4x$.

    b Solve for x:

        i $2^x - 4x < 0$ **ii** $2^x - 4x < 3$

    c Find the values of k such that $2^x - 4x < k$ has no solutions.

F   LINEAR INEQUALITIES IN THE CARTESIAN PLANE   [E4.7]

In **Sections A** and **B** we studied linear inequalities in a single variable. We represented the solution to the inequality on a one-dimensional number line.

We can also consider linear inequalities in two variables, usually x and y. Examples of such inequalities include $2x + 5y \leqslant 10$ or $x - 3y < -9$.

We can represent the solutions to these inequalities as regions of the two-dimensional Cartesian plane.

Consider the region $\mathcal{R}$ which is on or to the right of the line $x = 3$. This region is specified by the linear inequality $x \geqslant 3$, since all points within $\mathcal{R}$ have x-coordinates which are more than 3.

To illustrate this region we shade out all **unwanted** points. This makes it easier to identify the required region $\mathcal{R}$ when several inequalities define a region, as $\mathcal{R}$ is the region left unshaded.

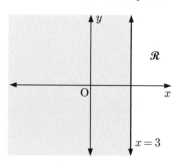

We use a solid boundary line to indicate that points on the boundary are wanted.

If the boundary is unwanted, we use a dashed boundary line.

For example, to illustrate the region specified by $x > 2$ and $y > 4$, we shade the region on and to the left of the line $x = 2$, and the region on and below the line $y = 4$. The region $\mathcal{R}$ left completely unshaded is the region specified by $x > 2$ and $y > 4$. The lines $x = 2$ and $y = 4$ are dashed, which indicates the boundaries are not included in the region.

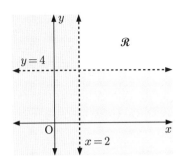

Example 7   ◀》 *Self Tutor*

Write inequalities to represent the following unshaded regions:

a

b

c

a $x \leqslant 0$ and $y \leqslant 0$

b $-2 < y < 3$

c $0 \leqslant x \leqslant 3$ and $0 \leqslant y \leqslant 2$

Discovery 2   *Linear inequalities*

In this Discovery we consider the regions on either side of the line with equation $3x + 2y = 6$.

What to do:

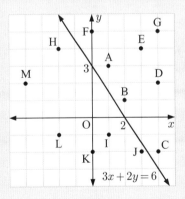

1 Copy and complete:

Point	$3x + 2y$
A(1, 3)	$3(1) + 2(3) = 9$
B(,)	
C(,)	
D(,)	
E(,)	
F(,)	
G(,)	

Point	$3x + 2y$
H(−2, 4)	$3(-2) + 2(4) = 2$
I(,)	
J(,)	
K(,)	
L(,)	
M(,)	
O(0, 0)	

2 Which points are solutions to the inequality $3x + 2y < 6$? What do you notice about these points?

3 Which points are solutions to the inequality $3x + 2y > 6$? What do you notice about these points?

You should have discovered that:

> All points satisfying $ax + by < d$ lie on one side of the line $ax + by = d$, and all points satisfying $ax + by > d$ lie on the other side.

To find the region which corresponds to an inequality, we substitute a point not on the boundary line into the inequality. The origin $(0, 0)$ is the easiest to substitute, provided it is not on the line.

Example 8
◀) **Self Tutor**

Graph $3x - 4y > 12$.

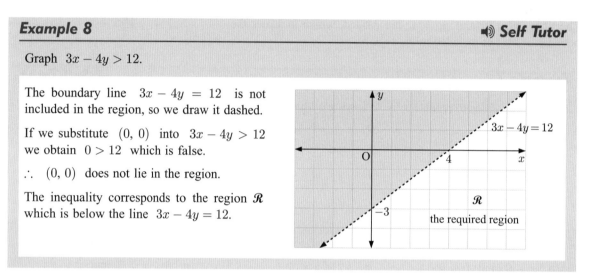

The boundary line $3x - 4y = 12$ is not included in the region, so we draw it dashed.

If we substitute $(0, 0)$ into $3x - 4y > 12$ we obtain $0 > 12$ which is false.

$\therefore$ $(0, 0)$ does not lie in the region.

The inequality corresponds to the region $\mathcal{R}$ which is below the line $3x - 4y = 12$.

EXERCISE 35F

1 Write inequalities to represent the unshaded region $\mathcal{R}$:

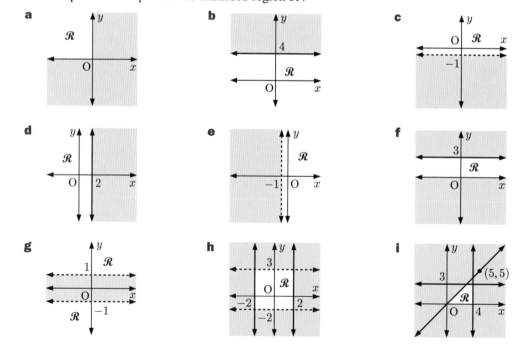

2 Graph the region defined by:

a $x < 4$ **b** $x \geqslant -1$ **c** $y \geqslant 2$

d $y < -1$ **e** $0 < x < 3$ **f** $-1 \leqslant y \leqslant 2$

g $-2 < x \leqslant 3$ **h** $-1 \leqslant y < 4$ **i** $0 \leqslant x \leqslant 3$ and $1 \leqslant y \leqslant 4$

3 Graph the region defined by:

a $x + 2y \leqslant 4$ **b** $2x + y > 5$ **c** $3x + 2y < 6$

d $2x + 3y \geqslant 6$ **e** $2x - 3y < 12$ **f** $5x + 2y > 10$

g $2x - 5y < -10$ **h** $4x + 3y < 6$ **i** $4x - 3y \geqslant 12$

j $y \geqslant x$ **k** $y < -x$ **l** $2x + 5y \geqslant 0$

4 Graph the region defined by:

a $x \geqslant 0$ and $y \geqslant 2$ **b** $x \leqslant -2$ and $y \geqslant 4$

c $x \geqslant 0$, $y \geqslant 0$, and $x + y \leqslant 4$ **d** $x \geqslant 0$, $y \geqslant 0$, and $2x + y < 6$

e $x \geqslant 2$, $y \geqslant 0$, and $x + y \geqslant 6$ **f** $x \geqslant 0$, $y \geqslant 3$, and $2x + 3y \geqslant 12$

Example 9   ◀» *Self Tutor*

Write an inequality to represent the unshaded region $\mathcal{R}$:

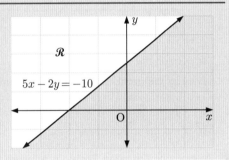

The boundary has equation $5x - 2y = -10$, and is included in $\mathcal{R}$.

Substituting $(0, 0)$, $5x - 2y = 0$. Since $0 > -10$ and the origin is *outside* $\mathcal{R}$, $\mathcal{R}$ is defined by $5x - 2y \leqslant -10$.

---

5 Write an inequality to represent the unshaded region $\mathcal{R}$:

a
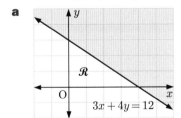

b
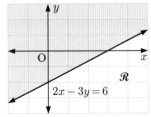

c
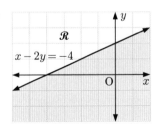

d
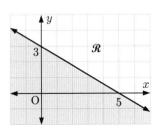

e
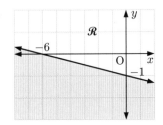

f
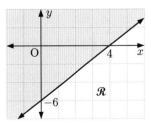

6 Write down inequalities which represent the unshaded region $\mathcal{R}$:

a
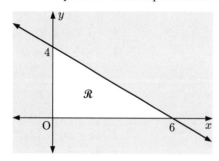

b
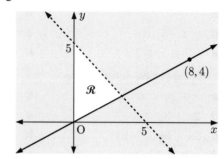

c
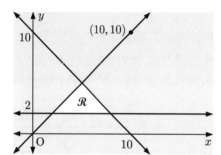

d
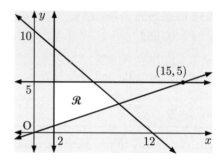

7 **a** Graph the region $\mathcal{R}$ defined by $y \geqslant 2x$, $x + y \leqslant 6$, $x \geqslant 0$.

  b List the points in $\mathcal{R}$ which have integer coordinates.

8 **a** Graph the region $\mathcal{R}$ defined by $x \geqslant 1$, $x + 2y \leqslant 10$, $x - y \leqslant -1$.

  b Find the minimum and maximum values of y in the region.

9 Answer the **Opening Problem** on page 613, assuming positive x is east and positive y is north.

Review set 35A

1 Solve for x:

  a $3x + 1 \leqslant 16$ **b** $-\dfrac{x}{3} > 7$ **c** $\dfrac{x}{4} - 7 \geqslant -2$

2 Solve the following inequalities, and show their solutions on separate number lines:

  a $3 - 2x \geqslant -4$ **b** $\dfrac{2x + 3}{2} < -3$ **c** $3(x + 2) - 1 \leqslant 1 - 4x$

3 **a** Solve the inequality $\dfrac{x}{5} - 3 > -5$ and display the solution on a number line.

  b Solve the inequality $8 - 3(x + 2) \geqslant 1$ and display the solution on a number line.

  c Find the values of x which satisfy *both* inequalities.

4 Find the smallest integer which satisfies $5x + 7 > 2x - 13$.

5 Draw a sign diagram for:

  a $(x + 4)(x - 1)$ **b** $-x^2 + 2x + 15$

6 Solve for x:

   a $(x+2)(x+6) < 0$ **b** $x^2 + 5x \geqslant 36$ **c** $2x^2 - 15 < 7x$

7 Solve $4x(x+2) \geqslant 3x + 6$, and show the solution on a number line.

8 Use technology to solve:

   a $5^x - 4 \leqslant 0$ **b** $x^2 + 4x - 1 > 0$ **c** $x^3 + 11x < 6x^2 + 5$

9 Write inequalities which represent the unshaded region $\mathcal{R}$:

   a 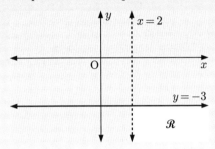   **b**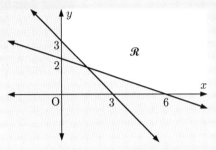

10 **a** Graph the region $\mathcal{R}$ defined by $x \geqslant 0$, $y \geqslant 0$, $x + 2y \leqslant 12$.

    b List the points in $\mathcal{R}$ which have integer coordinates and which also satisfy $y = x + 1$.

Review set 35B

1 Solve for x:

   a $8 - x < -1$ **b** $4x - 3 \geqslant x + 1$ **c** $\dfrac{x - 5}{3} \leqslant 1 - 2x$

2 Solve the following inequalities:

   a $3 - 2x \geqslant 0$ **b** $\dfrac{x}{5} - 3 < -1$ **c** $6(2x + 1) \geqslant 6 - 13x$

3 **a** Draw a sign diagram for $2x^2 - 16x + 32$.

    b Hence solve $2x^2 - 16x + 32 > 0$.

4 Solve for x:

   a $-x^2 - 2x + 35 > 0$ **b** $(x + 5)(6 - x) \leqslant 0$ **c** $2(x^2 - 6) < 5x$

5 Solve $x(x + 6) < 27$, and show the solution on a number line.

6 **a** Sketch the graphs of $f(x) = 4^x - 5$ and $g(x) = 2x - x^2$ on the same set of axes.

    b Hence solve $4^x - 5 \leqslant 2x - x^2$.

7 **a** Sketch the graph of $f(x) = \log(x^2 + x + 4) - 1$.

    b Hence solve $\log(x^2 + x + 4) - 1 \leqslant 0$.

    c Find the values of k such that $\log(x^2 + x + 4) - 1 \leqslant k$ has no solutions.

8 Graph the region defined by:

   a $x \geqslant 4$ **b** $5x - y \leqslant -10$

9 Write inequalities which represent the unshaded region $\mathcal{R}$:

a

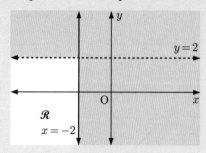

b

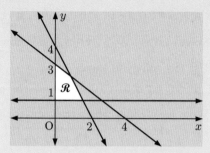

10 **a** Graph the region defined by $y \geqslant x$, $y \geqslant 0$, $x - 4y \geqslant -4$.

   b Find the maximum value of x in the region.

Multi-topic questions

36

The questions from past examination papers in this Chapter are reproduced by permission of Cambridge Assessment International Education.

MULTI-TOPIC QUESTIONS

1 The diagram shows a solid trophy for a football tournament.
The sphere on the top has a radius of 15 cm.
The sphere rests on a cylinder with the same radius as the sphere and height 40 cm.
The base is a cylinder with radius 25 cm and height 12 cm.

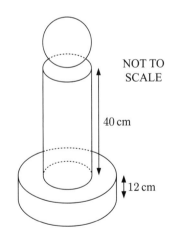

NOT TO SCALE

40 cm

12 cm

  a Calculate the volume of the trophy.

  b The mass of the trophy is 15 kg.
  Each member of the winning team receives a model of the trophy made from the same material.
  The model is similar to the real trophy and one fifth of the height.

    i Calculate the total height of each model trophy.

    ii Calculate the mass, in grams, of each model trophy.

(Cambridge IGCSE International Mathematics 0607, Paper 41 Q4, May/June 2016)

2 Sunil has $80 and Asha has $75.

  a Write the ratio 80 : 75 in its simplest form.

  b **i** Sunil spends $24. Work out $24 as a percentage of $80.

  ii Sunil invests $50 at a rate of 2% per year compound interest. Calculate the **interest** Sunil has after 20 years.

c During each month, Asha spends $\frac{1}{5}$ of the money that she had at the beginning of the month.

   i Work out how much of the $75 Asha has at the end of the 2nd month.

   ii Calculate the number of **whole** months it takes for Asha to have less than $5.

(Cambridge IGCSE International Mathematics 0607, Paper 41 Q1, October/November 2015)

3 Squash balls have radius 1.5 cm. They are sold in boxes. Each box is a cuboid. Each box has length 15 cm, width 12 cm, and height 3 cm.

   a Show that the maximum number of balls in a box is 20.

   b Calculate the volume of **one** ball.

   c Calculate the total volume of 20 balls.

   d Write your answer to part **c** in standard form.

   e Calculate the percentage of the volume of the box that the 20 balls fill.

(Cambridge IGCSE International Mathematics 0607, Paper 41 Q7, May/June 2015)

4 The diagram alongside shows the cylindrical tank in which Dipak stores his heating oil.
The length of the tank is 2.5 m and its radius is 0.9 m.
Dipak measures the depth of the oil to be 0.2 m.

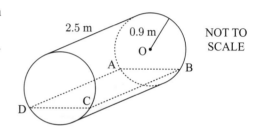

The diagram alongside shows the cross-section of the tank and the oil.

   a Calculate the rectangular surface area of the oil, ABCD.

   b Calculate angle AOB and show that it rounds to 77.9° correct to 1 decimal place.

   c Find the number of **extra** litres of oil that Dipak needs to fill the tank.

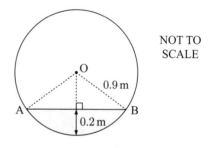

(Cambridge IGCSE International Mathematics 0607, Paper 41 Q5, October/November 2014)

5 Consider the functions $f(x) = x^2 + 5x$ and $g(x) = 4 - 3x$.

   a Find:

   i $f(g(x))$ **ii** $g(g(x))$ **iii** $g(f(2))$

   b Solve for x:

   i $f(g(x)) = 24$ **ii** $f(g(x)) \leqslant 0$

6 Calculate:

   a BC

   b angle CAD

   c the area of the quadrilateral ABCD.

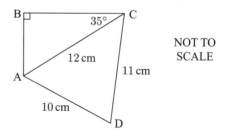

(Cambridge IGCSE International Mathematics 0607, Paper 41 Q5, October/November 2015)

7 The points A(3, 4), B(9, 2), and C(6, 7) are shown on the diagram below.

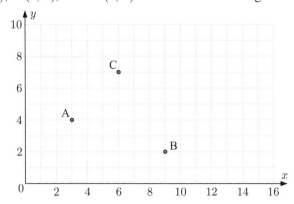

  a Write $\overrightarrow{AB}$ as a column vector.

  b Find the gradient of the line AB.

  c Find the equation of the line AB. Give your answer in the form $y = mx + c$.

  d C is the midpoint of AM. Find the coordinates of M.

  e The point N is such that ABNM is a parallelogram. Find the coordinates of N.

  f Find the length BM.

(Cambridge IGCSE International Mathematics 0607, Paper 41 Q2, May/June 2014)

8 A circular target of diameter 20 cm is placed in the centre of a regular hexagonal board. The shortest distance from the edge of the board to the target is 5 cm.

  a Find the measure of the shaded angle.

  b Find the length of each side of the hexagon.

  c Find the area of the hexagon.

  d What percentage of the board is covered by the target?

  e Two darts are thrown. They each hit a point on the board at random. Find the probability that one dart hits the target and the other misses it.

9 In this question all lengths are in centimetres.

  a Write down a quadratic equation, in terms of x, and show that it simplifies to $7x^2 - 24x - 16 = 0$.

  b Factorise $7x^2 - 24x - 16$.

  c Show that the area of the triangle is 84 cm².

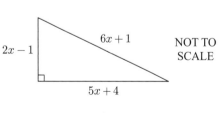

NOT TO SCALE

  d The area of this rectangle is equal to the area of the triangle. Find the value of y.

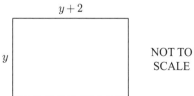

NOT TO SCALE

(Cambridge IGCSE International Mathematics 0607, Paper 41 Q13, May/June 2015)

10 In Kim's game a player looks at a fixed number of objects on a tray for a length of time, t seconds. The player is then tested to find how many objects they remember.

The table shows the results for 10 players.

Time in seconds (t)	30	40	50	60	70	80	90	100	110	120
Number of objects (n)	8	10	15	12	16	20	18	23	19	25

a Copy and complete the scatter diagram. The first six points have been plotted for you.

b What type of correlation is shown by the scatter diagram?

c **i** Calculate the mean time.
    ii Calculate the mean number of objects.

d **i** Find the equation of the regression line. Give your answer in the form $n = mt + c$.
    ii Errol looks at the tray for 85 seconds. Use your equation to estimate the number of objects he remembers.

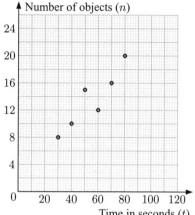

(Cambridge IGCSE International Mathematics 0607, Paper 41 Q5, May/June 2016)

11 $f(x) = 2x + 3, \quad g(x) = x - 1, \quad h(x) = \log(x + 1)$

a Find $f(h(9))$.   **b** Find $g(f(x))$ in its simplest form.

c Find $\dfrac{1}{f(x)} + \dfrac{1}{g(x)}$ in terms of x. Give your answer as a single fraction.

d Solve the equation $h(x) = -1$.

e Solve the equation $(g(x))^2 = 5$. Give exact answers.

(Cambridge IGCSE International Mathematics 0607, Paper 41 Q10, October/November 2015)

12 A library allows each member to have up to 10 books on loan. The table shows the number of books currently on loan to a random sample of 75 members.

Number of books on loan	0	1	2	3	4, 5, or 6	7	8 or 9	10
Number of members	7	4	20	14	10	8	8	4

a Write down the mode.   **b** Work out the range.

c Find the median.   **d** Find the interquartile range.

e Calculate an estimate of the mean.

f Two members are chosen at random. Find the probability that they both have at least seven books out on loan.

(Cambridge IGCSE International Mathematics 0607, Paper 41 Q7, May/June 2014)

13 Consider the points A(2, 2), B($\sqrt{11}$, 7), and C(−1, −3).

a Find the length of AC.

b How far is B from the origin? Give your answer in simplest form.

c Find the gradient of AB. Give your answer in the form $a + b\sqrt{11}$ where $a, b \in \mathbb{Q}$.

d Point D lies on the x-axis, and AD is perpendicular to AC. Find the coordinates of D.

14   **a** Solve the equation $3\log 2 - 2\log 3 + \log x = 3\log 4$.

    b Solve the simultaneous equations: $\begin{aligned} 5x - 4y &= 1 \\ 4x - 5y &= 8 \end{aligned}$

(Cambridge IGCSE International Mathematics 0607, Paper 41 Q5, May/June 2014)

15 You may use these axes to help you answer this question.
The transformation P is a rotation of $90°$ clockwise about the origin.
The transformation Q is a reflection in the line $y = -x$.

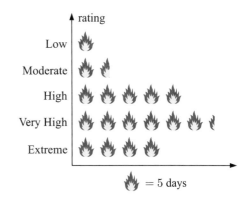

    a Find the coordinates of the image of the point $(4,\ 1)$ under the transformation P.

    b Find the coordinates of the image of the point $(4,\ 1)$ under the transformation Q.

    c Find the coordinates of the image of the point $(x,\ y)$ under the transformation P followed by the transformation Q.

    d Describe fully the **single** transformation equivalent to P followed by Q.

(Cambridge IGCSE International Mathematics 0607, Paper 41 Q1, May/June 2014)

16 A is the point $(-2,\ -1)$ and B is the point $(6,\ 3)$.

    a Calculate $|\overrightarrow{AB}|$.

    b The point P has coordinates $(x,\ y)$ and $PA = PB$. Show that $2x + y = 5$.

    c If P is also on the line $y = x$, find the coordinates of P.

(Cambridge IGCSE International Mathematics 0607, Paper 41 Q10, May/June 2016)

17 This pictograph shows the fire danger rating of 90 summer days in California.

    a On how many days was the rating:

       i High   **ii** Very High?

    b On what percentage of the days was the rating Low?

    c Write the ratio of Extreme : Very High days in simplest form.

    d Two summer days are randomly selected. Find the probability that the rating on both days was High.

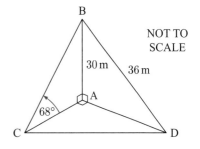

18 AB is a vertical tower of height 30 m.
BC and BD are straight wires attached to B.
A, C, and D are on horizontal ground with C due west of D.
Angle $BCA = 68°$ and $BD = 36$ m.

    a Calculate AD.

    b Calculate AC and show that it rounds to 12.1 m, correct to 3 significant figures.

    c Calculate the bearing of A from D.

(Cambridge IGCSE International Mathematics 0607, Paper 41 Q7, May/June 2016)

19 P and Q are points on the unit circle. P has y-coordinate $\frac{4}{5}$, and Q has x-coordinate $\frac{2}{\sqrt{5}}$.

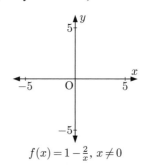

   a Find the coordinates of P and Q.

   b Find the measure of θ.

   c Find the distance PQ. Give your answer in the form $\sqrt{a + b\sqrt{5}}$ where $a, b \in \mathbb{Q}$.

   d Find the size of $\widehat{POQ}$.

   e Find the gradient of the tangent to the circle at:

      i P   **ii** Q.

20 Paula invests $3000 in Bank A and $3000 in Bank B.

   a Bank A pays compound interest at a rate of 4% each year.

      i Find the total amount that Paula has in Bank A at the end of 3 years.

      ii After how many complete years is the total amount that Paula has in Bank A greater than $4000?

   b Bank B pays simple interest at a rate of 5% each year.

      i Find the total amount that Paula has in Bank B at the end of 3 years.

      ii After how many complete years is the total amount that Paula has in Bank B greater than $4000?

   c After how many complete years will the total amount that Paula has in Bank A be greater than the total amount that Paula has in Bank B?

(Cambridge IGCSE International Mathematics 0607, Paper 41 Q11, May/June 2015)

21   **a** On a diagram like the one alongside, sketch the graph of $y = f(x)$, for values between $x = -5$ and $x = 5$.

   b Solve the inequality $f(x) < 0$.

   c Find $f^{-1}(x)$.

   d On your diagram, sketch the graph of $y = f^{-1}(x)$, for values between $x = -5$ and $x = 5$.

   e Describe fully the **single** transformation that maps the graph of $y = f(x)$ onto the graph of $y = f^{-1}(x)$.

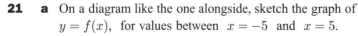

$f(x) = 1 - \frac{2}{x}, \ x \neq 0$

(Cambridge IGCSE International Mathematics 0607, Paper 41 Q3, October/November 2015)

22 This sector has radius x m and arc length $(x - 2)$ m. The area of the sector is 24 m^2.

   a Show that $\frac{1}{2}x(x - 2) = 24$.

   b Find the radius of the sector.

   c What percentage of the sector does the triangle ABC occupy?

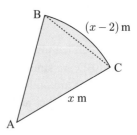

23   **a** Find the nth term of the sequence:

      i 1, 4, 9, 16, 25, ...   **ii** 7, 10, 13, 16, 19, ...

   b Hence find the nth term of the sequence 8, 14, 22, 32, 44, ...

   c The kth term of the sequence in **b** is 158. Find k.

24   a   AB and CD are parallel.
AD and CB intersect at X.
CD $= 9$ cm, AB $= 4$ cm, AX $= 4.5$ cm,
and BX $= 3$ cm.
Calculate the length of CX.

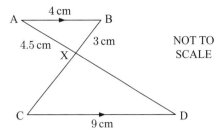

b

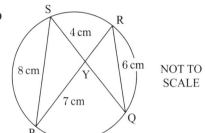

P, Q, R, and S lie on a circle.
PR and QS intersect at Y.
QR $= 6$ cm, PS $= 8$ cm, PY $= 7$ cm, and
YS $= 4$ cm.
Calculate the length of RY.

c   The two shapes are mathematically similar.
The area of E is 90 cm^2 and the area of F is
45 cm^2.
Find the value of w.

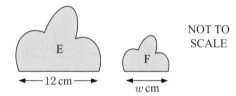

(Cambridge IGCSE International Mathematics 0607, Paper 41 Q4, October/November 2015)

25   The frequency of a radio wave, f, is inversely proportional to the wavelength, L metres.
A radio station broadcasts on a frequency of 93.7 and a wavelength of 3.2 m.
   a   Find a formula for f, in terms of L, writing any constants correct to 3 significant figures.
   b   Chat Radio broadcasts with a wavelength of 2.8 m. Find the frequency of Chat Radio.
   c   Allsports Radio broadcasts with a frequency of 0.35. Find the wavelength of Allsports Radio.
(Cambridge IGCSE International Mathematics 0607, Paper 41 Q2, May/June 2016)

26   Points A, B, and C lie on a circle. The tangent to the
circle at C meets BA extended at D.
   a   Find the measure of $A\widehat{C}D$.
   b   Find the area of the shaded triangle.

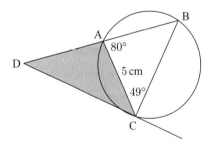

27   a   These are the first four terms of a sequence: 5, 8, 11, 14.
Write down an expression in terms of n for the nth term, s_n, of the sequence.
   b   The nth term, t_n, of another sequence is $2n^2 + n - 6$. Write down the first four terms of this
sequence.
   c   The nth term of a third sequence, u_n, is given by $u_n = \dfrac{t_n}{n+2}$. Find an expression for u_n, in
terms of n, giving your answer in its simplest form.
   d   The nth term of a fourth sequence is given by $s_n + u_n$. Is 501 a term of this fourth sequence?
Give your reasons.
(Cambridge IGCSE International Mathematics 0607, Paper 41 Q6, May/June 2016)

28 In a survey, 200 people were asked whether they owned a vehicle.

130 owned a car (C), 30 owned a motorcycle (M), and 85 owned a bicycle (B).

18 owned a car and a motorcycle.

17 owned a motorcycle and a bicycle.

60 owned a car and a bicycle.

8 owned a car and a motorcycle and a bicycle.

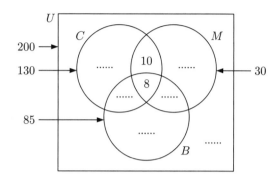

   a Copy and complete this Venn diagram.

   b Find the probability that a person, chosen at random from these 200 people:

     i does not own any of the three vehicles

     ii is an element of the set $B \cap M \cap C'$.

   c Two of the 200 people are chosen at random, without replacement. Calculate the probability that:

     i both own a motorcycle   **ii** one owns only a car and the other owns only a bicycle.

(Cambridge IGCSE International Mathematics 0607, Paper 41 Q7, October/November 2014)

29 A ship sails from S on a bearing of $020°$. There is a lighthouse at L, 35 km due north of S. The light from the lighthouse has a range of 25 km. SP $= x$ km.

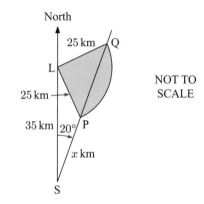

   a Use the cosine rule to show that $x^2 - kx + 600 = 0$, where $k = 65.78$ correct to 2 decimal places.

   b **i** Solve the equation $x^2 - 65.78x + 600 = 0$, giving your answers correct to 2 decimal places.

     ii Write down the distance SQ.

   c The ship is sailing at 30 km/h. Use your answers to part **b** to find the length of time the light is visible from the ship. Give your answer in hours and minutes correct to the nearest minute.

(Cambridge IGCSE International Mathematics 0607, Paper 41 Q12, October/November 2014)

30 The diagram shows the top of a circular cake of **diameter** 30 cm. The cake is cut into 16 pieces as shown in the diagram.

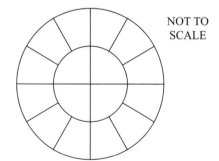

   a **i** The top of each of the 16 pieces of cake has the same area. Find the area of one of the pieces in square centimetres.

     ii Write your answer to part **a i** in square metres.

     iii Show that the radius of the inner circle is 7.5 cm.

   b The diagram shows the top of one of the outer pieces of cake.

     i Calculate the perimeter of the top of this piece of cake.

     ii The depth of the cake is 8 cm. Calculate the **total** surface area of this piece of cake.

(Cambridge IGCSE International Mathematics 0607, Paper 41 Q11, May/June 2014)

Investigation and modelling questions

37

Contents:

A Investigation questions
B Modelling questions

The questions from past examination papers in this Chapter are reproduced by permission of Cambridge Assessment International Education.

A INVESTIGATION QUESTIONS

1 The sum of the squares of the first n integers is given by the formula

$$1^2 + 2^2 + 3^2 + ... + n^2 = \frac{n(n+1)(2n+1)}{k} \text{ where } k \text{ is an integer.}$$

    a Use the case $n = 1$ to find the value of k.

    b Verify the formula is true for $n = 2$ and $n = 3$.

    c Use the formula to find the value of $1^2 + 2^2 + 3^2 + ... + 100^2$.

    d Notice that $2^2 + 4^2 + 6^2 = (2 \times 1)^2 + (2 \times 2)^2 + (2 \times 3)^2$
$$= 2^2 1^2 + 2^2 2^2 + 2^2 3^2$$
$$= 2^2 (1^2 + 2^2 + 3^3)$$

    Hence find the value of $2^2 + 4^2 + 6^2 + ... + 100^2$.

    e Use **c** and **d** to find the value of $1^2 + 3^2 + 5^2 + ... + 99^2$.

    f Find the value of $1^2 - 2^2 + 3^2 - 4^2 + 5^2 - 6^2 + ... + 99^2 - 100^2$.

2 A farmer makes a sheep pen in the shape of a quadrilateral from four pieces of fencing. Each side of the quadrilateral is 5 metres long, and one of the angles is $60°$.

    a Using a scale of 1 to 100, make an accurate drawing of the quadrilateral.

    b Mark in its axes of symmetry and describe how they cut each other.

    c What is the special geometrical name of this shape?

    d Calculate the area enclosed by the sheep pen.

  e By changing the angles but leaving the lengths of the sides unchanged, the area of the pen can be varied. What is the greatest possible area that can be enclosed? Justify your answer.

3 **a** Find a prime number which can be written as the sum of two prime numbers.

   b Consider the statement "All even numbers greater than 15 can be written as the sum of two different prime numbers in at least two different ways." For example, $20 = 3 + 17 = 7 + 13$.

   i Show that the above statement is true for 16.

   ii Find a number between 30 and 50 which shows that the statement is false.

   c Show that 16 can be written as the sum of three different prime numbers.

4 **a** The shapes below form a sequence. The shapes are made with 1 cm rods.

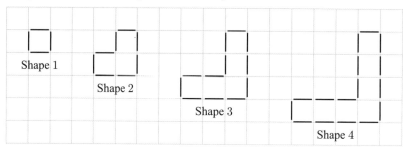

   i Copy and complete the table below.

Shape number	1	2	3	4		7		n
Number of rods	4	8	12	16				
Number of squares enclosed	1	3	5	7				

   ii Find the number of squares enclosed by Shape 100.

   b Here is another sequence of shapes made with 1 cm rods.

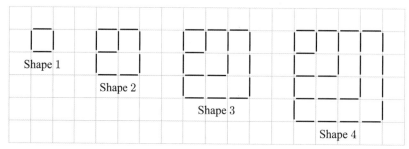

   i Find the number of rods in Shape 5.

   ii Find an expression, in terms of n, for the number of rods in Shape n.

(Cambridge IGCSE International Mathematics 0607, Paper 41 Q4, October/November 2014)

5 **a** Two circles touch each other and the coordinate axes as shown.

   Suppose the smaller circle has radius r and the larger circle has radius R.

   i Explain why $r\sqrt{2} + r + R = R\sqrt{2}$.

   ii Hence show that $\dfrac{r}{R} = 3 - 2\sqrt{2}$.

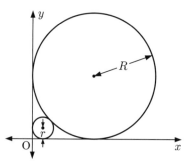

b Consider a more general scenario in which the larger circle touches the x-axis, and has centre (a, R) where $a > 0$. The smaller circle touches the larger circle and both coordinate axes.

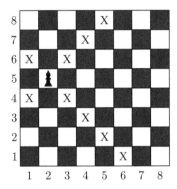

   i Show that $a^2 + r^2 = (2a + 4R)r$.

   ii Find r if the larger circle has centre $(6, 4)$.

   iii Find the ratio $\dfrac{r}{R}$ if $a = R$. Compare this with your answer to **a**.

   iv Illustrate the case where $r = R$. Find a in terms of R in this case.

   v If $a = kR$, $1 < k \leqslant 3$, find the ratio $\dfrac{r}{R}$ in terms of k.

6 In chess, a bishop is only allowed to move diagonally. For example, a bishop in position $(2, 5)$ can move to 9 possible squares (marked X).

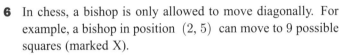

  a Find the number of possible squares a bishop can move to if it is currently at:

    i $(2, 3)$ **ii** $(5, 5)$ **iii** $(8, 1)$

  b Consider a bishop in the position (x, y).

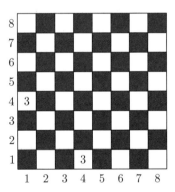

    i Copy and complete this chessboard, showing the value $|x - y|$ in each square.

    ii Explain why the number of possible squares it can move to in the ↗ direction is maximised at 7, when $|x - y| = 0$.

    iii Explain why the bishop can move to $7 - |x - y|$ possible squares in the direction ↗.

    iv Explain why the bishop can move to $7 - |9 - (x + y)|$ possible squares in the direction ↘.

    v Hence find the total number of squares a bishop at (x, y) can move to. Check your formula with your results to **a**.

  c **i** Generalise your result to find the number of squares a bishop at (x, y) can move to on an $n \times n$ chessboard.

    ii Suppose a bishop is at $(32, 17)$ on a 100×100 chessboard. How many possible squares can the bishop move to?

  d The queen, in addition to moving diagonally, can also move horizontally and vertically.

    i Find the number of possible squares a queen can move to on an 8×8 chessboard if it is at:

      (1) $(2, 3)$ **(2)** $(5, 5)$ **(3)** $(8, 1)$

    ii Find the number of squares a queen at (x, y) can move to on:

      (1) an 8×8 chessboard   **(2)** an $n \times n$ chessboard.

7 The first three rows of **Pascal's triangle** are shown
alongside. Each term along the outside edge is 1, and
every other term is the sum of the two terms above it.

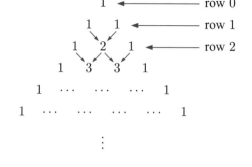

- **a** Write down the terms in the:
  - **i** 4th row   **ii** 5th row of Pascal's triangle.
- **b** **i** Find the sum of the terms in each of the first
  5 rows of Pascal's triangle.
  - **ii** Write down a formula, in terms of n, for
    the sum of the terms in row n of Pascal's
    triangle.
  - **iii** Find the sum of the terms in row 20 of Pascal's triangle.
- **c** **i** Find the sum of *all* the terms in Pascal's triangle up to and including:
  - **(1)** row 1   **(2)** row 2   **(3)** row 3   **(4)** row 4.
  - **ii** Write a formula for the sum of all the terms in Pascal's triangle up to and including row n.
  - **iii** Find the sum of all the terms in Pascal's triangle up to and including row 30.

Click on the icon to obtain Investigation questions from past examination papers.

**INVESTIGATION
QUESTIONS**

B   MODELLING QUESTIONS

1 The depth d of water in a harbour is given by the formula $d = a + b\sin(ct)°$ metres, where a, b, and
c are constants, and t is the time in hours after midnight. It is known that both b and c are non-zero,
and that $20 < c < 35$.

The table alongside gives depths at particular times:

t	midnight	noon	1300	1400
d	5	5	7	8.46

- **a** Use the first three pieces of information in the table to deduce the values of a, b, and c.
- **b** Check that the formula is correct by substituting the fourth piece of information.
- **c** Find the depth of water at 10 am.
- **d** Find the greatest depth of water in the harbour.
- **e** At what times during the day is the depth of water greatest?
- **f** Find the lowest depth of water in the harbour.

2 The *surge model* has the form $y = \dfrac{at}{2^{bt}}$ where a and b are constants, and $t \geqslant 0$ is the time.

This model is used in the study of the impact of medicines where there is an initial rapid increase to a
maximum and then a slow decay to zero.

- **a** Use a graphics calculator to help sketch, on the same set of axes, the graphs $y = \dfrac{10t}{2^{2t}}$ and $y = \dfrac{15t}{2^{3t}}$.

- **b** The effect of a pain killing injection after t hours
  is shown in the table.
  The effect E follows a surge model of the form
  $E = \dfrac{at}{2^{bt}}$.

Time (t hours)	0	2	4	6	12
Effect (E units)	0	25	25	r	s

  - **i** Use *two* of the points in the table to find a and b.   **ii** Hence find r and s.

      iii Use your calculator to find the maximum effect of the injection, and the time at which it occurs.

      iv Surgical operations can only take place when the effectiveness is more than 15 units. Between what two times can an operation take place?

3 The *logistic model* has the form $y = \dfrac{a \times 2^{bt}}{2^{bt} + c}$ where $t \geqslant 0$ is the time. The logistic model is useful in describing limited growth problems such as a population growing under limited resources.

  a **i** Use technology to help graph the logistic model $y = \dfrac{3 \times 2^{\frac{1}{2}t}}{2^{\frac{1}{2}t} + 2}$.

     ii What feature of the graph indicates a limiting value? Identify this limiting value.

  b The quantity of bacteria B present in a mug of milk after t hours out of the fridge is shown alongside.

It is known that B follows a logistic model with $c = 1$.

t	0	1	2
$B(t)$	10	12.70	15.03

    i Use the first two data points to find a and b, and hence determine the logistic model.

    ii Check your model using the third data point.

   iii What is the limiting quantity of bacteria for this model?

    iv In the general model $y = \dfrac{a \times 2^{bt}}{2^{bt} + c}$, explain why the limiting quantity is a.

4 **a** Consider a square ABCD inscribed in a circle. The tangents to the circle at A, B, C, and D form a larger square outside the circle.

    i Show that the shaded triangles are similar.

    ii Find the scale factor for enlarging the red triangle to the blue triangle.

   iii What combination of transformations maps the red triangle onto the blue triangle?

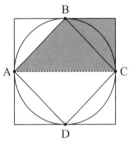

  b Now consider a regular pentagon ABCDE inscribed in a circle, with tangents drawn at A, B, C, D, and E.

    i Show that the shaded triangles are similar.

    ii Find the exact scale factor for enlarging the red triangle to the blue triangle.

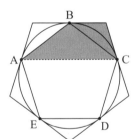

  c Suppose a regular n-sided polygon is inscribed in a circle, and tangents are drawn at each vertex of the polygon.

    i Show that the shaded triangles are similar.

    ii Show that the scale factor for enlarging the red triangle to the blue triangle is $2 \sin\left(\dfrac{90(n-2)}{n}\right)^{\circ}$.

   iii Find the scale factor when $n = 3$. Explain what this means about the triangles in this case.

    iv Find the scale factor when: **(1)** $n = 10$ **(2)** $n = 50$ **(3)** $n = 100$

    v Copy and complete:
As the number of sides of the polygon increases, the scale factor gets closer and closer to ......

5   A rubber ball is projected into the air, and it returns to 80% of its previous height each time it bounces.

The graph alongside shows the height of the ball over time.

Denise wonders whether the time interval between two bounces is also 80% of the previous time interval.

The height of a ball projected from ground level after t seconds is $H_1(t) = -4.9t^2 + b_1 t$ metres, where b_1 is a constant.

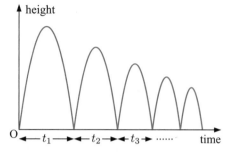

a   Suppose the ball takes 5 seconds to reach its maximum height.

   i   Find b_1.

   ii   Determine the maximum height which the ball reaches.

   iii   How long will it take for the ball to return to the ground?

b   The ball then bounces back to 80% of its previous height.

   i   Find the maximum height reached on the second bounce.

   ii   Let $H_2(t) = -4.9t^2 + b_2 t$ be the height in metres of the ball t seconds after the ball bounces for the first time.

   (1)   Show that the maximum height is reached when $t = \dfrac{b_2}{9.8}$.

   (2)   Find an expression for the maximum height reached in terms of b_2 only.

   (3)   Hence find b_2, and find the time interval between the first and second bounces.

c   Find the time interval between the second and third bounces.

d   Is the time interval between two bounces 80% of the previous time interval? If not, explain what is happening.

e   Find an expression for the time interval between the nth and $(n+1)$th bounces.

f   How many times will the ball hit the ground in the first 40 seconds?

6   A manufacturer produces two kinds of table-tennis sets:

   ● Set A contains 2 bats and 3 balls.

   ● Set B contains 2 bats, 5 balls, and 1 net.

In one hour the factory can produce at most 560 bats, 1080 balls, and 180 nets. Set A earns a profit of $3 and Set B earns a profit of $5.

Suppose the manufacturer produces x lots of set A and y lots of set B each hour.

a   Write an expression for the total profit made P.

b   Explain why $2x + 2y \leqslant 560$.

c   Write down *four* more inequalities which x and y must satisfy.

d   Graph the region of the Cartesian plane satisfied by *all* of the inequalities.

e   How many of each set should the manufacturer make each hour to maximise their profit? Are any components under-utilised in this case?

Click on the icon to obtain Modelling questions from past examination papers.

MODELLING QUESTIONS

ANSWERS

EXERCISE 1A

1 a 8 **b** 16 **c** 27 **d** 50
e 100 **f** 135 **g** 315 **h** 1188

2 a 104 544 **b** 42 017 500 **c** 5 282 739 **d** 178 200

3 a 2×3^2 **b** 2×5^3 **c** $2^3 \times 5 \times 7$
d $3^3 \times 7^2$ **e** $3^4 \times 5^2$ **f** $7^5 \times 11^3$

4 a -9 **b** 9 **c** -1 **d** -1 **e** 25 **f** -25
g 16 **h** -16 **i** -27 **j** -27 **k** 27 **l** 64

5 a -72 **b** 108 **c** -648

6 a 256 **b** 625 **c** -243 **d** 117 649
e $-117\,649$ **f** 1.795 856 326
g $-0.005\,487\,423\,935$ **h** $-325\,687.9871$

7 a 2^2 **b** 2^4 **c** 2^6 **d** 2^{12}
8 a 3^3 **b** 3^4 **c** 3^6 **d** 3^{10} **9** 3 **10** 7
11 a $n = 625$ **b** $n = 7$ **c** $n = 5$ **d** $n = 6$

EXERCISE 1B

1 a 2^3 **b** 3^3 **c** 5^3 **d** 2^7 **e** 7^3 **f** 3^6
g 19^2 **h** 11^3

2 a $54 = 2 \times 3^3$ **b** $108 = 2^2 \times 3^3$
c $360 = 2^3 \times 3^2 \times 5$ **d** $228 = 2^2 \times 3 \times 19$
e $196 = 2^2 \times 7^2$ **f** $756 = 2^2 \times 3^3 \times 7$
g $936 = 2^3 \times 3^2 \times 13$ **h** $1225 = 5^2 \times 7^2$
i $588 = 2^2 \times 3 \times 7^2$ **j** $945 = 3^3 \times 5 \times 7$
k $910 = 2 \times 5 \times 7 \times 13$ **l** $1274 = 2 \times 7^2 \times 13$

EXERCISE 1C

1 a $3^5 = 243$ **b** $2^4 = 16$ **c** $5^6 = 15\,625$
d $3^7 = 2187$ **e** $7^5 = 16\,807$ **f** $(-2)^3 = -8$
g x^2 **h** y^3 **i** a^5 **j** n^3 **k** x^9 **l** y^8

2 a $2^2 = 4$ **b** $3^2 = 9$ **c** $7^3 = 343$
d $10^1 = 10$ **e** x^4 **f** y^4 **g** c^2 **h** b^3

3 a $2^6 = 64$ **b** $10^8 = 100\,000\,000$ **c** $3^6 = 729$
d $2^{12} = 4096$ **e** x^{10} **f** p^9 **g** t^{12} **h** z^{12}

4 a c^6 **b** b^5 **c** y^{15} **d** y^{10} **e** q^7 **f** z^{30}
g t^3 **h** a^{2+n} **i** g^3 **j** n^{10} **k** k^7 **l** p^6

5 a $(7^2)^3 = 7^6$ **b** $2^4 \div 2 = 2^3$ **c** $2^2 \times 2^7 = 2^9$
d $(x^3)^4 = x^{12}$ **e** $a^5 \times a^5 = a^{10}$ **f** $5^9 \div 5^3 = 5^6$

6 a $5a^2$ **b** $15q^3$ **c** $16x^3 y^4$ **d** $7t$

7 a $p^2 q^2$ **b** $x^4 y^4$ **c** $a^6 b^6$ **d** $a^3 b^3 c^3$
e $8a^3$ **f** $243 d^5$ **g** $32k^5$ **h** $25g^2 h^2$

8 a $\dfrac{a^2}{b^2}$ **b** $\dfrac{b^3}{8}$ **c** $\dfrac{j^4}{k^4}$ **d** $\dfrac{16}{z^4}$
e $\dfrac{16}{x^2}$ **f** $\dfrac{32}{b^5}$ **g** $\dfrac{q^4}{16}$ **h** $\dfrac{27}{b^3}$

9 a $8b^{12}$ **b** $\dfrac{9}{x^4 y^2}$ **c** $25a^8 b^2$ **d** $\dfrac{m^{12}}{16n^8}$
e $\dfrac{27a^9}{b^{15}}$ **f** $32m^{15} n^{10}$ **g** $\dfrac{16a^8}{b^4}$ **h** $125x^6 y^9$

EXERCISE 1D

1 a 1 **b** 1 **c** 1 $(x \neq 0)$ **d** 5 **e** 9 **f** 5
g 11 **h** p^6 $(p \neq 0)$ **i** 1 **j** 1 **k** 7 **l** 1
2 a 1 $(n \neq 0)$ **b** 1 $(k \neq 0)$ **c** x $(y \neq 0)$
d a^3 $(b \neq 0)$

3 a 3^{-2} **b** 5^{-1} **c** 2^{-2} **d** 3^{-2} **e** 7^{-1}
4 a $\frac{1}{5}$ **b** $\frac{1}{4}$ **c** $\frac{1}{8}$ **d** $\frac{1}{10}$ **e** $\frac{1}{9}$
f $\frac{1}{4}$ **g** $\frac{1}{121}$ **h** $\frac{1}{49}$ **i** $\frac{1}{27}$ **j** $\frac{1}{128}$

5 a $2\frac{2}{3}$ **b** $1\frac{1}{3}$ **c** $\frac{6}{7}$ **d** $5\frac{4}{5}$

6 a $\dfrac{1}{x}$ **b** $\dfrac{1}{k}$ **c** $\dfrac{1}{t^3}$ **d** $\dfrac{1}{r^5}$

7 a 3 **b** 5 **c** $\frac{7}{3}$ **d** $\frac{2}{5}$ **e** 10
f $\frac{36}{25}$ **g** $\frac{16}{81}$ **h** $\frac{27}{8}$

8 a $\dfrac{2}{x}$ **b** $\dfrac{1}{2x}$ **c** $\dfrac{1}{3q}$ **d** $\dfrac{3}{q}$ **e** $\dfrac{7}{a^2}$ **f** t^2
g $\dfrac{1}{25z^2}$ **h** $\dfrac{z^2}{5}$ **i** $\dfrac{s}{t}$ **j** $\dfrac{1}{st}$ **k** $\dfrac{g}{h^3}$
l $\dfrac{1}{g^3 h^3}$ **m** $\dfrac{4c}{d^2}$ **n** $\dfrac{1}{16c^2 d^2}$ **o** $4c^3 d^3$ **p** $\dfrac{m^3}{7}$

9 a 2^4 **b** 2^{-4} **c** 5^2 **d** 5^{-2} **e** 3^4
f 3^{-4} **g** 2^{-10} **h** 2^{-a} **i** $3^2 \times 5^{-2}$
j $2^5 \times 3^{-4}$ **k** $2^2 \times 3 \times 5^{-1}$ **l** $2^{-3} \times 3 \times 5^2$

EXERCISE 1E.1

1 a 10^2 **b** 10^3 **c** 10^1 **d** 10^5
e 10^{-1} **f** 10^{-2} **g** 10^{-4} **h** 10^8

2 c

3 a $376 = 3.76 \times 10^2$ **b** $8000 = 8 \times 10^3$
c $0.04 = 4 \times 10^{-2}$ **d** $0.005\,07 = 5.07 \times 10^{-3}$
e $9\,040\,000 = 9.04 \times 10^6$ **f** $0.000\,000\,23 = 2.3 \times 10^{-7}$

4 a 4.25×10^2 **b** 4.25×10^5 **c** 4.25×10^0
d 4.25×10^{-1} **e** 2.01×10^1 **f** 2.01×10^4
g 2.01×10^{-3} **h** 2.01×10^6 **i** 3.87×10^3
j 3.87×10^{-2} **k** 3.87×10^7 **l** 3.87×10^{-4}

5 a 4.0075×10^4 km **b** 4×10^{-4} mm
c 4×10^7 bacteria **d** 1.4162×10^{-7}
e 1×10^{-2} mm **f** 1.5×10^7 °C

6 a 50 000 **b** 3000 **c** 18 000 000 **d** 810
e 650 000 **f** 11 **g** 275 000 000 **h** 8 000 000

7 a 0.03 **b** 0.000 09 **c** 0.007
d 0.000 41 **e** 0.000 008 2 **f** 0.761
g 0.000 000 325 **h** 0.000 000 02

8 a 0.000 000 475 m **b** 7 530 000 000 people
c 0.000 012 m **d** 40 100 km **e** 0.000 001 5 kg

9 a 1.817×10^7 **b** 9.34×10^{10} **c** 4.1×10^{-4}

10 a 602 000 000 000 000 000 000 000
b 6.02×10^{29} atoms **c** ≈ 1.66 tonnes

11 a 2.2×10^8 **b** 3.5×10^{-5} **c** 4.9×10^3
d 6.41×10^8 **e** 1.01×10^{-6} **f** 9×10^{-8}

12 a 6×10^7 **b** 2.4×10^7 **c** 4×10^{12}
d 8.1×10^{19} **e** 9×10^{-5} **f** 4.9×10^{-5}
g 4×10^{-1} **h** 2×10^{11} **i** 2.5×10^3

13 a 9×10^8 **b** 5×10^4 **c** 2.7×10^5
d 3.77×10^{-4} **e** 5.67×10^4 **f** 2.37×10^8
g 3.625×10^{-7} **h** 2.3×10^{-6}

14 a France **b** 2.5×10^{10} kg **c** 3.41×10^7 tonnes
d 2.81×10^6 tonnes **e** 400 times more

EXERCISE 1E.2

1 a 6.00×10^{-10} **b** 2.39×10^{10} **c** 2.19×10^{11}
  d 4.01×10^{10} **e** 6.24×10^{-10} **f** 1.03×10^{-7}

2 a 9.55×10^9 **b** 9.62×10^{-7} **c** 4.90×10^{-14}
  d 6.50×10^{-7} **e** 4.00×10^{-7} **f** 4.37×10^{14}

3 a 4.80×10^8 mm **b** 3.15×10^7 seconds
  c 3.15×10^{10} seconds **d** 5×10^{-7} kg

4 a 8.64×10^4 km **b** 6.05×10^5 km **c** 6.31×10^7 km

5 a 1.8×10^{10} m **b** 2.59×10^{13} m **c** 9.46×10^{15} m

REVIEW SET 1A

1 a k^9 **b** b^{12} **c** p^8 **2 a** 5^7 **b** 5^6 **c** 5^0

3 a $3b^2$ **b** $-3m^3$ **c** $6x^3y^3$

4 a $25x^2$ **b** $27m^3n^3$ **c** $\dfrac{p^4}{16q^4}$

5 a 1 **b** 13 **c** 6 **6 a** $\dfrac{1}{9}$ **b** $\dfrac{1}{36}$ **c** $\dfrac{1}{1000}$

7 a 5^{-1} **b** b^9 **c** x^{-8} **8 a** $\dfrac{1}{5c}$ **b** $\dfrac{7}{k^2}$ **c** $\dfrac{1}{64d^6}$

9 a 9×10^0 **b** 3.49×10^4 **c** 7.5×10^{-3}

10 a $2\,810\,000$ **b** 2.81 **c** 0.002 81

11 a 4.26×10^8 **b** 6×10^3 **c** 2.95×10^6
  d 6.15×10^{-2}

12 a 2.57×10^6 km **b** 1.80×10^7 km **c** 9.37×10^8 km

REVIEW SET 1B

1 a x^6 **b** c^5 **c** d^{33}

2 a $3^8 = 6561$ **b** $2^0 = 1$ **c** y^{-3}

3 a $3^5 \div 3^2 = 3^3$ **b** $(x^3)^2 = x^6$ **c** $(4a)^3 \times a^3 = 64a^6$

4 a $-8x^3$ **b** $9m^4$ **c** $\dfrac{m^3}{64n^3}$

5 a -2 **b** 1 $(y \neq 0)$ **c** $\dfrac{27}{125}$

6 a $\dfrac{c^2}{d^2}$ **b** $\dfrac{q^3}{64}$ **c** $\dfrac{a^2b^2}{64}$

7 a $\dfrac{5}{4}$ **b** $\dfrac{49}{4}$ **c** $\dfrac{9}{100}$ **8 a** $\dfrac{b}{a^2}$ **b** $\dfrac{25}{a^4}$ **c** $\dfrac{p^3}{5}$

9 a 2.6357×10^2 **b** 5.11×10^{-4} **c** 8.634×10^8

10 a 2.78 **b** $39\,900\,000$ **c** 0.002 081

11 a 6.4×10^7 **b** 6×10^6 **c** 1.383×10^5
  d 5.72×10^{-3}

12 2.1×10^{-7} km

EXERCISE 2A

1 a $3x + 3$ **b** $10 - 2x$ **c** $5x + 10$ **d** $12 - 4x$
  e $4a + 8b$ **f** $6x + 3y$ **g** $5x - 5y$ **h** $-6x^2 + 6y^2$
  i $-2x - 8$ **j** $-6x + 3$ **k** $x^2 + 3x$ **l** $2x^2 - 10x$
  m $-3x - 6$ **n** $-4x + 12$ **o** $2x - 7$ **p** $-2x + 2y$
  q $a^2 + ab$ **r** $ab - a^2$ **s** $2x^2 - x$ **t** $x^2 - 2x$

2 a $3x - 3y + 3$ **b** $-x^2 - x + 4$
  c $2a - 6b - 2ab$ **d** $6x^2 + 3xy - 3x$
  e $2x^3 - 2x^2 - 4x$ **f** $3x^3 - 3x^2 - 3x$

3 a $2x + 5$ **b** $1 - 4x$ **c** $3x - 1$ **d** $2 - 4x$ **e** x^2
  f $6x - x^2$ **g** $2ab + a^2$ **h** $7x - 3x^2$ **i** $2x^2 - 10x$

4 a $5x - 2$ **b** $3a - 2b$ **c** $a + 2b$ **d** $15 - 3y$
  e $-6y - 10$ **f** $15x - 8$ **g** $a + 5b$ **h** $x^2 + 6x - 6$
  i $x^2 + 2x + 6$ **j** $2x^2 - x$ **k** $-2x^2 + 2x$
  l $x^2 - y^2$ **m** $5 - 3x$ **n** $8x - 8$ **o** $6x^2 - 22x$

EXERCISE 2B

1 a ac **b** ad **c** bc **d** bd **e** $(a+b)(c+d)$
  $(a+b)(c+d) = ac + ad + bc + bd$

2 a $x^2 + 10x + 21$ **b** $x^2 + x - 20$ **c** $x^2 + 3x - 18$
  d $x^2 - 4$ **e** $x^2 - 5x - 24$ **f** $6x^2 + 11x + 4$
  g $1 + 2x - 8x^2$ **h** $12 + 5x - 2x^2$ **i** $6x^2 - x - 2$
  j $25 - 10x - 3x^2$ **k** $-4x^2 + 29x - 7$ **l** $3 - 7x - 6x^2$

3 a $x^2 - 4$ **b** $a^2 - 25$ **c** $16 - x^2$ **d** $4x^2 - 1$
  e $25a^2 - 9$ **f** $16 - 9a^2$

4 a $x^2 + 6x + 9$ **b** $x^2 - 4x + 4$ **c** $9x^2 - 12x + 4$
  d $1 - 6x + 9x^2$ **e** $9 - 24x + 16x^2$ **f** $25x^2 - 10xy + y^2$

5 a $x^2 + 8x + 1$ **b** $x^2 + 7x - 10$ **c** $3a^2 - 30$
  d $5x^2 - 2x - 15$ **e** $3x^2 + 8x - 24$ **f** $-y - 31$
  g $-k^2 + 2k - 7$ **h** $2x^2 - 40$

EXERCISE 2C

1 a $x^2 - 4$ **b** $x^2 - 4$ **c** $4 - x^2$ **d** $4 - x^2$
  e $x^2 - 1$ **f** $1 - x^2$ **g** $x^2 - 49$ **h** $c^2 - 64$
  i $d^2 - 25$ **j** $x^2 - y^2$ **k** $16 - d^2$ **l** $25 - e^2$

2 a $4x^2 - 1$ **b** $9x^2 - 4$ **c** $16y^2 - 25$ **d** $4y^2 - 25$
  e $9x^2 - 1$ **f** $1 - 9x^2$ **g** $4 - 25y^2$ **h** $9 - 16a^2$
  i $16 - 9a^2$ **j** $4a^2 - b^2$ **k** $a^2 - 4b^2$ **l** $16x^2 - y^2$
  m $16x^2 - 25y^2$ **n** $4x^2 - 9y^2$ **o** $49x^2 - 4y^2$

3 a i 43×37 **ii** 24×26
  $= (40+3)(40-3)$ $= (25-1)(25+1)$
  $= 40^2 - 3^2$ $= 25^2 - 1^2$

  b i 396 **ii** 2499 **iii** 9991

EXERCISE 2D

1 a a^2 **b** ab **c** ab **d** b^2 **e** $(a+b)^2$
  $(a+b)^2 = a^2 + 2ab + b^2$

2 a $x^2 + 10x + 25$ **b** $x^2 + 8x + 16$ **c** $x^2 + 14x + 49$
  d $a^2 + 4a + 4$ **e** $9 + 6c + c^2$ **f** $25 + 10x + x^2$

3 a $x^2 - 6x + 9$ **b** $x^2 - 4x + 4$ **c** $y^2 - 16y + 64$
  d $a^2 - 14a + 49$ **e** $25 - 10x + x^2$ **f** $16 - 8y + y^2$

4 a $9x^2 + 24x + 16$ **b** $4a^2 - 12a + 9$ **c** $9y^2 + 6y + 1$
  d $4x^2 - 20x + 25$ **e** $9y^2 - 30y + 25$ **f** $49 + 28a + 4a^2$
  g $1 + 10x + 25x^2$ **h** $49 - 42y + 9y^2$ **i** $9 + 24a + 16a^2$

5 a $x^4 + 4x^2 + 4$ **b** $y^4 - 6y^2 + 9$ **c** $9a^4 + 24a^2 + 16$
  d $1 - 4x^2 + 4x^4$ **e** $x^4 + 2x^2y^2 + y^4$ **f** $x^4 - 2a^2x^2 + a^4$

6 a $-x^2 - 3x - 8$ **b** $x^2 + x + 2$ **c** $2x^2 + 6x + 5$
  d $-6x - 13$ **e** $11 - 13x + 3x^2$ **f** $10x^2 - 7x - 5$
  g $3x^2 - 2x - 10$ **h** $3x^2 - x - 10$ **i** $2x^2 + 2x + 5$
  j $-6x - 3$

EXERCISE 2E

1 a $x^3 + 3x^2 + 6x + 8$ **b** $x^3 + 5x^2 + 3x - 9$
  c $x^3 + 5x^2 + 7x + 3$ **d** $2x^3 + x^2 - 6x - 5$
  e $2x^3 + 7x^2 + 8x + 3$ **f** $2x^3 - 9x^2 + 4x + 15$
  g $3x^3 + 14x^2 - x + 20$ **h** $8x^3 - 14x^2 + 7x - 1$

2 a $x^3 + 3x^2 + 3x + 1$ **b** $x^3 + 9x^2 + 27x + 27$
  c $x^3 - 12x^2 + 48x - 64$ **d** $x^3 - 9x^2 + 27x - 27$
  e $27x^3 + 27x^2 + 9x + 1$ **f** $8x^3 - 36x^2 + 54x - 27$
  g $x^4 + 4x^3 + 6x^2 + 4x + 1$ **h** $x^4 - 4x^3 + 6x^2 - 4x + 1$

3 **a** $x^3 + 6x^2 + 8x$ **b** $x^3 - x^2 - 6x$ **c** $x^3 - 9x^2 + 20x$
  d $2x^3 + 14x^2 + 20x$ **e** $-3x^3 + 15x^2 - 18x$
  f $x^3 - 4x^2 - 12x$ **g** $-9x^3 - 33x^2 + 12x$
  h $-10x^3 - 13x^2 + 3x$ **i** $x^3 - 3x^2 - 4x + 12$

4 **a** $x^3 + 9x^2 + 26x + 24$ **b** $x^3 - x^2 - 14x + 24$
  c $x^3 - 10x^2 + 31x - 30$ **d** $2x^3 + x^2 - 12x + 9$
  e $3x^3 + 14x^2 + 21x + 10$ **f** $12x^3 + 11x^2 - 2x - 1$
  g $-3x^3 + 26x^2 - 33x - 14$ **h** $-3x^3 + 16x^2 - 12x - 16$

5 **a** 4 **b** 6 **c** 6 **d** 9 **e** 8 **f** 12 **g** 8 **h** 12

REVIEW SET 2A

1 **a** $6 + 3x$ **b** $-4x + 2$ **c** $3x^2 + 9x$
2 **a** $4x - 1$ **b** $-2x - 5$ **c** $-9x + 11$
3 **a** $x^2 + 11x + 28$ **b** $x^2 + 6x - 16$
  c $-5x^2 - x + 6$ **d** $2a^2 - 21a + 27$
  e $-12x^2 + x + 1$ **f** $20x^2 - 11x - 4$
4 **a** $x^2 + 8x - 6$ **b** $n - 9$
5 **a** $x^2 + 8x + 16$ **b** $x^2 - 20x + 100$
  c $4x^2 + 20x + 25$ **d** $9 - 24x + 16x^2$
  e $x^2 + 4xy + 4y^2$ **f** $8x^3 - 12x^2 + 6x - 1$
6 **a** $x^2 - 81$ **b** $9x^2 - 4$ **c** $1 - 49x^2$
7 **a** $x^3 + 5x^2 - 3x - 28$ **b** $4x^3 - 7x^2 - 17x + 15$
  c $-x^3 + 2x^2 - 3x + 2$

REVIEW SET 2B

1 **a** $-3x - 12$ **b** $xy + 3x$ **c** $2a^2 - 10a$
2 **a** $10x - 11$ **b** $x^2 - 3x + 8$ **c** $x^2 + 4x - 3$
3 **a** $x^2 + 5x - 36$ **b** $2x^2 + 5x - 42$ **c** $2a^2 - 11a + 12$
  d $x^2 - 5x - 24$ **e** $2a^2 + ab - b^2$ **f** $12x^2 - 5x - 2$
4 **a** $y^2 + 6y + 9$ **b** $9x^2 + 12x + 4$ **c** $16a^2 - 8ab + b^2$
5 **a** $25 - x^2$ **b** $9y^2 - 16$ **c** $1 - 16x^2$
6 **a** $-x^2 - 6x - 9$ **b** $y^2 + 5y - 40$
7 **a** $x^3 + 6x^2 - 32$ **b** $x^3 - 4x^2 - 3x + 18$
  c $x^3 - 15x^2 + 75x - 125$ **d** $-x^3 + 5x^2 - 10x + 8$
  e $-x^3 + 3x^2 - 4$ **f** $x^4 - 12x^3 + 54x^2 - 108x + 81$

EXERCISE 3A

1 **a** $2a$ **b** $5b$ **c** $4xy$ **d** $4x$ **e** x **f** $-2x$
  g $-b$ **h** $4a$ **i** $-3xy$
2 **a** 2 **b** c **c** 1 **d** k **e** $3a$ **f** $5x$
  g $5x$ **h** $8y$ **i** 18
3 **a** ab **b** abc **c** $12a$ **d** r **e** q **f** $4r$
  g $3pq$ **h** $2ab$ **i** $6xy$ **j** 5 **k** $12wz$ **l** $12pqr$
4 **a** $(x + 2)$ **b** $2(x + 5)$ **c** x **d** $2(x + 1)$
  e $2(x + 3)$ **f** $2x(x - 3)$

EXERCISE 3B

1 **a** $2(x + 2)$ **b** $3(a - 4)$ **c** $5(3 - p)$
  d $6(3x + 2)$ **e** $4x(x - 2)$ **f** $2m(1 + 4m)$
2 **a** $4(x + 4)$ **b** $5(2 + d)$ **c** $5(c - 1)$ **d** $d(c + e)$
  e $2a(3 + 4b)$ **f** $2x(3 - x)$ **g** $7a(b - 1)$ **h** $2b(2a - 3c)$
3 **a** $3(a + b)$ **b** $8(x - 2)$ **c** $3(p + 6)$ **d** $14(2 - x)$
  e $7(x - 2)$ **f** $6(2 + x)$ **g** $c(a + b)$ **h** $6(2y - a)$
  i $a(5 + b)$ **j** $c(b - 6d)$ **k** $x(7 - y)$ **l** $y(x + 1)$
  m $a(1 + b)$ **n** $y(x - z)$ **o** $p(3q + r)$ **p** $c(d - 1)$

4 **a** $x(x + 2)$ **b** $x(5 - 2x)$ **c** $4x(x + 2)$
  d $7x(2 - x)$ **e** $6x(x + 2)$ **f** $x^2(x + 9)$
  g $xy(x + y)$ **h** $2x^2(2x - 3)$ **i** $9x(x^2 - 2y)$
  j $a(a^2 + a + 1)$ **k** $2(a^2 + 2a + 4)$ **l** $3a(a^2 - 2a + 3)$
5 **a** $9(b - a)$ **b** $3(2b - 1)$ **c** $4(b - 2a)$
  d $c(d - 7)$ **e** $a(b - 1)$ **f** $6x(2 - x)$
  g $5x(3x - 1)$ **h** $2b(2a - b)$ **i** $a(a - 1)$
6 **a** $-6(a + b)$ **b** $-4(1 + 2x)$ **c** $-3(y + 2z)$
  d $-c(9 + d)$ **e** $-x(1 + y)$ **f** $-5x(x + 4)$
  g $-3y(4 + y)$ **h** $-9a(2a + b)$ **i** $-8x(2x + 3)$
7 **a** $(x - 7)(2 + x)$ **b** $(x + 3)(a + b)$ **c** $(x + 2)(4 - x)$
  d $(x + 9)(x + 1)$ **e** $(b + 4)(a - 1)$ **f** $(b + c)(a + d)$
  g $(m + n)(a - b)$ **h** $(x + 3)(x - 1)$
8 **a** $(x + 3)(x - 1)$ **b** $(x - 7)(x + 7)$ **c** $(x + 6)(x - 4)$
  d $(x - 2)(x - 8)$ **e** $x + 2$ **f** $(a + b)(4 - a)$
  g $3(a - 2)(a - 4)$ **h** $(x + 4)(4x + 1)$
  i $5(x - 1)(6 - x)$ **j** $-(x + 5)(4x + 17)$
9 **a** $6(2x^2 - 3xy)$ has a common factor of x within the brackets.
  b $12x^2 - 18xy = 6x(2x - 3y)$

EXERCISE 3C

1 **a** $(x + y)(x - y)$ **b** $(p + q)(p - q)$
  c $(n + m)(n - m)$ **d** $(x + 2)(x - 2)$
  e $(2 + x)(2 - x)$ **f** $(x + 9)(x - 9)$
  g $(5 + x)(5 - x)$ **h** $(8 + a)(8 - a)$
  i $(2x + 1)(2x - 1)$ **j** $(3x + 4)(3x - 4)$
  k $(2x + 3)(2x - 3)$ **l** $(6 + 7x)(6 - 7x)$
  m $(x + 2y)(x - 2y)$ **n** $(ab + 6)(ab - 6)$
  o $(4x + 3y)(4x - 3y)$
2 **a** $3(2 + x)(2 - x)$ **b** $2(x + 3)(x - 3)$
  c $3(x + 3)(x - 3)$ **d** $-2(x + 2)(x - 2)$
  e $3(x + 5)(x - 5)$ **f** $-5(x + 1)(x - 1)$
  g $2(2x + 3)(2x - 3)$ **h** $-3(3x + 5)(3x - 5)$
  i $3(x + 2y)(x - 2y)$
3 **a** $(x + 3)(x - 1)$ **b** $4(x + 2)(x - 1)$
  c $(x - 5)(x + 3)$ **d** $3(x + 1)(3 - x)$
  e $(3x + 2)(x - 2)$ **f** $(2x + 3)(4x - 3)$
  g $(3x - 1)(x + 3)$ **h** $8x(x - 1)$ **i** $-3(4x + 3)$
4 **a** **i** Area of garden and path $= (x + 2)^2$ m^2
      Area of path $= (x + 2)^2 -$ area of garden
                  $= [(x + 2)^2 - x^2]$ m^2
    ii Area of path $= 4(x + 1) \times 1$ m^2
                  $= (4x + 4)$ m^2
  b $(x + 2)^2 - x^2 = [(x + 2) + x][(x + 2) - x]$
            $= (2x + 2)(2)$
            $= 2(2x + 2)$
5 **a** $(x + \sqrt{3})(x - \sqrt{3})$ **b** no linear factors
  c $(x + \sqrt{15})(x - \sqrt{15})$ **d** $(\sqrt{7} + x)(\sqrt{7} - x)$
6 **a** $(x + 1 + \sqrt{6})(x + 1 - \sqrt{6})$ **b** no linear factors
  c $(x - 2 + \sqrt{7})(x - 2 - \sqrt{7})$
  d $(x + 3 + \sqrt{17})(x + 3 - \sqrt{17})$ **e** no linear factors
  f $(x + 1)(3x - 1)$

7 $391 = 20^2 - 3^2$
$$= (20+3)(20-3)$$
$$= 23 \times 17$$

EXERCISE 3D

1 a not a perfect square   **b** perfect square
   c not a perfect square   **d** perfect square
   e not a perfect square   **f** not a perfect square

2 a $(x+3)^2$ **b** $(x+4)^2$ **c** $(x-3)^2$
   d $(x-4)^2$ **e** $(x+1)^2$ **f** $(x-5)^2$
   g $(y+9)^2$ **h** $(m-10)^2$ **i** $(t+6)^2$

3 a $(3x+1)^2$ **b** $(2x-1)^2$ **c** $(3x+2)^2$
   d $(5x-1)^2$ **e** $(4x+3)^2$ **f** $(5x-2)^2$
   g $(3x-7)^2$ **h** $(6x+5)^2$ **i** $(2x-7)^2$

4 a $2(x+1)^2$ **b** $2(x-3)^2$ **c** $4(x-4)^2$
   d $-(x-1)^2$ **e** $-2(x+2)^2$ **f** $-3(x+5)^2$

5 a $x^2 + 12x + 36 = (x+6)^2$ and no perfect square is ever negative for real x.
   b Consider $x^2 - 4x + 4$
      $$x^2 - 4x + 4 = (x-2)^2$$
      where $(x-2)^2 \geqslant 0$ for all real x
      $\therefore$ $x^2 - 4x + 4 \geqslant 0$
      $\therefore$ $x^2 + 4 \geqslant 4x$ for all real x

EXERCISE 3E

1 a $(b+2)(a+1)$ **b** $(a+4)(c+d)$ **c** $(a+2)(b+3)$
   d $(m+p)(n+3)$ **e** $(x+3)(x+7)$ **f** $(x+4)(x+5)$
   g $(2x+1)(x+3)$ **h** $(3x+2)(x+4)$ **i** $(5x+3)(4x+1)$

2 a $(x+5)(x-4)$ **b** $(x+2)(x-7)$ **c** $(x-3)(x-2)$
   d $(x-5)(x-3)$ **e** $(x+7)(x-8)$ **f** $(2x+1)(x-3)$
   g $(3x+2)(x-4)$ **h** $(4x-3)(x-2)$ **i** $(9x+2)(x-1)$

EXERCISE 3F

1 a $3, 4$ **b** $3, 5$ **c** $2, 8$ **d** $2, 9$ **e** $-3, 7$
   f $3, -7$ **g** $-6, 2$ **h** $-2, 15$

2 a $(x+1)(x+3)$ **b** $(x+12)(x+2)$ **c** $(x+3)(x+7)$
   d $(x+6)(x+9)$ **e** $(x+4)(x+5)$ **f** $(x+3)(x+5)$
   g $(x+4)(x+6)$ **h** $(x+2)(x+7)$ **i** $(x+2)(x+4)$

3 a $(x-1)(x-2)$ **b** $(x-1)(x-3)$ **c** $(x-2)(x-3)$
   d $(x-3)(x-11)$ **e** $(x-3)(x-13)$ **f** $(x-3)(x-16)$
   g $(x-4)(x-7)$ **h** $(x-2)(x-12)$ **i** $(x-2)(x-18)$

4 a $(x-8)(x+1)$ **b** $(x+7)(x-3)$ **c** $(x-2)(x+1)$
   d $(x-4)(x+2)$ **e** $(x+8)(x-3)$ **f** $(x-5)(x+2)$
   g $(x+9)(x-6)$ **h** $(x+9)(x-8)$ **i** $(x-7)(x+3)$
   j $(x-3)(x+2)$ **k** $(x-12)(x+5)$ **l** $(x+12)(x-5)$
   m $(x+6)(x-3)$ **n** $(x+2)(x-9)$ **o** $(x-15)(x+3)$

5 a $(x+6)(x+1)$ **b** $(x-9)(x+7)$ **c** $(x-2)(x-9)$
   d $(x+8)(x-2)$ **e** $(x-1)(x-4)$ **f** $(x+7)(x+5)$
   g $(x-5)(x+4)$ **h** $(x-11)(x+2)$ **i** $(x+12)(x-4)$
   j $(x-7)(x+4)$ **k** $x(x+13)$ **l** $(x-7)^2$

6 a $2(x+1)(x+4)$ **b** $3(x-1)(x-6)$
   c $2(x+3)(x+4)$ **d** $-(x-1)(x-3)$
   e $-(x-2)^2$ **f** $-(x+3)(x-1)$
   g $-2(x-10)(x-12)$ **h** $4(x-3)(x+1)$

i $-3(x-3)(x-11)$ **j** $2(x-10)(x+9)$
k $3(x-4)(x+2)$ **l** $-2(x+4)(x+5)$
m $x(x-8)(x+1)$ **n** $-4(x-3)^2$
o $7(x+5)(x-2)$ **p** $-5(x-8)(x+2)$
q $x(x-7)(x+4)$ **r** $x^2(x+1)^2$

7 a $-(x+9)(x-6)$ **b** $2(x+5)(x+2)$
   c $-(x+3)(x+7)$ **d** $2(x+8)(x-6)$
   e $-3(x-3)^2$ **f** $2(x-7)(x-3)$
   g $-2(x-9)(x+7)$ **h** $-2(x-5)^2$
   i $-x(x-2)(x+1)$

EXERCISE 3G

1 a $(2x+3)(x+1)$ **b** $(2x+5)(x+1)$
   c $(7x+2)(x+1)$ **d** $(3x+4)(x+1)$
   e $(3x+1)(x+4)$ **f** $(3x+2)(x+2)$
   g $(4x+1)(2x+3)$ **h** $(7x+1)(3x+2)$
   i $(3x+1)(2x+1)$ **j** $(6x+1)(x+3)$
   k $(5x+1)(2x+3)$ **l** $(7x+1)(2x+5)$

2 a $(2x+1)(x-5)$ **b** $(3x-1)(x+2)$
   c $(3x+1)(x-2)$ **d** $(2x-1)(x+2)$
   e $(2x+5)(x-1)$ **f** $(5x+1)(x-3)$
   g $(5x-3)(x-1)$ **h** $(11x+2)(x-1)$
   i $(3x+2)(x-3)$ **j** $(2x+3)(x-3)$
   k $(3x-2)(x-5)$ **l** $(5x+2)(x-3)$
   m $(3x-2)(x+4)$ **n** $(2x-1)(x+9)$
   o $(2x-3)(x+6)$ **p** $(2x-3)(x+7)$
   q $(5x+2)(3x-1)$ **r** $(21x+1)(x-3)$

3 a $(3x+2)(5x+3)$ **b** $(3x+2)(5x-3)$
   c $(3x-2)(5x+3)$ **d** $2(3x-2)(5x-3)$
   e $2(3x-1)^2$ **f** $3(4x+3)^2$
   g $2(4x+1)(2x+1)$ **h** $2(4x-1)(2x+1)$
   i $5(4x+1)(2x-1)$ **j** $4(4x-1)(2x-1)$
   k $(5x+3)(5x+2)$ **l** $(5x-3)(5x-2)$
   m $(5x-4)(5x+2)$ **n** $(25x+1)(x-6)$
   o $(6x+5)(6x-1)$ **p** $(9x+5)(4x-1)$
   q $(12x-5)(3x+2)$ **r** $(18x-1)(2x+3)$

EXERCISE 3H

1 a $x(3x+2)$ **b** $(x+9)(x-9)$ **c** $2(p^2+4)$
   d $3(b+5)(b-5)$ **e** $2(x+4)(x-4)$
   f $n^2(n+2)(n-2)$ **g** $(x-9)(x+1)$
   h $(d+7)(d-1)$ **i** $(x+9)(x-1)$ **j** $4t(1+2t)$
   k $3(x+6)(x-6)$ **l** $2(g-11)(g+5)$
   m $(2a+3d)(2a-3d)$ **n** $5(a-2)(a+1)$
   o $2(c-3)(c-1)$ **p** $x^2(x+1)(x-1)$
   q $d^2(d+3)(d-1)$ **r** $x(x+2)^2$

2 a $(x-3)^2$ **b** $(x+11)(x-11)$ **c** $(x-1)^2$
   d $(y+5)^2$ **e** $(x+11)^2$ **f** $(x-y)^2$
   g $(1+x)(1-x)$ **h** $(5y+1)(5y-1)$
   i $(7y+6z)(7y-6z)$ **j** $(2d+7)^2$
   k $a(2b+c)(2b-c)$ **l** $2\pi(R+r)(R-r)$

3 a $a(b+c-2)$ **b** $ab(ab-2)$
   c $2x(3+x)(3-x)$ **d** $(x+7)^2$
   e $4a(a+b)(a-b)$ **f** $xy(x+2)(x-2)$

g $4x^2(x+1)(x-1)$ **h** $(x-2)(y-z)$
i $(a+b)(x+1)$ **j** $(x-y)(a+1)$
k $(x+2)(x+3)$ **l** $(x^2+1)(x+1)$

4   **a** $7(x-5y)$ **b** $2(g+2)(g-2)$ **c** $-5x(x+2)$
   d $m(m+3p)$ **e** $(a+3)(a+5)$ **f** $(m-3)^2$
   g $5x(x+y-xy)$ **h** $(x+2)(y+2)$ **i** $(y+5)(y-9)$
   j $(2x+1)(x+5)$ **k** $3(y+7)(y-7)$
   l $3(p+q)(p-q)$ **m** $(2c+1)(2c-1)$
   n $3(x+4)(x-3)$ **o** $2(b+5)(x-3)$

5   **a** $(\sqrt{12}+x)(\sqrt{12}-x)$ **b** $-(x-1)(x+12)$
   c $-2(x-1)(x-3)$ **d** $-(x+7)(x-2)$
   e $(x+1+\sqrt{2})(x+1-\sqrt{2})$
   f $-2x(x-1)^2$ **g** $(a+b+3)(a+b-3)$
   h $x(x+4)$ **i** cannot be factorised

6   **a** $(2x+3)(x+7)$ **b** $(2x+5)(x+3)$
   c $(2x+1)(2x+5)$ **d** $(4x+3)(3x+1)$
   e $(x-5)(6x+1)$ **f** $(4x+1)^2$
   g $(5x+4)(5x-4)$ **h** $(12x+1)(x-6)$
   i $2(6x-1)(x-3)$ **j** $3(3x+4)(x-1)$
   k $(3x-5)(4x-3)$ **l** $(3x+2)(12x-7)$

REVIEW SET 3A

1   **a** $3x(x-4)$ **b** $3x(5-2x)$ **c** $2(x+7)(x-7)$
   d $(x-3)^2$ **e** $(a+b)^2$ **f** $(x+2)(x-1)$

2   **a** $(x+\sqrt{10})(x-\sqrt{10})$ **b** cannot be done
   c $(x-4+\sqrt{13})(x-4-\sqrt{13})$

3   **a** $(x-1)(5+y)$ **b** $(3x+7)(1+2b)$ **c** $(2x+1)(y-z)$

4   **a** $(x+3)(x+7)$ **b** $(x-3)(x+7)$ **c** $(x-7)(x+3)$
   d $(x-2)(x-3)$ **e** $4(x-3)(x+1)$ **f** $-(x+4)(x+9)$

5   **a** $(4x+5)(2x+3)$ **b** $(6x-1)(2x-3)$
   c $(4x-5)(3x+2)$

REVIEW SET 3B

1   **a** $5b(a+2b)$ **b** $3(x+2)(x-2)$ **c** $(x+4)^2$
   d $2(a-b)^2$ **e** $3x(x+3)(x-1)$ **f** $(x-3)(x-6)$

2   **a** $(x+9)(x-9)$ **b** $2(x+\sqrt{19})(x-\sqrt{19})$
   c cannot be done

3   **a** $(x+5)(x+7)$ **b** $(x+7)(x-5)$
   c $(x-5)(x-7)$ **d** $2(x-7)(x+5)$
   e $(x-5)(x-6)$ **f** $-(x-2)(x-10)$

4   **a** $(c+3)(d+3)$ **b** $(4-x)(x-1)$ **c** $(3x-4)(2x-3)$

5   **a** $(3x+2)(4x-1)$ **b** $(3x-2)(4x+3)$
   c $4(3x-1)(2x+3)$

EXERCISE 4A

1   **a** concert   **b** ≈ 1000 people   **c** $\approx 29.7\%$

2   **a**

Level of achievement	Tally	Frequency
A	|||	3
B	⊬⊬	5
C	⊬⊬ ⊬⊬ ⊬⊬		16
D	|||	3
E			1
	Total	28

b 16 students   **c** $\frac{5}{28}$

d

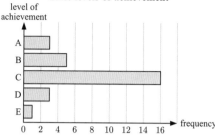
Class levels of achievement

3   **a**

Attraction	Tally	Frequency
Sideshows	⊬⊬ ||||	9
Farm animals	|||	3
Ring events	⊬⊬ ||	7
Cats	||	2
Wood chopping	||||	4
	Total	25

b 16%

c

Preferred show event

4   **a**

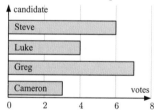
Votes for team captain

b Greg   **c** **i** 20%   **ii** 65%

5   **a**

Ice cream flavour	Tally	Frequency
Chocolate	⊬⊬ ⊬⊬ ⊬⊬ |||	18
Strawberry	⊬⊬ ⊬⊬	10
Vanilla	⊬⊬ ⊬⊬ |||	13
Lime	⊬⊬ ||||	9
	Total	50

b 13 students
c 18%
d chocolate

e Favourite ice cream flavours

6 **a** 15 flights **b** Friday **c** 31 flights

7

Sunday activities		
Walking	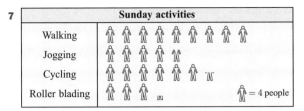	
Jogging		
Cycling		
Roller blading		👤 = 4 people

8 **a** 7 "get well" cards sold

b

Types of cards	
Anniversary	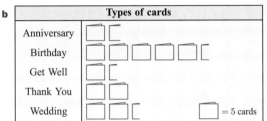
Birthday	
Get Well	
Thank You	
Wedding	▭ = 5 cards

c 18.75%

9 **a**

Eye colour

Grey ≈ 23% Blue 30% 84° 108°
Green ≈ 7% 24° 144° Brown 40%

b **i** ≈ 6.67% **ii** ≈ 53.3%

10 **a** 60 fines **b**

Driving offences

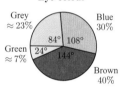

Speeding ≈ 26.7%
Mobile phone offence ≈ 41.7% 96° 54° Drink driving 15%
150° 60°
Seatbelt offence ≈ 16.7%

c **i** false **ii** true **iii** true

11 **a** 188 people **b** 9.5 **c** 1440 people

12 **a**

Response	Frequency
Excellent	8
Good	30
Fair	25
Poor	27

b

Poor 30%
Excellent ≈ 8.9%
108° 32°
100° 120°
Fair ≈ 27.8% Good ≈ 33.3%

EXERCISE 4B

1 **a** 4 students **b** 6 students **c** **i** east **ii** south
d class A **e** 40%

2 **a** **i** 25 members **ii** 25 members
b adult members **c** squash **d** $2200

3 **a** 10 students **b** Redstone
c **i** Redstone **ii** Hillsvale

4 **a** • Graph for soft drink (lunch) is incorrect.
• Graph for water (lunch) too large, and graph for water (recess) too small. (The numbers were reversed.)

b

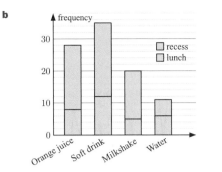

c lunch
d 23.8%

5 **a** Tuesday **b** 87.5% **c** small
d Monday; this is the only day that large outsold the other sizes.

6 **a**

Most enjoyed newspaper section

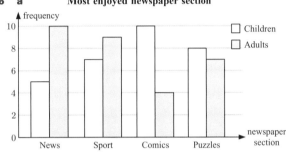

b **i** comics **ii** news
c News and comics, as adults are more interested in the news whilst children are more interested in comics.

7 **a**

Call-outs

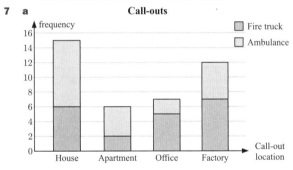

b **i** factory **ii** house **c** fire truck

EXERCISE 4C

1 **a** The volume of water in a lake from March to September.
b **i** ≈ 22 300 Ml **ii** ≈ 24 800 Ml
c **i** May **ii** August **d** ≈ 25 200 Ml
e ≈ 18% increase

2 **a**

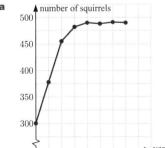

b The squirrel population increased rapidly from 2011 to 2015, at an ever decreasing rate. It then seemed to stabilise from 2015 onwards with only minimal change.

3 a

distance (km) vs day graph, y-axis from 0 to 6.0, x-axis from 0 to 28.

b 12 days   **c** 8th February

4 a

heart rate (bpm) vs time (minutes) graph, y-axis from 50 to 150, x-axis from 0 to 60.

b After 50 minutes.

c There is an upward trend for the first 50 minutes, after which Jana's heart rate begins to decrease.

5 a

Household water consumption

usage (litres × 1000) vs quarter graph, y-axis from 50 to 85, x-axis quarters 1–4 for 2017 and 2018.

b **i** 3rd quarter   **ii** 1st quarter

People tend to use more water in summer (July to September) than in winter (January to March).

6 a

profit ($ × 1000) vs quarter graph, y-axis from 0 to 40, x-axis quarters 1–4 for 2014, 2015, 2016.

b The shop generally makes the most profit in the 4th quarter. This could result from increased sales in the holiday period.

c There is an increasing trend in profit.

REVIEW SET 4A

1 a   **Hair colour of students**

bar chart: Blond, Black, Brown, Red with frequency axis 0 to 20.

b brown
c 47.5%

2 a 5 litres   **b i** Friday   **ii** Wednesday

c i 30 litres   **ii** 55 litres

3 a   **Animal numbers data**

bar chart: number vs animal (Chickens, Cows, Donkeys, Ducks, Geese, Goats, Horses, Sheep), y-axis 0 to 40.

b $\frac{11}{120}$

c cows, goats, sheep

d i 10%
ii 22.5%

4 a 150 litres   **b** 50 litres   **c** 600 litres

5 a 360 students   **b**

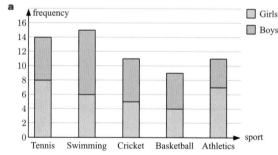

Participation ≈ 28.1%, High distinction ≈ 14.4%, Distinction ≈ 24.7%, Credit ≈ 32.8%. Angles: 118°, 101°, 89°, 52°.

c As we do not know how many students are from School B, we cannot say whether this statement is valid. It would be appropriate to say that "School B had a higher proportion of students who scored a distinction than School A".

6 a i 3 calf injuries   **ii** 5 calf injuries   **b** Panthers

c i hamstring injuries   **ii** knee injuries

7 a

frequency bar chart by sport (Tennis, Swimming, Cricket, Basketball, Athletics), y-axis 0 to 16, showing Girls and Boys.

b girls   **c** 36.4%   **d** swimming

8 a

attendance (× 1000) vs game graph, y-axis 10 to 50, x-axis 0 to 12.

b The data shows a decrease in attendance rates as the season progresses.

REVIEW SET 4B

1 **a** 955 billion barrels **b** 120 billion barrels **c** $\approx 15.7\%$

2 **a**

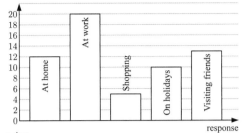

Location during burglary

b 8.3%

3 **a** **i** $10°C$ **ii** $20°C$ **b** **i** $25°C$ **ii** 2 pm
c decreasing; the line is sloping downwards at 4 pm.
d $20°C$

4 **a** There is a slowly increasing trend.
b International sales have increased and are now much larger than the UK sales.
c 2017; international exposure could be a reason for the increase in international sales.

5

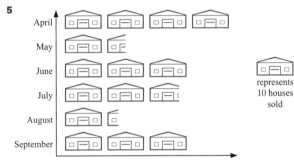

represents 10 houses sold

6 **a** 7 hours **b** 1 hour **c** REM sleep **d** Wednesday

7 **a** • missed day 7 from the line
• did not connect day 13 to day 14
b

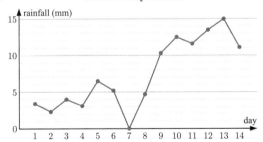

Lisbon's daily rainfall

c The trend is generally increasing throughout the fortnight but has decreased from day 13 to day 14.

8 **a**

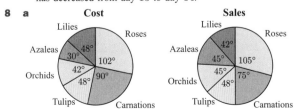

Cost   Sales

b Roses and Carnations **c** Roses and Carnations
d Lilies as he makes least profit (only $6000).

EXERCISE 5A

1 **a** $x = 5$ **b** $x = 9$ **c** $5x = 15$ **d** $7x = x + 6$
2 **a** $x = 4$ **b** $2x = 4$ **c** $3x = -3$ **d** $4x = 3x + 2$
3 **a** $x = 16$ **b** $x - 1 = 5$ **c** $3x = 14$ **d** $3x - 4 = -40$
4 **a** $x = -10$ **b** $x = -9$ **c** $2 - x = 5$ **d** $2x - 1 = 11$

EXERCISE 5B

1 **a** -3 **b** $+8$ **c** $\div 2$ **d** $\times 5$ **e** -12 **f** $\times 6$
g $+5$ **h** $\div 9$ **i** $-\frac{2}{3}$ **j** $\times 13$ **k** $\div 15$ **l** $+\frac{4}{5}$
2 **a** x **b** x **c** x **d** x **e** p **f** q **g** $8r$ **h** s
3 **a** $x = 6$ **b** $x = 10$ **c** $x = 7$ **d** $x = 6$
e $x = 6$ **f** $x = -2$ **g** $x = -35$ **h** $x = -11$
i $x = -32$ **j** $x = -3$ **k** $x = -7$ **l** $x = -9$
m $x = -9$ **n** $x = 4$ **o** $x = 9$ **p** $x = -18$

EXERCISE 5C

1 **a** $x = 2$ **b** $x = 5$ **c** $x = 4$ **d** $x = -8$
e $x = 4$ **f** $x = \frac{3}{8}$ **g** $x = 1\frac{1}{2}$ **h** $x = 17$
i $x = -2$ **j** $x = -2$ **k** $x = 2$ **l** $x = -4\frac{1}{4}$
2 **a** $x = 4$ **b** $x = -2$ **c** $x = 4$ **d** $x = 5$
e $x = 2$ **f** $x = 7$ **g** $x = 15$ **h** $x = 7$ **i** $x = 4$
3 **a** $x = 4$ **b** $x = 22$ **c** $x = 16$ **d** $x = 9$
e $x = -21$ **f** $x = -24$ **g** $x = 63$ **h** $x = -56$
i $x = 22$
4 **a** $x = 11$ **b** $x = 9$ **c** $x = 3\frac{1}{2}$ **d** $x = -7$
e $x = -4$ **f** $x = -28$ **g** $x = -5$ **h** $x = 2$
i $x = -11$
5 **a** $x = 10$ **b** $x = 2$ **c** $x = 4\frac{1}{2}$ **d** $x = -\frac{2}{3}$
e $x = -3$ **f** $x = 0$ **g** $x = 1\frac{1}{3}$ **h** $x = \frac{1}{2}$ **i** $x = 0$
6 **a** $a = 3$ **b** $x = 448$ **c** $x = 5$ **d** $x = 1$
e $n = 4$ **f** $a = -8$ **g** $x = 2\frac{1}{2}$ **h** $x = 75$
i $x = 3$ **j** $n = -3$ **k** $k = 7$ **l** $z = -\frac{4}{5}$

EXERCISE 5D

1 **a** $x = 2$ **b** $x = -5$ **c** $x = 15$ **d** $y = 0$
e $t = 6$ **f** $d = -10$ **g** $x = -6$ **h** $x = 12$
2 **a** $x = 9$ **b** $x = 1$ **c** $x = -2$ **d** $x = -3$
e $x = -3$ **f** $x = 1$
3 **a** $x = 6$ **b** $x = 2$ **c** $x = -4$ **d** $x = 3$
e $x = 4$ **f** $x = -2\frac{1}{2}$
4 **a** $x = 1$ **b** $x = 1$ **c** $x = \frac{1}{10}$ **d** $x = 4$
e $x = 1$ **f** $x = -1\frac{1}{3}$
5 **a** $x = 3$ **b** $t = 5$ **c** $x = 1$ **d** $y = \frac{1}{2}$
e $a = 3$ **f** $p = -3$
6 **a** $7(a + 3) = 21 + 7a$ reduces to $0 = 0$.
The equation is true for all real values of a. So, infinitely many values of a satisfy this equation.
b We get $3 = 4$ which is absurd. So, this equation has no solution. No values of a satisfy the equation.
7 **a** $x = \frac{1}{3}$ **b** $x = 2\frac{2}{9}$ **c** $x = 3$ **d** $p = -\frac{1}{4}$
8 **a** $x = -8$ **b** $x = 1\frac{3}{5}$ **c** $x = -1$ **d** $x = -2$
e $x = 5$ **f** $x = -1$ **g** $x = 1$ **h** $x = -2$

EXERCISE 5E

1 **a** $x = \frac{10}{9}$ **b** $x = 2$ **c** $x = -3$ **d** $x = \frac{13}{11}$
e $x = \frac{24}{19}$ **f** $x = \frac{7}{8}$ **g** $x = -1$ **h** $x = -5$
i no solution

2 **a** $x = \frac{1}{3}$ **b** $x = -\frac{1}{4}$ **c** $x = \frac{3}{2}$ **d** $x = -\frac{1}{6}$
 e $x = \frac{21}{2}$ **f** $x = \frac{10}{3}$ **g** $x = \frac{7}{6}$ **h** $x = -28$

3 **a** $x = -2$ **b** $x = -\frac{1}{2}$ **c** $x = -1$ **d** $x = -\frac{7}{2}$
 e $x = \frac{17}{2}$ **f** $x = -12$ **g** $x = \frac{1}{5}$ **h** $x = -1$

4 **a** $x = -\frac{36}{5}$ **b** $x = -\frac{16}{5}$ **c** $x = 16$ **d** $x = \frac{16}{3}$
 e $x = \frac{4}{5}$ **f** $x = \frac{17}{24}$

EXERCISE 5F

1 The number is 9. **2** The number is 5.
3 The number is 8. **4** The numbers are 86 and 87.
5 The smallest integer is 35. **6** The number is 91.
7 The number is $4\frac{1}{4}$. **8** 7 packs **9** 6 shirts
10 There are 7 passengers in each row.
11 Paige ate 5 sweets. **12** Carol drank 580 ml of water.
13 Emma scored 37 runs, Alex scored 42 runs, and Toni scored 14 runs.
14 **a** Stan has only considered positive numbers.
 b If the denominator is x, then $\frac{x+4}{x} = \frac{1}{3}$. Solving gives $x = -6$, so the fraction is $\frac{-2}{-6}$.
15 Isaac buys 6 shirts. **16** eight 5-cent coins **17** 6 apples
18 Ellie's son is 10 years old now **19** Adrian is 7 years old now

REVIEW SET 5A

1 **a** $3x = -9$ **b** $4x = -10$
2 **a** $x = 2$ **b** $x = 6$ **c** $x = -3$ **d** $x = -2$
 e $x = 1$ **f** $x = -2$
3 **a** $x = 5$ **b** $x = \frac{1}{2}$ **c** $x = -9$ **d** $x = \frac{3}{5}$
 e $x = 1$ **f** $x = \frac{6}{7}$
4 **a** $x = \frac{26}{3}$ **b** $x = \frac{14}{15}$ **c** $x = -\frac{5}{2}$ **d** $x = 9$
 e $x = -\frac{1}{7}$ **f** $x = \frac{11}{5}$
5 The number is 13. **6** The smallest integer is 20.
7 The number is 7. **8** twelve 5-cent coins

REVIEW SET 5B

1 **a** $x = 4$ **b** $x = -48$ **c** $x = -1$
2 **a** $x = 7$ **b** $x = -\frac{3}{4}$ **c** $x = 4\frac{1}{4}$
3 **a** $x = 5$ **b** $x = 2$ **c** $x = 1\frac{2}{3}$ **d** $x = \frac{2}{3}$
4 **a** **i** $x + 6 = 21$ **ii** $x = 15$
 b **i** $\frac{x}{3} = 5$ **ii** $x = 15$ **c** yes
5 **a** $x = -5$ **b** $x = -\frac{24}{35}$ **c** $x = -2\frac{2}{3}$ **d** $x = 1$
 e $x = -2$
6 The larger integer is 19. **7** The number is 7.
8 6 writing pads **9** 13 chogokin

EXERCISE 6A

1 **a** $A = \{$Sunday, Monday, Tuesday, Wednesday, Thursday, Friday, Saturday$\}$
 b $A = \{$F, O, T, B, A, L$\}$
 c $A = \{2, 3, 5, 7, 11, 13, 17, 19\}$ **d** $A = \{$a, e, i, o, u$\}$
 e $A = \{1, 3, 7, 21\}$
2 **a** The set has an endless number of elements. It is infinite.
 b 123 456 has a finite number of factors, so the set is finite.
 c The set is finite.

3 **a** **i** $n(S) = 6$ **ii** $n(T) = 4$
 b **i** true **ii** true **iii** false **iv** true **c** no
4 **a** **i** $A = \{1, 4, 9\}$
 ii $B = \{4, 6, 8, 9, 10, 12, 14, 15, 16, 18\}$
 iii $C = \{1, 2, 3, 4, 6, 9, 12, 18, 36\}$
 b **i** $n(A) = 3$ **ii** $n(B) = 10$ **iii** $n(C) = 9$
 c **i** false **ii** true
5 **a** $\varnothing, \{a\}$
 b $\varnothing, \{a\}, \{b\}, \{c\}, \{a, b\}, \{b, c\}, \{a, c\}, \{a, b, c\}$
 c $2^4 = 16$ (For a set with 1 element, 2 subsets; for a set with 2 elements, 4 subsets; for a set with 3 elements, 8 subsets.)
6 **a** $S = \{1, 2, 3, 6\}$, $n(S) = 4$
 b $S = \{6, 12, 18, 24, ...\}$, $n(S)$ is infinite
 c $S = \{1, 17\}$, $n(S) = 2$
 d $S = \{17, 34, 51, 68, ...\}$, $n(S)$ is infinite
 e $S = \{2, 3, 5, 7, 11, 13, 17, 19\}$, $n(S) = 8$
 f $S = \{12, 14, 15, 16, 18, 20, 21, 22, 24, 25, 26, 27, 28\}$, $n(S) = 13$
7 **a** $A = \{$red, blue, green$\}$,
 $B = \{$orange, red, yellow, blue, pink, green$\}$
 b yes **c** **i** $n(A) = 3$ **ii** $n(B) = 6$ **d** yes
8 $x = 3, 6, 7$, or 11 **9** $x = 0, -2, -4$, or 4
10 **a** $A = \{23, 29\}$, $B = \{22, 24, 26, 28\}$,
 $C = \{21, 22, 24, 25, 26, 27, 28\}$, $D = \varnothing$
 b **i** 2 **ii** 0 **c** **i** A and D **ii** B and D
 d **i** false **ii** true **iii** false

EXERCISE 6B

1 **a** $A' = \{1, 3, 5, 7, 8, 9\}$ **b** $B' = \{2, 4, 6, 8\}$
 c $C' = \{1, 2, 5, 6, 9\}$ **d** $D' = \{4, 5, 6\}$
2 **a** $P = \{1, 2, 3, 4, 6, 12\}$ **b** $Q = \{11, 13, 17, 19\}$
 c $P' = \{5, 7, 8, 9, 10, 11, 13, 14, 15, 16, 17, 18, 19\}$
 d $Q' = \{1, 2, 3, 4, 5, 6, 7, 8, 9, 10, 12, 14, 15, 16, 18\}$
3 **a** **i** $U = \{$Rugby, Athletics, Volleyball, Baseball, Cricket, Archery, Netball, Tennis$\}$
 ii $K = \{$Baseball, Cricket, Tennis$\}$
 iii $K' = \{$Rugby, Athletics, Volleyball, Archery, Netball$\}$
 b K' represents sports played at school which do not involve hitting a ball with a bat or racquet.
4 **a** **i** 7 **ii** 4 **iii** 3 **iv** 2 **v** 5
 b $n(S) + n(S') = n(U)$

EXERCISE 6C

1 **a** $A \cap B = \{3, 5\}$ **b** $A \cup B = \{1, 3, 5, 6, 7, 9\}$
2 **a** $P \cap Q = \{$Dragons, Tigers$\}$
 $P \cup Q = \{$Dragons, Tigers, Roosters, Raiders, Storm, Knights$\}$
 b $P \cap Q = \{1\}$, $P \cup Q = \{1, 3, 4, 6, 9, 10, 15, 16\}$
 c $P \cap Q = \{g, m\}$, $P \cup Q = \{d, e, g, h, k, l, m, p\}$
3 B and C
4 **a** $X = \{2, 3, 5, 7, 11, 13, 17, 19\}$,
 $Y = \{1, 2, 4, 5, 10, 20\}$
 b **i** $X \cap Y = \{2, 5\}$ **ii** $n(X \cap Y) = 2$
 iii $X \cup Y = \{1, 2, 3, 4, 5, 7, 10, 11, 13, 17, 19, 20\}$
 iv $n(X \cup Y) = 12$

5 **a** $U = \{$January, February, March, April, May, June, July, August, September, October, November, December$\}$

    b $G = \{$September, October, November, December$\}$
      $R = \{$October, November, December, January, February, March$\}$

    c $G \cap R = \{$October, November, December$\}$
      This set represents the months when both gardenias and roses are in flower.

    d $G \cup R = \{$September, October, November, December, January, February, March$\}$
      This set represents the months when either gardenias or roses (or both) are in flower.

    e $(G \cup R)' = \{$April, May, June, July, August$\}$
      This set represents the months when neither flower is in bloom.

6 **a** $A = \{4, 8\}$, $B = \{1, 2, 4, 8, 16\}$ **b** yes

    c   **i** $A \cap B = \{4, 8\}$ **ii** $A \cup B = \{1, 2, 4, 8, 16\}$

    d "If $A \subseteq B$, then $A \cap B = A$ and $A \cup B = B$."

7 **a**   **i** $\varnothing$ **ii** $\{1, 2, 3, 4, 5, 6, 7, 8\}$ **b**   **i** $\varnothing$ **ii** U

EXERCISE 6D

1

Number	$\mathbb{N}$	$\mathbb{Z}$	$\mathbb{Q}$	$\mathbb{R}$
19	✓	✓	✓	✓
$-\frac{2}{3}$	✗	✗	✓	✓
$\sqrt{7}$	✗	✗	✗	✓
5.6389	✗	✗	✓	✓
$\sqrt{16}$	✓	✓	✓	✓
2π	✗	✗	✗	✓
-11	✗	✓	✓	✓
$\frac{6}{0}$	✗	✗	✗	✗
$\sqrt{-2}$	✗	✗	✗	✗

2 **a** true   **b** true   **c** true   **d** true   **e** false   **f** false   **g** true   **h** true

3 **a, b, c, d, f, g, h** are rational;   **e** is irrational

4 **a** $0.\dot{7} = \frac{7}{9}$ **b** $0.\dot{4}\dot{1} = \frac{41}{99}$ **c** $0.\dot{3}2\dot{4} = \frac{12}{37}$

5 **a** 0.527 can be written as $\frac{527}{1000}$, and 527, 1000 are integers

    b $0.\dot{9} = 1$

6 **a** $\sqrt{2} + (-\sqrt{2}) = 0$ which is rational

    b $\sqrt{2} \times \sqrt{50} = \sqrt{100} = 10$ which is rational

7 **a** true   **b** false   **c** true

EXERCISE 6E

1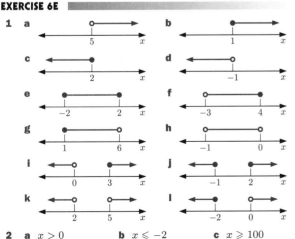

2 **a** $x > 0$ **b** $x \leqslant -2$ **c** $x \geqslant 100$
    d $x < 0.2$ **e** $-1 \leqslant x \leqslant 4$ **f** $3 \leqslant x < 10$

g $-5 < x < 5$ **h** $7 < x \leqslant 20$
i $x < 2$ or $x \geqslant 7$ **j** $x < -3$ or $x > 0$
k $x \leqslant 4$ or $x \geqslant 17$ **l** $x \leqslant 21$ or $x > 33$

3 **a** The set of all real x such that x is greater than 4.

    b The set of all natural numbers x such that x lies between 0 and 5, both inclusive.

    c The set of all integers y such that y lies between 0 and 8.

    d The set of all real x such that x lies between 1 and 4 inclusive.

    e The set of all positive integers t such that t lies between 2 and 7.

    f The set of all real n such that n is less than or equal to 3 or n is greater than 6.

4 **a** $\{2, 3, 4, 5, 6\}$ **b** $\{...., -2, -1, 0, 1, 2, 3, 4, 5\}$
    c $\{3, 4, 5, 6, ...\}$ **d** $\{-3, -2, -1, 0, 1, 2, 3, 4, 5\}$
    e $\{...., -8, -7, -6, -5\}$ **f** $\{7, 8, 9, 10, ...\}$

5 **a** $\{x \mid -5 \leqslant x \leqslant -1, \ x \in \mathbb{Z}\}$

    b $\{x \mid 0 \leqslant x \leqslant 5, \ x \in \mathbb{N}\}$ or $\{x \mid 0 \leqslant x \leqslant 5, \ x \in \mathbb{Z}\}$

    c $\{x \mid x \geqslant 4, \ x \in \mathbb{Z}\}$ or $\{x \mid x \geqslant 4, \ x \in \mathbb{N}\}$

    d $\{x \mid x \leqslant 1, \ x \in \mathbb{Z}\}$ **e** $\{x \mid -5 \leqslant x \leqslant 1, \ x \in \mathbb{Z}\}$

    f $\{x \mid x \leqslant 44, \ x \in \mathbb{Z}\}$

6 **a** $\{x \mid x > 3\}$ **b** $\{x \mid 2 < x \leqslant 5\}$
    c $\{x \mid x \leqslant -1$ or $x \geqslant 2\}$ **d** $\{x \mid -1 \leqslant x \leqslant 4, \ x \in \mathbb{Z}\}$
    e $\{x \mid 0 \leqslant x \leqslant 6, \ x \in \mathbb{N}\}$ **f** $\{x \mid x < 0\}$

7 **a**   **b**

    c   **d**

    e   **f**

8 **a** finite   **b** infinite   **c** infinite   **d** finite
    e finite   **f** infinite

EXERCISE 6F

1 **a** $A' = \{1, 4, 6, 8\}$

    b $A = \{2, 3, 5, 7\}$
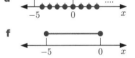

    c $4, 4$

2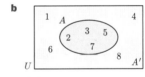

3 **a**   **i** $U = \{1, 2, 3, 4, 5, 6, 7, 8, 9, 10\}$
       ii $N = \{3, 8\}$ **iii** $M = \{1, 3, 4, 7, 8\}$
    b $n(N) = 2$, $n(M) = 5$ **c** No, $N \subseteq M$.

4 **a**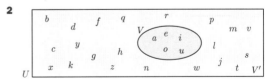
                         b   **i** true
                                       ii true
                                       iii true

                                     c (shaded section of diagram alongside)

5 **a**
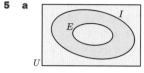

b

c
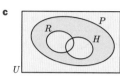

d

e
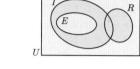

6 **a** **i** $A = \{2, 7\}$ **ii** $B = \{1, 2, 4, 6, 7\}$
 iii $U = \{1, 2, 3, 4, 5, 6, 7, 8\}$ **iv** $A \cap B = \{2, 7\}$
 v $A \cup B = \{1, 2, 4, 6, 7\}$
 b **i** $n(A) = 2$ **ii** $n(B) = 5$ **iii** $n(U) = 8$
 iv $n(A \cap B) = 2$ **v** $n(A \cup B) = 5$

7 **a** **i** $C = \{1, 3, 7, 9\}$ **ii** $D = \{1, 2, 5\}$
 iii $U = \{1, 2, 3, 4, 5, 6, 7, 8, 9\}$ **iv** $C \cap D = \{1\}$
 v $C \cup D = \{1, 2, 3, 5, 7, 9\}$
 b **i** $n(C) = 4$ **ii** $n(D) = 3$ **iii** $n(U) = 9$
 iv $n(C \cap D) = 1$ **v** $n(C \cup D) = 6$

8 **a** $A \cap B = \{3, 4\}$,
 $A \cup B = \{1, 2, 3, 4, 5, 6\}$
 b

9 **a** $A \cap B = \varnothing$. There are no
 elements common to sets A
 and B.
 These sets are disjoint.
 b

10
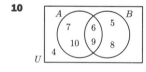

11 **a** **i** $A = \{1, 2, 3, 5, 6, 10, 15, 30\}$
 ii $B = \{2, 3, 5, 7, 11, 13, 17, 19, 23, 29\}$
 iii $A \cap B = \{2, 3, 5\}$
 iv $A \cup B = \{1, 2, 3, 5, 6, 7, 10, 11, 13, 15, 17, 19, 23,$
 $29, 30\}$
 b **i** $n(A) = 8$ **ii** $n(B) = 10$
 iii $n(A \cap B) = 3$ **iv** $n(A \cup B) = 15$
 c $n(A) + n(B) - n(A \cap B) = 8 + 10 - 3 = 15$
 $= n(A \cup B)$
 d

12
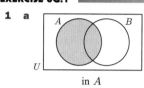

1 **a**

b
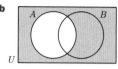

in A

not in A

c

d
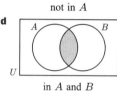

neither in A nor B

in A and B

e

in either A or B, but not both

2 **a**

b
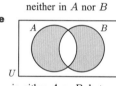

B

B'

c

d
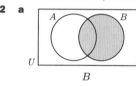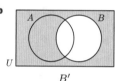

$A \cap B'$

$A \cup B'$

e

f
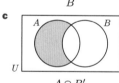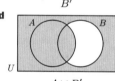

$(A \cap B)'$

$(A \cup B)'$

3 **a** In X but not in Y.
 b Outside of X and Y or in both X and Y.
 c In at least 2 of X, Y, and Z.

4 **a** A **b** B **c** C'
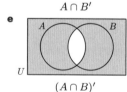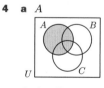

d $A \cup B$ **e** $B \cap C$ **f** $A \cap B \cap C$
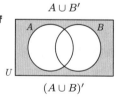

g $A \cap B' \cap C$ **h** $(A \cup B)'$ **i** $A' \cup (B \cap C)$

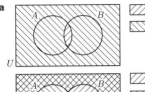

5 a

represents $A \cap B$
represents $(A \cap B)'$

represents A'
represents B'
whole shaded region is $A' \cup B'$

b

represents $B \cap C$
represents A
whole shaded region represents
$A \cup (B \cap C)$

represents $A \cup B$
represents $A \cup C$
represents
$(A \cup B) \cap (A \cup C)$

c

represents A
represents $B \cup C$
represents $A \cap (B \cup C)$

represents $A \cap B$
represents $A \cap C$
whole shaded region represents
$(A \cap B) \cup (A \cap C)$

EXERCISE 6G.2

1 a 7   **b** 9   **c** 15   **d** 8   **e** 5   **f** 19
2 a $b+c$ **b** $c+d$ **c** $a+c$ **d** b **e** $a+c+d$ **f** d
3 a   i $2a-4$ **ii** $5a-4$ **iii** $4a+5$ **iv** $6a+1$
   b $a=7$
4 a $n(A) + n(B) - n(A \cap B) = a+b+b+c-b$
$$= a+b+c$$
$$= n(A \cup B)$$
   b If A and B are disjoint events, then $n(A \cap B) = 0$.
   So, $n(A \cup B) = n(A) + n(B) - n(A \cap B)$
   $$= n(A) + n(B)$$

EXERCISE 6H

1 a 26   **b** 20   **c** 25   **d** 5   **e** 7
2 a 48   **b** 27   **c** 23   **d** 16   **e** 30
3 a

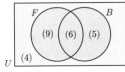

   b   i 5   **ii** 20
   iii 9   **iv** 4
   v 14

4 a

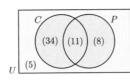

   b   i 13   **ii** 53
   iii 42   **iv** 8
   v 34

5 6 girls   **6 a** 12 books   **b** 14 books
7 a 150 people   **b** 150 people
8 a 7 shops   **b** 12 shops   **c** 18 shops
9 39 people attended   **10** 14 cars
11 7% of them   **12** 1 worker uses both
13 a

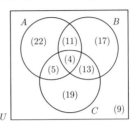

   b   i 9%   **ii** 91%   **iii** 58%   **iv** 72%   **v** 19%
14 7 women
15 a

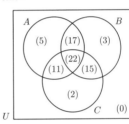

   b   i 11 of them
   ii 65 of them

16 5 students

REVIEW SET 6A

1 a 1.3 can be written as $\frac{13}{10}$, and 13, 10 are integers
   b $\{23, 29, 31, 37\}$
   c The set of all real t such that t lies between -1 and 3, including -1.
   d $\{x \mid 0 < x \leqslant 5\}$ **e**

   f $\varnothing$, $\{1\}$, $\{3\}$, $\{6\}$, $\{8\}$, $\{1, 3\}$, $\{1, 6\}$, $\{1, 8\}$, $\{3, 6\}$, $\{3, 8\}$, $\{6, 8\}$, $\{1, 3, 6\}$, $\{1, 3, 8\}$, $\{1, 6, 8\}$, $\{3, 6, 8\}$ (15 of them)

2 a   i $A = \{1, 2, 3, 4, 5\}$ **ii** $B = \{1, 2, 7\}$
   iii $U = \{1, 2, 3, 4, 5, 6, 7\}$
   iv $A \cup B = \{1, 2, 3, 4, 5, 7\}$ **v** $A \cap B = \{1, 2\}$
   b   i $n(A) = 5$ **ii** $n(B) = 3$ **iii** $n(A \cup B) = 6$
3 a $S \cap T = \{$English, German$\}$
   b $S \cup T = \{$English, French, German, Spanish, Japanese$\}$
   c $S \cap T' = \{$French, Spanish$\}$
4 a false   **b** false   **c** false
5 a

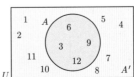

   b $A' = \{1, 2, 4, 5, 7, 8, 10, 11\}$ **c** $n(A') = 8$ **d** no

6 **a**

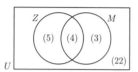

b **i** $P \cup Q = \{2, 3, 4, 5, 6, 7, 8\}$
ii $Q' = \{1, 3, 5, 7, 9, 10\}$
c **i** $n(P') = 6$ **ii** $n(P \cap Q) = 1$ **d** true

7 **a** The shaded region is the complement of X, that is, everything not in X.
b The shaded region represents "in exactly one of X or Y but not both".
c The shaded region represents everything in X or in neither set.

8 **a**

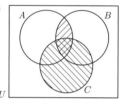

b **i** 5 times
ii 3 times

9

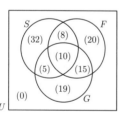

represents $A \cap B$
represents C
whole shaded region
represents $(A \cap B) \cup C$

represents $A \cup C$
represents $B \cup C$
represents
$(A \cup C) \cap (B \cup C)$

Area shaded is the same in each case.

10 **a**

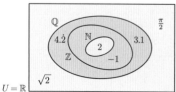

b 109 took part

REVIEW SET 6B

1 **a** false **b** false

2 **a** $0.\dot{5}\dot{1} = \frac{51}{99}$, and 51, 99 are integers
b $\{t \mid t \leqslant -3 \text{ or } t > 4\}$ **c**

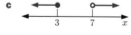

3

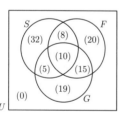

$U = \mathbb{R}$

4 **a** $A \cap B = \{1, 2, 3, 6\}$
b $A \cup B = \{1, 2, 3, 4, 6, 8, 9, 12, 18, 24\}$

5 **a**

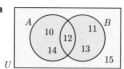

b

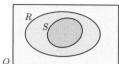

$U = Q$

c

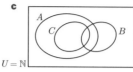

$U = \mathbb{N}$

6 **a** **i** $U = \{12, 13, 14, 15, 16, 17, 18, 19, 20\}$
ii $A' = \{13, 15, 17, 19, 20\}$
iii $B' = \{13, 14, 16, 17, 19, 20\}$
iv $A \cup B = \{12, 14, 15, 16, 18\}$
v $A' \cap B' = \{13, 17, 19, 20\}$
b $(A \cup B)' = \{13, 17, 19, 20\}$ {using **a iv**}
  $= A' \cap B'$ {**a v**}

7 **a**

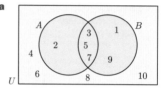

b **i** $A' = \{1, 4, 6, 8, 9, 10\}$ **ii** $A \cap B = \{3, 5, 7\}$
c **i** $n(A) = 4$ **ii** $n(B') = 5$ **iii** $n(A \cup B) = 6$
d **i** false **ii** true

8 **a**

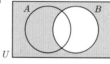

b

c

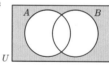

9 **a**

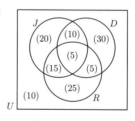

b **i** $n(J \cap D \cap R) = 5$ **ii** $n(J \cap R \cap D') = 15$
iii $n(R \cap J') = 30$

EXERCISE 7A

1 **a** supplementary **b** neither **c** complementary
d neither **e** neither **f** supplementary
2 **a** $75°$ **b** $3°$ **c** $47°$ **3** **a** $51°$ **b** $123°$ **c** $90°$
4 **a** supplementary **b** neither **c** complementary
d neither
5 **a** The size of the angle complementary to $x°$ is $(90 - x)°$.
b The size of the angle supplementary to $y°$ is $(180 - y)°$.
c Two lines are perpendicular if they meet at $90°$.

6 **a** $p = 125$ **b** $q = 38$ **c** $k = 94$ **d** $x = 112$
   e $q = 26$ **f** $t = 45$ **g** $c = 90$ **h** $s = 21$
   i $x = 66$ **j** $j = 161$ **k** $b = 115$ **l** $s = 75$
   m $x = 45$ **n** $x = 15$ **o** $x = 42$

EXERCISE 7B

1 **a** $x = 124$ {equal corresponding angles}
   b $b = 82$ {supplementary co-interior angles}
   c $q = 42$ {equal alternate angles}
   d $y = 57$ {equal corresponding angles}
   e $k = 62$ {equal alternate angles}
   f $a = 135$ {equal corresponding angles}
   g $x = 147$ {equal alternate angles}
   h $y = 73$ {supplementary co-interior angles}
   i $d = 15$ {equal corresponding angles}

2 **a** $a = 76$ {vertically opposite angles}
     $b = 104$ {supplementary co-interior angles}
   b $a = 117$ {equal corresponding angles}
     $b = 117$ {vertically opposite angles}
   c $a = 38$ {vertically opposite angles}
     $b = 38$ {equal alternate angles}

3 **a** $x = y$ {equal alternate angles}
   b $a + b = 180$ {supplementary co-interior angles}
   c $p = q$ {equal corresponding angles}
   d $a + b = c$ {equal alternate angles}

4 **a** parallel   {equal alternate angles}
   b not parallel   {co-interior angles do not sum to $180°$}
   c not parallel   {alternate angles are not equal}
   d parallel   {equal corresponding angles}
   e parallel   {angles on a straight line,
             equal corresponding angles}
   f parallel   {angles on a straight line,
             equal corresponding angles}

5 **a** $x = 60$, $y = 60$ **b** $a = 90$, $b = 35$
   c $p = 90$, $q = 25$, $r = 25$

EXERCISE 7C

1 **a** $a = 130$ **b** $b = 90$ **c** $c = 43$ **d** $d = 129$
   e $e = 53$ **f** $x = 131$

2 **a** true   **b** false   **c** false   **d** false

3 **a** AB   **b** AC   **c** BC   **d** BC   **e** AC   **f** AC

4 **a** $a = 55$ **b** $b = 55$ **c** $x = 20$ **d** $a = 55$, $b = 77$
   e $x = 45$, $y = 70$ **f** $a = 45$, $b = 85$, $c = 130$, $d = 50$

5 **a** $\widehat{CBD} = 180° - \widehat{ABD}$ {angles on a straight line}
       $= 180° - 90°$
       $= 90°$
   b $\widehat{BDC} = 55°$ **c** $\widehat{ADB} = 55°$

6 $46.5°$, $34.5°$, $99°$

EXERCISE 7D

1 **a** $x = 74$ {isosceles triangle theorem}
   b $x = 64$ {isosceles triangle theorem,
             angle sum of a triangle}
   c $x = 69$ {isosceles triangle theorem,
             angle sum of a triangle}
   d $x = 24$ {isosceles triangle theorem,
             angle sum of a triangle}
   e $x = 45$ {isosceles triangle theorem}

f $x = 22.5$ {isosceles triangle theorem,
             angle sum of a triangle}
g $x = 140$ {isosceles triangle theorem,
             exterior angle of a triangle}
h $x = 103$ {isosceles triangle theorem, angle sum of a
             triangle, exterior angle of a triangle}
i $x = 33$ {isosceles triangle theorem (twice),
             angle sum of a triangle (twice)}

2 **a** $x = 12$ {equal sides of isosceles triangle}
   b $x = 8$ {isosceles triangles, QR = QS = PS}
   c $x = 90$ {line from apex to midpoint of base in an
             isosceles triangle is perpendicular to base}
   d $x = 50$ {line from apex to midpoint of base in an
             isosceles triangle is perpendicular to base}
   e $x = 140$ {if line from apex perpendicular to base bisects
             the base, it is an isosceles triangle}
   f $x = 4$ {equilateral triangle, all angles $60°$}

3 **a** $x = 66$ **b** $\triangle$ABC is isosceles, AC = BC

4 **a** $\widehat{ABD} = 48°$ **b** $\triangle$ABD is isosceles, AD = BD
   c $x = 3$

5 **a** $\theta = 72$ **b** $\phi = 54$ **c** $\widehat{ABC} = 108°$

EXERCISE 7E

1 **a** $540°$ **b** $900°$ **c** $720°$
   d $1080°$ **e** $1800°$ **f** $2340°$

2 **a** $x = 87$ **b** $x = 43$ **c** $x = 52.5$
   d $x = 108$ **e** $x = 150$ **f** $x = 60$
   g $x = 120$ **h** $x = 125$ **i** $x = 135$

3 $135°$ **4** 13 sides

5 The sum of the sizes of the interior angles of a polygon is always
   a multiple of 180, but 2060 is *not* a multiple of 180.
   $\therefore$ no such polygon exists.

6 **a**

Regular polygon	Number of sides	Sum of angles	Size of each angle
triangle	3	$180°$	$60°$
quadrilateral	4	$360°$	$90°$
pentagon	5	$540°$	$108°$
hexagon	6	$720°$	$120°$
octagon	8	$1080°$	$135°$
decagon	10	$1440°$	$144°$

   b **i** The sum of the angles of an n-sided polygon is
         $(n - 2) \times 180°$.
      ii The size of each angle of a regular n-sided polygon is
         $\dfrac{(n - 2) \times 180°}{n}$.

   c $150°$

7 **a** 3 reflex angles   **b**

8 **a** yes   **b** each angle is $30°$
   c yes, the two inner triangles contain right angles.

9 **a** $128\frac{4}{7}°$
   b $\alpha = 25\frac{5}{7}$, $\beta = 102\frac{6}{7}$, $\gamma = 77\frac{1}{7}$, $\delta = 51\frac{3}{7}$

10 $\alpha = 60$, $\beta = 80$

EXERCISE 7F

1 a $x = 120$ **b** $x = 95$ **c** $x = 60$

2 a $108°$ **b** $135°$ **c** $144°$ **d** $162°$ **e** $176.4°$

f $\left(180 - \dfrac{360}{n}\right)°$

3 a 8 sides **b** 24 sides **c** 180 sides **d** 720 sides

4 a 6 sides **b** 12 sides **c** 72 sides **d** 360 sides

REVIEW SET 7A

1 a ...... equal in size. **b** ...... supplementary.

2 a $x = 72$ {equal corresponding angles}

b $x = 20$ {angles on a straight line}

c $x = 242$ {angles at a point}

d $x = 65$ {angles on a straight line, equal alternate angles}

e $x = 40$ {vertically opposite angles, supplementary co-interior angles}

3 yes {angles on a straight line, equal alternate angles}

4 a $x = 62$ **b** $x = 152$ **c** $x = 68$

5 $\triangle$ABC is isosceles since $A\widehat{C}B = A\widehat{B}C = 62°$ {angles on a straight line, angle sum of a triangle, isosceles triangle theorem}

6 a $x = 122$ {angle sum of a quadrilateral}

b $x = 60$ {opposite angles of parallelogram}
$y = 5$ {opposite sides of parallelogram}

c Must be a parallelogram and so a rectangle. {equal opposite sides and one right angle}
$x = 35$ {interior angle of rectangle}
$y = 55$ {alternate angles}

7 a $x = 110$ {angle sum of a pentagon}

b $x = 120$ {angle sum of a hexagon}

c $x = 100$ {exterior angles of a polygon}

d $x = 75$ {exterior angles of a polygon}

REVIEW SET 7B

1 a $a = 73$ {angles on a straight line}

b $b = 90$ {angles on a straight line}

c $c = 56$ {vertically opposite angles}

d $a = 110$ {equal alternate angles}
$b = 110$ {vertically opposite angles}

e $x = 40$ {angles on a straight line}

f $x = y = 96$ {isosceles triangle theorem, angle sum of a triangle, equal corresponding angles}

2 a $x = 60$ {angle sum of a triangle}

b $a = 131$ {exterior angle of a triangle}

c $x = 2$ {equal sides of equilateral triangle}

3 a right angled, scalene **b** obtuse angled, scalene

c obtuse angled, isosceles

4 a $x = 56$ **b** $a = 44$, $b = 46$, $c = 88$

5

Polygon	Number of sides	Sum of interior angles	Sum of exterior angles
pentagon	5	540°	360°
hexagon	6	720°	360°
octagon	8	1080°	360°

6 $160°$ **7 a** $x = 100$ **b** $x = 140$

EXERCISE 8A

1 a $\sqrt{5}$ is a surd, $\sqrt{5} \approx 2.2361$

b $\sqrt{36} = 6$, $\sqrt{36}$ is not a surd.

c $\sqrt{72}$ is a surd, $\sqrt{72} \approx 8.4853$

d $\sqrt{81} = 9$, $\sqrt{81}$ is not a surd.

e $\sqrt{200}$ is a surd, $\sqrt{200} \approx 14.1421$

f $\sqrt{\frac{1}{10}}$ is a surd, $\sqrt{\frac{1}{10}} \approx 0.3162$

g $\sqrt{\frac{1}{64}} = \frac{1}{8}$, $\sqrt{\frac{1}{64}}$ is not a surd.

h $\sqrt{\frac{3}{14}}$ is a surd, $\sqrt{\frac{3}{14}} \approx 0.4629$

2 $\sqrt{1}$, $\sqrt{4}$, $\sqrt{9}$, $\sqrt{16}$, ..., $\sqrt{961} = 31$ are all rational numbers from the given set.

$\therefore$ $1000 - 31 = 969$ are surds.

3 a 3 **b** $3\sqrt{3}$ **c** $9\sqrt{3}$ **d** $\frac{1}{3}$ **e** 5 **f** 25

g 5 **h** 20

4 a 8 **b** 32 **c** 12 **d** 27 **e** 20 **f** 45

g 28 **h** 40 **i** 490

5 a 24 **b** 30 **c** 70 **d** 32 **e** 147 **f** -6

g 30 **h** -42 **i** -22

EXERCISE 8B

1 a $x \approx \pm 3.32$ **b** no real solution **c** $x \approx \pm 8.43$

d $x \approx 9.43$ **e** $x = 2$ **f** $x \approx 2.22$ **g** $x \approx -2.22$

h $x = \pm 3$ **i** no real solution **j** $x \approx 1.87$

k $x \approx -2.57$ **l** $x \approx 1.84$

2 a $x = \pm\sqrt{12}$ **b** $x = \pm 6$ **c** $x = \pm\sqrt{3}$

d $x = \pm 7$ **e** $x = \pm\sqrt{10}$ **f** $x = \pm\sqrt{35}$

g $x = \pm 4$ **h** no real solution

EXERCISE 8C

1 a $\sqrt{6}$ **b** $\sqrt{34}$ **c** $\sqrt{21}$ **d** $10\sqrt{6}$ **e** $5\sqrt{14}$

f $-10\sqrt{14}$ **g** $2\sqrt{21}$ **h** $24\sqrt{5}$ **i** $80\sqrt{6}$

2 a 2 **b** $\frac{1}{3}$ **c** $\sqrt{6}$ **d** $\frac{1}{5}$ **e** $\sqrt{15}$

f $\sqrt{\frac{1}{15}}$ **g** 3 **h** $\frac{1}{4}$

3 a $\frac{1}{4}$ **b** $\frac{3}{4}$ **c** $\frac{7}{8}$ **d** $\frac{11}{3}$ **e** $\frac{5}{2}$ **f** $\frac{4}{3}$ **g** $\frac{8}{5}$ **h** $\frac{8}{3}$

4 a $2\sqrt{2}$ **b** $3\sqrt{2}$ **c** $5\sqrt{2}$ **d** $7\sqrt{2}$

e $10\sqrt{2}$ **f** $12\sqrt{2}$ **g** $100\sqrt{2}$ **h** $\frac{1}{2}\sqrt{2}$

5 a $2\sqrt{3}$ **b** $3\sqrt{3}$ **c** $5\sqrt{3}$ **d** $\frac{1}{3}\sqrt{3}$

6 a $2\sqrt{5}$ **b** $3\sqrt{5}$ **c** $5\sqrt{5}$ **d** $\frac{1}{5}\sqrt{5}$

EXERCISE 8D

1 a $2\sqrt{3}$ **b** $2\sqrt{7}$ **c** $3\sqrt{6}$ **d** $2\sqrt{15}$

e $3\sqrt{11}$ **f** $2\sqrt{13}$ **g** $2\sqrt{10}$ **h** $3\sqrt{7}$

i $4\sqrt{3}$ **j** $5\sqrt{5}$ **k** $7\sqrt{3}$ **l** $5\sqrt{7}$

m $4\sqrt{11}$ **n** $5\sqrt{6}$ **o** $5\sqrt{11}$ **p** $20\sqrt{5}$

2 a $\dfrac{\sqrt{96}}{\sqrt{6}} = \sqrt{\dfrac{96}{6}} = \sqrt{16} = 4$

b $\sqrt{96} = \sqrt{16 \times 6} = 4\sqrt{6}$ $\therefore$ $\dfrac{\sqrt{96}}{\sqrt{6}} = \dfrac{4\sqrt{6}}{\sqrt{6}} = 4$

EXERCISE 8E

1 a $2\sqrt{2}$ **b** 0 **c** $\sqrt{2}$ **d** $\sqrt{3}$

e $7\sqrt{7}$ **f** $-3\sqrt{5}$ **g** $-3\sqrt{2}$ **h** $8\sqrt{5}$

i $6\sqrt{2}$ **j** $-3\sqrt{2}$ **k** $4\sqrt{3}$ **l** $10\sqrt{5} - 10$

2 a $2\sqrt{2} + 7\sqrt{3}$ **b** $5\sqrt{2} - \sqrt{3}$ **c** $-7\sqrt{2} + 4\sqrt{3}$

d $11\sqrt{5} - 5\sqrt{2}$ **e** $2\sqrt{2} - 10\sqrt{7}$ **f** $2\sqrt{2} + 3\sqrt{11}$

g $1 - 3\sqrt{2}$ **h** $9\sqrt{3} - 13$

3 a $6\sqrt{2}$ **b** $8\sqrt{3}$ **c** $4\sqrt{5}$

4 a $\sqrt{12} + \sqrt{27} = 2\sqrt{3} + 3\sqrt{3} = 5\sqrt{3} = \sqrt{75}$

b $\sqrt{80} - \sqrt{5} = 4\sqrt{5} - \sqrt{5} = 3\sqrt{5} = \sqrt{45}$

5 a $12 + 4\sqrt{2}$ **b** $3\sqrt{2} + 3\sqrt{3}$ **c** $20 - 5\sqrt{7}$
d $6\sqrt{11} - 24$ **e** $\sqrt{2} + 2$ **f** $2 - 5\sqrt{2}$
g $2\sqrt{3} + 6$ **h** $3 - \sqrt{6}$ **i** $6\sqrt{5} - 5$
j $10 - \sqrt{5}$ **k** $10 + \sqrt{15}$ **l** $2\sqrt{7} + 7 + \sqrt{14}$

6 a $-4\sqrt{2} - 2$ **b** $-3\sqrt{2} + 2$ **c** $-2 + \sqrt{14}$
d $-3\sqrt{3} - 3$ **e** $-5\sqrt{3} + 3$ **f** $-6 - \sqrt{15}$
g $-2\sqrt{10} + \sqrt{15}$ **h** $-4 - 2\sqrt{6}$ **i** $-20\sqrt{2} + 20$
j $-14 - 4\sqrt{7}$ **k** $-2\sqrt{11} + 11$ **l** $-2\sqrt{3} + 4\sqrt{6}$

7 a $7 + 6\sqrt{2}$ **b** $11 + 6\sqrt{2}$ **c** $\sqrt{2}$
d $9 + \sqrt{3}$ **e** 1 **f** $1 - \sqrt{7}$
g 9 **h** $2\sqrt{2} + 1$ **i** $8 + 2\sqrt{2}$

8 a $4 + 2\sqrt{3}$ **b** $27 + 10\sqrt{2}$ **c** $11 - 6\sqrt{2}$
d $8 + 2\sqrt{7}$ **e** $5 - 2\sqrt{6}$ **f** $21 - 8\sqrt{5}$
g $8 + 2\sqrt{15}$ **h** $15 - 6\sqrt{6}$ **i** $9 - 6\sqrt{2}$
j $17 + 12\sqrt{2}$ **k** $17 - 12\sqrt{2}$ **l** $59 - 30\sqrt{2}$

9 a 7 **b** 2 **c** 22 **d** -13 **e** -2 **f** 2
g -18 **h** -16 **i** 14 **j** 3 **k** -4 **l** 7

EXERCISE 8F

1 a $\frac{\sqrt{5}}{5}$ **b** $\frac{\sqrt{2}}{1} = \sqrt{2}$ **c** $\frac{5\sqrt{3}}{3}$ **d** $\frac{\sqrt{8}}{8} = \frac{\sqrt{2}}{4}$
e $\frac{\sqrt{6}}{3}$ **f** $\frac{4\sqrt{7}}{7}$ **g** $\frac{\sqrt{3}}{6}$ **h** $-3\sqrt{2}$
i $\frac{2\sqrt{2}}{3}$ **j** $\frac{\sqrt{6}}{2}$ **k** $\frac{2\sqrt{15}}{3}$ **l** $\frac{\sqrt{21}}{7}$
m $\frac{\sqrt{14}}{6}$ **n** $\frac{2\sqrt{11}}{1} = 2\sqrt{11}$ **o** $\frac{\sqrt{3}}{9}$

2 a $\frac{3 + \sqrt{5}}{4}$ **b** $2 - \sqrt{3}$ **c** $\frac{4 + \sqrt{11}}{5}$
d $\frac{5\sqrt{2} - 2}{23}$ **e** $\frac{\sqrt{3} - 1}{2}$ **f** $\frac{-10 - 15\sqrt{2}}{14}$
g $\frac{3\sqrt{5} - 10}{11}$ **h** $\frac{5\sqrt{7} - 13}{3}$

3 a $4 + 2\sqrt{2}$ **b** $5 - 5\sqrt{2}$ **c** $-3 + 2\sqrt{2}$
d $-\frac{4}{7} + \frac{1}{7}\sqrt{2}$ **e** $1 + \sqrt{2}$ **f** $3 + 2\sqrt{2}$
g $\frac{9}{7} + \frac{3}{7}\sqrt{2}$ **h** $\frac{10}{7} + \frac{6}{7}\sqrt{2}$

4 a -4 **b** $\frac{9\sqrt{2} - 9}{7}$ **c** $\frac{11 + 7\sqrt{5}}{4}$ **5** $3 + 2\sqrt{2}$

6 a Hint: $\left(\sqrt{a+b}\right)^2 = \left(\sqrt{a} + \sqrt{b}\right)^2$
$\therefore \quad a + b = ...,$ and so on.
b $b = 0$ or $a = b$

7 a $\sqrt{5}, \sqrt{5}, 2\sqrt{5}, 3\sqrt{5}$
b The answer always has the form $k\sqrt{5}$ where $k \in \mathbb{Z}^+$.
(In fact the successive values of k are 1, 1, 2, 3, 5, 8, ...
which are the numbers of the Fibonacci sequence.)

REVIEW SET 8A

1 a $\sqrt{7} \approx 2.646$ **b** $\sqrt{22} \approx 4.690$ **c** $\sqrt{187} \approx 13.675$

2 a 12 **b** 32 **c** $6\sqrt{10}$ **d** $\frac{7}{2}$

3 a $\sqrt{5}$ **b** $\sqrt{5}$ **c** $\sqrt{7}$ **d** $\frac{1}{\sqrt{10}} = \frac{\sqrt{10}}{10}$

4 a $3\sqrt{11}$ **b** $6\sqrt{7} - 3\sqrt{3}$

5 a i $\sqrt{15}$ cm **ii** $\sqrt{15} \approx 3.87$ cm
b i $(15 - 3\sqrt{15})$ cm^2 **ii** $(30 - 3\sqrt{15})$ cm^2
iii $(10 + 2\sqrt{15})$ cm

6 $4\sqrt{5}$

7 a $2\sqrt{3} + 2$ **b** $3\sqrt{2} - 2$ **c** $8 + 2\sqrt{7}$
d $9 - 4\sqrt{5}$ **e** 19 **f** $1 - 2\sqrt{2}$

8 a $2\sqrt{5}$ **b** $\frac{1 + \sqrt{3}}{2}$ **c** $\frac{-4 - \sqrt{7}}{3}$

9 a $-6 - 3\sqrt{5}$ **b** $\frac{5}{2} - \frac{1}{2}\sqrt{5}$ **c** $\frac{9}{2} - \frac{3}{2}\sqrt{5}$

10 a $9 - 4\sqrt{2}$
b As $\left(3 + \sqrt{2}\right)\left(5 - 3\sqrt{2}\right) = 9 - 4\sqrt{2}$
then $\frac{9 - 4\sqrt{2}}{3 + \sqrt{2}} = 5 - 3\sqrt{2}$
c Hint: $\frac{9 - 4\sqrt{2}}{3 + \sqrt{2}} = \left(\frac{9 - 4\sqrt{2}}{3 + \sqrt{2}}\right)\left(\frac{3 - \sqrt{2}}{3 - \sqrt{2}}\right)$

REVIEW SET 8B

1 a $\sqrt{10}$ **b** 2 **c** 54 **2 a** $\frac{1}{2\sqrt{2}}$ **b** $\frac{1}{7}$ **c** $\frac{10}{3}$

3 a $2\sqrt{11}$ **b** $3\sqrt{10}$

4 a $6\sqrt{2} + 2\sqrt{5}$ **b** $-4 + 3\sqrt{7}$

5 a $\sqrt{14} - \sqrt{7}$ **b** $27 - 10\sqrt{2}$ **6 a** $5 + 2\sqrt{6}$ **b** -1

7 a $\frac{8\sqrt{3}}{3}$ **b** $\frac{\sqrt{91}}{13}$ **c** $\frac{17 - 7\sqrt{5}}{4}$

8 a $\frac{45}{11} + \frac{9}{11}\sqrt{3}$ **b** $-2 - \sqrt{3}$ **c** $\frac{1}{2} - \frac{1}{2}\sqrt{3}$

9 a i 10 and 2 **ii** 6 and $\frac{1}{2}$
b Let $\sqrt{a}\sqrt{b} = k$ where $a, b \in \mathbb{Z}^+, k \in \mathbb{Z}$
then $\frac{\sqrt{a}}{\sqrt{b}} = \frac{\sqrt{a}}{\sqrt{b}} \times \frac{\sqrt{b}}{\sqrt{b}} = \frac{\sqrt{a}\sqrt{b}}{b} = \frac{k}{b}$

10 $\frac{1 - 10\sqrt{2}}{7}$

EXERCISE 9A

1 a ≈ 6.32 m **b** ≈ 4.24 m **c** ≈ 10.0 cm
2 a 6 cm **b** ≈ 4.49 cm **c** ≈ 7.07 m
3 a ≈ 6.40 cm **b** ≈ 5.74 m **c** ≈ 4.36 cm
4 a $x = \sqrt{3}$ **b** $x = \frac{\sqrt{5}}{2}$ **c** $x - \sqrt{6}$
d $x = \frac{\sqrt{10}}{2}$ **e** $x = \frac{1}{2}$ **f** $x = \sqrt{6}$
5 a $x = 3\sqrt{3}$ **b** $x = 2\sqrt{13}$ **c** $x = 2$
6 a $x = \sqrt{5}, y = \sqrt{6}$ **b** $x = 5, y = \sqrt{26}$
c $x = 2\sqrt{51}$ **d** $x = \sqrt{37}$
e $x = \sqrt{13}, y = \sqrt{29}$ **f** $x = \sqrt{2}, y = \sqrt{3}, z = 2$

7 $AC = \sqrt{39}$ m ≈ 6.24 m

8
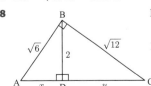
In $\triangle ABD$, $x^2 = 6 - 2^2$
$\therefore x = \sqrt{2}, x > 0$
In $\triangle BCD$,
$y^2 + 2^2 = 12$
$\therefore y = \sqrt{8}, y > 0$
In $\triangle ABC$, $AC^2 = (\sqrt{6})^2 + (\sqrt{12})^2 = 18$
$\therefore x + y = \sqrt{2} + \sqrt{8} = \sqrt{18}$

9 a $\sqrt{17}$ cm **b** $\sqrt{29}$ m **c** $\sqrt{41}$ m

EXERCISE 9B

1 **b**, **e**, **f** are right angled.   **2 a** $\widehat{BAC}$ **b** $\widehat{ABC}$ **c** $\widehat{ACB}$

3 $40^2 + 42^2 = 3364$, $58^2 = 3364$
  $\therefore$ the triangle is right angled.

4 **a** The ground is flat and the street lamp is straight.   **b** no

5 $AB = \sqrt{117}$ cm, $BC = \sqrt{52}$ cm
  $AB^2 + BC^2 = 169 = 13^2 = AC^2$
  $\therefore$ $\triangle ABC$ is right angled at B.

EXERCISE 9C

1 ≈ 8.54 cm   **2** ≈ 3.16 cm $\times \approx 9.49$ cm

3 a ≈ 53.7 cm   **b** 160 cm^2

4 ≈ 6.63 cm   **5** ≈ 7.07 cm   **6** ≈ 25.6 cm

7 a ≈ 15.8 km   **b** ≈ 22.4 km   **c** ≈ 22.4 km
  d ≈ 25.5 km   **e** ≈ 29.2 km   **f** ≈ 31.6 km

8 ≈ 4.59 m

9 a ≈ 36.7 km   **b** ≈ 1.02 hours (or 1 h 1 min 12 s)

10 $8^2 + 11.55^2 = 197.4025$ and $14.05^2 - 197.4025$
  $\therefore$ it is right angled.

11 a Train A: 135 km,   Train B: 210 km   **b** ≈ 250 km

12 ≈ 58.0 m

13 a ≈ 21.5 m   **b** 8 m   **c** ≈ 21.5 m   **d** ≈ 40.8 m

14 ≈ 8.66 cm   **15** 8 cm   **16** ≈ 7.52 m

17 ≈ 2.72 m   **18** ≈ 18.5 cm   **19** ≈ 2.24 km

20 ≈ 13.4 km   **21** 15 cm

22 When placed like this, the greatest length a stirrer could be and lie within the glass is 11.6 cm. So a 12 cm stirrer would go outside the glass.

23 ≈ 3.16 cm   **24** $2\sqrt{3}$ cm   **25** ≈ 6.80 m

26 No, the maximum length would be about 8.06 m.

27 ≈ 71 m   **28** ≈ 42.9 m

29 a The square base has right angles. The line from the vertex to the point of intersection of the diagonals of the base is at right angles to the base. The line from the vertex to the midpoint of each side of the base is at right angles to the base.
  b ≈ 32.2 m

30 $\sqrt{18} \approx 4.24$ cm   **31** $\sqrt{50^2 + (20\pi)^2} \approx 80.30$ m

REVIEW SET 9A

1 a $x \approx 6.71$ **b** $x \approx 12.09$ **c** $x \approx 5.66$ **2** ≈ 9.2 cm

3 a ≈ 12.6 km   **b** ≈ 14.4 km   **c** ≈ 16.5 km

4 a no, $8^2 + 9^2 \neq 11^2$ **b** yes, $(\sqrt{2})^2 + 3^2 = (\sqrt{11})^2$

5 ≈ 10.8 cm   **6 a** ≈ 2.68 m   **b** ≈ 9.88 m

7 Hint: Find the two lengths that make up the base of the triangle, then use Pythagoras in the largest triangle.

8 ≈ 7.54 m   **9** ≈ 5.77 m

REVIEW SET 9B

1 a $x \approx 4.24$ **b** $x \approx 7.81$ **c** $x \approx 1.41$

2 No, $(\sqrt{41})^2 + (\sqrt{61})^2 \neq 10^2$ **3** ≈ 42.4 m

4 a $x = 40$ **b** **i** ≈ 2.26 m   **ii** ≈ 9.05 m
  c ≈ 22.6 m

5 ≈ 2.37 m   **6** ≈ 21.5 m

7 a As $PQ^2 + QR^2 = PR^2$, the triangle is right angled.
    {converse of Pythagoras}
  b $\widehat{PQR}$

8 ≈ 17.7 m

EXERCISE 10A

1 a $A = 5 \times 15$ **b** $A = 5p$ **c** $A = tp$

2 a $A = 2000 + 150 \times 8$ **b** $A = 2000 + 150w$
  c $A = 2000 + dw$ **d** $A = P + dw$

3 a $C = 40 + 60 \times 5$ **b** $C = 40 + 60t$
  c $C = 40 + xt$ **d** $C = F + xt$

4 a $P = 3 \times 10 - 1(15 - 10)$ **b** $P = 3c - 1(20 - c)$
  c $P = 3c - 1(a - c)$

5 a $D = 4 \times 6 + 2 \times (4 - 1)$ **b** $D = 5m + 3 \times (5 - 1)$
  c $D = 8m + b(8 - 1)$ **d** $D = mp + b(p - 1)$

6 a $G = 2 \times (3 - 1) + 3 \times (2 - 1)$
  b $G = 3 \times (5 - 1) + 5 \times (3 - 1)$
  c $G = 4 \times (4 - 1) + 4 \times (4 - 1)$
  d $G = m(n - 1) + n(m - 1)$

EXERCISE 10B

1 a ≈ 26.4 cm   **b** ≈ 17.8 cm   **c** ≈ 127 m

2 a 19.6 m   **b** ≈ 4.52 s

3 a ≈ 129 cm^2 **b** ≈ 7.14 m

4 a ≈ 4260 cm^3 **b** ≈ 1.06 cm   **c** ≈ 4.99 mm

5 a ≈ 707 cm^2 **b** ≈ 39.9 cm

6 a ≈ 71.4 km/h   **b** 220 km   **c** ≈ 8 h 19 min

7 a ≈ 55.8 m^3 **b** ≈ 8.42 cm

8 a ≈ 1.34 s   **b** 81 cm

9 a ≈ 15.9 km   **b** ≈ 49.3 m

EXERCISE 10C

1 a $y = 7 - x$ **b** $y = x - 3$ **c** $y = \frac{1}{2} - \frac{1}{2}x$
  d $y = 2 - \frac{2}{5}x$ **e** $y = 5 - \frac{3}{4}x$ **f** $y = 2x - 8$
  g $y = 2 - \frac{2}{7}x$ **h** $y = 10 - \frac{5}{2}x$ **i** $y = \frac{2}{3}x + 4$

2 a $x = r - p$ **b** $x = \dfrac{z}{y}$ **c** $x = \dfrac{d - a}{3}$
  d $x = \dfrac{d - 2y}{5}$ **e** $x = \dfrac{p - by}{a}$ **f** $x = \dfrac{y - c}{m}$
  g $x = \dfrac{s - 2}{t}$ **h** $x = \dfrac{m - p}{q}$ **i** $x = \dfrac{6 - a}{b}$

3 a $y = \dfrac{t - z}{5}$ **b** $y = \dfrac{c - p}{2}$ **c** $y = \dfrac{a - t}{3}$
  d $y = \dfrac{n - 5}{k}$ **e** $y = \dfrac{a - n}{b}$ **f** $y = \dfrac{a - p}{n}$
  g $y = \dfrac{4 - c}{x}$ **h** $y = \dfrac{6 - w}{a}$ **i** $y = \dfrac{m + k}{t}$

4 a $z = \dfrac{b}{ac}$ **b** $z = \dfrac{q}{p}$ **c** $z = \dfrac{a}{d}$
  d $z = \dfrac{2d}{3}$ **e** $z = \dfrac{7n}{k}$ **f** $z = -\dfrac{pt}{q}$
  g $z = \pm\sqrt{2a}$ **h** $z = \pm\sqrt{bn}$ **i** $z = \pm\sqrt{m(a - b)}$

5 a $a = \dfrac{F}{m}$ **b** $r = \dfrac{C}{2\pi}$ **c** $d = \dfrac{V}{lh}$
  d $K = \dfrac{b}{A}$ **e** $h = \dfrac{2A}{b}$ **f** $T = \dfrac{100I}{PR}$
  g $m = \dfrac{E}{c^2}$ **h** $a = 2M - b$

6 $h = \dfrac{A - 2\pi r^2}{2\pi r}$ or $h = \dfrac{A}{2\pi r} - r$

7 **a** $r = \sqrt{\dfrac{A}{\pi}}$ **b** $x = \pm\sqrt{aN}$ **c** $k = \pm\sqrt{\dfrac{M}{5}}$

     d $x = \sqrt[3]{\dfrac{n}{D}}$ **e** $x = -\sqrt{\dfrac{y+7}{4}}$ **f** $Q = \pm\sqrt{P^2 - R^2}$

8 **a** $a = d^2 n^2$ **b** $l = 25T^2$ **c** $a = \pm\sqrt{b^2 + c^2}$

     d $d = \dfrac{25a^2}{k^2}$ **e** $l = \dfrac{gT^2}{4\pi^2}$ **f** $b = \dfrac{16a}{A^2}$

9 **a** $x = \dfrac{c-a}{3-b}$ **b** $x = \dfrac{c}{a+b}$ **c** $x = \dfrac{a+2}{n-m}$

     d $x = -\dfrac{a}{b+8}$ **e** $x = \dfrac{a-b}{1-c}$ **f** $x = \dfrac{e-d}{r+s}$

10 **a** $x = \dfrac{1-4y}{3}$ **b** $x = \dfrac{6+z}{7}$ **c** $x = \dfrac{5a+b}{b-a}$

     d $x = \dfrac{k-7}{2k-1}$ **e** $x = \dfrac{6}{2-3y}$ **f** $x = \dfrac{2m}{4m+n}$

11 **a** $a = \dfrac{2-bP}{P}$ **b** $r = \dfrac{8-qT}{T}$ **c** $q = \dfrac{Ap-B}{A}$

     d $x = \dfrac{3-Ay}{2A}$ **e** $y = \sqrt{\dfrac{4-Mx^2}{M}}$

12 **a** $x = \dfrac{y}{1-y}$ **b** $x = \dfrac{2y+3}{1-y}$ **c** $x = \dfrac{3y+1}{3-y}$

     d $x = \dfrac{y-2}{y-5}$ **e** $x = \dfrac{2y+1}{y+4}$ **f** $x = \dfrac{3y-7}{2y+3}$

     g $x = \dfrac{3y-1}{y-1}$ **h** $x = -\dfrac{4y+3}{y+2}$ **i** $x = \dfrac{2y}{y+3}$

EXERCISE 10D

1 **a** $\theta = \dfrac{360A}{\pi r^2}$ **b** **i** $\approx 63.7°$ **ii** $\approx 105°$ **iii** $\approx 214°$

2 **a** $a = \dfrac{d^2}{2bK}$ **b** **i** $a = \tfrac{9}{7}$ **ii** $a = \tfrac{81}{5}$

3 **a** $t = (H-1)^2$

     b **i** 1 year   **ii** 4 years   **iii** $6\tfrac{1}{4}$ years

4 **a** $r = \sqrt[3]{\dfrac{3V}{4\pi}}$

     b **i** ≈ 2.12 cm   **ii** ≈ 5.76 cm   **iii** ≈ 62.0 cm

5 **a** $v = \sqrt{u^2 + 2as}$ **b** **i** ≈ 20.6 m/s   **ii** ≈ 52.9 m/s

6 **a** $\approx 58.8\%$ **b** $w = \dfrac{Pl}{100-P}$ **c** 9 matches

     d 7 consecutive matches

7 **a** $\approx 2.01 \times 10^{20}$ Newtons   **b** $d = \sqrt{\dfrac{Gm_1 m_2}{F}}$

     c **i** $\approx 1.50 \times 10^{11}$ m   **ii** $\approx 1.43 \times 10^{14}$ m

8 **b** $p = \dfrac{3g}{g-1}$ **c** $0g$ $0p$, $4g$ $4p$

9 **a** $v = \sqrt{c^2\left(1 - \dfrac{m_0^2}{m^2}\right)} = \dfrac{c}{m}\sqrt{m^2 - m_0^2}$

     b $v = \dfrac{\sqrt{8}}{3}c$ **c** 2.998×10^8 m/s

REVIEW SET 10A

1 **a** **i** $V = 6 \times 8$ litres   **ii** $V = 8n$ litres

     iii $V = ln$ litres

     b $V = 25 + ln$ litres

2 **a** ≈ 11.4 g/cm^3 **b** 37.94 g   **c** ≈ 9230 cm^3

3 **a** $x = \dfrac{3p-n}{m}$ **b** $x = \dfrac{5y}{7}$ **c** $x = \dfrac{2y-3}{y-2}$

4 **a** $k = T^2 + l^2$ **b** $k = -\sqrt{\dfrac{P+r}{2}}$

5 **a** $c = -3$ **b** $c = 6$ **c** $c = -10$

6 **a** 8 amperes   **b** $r = \dfrac{E-IR}{I}$ **c** 0.15 ohms

7 **a** **i** ≈ 283.2 K   **ii** ≈ 183.2 K   **iii** ≈ 338.7 K

     b $F = \tfrac{9}{5}(K - 273.15) + 32$

     c **i** $104°$F   **ii** $-459.67°$F   **iii** $-99.67°$F

REVIEW SET 10B

1 **a** $B = 15 + 25 \times 5$ **b** $B = s + 25p$ **c** $B = s + mp$

2 **a** $E = 2 \times (3-2) + 2 \times (5-2)$

     b $E = 2 \times (4-2) + 2 \times (8-2)$

     c $E = 2(m-2) + 2(n-2)$

3 **a** $M = 37$ **b** $r = 8$

4 **a** 204 800 units   **b** ≈ 7.75 cm

5 **a** $a = \dfrac{B+f}{d}$ **b** $a = \dfrac{9Q^2}{t^2}$ **c** $a = \dfrac{5-G^2}{G^2}$

6 ≈ 4.46 cm   **7** **a** 1000 joules   **b** $v = \sqrt{\dfrac{2E}{m}}$ **c** 8 m/s

EXERCISE 11A

1 **a** 38.8 cm   **b** 17.8 cm   **c** 11.9 km   **d** 29 m

     e 11.6 cm   **f** 30 m   **g** 17.6 m   **h** 99.6 km   **i** 19.1 m

2 **a** ≈ 50.3 cm   **b** ≈ 3.39 m   **c** ≈ 34.6 cm

3 **a** ≈ 10.7 m   **b** ≈ 441 m   **c** ≈ 14.3 cm

4 **a** ≈ 85.7 cm   **b** ≈ 22.8 cm   **c** ≈ 75.4 cm

5 11.1 cm   **6** 18.8 cm

7 **a** ≈ 8.09 cm   **b** ≈ 19.6 mm   **c** ≈ 8.09 cm

8 38.4 m   **9** **a** ≈ 13.1 cm   **b** ≈ 17.6 m

10 **a** $P = 2x + y$ cm   **b** $P = 2(2x + 3)$ m

     c $P = 2\pi r + 2d$ m

11 **a** **i** ≈ 565.5 m   **ii** ≈ 502.7 m   **b** ≈ 62.8 m

12 **a** 69.38 m   **b** 146.08 m   **13** \$1531.53

14 **a** ≈ 16.8 cm   **b** ≈ 30.6 cm   **15** ≈ 20.9 cm

16 155 cm   **17** **a** ≈ 39.0 m   **b** 14 posts   **c** \$936.16

EXERCISE 11B

1 **a** 49 cm^2 **b** 7.5 mm^2 **c** 13 cm^2

     d 186.34 mm^2 **e** 5.46 cm^2 **f** 1.02 m^2

2 **a** 30 cm^2 **b** ≈ 31.2 cm^2 **c** ≈ 26.9 cm^2

3 **a** $h = 6$ **b** $h = 3.6$ **c** $h = 5$

4 The square has greater area (306.25 cm^2).
     Area of rectangle is 300 cm^2.

5 **a** ≈ 6.09 m^2 **b** ≈ 7.31 m^2 **c** \$207.68

6 5.09 m^2 **7** 375 tiles   **8** 48 cm^2 **9** ≈ 5.66 cm

10 144 cm^2 **11** **a** 80 cm^2 **b** $\tfrac{1}{2}ab$ cm^2 **12** $5\tfrac{1}{3}$ cm

13 ≈ 9.98 cm^2 **14** ≈ 27.4 mm

15 **a** 112 m^2 **b** 74 m^2 **c** 84 cm^2

     d 31.5 cm^2 **e** 189 cm^2 **f** 36 cm^2

16 **a** 160 tiles   **b** \$1504   **17** $\approx 25.5\%$

18 **a** $A = \dfrac{a^2\sqrt{3}}{4}$ **b** $A = b\sqrt{a^2 - b^2}$

     c $A = \tfrac{1}{2}\left(ab + c\sqrt{a^2 + b^2 - c^2}\right)$

19 204 m^2

EXERCISE 11C

1   **a** ≈ 314 cm^2 **b** ≈ 468 m^2 **c** ≈ 73.9 cm^2
2   **a** ≈ 56.5 m^2 **b** ≈ 12.6 cm^2 **c** ≈ 26.2 m^2
    d ≈ 30.2 cm^2
3   **a** ≈ 22.1 m^2 **b** ≈ 139 cm^2
4   **a** $\frac{4}{3}\pi$ cm   **b** $16 + \frac{4}{3}\pi$ cm   **c** $\frac{16}{3}\pi$ cm^2
5   **a** ≈ 3.18 cm   **b** ≈ 2.52 cm   **c** 3 m
6   $\approx 23.9°$ 7 ≈ 154 m^2
8   **a** ≈ 6.85 cm^2 **b** ≈ 30.6 cm^2 **c** ≈ 30.9 cm^2
    d ≈ 6430 m^2 **e** ≈ 113 cm^2 **f** ≈ 36.9 cm^2
9   ≈ 2.85 m^2 10 $\approx 46.2\%$ 11 $\approx 21.5\%$
12   **a** ≈ 9.42 m^2 **b** \$74.46
13   **a** $P \approx 34.6$ cm, $A \approx 77.9$ cm^2
    b $P \approx 62.8$ cm, $A \approx 157$ cm^2
    c $P \approx 37.7$ cm, $A \approx 37.7$ cm^2
14   **a** ≈ 731 m   **b** ≈ 3480 m^2
15   **a** $A - 2ab + \pi a^2$ **b** $A = \pi(R^2 - r^2)$
    c $A = (x + 2a)^2 - \pi a^2$ **d** $A = 2ar - \pi r^2$
    e $A = (5 + \pi)a^2$ **f** $A = (\sqrt{3} + \frac{\pi}{2})x^2$
16   $\approx 18.2\%$
17   **a** ≈ 108 cm   **b** ≈ 3.27 cm
    c **i** ≈ 1.13 cm^2 **ii** ≈ 6.91 cm^2 **iii** ≈ 39.3 cm^2
        iv ≈ 43.6 cm^2 **v** ≈ 46.1 cm^2

REVIEW SET 11A

1   **a** $P = 42$ m, $A = 60$ m^2
    b $P \approx 256$ mm, $A \approx 3320$ mm^2
    c $P = 28$ cm, $A = 40$ cm^2 **d** $P = 9.2$ m, $A \approx 4.51$ m^2
2   **a** 9.1 m   **b** \$305   3 ≈ 565 m
4   **a** ≈ 105 cm^2 **b** 30 cm^2 **c** ≈ 177 cm^2
5   1273 revolutions
6   **a** ≈ 1.60 m   **b** ≈ 10.0 m   7 $\approx 262°$
8   **a** $P = a + h + \sqrt{h^2 - a^2}$ cm, $A = \frac{1}{2}a\sqrt{h^2 - a^2}$ cm^2
    b $P = (10 + \pi)x$ m, $A = (8 + \frac{\pi}{2})x^2$ m^2
9   Area $= \frac{1}{2} \times 12 \times 5$ or $\frac{1}{2} \times 13 \times d$,   and so on.

REVIEW SET 11B

1   **a** $P \approx 20.8$ cm, $A \approx 20$ cm^2
    b $P \approx 19.8$ m, $A \approx 22.5$ m^2
    c $P \approx 41.7$ cm, $A \approx 37.7$ cm^2
    d $P \approx 85.1$ cm, $A \approx 267$ cm^2
2   ≈ 31.9 cm   3 ≈ 2.43 m^2 4   6 hectares
5   **a** $\frac{3}{8}$ **b** ≈ 52.3 cm   **c** ≈ 170 cm^2
6   **a** ≈ 6.49 m   **b** ≈ 132 m^2 7 ≈ 10.8 km
8   **a** $A = (4 + \frac{\pi}{2})x^2$ **b** $A = (2 - \frac{\pi}{4})x^2$
    c $A = \left(\dfrac{a+b}{2}\right)h + bc$
9   $P = \pi$ m, $A = (\frac{\pi}{2} - 1)$ m^2

EXERCISE 12A.1

1   **a** 54 cm^2 **b** 121.5 cm^2 **c** 576.24 mm^2
2   **a** 276 cm^2 **b** 6880 mm^2 **c** 8802 m^2
3   **a** ≈ 198 m^2 **b** ≈ 496 cm^2 **c** ≈ 148 cm^2
4   **a** 360 cm^2 **b** 340 m^2 **c** ≈ 9840 cm^2
5   **a** 576 cm^2 **b** 384 m^2 **c** ≈ 823 m^2
    d ≈ 1.73 m^2 **e** $\approx 63\,500$ cm^2

6   1160 cm^2 7   **a** ≈ 1011 m^2 **b** $\approx \$25\,300$
8   \$3717   9   26.52 m^2 10   167.4 m^2
11   **a** $A = 2(ab + ac + bc)$ **b** $A = 8ab + 6a^2$
    c $A = a\sqrt{4b^2 - a^2} + a^2$

EXERCISE 12A.2

1   **a** ≈ 207 cm^2 **b** ≈ 339 cm^2 **c** ≈ 196 cm^2
    d ≈ 56.7 m^2 **e** ≈ 124 m^2 **f** ≈ 79.5 cm^2
2   **a** ≈ 707 m^2 **b** ≈ 145 km^2 **c** ≈ 84.8 cm^2
3   **a** ≈ 204 cm^2 **b** ≈ 56.5 m^2 **c** ≈ 298 cm^2
    d ≈ 49.5 mm^2 **e** ≈ 302 cm^2 **f** ≈ 95.1 m^2
4   **a** ≈ 1640 cm^2 **b** ≈ 758 cm^2 **c** ≈ 452 cm^2
    d ≈ 942 m^2 **e** ≈ 603 cm^2
5   **a** $s \approx 5.39$ **b** ≈ 33.8 cm^2
6   **a** ≈ 251 m^2 **b** 11 cans   **c** \$577.50
7   **a** ≈ 5.64 m   **b** ≈ 21.8 cm   **c** ≈ 25.8 m
8   **a** $\approx 5.15 \times 10^8$ km^2 **b** $\approx 3.65 \times 10^8$ km^2
    c **i** $\approx 1.89\%$ **ii** $\approx 6.50\%$
9   **a** ≈ 179.1 cm^2 **b** ≈ 238.8 cm^2 **c** ≈ 216.8 cm^2
10   \$1100   11 ≈ 213 cm^2
12   **a** $A = 8\pi r^2$ **b** $A = \pi r(r + 2h + s)$
    c $A = 6r^2 + 10rh + 4\pi r^2$
    d $A = \frac{1}{2}\pi r^2 + rh + \frac{1}{2}\pi r\sqrt{h^2 + r^2}$

EXERCISE 12B.1

1   **a** 96 m^3 **b** 343 mm^3 **c** 12 cm^3
2   **a** ≈ 352 cm^3 **b** ≈ 35.3 m^3 **c** ≈ 1.54 m^3
3   **a** 45 cm^3 **b** 320 cm^3 **c** 704 cm^3
    d 432 cm^3 **e** 288 cm^3 **f** ≈ 2320 cm^3
4   **a** 2000 cm^3 **b** ≈ 0.982 cm^3 **c** ≈ 183 cm^3
    d 2196 cm^3 **e** ≈ 2380 cm^3
5   15 915 handles   6   **a** 32.5 m^2 **b** 195 m^3
7   **a** **i** ≈ 3.93 m^3 **ii** ≈ 9.05 m^3 **b** ≈ 13.0 m^3
    c \$1846 (buy 13 m^3)
8   **a** ≈ 5.94 m^2 **b** ≈ 3.56 m^3
9   **a** $V = \frac{1}{4}\pi d^2 h$ **b** $V = \frac{1}{2}abc$ **c** $V = c(a^2 - b^2)$

EXERCISE 12B.2

1   **a** 32 m^3 **b** ≈ 66.0 cm^3 **c** 120 cm^3 **d** ≈ 233 m^3
2   **a** ≈ 37.7 m^3 **b** ≈ 738 cm^3 **c** ≈ 42.7 m^3
    d ≈ 1.89 m^3
3   4500 m^3 4 ≈ 2.48 m^3 5 ≈ 258 cm^3
6   611 garden stakes   7 ≈ 1.79 m high   8 $V = \frac{1}{12}\pi d^3$

EXERCISE 12B.3

1   **a** ≈ 268 cm^3 **b** ≈ 102 cm^3 **c** ≈ 82.3 cm^3
    d ≈ 1.07 m^3
2   **a** ≈ 80.4 cm^3 **b** ≈ 101 m^3 **c** ≈ 22.4 m^3
3   ≈ 0.905 m^3 4 ≈ 0.116 m^3 5 ≈ 15.0 cm^3
6   **a** 30.912 cm^3 **b** ≈ 905 mm^3 **c** 34 spheres
    d $\approx 0.484\%$
7   **a** $V = \pi r^2(h + \frac{2}{3}r)$ **b** $V = x^3(1 + \frac{\pi}{12})$

EXERCISE 12C

1   **a** 24 ml   **b** ≈ 23.6 ml   **c** ≈ 9.11 ml   **d** 300 000 litres
2   368 bottles   3 ≈ 24.4 ml   4 ≈ 817 ml
5   ≈ 12.7 cm   6   **a** 13 500 m^2 **b** $\approx 23\,000\,000$ litres
7   **a** ≈ 53.8 litres   **b** ≈ 618 km

8 $\approx 1\,410\,000$ litres   **9** ≈ 888 ml

10 a 1000 cm^3 **b** ≈ 6.20 cm   **c** ≈ 484 cm^2

11 ≈ 0.707 m   **12 a** $\approx 18\,100$ litres   **b** ≈ 0.177 m

13 ≈ 3.07 cm

14 a $(1 + \frac{\pi}{4})a^3$ m^3 **b** $a \approx 6.05$

   c Each 4 m^2 of floor space has a "double bunk" bed.

15 $\frac{91}{108}$ cm

EXERCISE 12D

1 a ≈ 1.26 g per cm^3 **b** ≈ 1.08 g per cm^3

2 a 2.25 g per cm^3 **b** 20 g per cm^3

3 ≈ 312 cm^3 **4** ≈ 569 g   **5** ≈ 19.3 g per cm^3

6 ≈ 4.90 cm   **7** $\approx 472\,000$ beads

8 a ≈ 2.54 cm^2 **b** ≈ 6360 cm^3 **c** ≈ 9.54 kg

9 $4\,240\,000$ t

10 a **i** $A = (4 + 3\pi)a^2 + 8ab$ cm^2

   ii $V = a^2(4b + \pi a)$ cm^3 **iii** $M = a^2d(4b + \pi a)$ g

   b **i** $A = 5\pi x^2$ cm^2 **ii** $V = \frac{5}{3}\pi x^3$ cm^3

   iii $M = \frac{5}{3}\pi dx^3$ g

REVIEW SET 12A

1 a 182.88 cm^2 **b** ≈ 2630 mm^2 **c** ≈ 102 cm^2

2 a ≈ 729 cm^3 **b** ≈ 303 cm^3 **c** ≈ 65.4 cm^3

3 a ≈ 209 cm^3 **b** ≈ 227 cm^2 **4** ≈ 1.24 cm

5 a 5196 cans   **b** ≈ 154 m^2

6 a ≈ 212 m^2 **b** $\approx 46\,700$ m^3 **c** $\approx \$11\,900\,000$

7 a $375\,000$ litres   **b** $350\,000$ litres   **8** ≈ 1.24 m

9 a $V = \left(\dfrac{\theta}{360}\right) \times \pi r^2 h$

   b $A = \left(\dfrac{\theta}{360}\right) \times 2\pi r(r + h) + 2hr$

10 a $\approx 2\,460\,000$ m^3 **b** $\approx 6.56 \times 10^6$ tonnes

   c $\approx 327\,000$ litres

REVIEW SET 12B

1 a ≈ 138 mm^2 **b** ≈ 692 cm^2 **c** 3024 m^2

   d ≈ 37.7 m^2

2 a $\approx 10\,900$ km   **b** $\approx 3.79 \times 10^7$ km^2

3 a ≈ 339 cm^3 **b** ≈ 1270 cm^3 **c** $\approx 14\,100$ cm^3

4 2842 m^3 **5 a** $A = 16x^2$ **b** $A = 6\pi x^2$ **c** $A = 7x^2$

6 ≈ 3.99 cm   **7** slant length is 3 m   **8** no

9 a 4 m   **b** ≈ 527 m^2

10 a $\approx 23\,979.2$ cm^3 **b** ≈ 5184.2 cm^2 **c** $\approx 19\,423.2$ g

11 $\approx 53\,100\,000$ litres

EXERCISE 13A

1 a 9 **b** 7 **c** 9 **d** $\$1512$ **e** $\$750$ **f** 4.75 tonnes

   g 3.8 m   **h** 5600 ml   **i** 18.69 tonnes

   j $\$16\,469.78$ **k** 9 min   **l** 290 kg

2 7 sweets   **3** 132 seeds   **4** 54 laps

5 a 2.16 kg   **b** 69.84 kg

6 a $\$345$ **b** $\$4355$ **c** $\approx 7.34\%$

EXERCISE 13B.1

1 a 1.3 **b** 0.9 **c** 1.15 **d** 0.65 **e** 1.12

   f 0.925

2 $\$4.20$/kg   **3** $\$64\,800$ **4** 800 kg   **5** 44 minutes

6 772.8 m

EXERCISE 13B.2

1 a 10% increase   **b** 15% decrease   **c** 40% decrease

   d 50% increase

2 a 15% increase   **b** 28% decrease   **c** 7.5% increase

   d 12.5% decrease

3 a **i** $\approx 36.2\%$ **ii** $\approx 19.0\%$ **iii** $\approx 13.8\%$

   b $\approx 84.5\%$

4 a Germany: $\approx 0.364\%$ increase, Italy: $\approx 4.30\%$ increase,
   France: $\approx 5.19\%$ increase, Spain: $\approx 4.25\%$ increase,
   Greece: $\approx 2.73\%$ decrease, Portugal: $\approx 1.90\%$ decrease,
   United Kingdom: $\approx 7.89\%$ increase

   b **i** United Kingdom   **ii** Greece

5 21% **6 a** 20% **b** 36%

EXERCISE 13C

1 75 marks   **2** 620 students   **3** 40 kg

4 a $\$4700$ **b** $\$235$ **5** 2250 m

6 a 20 cm   **b** 60 kg   **c** $\$125$

   d 4000 litres   **e** $50\,000$ people

7 $\$950$ **8** $\$8400$

9 ≈ 2475 black rhinoceroses   **10** $\$420$

EXERCISE 13D

1 a $\$37$ **b** $\approx 38.9\%$ **2 a** $\$60$ **b** $\approx 33.3\%$

3 80% **4 a** $\$812.50$ **b** $\$377.50$ **c** $\approx 86.8\%$

5 a $\$4600$ **b** $\approx 25.3\%$ **6 a** $\$470$ **b** $\approx 32.4\%$

7 a $\$1.60$ **b** $\$1.25$ **c** $\approx 78.1\%$

8 a $\$140\,300$ **b** $\approx 23.4\%$

9 $\$24$ **10** $\$225$ **11** $\$180$ **12** $\$34.50$ per kg

EXERCISE 13E

1 $\$40.92$ **2** ≈ 125 cm   **3** $\$504$ **4** $27\,025$ people

5 $\$42$ **6 a** $\$336\,000$ **b** $\approx \$310\,000$

7 $\$1.40$ **8** 9.18% **9** 20% mark-up   **10** ≈ 3.61 kg

11 No, $0.87 \times 1.13 \approx 0.9831$
   So the yield after 2 years is only 98.31% of the original yield.

12 No, $1.2 \times 1.2 \times 1.2 = 1.728$
   Julia's allowance will be 72.8% higher when she is 12.

EXERCISE 13F

1 a $\$600$ **b** $\$400$ **2 a** $\$6000$ **b** $\$3750$

3 a $\$3120$ **b** $\$14\,720$ **4 a** $\$7912.50$ **b** $\$23\,115$

5 a $\$31\,000$ **b** $\$645.84$

6 a $\$8695$ **b** $\$144.92$ **7** 5 years   **8** $\$3500$

9 a The simple interest earned in one year is $P \times r$.
   $\therefore$ the total interest earned over n years $I = Prn$.

   b **i** $\$432$ **ii** 1.8% **iii** $2\frac{1}{2}$ years

EXERCISE 13G

1 $\$4410$ **2 a** $\$7498.58$ **b** $\$498.58$

3 a $\$7311.62$ **b** $\$811.62$ **4** $\$1270.50$

5 a $\$7827.36$ **b** $\approx 26.2\%$

6 a $\$9478.84$ **b** 5 years

7 a Option 1: $\$10\,160$ after 3 years
   Option 2: $\$10\,077.70$ after 3 years
   Option 1 should be chosen as you would have about $\$82$
   more than option 2.

   b Yes. Option 1: $\$11\,600$,   Option 2: $\approx \$11\,754.62$
   After 5 years, option 2 would be worth $\$154.62$ more than
   option 1.

8 a $\$2407.26$ **b** Yes, but only by about $\$23.75$.

9 a After n years, the amount in the account would be

$$A = 5000 \times \underbrace{1.04 \times 1.04 \times .... \times 1.04}_{n \text{ times}}$$

$$= 5000 \times 1.04^n$$

b i $5624.32   **ii** $6579.66   **c** 12 years

10 $\approx 5.84\%$ **11** $\approx 20.6\%$ **12** $\approx 12.0\%$

REVIEW SET 13A

1 a $12   **b** 52 ml   **c** 64 kg

2 a $2900   **b** 58.5 kg   **3** ≈ 6.05 m   **4** $290

5 $\approx 11.1\%$ **6** $68   **7** $\approx 180\%$ increase

8 $38.50   **9** 4 hectares   **10** $840

11 a $6700   **b** $139.59

12 a $10\,099.82   **b** $2099.82

13 a As the caravan is depreciating, its value is multiplied by 0.84 each year. After n years, the value of the caravan will be

$$V = 15\,000 \times \underbrace{0.84 \times 0.84 \times .... \times 0.84}_{n \text{ times}}$$

$$= 15\,000 \times 0.84^n$$

b $6273.18   **c** 7 years

REVIEW SET 13B

1 51 000 people

2

Offence	Old fine	New fine
Speeding	$200	$210
Drink driving	$840	$882
Not wearing seatbelt	$260	$273
Illegal parking	$50	$52.50

3 $41.65   **4** 6 cm   **5 a** $350   **b** $\approx 21.2\%$

6 a $513   **b** $384.75   **7** $70\,400   **8** $52.46

9 $80   **10 a** $\approx 26.0\%$ **b** 1950 customers

11 a $1896.26   **b** $396.26   **12** $20\,100

13 a $34\,333.36   **b** 7 years

EXERCISE 14A

1 P(4, 2), Q(−1, −3), R(3, −1), S(−2, 5), T(7, −3)

2 a

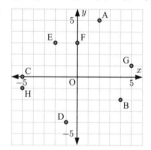

b A - first,
B - fourth,
C - on x-axis,
D - third,
E - second,
F - on y-axis,
G - first,
H - third

3 a quadrants 1 and 3   **b** quadrants 2 and 4

4 a

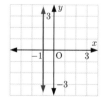

b

All points on a vertical line 1 unit left of the y-axis.

All points on a horizontal line 3 units above the x-axis.

c

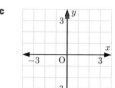

All points on the y-axis.

d

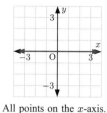

All points on the x-axis.

e

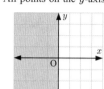

All points left of the y-axis.

f

All points above the x-axis.

g

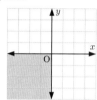

All points in quadrant 3.

h

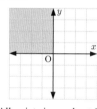

All points in quadrant 2.

5 a P(5, 1), Q(4, 3)   **b** R(0, 1)   **c** S(4, −1)

EXERCISE 14B

1 a $2\sqrt{2}$ units   **b** 7 units   **c** $2\sqrt{5}$ units   **d** $3\sqrt{5}$ units

e 7 units   **f** $\sqrt{5}$ units   **g** $\sqrt{10}$ units   **h** $\frac{\sqrt{5}}{2}$ units

2 a $10\sqrt{2} \approx 14.1$ km   **b** $20\sqrt{5} \approx 44.7$ km

c $10\sqrt{26} \approx 51.0$ km

3 a isosceles with AB = AC = $\sqrt{85}$ units   **b** scalene

c isosceles (and right angled at B) with AB = BC

d isosceles with BC = AC = $\sqrt{7}$ units

e equilateral, all sides $2\sqrt{3}$ units

f isosceles (AC = BC) if $b \neq 2 \pm a\sqrt{3}$
equilateral if $b = 2 \pm a\sqrt{3}$

4 a right angled at B   **b** not right angled

c right angled at A   **d** not right angled

5 a $a = 2$

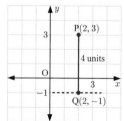

b $a = -5$ or 3

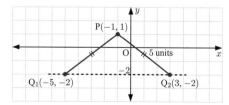

c $a = \pm 2$

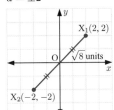

d $a = -1$

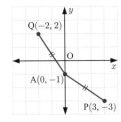

6 a   i $x^2 + y^2 = 9$ **ii** $(x-1)^2 + (y-3)^2 = 4$

b

This set represents a circle with centre $(0, 0)$ and radius 1 unit.

7 Let R be $(a, 0)$. Find PQ, PR, and RQ.
Solve PQ = PR, PQ = RQ, PR = RQ.
$(10, 0)$, $(-8, 0)$, $(-3, 0)$, $(-7, 0)$, and $(-\frac{101}{12}, 0)$

EXERCISE 14C

1 a $(-1\frac{1}{2}, 3\frac{1}{2})$ **b** $(-1, -2)$ **c** $(1, 1\frac{1}{2})$ **d** $(2, 1)$
  e $(1, -1\frac{1}{2})$ **f** $(-4, 1\frac{1}{2})$ **g** $(-4\frac{1}{2}, \frac{1}{2})$ **h** $(-1\frac{1}{2}, \frac{1}{2})$

2 a $(5, 3)$ **b** $(1, -1)$ **c** $(1\frac{1}{2}, 3)$ **d** $(0, 4)$
  e $(2, -1\frac{1}{2})$ **f** $(1, 2\frac{1}{2})$

3 a B$(0, -6)$ **b** B$(5, -2)$ **c** B$(0, 6)$ **d** B$(0, 7)$
  e B$(-7, 3)$ **f** B$(-3, 0)$

4 C$(1, -3)$ **5** P$(7, -3)$ **6** S$(-2, 0)$

7 $\frac{\sqrt{89}}{2} \approx 4.72$ units   **8** $a = \frac{7}{3}$, $b = \frac{11}{2}$

9 Hint: Let the vertices be A(a, b), B(c, d), C(e, f).
Use the midpoint formula to find six simple equations and solve them simultaneously.
Points are $(3, -1)$, $(7, 9)$, $(9, 1)$.

EXERCISE 14D.1

1 a $\frac{2}{3}$ **b** -1 **c** $\frac{1}{3}$ **d** $-\frac{4}{3}$ **e** $\frac{1}{6}$
  f undefined **g** -3 **h** $-\frac{1}{8}$ **i** 0

2 a   **b**   **c**   **d**
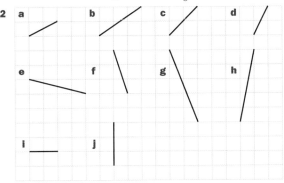
  e   **f**   **g**   **h**
  i   **j**

3 a

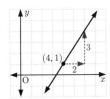

b

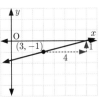

c

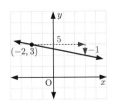

d

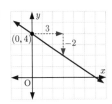

4

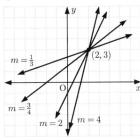

5

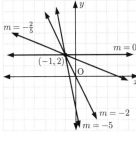

EXERCISE 14D.2

1 $\frac{4}{7}$

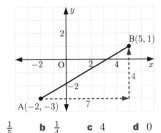

2 a $\frac{1}{5}$ **b** $\frac{1}{4}$ **c** 4 **d** 0 **e** undefined
  f $\frac{2}{7}$ **g** $-\frac{2}{7}$ **h** 1 **i** $-\frac{4}{3}$

3 a $t = 19$ **b** $t = \frac{29}{2}$ **c** $t = \frac{13}{3}$ **d** $t = \frac{2}{3}$
  e $t = 9$ **f** $t = 5$

4 R$(\frac{28}{3}, 0)$

EXERCISE 14E

1 a -2 **b** $-\frac{5}{2}$ **c** $-\frac{1}{3}$ **d** $-\frac{1}{7}$ **e** $\frac{5}{2}$ **f** $\frac{2}{7}$
  g $\frac{3}{4}$ **h** 1

2 The line pairs in **c**, **d**, **f**, and **h** are perpendicular.

3 a AB: $\frac{3}{5}$, BC: -2, CD: $\frac{9}{2}$, DE: $-\frac{1}{2}$, EF: -2, FA: 2
  b i BC ∥ EF   **ii** DE ⊥ FA

4 a $a = 9$ **b** $a = 1$ **c** $a = 6\frac{1}{3}$

5 a $t = \frac{1}{5}$ **b** $t = 5$ **c** $t = 3\frac{3}{5}$

6 a $t = 4$ **b** $t = 4$ **c** $t = 14$ **d** $t = 3\frac{1}{7}$

7 $k = -2$

EXERCISE 14F

1 a gradient of AB $= \frac{4}{3}$, gradient of BC $= \frac{5}{4}$
    ∴ not collinear
  b gradient of PQ = gradient of QR $= \frac{6}{5}$
    ∴ P, Q, R are collinear
  c gradient of RS $= -\frac{3}{11}$, gradient of ST $= -\frac{3}{2}$
    ∴ not collinear
  d gradient of AB = gradient of BC $= 3$
    ∴ A, B, C are collinear

2 a $c = 3$ **b** $c = -5$

EXERCISE 14G

1 **a** PQ = PR = $2\sqrt{5}$ units
     b M(4, 4)
     c gradient of PM = $-\frac{1}{3}$,
         gradient of QR = 3,
         and their product is -1
         $\therefore$ PM $\perp$ QR
     d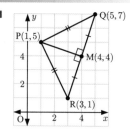

2 M(0, 3) and N(3, 3)
     a gradient of MN = 0,   gradient of AC = 0
         $\therefore$ MN $\parallel$ AC
     b MN = 3 units   and   AC = 6 units $\therefore$ MN = $\frac{1}{2}$(AC)

3 **a** All sides have length 5 units. $\therefore$ ABCD is a rhombus.
     b (2, 1) and (2, 1)
     c gradient of AC = -2,
         gradient of BD = $\frac{1}{2}$
         and their product = -1
         $\therefore$ AC $\perp$ BD
     d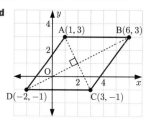

4 **a** M(1, -4)
     b gradient of AM = gradient of MC = 1, $\therefore$ collinear
     c gradient of AC = 1,   gradient of BD = -1,
         $\therefore$ perpendicular

5 **a** **i** P(0, 5)   **ii** Q(4$\frac{1}{2}$, 2)   **iii** R($\frac{1}{2}$, $-2\frac{1}{2}$)
         iv S(-4, $\frac{1}{2}$)
     b **i** $-\frac{2}{3}$ **ii** $\frac{9}{8}$ **iii** $-\frac{2}{3}$ **iv** $\frac{9}{8}$
     c PQRS is a parallelogram.

6 **a** s = 6   **b** **i** $\frac{1}{2}$ **ii** -2
     c gradient of PS $\times$ gradient of SQ = -1
         $\therefore$ $\widehat{PSQ}$ = 90°

7 **a** B($a + b$, c)   **b** midpoint of AC is $\left(\dfrac{a+b}{2}, \dfrac{c}{2}\right)$
         midpoint of OB is $\left(\dfrac{a+b}{2}, \dfrac{c}{2}\right)$
     c The diagonals of a parallelogram bisect each other.

REVIEW SET 14A

1
     2 **a** 5 units   **b** $\sqrt{13}$ units
     3 (5, -1)
     4 **a** $\frac{2}{5}$ **b** $-\frac{15}{4}$

5 **a** isosceles with AB = BC = $\sqrt{65}$ units, AC = $\sqrt{26}$ units
     b not right angled

6 **a** $k = -4\frac{1}{2}$ **b** $k = -15$

7 gradient of AB = gradient of BC = 2 and B is common

8 $-\frac{3}{2}$ **9** $m = 6$ or -2 **10** $a = 4$

11 **a** AB = BC = 5 units, $m_{AB} = \frac{3}{4}$, $m_{BC} = -\frac{4}{3}$
         $\therefore$ right angled at B.
     b X($\frac{1}{2}$, $\frac{1}{2}$)

c gradient of BX = 7,   gradient of AC = $-\frac{1}{7}$
     and $7 \times -\frac{1}{7} = -1$, $\therefore$ BX $\perp$ AC.

REVIEW SET 14B

1 **a** 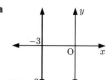   **b**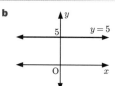
     c

2 B(5, -4)   **3** **a** -1 **b** undefined
4 **a** ST = $\sqrt{73}$ units   **b** (3, $-\frac{1}{2}$)   **5** 2
6 $a = -1$ or -3 **7** $b = -3$
8 **a** D(4, -3)   **b** 5 units   **9** $c = 20$
10 **a** AB: $\frac{1}{5}$, BC: -2, CD: $\frac{1}{5}$, AD: -2
     b ($\frac{1}{2}$, $\frac{1}{2}$) for both diagonals.   **c** AC: $-\frac{3}{7}$, BD: $\frac{5}{3}$
     d The quadrilateral ABCD is a parallelogram but not a rhombus.

EXERCISE 15A

1 $\approx$ 764 km/h   **2** **a** $\approx$ 9.95 m/s   **b** $\approx$ 35.8 km/h
3 37.5 km   **4** $\approx$ 152 km   **5** $\approx$ 13.8 km/h
6 4 h 20 min   **7** $\approx$ 54 min 33 s   **8** 7.875 km
9 **a** 9 km   **b** 3 km/h
10 **a** 1 h 15 min   **b** 84 km/h   **11** $\approx$ 7.94 km/h
12 $\approx$ 92.3 km/h   **13** **a** 14.4 s   **b** 124 m   **14** 200 m

EXERCISE 15B

1 **a** Chloe walks at a constant speed for 300 metres, stops for
         50 seconds, then walks at a constant speed (slower than
         before) for a further 300 metres.
     b 600 metres   **c** 1.5 m/s
     d Slower. Chloe walked the first 300 m in 200 s, and the
         second 300 m in 300 s.
2 **a** 1.25 m/s; this is Tan's walking speed.
     b constant; the graph is a straight line.

3 **a**
```
distance (km)
120
 80
 40
  0
    0      2      6      time (h)
```
     b 60 km
     c 5 h
     d 20 km/h

4 **a** 12 min   **b** 80 km   **c** 20 km
     d A: 1 h 48 min, B: 2 h 12 min
     e A: $\approx$ 44.4 km/h, B: $\approx$ 36.4 km/h

5 **a** the Smith family   **b** the Reynolds family

c the Reynolds family   **d** $1\frac{1}{2}$ hours   **e** 100 km

6 a after 2 min   **b** 1 min   **c** 3 min
d 2 km   **e** between the 3 and 4 minute marks

REVIEW SET 15A

1 train (96.25 km/h versus ≈ 84.7 km/h)
2 ≈ 4 h 21 min 26 s   **3 a** 105 km   **b** 70 km/h
4 a 165 km   **b** 1 h 49 min
5 a Yes, the graph is a straight line.   **b** 150 km   **c** 75 km/h
6 a 150 km   **b** 2 h   **c** 50 km/h
7 a 100 km   **b** 2 h
  c **i** 50 km/h   **ii** 100 km/h   **d** ≈ 66.7 km/h

REVIEW SET 15B

1 a 13 km/h   **b** ≈ 3.61 m/s
2 a 50 km/h   **b** $6\frac{1}{2}$ h   **c** ≈ 13.9 m/s   **3** 1300 km
4 a Yiren: ≈ 2.67 m/s, Sean: 2.5 m/s
  b Yiren, by 50 seconds
5 a 400 km   **b** 5 h   **c** Yes, the graph is a straight line.
  d 80 km/h
6 a 20 miles   **b** 30 min   **c** 40 miles/h   **d** 52 miles/h
  e C and D
7 a 325 km   **b** 20 min
  c Johnson: 87.5 km/h, Maple: 100 km/h
  d ≈ 88.6 km/h

EXERCISE 16A

1 a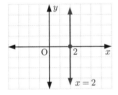
gradient is undefined
b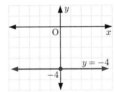
gradient is 0
c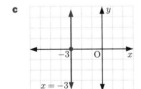
gradient is undefined
d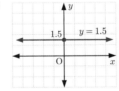
gradient is 0
e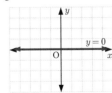
gradient is 0

2 a $y=0$ **b** $x=0$ **c** $y=-3$ **d** $x=4$
3 a $y=3$ **b** $x=4$
4 a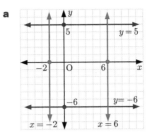
b i A(5, 0), B(0, −3)
  ii $\frac{3}{5}$

5 a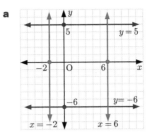
b i rectangle
  ii 88 units^2
  iii $\frac{11}{8}$ and $-\frac{11}{8}$

EXERCISE 16B

1 a i
x	−3	−2	−1	0	1	2	3
y	−3	−2	−1	0	1	2	3

ii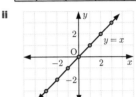
iii gradient is 1, x-intercept is 0, y-intercept is 0

b i
x	−3	−2	−1	0	1	2	3
y	3	2	1	0	−1	−2	−3

ii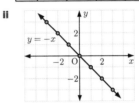
iii gradient is −1, x-intercept is 0, y-intercept is 0

c i
x	−3	−2	−1	0	1	2	3
y	−6	−4	−2	0	2	4	6

ii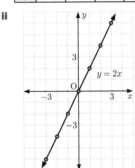
iii gradient is 2, x-intercept is 0, y-intercept is 0

d i
x	−3	−2	−1	0	1	2	3
y	6	4	2	0	−2	−4	−6

ii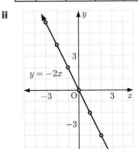
iii gradient is −2, x-intercept is 0, y-intercept is 0

e **i**

x	-3	-2	-1	0	1	2	3
y	-7	-5	-3	-1	1	3	5

ii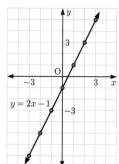

iii gradient is 2, x-intercept is $\frac{1}{2}$, y-intercept is -1

f **i**

x	-3	-2	-1	0	1	2	3
y	$\frac{1}{2}$	1	$1\frac{1}{2}$	2	$2\frac{1}{2}$	3	$3\frac{1}{2}$

ii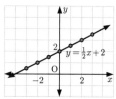

iii gradient is $\frac{1}{2}$, x-intercept is -4, y-intercept is 2

g **i**

x	-3	-2	-1	0	1	2	3
y	$3\frac{1}{2}$	3	$2\frac{1}{2}$	2	$1\frac{1}{2}$	1	$\frac{1}{2}$

ii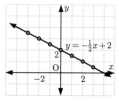

iii gradient is $-\frac{1}{2}$, x-intercept is 4, y-intercept is 2

h **i**

x	-3	-2	-1	0	1	2	3
y	5	4	3	2	1	0	-1

ii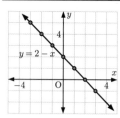

iii gradient is -1, x-intercept is 2, y-intercept is 2

i **i**

x	-3	-2	-1	0	1	2	3
y	$3\frac{1}{2}$	2	$\frac{1}{2}$	-1	$-2\frac{1}{2}$	-4	$-5\frac{1}{2}$

ii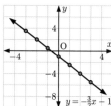

iii gradient is $-\frac{3}{2}$, x-intercept is $-\frac{2}{3}$, y-intercept is -1

2 **a** yes **b** no **c** yes **d** no **e** yes **f** no

3 **a** $a = 2$ **b** $a = 13$ **c** $a = 5$ **d** $a = 4$
e $a = 3$ **f** $a = -2$ **g** $a = 2$ **h** $a = -2$

4 **a** **i**

x	-3	-2	-1	0	1	2	3
y	0	1	2	3	4	5	6

ii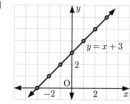

iii yes

b **i**

x	-3	-2	-1	0	1	2	3
y	-3	$-3\frac{1}{3}$	$-3\frac{2}{3}$	-4	$-4\frac{1}{3}$	$-4\frac{2}{3}$	-5

ii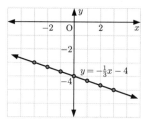

iii no

c **i**

x	-3	-2	-1	0	1	2	3
y	-2	$-1\frac{2}{3}$	$-1\frac{1}{3}$	-1	$-\frac{2}{3}$	$-\frac{1}{3}$	0

ii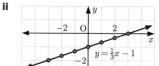

iii yes

5 **a** 4 **b** -2 **c** 1 **d** -3 **e** 4
f 3 **g** 6 **h** -4 **i** -5

6 **a**

x	-2	0	2	$-\dfrac{c}{m}$
y	$-2m + c$	c	$2m + c$	0

b x-intercept $-\dfrac{c}{m}$, y-intercept c **c** gradient is m

d A straight line with equation $y = mx + c$ has gradient m and y-intercept c.

EXERCISE 16C

1 **a** gradient is 4, y-int. is 8 **b** gradient is -3, y-int. is 2
c gradient is -1, y-int. is 6 **d** gradient is -2, y-int. is 3
e gradient is 0, y-int. is -2 **f** gradient is -3, y-int. is 11
g gradient is $\frac{1}{2}$, y-int. is -5 **h** gradient is $-\frac{3}{2}$, y-int. is 3
i gradient is $\frac{2}{5}$, y-int. is $\frac{4}{5}$ **j** gradient is $\frac{1}{2}$, y-int. is $\frac{1}{2}$
k gradient is $\frac{2}{5}$, y-int. is -2 **l** gradient is $-\frac{3}{2}$, y-int. is $\frac{11}{2}$

2 **a** 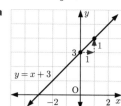 **b**

c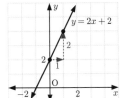

d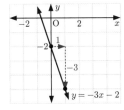

e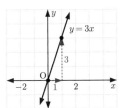

f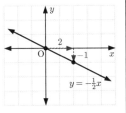

g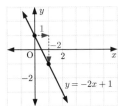

h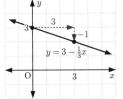

i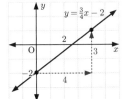

j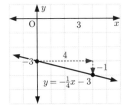

k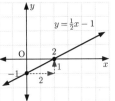

l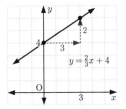

3 a   i gradient is $-\frac{2}{3}$

  ii y-intercept is 2

  iii x-intercept is 3

 c yes

b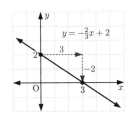

EXERCISE 16D

1 a $2x + y = 11$ **b** $3x - y = 4$ **c** $x + 5y = 6$
 d $6x + 7y = 5$ **e** $5x - 8y = 1$ **f** $4x - 9y = -18$

2 a   i $y = -3x + 5$ **ii** -3
 b   i $y = -\frac{2}{5}x + 2$ **ii** $-\frac{2}{5}$
 c   i $y = -\frac{7}{4}x - \frac{9}{4}$ **ii** $-\frac{7}{4}$
 d   i $y = 6x - 1$ **ii** 6
 e   i $y = \frac{5}{11}x - \frac{2}{11}$ **ii** $\frac{5}{11}$
 f   i $y = \frac{9}{2}x + \frac{5}{2}$ **ii** $\frac{9}{2}$

3 a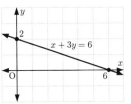

b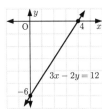

c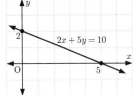

d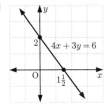

e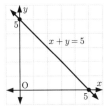

f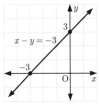

g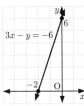

h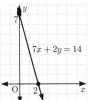

i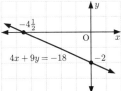

4 a x-intercept 5, y-intercept -3

 b   i yes **ii** no

 c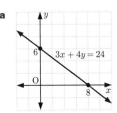

5 a

 b D

6 $ax - by = d$

$\therefore \quad by = ax - d$

$\therefore \quad y = \dfrac{a}{b}x - \dfrac{d}{b}$ which is a line with gradient $\dfrac{a}{b}$.

EXERCISE 16E.1

1 a $y = 3x + 4$ **b** $y = 7x - 1$ **c** $y = -x + \frac{1}{3}$

d $y = \frac{1}{2}x$ **e** $y = 5$ **f** $y = -\frac{5}{2}x - \frac{2}{3}$

2 a $2x - y = -4$ **b** $3x + y = -2$ **c** $2x - 4y = -1$

d $x + 3y = 0$ **e** $3x + 4y = 8$ **f** $2x - 5y = 5$

EXERCISE 16E.2

1 a $y = 2x + 6$ **b** $y = -3x - 4$ **c** $y = 5x + 14$

d $y = \frac{3}{4}x + 6$ **e** $y = 4$ **f** $y = -\frac{1}{2}x - \frac{13}{2}$

g $y = -\frac{1}{3}x + \frac{13}{3}$ **h** $y = \frac{2}{3}x + \frac{19}{3}$

2 a $y = 3x - 2$ **b** $y = -\frac{1}{4}x - 1$ **c** $y = \frac{2}{5}x + 3$

d $y = -\frac{4}{3}x + \frac{20}{3}$ **e** $y = \frac{1}{2}x + 4$

3 a $x - 2y - 2$ **b** $3x - 4y - 15$ **c** $3x - y = 11$

d $3x + 4y = -6$ **e** $2x + y = 4$ **f** $3x + y = 4$

4 a Lines parallel to $3x + 5y = 2$ have the same gradient of $-\frac{3}{5}$. These lines have the form $3x + 5y = d$, where d is a constant.

b Lines perpendicular to $3x + 5y = 2$ have gradient $\frac{5}{3}$. These lines have the form $5x - 3y = d$, where d is a constant.

5 a $3x + 4y = 10$ **b** $2x - 5y = 3$ **c** $3x + y = -12$

d $x - 3y = 0$

6 a $\frac{2}{3}, -\dfrac{6}{k}$ **b i** $k = -9$ **ii** $k = 4$

EXERCISE 16E.3

1 a $y = 2x + 2$ **b** $y = \frac{2}{5}x + 3$ **c** $y = -x - 1$

d $y = -2x + 4$ **e** $y = \frac{1}{2}x - \frac{1}{2}$ **f** $y = -\frac{2}{5}x$

2 a $y = 4x - 5$ **b** $y = -3x + 7$ **c** $y = \frac{3}{8}x - 1$

3 a $y = x - 1$ **b** $y = \frac{1}{2}x + 1$ **c** $y = -\frac{3}{4}x + 3$

d $y = -\frac{1}{3}x + 3$ **e** $y = -2x - 4$ **f** $y = 3$

4 a $y = 2x + 3$ **b** $y = -2x + 12$ **c** $y = \frac{2}{3}x - 2$

d $y = -3$ **e** $y = \frac{3}{2}x - 5$ **f** $y = -\frac{4}{3}x + \frac{1}{3}$

5 a $y = \frac{2}{5}x - 2$ **b** $y = -2x - 2$

6 a $y = 3x - 2$ **b** $y = -\frac{1}{3}x + 4$ **c** $y = 7$

d $y = -\frac{2}{5}x - 2$ **e** $y = \frac{5}{4}x + \frac{5}{2}$ **f** $x = -4$

7 a $3x + y = 4$ **b** $y = 2$ **c** $x = 3$

d $5x + 3y = 12$ **e** $5x - 4y = -14$ **f** $x - 5y = 9$

8 a $V = \frac{1}{2}t + 1$ **b** $N = 3 - d$ **c** $C = \frac{1}{2}t + 2$

d $H = 2 - g$ **e** $F = \frac{3}{10}x + 5$ **f** $P = -\frac{1}{3}t - 2$

9 a $y = -\frac{3}{5}x + 11$ **b** $y = -\frac{3}{5}x + \frac{27}{5}$

10 a $y = 4x + 13$ **b** $y = 5$ **c** $y = 4x - 23$ **d** $y = -3$

EXERCISE 16F

1 a

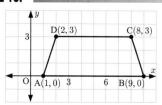

b a trapezium

c $x = 5$

---

2 a

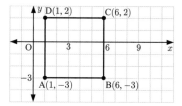

ABCD is a square.

b 4 lines   **c** $x = \frac{7}{2}$, $y = -\frac{1}{2}$, $y = x - 4$, $y = 3 - x$

3 a i $R(7, -2)$ **ii** $(4, \frac{1}{2})$ and $(4, \frac{1}{2})$ **iii** $x = 4$, $y = \frac{1}{2}$

b The diagonals of a rectangle bisect each other.

4 a gradient of AC $= \dfrac{k}{3}$,   gradient of BC $= -\dfrac{k}{3}$

b As the right angle must be at C, $\dfrac{k}{3} = \dfrac{3}{k}$

$\therefore \quad k^2 = 9$ and so $k = 3$ {as $k > 0$}

c right angled isosceles   **d** $x = 0$

5

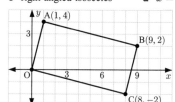

a gradient of OA $= 4$, gradient of BC $= 4$ $\therefore$ OA $\parallel$ BC

OA $=$ BC $= \sqrt{17}$ units

b gradient of OA $= 4$,   gradient of AB $= -\frac{1}{4}$

and $4 \times -\frac{1}{4} = -1$ $\therefore$ OA and AB are perpendicular.

c From **a**, a pair of opposite sides are parallel and equal in length, $\therefore$ OABC is a parallelogram.

From **b**, angle OAB is a right angle

$\therefore$ the parallelogram is a rectangle.

d $(\frac{1}{2}, 2)$ and $(5, 3)$ **e** $2x + 8y = 17$ and $4x - y = 17$

6 a

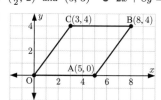

b $y = 4$

c OA $=$ AB $=$ BC $=$ CO $= 5$ units

$\therefore$ OABC is a rhombus

d $(4, 2)$ and $(4, 2)$

The diagonals of a rhombus bisect each other.

e $y = \frac{1}{2}x$ and $2x + y = 10$

These are the diagonals of the rhombus.

7 a $C(0, 2\sqrt{3})$ **b** $M(1, \sqrt{3})$, $N(-1, \sqrt{3})$

c $x = 0$, $\sqrt{3}x - 3y = -2\sqrt{3}$, $\sqrt{3}x + 3y = 2\sqrt{3}$

REVIEW SET 16A

1

2 a gradient is 4, y-intercept is -3

b gradient is -1, y-intercept is 2

c gradient is $\frac{3}{2}$, y-intercept is $-\frac{1}{2}$

3 a 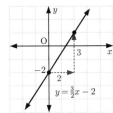 **b**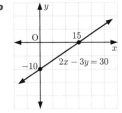

c 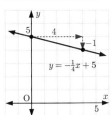 **d**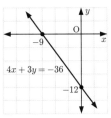

4 x-intercept is 3, y-intercept is 2, gradient is $-\frac{2}{3}$

5 a $y = -2x + 3$ **b** $y = -4$
  c $2x - 3y = -18$ **d** $y = 3x - 5$

6 $k = -11$ **7 a** $8x - 3y = -7$ **b** $2x - 3y = 18$

8 a $y = x - 3$ **b** $2x + 3y = 2$ **c** $x + 2y = 8$

  d line 1: $y = \frac{6}{5}x + \frac{8}{5}$,   line 2: $y = -\frac{5}{6}x + \frac{29}{6}$

9

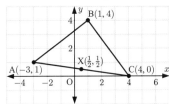

  a $AB = BC = 5$ units $\therefore$ $\triangle ABC$ is isosceles
  b $X(\frac{1}{2}, \frac{1}{2})$
  c gradient of BX $= 7$,   gradient of AC $= -\frac{1}{7}$
    $\therefore$ BX and AC are perpendicular, as their gradients are
    negative reciprocals.
  d BX is a line of symmetry with equation $y = 7x - 3$.

10

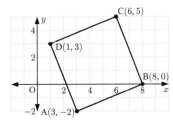

  a gradient of AB $= \frac{2}{5}$,   gradient of DC $= \frac{2}{5}$, $\therefore$ AB $\parallel$ DC.
    Also AB $=$ DC $= \sqrt{29}$ units.
  b gradient of AB $= \frac{2}{5}$,   gradient of BC $= -\frac{5}{2}$,   and as these
    are negative reciprocals, AB is perpendicular to BC.
    Also AB $=$ BC $= \sqrt{29}$ units.
  c ABCD is a square.
  d $7x - 3y = 27$, $3x + 7y = 24$, $4x - 10y = 3$,
    $10x + 4y = 51$

REVIEW SET 16B

1 a yes   **b** yes   **2** gradient is -2, y-intercept is 5

3 a x-intercept is 5, y-intercept is -2 **b** gradient is $\frac{2}{5}$

c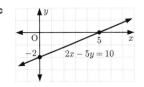

4 a $y = 3$ **b** $x = -1$ **c** $y = \frac{8}{5}x + 20$

5 a   **b**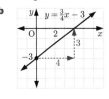

c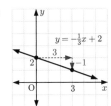

6 $k = -1$

7 a $y = 2x - 3$ **b** $x + 2y = 4$ **c** $y = 2 - x$
  d $y = \frac{3}{2}x - 5$

8 a $R = -\frac{3}{4}t + 3$ **b** $P = r + 4$

9 a $4x + 7y = 6$ **b** $x + 2y = 6$

10 a

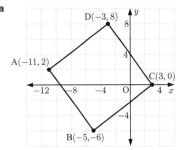

  b $AB = BC = CD = DA = 10$ units
  c gradient of AB $= -\frac{4}{3}$,   gradient of BC $= \frac{3}{4}$
    $\therefore$ AB and BC are perpendicular, as their gradients are
    negative reciprocals.
  From **b**, ABCD is a rhombus and from **c**, one angle is a right
  angle. $\therefore$ ABCD is a square.
  d $x + 7y = 3$, $7x - y = -29$, $4x + 3y = -13$,
    $3x - 4y = -16$
  e midpoint is $(-4, 1)$ **f** $x + 7y = -4 + 7 = 3$ ✓
              $7x - y = -28 - 1 = -29$ ✓
              $4x + 3y = -16 + 3 = -13$ ✓
              $3x - 4y = -12 - 4 = -16$ ✓

EXERCISE 17A

1 a

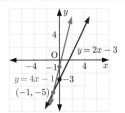

              $x = -1$, $y = -5$

b

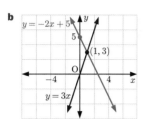

$x = 1, \; y = 3$

c

$x = -2, \; y = 0$

$x = 5, \; y = 2$

2 a

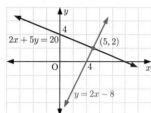

b

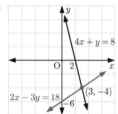

$x = 3, \; y = -4$

c

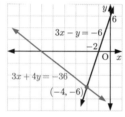

$x = -4, \; y = -6$

3 a

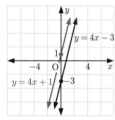

No solutions, the lines are parallel.

b

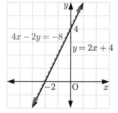

Infinitely many solutions, the lines are coincident.

EXERCISE 17B

1 a $x = 4, \; y = 5$ **b** $x = -1, \; y = 3$ **c** $x = 1, \; y = 3$
2 a $x = 0, \; y = -4$ **b** $x = 4, \; y = 0$
  c $x = -5, \; y = 3$ **d** $x = -\frac{13}{4}, \; y = -\frac{11}{4}$
  e $x = 8, \; y = 6$ **f** $x = \frac{5}{3}, \; y = 0$
3 No solutions, the lines are parallel.

EXERCISE 17C

1 a $x = 3, \; y = 5$ **b** $x = -2, \; y = -3$
  c $x = 1, \; y = -6$ **d** $x = -7, \; y = -3$
  e $x = 0, \; y = 3$ **f** $x = -\frac{1}{2}, \; y = \frac{1}{2}$
2 a $x = \frac{2}{5}, \; y = -\frac{7}{5}$ **b** $x = \frac{5}{4}, \; y = 3$
  c $x = \frac{25}{17}, \; y = \frac{10}{17}$
3 a $(2, 5)$ **b** $(3, 1)$ **c** $(0, 5)$ **d** $(0, 4)$
4 a No solutions as the lines are parallel.
  b There are infinitely many solutions as the lines are coincident.

EXERCISE 17D.1

1 a $6x = 6$ **b** $-y = 8$ **c** $5x = 7$
  d $-6x = -30$ **e** $8y = 4$ **f** $-2y = -16$

2 a $x = 2, \; y = -1$ **b** $x = -2, \; y = 5$
  c $x = 3, \; y = 2$ **d** $x = -2, \; y = -1$
  e $x = 5, \; y = -3$ **f** $x = 4, \; y = -3$

EXERCISE 17D.2

1 a $9x + 12y = 6$ **b** $-2x + 8y = -14$
  c $25x - 5y = -15$ **d** $-21x - 9y = 12$
  e $8x + 20y = -4$ **f** $-3x + y = 1$
2 a $x = 3, \; y = 2$ **b** $x = 8, \; y = 7$ **c** $x = -2, \; y = 3$
  d $x = 5, \; y = -1$ **e** $x = -\frac{5}{2}, \; y = 0$ **f** $x = 4, \; y = -\frac{3}{2}$
3 a $x = -3, \; y = 1$ **b** $x = 2, \; y = 1$
  c $x = 3, \; y = 1$ **d** $x = 3, \; y = 2$ **e** $x = 5, \; y = 2$
  f $x = 4, \; y = 1$ **g** $x = -1, \; y = -3$
  h $x = 2, \; y = -5$ **i** $x = 19, \; y = -17$
4 a Yes, dividing an equation by a non-zero constant is equivalent to multiplying the equation by a fraction, which will not change its solution.
  b Dividing $5x - 10y = 15$ by 5, we obtain $x - 2y = 3$.
  c $x = 5, \; y = 1$
5 a Infinitely many solutions.
  b No solutions as the lines are parallel.

EXERCISE 17E

1 97 and 181   **2** $81\frac{1}{2}$ and $118\frac{1}{2}$ **3** 9 and 17
4 hammer \$14, screwdriver \$6
5 adult's ticket \$28, child's ticket \$12
6 A nectarine costs 56 cents and a peach costs 22 cents.
7 19 five cent coins and 14 twenty cent coins
8 14 rabbits and 21 pheasants
9 74 one litre cartons and 23 two litre cartons
10 a $x = 3, \; y = 5$ **b** 8 cm^2
11 a $x = \frac{3}{5}, \; y = 1$ **b** 36 cm
12 a $a = \frac{5}{9}, \; b = -\frac{160}{9}$ **b** 25°C

REVIEW SET 17A

1

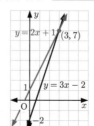

$x = -1, \; y = -3$

2 $x = 8, \; y = -13$
3 a $x = -5, \; y = -7$
  b no solutions
4 a $x = 4, \; y = -2$
  b $x = 2, \; y = -1$

5 pencil 24 cents, ruler 50 cents
6 a $y = 29 - 4x$ **b** $x = 8, \; y = -3$
7 $x = 3, \; y = -4$ **8 a** $x = 5, \; y = 4$ **b** 13 cm^2

REVIEW SET 17B

1 a

b $x = 3, \; y = 7$

2 $x = 4$, $y = 4$ **3** $x = 2$, $y = 1$

4 **a** $x = -1$, $y = -7$ **b** $x = 2$, $y = -1$

5 37 and 48   **6** 13 ten cent coins and 8 fifty cent coins

7 **a** $x = -9$, $y = 23$ **b** no solutions

8 **a** $x = \frac{14}{11}$, $y = \frac{57}{11}$ **b** $\frac{125}{11}$ cm ≈ 11.4 cm

EXERCISE 18A

1 **a** categorical   **b** quantitative   **c** categorical
   d quantitative   **e** quantitative   **f** categorical
   g categorical   **h** quantitative

2 **a** male, female   **b** black, blond, brown, grey, red
   c strings, woodwind, brass, percussion

3 **a** Sample, it is not realistic to ask every person using a taxi.
   b Census, we can measure the height of every person on the team.
   c Sample, we cannot realistically collect data from every person in a city.
   d Census, we can find the resting pulse rate of every person on the team.
   e Sample, we cannot realistically collect data from every household in a country.
   f Sample, it is impractical to collect this data for every day.

4 **a** quantitative discrete   **b** quantitative continuous
   c quantitative discrete   **d** quantitative discrete
   e quantitative discrete   **f** quantitative continuous
   g quantitative discrete   **h** quantitative continuous
   i quantitative continuous   **j** quantitative discrete

5 **a** The sample is not representative of the whole population, it does not account for students in different year levels.
   b The data collection process is unfairly influenced. Only motorists stopped by traffic can be interviewed.
   c The poll can only be completed by those who own mobile phones.
   d The participants in the survey will be those of a higher income, and will not represent the entire population.

EXERCISE 18B.1

1 **a** 45 shoppers   **b** 18 shoppers   **c** $\approx 15.6\%$
   d 3, more people shopped 3 times in the past week than any other number of times.
   e positively skewed

2 **a** number of pets in a household
   b The variable is discrete since you cannot have part of a pet.
   c

Number of pets	Tally	Frequency
0	⫼⫼ |	6
1	⫼⫼ ||	7
2	||||	4
3	||	2
4	|	1
	Total	20

   d

Number of household pets

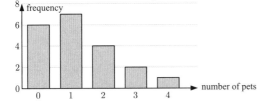

e 1 pet   **f** positively skewed   **g** 30%   **h** 15%

3 **a** 17 games   **b** **i** 76 points   **ii** 137 points
   c positively skewed   **d** 10 times   **e** $\approx 11.8\%$

4 **a**

Number of goals	Tally	Frequency
0	⫼⫼	5
1	⫼⫼ |||	8
2	⫼⫼ ||	7
3	⫼⫼	5
4	|||	3
5	|	1
6		0
7	|	1
	Total	30

   b

Goals scored

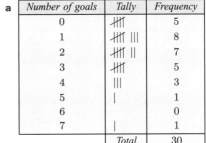

   c positively skewed   **d** 7 goals   **e** $\frac{1}{3}$

5 **a**   **Test results**

Stem	Leaf
0	7
1	8
2	7 9
3	2 2 5 6 8 9 9
4	0 3 4 4 5 6 6 7 8

Key: $1 \mid 8 = 18$ marks

   b 9 students   **c** 20%   **d** 90%   **e** negatively skewed

6 **a**

Number of toothpicks	Tally	Frequency
47	|	1
48	⫼⫼	5
49	⫼⫼ ⫼⫼	10
50	⫼⫼ ⫼⫼ ⫼⫼ ⫼⫼ |||	23
51	⫼⫼ ⫼⫼	10
52	⫼⫼ ||||	9
53	||	2
	Total	60

   b

Number of toothpicks in boxes

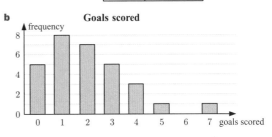

   c approximately symmetrical   **d** $\approx 38.3\%$

7 **a** 62 runs   **b** 14 runs
   c In 2018 as the scores are more closely grouped.
   d In 2018, 842 compared with 559 in 2017.

8 a   **Travel times to university**

Alex (train)		Stan (bus)
7 5	1	8 9
7 5 3 2	2	2 4 5 8 9
6 4 4 0	3	0 1 1 2 4 6 8
8 5 1	4	2
5	5	
0	6	

Key: 4 | 2 means 42 min

b Alex had the fastest journey, which was 15 minutes.

c As the bus data is less spread out, travelling by bus is more reliable.

9 a   **Leeds hotel**

Number of nights stayed	Tally	Frequency
1	⊮ I	6
2	⊮ ⊮	10
3	⊮ III	8
4	⊮	5
5	IIII	4
6	III	3
7	I	1
8	III	3
	Total	40

Manchester hotel

Number of nights stayed	Tally	Frequency
1	IIII	4
2	⊮ I	6
3	⊮ II	7
4	⊮ II	7
5	⊮ I	6
6	IIII	4
7	IIII	4
8	II	2
	Total	40

b
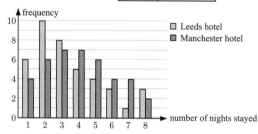

c The Leeds hotel data is positively skewed, the Manchester hotel data is slightly positively skewed.

d the Manchester hotel

10 a

Before program		After program
	6	7
8 8 6 6 2	7	1 2 2 6 7 8 8 8 9 9
9 8 7 6 4 3 3 2 0	8	0 1 3 7 9
6 6 6 5 5 4 4 2 0	9	0 1 1 1 4 4 5 6 7 7 8
8 6 6 5 3 2	10	1 2 4 7
5 1	11	1
4	12	

Key: 10 | 7 means 107 kg

b 124 kg

c Yes, the weights of the participants were generally lower after the program.

EXERCISE 18B.2

1 a

Chairs completed per day	Tally	Frequency
10 - 19	IIII	4
20 - 29	⊮ ⊮	10
30 - 39	⊮ IIII	9
40 - 49	III	3
	Total	26

b
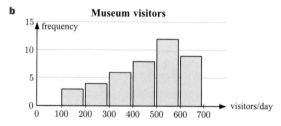

c ≈ 88.5%   **d** 12 days   **e** 20 - 29 chairs/day

2 a

Visitors	Tally	Frequency
0 - 99		0
100 - 199	III	3
200 - 299	IIII	4
300 - 399	⊮ I	6
400 - 499	⊮ III	8
500 - 599	⊮ ⊮ II	12
600 - 699	⊮ IIII	9
	Total	42

b   **Museum visitors**
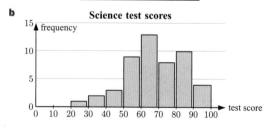

c 21 days   **d** 500 - 599 visitors   **e** negatively skewed

3 a

Test score	Tally	Frequency
20 - 29	I	1
30 - 39	II	2
40 - 49	III	3
50 - 59	⊮ IIII	9
60 - 69	⊮ ⊮ III	13
70 - 79	⊮ III	8
80 - 89	⊮ ⊮	10
90 - 100	IIII	4
	Total	50

b   **Science test scores**

c 28%   **d** 12%

e More students had a test score in the interval 60 - 69 than in any other interval.

f negatively skewed

4 a

Test score	Tally	Frequency
15 - 19	|	1
20 - 24		0
25 - 29	|||	3
30 - 34	|||||	5
35 - 39	||||| |	6
40 - 44	||||| ||||| |||||	15
45 - 49	|||||	5
50 - 54	||||| |	6
55 - 60	||||	4
	Total	45

b

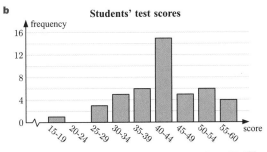

Students' test scores

c negatively skewed with no outliers   **d** $\approx 22.2\%$

EXERCISE 18B.3

1 a approximately symmetrical   **b** $14 \leqslant d < 16$ m   **c** 35%

2 a *Weight* can take any value in the given range, and is measured, not counted.

b approximately symmetrical

c $85 \leqslant w < 90$ kg. More people in the volleyball squad have weights between 85 kg and 90 kg than in any other interval.

d 28 players   **e** $\approx 21.4\%$ of players

3 a positively skewed

b **i, ii**

Height (h mm)	Frequency
$20 \leqslant h < 40$	4
$40 \leqslant h < 60$	17
$60 \leqslant h < 80$	15
$80 \leqslant h < 100$	8
$100 \leqslant h < 120$	2
$120 \leqslant h < 140$	4

c **i** 6 seedlings   **ii** 30%

d **i** ≈ 754 seedlings   **ii** ≈ 686 seedlings

4 a **i** Girls: approximately symmetrical
Boys: negatively skewed

ii Girls: $15 \leqslant t < 15.5$ s, Boys: $15 \leqslant t < 15.5$ s

b boys   **c** boys

d The boys data set, as the 1 runner in the $11.5 \leqslant t < 12$ s interval is separated from the main body of the data.

EXERCISE 18C

1 a **i** 25   **ii** 24   **iii** 30

b **i** ≈ 13.3 **ii** 11.5   **iii** 8

c **i** ≈ 10.3 **ii** 10   **iii** 11.2

d **i** ≈ 429 **ii** 428   **iii** 415, 427

2 a *data set A*: $\overline{x} \approx 7.73$ *data set B*: $\overline{x} \approx 8.45$

b *data set A*: 7   *data set B*: 7

c The data sets are the same except for the last value. Since the last value of A is less than the last value of B, the mean of A is less than the mean of B.

d The middle value of both data sets is the same, so the median is the same.

3 a mean: $295\,900$, median: $262\,500$, mode: $240\,000$

b The mode is the second lowest value, so does not take the higher values into account.

c The median; it is unaffected by large values.

4 a mean: ≈ 3.11 mm, median: 0 mm, mode: 0 mm

b **i** 15 and 27

ii The outliers should not be removed unless they are a result of a recording error.

5 a 44 points   **b** 44 points   **c** ≈ 40.6 points

d **i** Increase, as 42 is greater than the mean calculated in **c**.

ii 40.75 points

6 a 1 head   **b** 1 head   **c** 1.4 heads

7 a

Donation ($)	Frequency
1	7
2	9
5	2
10	4
20	8
Total	30

b 30 donations

c **i** $\approx \$7.83$

ii $2

iii $2

d the mode

8 a **i** 4.25 ducklings   **ii** 5 ducklings   **iii** 5 ducklings

b Yes, it is negatively skewed.

c The mean is lower than the mode and median.

9 a **i** Leeds: 3.475 nights, Manchester: 4.075 nights

ii Leeds: 2 nights, Manchester: 3 nights and 4 nights

iii Leeds: 3 nights, Manchester: 4 nights

b the Manchester hotel

10 a *Group A*: mean $= 19.91$ cm, median $= 19.85$ cm
Group B: mean $= 17.86$ cm, median $= 17.6$ cm

b The mean and median are higher for the plants which were fertilised than for those which were not. This suggests that the fertiliser is effective.

11 105.6   **12** 99.2 km   **13** $2\,592\,000   **14** $x = 12$

15 $a = 8$ **16** 27   **17** 7.875

18 $A = \dfrac{30S + 31O + 30N}{91}$ **19** 15

EXERCISE 18D

1 a **i** 9   **ii** $Q_1 = 7$, $Q_3 = 10$ **iii** 7   **iv** 3

b **i** 18.5   **ii** $Q_1 = 16$, $Q_3 = 20$ **iii** 14   **iv** 4

c **i** 26.9   **ii** $Q_1 = 25.5$, $Q_3 = 28.1$ **iii** 7.7   **iv** 2.6

2 a $120   **b** $Q_1 = \$90$ **c** $Q_3 = \$150$ **d** IQR $= \$60$

3 a **i** median $= 2.35$ **ii** $Q_1 = 1.4$ **iii** $Q_3 = 3.7$

b range $= 5.1$, IQR $= 2.3$

c **i** ...... greater than 2.35 minutes

ii ...... less than 3.7 minutes

iii The minimum waiting time was 0.1 minutes and the maximum waiting time was 5.2 minutes. The waiting times were spread over 5.1 minutes.

4 a 6 cm   **b** 10.1 cm   **c** 8.2 cm   **d** 7.3 cm

e 8.95 cm   **f** 4.1 cm   **g** 1.65 cm

5 a range $= 27$, IQR $= 12$ **b** range $= 38$, IQR $= 12$

c range $= 47$, IQR $= 14.5$ **d** range

EXERCISE 18E

1 a

Number of times	Frequency	Interval midpoint	Product
0 - 4	19	2	38
5 - 9	24	7	168
10 - 14	10	12	120
15 - 19	5	17	85
20 - 24	2	22	44
Total	60		455

b $\overline{x} \approx 7.58$ times

2 a Distance kicked is a continuous variable since it takes a numerical value and is a result of measuring.

b No; as the actual data values are lost when combining them in classes.

c

Distance (d m)	Frequency	Interval midpoint	Product
$20 \leqslant d < 30$	10	25	250
$30 \leqslant d < 40$	19	35	665
$40 \leqslant d < 50$	14	45	630
$50 \leqslant d < 60$	7	55	385
Total	50		1930

d ≈ 38.6 m

3 a $600 \leqslant A < 700$ m^2 **b** $\overline{x} \approx 661$ m^2

4 a positively skewed

b

Weight (w kg)	Frequency	Interval midpoint	Product
$0 \leqslant w < 1$	10	0.5	5
$1 \leqslant w < 2$	25	1.5	37.5
$2 \leqslant w < 3$	20	2.5	50
$3 \leqslant w < 4$	15	3.5	52.5
$4 \leqslant w < 5$	10	4.5	45
$5 \leqslant w < 6$	10	5.5	55
$6 \leqslant w < 7$	5	6.5	32.5
$7 \leqslant w < 8$	5	7.5	37.5
Total	100		315

c $\overline{x} \approx 3.15$ kg

5 a $165 \leqslant s < 170$ km/h

b **i** 76 serves   **ii** not possible   **iii** 73.5%

c ≈ 167 km/h

6 a $\overline{x} = 71.225$, median $= 73.5$

b

Chemistry exam mark	Frequency	Interval midpoint	Product
30 - 39	1	34.5	34.5
40 - 49	2	44.5	89.0
50 - 59	7	54.5	381.5
60 - 69	6	64.5	387.0
70 - 79	10	74.5	745.0
80 - 89	10	84.5	845.0
90 - 99	4	94.5	378.0
Total	40		2860

c $\overline{x} \approx 71.5$ using the grouped data, which is very close to our answer in **a**.

7 a $75 \leqslant h < 80$ mm   **b** ≈ 78.1 mm   **c** 22 plants

d $\approx 20.3\%$ **e** **i** ≈ 363 plants   **ii** ≈ 530 plants

8 Girls' mean ≈ 55.2,   boys' mean ≈ 58.3
The boys performed better on the test than the girls.

9 a 32.5%   **b** ≈ 22.9 min   **c** ≈ 1490 people

EXERCISE 18F

1 a 120 goats   **b** ≈ 29 kg   **c** 48 goats   **d** ≈ 17.5 kg

2 a

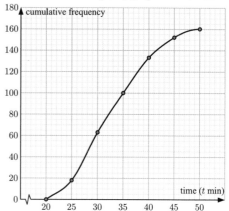

Cumulative frequency graph of race data

b **i** ≈ 32 min   **ii** ≈ 80 runners   **iii** ≈ 28 min
iv IQR ≈ 10 min

3 a

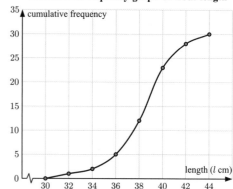

Cumulative frequency graph of trout length

b **i** $\approx 57\%$ **ii** ≈ 38.6 cm
iii ≈ 3.0 cm, this is the range in the lengths of the middle 50% of the population of trout.
iv ≈ 37.6 cm. 35% of the trout have lengths less than or equal to 37.6 cm.

c ≈ 38.3 cm   **d** negatively skewed

4 a **i** 4 kg   **ii** ≈ 2.0 kg

b

Weight (w kg)	Frequency	Cumulative frequency
$0 \leqslant w < 1$	1	1
$1 \leqslant w < 2$	2	3
$2 \leqslant w < 3$	5	8
$3 \leqslant w < 4$	12	20
$4 \leqslant w < 5$	8	28
$5 \leqslant w < 6$	6	34
$6 \leqslant w < 7$	3	37
$7 \leqslant w < 8$	2	39
$8 \leqslant w < 9$	1	40

c ≈ 4.25 kg

5 a Cumulative frequency graph of Ben Nevis climb data

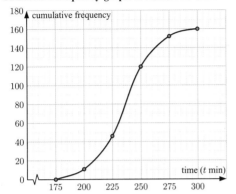

b ≈ 235 min

c ≈ 30 min. This is the range in times for the middle 50% of the data.

d ≈ 5%   **e** symmetrical

6 a Cumulative frequency graphs of cabbage weight data

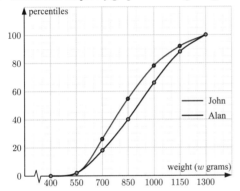

b **i** Alan: ≈ 910 g, John: ≈ 830 g
ii Alan: ≈ 310 g, John: ≈ 290 g

c Alan: ≈ 970 g, John: ≈ 890 g

d Alan's cabbages are generally heavier than John's. The spread of each data set is about the same.

REVIEW SET 18A

1 a discrete   **b** continuous   **c** discrete

2 a 49 businesses   **b** 15 businesses   **c** ≈ 26.5%
d positively skewed   **e** ≈ 3.51 employees

3 a

Test scores	Tally	Frequency
0 - 9			1
10 - 19	|||	3
20 - 29	₩₩ ₩₩ ||	12
30 - 39	₩₩ ₩₩ ||||	14
	Total	30

b Test scores

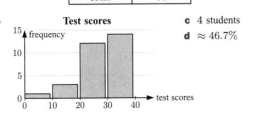

c 4 students
d ≈ 46.7%

4 a 5 | 1 means that a calf weighs 51 kg.
b 28 kg   **c** 37 kg   **d** 54 kg   **e** $\frac{7}{18}$

5 a

Number call-outs/day	Tally	Frequency
0 - 9	||	2
10 - 19	₩₩		6
20 - 29	₩₩ ₩₩	10
30 - 39	₩₩ ||	7
	Total	25

b Fire department call-outs

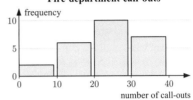

c 17 days   **d** 8%   **e** 20 - 29 call-outs/day

6 a $\bar{x} \approx 29.6$ **b** 16 and 28   **c** 29   **d** 45
e $Q_1 = 22$, $Q_3 = 41.5$ **f** 19.5

7 $x = 7$

8 a 12   **b** 43   **c** 29   **d** 20
e 34.5   **f** 31   **g** 14.5

9 a

Goals/game	Frequency
0	8
1	7
2	4
3	1
Total	20

b **i** 20 games   **ii** 18 goals
c **i** 0.9 goals   **ii** 1 goals   **iii** 0 goals   **iv** 3 goals

10 a **i** $\bar{x} = 371.12$ **ii** 372
iii $Q_1 = 228.5$ **iv** $Q_3 = 469.5$
b range = 682, IQR = 241

11 ≈ 8.53 potatoes per plant

12 a ≈ 54.9 km/h   **b** $55 \leqslant v < 60$ **c** ≈ 24.3%
d approximately symmetrical

13 a Cumulative frequency graph of wage data

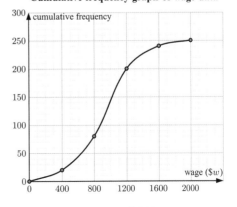

b **i** ≈ $950   **ii** ≈ $1200

14 **a**

Time (t min)	Frequency	Cumulative frequency
$0 \leqslant t < 5$	2	2
$5 \leqslant t < 10$	3	5
$10 \leqslant t < 15$	5	10
$15 \leqslant t < 20$	10	20
$20 \leqslant t < 25$	20	40
$25 \leqslant t < 30$	15	55
$30 \leqslant t < 35$	5	60
$35 \leqslant t < 40$	10	70
$40 \leqslant t < 45$	6	76
$45 \leqslant t < 50$	4	80

b **i** ≈ 25 min
ii ≈ 15 min
iii ≈ 37 min

c **i** 27
ii 18

REVIEW SET 18B

1 **a** categorical variable
  b • The sample is only of Chinese people already at the airport, it is not representative of the whole population.
  • The responses could be influenced by the time of year.

2 **a** The number of children per household.
  b Discrete, you cannot have part of a child.
  c

Number of children	Tally	Frequency
0		0
1	$\parallel\!\parallel\!\parallel$	5
2	$\parallel\!\parallel\!\parallel$ $\parallel$	7
3	$\parallel\parallel\parallel\parallel$	4
4	$\parallel$	2
5	$\vert$	1
6		0
7		0
8	$\vert$	1
	Total	20

Number of children in a household

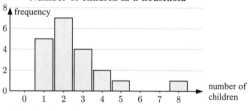

d positively skewed **e** mode = 2

3 **a**

Emails sent last week	Tally	Frequency
0 - 9	$\parallel\!\parallel\!\parallel$ $\vert$	6
10 - 19	$\parallel\!\parallel\!\parallel$ $\parallel\parallel\parallel\parallel$	9
20 - 29	$\parallel\!\parallel\!\parallel$ $\parallel$	7
30 - 39	$\parallel\!\parallel\!\parallel$	5
40 - 49	$\parallel$	2
50 - 59	$\vert$	1
	Total	30

b **Email data**

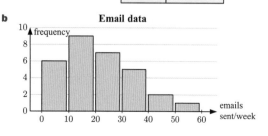

c 10 - 19 emails **d** $\approx 26.7\%$ **e** positively skewed

4 **a**

	Last season		This season
	6	20	4 7 8 8 8 9
9 7 7 6 4 4 4 3 3 1 0 0		21	0 1 2 4 5 8 8
8 6 3 1 1		22	2 4 5 6 9 9
5 4 1		23	3

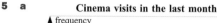

Key: 20 | 4 = 20.4 seconds

b Yes, the best times were generally lower in the season following the training program.

5 **a** **Cinema visits in the last month**

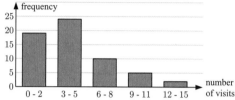

b No, we do not know the exact number of visits for those in the 0 - 2 class interval.
c $\approx 56.7\%$ **d** positively skewed

6 **a** approximately symmetrical **b** 27 babies **c** 70%
  d about 17 babies

7 ≈ 13.6 **8** $x = 2$

9 **a** median = 101.5, $Q_1 = 98$, $Q_3 = 105.5$
  b IQR = 7.5. The middle 50% of the data lies within an interval of length 7.5.

10 **a** $\overline{x} \approx 52.3$ **b** 51 **c** $Q_1 = 42$
  d $Q_3 = 61$ **e** 32 **f** IQR = 19

11 **a** **i** $\overline{x} \approx 8.47$ **ii** 9 **iii** 9 **iv** 4
  b well above the average **c** negatively skewed

12 **a** 10 days **b** 50% **c** 160 - 179 vehicles
  d ≈ 159 vehicles

13 **a** $70 \leqslant w < 80$ kg **b** ≈ 75.8 kg
  c **Weight of boxers**

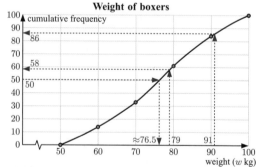

d ≈ 28 boxers **e** ≈ 76.5 kg

14 **a**

Percentage score (s)	Cumulative frequency		Percentiles	
	Boys	Girls	Boys	Girls
$0 \leqslant s < 10$	5	0	3.3	0
$10 \leqslant s < 20$	13	4	8.7	3.3
$20 \leqslant s < 30$	25	12	16.7	10
$30 \leqslant s < 40$	35	22	23.3	18.3
$40 \leqslant s < 50$	65	37	43.3	30.8
$50 \leqslant s < 60$	115	62	76.7	51.7
$60 \leqslant s < 70$	135	102	90	85
$70 \leqslant s < 80$	145	112	96.7	93.3
$80 \leqslant s < 90$	150	117	100	97.5
$90 \leqslant s < 100$	150	120	100	100

Cumulative frequency graph of test scores

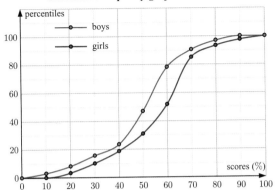

b For boys: median ≈ 52,   IQR ≈ 19
   For girls: median ≈ 59,   IQR ≈ 22

c As the girls graph is further to the right of the boys graph, the girls are outperforming the boys. Both distributions are negatively skewed.

EXERCISE 19A

1 **a i** negative association **ii** linear **iii** strong
   b i no association **ii** not linear **iii** zero
   c i positive association **ii** linear **iii** moderate
   d i positive association **ii** linear **iii** weak
   e i positive association **ii** not linear **iii** moderate
   f i negative association **ii** not linear **iii** strong

2 **a** as x increases, y increases   **b** as T increases, d decreases
   c If there is no association between two variables then the points on the scatter graph are randomly scattered.

3 **a**

   b A moderate, positive, linear correlation.

4 **a i**
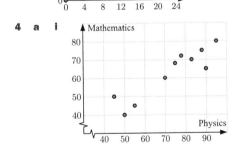
   ii A moderate, positive, linear correlation.

   b
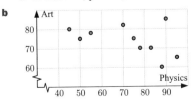
   A weak, negative, linear correlation (virtually zero correlation).

5 **a**
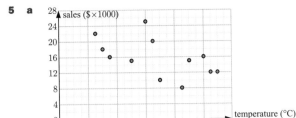
   b There is a weak, negative, linear correlation between sales and temperature.

6 **a**
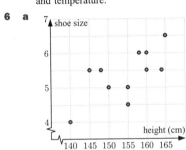
   b A weak, positive, linear association exists between *shoe size* and *height*.

EXERCISE 19B

1 **a** $\overline{x} = 7.2$, $\overline{y} = 10$
   c negatively correlated
   e when $x = 8$, $y \approx 9$
   b, d
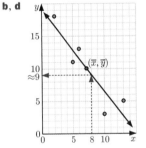

2 **a** $\overline{x} = 7$, $\overline{y} = 85$
   b, c, d
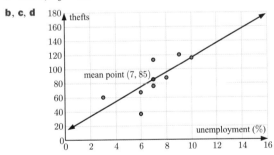
   e i ≈ 170 thefts
   ii Unreliable as it is an extrapolation well beyond the upper pole.

3 **a** $\overline{x} = 50$, $\overline{y} = 38$
   b
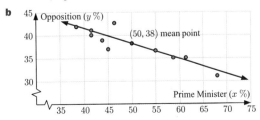
   c $\approx 39\%$

4 a (13.3, 78.8)

b

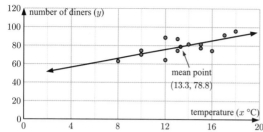

c i ≈ 73 diners   **ii** ≈ 56 diners

d We expect the first estimate to be reliable as it is an interpolation, but the second may not be reliable as it is an extrapolation.

5 a, b, c

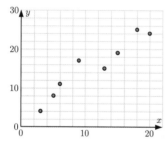

d The line of best fit in **b** is skewed towards the outlier and thus is not very close to the points to the left of the mean point.

The line of best fit in **c** however, is very close to all of the points except the outlier. This line of best fit therefore better describes the trend seen in the main body of data.

EXERCISE 19C

1 a i

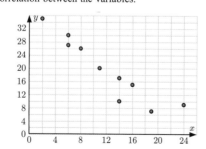

ii $y \approx 1.12x + 2.90$

iii $r > 0$ and $r^2 \approx 0.908$, there is a very strong positive correlation between the variables.

b i

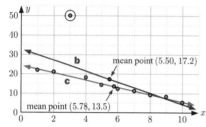

ii $y \approx -1.34x + 35.7$

iii $r < 0$ and $r^2 \approx 0.879$, there is a strong negative correlation between the variables.

2 a

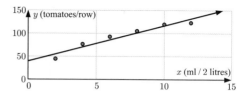

b $y \approx 7.66x + 40.1$

c The y-intercept indicates that a row can be expected to produce on average 40.1 tomatoes when no spray is applied.

d $r > 0$ and $r^2 \approx 0.939$, there is a very strong positive correlation between the variables.

e ≈ 94 tomatoes/row. Even though this is an interpolation, this seems low compared with the yield at 6 and 8 ml/2 litres. Looking at the graph it would appear that the relationship is not linear.

3 a

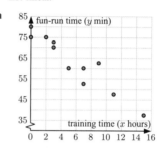

b $r \approx -0.952$, $r^2 \approx 0.907$
As $r < 0$ and $r^2 \approx 0.907$, there is a very strong negative correlation between the variables.

c $y \approx -2.69x + 77.9$

d The gradient indicates that an increase in training time of 1 hour will decrease the fun-run time by ≈ 2.7 minutes.

e i ≈ −2.86 minutes
ii This value is clearly absurd as one cannot record a negative time for a fun-run. It is very unreliable as it is an extrapolation well beyond the upper pole.

4 a

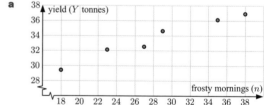

b $Y \approx 0.371n + 23.1$, as $r^2 \approx 0.965$ there is a very strong correlation between the variables and hence the linear model is suitable.

c ≈ 34.6 tonnes

d "...... , the *greater* the yield of cherries."

5 a

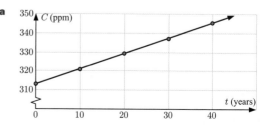

b $r = 1$, perfect positive linear correlation

c $C = 0.8t + 313$ **d** 334.6 parts per million

e 361 parts per million

6 a quantitative   **b** weight

c

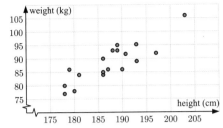

d An increase in height generally corresponds to an increase in weight.

e By calculating the Pearson's correlation coefficient r and the coefficient of determination r^2.
Here $r \approx 0.864$ and $r^2 \approx 0.747$

f We can make estimations using the equation of the least squares regression line. As the estimate is an interpolation, we expect it to be reliable.

7 a

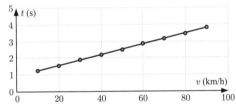

b $t \approx 0.0322v + 0.906$

c $r > 0$ and $r^2 \approx 0.9997$, there is a very strong positive correlation between the variables.

d **i** ≈ 2.68 s   **ii** ≈ 4.44 s

e 55 lies within the poles
∴ **d i** should be reasonably reliable.
110 lies outside the poles
∴ **d ii** could be unreliable.

f The vertical intercept is the reaction time, that is, the time taken for the driver to respond to the red light when the car is stationary.

g A three second margin should allow sufficient time to avoid a collision with the car in front, taking into consideration that the car is slowing down as it comes to a stop.

REVIEW SET 19A

1 a independent : weeks of experience
dependent : defective items

b There is a weak, negative, linear correlation between the variables.

2 a

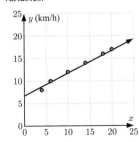

b $\overline{x} = 12$, $\overline{y} \approx 12.8$ **c** On the graph.

d **i** ≈ 13 km/h   **ii** ≈ 19 km/h

3 a, b

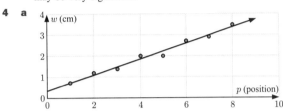

c We estimate that there will be about 210 diagnosed cases on day 14. This estimate is very unreliable as 14 is outside the poles. The medical team have probably isolated those infected at this stage and there could be a downturn which may be very significant.

4 a

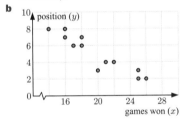

b $r \approx 0.990$, $r^2 \approx 0.980$ There is a very strong positive correlation between the variables.

c $w \approx 0.381p + 0.336$

d **i** ≈ 5.7 cm

ii As $p = 14$ is outside the poles, this prediction could be unreliable.

5 a Negatively correlated. The more games won, the higher the team's position on the ladder (and so the value for *Position* is smaller).

b

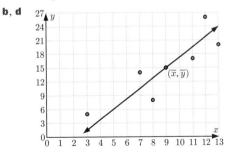

c $r < 0$ and $r^2 \approx 0.879$, there is a strong negative correlation between the variables.

d $y \approx -0.529x + 15.5$ **e** 4th

REVIEW SET 19B

1 a The independent variable is *age*.   **b** No association exists.

c It is not sensible to find it as the variables are not linearly related.

2 a $\overline{x} = 9$, $\overline{y} = 15$

b, d

c positively correlated

e $y \approx 6$. Reasonably accurate by interpolation.

3 a i Positive, as numbers get larger they have more possible factors.

ii Weak, the larger the number, the more prime, square, cubic, etc. numbers you encounter that have very small numbers of factors.

b

Number	1	2	3	4	5	6	7	8	9	10
Number of factors	1	2	2	3	2	4	2	4	3	4

Number	11	12	13	14	15	16	17	18	19	20
Number of factors	2	6	2	4	4	5	2	6	2	6

c

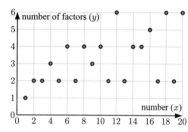

d $r \approx 0.531$, $r^2 \approx 0.282$ there is a weak positive linear correlation between the variables.

4 a

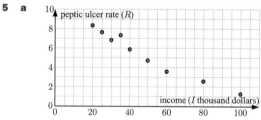

b $r > 0$ and $r^2 \approx 0.770$, there is a strong positive correlation between the variables.

c $v \approx 0.114n + 0.100$

d Each coin added to a wallet or purse increases the value by 11.4 cents on average.

e i $\approx \$2.38$

ii 20 coins is too far beyond the upper pole to extrapolate with any reliable accuracy.

5 a

b $R \approx -0.0907I + 9.79$

c There is a very strong negative correlation between the variables.

d when $I = 55$, $R \approx 4.8$

e $\$120\,000$ gives a rate of -1.09 which is meaningless. So, $\$120\,000$ is outside the data range of this model.

f i The point $(35, 7.3)$, as it does not follow the general trend of the data in that area.

ii $R \approx -0.0887I + 9.61$ There is a very strong negative correlation between the variables. When $I = 55$, $R \approx 4.7$

EXERCISE 20A

1 a 1 **b** $\frac{1}{2}$ **c** 2 **d** $1\frac{3}{5}$ **e** 1 **f** $4\frac{1}{3}$

g 2 **h** -1 **i** 2 **j** 1 **k** 1 **l** $\frac{1}{2}$

2 a -2 **b** 3 **c** 1 **d** -1 **e** 5 **f** 1

g $-\frac{1}{2}$ **h** $-\frac{1}{3}$ **i** -1 **j** $-\frac{1}{2}$ **k** $\frac{1}{2}$ **l** 5

m -5 **n** $1\frac{1}{4}$ **o** $-\frac{7}{9}$ **p** $-\frac{1}{3}$

EXERCISE 20B.1

1 a $\frac{a}{2}$ **b** $2m$ **c** 6 **d** 3 **e** $2a$ **f** x^2

g $2x$ **h** 2 **i** $\frac{1}{2a}$ **j** $2m$ **k** 4 **l** $\frac{2}{t}$

m $2d$ **n** $\frac{b}{2}$ **o** $\frac{2b}{3a}$

2 a t **b** cannot be simplified **c** y

d cannot be simplified **e** $\frac{a}{b}$ **f** cannot be simplified

g $\frac{a}{2}$ **h** cannot be simplified **i** $\frac{7c}{4d}$

3 a 4 **b** $2n$ **c** a **d** 1

e a^2 **f** $\frac{3n}{2}$ **g** $\frac{1}{2b^3}$ **h** $\frac{k^4}{2a^3}$

4 a $2(x+5)$ **b** $\frac{n+5}{6}$ **c** $\frac{b+2}{2}$ **d** $\frac{3(k-2)}{4}$

e $\frac{5}{t-1}$ **f** $\frac{2}{5(k+4)}$ **g** $\frac{1}{3(x-3)}$ **h** $\frac{5(p+4)}{3}$

5 a $\frac{x+2}{9}$ **b** $\frac{12}{a+1}$ **c** $\frac{x+y}{3}$ **d** $x+y$

e $\frac{2}{x+2}$ **f** $\frac{a+5}{3}$ **g** $\frac{y}{3}$ **h** $\frac{y-3}{3}$

i $\frac{x+1}{3}$ **j** $\frac{1}{2(b-4)}$ **k** $\frac{2(p+q)}{3}$ **l** $\frac{8}{5(r-2)}$

m $\frac{x}{x-1}$ **n** $\frac{(x+2)(x+1)}{4}$ **o** $\frac{(x+2)(x-1)^2}{4x}$

EXERCISE 20B.2

1 a $x+2$ **b** $x-2$ **c** $\frac{x+2}{2}$ **d** $\frac{x-5}{2}$

e $\frac{y+3}{3}$ **f** $\frac{3x-15}{2}$ **g** $a+b$ **h** $\frac{a+b}{c+d}$

2 a $\frac{2x+3}{3}$ **b** cannot be simplified

c cannot be simplified **d** $2a-1$ **e** $\frac{3a+1}{2}$

f cannot be simplified **g** $\frac{b+3}{2}$ **h** $\frac{4b-6}{3}$

3 a $\frac{3}{4}$ **b** $\frac{5}{3}$ **c** x **d** $\frac{4}{5}$ **e** $\frac{1}{y}$ **f** $\frac{x}{y}$ **g** $4x$

h $3x$ **i** $\frac{5x}{7}$ **j** $\frac{3b}{4}$ **k** $\frac{2x}{3}$ **l** $\frac{3(a+b)}{2a^2(2a+b)}$

4 a -2 **b** $-\frac{3}{2}$ **c** -1 **d** $-\frac{1}{2}$ **e** -3

f $-\frac{2}{x}$ **g** $\frac{ab}{2}$ **h** $-2x$

5 a $x+1$ **b** $x-1$ **c** $-(x+1)$ **d** $\frac{1}{x-2}$

e $a-b$ **f** $-(a+b)$ **g** $\frac{2}{x-1}$ **h** $\frac{3+x}{x}$

i $\frac{3(x+y)}{2y}$ **j** $-\frac{2(b+a)}{a}$ **k** $\frac{y}{4x+y}$ **l** $-\frac{4x}{x+4}$

6 a $x + 1$ **b** $\dfrac{1}{a-5}$ **c** $\dfrac{2x}{x-5}$ **d** $\dfrac{x-2}{x+2}$

e $\dfrac{x+3}{x-1}$ **f** $\dfrac{x+1}{1-x}$ **g** $\dfrac{n-5}{n+3}$ **h** $\dfrac{x+2}{x+3}$

i $\dfrac{x+2}{2x-1}$ **j** $\dfrac{2x+1}{x-1}$ **k** $\dfrac{4x-3}{2x+1}$ **l** $\dfrac{3x+4}{x+2}$

7 $\dfrac{2k^2 - 7k - 15}{k - 5} = \dfrac{(2k+3)\cancel{(k-5)}^{1}}{\cancel{k-5}\,1} = 2k + 3$

For $k \in \mathbb{Z}$, $2k$ is always an even integer, so $(2k+3)$ is always an odd integer.

EXERCISE 20C

1 a $\dfrac{xy}{10}$ **b** $\dfrac{3}{2}$ **c** $\dfrac{a^2}{2}$ **d** $\dfrac{1}{6}$ **e** $\dfrac{1}{5}$ **f** $\dfrac{c^2}{10}$

g $\dfrac{ac}{bd}$ **h** 1 **i** $\dfrac{1}{2m}$ **j** 2 **k** $\dfrac{a}{b}$ **l** 4

m $\dfrac{3}{m}$ **n** $\dfrac{a^2}{b^2}$ **o** $\dfrac{4}{x^2}$ **p** $\dfrac{1}{c}$

2 a $\dfrac{3}{2}$ **b** $\dfrac{3}{a}$ **c** $\dfrac{3x}{16}$ **d** $\dfrac{3}{4}$ **e** 2 **f** $\dfrac{c}{25}$

g $\dfrac{1}{5}$ **h** $\dfrac{m^2}{2}$ **i** 2 **j** $\dfrac{n}{m}$ **k** $\dfrac{3}{4g}$ **l** $\dfrac{g}{3}$

m $\dfrac{8}{x^3}$ **n** $\dfrac{x^2}{3}$ **o** $\dfrac{1}{a}$ **p** $\dfrac{3a}{5}$

3 a $\dfrac{5x}{2(x-2)}$ **b** $\dfrac{4}{3t}$ **c** $\dfrac{20}{a}$ **d** $\dfrac{4k}{3}$

e $-\dfrac{x}{2}$ **f** $\dfrac{3m}{2(5m-1)}$

EXERCISE 20D

1 a $\dfrac{5a}{6}$ **b** $\dfrac{b}{10}$ **c** $\dfrac{7c}{4}$ **d** $\dfrac{5d-6}{10}$

e $\dfrac{2x+15}{24}$ **f** $-\dfrac{5x}{14}$ **g** $\dfrac{4a+3b}{12}$ **h** $-\dfrac{2t}{9}$

i $\dfrac{5m}{21}$ **j** $\dfrac{d}{2}$ **k** $\dfrac{11p}{35}$ **l** $\dfrac{22t}{45}$

m $\dfrac{19k}{72}$ **n** m **o** $\dfrac{5a}{12}$ **p** $\dfrac{x}{12}$

q $\dfrac{11z}{20}$ **r** $\dfrac{41q}{21}$

2 a $\dfrac{7b+3a}{ab}$ **b** $\dfrac{3c+2a}{ac}$ **c** $\dfrac{4d+5a}{ad}$ **d** $\dfrac{2an-am}{mn}$

e $\dfrac{2a+b}{2x}$ **f** $\dfrac{5}{2a}$ **g** $\dfrac{4y-1}{xy}$ **h** $\dfrac{31}{5x}$

i $\dfrac{35}{12z}$ **j** $\dfrac{ad+bc}{bd}$ **k** $\dfrac{6+a^2}{2a}$ **l** $\dfrac{3x+2y}{3y}$

m $\dfrac{40-2p}{5p}$ **n** $\dfrac{7x}{18y}$ **o** $-\dfrac{19}{40t}$ **p** $\dfrac{x+1}{x^2}$

q $\dfrac{x-2}{x^2}$ **r** $\dfrac{5x+6}{2x^2}$ **s** $\dfrac{1+2x}{x^2y}$ **t** $\dfrac{2y^2-1}{xy^2}$

u $\dfrac{3-8x}{2x^2}$ **v** $\dfrac{q^2-p}{p^2q}$ **w** $\dfrac{3s+2r^2}{rs^2}$ **x** $\dfrac{6y-x^2}{2x^2y^2}$

3 a $\dfrac{x+2}{2}$ **b** $\dfrac{y-3}{3}$ **c** $\dfrac{3a}{2}$ **d** $\dfrac{b-12}{4}$

e $\dfrac{x-8}{2}$ **f** $\dfrac{6+a}{3}$ **g** $\dfrac{4x}{5}$ **h** $\dfrac{2x+1}{x}$

i $\dfrac{5x-2}{x}$ **j** $\dfrac{a^2+2}{a}$ **k** $\dfrac{3+b^2}{b}$ **l** $\dfrac{1-2x^3}{x^2}$

4 a $\dfrac{5x+2}{6}$ **b** $\dfrac{-x-1}{4}$ **c** $\dfrac{11x+9}{12}$ **d** $\dfrac{x+5}{6}$

e $\dfrac{-2x-1}{12}$ **f** $\dfrac{10x+3}{6}$ **g** $\dfrac{x-3}{12}$ **h** $\dfrac{23x-6}{30}$

i $\dfrac{5a-b}{6}$ **j** $\dfrac{14x-1}{20}$ **k** $\dfrac{11x-12}{30}$ **l** $\dfrac{3x-4}{20}$

m $\dfrac{3x-2}{8}$ **n** $\dfrac{13x-38}{15}$ **o** $\dfrac{-17x-1}{12}$

5 a $\dfrac{7x+3}{x(x+1)}$ **b** $\dfrac{2x-6}{x(x+2)}$ **c** $\dfrac{x-7}{(x+1)(x-1)}$

d $\dfrac{3x+7}{x+2}$ **e** $\dfrac{5x-4}{x(x-4)}$ **f** $\dfrac{-4x-10}{x+3}$

g $\dfrac{2x^2+x+1}{(x+1)(x-1)}$ **h** $\dfrac{11x-10}{x(x-2)}$

i $\dfrac{-2x-6}{(x+1)(x+2)}$ **j** $\dfrac{2x^2+5x-4}{(x-1)(2x+1)}$

k $\dfrac{x^2+2x+17}{(x-1)(x+3)}$ **l** $\dfrac{-8x}{(x+5)(x-3)}$

m $\dfrac{3x^2+6x+2}{x(x+1)(x+2)}$ **n** $\dfrac{27x-24}{x(x+3)(x-4)}$

o $\dfrac{2x^3-x^2+1}{x(x-1)(x+1)}$

6 a $\$\left(\dfrac{210x+150}{x(x+1)}\right)$ **b i** \$49.50 **ii** \$40

7 a $\dfrac{2+x}{x(x+1)}$ **b** $\dfrac{2(x^2+2x+2)}{(x+2)(x-3)}$

c $\dfrac{x^2-2x+3}{(x-2)(x+3)}$ **d** $\dfrac{x+14}{x+7}$ **e** $\dfrac{3+5x}{x(x+2)}$

f $\dfrac{7x-25}{x(x-3)}$ **g** $\dfrac{6x+13}{(x-4)(x+2)}$ **h** $\dfrac{-2x}{x-1}$

8 a $\dfrac{-1}{a(a+1)}$

b If a is positive, then $(a+1)$ is positive.

$\therefore \dfrac{-1}{a(a+1)}$ is negative.

$\therefore \dfrac{a+2}{a+1} - \dfrac{a+1}{a}$ is negative.

9 b i $\dfrac{1}{2} = \dfrac{1}{3} + \dfrac{1}{6}$ **ii** $\dfrac{1}{5} = \dfrac{1}{6} + \dfrac{1}{30}$ **iii** $\dfrac{1}{9} = \dfrac{1}{10} + \dfrac{1}{90}$

10 a $\dfrac{-2}{x-2}$ **b** $\dfrac{2}{x+4}$ **c** $\dfrac{x-2}{x+2}$

d $\dfrac{x-6}{2-x}$ **e** $\dfrac{-(x+2)}{4x^2}$ **f** $\dfrac{12-x}{16x^2}$

11 a i $\dfrac{2x}{x+1} - \dfrac{4}{(x-1)(x+1)} = \dfrac{2(x-2)}{x-1}$

ii $\dfrac{2(x-2)}{x-1} = 0$ when $x = 2$

iii It is undefined when $x = \pm 1$.

b i $\dfrac{6}{(x+2)(x+5)} + \dfrac{x}{x+2} = \dfrac{x+3}{x+5}$

ii $\dfrac{x+3}{x+5} = 0$ when $x = -3$

iii It is undefined when $x = -5$ or -2.

REVIEW SET 20A

1 a -2 **b** 4 **c** $\frac{1}{3}$ **d** -1 **2 a** 9 **b** -1

3 a $\dfrac{2t}{3}$ **b** $\dfrac{8}{3}$ **c** $\dfrac{x}{3}$ **d** $\dfrac{2}{x+2}$

4 a $\dfrac{2}{x-3}$ **b** $\dfrac{x+2}{x}$ **c** $\dfrac{3x}{3x+1}$

5 a -2 **b** $-\dfrac{5}{x}$ **c** $-\dfrac{x+4}{2}$

6 a $\dfrac{a}{3}$ **b** $\dfrac{3a}{b^2}$ **c** $\dfrac{3a+b^2}{3b}$ **d** $\dfrac{3a-b^2}{3b}$

7 a $\dfrac{21}{x}$ **b** $\dfrac{t}{24}$ **8 a** $\dfrac{3}{2n}$ **b** $\dfrac{7x}{3(x+5)}$

9 a $\dfrac{11x}{12}$ **b** $\dfrac{14+x}{7}$ **c** $\dfrac{x-4}{4}$ **d** $\dfrac{5x}{12}$

10 a $\dfrac{7x-3}{12}$ **b** $\dfrac{3x+2}{6}$ **c** $\dfrac{3x+3}{10}$

11 a $\dfrac{3x}{(x+1)(x-2)}$ **b** $\dfrac{x+9}{(x-1)(x+1)}$ **c** $\dfrac{x^2+x+1}{x^2(x+1)}$

12 a i $\dfrac{a^2-9}{a}$ **ii** $\dfrac{3-a}{3}$ **b** $-\dfrac{3(a+3)}{a}$

c i -12 **ii** undefined **iii** $-\frac{24}{5}$

REVIEW SET 20B

1 a -6 **b** 0 **c** 2

2 a $\dfrac{3}{2x}$ **b** $a+2b$ **c** $\dfrac{x+2}{x}$

3 a $\frac{1}{3}$ **b** $2(x-2)$ **c** $\dfrac{x-3}{4}$

4 a $\dfrac{2m}{n^2}$ **b** $\dfrac{m}{2}$ **c** $\dfrac{m^3}{n}$

5 a $\dfrac{11}{2x}$ **b** $\dfrac{6b-ay}{by}$ **c** $\dfrac{35}{12x}$

6 a $\dfrac{5x}{14}$ **b** $\dfrac{4x+9}{3x^2}$

7 a $\dfrac{10+x}{2}$ **b** $\dfrac{3x-y}{x}$ **c** $\dfrac{6+3x+2y}{6}$

8 a $\dfrac{3y}{2(y+2)}$ **b** $-\dfrac{3}{4x}$

9 a $\dfrac{3x-2}{8}$ **b** $\dfrac{9x+27}{10}$ **c** $\dfrac{9-7x}{18}$

10 a $\dfrac{7-x}{(x-1)(x+2)}$ **b** $\dfrac{x^2-2x+2}{x^2(x-1)}$

c $\dfrac{2x^3+3x^2-10x-12}{x(x+3)(x+2)}$

11 $\dfrac{70-m^2-3m}{m+10} = \dfrac{-(m+10)(m-7)}{m+10} = -m+7$

If m is an even integer, then $-m+7$ must be an odd integer, as even + odd = odd.

$\therefore \ \dfrac{70-m^2-3m}{m+10}$ is an odd integer.

12 a i 12 **ii** 50 **b** xy

c $(x+y) \div \left(\dfrac{1}{x} + \dfrac{1}{y}\right) = (x+y) \div \left(\dfrac{y+x}{xy}\right)$
$$= (x+y) \times \dfrac{xy}{x+y}$$
$$= xy$$

d 420

13 a $\dfrac{-3(x-4)}{x-2}$ **b** $x=4$ **c** $x = \pm 2$

EXERCISE 21A

1 a $\dfrac{A'B'}{AB} = \dfrac{3}{4}$, $\dfrac{B'C'}{BC} = \dfrac{2}{3}$ $\therefore$ not similar **b** similar

2 no, $\dfrac{140}{100} \neq \dfrac{100}{60}$

3 a true **b** false

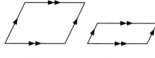

c true **d** false

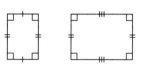

4 a $x = 8.75$ **b** $x = 4.8$ **c** $x = 7.5$ **d** $x = 127$

5 a 6 cm **b** 60

6 a 6 cm **b** $k = 1.5$ **7** FG $= 2.4$ m

8 a $x = 4.8$ **b** $x = 9$ **c** $x = 100$ **d** $x = 16$

9 a

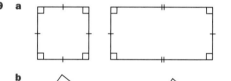

Note: Other answers are possible.

b

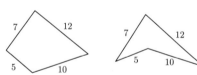

10 no

EXERCISE 21B.1

1 a $\widehat{\text{VUW}} = \widehat{\text{XYW}}$, $\widehat{\text{VWU}} = \widehat{\text{XWY}}$ {vertically opposite}

b $\widehat{\text{FGH}} = \widehat{\text{FDE}}$, angle F is common.

c $\widehat{\text{RST}} = \widehat{\text{RQP}}$, $\widehat{\text{SRT}} = \widehat{\text{QRP}}$ {vertically opposite}

d $\widehat{\text{ABC}} = \widehat{\text{EDC}}$ {equal alternate angles},
$\widehat{\text{ACB}} = \widehat{\text{ECD}}$ {vertically opposite}

e $\widehat{\text{LKM}} = \widehat{\text{LNJ}}$, angle L is common

f VX $= 15$ m, XY $= 34$ m {Pythagoras}
$\therefore$ YZ $= 2$WV, XY $= 2$XW, XZ $= 2$XV

2 Hint: Find the unknown angles in terms of α.

EXERCISE 21B.2

1 a $x = 5$ **b** $x = 2.8$ **c** $x = \frac{36}{11} \approx 3.27$

d $x = \frac{20}{3} \approx 6.67$ **e** $x = 7$ **f** $x = 7.2$

g $x = 12$ **h** $x = 7$ **i** $x = 10$

2 BE $= 7.5$ m

EXERCISE 21C

1 a 7 m **b** 7.5 m **2** ≈ 9.22 m **3** 180 cm or 1.8 m

4 a ≈ 2.67 m **b** ≈ 5.67 m **5** 39 m **6** 1.52 m

7 ≈ 117 m **8** 9.9 seconds

9 a i SU = 5.5 m   **ii** BC = 8.2 m
   b No, the ball's centre is ≈ 11 cm on the D side of C.

10 PR ≈ 3.67 m   **11 a** $\frac{9}{20}$ **b** 9 : 2

EXERCISE 21D

1 a $x = 32$ **b** $x = 16$ **2 a** $x = 5$ **b** $x = 4.8$
3 a $k = 4$ **b** 20 cm and 24 cm   **c** 16 times
4 b $k = \frac{5}{2}$ **c** **i** 100 cm^2 **ii** 84 cm^2
5 ≈ 1.45 cm   **6** 4 units^2

EXERCISE 21E

1 a $V = 270$ **b** $V = 31.25$ **2 a** $x = 8$ **b** $x \approx 5.26$
3 6750 cm^3 **4** 12 cm   **5** $k \approx 1.19$
6 a 4.116 m^3 **b** 3.75 m^2
7 No, comparing lengths $k = 1.6$, comparing capacities $k \approx 1.37$.
8 a 4 cm   **b** 648 cm^3
9 a $k = \frac{2}{3}$ **b** 14 850 cm^3 **c** 280 cm^2
10 a The dimensions are in the same ratio.
   b **i** $6 : 10 : 15$ **ii** $\sqrt[3]{6} : \sqrt[3]{10} : \sqrt[3]{15}$
     iii $(\sqrt[3]{6})^2 : (\sqrt[3]{10})^2 : (\sqrt[3]{15})^2$
   c **i** ≈ 8.43 cm   **ii** ≈ 4.58 cm   **iii** ≈ 215 cm^2

REVIEW SET 21A

1 similar
2
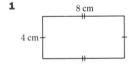 and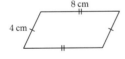

3 $x = 2.8$
4 Hint: Carefully show that triangles are equiangular, giving reasons.
5 No, even if corresponding side lengths of rhombuses are always in the same ratio, the rhombuses are not always equiangular.
6 a $x \approx 1.71$ **b** $x \approx 6.47$ **c** $x \approx 4.90$ **d** $x = 13.5$
7 ≈ 10.4 m
8 a $A = 7$ **b** $x \approx 8.14$ **c** $x = 15$, $y = 32$
9 ≈ 66.7 m wide   **10 a** $k = 4$ **b** 0.99 cm   **c** 0.5 cm^3

REVIEW SET 21B

1

2 a $x = 3$ **b** $x = 4$ **c** $x = 12$
3 a $\widehat{ABC} = \widehat{EDC}$, $\widehat{ACB} = \widehat{ECD}$ {vertically opposite}
   b 3.2 cm
4 a **i** 3 cm   **ii** 5 cm   **b** 128 cm^2 **5** 6.4 cm
6 a $x = 4$ **b** $x \approx 42.7$ **c** $x = 3.6$, $y = 6.4$
7 a 7 : 5   **b** 49 : 25
8 $2\sqrt{13} \approx 7.21$ cm by $3\sqrt{13} \approx 10.8$ cm   **9** $x = 12$
10 a CD = 7.2 cm   **b** 22.4 cm^2 **11** 648 cm^3

EXERCISE 22A

1 a **i** BC   **ii** AC   **iii** AB
   b **i** KM   **ii** KL   **iii** LM
   c **i** PR   **ii** QR   **iii** PQ
2 a **i** PR   **ii** QR   **iii** PQ   **iv** PQ   **v** QR

   b **i** AC   **ii** AB   **iii** BC   **iv** BC   **v** AB
   c **i** LM   **ii** MN   **iii** LN   **iv** LN   **v** MN

EXERCISE 22B

1 a **i** $\frac{3}{5}$ **ii** $\frac{4}{5}$ **iii** $\frac{3}{4}$ **b** **i** $\frac{5}{13}$ **ii** $\frac{12}{13}$ **iii** $\frac{5}{12}$
   c **i** $\frac{15}{17}$ **ii** $\frac{8}{17}$ **iii** $\frac{15}{8}$ **d** **i** $\frac{1}{\sqrt{5}}$ **ii** $\frac{2}{\sqrt{5}}$ **iii** $\frac{1}{2}$
   e **i** $\frac{4}{7}$ **ii** $\frac{\sqrt{33}}{7}$ **iii** $\frac{4}{\sqrt{33}}$
   f **i** $\frac{8}{\sqrt{73}}$ **ii** $\frac{3}{\sqrt{73}}$ **iii** $\frac{8}{3}$
2 a PQ ≈ 59 mm, PR ≈ 54 mm, QR ≈ 24 mm
   b **i** ≈ 0.407 **ii** ≈ 0.915 **iii** ≈ 0.444
   c **i** ≈ 0.407 **ii** ≈ 0.914 **iii** ≈ 0.445
3 a **i** ≈ 0.587 **ii** ≈ 0.630 **iii** ≈ 1.378 **iv** ≈ 0.778
   b **i** ≈ 0.588 **ii** ≈ 0.629 **iii** ≈ 1.376 **iv** ≈ 0.777
4 a **i** ≈ 0.9240 **ii** ≈ 0.0760 **iii** 1
     iv ≈ 0.1786 **v** ≈ 0.8214 **vi** 1
   b $\cos^2 \theta + \sin^2 \theta = 1$
5 a **i** 1   **ii** 1   **iii** 1
   b $\tan \theta \times \tan(90° - \theta)$ is always 1
6 Hint: Show QX $= \sqrt{3}$.

7 a $\widehat{PYX} = 15°$
   b **Hint:** Find the length of XQ and the size of $\widehat{PYQ}$.

EXERCISE 22C

1 a $\sin 65° = \dfrac{x}{a}$ **b** $\cos 32° = \dfrac{x}{b}$ **c** $\tan 56° = \dfrac{x}{c}$
   d $\cos 37° = \dfrac{d}{x}$ **e** $\tan 49° = \dfrac{e}{x}$ **f** $\tan 73° = \dfrac{f}{x}$
2 a $x \approx 17.62$ **b** $x \approx 8.91$ **c** $x \approx 6.88$
   d $x \approx 16.73$ **e** $x \approx 14.98$ **f** $x \approx 22.94$
   g $x \approx 23.47$ **h** $x \approx 36.05$ **i** $x \approx 7.42$
   j $x \approx 13.77$ **k** $x \approx 13.07$ **l** $x \approx 20.78$
3 a $\theta = 62°$, $a \approx 12.4$, $b \approx 6.6$
   b $\theta = 27°$, $a \approx 15.7$, $b \approx 7.1$
   c $\theta = 52°$, $a \approx 54.6$, $b \approx 33.6$
4 ≈ 28.8 cm

EXERCISE 22D

1 a $\theta \approx 51.3°$ **b** $\theta \approx 41.8°$ **c** $\theta \approx 39.6°$
   d $\theta \approx 38.0°$ **e** $\theta \approx 34.1°$ **f** $\theta \approx 47.6°$
   g $\theta \approx 36.5°$ **h** $\theta \approx 35.8°$ **i** $\theta \approx 36.9°$
2 a $\theta \approx 38.7°$, $\phi \approx 51.3°$, $x \approx 6.2$
   b $\alpha \approx 60.2°$, $\beta \approx 29.8°$, $x \approx 7.0$
   c $a \approx 41.5°$, $b \approx 48.5°$, $x \approx 8.4$
3 These three triangles do not exist. The hypotenuse must be longer than the other sides.

EXERCISE 22E

1 ≈ 110 m   **2** $\approx 32.9°$ **3** ≈ 238 m   **4** ≈ 765 m
5 ≈ 280 m   **6** $\approx 6.89°$ **7** ≈ 2.65 m   **8** ≈ 54.6 m
9 $\approx 44.4°$ **10** ≈ 23.5 m   **11** ≈ 73.2 m
12 $\approx 67.4°$ **13** $\approx 21.8°$ **14** ≈ 15.8 cm
15 a ≈ 18.7 mm   **b** $\approx 35.7°$ **16** ≈ 35.3 cm^2

17 No, ≈ 0.721 cm **18** $\approx 118°$ **19** $\approx 41.4°$

20 $\approx 53.2°$

21 **a** **i** ≈ 7.98 m **ii** ≈ 12.6 m **b** $\approx 21.1°$

22 ≈ 7.48 m **23** **a** ≈ 248 m **b** ≈ 128 m

24 $\approx 14.3°$ **25** ≈ 729 m

26 **a** ≈ 1.66 units **b** ≈ 1.66 units

27 AB ≈ 6.43 m, BC ≈ 9.85 m, AC ≈ 8.66 m

28 **a** ≈ 21.2 cm **b** $\approx 35.3°$

29 **a** ≈ 9.43 cm **b** $\approx 32.5°$ **c** ≈ 10.8 cm **d** $\approx 29.1°$

30 **a** ≈ 8.94 cm **b** $\approx 18.5°$

31 ≈ 69.2 cm **32** **a** $45°$ **33** $\theta \approx 61.9°$

34 ≈ 163 m **35** **a** 13 cm **b** $\approx 47.3°$

EXERCISE 22F

1 **a** **b** **c** **d**

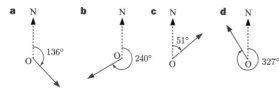

2 **a** $234°$ **b** $293°$ **c** $083°$ **d** $124°$

3 **a** $040°$ **b** $235°$ **c** $297°$

4 **a** $041°$ **b** $142°$ **c** $322°$ **d** $099°$ **e** $221°$
  f $279°$

5 **a** $055°$ **b** $235°$ **c** $095°$ **d** $275°$ **e** $130°$
  f $310°$

6 **a** $\approx 062.6°$ **b** $\approx 243°$

7 **a** ≈ 3.49 km **b** $\approx 027.3°$ **8** ≈ 46.0 km

9 **a**

N
S 164°
F

b 2.8 km

c **i** ≈ 772 m east
  ii ≈ 2.69 km south

10 ≈ 2.44 km

11 **a**

N
R 197°
2.3 km
N
107°
T
1.8 km S

b ≈ 2.92 km
c $\approx 159°$

12 ≈ 33.5 km on bearing $\approx 025.6°$

13 ≈ 2.62 km on bearing $\approx 058.4°$

EXERCISE 22G

1 **a** **i** GF **ii** HG **iii** HF **iv** GM
  b **i** CD **ii** DE **iii** DF **iv** DX

2 **a** **i** $B\widehat{G}F$ **ii** $B\widehat{H}F$ **iii** $D\widehat{F}H$ **iv** $A\widehat{X}E$
  b **i** $P\widehat{Z}S$ **ii** $Q\widehat{Y}R$ **iii** $P\widehat{W}S$ **iv** $Q\widehat{W}R$
  c **i** $A\widehat{S}X$ **ii** $A\widehat{Y}X$

3 **a** **i** $45°$ **ii** $\approx 35.3°$ **iii** $\approx 63.4°$ **iv** $\approx 41.8°$
  b **i** $\approx 18.4°$ **ii** $\approx 15.5°$ **iii** $\approx 17.5°$
  c **i** $\approx 26.6°$ **ii** $\approx 22.6°$ **iii** $\approx 25.4°$
  d **i** $\approx 61.9°$ **ii** $\approx 69.3°$

EXERCISE 22H

1 $\approx 54.7°$ **2** $\approx 29.5°$ **3** $\approx 71.7°$ **4** $\approx 51.6°$

REVIEW SET 22A

1 $\sin\theta = \frac{5}{13}$, $\cos\theta = \frac{12}{13}$, $\tan\theta = \frac{5}{12}$

2 **a** $x \approx 14.0$ **b** $x \approx 35.2$

3 $\theta = 36°$, $x \approx 12.4$, $y \approx 21.0$ **4** ≈ 55.2 m

5 **a** $157°$ **b** $281°$ **6** ≈ 8.54 km, on bearing $\approx 201°$

7 ≈ 9.38 m **8** **a** $\approx 56.3°$ **b** $\approx 33.9°$

9 ≈ 294 km, on bearing $\approx 264°$

REVIEW SET 22B

1 **a** $\theta \approx 38.7°$ **b** $\theta \approx 37.1°$

2 **a** $x \approx 3.18$ **b** $x \approx 9.40$

3 $\alpha \approx 36.4°$, $\theta \approx 53.6°$, $x \approx 25.7$

4 $\approx 32.2°$ **5** ≈ 638 m **6** ≈ 22.4 km

7 **a** $230°$ **b** $165°$ **c** $140°$

8 **a**

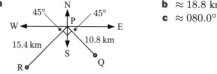

b ≈ 18.8 km
c $\approx 080.0°$

9 $(30 - 6\sqrt{3})$ cm ≈ 19.6 cm **10** **a** $45°$ **b** $\approx 54.7°$

EXERCISE 23A

1 **a** $x = \pm 10$ **b** $x = \pm 5$ **c** $x = \pm 2$
  d $x = \pm 3$ **e** no real solutions **f** $x = 0$
  g $x = \pm 3$ **h** no real solutions **i** $x = \pm\sqrt{2}$

2 **a** $x = 4$ or -2 **b** $x = 0$ or -8 **c** no real solutions
  d $x = 4 \pm \sqrt{5}$ **e** no real solutions **f** $x = -2$
  g $x = 2\frac{1}{2}$ **h** $x = 0$ or $-\frac{4}{3}$ **i** $x = \frac{8}{3}$ or $-\frac{10}{3}$
  j $x = -\frac{1}{2} \pm 2\sqrt{3}$ **k** $x = \dfrac{3 \pm \sqrt{7}}{2}$ **l** $x = \dfrac{\pm\sqrt{6} - 3}{2}$

3 **a** $x = \pm 2$ **b** $x = \pm\sqrt{10}$ **c** $x = \pm 4$

4 **a** $x = 1$ **b** $x = \frac{3}{5}$ or 1

EXERCISE 23B

1 **a** $m = 0$ or $n = 0$ **b** $p = 0$ or $q = 0$
  c $x = 0$ or $y = 0$

2 **a** $x = 0$ or 5 **b** $x = 0$ or -3 **c** $x = -1$ or 3
  d $x = 0$ or 7 **e** $x = 0$ or -1 **f** $x = -6$ or $\frac{3}{2}$
  g $x = \pm\frac{1}{2}$ **h** $x = -2$ or 7 **i** $x = 5$ or $-\frac{2}{3}$

3 **a** $x = 0$ or 7 **b** $x = 0$ or 5 **c** $x = 0$ or 8
  d $x = 0$ or 4 **e** $x = 0$ or -2 **f** $x = 0$ or $-\frac{5}{2}$
  g $x = 0$ or $\frac{3}{4}$ **h** $x = 0$ or $\frac{5}{4}$ **i** $x = 0$ or 3

4 **a** $x = -1$ or -2 **b** $x = 1$ or 2 **c** $x = 5$
  d $x = -2$ or -3 **e** $x = 2$ or 3 **f** $x = -1$ or -6
  g $x = -2$ or -7 **h** $x = -5$ or -6 **i** $x = -5$ or 3
  j $x = -6$ or 2 **k** $x = 3$ or 8 **l** $x = 7$

5 **a** $x = -3$ or -6 **b** $x = -4$ or -7 **c** $x = -4$ or 2
  d $x = -4$ or 3 **e** $x = 3$ or 2 **f** $x = 2$
  g $x = 3$ or -2 **h** $x = -12$ or 5 **i** $x = 10$ or -7

6 **a** $x = \frac{1}{2}$ or 2 **b** $x = -3$ or $\frac{1}{3}$ **c** $x = -4$ or $-\frac{5}{3}$

  d $x = \frac{1}{2}$ or -3 **e** $x = \frac{1}{2}$ or 5 **f** $x = -1$ or $-\frac{5}{2}$

  g $x = -\frac{1}{3}$ or -4 **h** $x = -\frac{2}{5}$ or 3 **i** $x = \frac{1}{2}$ or -9

  j $x = -1$ or $\frac{5}{2}$ **k** $x = \frac{4}{3}$ or -2 **l** $x = \frac{3}{2}$ or -6

  m $x = -\frac{1}{6}$ or 3 **n** $x = \frac{3}{2}$ or -4 **o** $x = \frac{3}{2}$ or $\frac{1}{3}$

  p $x = -\frac{8}{3}$ or 2 **q** $x = \frac{4}{7}$ or $-\frac{1}{2}$ **r** $x = \frac{1}{4}$ or $-\frac{4}{3}$

7 **a** $x = -4$ or -3 **b** $x = -3$ or 1 **c** $x = \pm 3$

  d $x = -1$ or $\frac{2}{3}$ **e** $x = -\frac{1}{2}$ **f** $x = \frac{5}{2}$ or 4

  g $x = 11$ or -3 **h** $x = -\frac{3}{4}$ or $\frac{5}{2}$

8 **a** $x = -2$ or 1 **b** $x = -6$ or 2 **c** $x = 2$ or -1

  d $x = 4$ or -1 **e** $x = 1$ or $-\frac{1}{3}$ **f** $x = \frac{1}{2}$ or -1

9 **a** $x = 4$ or -1 **b** $x = 15$ or 2 **c** $x = -9$ or -2

  d $x = 3$ or $-\frac{7}{2}$ **e** $x = 4$ or $\frac{4}{3}$ **f** $x = 1$ or $\frac{6}{5}$

  g $x = 0$ or $\pm\sqrt{11}$ **h** $x = 0$ or -3

10 **a** $x = \pm 1$ or ± 2 **b** $x = \pm\sqrt{3}$ or ± 2 **c** $x = \pm\sqrt{5}$

EXERCISE 23C

1 **a** **i, ii** $x = -2$ or -4 **b** **i, ii** $x = 5$

  c **i, ii** $x = -\frac{2}{3}$ or 3

2 **a** $x = \dfrac{-1 \pm \sqrt{21}}{2}$ **b** $x = \dfrac{5 \pm \sqrt{5}}{2}$ **c** $x = 2 \pm \sqrt{5}$

  d $x = \dfrac{3 \pm \sqrt{5}}{2}$ **e** $x = \dfrac{1 \pm \sqrt{7}}{2}$ **f** $x = \dfrac{1 \pm \sqrt{2}}{3}$

3 **a** $x \approx -1.85$ or 0.18 **b** $x \approx -1.64$ or 2.14

  c $x \approx 0.14$ or 1.46 **d** $x \approx -0.16$ or 0.88

  e $x \approx -1.22$ or 0.55 **f** $x \approx 0.05$ or 0.75

4 **a** $\Delta = -39$ which is < 0 ∴ no real solutions exist

  b $\Delta = -12$ which is < 0 ∴ no real solutions exist

  c $\Delta = -7$ which is < 0 ∴ no real solutions exist

5 **a** $x = \pm 5$ **b** no real solutions **c** $x = \pm\sqrt{7}$

  d no real solutions **e** $x = \pm\frac{3}{2}$

  f no real solutions **g** no real solutions

  h $x = 5$ or -1 **i** no real solutions

  j no real solutions **k** $x = \dfrac{3 \pm \sqrt{19}}{2}$ **l** $x = \dfrac{-1 \pm \sqrt{17}}{4}$

6 **a** $x = \dfrac{-1 \pm \sqrt{29}}{2}$ **b** $x = \dfrac{1 \pm \sqrt{5}}{2}$ **c** no real solutions

  d $x = 1 \pm 2\sqrt{2}$ **e** $x = \dfrac{7 \pm \sqrt{217}}{6}$ **f** $x = \dfrac{3 \pm \sqrt{13}}{2}$

EXERCISE 23D

1 The number is -11 or 10. **2** The number is -3 or 8.

3 The numbers are $3 + \sqrt{5}$ and $3 - \sqrt{5}$.

4 The numbers are -2 and 5, or 2 and -5.

5 8 cm **6** 10 m **7** 18 m by 12 m

8

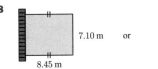

7.10 m or 16.90 m

8.45 m   3.55 m

9 ≈ 17.9 cm **10** BC $= 16$ cm or 5 cm

11 **a** $x = 2$ **b** $x = 5$ **c** $x = 6$ **d** $x = \sqrt{31} - 1$

  e $x = \dfrac{3 + \sqrt{5}}{2}$ **f** $x = 3 + \sqrt{34}$

12 BE $= 6$ cm **13** CD $= (1 + \sqrt{41})$ m **14** $n = 6$

15 $\frac{2}{5}$ or $\frac{-9}{-6}$ **16** 40 oranges **17** The number is $\frac{4}{3}$ or $\frac{3}{4}$.

18 The numbers are $\dfrac{4 + \sqrt{14}}{2}$ and $\dfrac{4 - \sqrt{14}}{2}$.

19 Cut out squares with sides 2 cm.

20 **a** If each flower bed has radius r m, then $x + 2r = 10$

  $\therefore r = 5 - \dfrac{x}{2}$

  b Hint: Lawn area $= 4 \times$ total of flower bed areas

  $\therefore 2(\pi \times 5^2) = 4 \times \pi r^2$

  $\therefore 50\pi = 4\pi\left(5 - \dfrac{x}{2}\right)^2$, and so on.

  c ≈ 2.93 m

21 $x = 5$

22 **a** Hint: Draw a diagram and show that area of pavement $= 2\left[x(12 + 2x) + 6x\right]$.

  b $4x^2 + 36x = \frac{7}{8}(6 \times 12) = 63$ **c** 1.5 m

23 3.2 cm

REVIEW SET 23A

1 **a** $x = \pm\sqrt{2}$ **b** no real solutions **c** $x = 0$ or 3

  d $x = 3$ or 8 **e** $x = -\frac{2}{5}$ or $\frac{3}{2}$ **f** $x = -\frac{7}{3}$ or 3

2 **a** $x = 0$ or 1 **b** no real solutions **c** $x = 2 \pm \sqrt{5}$

  d no real solutions **e** $x = 1$ or $-3\frac{1}{3}$ **f** $x = 5$ or $-1\frac{1}{2}$

3 **a** $x = 7$ or -3 **b** $x = \pm\frac{5}{2}$ **c** $x = \frac{2}{3}$ or $-\frac{1}{2}$

  d $x = 6$ or -4 **e** $x = -3$ **f** $x = \frac{1}{2}$ or 4

4 The number is $\frac{2}{3}$ or $\frac{3}{2}$.

5 **a** $x = -12 \pm \sqrt{155}$ **b** $x = 9$ or -2 **c** $x = -\frac{2}{5}$ or $\frac{3}{2}$

6 **a** $x = 2$ or $-\frac{1}{2}$ **b** $x = \dfrac{-2 \pm \sqrt{19}}{3}$ **c** $x = \dfrac{13 \pm \sqrt{105}}{8}$

7 $x = 7$ **8** $\dfrac{15 + 30\sqrt{2}}{7}$ cm **9** $x \approx 5.46$

10

x cm

$(20 - x)$ cm

  a **i** $(10 + 2\sqrt{10})$ cm, $(10 - 2\sqrt{10})$ cm, and hypotenuse $2\sqrt{70}$ cm

  ii $(20 + 2\sqrt{70})$ cm

  b Hint: We require $\frac{1}{2}x(20 - x) = 51$.

11 $x = 1$ or 5

REVIEW SET 23B

1 **a** $x = 3$ **b** $x = -5$ or 4 **c** no real solutions

  d $x = 8$ or -3 **e** $x = \pm 2$ **f** $x = -\frac{1}{2}$ or $\frac{2}{3}$

2 **a** $x = 2 \pm \sqrt{14}$ **b** $x = \dfrac{-1 \pm \sqrt{37}}{2}$

3 **a** $x = -5$ or 3 **b** $x = 2\frac{1}{2}$ or 4 **c** $x = -\frac{1}{3}$ or 3

4 **a** $x = \pm\sqrt{6}$ **b** $x = \pm 1$ **c** $x = \dfrac{1 \pm \sqrt{17}}{3}$

  d $x = 11$ or -3 **e** $x = \frac{1}{2}$ or $-\frac{3}{4}$ **f** $x = \frac{2}{3}$ or -5

5 8 cm, 15 cm, and 17 cm **6** 12 people, \$40 each

7 10 cm **8** The number is $\frac{4}{5}$ or -1.

9 The numbers are $\sqrt{3} - \frac{3}{2}$ and $\sqrt{3} + \frac{3}{2}$.

10 12 grandchildren **11** CX $= 60$ m, AY ≈ 34.38 m

EXERCISE 24A

1 **a** $(5, 3)$ **b** $(4, 6)$ **2** **a** $\binom{0}{3}$ **b** $\binom{5}{-5}$ **3** $(0, 1)$

4 **a** $\binom{8}{0}$ **b** $\binom{-8}{0}$ **c** $\binom{0}{-4}$ **d** $\binom{0}{4}$ **e** $\binom{4}{1}$

 f $\binom{4}{6}$ **g** $\binom{-8}{-4}$ **h** $\binom{-4}{-6}$ **i** $\binom{0}{5}$ **j** $\binom{4}{-6}$

5 **a** P$(-3, 1)$, Q$(-1, 1)$, R$(-1, -2)$, S$(-3, -2)$

 b

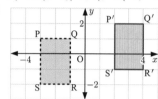

 c P$'(2, 2)$, Q$'(4, 2)$, R$'(4, -1)$, S$'(2, -1)$

6 **a, b**

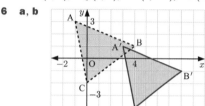

 c A$'(3, 1)$, B$'(8, -1)$, C$'(4, -4)$ **d** $2\sqrt{5}$ units

7 **a** translation of $\binom{5}{5}$

8 **a** $y = 2x + 7$ **b** $y = \frac{1}{3}x + 1$ **c** $y = -x + 7$

 d $y = -\frac{1}{2}x - 6$ **e** $3x + 2y = 11$ **f** $x = 6$

 g $y = 2x$ **h** $y = 0$

EXERCISE 24B

1

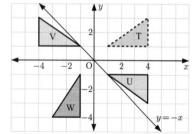

2 **a** $(4, 1)$ **b** $(-4, -1)$ **c** $(-1, 4)$ **d** $(1, -4)$

3 **a** $(1, -3)$ **b** $(3, 1)$ **c** $(5, -3)$ **d** $(-1, 1)$

 e $(-1, 3)$ **f** $(-5, -3)$ **g** $(-3, -1)$ **h** $(-1, 7)$

4

5 **a** $(1, -1)$ **b** $(5, -1)$ **c** $(3, -9)$ **d** $(1, 7)$

 e $(5, 1)$ **f** $(-8, 3)$

6 **a** $y = -2x$ **b** $y = \frac{1}{2}x$ **c** $y = -2x + 4$

 d $y = -2x + 6$

7 **a** $y = -\frac{1}{2}x$ **b** $3x - 2y = -12$

 c $3x + 2y = -4$ **d** $y = x - 5$

8 **a** $y = 2x - 5$ **b** $y = -2x + 5$

c

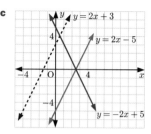

 d A reflection of $y = 2x + 3$ in the line $x = \frac{1}{2}$.

EXERCISE 24C

1 **a** $(-3, -2)$ **b** $(3, 2)$ **c** $(2, -3)$

2 **a** $(3, 6)$ **b** $(-3, -2)$ **c** $(-4, 5)$

3 **a**

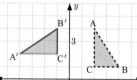

 b A$'(-4, 2)$,
  B$'(-1, 4)$,
  C$'(-1, 2)$

4 **a**

 b P$'(-5, 4)$,
  Q$'(-3, -2)$,
  R$'(-1, 1)$

5 **a** $(-3, -2)$ **b** $(2, 5)$ **c** $(1, 3)$ **d** $(0, 1)$

6 **a**

 b An anticlockwise rotation of $90°$ about O.

7 **a**

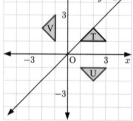

 b A rotation of $180°$ about O.

8 **a** $3x - 2y = -12$ **b** $x = 3$ **c** $x = -7$

 d $4x + 3y = -7$

9 A rotation about O through $(\theta + \phi)°$.

10 **a** $2x - y = 5$ **b** $y = x - 1$

EXERCISE 24D

1 **a**
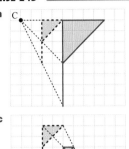

c
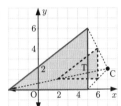

2 **a**
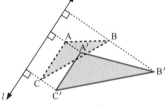

3 **a** $(4\frac{1}{2}, 6)$ **b** $(0, 2)$ **c** (kx, ky) **4** $y = 2x + 6$

5 A reduction with centre $O(0, 0)$ and scale factor $\frac{1}{2}$.

EXERCISE 24E

1 **a**
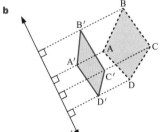

b

c

d
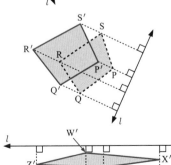

2 **a**
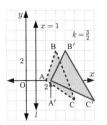

b
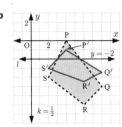

3 **a** $(3, -4)$ **b** $(4, 10)$ **c** $(-1, 1)$ **d** $(4\frac{1}{2}, -4)$
   e $(\frac{3}{4}, 1\frac{3}{4})$ **f** (x, ky) **g** (kx, y)

4 **a**
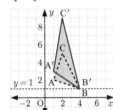

b

A′(1, 3), B′(4, 1),   A′(0, 2), B′(1$\frac{1}{2}$, 1),
C′(2, 9)   C′($\frac{1}{2}$, 5)

5 **a** Stretch with invariant x-axis and scale factor $k = \frac{3}{4}$.
   b Stretch with invariant y-axis and scale factor $k = 2$.
   c Stretch with invariant y-axis and scale factor $k = 4$.
   d Stretch with $x = -1$ the invariant line and scale factor $k = \frac{1}{4}$.

6 **a** $y = 6x$ **b** $y = \frac{9}{4}x$ **c** $y = \frac{1}{4}x + 2\frac{1}{4}$

EXERCISE 24F

1 **a** a reflection in the y-axis
   b a rotation about $O(0, 0)$ through $180°$
   c a translation of $\begin{pmatrix} -3 \\ 0 \end{pmatrix}$ **d** a translation of $\begin{pmatrix} 0 \\ 2 \end{pmatrix}$
   e a translation of $\begin{pmatrix} -3 \\ 1 \end{pmatrix}$
   f a $90°$ anticlockwise rotation about $O(0, 0)$
   g a reduction, centre $O(0, 0)$, scale factor $\frac{1}{4}$
   h an enlargement, centre $C(6, 3)$, scale factor 2
   i a reflection in $y = -x$
   j a stretch with invariant x-axis and scale factor $\frac{2}{3}$
   k a reflection in $y = -2$
   l a stretch with invariant y-axis and scale factor 2

2 **a** a translation of $\begin{pmatrix} -h \\ -k \end{pmatrix}$ **b** a reflection in the line M
   c a rotation with centre C through $(-\theta°)$
   d a reduction with centre C and scale factor $\frac{1}{k}$
   e a stretch with invariant line l and scale factor $\frac{1}{k}$

EXERCISE 24G

1 **a** **i**
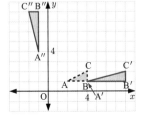

ii
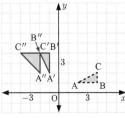

b **i**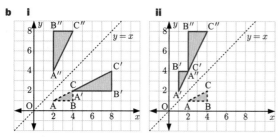

c **i** a 90° anticlockwise rotation about O
  ii a 90° clockwise rotation about O

d **i** a reflection in the x-axis **ii** a reflection in the x-axis

2 **a** **i** T_3 **ii** T_3 **iii** T_6 **iv** T_0 **v** T_1

b

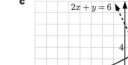

second transformation

	T_0	T_1	T_2	T_3	T_4	T_5	T_6	T_7
T_0	T_0	T_1	T_2	T_3	T_4	T_5	T_6	T_7
T_1	T_1	T_0	T_3	T_2	T_5	T_4	T_7	T_6
T_2	T_2	T_7	T_4	T_1	T_6	T_3	T_0	T_5
T_3	T_3	T_6	T_5	T_0	T_7	T_2	T_1	T_4
T_4	T_4	T_5	T_6	T_7	T_0	T_1	T_2	T_3
T_5	T_5	T_4	T_7	T_6	T_1	T_0	T_3	T_2
T_6	T_6	T_3	T_0	T_5	T_2	T_7	T_4	T_1
T_7	T_7	T_2	T_1	T_4	T_3	T_6	T_5	T_0

first transformation

REVIEW SET 24A

1 **a** $(2, 5)$ **b** $(-5, 2)$ **c** $(4, -5)$

2 **a** $(4, 1)$ **b** $(5, 4)$

3 **a** $(0, 3)$ **b** $(6, -2)$ **c** $(3, -2\frac{1}{2})$ **d** $(2\frac{1}{2}, -1)$

4 $(-8, 1)$

5 **a** $y = 2x - 9$ **b** $y = -2x + 1$ **c** $y = -\frac{1}{2}x - \frac{1}{2}$
  d $y = x - 1$

6 **a** $x - 2y = -6$ **b** $x - 2y = -1$
  c

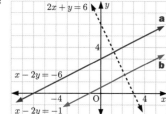

7 a stretch with invariant x-axis and scale factor $\frac{5}{3}$

8 **a** $y = 3x + 6$ **b** $4x - 5y = 20$ **c** $y = -4x + 1$

9 **a** a translation of $\begin{pmatrix} -2 \\ 3 \end{pmatrix}$ **b** a reflection in the line $y = -x$
  c a stretch with invariant y-axis and scale factor $\frac{1}{2}$

10 **a** a reflection in the y-axis **b** a reflection in the x-axis

REVIEW SET 24B

1 **a** $(3, 2)$ **b** $(2, -3)$ **c** $(3, 10)$

2 **a** $(-5, -11)$ **b** $(-7, -3)$

3 **a** $(9, 15)$ **b** $(-4, 3)$ **c** $(-5, -1\frac{1}{2})$

4 **a** $y = -2x + 6$ **b** $x + 2y = 1$ **c** $x - 2y = -1$
  d $2x + 2y = 1$

5 **a** $5x - 2y = 27$ **b** $4x - 3y = -8$ **c** $3x - 2y = -9$

6 a stretch with invariant y-axis and scale factor 3

7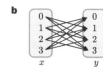

8 **a** **i** a translation of $\begin{pmatrix} -1 \\ -3 \end{pmatrix}$
   ii a reflection in the line $y = x$
   iii a rotation of 180° about the origin
   iv a stretch with invariant y-axis and scale factor $\frac{1}{3}$
  b Rotation of 180° about $(-\frac{1}{2}, -\frac{3}{2})$.

9 **a** a reflection in the x-axis
  b a rotation of 180° about $O(0, 0)$
  c A reduction with centre $O(0, 0)$ and scale factor $\frac{1}{3}$.

10 **a** a reflection in $y = x$ **b** a reflection in $y = -x$

EXERCISE 25A

1 **a**
  one-to-one

  b many-to-many

  c one-to-many **d** many-to-many

  e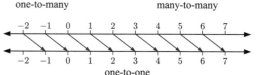
  one-to-one

2 **a** {real numbers}
  b {multiples of 2 which are not multiples of 4}
  c {positive real numbers} **d** {real numbers $\geqslant 10$}
  e {all integers}

3 **a** Domain is $\{x \mid x > -4\}$. Range is $\{y \mid y > -2\}$.
  b Domain is $\{x \mid -3 \leqslant x \leqslant 4\}$. Range is $\{y \mid -5 \leqslant y \leqslant 2\}$.
  c Domain is $\{x \mid -3 < x < 4\}$. Range is $\{y \mid -5 < y < 6\}$.
  d Domain is $\{x \mid x = 2\}$. Range is $\{y \mid y \in \mathbb{R}\}$.
  e Domain is $\{x \mid -3 \leqslant x \leqslant 3\}$. Range is $\{y \mid -3 \leqslant y \leqslant 3\}$.
  f Domain is $\{x \mid x \in \mathbb{R}\}$. Range is $\{y \mid y \leqslant 0\}$.
  g Domain is $\{x \mid x \in \mathbb{R}\}$. Range is $\{y \mid y = -5\}$.
  h Domain is $\{x \mid x \in \mathbb{R}\}$. Range is $\{y \mid y \geqslant 1\}$.
  i Domain is $\{x \mid x \geqslant -5\}$. Range is $\{y \mid y \leqslant 7\}$.
  j Domain is $\{x \mid x \in \mathbb{R}\}$. Range is $\{y \mid y \leqslant 4\}$.
  k Domain is $\{x \mid x \geqslant -5\}$. Range is $\{y \mid y \in \mathbb{R}\}$.
  l Domain is $\{x \mid x \in \mathbb{R}, x \neq 1\}$.
   Range is $\{y \mid y \in \mathbb{R}, y \neq 0\}$.

4 **a** Domain is $\{x \mid 0 \leqslant x \leqslant 2\}$. Range is $\{y \mid -3 \leqslant y \leqslant 2\}$.
  b Domain is $\{x \mid -2 < x < 2\}$. Range is $\{y \mid -1 < y < 3\}$.
  c Domain is $\{x \mid -4 \leqslant x \leqslant 4\}$. Range is $\{y \mid -2 \leqslant y \leqslant 2\}$.

5 a Domain $= \{-3, -2, -1, 0, 6\}$. Range $= \{-1, 3, 4, 5, 8\}$.
   b Domain $= \{-3, -1, 0, 2, 4, 5, 7\}$. Range $= \{3, 4\}$.

6 a $\{2, 3, 5, 10, 12\}$ **b** $\{0, \frac{1}{2}, 2\}$
   c $\{y \mid -3 < y < 5\}$ **d** $\{y \mid -27 \leqslant y \leqslant 64\}$

EXERCISE 25B

1 a, **b**, and **e** are functions as no two ordered pairs have the same x-coordinate.

2 a, b, d, e, g, h, and **i** are functions.

3 No, a vertical line is not a function as it does not satisfy the vertical line test.

4 a i 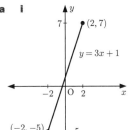   **b i**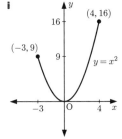

   ii Range is $\{y \mid -5 \leqslant y \leqslant 7\}$.   **ii** Range is $\{y \mid 0 \leqslant y \leqslant 16\}$.

c i 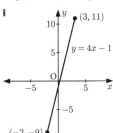   **d i**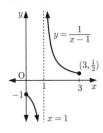

   ii Range is $\{y \mid -9 \leqslant y \leqslant 11\}$.   **ii** Range is $\{y \mid y \leqslant -1 \text{ or } y \geqslant \frac{1}{2}\}$.

e i 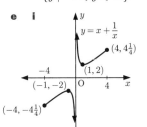   **f i**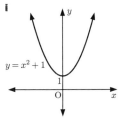

   ii Range is $\{y \mid y \leqslant -2 \text{ or } y \geqslant 2\}$.   **ii** Range is $\{y \mid y \geqslant 1\}$.

g i 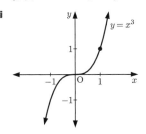   **ii** Range is $\{y \mid y \in \mathbb{R}\}$.

EXERCISE 25C

1 a 3   **b** 7   **c** 1   **d** -7 **e** 2
2 a -6 **b** -4 **c** 4   **d** -10 **e** 1
3 a -2 **b** $\frac{5}{2}$ **c** $\frac{10}{7}$ **d** 0   **e** $\frac{7}{10}$
4 a -2 **b** -17 **c** 13   **d** $5x+3$ **e** $-5x-17$
5 a 2   **b** 11   **c** 46   **d** $2x^2+3x+2$
   e $2x^2+x+1$
6 a 45   **b** -3 **c** 0   **d** $4x^2-20x+21$
   e $16x^2+8x-3$
7 a $a=5$ **b** $a=-4$ **c** $a=-\frac{9}{2}$
8 a i $-\frac{3}{2}$ **ii** $-\frac{1}{3}$ **iii** $-\frac{8}{3}$ **b** $x=-2$
   c $2-\dfrac{7}{x}$ **d** $x=-1$
9 a $V(4)=12\,000$. The value of the car after 4 years is $12\,000.
   b $V(t)=8000$ when $t=5$. 5 years after purchase the value of the car is $8000.
   c $28\,000
10 a i $f(2)=1$ **ii** $f(3)=-1$ **b** $x=-4$
11 a i $f(4)=2$ **ii** $g(0)=-6$ **iii** $g(5)=-1$
   b $x=0$ and $x=3$ **c** $x=2$
   d g has gradient 1 and y-intercept -6.
12 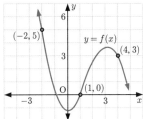 Other graphs are possible.
13 a 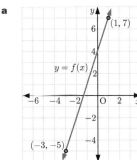   **b** $f(-3)=-5$, $f(1)=7$ **c** $f(x)=3x+4$

EXERCISE 25D

1 a $2-3x$ **b** $6-3x$ **c** $9x-16$ **d** x
2 a $\sqrt{4x-3}$ **b** $4\sqrt{x}-3$ **c** 5   **d** 5
3 a $f(x)=\sqrt{x}, g(x)=x-3$ **b** $f(x)=x^3, g(x)=x+5$
   c $f(x)=\dfrac{5}{x}, g(x)=x+7$ **d** $f(x)=3-4x, g(x)=\dfrac{1}{\sqrt{x}}$
   e $f(x)=x^2,\ g(x)=3^x$ **f** $f(x)=\dfrac{x+1}{x-1},\ g(x)=x^2$
   (**Note:** There may be other answers.)
4 a $f(g(x))=3x^2+6x+1$ **b** $x=-3$ or 1
5 a $f(g(x))=\dfrac{1}{4x+3}$ **b** -1 **c** $x=-\frac{2}{3}$

6 **a** **i** 13   **ii** 4   **iii** 6   **iv** 17
   b $f(g(x)) = x$ and $g(f(x)) = x$ **c** **i** 3   **ii** -7

EXERCISE 25E

1 **a** 7   **b** 7   **c** 0.93   **d** $2\frac{1}{4}$ **e** 0.0932

2 **a** 2   **b** 10   **c** 5   **d** 11   **e** 11   **f** 40
   g 40   **h** -2

3 **a** 3   **b** 10   **c** 7   **d** 3   **e** 13   **f** 2
   g $\frac{5}{2}$ **h** $\frac{4}{5}$

4 **a**

x	9	3	0	-3	-9
x^2	81	9	0	9	81
$|x|^2$	81	9	0	9	81

   b $x^2 = |x|^2$

5 **a**

a	b	$|ab|$	$|a||b|$	$\left|\dfrac{a}{b}\right|$	$\dfrac{|a|}{|b|}$
12	3	36	36	4	4
12	-3	36	36	4	4
-12	3	36	36	4	4
-12	-3	36	36	4	4

   b It is likely that $|ab| = |a||b|$ and $\left|\dfrac{a}{b}\right| = \dfrac{|a|}{|b|}$, $b \neq 0$.

6 **a**

a	b	$|a+b|$	$|a|+|b|$	$|a-b|$	$|a|-|b|$
2	5	7	7	3	-3
2	-5	3	7	7	-3
-2	5	3	7	7	-3
-2	-5	7	7	3	-3

   b $|a+b| \neq |a|+|b|$, $|a-b| \neq |a|-|b|$

7 **a** $f(x) = \begin{cases} -x & \text{if } x \geqslant 0 \\ x & \text{if } x < 0 \end{cases}$

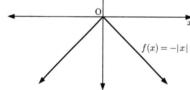

b $f(x) = \begin{cases} 2x & \text{if } x \geqslant 0 \\ 0 & \text{if } x < 0 \end{cases}$

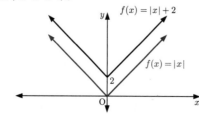

c $f(x) = \begin{cases} x+2 & \text{if } x \geqslant 0 \\ -x+2 & \text{if } x < 0 \end{cases}$

d $f(x) = \begin{cases} 5-x & \text{if } x \geqslant 0 \\ 5+x & \text{if } x < 0 \end{cases}$

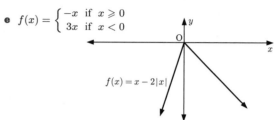

e $f(x) = \begin{cases} -x & \text{if } x \geqslant 0 \\ 3x & \text{if } x < 0 \end{cases}$

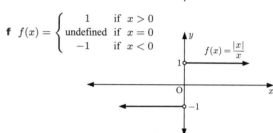

f $f(x) = \begin{cases} 1 & \text{if } x > 0 \\ \text{undefined} & \text{if } x = 0 \\ -1 & \text{if } x < 0 \end{cases}$

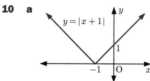
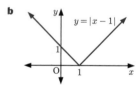

8 **a** $x = \pm 4$ **b** $x = \pm 1.4$
   c no solution as $|x| > 0$ for all x **d** $x = \pm 6$
   e $x = 2$ or -4 **f** $x = 7$ or -3 **g** $x = \pm 4$
   h $x = 4$ or 6

9 **a** **i** 15 cm   **ii** 4 cm   **iii** 0 cm   **iv** 4 cm   **v** 10 cm
   b $d = |x - 20|$

10 **a**

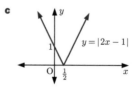

b

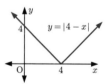

c

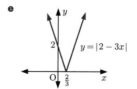

d

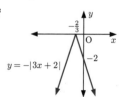

e

f

11 $x = -\dfrac{b}{a}$

12 **a** $f(x) = |x-2|$ **b** $f(x) = |2x+2|$
   c $f(x) = \left|\frac{1}{2}x + 1\right|$

EXERCISE 25F

1 a when x or $y = 0$, $xy = 0 \neq 5$

b vertical asymptote $x = 0$, horizontal asymptote $y = 0$

c **i** $y = 0.01$ **ii** $y = -0.01$

d **i** $x = 0.01$ **ii** $x = -0.01$

e $y = \dfrac{5}{x}$ **f** $y = -\dfrac{5}{x}$

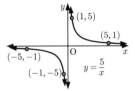 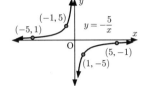

2 a

n	4	8	12	20
t	10	5	3.3	2

b

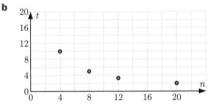

c One part of a hyperbola.   **d** $t = \dfrac{40}{n}$ or $nt = 40$

3 a $y = \dfrac{8}{x}$ **b** $y = \dfrac{3}{x}$ **c** $y = -\dfrac{12}{x}$

EXERCISE 25G

1 a i

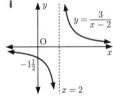

b i

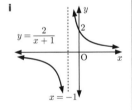

ii $x = 2$, $y = 0$ **ii** $x = -1$, $y = 0$

c i   **ii** $x = 3$, $y = 1$

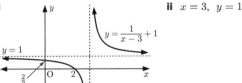

2 a i

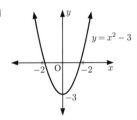

ii x-intercepts -1.73 and 1.73, y-intercept -3

iii local minimum at $(0, -3)$

b i

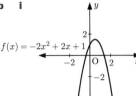

ii x-intercepts ≈ -0.367 and 1.37, y-intercept 1

iii local maximum at $\left(\frac{1}{2}, \frac{3}{2}\right)$

c i

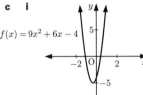

ii x-intercepts -1.08 and 0.412, y-intercept -4

iii local minimum at $\left(-\frac{1}{3}, -5\right)$

3 a $y = |2x - 1| + 2$ **b** $y = |x(x - 3)|$

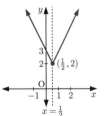 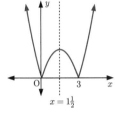

c $y = |(x - 2)(x - 4)|$ **d** $y = |x| + |x - 2|$

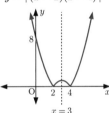 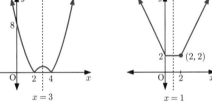

e $y = |x| - |x + 2|$ **f** $y = |9 - x^2|$

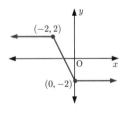 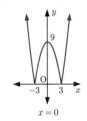

4 a $f(x) = x^3 - 4x^2 + 5x - 3$, $-1 \leqslant x \leqslant 4$

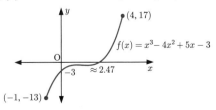

b x-intercept ≈ 2.47, y-intercept -3

c local maximum at $(1, -1)$, local minimum at $\approx (1.67, -1.15)$

d Range is $\{y \mid -13 \leqslant y \leqslant 17\}$

e

x	y
-1	-13
-0.5	-6.63
0	-3
0.5	-1.38
1	-1
1.5	-1.13

x	y
2	-1
2.5	0.125
3	3
3.5	8.38
4	17

5 a $f(x) = x^4 - 3x^3 - 10x^2 - 7x + 3, \quad -4 \leqslant x \leqslant 6$

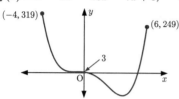

b ≈ 5.17 **c** $\approx (3.72, -124)$

d

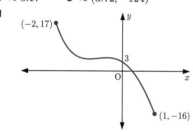

e local maximum at $\approx (-0.470, 4.44)$
local minimum at $(-1, 4)$

f

x	y
0	3
0.1	2.20
0.2	1.18
0.3	-0.07
0.4	-1.57
0.5	-3.31

x	y
0.6	-5.32
0.7	-7.59
0.8	-10.1
0.9	-12.9
1.0	-16

6 a **i, ii** $x = 2$ **b** **i, ii** $x = 5$
c **i, ii** $x = -3$ or 2 **d** **i, ii** $x = -1$ or 2
e **i, ii** $x = -\frac{1}{5}$ or 1 **f** **i, ii** $x = -3$ or $-\frac{1}{2}$

7 a **i** $f(x) = \dfrac{4}{x-2}$

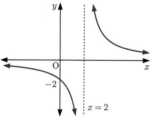

ii $x = 2, \ y = 0$
iii no x-intercept, y-intercept -2
iv no turning points exist

b **i** $f(x) = 2 - \dfrac{3}{x+1}$

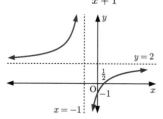

ii $x = -1, \ y = 2$
iii x-intercept $\frac{1}{2}$, y-intercept -1
iv no turning points exist

c **i** $f(x) = 2^x - 3$

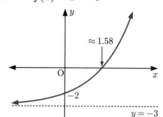

ii $y = -3$
iii x-intercept ≈ 1.58, y-intercept -2
iv no turning points exist

d **i** $f(x) = 2x + \dfrac{1}{x}$

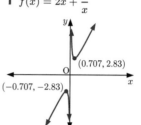

ii $x = 0$
iii no intercepts exist
iv local maximum at $\approx (-0.707, -2.83)$
local minimum at $\approx (0.707, 2.83)$

e **i** $f(x) = \dfrac{4x}{x^2 - 4x - 5}$

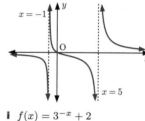

ii $x = -1, \ x = 5, \ y = 0$
iii x- and y-intercepts are both 0
iv no turning points exist

f **i** $f(x) = 3^{-x} + 2$

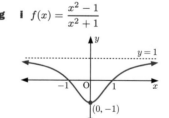

ii $y = 2$
iii no x-intercepts, y-intercept 3
iv no turning points exist

g **i** $f(x) = \dfrac{x^2 - 1}{x^2 + 1}$

ii $y = 1$
iii x-intercepts ± 1, y-intercept -1
iv minimum turning point at $(0, -1)$

h **i** $f(x) = \dfrac{x^2 + 1}{x^2 - 1}$

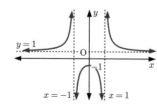

ii $x = -1, \ x = 1, \ y = 1$
iii no x-intercepts, y-intercept -1
iv maximum turning point at $(0, -1)$

i **i** $f(x) = \dfrac{2^x + 3}{2^x + 1}$

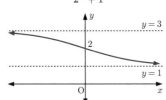

ii $y = 1$, $y = 3$

iii no x-intercepts, y-intercept 2

iv no turning points exist

8 **a** at $(-1.62, -1.24)$ and $(0.62, 3.24)$

b at $(4.71, 0.64)$

c They do not intersect, $\therefore$ no solutions exist.

d at $(-0.75, -0.43)$

9 $1 < k < 4$

10 **a** $x = -1.5$ or 1 **b** $x \approx -1.24$ or 3.24

c $x \approx -4.83$ or 0.828 **d** $x \approx -1.57$ or 0.319

e $x \approx 0.458$ or 3.31 **f** $x \approx 1.70$

g $x = -1$ or ≈ 1.35 **h** $x \approx -0.686$ **i** $x \approx -2.51$

j $x \approx -1.67$ **k** $x \approx -0.846, 0, 2,$ or 3.22

l $x \approx -1.37$ or 2.07 **m** no solutions

n $x \approx 3.21$ **o** $x \approx -1.21$ or 1

EXERCISE 25H

1 **a** **i** $y = f(x) + 4$ is a translation of $y = f(x)$ of $\binom{0}{4}$.

ii $y = f(x + 4)$ is a translation of $y = f(x)$ of $\binom{-4}{0}$.

b

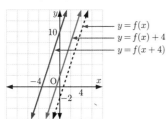

2 **a** **i** a vertical translation of $\binom{0}{-1}$

ii a horizontal translation of $\binom{3}{0}$

b

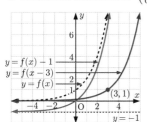

c a translation of $\binom{3}{1}$

3 **a**

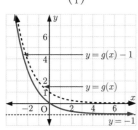

b $y = -1$

4 **a**

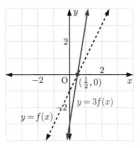

b points on the x-axis, such as $(\tfrac{1}{2}, 0)$

5 **a**

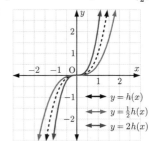

b a stretch with invariant x-axis, and scale factor $\tfrac{1}{4}$

6 **a, b** x-intercepts are ± 1, y-intercept is -1

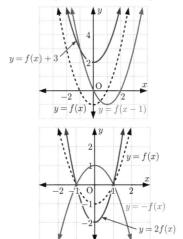

c A stretch with invariant x-axis and scale factor 2, followed by a reflection in the x-axis.

d

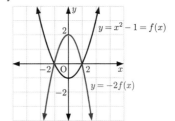

e $(-1, 0)$ and $(1, 0)$

7 **a** **i** A stretch with invariant x-axis and scale factor 3.

ii $g(x) = 3f(x)$

b **i** A vertical translation of $\binom{0}{-2}$.   **ii** $g(x) = f(x) - 2$

c **i** A stretch with invariant x-axis and scale factor $\tfrac{1}{2}$.

ii $g(x) = \tfrac{1}{2}f(x)$

·8 a 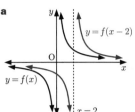   b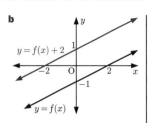

c d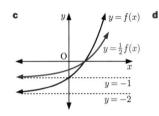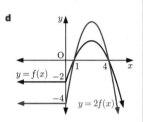

e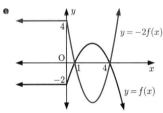

f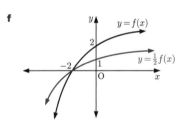

9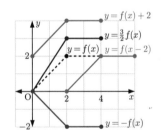

10 a $g(x) = 2x^2 - 8$, $h(x) = 4x^2 - 4$

b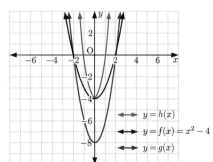

c i zeros are ± 2 ii zeros are ± 2 iii zeros are ± 1

EXERCISE 25I

1 a i $f^{-1}(x) = x - 3$
       ii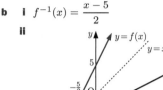

   b i $f^{-1}(x) = \dfrac{x - 5}{2}$
      ii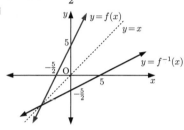

   c i $f^{-1}(x) = -2x + \dfrac{3}{2}$
      ii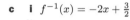
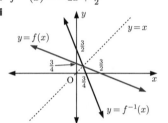

2 a 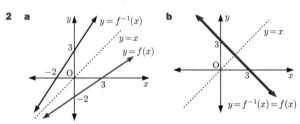   b

   c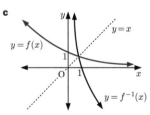

3 a $f^{-1}(x) = \dfrac{x - 7}{2}$ 4 a $f^{-1}(x) = \dfrac{1 - 3x}{x - 2}$

5 a $g^{-1}(x) = \dfrac{5x}{x - 1}$ c $g(6) = 6$, $g^{-1}(1)$ is undefined

6 a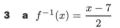
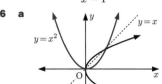

   b No, as the vertical line test fails.

   c Yes, it is $y = \sqrt{x}$ (not $y = \pm\sqrt{x}$).

7 **a** As f is the inverse of f^{-1}, $\therefore$ f^{-1} is one to one.
$\therefore$ every value in y must map to at most one value in x.

   b **i** and **iii** have inverse functions.

8 **a** **i** $f^{-1}(x) = 8 - x$ **ii** $f^{-1}(x) = \dfrac{9}{x}$

   b The functions are their own inverse.

   c The inverse is a reflection in the function in the line $y = x$.
$\therefore$ the reflection of the vertical asymptote $x = k$ is the horizontal asymptote $y = k$.

9 **a** $f^{-1}(x) = \dfrac{x - c}{m}$

   b **i** $f^{-1}(x) = \dfrac{x + 2}{3}$ **ii** $f^{-1}(x) = -2x + 4$

10 **a** **i** $f^{-1}(x) = \dfrac{2}{x} + 3$

     ii
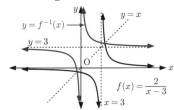

   b **i** $f^{-1}(x) = -1 - \dfrac{3}{x}$

     ii
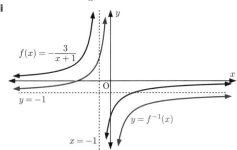

   c **i** $f^{-1}(x) = \dfrac{2x}{x - 1}$

     ii
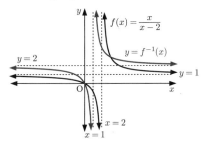

   d **i** $f^{-1}(x) = \dfrac{x + 1}{x - 1} = f(x)$

     ii
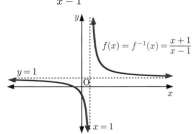

11 **a**
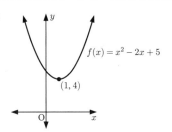

   b $f(x)$ passes the vertical line test but fails the horizontal line test.

   c $g(x)$ passes both the horizontal and vertical line tests.

   d
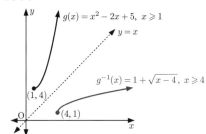

REVIEW SET 25A

1 **a**

     b A many-to-one function.

2 **a** 2   **b** -4 **c** $-x^2 + 9x - 18$

3 **a** function   **b** not a function

4 **a** 8   **b** $9x^2 + 6x$ **c** $x = -5$ or 3

5 **a** $f(g(x)) = \sqrt{5x - 3}$ **b** $g(f(x)) = 5\sqrt{x} - 3$
   c $g(g(x)) = 25x - 18$

6 **a** 7   **b** -1 **c** 0

7 **a** $f(x) = \begin{cases} 4x & \text{if } x \geqslant 0 \\ 2x & \text{if } x < 0 \end{cases}$ **b** $f(x) = \begin{cases} 2x - 4 & \text{if } x \geqslant 0 \\ -2x - 4 & \text{if } x < 0 \end{cases}$

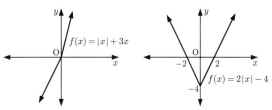

8 **a** $y = \dfrac{12}{x}$ **b** $y = -\dfrac{9}{x}$ **c** $y = -\dfrac{12}{x}$

9 **a**

     b $x = -3$, $y = -1$

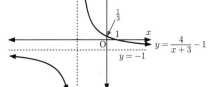

10 a

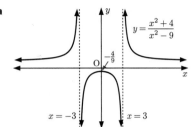

$$y = \frac{x^2 + 4}{x^2 - 9}$$

$x = -3$ $x = 3$

b $x = -3$, $x = 3$, $y = 1$
c Domain is $\{x \mid x \neq \pm 3, \ x \in \mathbb{R}\}$.
  Range is $\{y \mid y \leqslant -\frac{4}{9}, \ \text{or} \ y > 1\}$.
d $k > 1$ or $k < -\frac{4}{9}$

11 a $x \approx 2.01$ **b** $x \approx 1.38$ **c** $x \approx -7.26$, -1.65, or 1.34
12 a $\approx (-2.17, 2.41)$ and $(1.93, 0.457)$
  b $\approx (0.0773, 4.94)$, $(0.594, 4.49)$, and $(2.71, -0.521)$

13 a

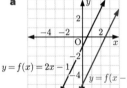

$y = f(x) = 2x - 1$ $y = f(x - 2)$

b

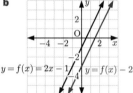

$y = f(x) = 2x - 1$ $y = f(x) - 2$

c

$y = f(x) = 2x - 1$ $y = 2f(x)$

d

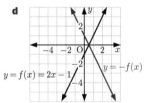

$y = f(x) = 2x - 1$ $y = -f(x)$

14

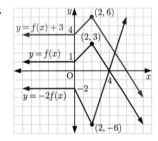

$y = f(x) + 3$ $(2, 6)$ $(2, 3)$
$y = f(x)$
$y = -2f(x)$ $(2, -6)$

15 a $f^{-1}(x) = 7x - 2$
  c

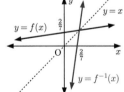

$y = f(x)$ $y = x$ $y = f^{-1}(x)$

16 a $f^{-1}(x) = \dfrac{x}{8}$ **b** $f^{-1}(x) = 1 + \dfrac{2}{x}$
  c $f^{-1}(x) = x^2 - 3$, $x \geqslant 0$

REVIEW SET 25B

1 a i Domain is $\{x \mid x > -6\}$.   Range is $\{y \mid y > -2\}$.
  ii function

b i Domain is $\{x \mid x \leqslant 1\}$.   Range is $\{y \mid y \in \mathbb{R}\}$.
  ii not a function
c i Domain is $\{x \mid x \neq -2, \ x \in \mathbb{R}\}$.
  Range is $\{y \mid y \neq 3, \ y \in \mathbb{R}\}$.
  ii function

2 a 42 **b** $5x^2 - x$ **c** $5x^2 + 11x + 6$

3 a

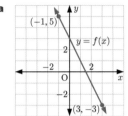

$(-1, 5)$ $y = f(x)$ $(3, -3)$

  b $f(-1) = 5$,
   $f(3) = -3$
  c $f(x) = -2x + 3$
  d $f^{-1}(x) = \dfrac{3 - x}{2}$

4 a $f(g(x)) = 15 - 2x$ **b** $g(f(x)) = 6 - 2x$
  c $f(g(-2)) = 19$

5 a 36 **b** 13 **c** $\frac{7}{4}$

6 a $f(g(x)) = \dfrac{1}{3x - 5}$ **b** $f(g(5)) = \frac{1}{10}$ **c** $x = 1$

7 a

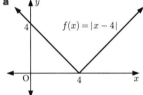

$f(x) = |x - 4|$

  b

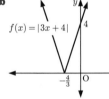

$f(x) = |3x + 4|$ $-\frac{4}{3}$

8 a i

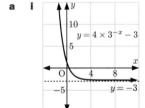

$y = 4 \times 3^{-x} - 3$ $y = -3$

  ii x-intercept ≈ 0.262,
   y-intercept 1
  iii $y = -3$

  b i

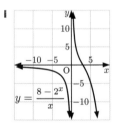

$y = \dfrac{8 - 2^x}{x}$

  ii x-intercept 3
  iii $x = 0$, $y = 0$

9 a

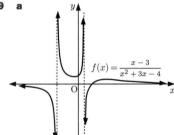

$f(x) = \dfrac{x - 3}{x^2 + 3x - 4}$ $x = -4$ $x = 1$

  b $x = -4$, $x = 1$,
   $y = 0$
  c x-intercept 3
   y-intercept $\frac{3}{4}$
  d local minimum at
   $\approx (-0.742, 0.659)$
   local maximum at
   $\approx (6.74, 0.0607)$

10 a $x \approx 2.18$ **b** $x \approx 3.29$ **c** $x \approx 0.505$
11 a $\approx (-1.70, -4.94)$ and $(1.26, 1.98)$
  b $\approx (-0.63, 2.50)$ and $(0.52, 3.76)$

12   **a**

x	$f(x)$	$g(x)$
-10	0.833	1.25
-5	0.913	1.118
0	1	1
5	1.095	0.894
10	1.2	0.8
15	1.315	0.716
20	1.44	0.64

b

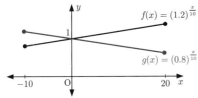

c $(0, 1)$ **d** $y = -0.01x + 1$ is one example.

13   **a**   **b**

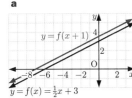   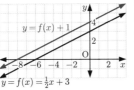

c   **d**

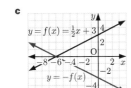

14   **a** A stretch with invariant x-axis and scale factor $k = 2$.
  b $g(x) = 2f(x)$

15   **a**   **b**

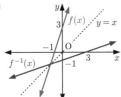   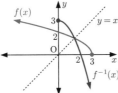

16   **a** $f^{-1}(x) = \dfrac{2x + 1}{x - 1}$ **c** 3

EXERCISE 26A

1 **b** and **c** are quadratic functions.

2   **a** $y = 0$ **b** $y = 5$ **c** $y = -15$ **d** $y = 12$

3   **a** no   **b** yes   **c** yes   **d** no   **e** no   **f** no

4   **a** $x = -3$ **b** $x = -2$ or -3 **c** $x = 1$ or 4
  d no real solution

5   **a** $x = 0$ or 1   **b** $x = -1$ or 3   **c** $x = -7$ or $\frac{1}{2}$
  d $x = 2$ or 3

6   **a** **i** 75 m   **ii** 195 m   **iii** 275 m
  b **i** At $t = 2$ s and $t = 14$ s.
      ii At $t = 0$ s and $t = 16$ s.
  c The object leaves the ground at $t = 0$ s.
      At $t = 2$ it is rising and at $t = 14$ it is falling.
      Height 0 m is ground level and the time of flight is 16 s.

7   **a** **i** $-\$40$, a loss of \$40   **ii** \$480 profit
  b 10 cakes or 62 cakes

EXERCISE 26B.1

1   **a**

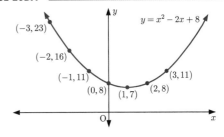

  b

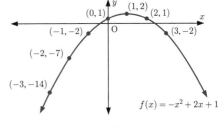

  c

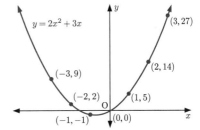

  d

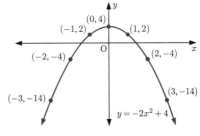

  e

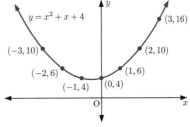

  f

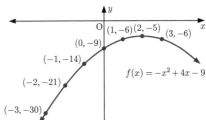

2   a

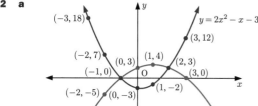

b $x = -1$ or 2 (where they meet)

c $2x^2 - x - 3 = -x^2 + 2x + 3$ becomes
  $3x^2 - 3x - 6 = 0$
  $\therefore \ x^2 - x - 2 = 0$,   and so on
  $\therefore \quad x = -1$ or 2

EXERCISE 26B.2

1   a

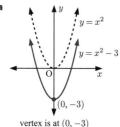

vertex is at $(0, -3)$

b

$y = x^2 - 1$
$(0, -1)$
vertex is at $(0, -1)$

c

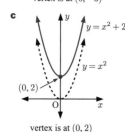

$y = x^2 + 2$
$y = x^2$
$(0, 2)$
vertex is at $(0, 2)$

d

$y = x^2$
$y = x^2 - 5$
$(0, -5)$
vertex is at $(0, -5)$

e

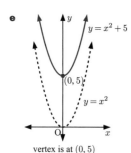

$y = x^2 + 5$
$(0, 5)$
$y = x^2$
vertex is at $(0, 5)$

f

$y = x^2$
$y = x^2 - \frac{1}{2}$
$(0, -\frac{1}{2})$
vertex is at $(0, -\frac{1}{2})$

2   a

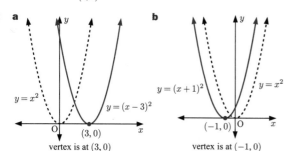

$y = x^2$
$y = (x - 3)^2$
$(3, 0)$
vertex is at $(3, 0)$

b

$y = (x + 1)^2$
$y = x^2$
$(-1, 0)$
vertex is at $(-1, 0)$

c

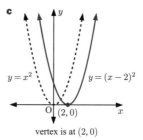

$y = x^2$ $y = (x - 2)^2$
$(2, 0)$
vertex is at $(2, 0)$

d

$y = (x - 5)^2$
$y = x^2$
$(5, 0)$
vertex is at $(5, 0)$

e

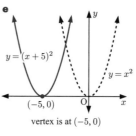

$y = (x + 5)^2$
$y = x^2$
$(-5, 0)$
vertex is at $(-5, 0)$

f

$y = x^2$ $y = (x - \frac{3}{2})^2$
$(\frac{3}{2}, 0)$
vertex is at $(\frac{3}{2}, 0)$

3   a $y = (x - 1)^2 + 3$

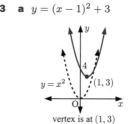

$y = x^2$ $(1, 3)$
vertex is at $(1, 3)$

b $y = (x - 2)^2 - 1$

$y = x^2$
$(2, -1)$
vertex is at $(2, -1)$

c $y = (x + 1)^2 + 4$

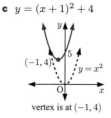

$(-1, 4)$ $y = x^2$
vertex is at $(-1, 4)$

d $y = (x + 2)^2 - 3$

$y = x^2$
$(-2, -3)$
vertex is at $(-2, -3)$

e $y = (x + 3)^2 - 2$

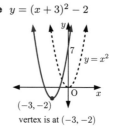

$y = x^2$
$(-3, -2)$
vertex is at $(-3, -2)$

f $y = (x - 3)^2 + 3$

$y = x^2$ $(3, 3)$
vertex is at $(3, 3)$

4   a

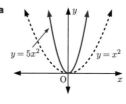

$y = 5x^2$ $y = x^2$

$y = 5x^2$ is "thinner" than $y = x^2$ and the graph opens upwards.

b

$y = x^2$
$y = -5x^2$

$y = -5x^2$ is "thinner" than $y = x^2$ and the graph opens downwards.

c

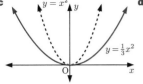

$y = \frac{1}{3}x^2$ is "wider" than $y = x^2$ and the graph opens upwards.

d

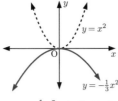

$y = -\frac{1}{3}x^2$ is "wider" than $y = x^2$ and the graph opens downwards.

e

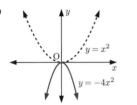

$y = -4x^2$ is "thinner" than $y = x^2$ and the graph opens downwards.

f

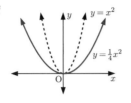

$y = \frac{1}{4}x^2$ is "wider" than $y = x^2$ and the graph opens upwards.

5 a

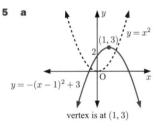

vertex is at $(1, 3)$

b

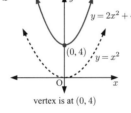

vertex is at $(0, 4)$

c

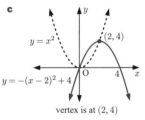

vertex is at $(2, 4)$

d

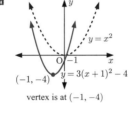

vertex is at $(-1, -4)$

e

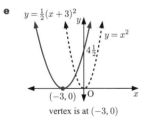

vertex is at $(-3, 0)$

f

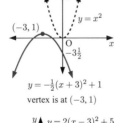

$y = -\frac{1}{2}(x + 3)^2 + 1$

vertex is at $(-3, 1)$

g

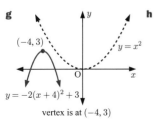

$y = -2(x + 4)^2 + 3$

vertex is at $(-4, 3)$

h

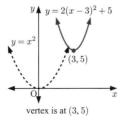

vertex is at $(3, 5)$

i

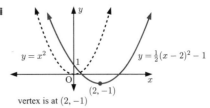

vertex is at $(2, -1)$

6   a F   **b** C   **c** B   **d** D   **e** E   **f** A

7   b

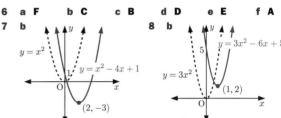

8   b

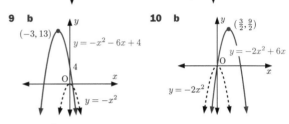

9   b

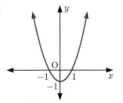

10   b

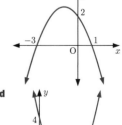

11   a $ax^2 + bx + c$

b Since $ax^2 + bx + c = a\left(x + \dfrac{b}{2a}\right)^2 + \left(c - \dfrac{b^2}{4a}\right)$, its graph has the same shape as $y = ax^2$, except that it has been translated by $\begin{pmatrix} -\dfrac{b}{2a} \\ c - \dfrac{b^2}{4a} \end{pmatrix}$.

EXERCISE 26C

1   a 3   **b** 2   **c** -8 **d** 1   **e** 6   **f** 5
   g 6   **h** 8   **i** -2

2   a 3 and -1 **b** 2 and 4   **c** -3 and -2
   d 4 and 5   **e** -3 (touching)   **f** 1 (touching)

3   a -3 and 3   **b** -5 and 5   **c** 0 and 6
   d -5 and -2 **e** -4 and 3   **f** 0 and 4
   g -2 and -4 **h** -1 (touching)   **i** 3 (touching)

4   a $2 \pm \sqrt{3}$ **b** $-2 \pm \sqrt{7}$ **c** $3 \pm \sqrt{5}$
   d $\dfrac{7 \pm \sqrt{73}}{6}$ **e** $\dfrac{1 \pm \sqrt{41}}{4}$ **f** $\dfrac{9 \pm \sqrt{33}}{8}$

5   a

b

c

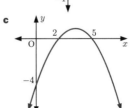

d

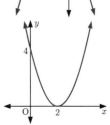

6 a i $a = 1$ **ii** 4
iii 2 (touching)

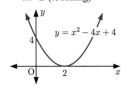

$y = x^2 - 4x + 4$

b i $a = 1$ **ii** -3
iii 1 and -3

$f(x) = (x-1)(x+3)$

c i $a = 2$ **ii** 8
iii -2 (touching)

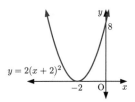

$y = 2(x+2)^2$

d i $a = -1$ **ii** 2
iii 2 and -1

$f(x) = -(x-2)(x+1)$

e i $a = -3$ **ii** -3
iii -1 (touching)

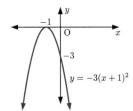

$y = -3(x+1)^2$

f i $a = -3$ **ii** -12
iii 4 and 1

$y = -3(x-4)(x-1)$

g i $a = 2$ **ii** 6
iii -3 and -1

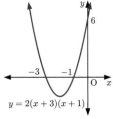

$y = 2(x+3)(x+1)$

h i $a = -2$ **ii** 5
iii $-\frac{5}{2}$ and 1

$y = -2x^2 - 3x + 5$

i i $a = -1$
ii -10
iii $4 \pm \sqrt{6}$

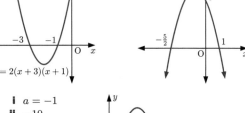

$4 - \sqrt{6}$ $4 + \sqrt{6}$

$f(x) = -x^2 + 8x - 10$

EXERCISE 26D

1 a $x = 2$ **b** $x = 1$ **c** $x = -2$ **d** $x = \frac{3}{2}$
 e $x = -\frac{5}{2}$ **f** $x = 2$

2 a $x = 3$ **b** $x = 2$ **c** $x = 0$ **d** $x = -\frac{5}{2}$
 e $x = -4$ **f** $x = \frac{3}{2}$

3 a $x = -2$ **b** $x = \frac{3}{2}$ **c** $x = -\frac{2}{3}$ **d** $x = -2$
 e $x = \frac{5}{4}$ **f** $x = 10$ **g** $x = -6$ **h** $x = 12\frac{1}{2}$
 i $x = 150$

4 a x-intercepts 1 and 3 **b** x-intercepts -1 and -2

5 a

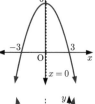

$x = 0$

b

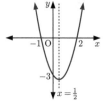

$x = \frac{1}{2}$

c

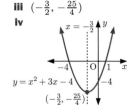

$x = -2$

EXERCISE 26E

1 a i $(2, -2)$ **ii** minimum   **iii** $\{y \mid y \geqslant -2\}$
 b i $(-1, -4)$ **ii** minimum   **iii** $\{y \mid y \geqslant -4\}$
 c i $(0, 4)$ **ii** minimum   **iii** $\{y \mid y \geqslant 4\}$
 d i $(0, 1)$ **ii** maximum   **iii** $\{y \mid y \leqslant 1\}$
 e i $(-2, 0)$ **ii** maximum   **iii** $\{y \mid y \leqslant 0\}$
 f i $\left(\frac{5}{2}, -\frac{19}{2}\right)$ **ii** minimum   **iii** $\{y \mid y \geqslant -\frac{19}{2}\}$

2 a i x-intercepts -2 and 4,
y-intercept -8
 ii $x = 1$ **iii** $(1, -9)$
 iv

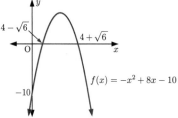

$x = 1$

$y = x^2 - 2x - 8$

$(1, -9)$

 b i x-intercepts 0 and 4,
y-intercept 0
 ii $x = 2$ **iii** $(2, 4)$
 iv

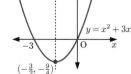

$(2, 4)$

$y = 4x - x^2$

$x = 2$

 c i x-intercepts 0 and
-3, y-intercept 0
 ii $x = -\frac{3}{2}$
 iii $\left(-\frac{3}{2}, -\frac{9}{4}\right)$
 iv

$x = -\frac{3}{2}$

$y = x^2 + 3x$

$\left(-\frac{3}{2}, -\frac{9}{4}\right)$

 d i x-intercept -2,
y-intercept 4
 ii $x = -2$
 iii $(-2, 0)$
 iv

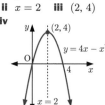

$x = -2$

$(-2, 0)$

$f(x) = x^2 + 4x + 4$

 e i x-intercepts -4 and
1, y-intercept -4
 ii $x = -\frac{3}{2}$
 iii $\left(-\frac{3}{2}, -\frac{25}{4}\right)$
 iv

$x = -\frac{3}{2}$

$y = x^2 + 3x - 4$

$\left(-\frac{3}{2}, -\frac{25}{4}\right)$

 f i x-intercept 1,
y-intercept -1
 ii $x = 1$
 iii $(1, 0)$
 iv

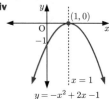

$(1, 0)$

$x = 1$

$y = -x^2 + 2x - 1$

g i x-intercepts -3 and $\frac{1}{2}$, y-intercept -3

ii $x = -\frac{5}{4}$

iii $\left(-\frac{5}{4}, -\frac{49}{8}\right)$

iv

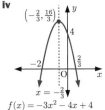

$y = 2x^2 + 5x - 3$

$\left(-\frac{5}{4}, -\frac{49}{8}\right)$

h i x-intercepts -2 and $\frac{2}{3}$, y-intercept 4

ii $x = -\frac{2}{3}$

iii $\left(-\frac{2}{3}, \frac{16}{3}\right)$

iv

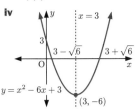

$f(x) = -3x^2 - 4x + 4$

i i x-intercepts $3 \pm \sqrt{6}$, y-intercept 3

ii $x = 3$

iii $(3, -6)$

iv

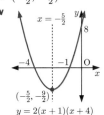

$y = x^2 - 6x + 3$

$(3, -6)$

3 a i x-intercepts 0 and 2, y-intercept 0

ii $x = 1$ **iii** $(1, -1)$

iv

$f(x) = x(x - 2)$

b i x-intercept 3, y-intercept 18

ii $x = 3$ **iii** $(3, 0)$

iv

$y = 2(x - 3)^2$

c i x-intercepts -3 and 1, y-intercept 3

ii $x = -1$ **iii** $(-1, 4)$

iv

$y = -(x - 1)(x + 3)$

d i x-intercept 1, y-intercept -2

ii $x = 1$ **iii** $(1, 0)$

iv

$y = -2(x - 1)^2$

e i x-intercepts -2 and 2, y-intercept 20

ii $x = 0$

iii $(0, 20)$

iv

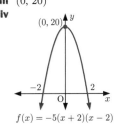

$f(x) = -5(x + 2)(x - 2)$

f i x-intercepts -1 and -4, y-intercept 8

ii $x = -\frac{5}{2}$

iii $\left(-\frac{5}{2}, -\frac{9}{2}\right)$

iv

$\left(-\frac{5}{2}, -\frac{9}{2}\right)$

$y = 2(x + 1)(x + 4)$

EXERCISE 26F

1 a $f(x) = 2(x - 2)^2 - 5$
b $f(x) = -(x + 4)^2 + 19$
c $f(x) = -(x - 1)^2 + 8$
d $f(x) = -2(x + 2)^2 + 11$

2 a $y = 2(x - 1)^2 + 3$
b $y = -(x + 2)^2 + 3$
c $y = -2(x + 1)^2 - 2$

3 a $f(x) = 2(x + 2)^2 - 5$
b $f(x) = 2(x - 3)^2 - 19$

4 a $b = -2$, $c = 4$
b $b = 0$, $c = 2$
c $b = -6$, $c = 9$
d $b = 6$, $c = 7$
e $b = -1$, $c = \frac{5}{4}$

5 a $f(x) = -3x^2 + 6x - 7$
b $f(x) = 3x^2 + 12x + 15$
c $f(x) = \frac{4}{3}x^2 + 8x + 7$
d $f(x) = -2x^2 + 12x - 10$
e $f(x) = 2x^2 - 8x + 5$
f $f(x) = -\frac{1}{2}x^2 - x + \frac{9}{2}$

6 a $b = -2$, $c = 0$
b $b = 3$, $c = -4$
c $b = 3$, $c = -10$
d $b = 7$, $c = 0$

7 a $f(x) = -2x^2 + 8$
b $f(x) = -3x^2 + 15x - 12$
c $f(x) = 3x^2 - 3x - 18$
d $f(x) = -2x^2 + 2x + 40$
e $f(x) = 2x^2 - 9x + 9$
f $f(x) = 16x^2 - 8x - 15$

EXERCISE 26G

1 a 2 seconds **b** 20 metres **c** 4 seconds

2 a 25 bicycles **b** \$425
c \$200 (Due to fixed daily costs such as wages and electricity.)

3 a 60 km/h (when $t = 0$) **b** $t = 1$ s **c** 66 km/h

4 a 30 taxis **b** \$1600/hour **c** \$200

5 a $25°C$ **b** 7:00 am the next day **c** $-11°C$

6 a 2 m **b** 3.8 m **c** 1 s

7 b $\dfrac{BF}{2} = \dfrac{1 - x}{1}$ and so on
c Area $= x(2(1 - x))$ and so on **d i** $x = \frac{1}{2}$ **ii** $\frac{1}{2}$ cm^2

EXERCISE 26H

1 a $f(x) = x^3 - 7x + 6$ **b** $f(x) = 2x^3 + 9x^2 + x - 12$
c $f(x) = 2x^3 + 3x^2 - 12x - 20$
d $f(x) = x^3 + 3x^2 + 3x + 3$

2 a

$f(x) = x(x - 3)(x + 2)$

b

$y = (x - 1)(x - 4)(x + 2)$

c

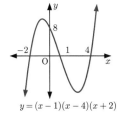

$f(x) = -(x + 3)(x - 2)(x - 4)$

d

$y = 2x(x - 1)(x + 1)$

e

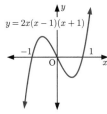

$f(x) = -\frac{1}{2}(x + 3)(x + 1)(x - 1)$

f

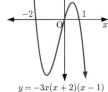

$y = -3x(x + 2)(x - 1)$

3 **a**
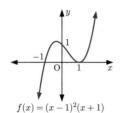
$f(x) = (x-1)^2(x+1)$

b
$y = -x(x+2)^2$

c
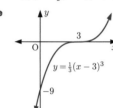
$f(x) = -\frac{1}{2}(x-2)(x+2)^2$

d
$y = \frac{1}{4}x^2(x+4)$

e
$y = \frac{1}{3}(x-3)^3$

f
$f(x) = -2(x+1)^3$

4 **a** $f(x) = 2(x+1)(x-2)(x-3)$
  b $f(x) = -2(x+3)(x+2)(2x+1)$
  c $f(x) = \frac{1}{4}(x+4)^2(x-3)$
  d $f(x) = -2(x-2)^2(x+1)$
  e $f(x) = -2(x+2)(x-1)(x-3)$
  f $f(x) = \frac{1}{2}(x+3)(x^2+x+1)$

5 **a** $f(x) = 2x^3 - 5x^2 - 6x + 9$
  b $f(x) = 3x^3 - 16x^2 + 15x + 18$

6 $b = 4$, $c = -10$ **7** $b = 2$, $d = -8$

REVIEW SET 26A

1 **a** $y = -11$ **b** $x = 6$ or -3

2 **a**
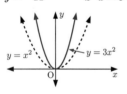

  b
$y = x^2$, $y = (x-2)^2 + 1$, $(2,1)$

  c
$(-3,-2)$, $y = x^2$, -11, $y = -(x+3)^2 - 2$

3 **b**
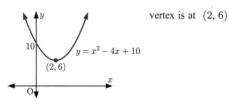
$y = x^2 - 4x + 10$, $(2,6)$, 10
vertex is at $(2, 6)$

4 **a** 0 and -4 **b** -7 and 4   **5** **a** $x = -\frac{3}{2}$ **b** $x = 2$

6 **a** **i** downwards   **b**
    ii 6
    iii -3 and 1
    iv $x = -1$
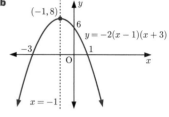
$(-1,8)$, 6, $y = -2(x-1)(x+3)$, -3, 1, $x = -1$

7 **a** $(4, -19)$ **b** $(\frac{1}{2}, -2)$

8 **a** **i** -15 **b**
    ii -3 and 5
    iii $x = 1$
    iv $(1, -16)$
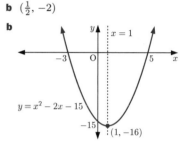
$x = 1$, -3, 5, $y = x^2 - 2x - 15$, -15, $(1, -16)$

9 $b = 6$, $c = -2$

10 **a** $(-1, -2)$ **c**
   b $-\frac{3}{2}$
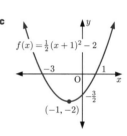
$f(x) = \frac{1}{2}(x+1)^2 - 2$, -3, 1, $-\frac{3}{2}$, $(-1, -2)$

11 $f(x) = 2(x+1)^2 - 5$

12 **a** unmarked side $= (40 - 2x)$ m
      $\therefore\ A = x(40 - 2x)$ m^2, and so on
   b $x = 10$ **c** 200 m^2

13 $f(x) = 9x^2 + 39x + 12$ **14** $f(x) = \frac{9}{2}x^2 - 54x + 160$

15 **a**
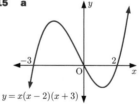
-3, 2, $y = x(x-2)(x+3)$

  b
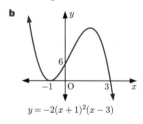
6, -1, 3, $y = -2(x+1)^2(x-3)$

16 $f(x) = -3x(x+1)(x-2)$ **17** $f(x) = 2(x+1)^2(x-3)$

REVIEW SET 26B

1 $x = -7$ or 6   **2** No, as $f(2) = 4 - 6 + 8 = 6 \neq 5$.

3
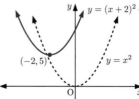
$y = (x+2)^2 + 5$, $(-2,5)$, $y = x^2$

4 **a** $\dfrac{1 \pm \sqrt{61}}{6}$
   b $1 \pm \sqrt{7}$

5

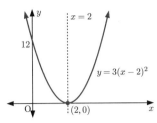

6 a $x = 1$
b $x = \frac{5}{6}$

7 a $(2, -3)$
b $\{y \mid y \leqslant -3\}$

8 a $f(-1) = 10$
b x-intercepts 1 and 4, y-intercept 4
c $x = \frac{5}{2}$
d $\left(\frac{5}{2}, -\frac{9}{4}\right)$
e

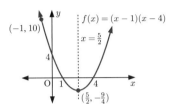

9 a $f(x)$ has x-intercepts -6 and -2 and y-intercept 12. $g(x)$ does not cut the x-axis and its y-intercept is -20.
b Both $f(x)$ and $g(x)$ have axis of symmetry $x = -4$. Both $f(x)$ and $g(x)$ have vertex $(-4, -4)$.
c Range of $f(x)$ is $\{y \mid y \geqslant -4\}$. Range of $g(x)$ is $\{y \mid y \leqslant -4\}$.
d

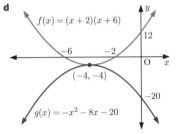

10 $b = 2$, $c = -15$

11 a **i** -10
ii 2 and 5
iii $x = \frac{7}{2}$
iv $\left(\frac{7}{2}, \frac{9}{4}\right)$
b

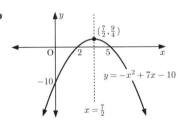

12 a
b

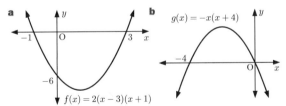

13 $f(x) = -(x - 2)^2 + 2$
14 $f(x) = -2x^2 - 16x - 17$

15 a $h = 2$
b $a = -\frac{3}{4}$, $k = 3\frac{1}{2}$

16 a
b

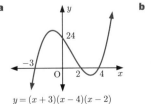
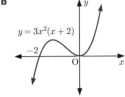

17 $c = 3$, $d = -10$

EXERCISE 27A

1 a Start with 8, then subtract 3 each time to get the next term.
b $u_2 = 5$, $u_4 = -1$ **c** $u_5 = -4$, $u_6 = -7$

2 a Start with 2, then add 4 each time to get the next term. $u_6 = 22$, $u_7 = 26$.
b Start with 2, then add 7 each time to get the next term. $u_6 = 37$, $u_7 = 44$.
c Start with 8, then add 11 each time to get the next term. $u_6 = 63$, $u_7 = 74$.
d Start with 20, then subtract 4 each time to get the next term. $u_6 = 0$, $u_7 = -4$.
e Start with 3, then subtract 5 each time to get the next term. $u_6 = -22$, $u_7 = -27$.
f Start with 10, then subtract $1\frac{1}{2}$ each time to get the next term. $u_5 = 4$, $u_6 = 2\frac{1}{2}$.

3 a Start with 1, then multiply by 2 each time to get the next term. $u_6 = 32$, $u_7 = 64$.
b Start with 1, then multiply by -2 each time to get the next term. $u_6 = -32$, $u_7 = 64$.
c Start with 36, then divide by 2 each time to get the next term. $u_5 = 2\frac{1}{4}$, $u_6 = 1\frac{1}{8}$.
d Start with $\frac{1}{81}$, then multiply by 3 each time to get the next term. $u_5 = 1$, $u_6 = 3$.
e Start with 405, then divide by 3 each time to get the next term. $u_5 = 5$, $u_6 = \frac{5}{3}$.
f Start with 1, then multiply by 1.1 each time to get the next term. $u_5 = 1.4641$, $u_6 = 1.61051$.

4 a The nth term is n^2. $u_6 = 36$, $u_7 = 49$.
b The nth term is n^3. $u_5 = 125$, $u_6 = 216$.
c The nth term is $\frac{1}{n^2}$. $u_5 = \frac{1}{25}$, $u_6 = \frac{1}{36}$.
d The first term is 2. Each term thereafter is the sum of the previous term and 2 to the power of 2 less than the term number. $u_6 = 33$, $u_7 = 65$.
e The first term is 2. Each term thereafter is the sum of the previous term and the previous term number. $u_6 = 17$, $u_7 = 23$.
f The nth term is the nth prime number. $u_6 = 13$, $u_7 = 17$.
g The first two terms are 0 and 1, and each term thereafter is the sum of the previous two terms. $u_7 = 8$, $u_8 = 13$.
h The first term is 1. Each term thereafter is the product of the previous term and the previous term number. $u_6 = 120$, $u_7 = 720$.
i Counting from 1, each term is the number of letters in the English word for that number. "One" has 3 letters, "two" has 3 letters, and so on. $u_7 = 5$, $u_8 = 5$.

5 a
b

3, 6, 9, 12, 15, ...
7, 10, 13, 16, 19, ...

c

4, 13, 26, 43, 64, ...

d
e

5, 12, 19, 26, 33, ...
6, 11, 16, 21, 26, ...

f

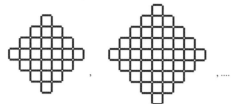

4, 16, 36, 64, 100, ...

6 **a**

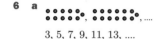

3, 5, 7, 9, 11, 13, ...

b

1, 4, 9, 16, 25, 36, ...

c

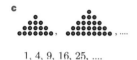

1, 4, 9, 16, 25, ...

d

2, 8, 18, 32, 50, ...

EXERCISE 27B

1 **a** $u_1 = 5$, $u_2 = 7$, $u_3 = 9$, $u_4 = 11$
 b $u_1 = 8$, $u_2 = 11$, $u_3 = 14$, $u_4 = 17$
 c $u_1 = -1$, $u_2 = -3$, $u_3 = -5$, $u_4 = -7$
 d $u_1 = 1$, $u_2 = -1$, $u_3 = -3$, $u_4 = -5$
 e $u_1 = 13$, $u_2 = 9$, $u_3 = 5$, $u_4 = 1$
 f $u_1 = 69$, $u_2 = 62$, $u_3 = 55$, $u_4 = 48$
2 **a** $u_1 = 0$, $u_2 = 3$, $u_3 = 8$, $u_4 = 15$
 b $u_1 = 2$, $u_2 = 6$, $u_3 = 12$, $u_4 = 20$
 c $u_1 = -1$, $u_2 = -4$, $u_3 = -9$, $u_4 = -16$
 d $u_1 = 4$, $u_2 = 10$, $u_3 = 18$, $u_4 = 28$
 e $u_1 = 0$, $u_2 = 7$, $u_3 = 26$, $u_4 = 63$
 f $u_1 = 2$, $u_2 = 15$, $u_3 = 44$, $u_4 = 95$
3 **a** $u_1 = 10$, $u_2 = 20$, $u_3 = 40$, $u_4 = 80$, $u_5 = 160$
 b $u_1 = 5$, $u_2 = 10$, $u_3 = 20$, $u_4 = 40$, $u_5 = 80$
 c $u_1 = 20$, $u_2 = 40$, $u_3 = 80$, $u_4 = 160$, $u_5 = 320$
 d $u_1 = 4$, $u_2 = 12$, $u_3 = 36$, $u_4 = 108$, $u_5 = 324$
 e $u_1 = 24$, $u_2 = 12$, $u_3 = 6$, $u_4 = 3$, $u_5 = \frac{3}{2}$
 f $u_1 = 36$, $u_2 = 12$, $u_3 = 4$, $u_4 = \frac{4}{3}$, $u_5 = \frac{4}{9}$
 g $u_1 = -48$, $u_2 = 96$, $u_3 = -192$, $u_4 = 384$, $u_5 = -768$
 h $u_1 = 8$, $u_2 = -8$, $u_3 = 8$, $u_4 = -8$, $u_5 = 8$
 i $u_1 = -4$, $u_2 = 2$, $u_3 = -1$, $u_4 = \frac{1}{2}$, $u_5 = -\frac{1}{4}$
4 **a** 1, 3, 6, 10, 15
 b **i** $u_1 = \frac{1}{2}(1)(2) = 1$ ✓ $u_2 = \frac{1}{2}(2)(3) = 3$ ✓
  $u_3 = \frac{1}{2}(3)(4) = 6$ ✓ $u_4 = \frac{1}{2}(4)(5) = 10$ ✓
  $u_5 = \frac{1}{2}(5)(6) = 15$ ✓
  ii $u_{10} = \frac{1}{2}(10)(11) = 55$
5 **a** 39 is the 7th term of the sequence.
 b No, 8 is *not* a term of the sequence.
 c Yes, −52 is the 20th term of the sequence.
6 **a** $u_4 = 21$ **b** Yes, 41 is the 6th term of the sequence.
 c No, 80 is *not* a term of the sequence.
7 **a** $u_n = 2n$
 b **i** $u_n = 2n + 2$ **ii** $u_n = 2n - 1$ **iii** $u_n = \dfrac{1}{2n}$
8 **a** $u_n = 5n$
 b **i** $u_n = 5n + 1$ **ii** $u_n = 5n - 2$ **iii** $u_n = \dfrac{1}{5n}$

9 **a** $u_n = 2^n$ **b** **i** $u_n = 3 \times 2^n$ **ii** $u_n = \dfrac{1}{2^n}$

10 **a** $u_n = n$ **b** $u_n = n + 1$ **c** $u_n = n + 2$ **d** $u_n = \dfrac{1}{n}$
 e $u_n = \dfrac{1}{n + 1}$ **f** $u_n = \dfrac{n}{n + 1}$ **g** $u_n = \dfrac{n + 2}{n}$
 h $u_n = n(n + 1)$ **i** $u_n = (n + 1)(n + 2)$
 j $u_n = n(n + 2)$ **k** $u_n = \dfrac{3n - 2}{3n}$

11 **a** $u_n = n^2$ **b** $u_n = (n - 1)^2$ **c** $u_n = n^2 + 1$
12 **a** $u_n = n^3$ **b** $u_n = n^3 - 1$
13 **a** $u_1 = a + b$, $u_2 = 2a + b$, $u_3 = 3a + b$, $u_4 = 4a + b$, $u_5 = 5a + b$
 b Each term differs from the previous term by the fixed number a. The value of a in our formula is the common difference.
 c **i** $u_n = 4n - 1$ **ii** $u_n = 6n - 1$ **iii** $u_n = 20 - 7n$

EXERCISE 27C

1 **a** $\frac{6}{3} = 2$, $\frac{12}{6} = 2$, and so on. $\therefore \dfrac{u_{n+1}}{u_n} = 2$, a constant.
 b $u_n = 3 \times 2^{n-1}$
2 **a** **i** $u_6 = -1$, $u_7 = 1$ **ii** $u_n = (-1)^{n-1}$
 b **i** $u_6 = 1$, $u_7 = -1$ **ii** $u_n = (-1)^n$
 c **i** $u_6 = 64$, $u_7 = 128$ **ii** $u_n = 2^n$
 d **i** $u_6 = -64$, $u_7 = 128$ **ii** $u_n = 2 \times (-2)^{n-1}$
 e **i** $u_5 = 486$, $u_6 = 1458$ **ii** $u_n = 6 \times 3^{n-1}$
 f **i** $u_5 = 486$, $u_6 = -1458$ **ii** $u_n = 6 \times (-3)^{n-1}$
3 **a** $u_n = 4 \times 3^{n-1}$ **b** $u_n = 2 \times (-7)^{n-1}$
 c $u_n = 3 \times (-2)^{n-1}$ **d** $u_n = -16 \times (-\frac{1}{2})^{n-1}$
 e $u_n = 12 \times (\frac{1}{2})^{n-1}$ **f** $u_n = 12 \times (-\frac{2}{3})^{n-1}$
4 **a** The first four terms of the sequence are 10, 20, 40, and 80.
 $\frac{20}{10} = 2$, $\frac{40}{20} = 2$, $\frac{80}{40} = 2$. $\therefore \dfrac{u_{n+1}}{u_n} = 2$, a constant.
 b $u_n = 10 \times 2^{n-1}$

EXERCISE 27D

1 **a** $u_n = 4n - 3$ **b** $u_n = 20 - 3n$ **c** $u_n = n^2 + n$
 d $u_n = n^2 + 3n - 4$ **e** $u_n = n^3 + 5$
 f $u_n = \frac{1}{2}n^3 + \frac{3}{2}n$ or $u_n = \dfrac{n(n^2 + 3)}{2}$
2 **a** $u_n = 4n^2 - 2n$
 b $u_1 = 1 \times 2$, $u_2 = 3 \times 4$, $u_3 = 5 \times 6$, $u_4 = 7 \times 8$, and so on.
 $\therefore \quad u_n = (2n - 1) \times 2n$
3 **a** $u_1 = 2$, $u_2 = 8$, $u_3 = 18$, $u_4 = 32$, $u_5 = 50$, $u_6 = 72$, $u_7 = 98$
 b $u_n = 2n^2$ **c** $u_{30} = 1800$ dots
4 **a**

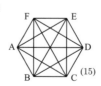 (15)
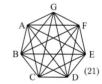 (21)

 b $u_n = \frac{1}{2}n^2 + \frac{1}{2}n$ or $u_n = \dfrac{n(n + 1)}{2}$
 c 15 931 handshakes
5 **a** $u_1 = 3$, $u_2 = 13$, $u_3 = 34$, $u_4 = 70$, $u_5 = 125$, $u_6 = 203$

b $u_n = \frac{2}{3}n^3 + \frac{3}{2}n^2 + \frac{5}{6}n$ or $u_n = \frac{n(n+1)(4n+5)}{6}$

c $u_{50} = 87\,125$

6 a $u_1 = 1,\ u_2 = 5,\ u_3 = 14,\ u_4 = 30,\ u_5 = 55,\ u_6 = 91,$
$u_7 = 140$

b $u_n = \frac{1}{3}n^3 + \frac{1}{2}n^2 + \frac{1}{6}n$ or $u_n = \frac{n(n+1)(2n+1)}{6}$

c $338\,350$ squares

7 a $u_3 = 20,\ u_4 = 40,\ u_5 = 70,\ u_6 = 112$

b $u_n = \frac{1}{3}n^3 + n^2 + \frac{2}{3}n$ or $u_n = \frac{n(n+1)(n+2)}{3}$

c 1360 squares

REVIEW SET 27A

1 a Start with 6, then add 4 each time to get the next term.
$u_6 = 26,\ u_7 = 30.$

b Start with 810, then divide by 3 each time to get the next
term. $u_5 = 10,\ u_6 = 3\frac{1}{3}.$

2 a

$2, 5, 8, 11, 14, ...$

b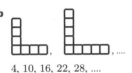

$4, 10, 16, 22, 28, ...$

3 a $u_1 = 5,\ u_2 = 11,\ u_3 = 17,\ u_4 = 23$

b $u_1 = 4,\ u_2 = 12,\ u_3 = 22,\ u_4 = 34$

4 a $u_n = 4n$ **b i** $u_n = 4n - 3$ **ii** $u_n = \frac{1}{4n-1}$

c i $u_{20} = 77$ **ii** $u_{20} = \frac{1}{79}$

5 a $u_1 = 18,\ u_2 = 12,\ u_3 = 8,\ u_4 = 5\frac{1}{3}$

b $u_1 = 5,\ u_2 = -10,\ u_3 = 20,\ u_4 = -40$

6 a $u_n = 3 \times 4^{n-1}$ **b** $u_n = 88 \times (-\frac{1}{2})^{n-1}$

7 a $u_n = 7n - 2$ **b** $u_n = n^2 + 4n - 6$

8 a $u_3 = 9,\ u_4 = 13,\ u_5 = 17$ **b** $u_n = 4n - 3$

c $u_{50} = 197$ triangles

9 a $u_n = n^3 + 3n^2 + 2n$

b $u_1 = 6 = 1 \times 2 \times 3,\quad u_2 = 24 = 2 \times 3 \times 4,$
$u_3 = 60 = 3 \times 4 \times 5,\quad u_4 = 120 = 4 \times 5 \times 6$
which suggests that $u_n = n(n+1)(n+2)$

10 a $u_4 = 11,\ u_5 = 16$

b $u_n = \frac{1}{2}n^2 + \frac{1}{2}n + 1$ or $u_n = \frac{n^2 + n + 2}{2}$

c $u_{10} = 56$ pieces

REVIEW SET 27B

1 a Start with 17, then subtract 5 each time to get the next term.
$u_5 = -3,\ u_6 = -8.$

b Start with -2, then multiply by -2 each time to get the next
term. $u_5 = -32,\ u_6 = 64.$

2 a

$4, 8, 12, 16, 20, ...$ $3, 8, 15, 24, 35, ...$

3 a $u_1 = 1,\ u_2 = -3,\ u_3 = -7,\ u_4 = -11$

b $u_1 = 0,\ u_2 = 4,\ u_3 = 10,\ u_4 = 18$

4 a $u_n = 6n + 10$ **b i** $u_n = 6n + 4$ **ii** $u_n = \frac{6n-1}{6n+1}$

c i $u_{15} = 94$ **ii** $u_{15} = \frac{89}{91}$

5 a $u_n = n^2 + 1$ **b** $u_n = \frac{1}{n^3}$

6 a $u_1 = 5,\ u_2 = 15,\ u_3 = 45,\ u_4 = 135$

b $u_1 = -12,\ u_2 = 3,\ u_3 = -\frac{3}{4},\ u_4 = \frac{3}{16}$

7 a $u_n = 4 \times (-3)^{n-1}$ **b** $u_n = 224 \times (\frac{1}{4})^{n-1}$

8 a $u_n = 52 - 9n$ **b** $u_n = n^2 + 5n - 2$

9 a $u_3 = 24,\ u_4 = 40,\ u_5 = 60,\ u_6 = 84$

b $u_n = 2n^2 + 2n$ or $u_n = 2n(n+1)$

c $u_{10} = 220$ matches

10 c $u_n = \frac{1}{24}n^4 + \frac{1}{12}n^3 - \frac{1}{24}n^2 - \frac{1}{12}n$

EXERCISE 28A

1 a 4 **b** $\frac{1}{4}$ **c** 5 **d** $\frac{1}{5}$ **e** 2 **f** $\frac{1}{2}$

g 3 **h** $\frac{1}{3}$ **i** 3 **j** $\frac{1}{3}$ **k** 2 **l** $\frac{1}{2}$

2 a not possible **b** -1 **c** $-\frac{1}{3}$ **d** not possible

3 a $10\frac{1}{2}$ **b** $10^{-\frac{1}{2}}$ **c** $15\frac{1}{3}$ **d** $15^{-\frac{1}{3}}$

e $19\frac{1}{4}$ **f** $19^{-\frac{1}{4}}$ **g** $13\frac{1}{5}$ **h** $13^{-\frac{1}{5}}$

4 a 27 **b** 64 **c** 243 **d** 4 **e** 8 **f** $\frac{1}{64}$

g $\frac{1}{8}$ **h** $\frac{1}{4}$ **i** $\frac{1}{125}$ **j** 27 **k** $\frac{1}{27}$ **l** 25

5 a ≈ 4.33 **b** ≈ 36.5 **c** ≈ 91.2 **d** ≈ 0.397

e $\approx 0.000\,264$

EXERCISE 28B

1 a, c, d, and **f** are exponential functions.

2 a 3 **b** 11 **c** $2\frac{1}{3}$ **d** $3^{2x} + 2$

3 a -2 **b** $-2\frac{4}{5}$ **c** 22 **d** $5^x - 3$

4 a $\frac{1}{9}$ **b** 9 **c** $\frac{1}{27}$ **d** 3^{x+3}

EXERCISE 28C

1 a

x	-3	-2	-1	0	1	2	3
y	$\frac{1}{27}$	$\frac{1}{9}$	$\frac{1}{3}$	1	3	9	27

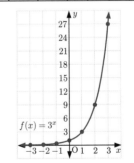

b

x	-3	-2	-1	0	1	2	3
y	$\frac{1}{64}$	$\frac{1}{16}$	$\frac{1}{4}$	1	4	16	64

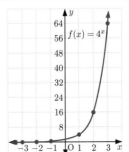

c

x	-3	-2	-1	0	1	2	3
y	8	4	2	1	$\frac{1}{2}$	$\frac{1}{4}$	$\frac{1}{8}$

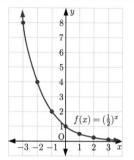

$f(x) = (\frac{1}{2})^x$

d

x	-3	-2	-1	0	1	2	3
y	27	9	3	1	$\frac{1}{3}$	$\frac{1}{9}$	$\frac{1}{27}$

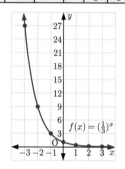

$f(x) = (\frac{1}{3})^x$

2

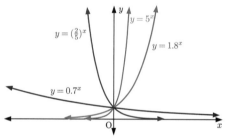

$y = (\frac{2}{5})^x$ $y = 5^x$ $y = 1.8^x$ $y = 0.7^x$

3   **a** D   **b** A   **c** F   **d** C   **e** B   **f** E

4   **a** A translation of $y = f(x)$ by $\binom{0}{k}$.

   b   **i**

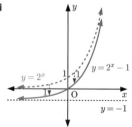

$y = 2^x$ $y = 2^x - 1$ $y = -1$

     ii

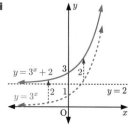

$y = 3^x + 2$ $y = 3^x$ $y = 2$

     iii

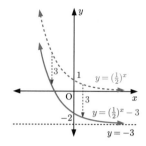

$y = (\frac{1}{2})^x$ $y = (\frac{1}{2})^x - 3$ $y = -3$

5   **a** A stretch with invariant x-axis and scale factor a.

   b   **i**   **ii**

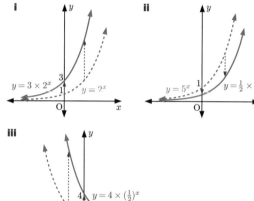

$y = 3 \times 2^x$ $y = 2^x$ $y = 5^x$ $y = \frac{1}{2} \times 5^x$

     iii

$y = 4 \times (\frac{1}{2})^x$ $y = (\frac{1}{2})^x$

6   **a** A translation of $y = f(x)$ by $\binom{h}{0}$.

   b   **i**   **ii**

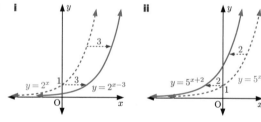

$y = 2^x$ $y = 2^{x-3}$ $y = 5^{x+2}$ $y = 5^x$

     iii

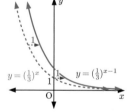

$y = (\frac{1}{3})^x$ $y = (\frac{1}{3})^{x-1}$

7   **a**   **i** A reflection of $y = f(x)$ in the x-axis.

       ii A reflection of $y = f(x)$ in the y-axis.

   b   **i**

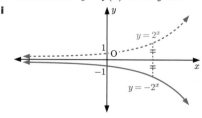

$y = 2^x$ $y = -2^x$

ii

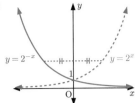

iii

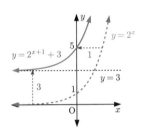

8 $y = 2^{x+1} + 3$

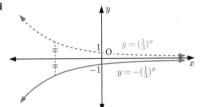

9 **a** $y = -2^{-x}$ **b** $y = 2^x$

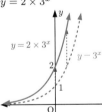

10 **a** $y = 2 \times 3^x$ **b** $y = 3^{3x}$

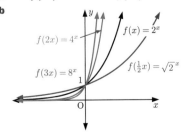

11 **a** **i** $f(2x) = 4^x$ **ii** $f(3x) = 8^x$ **iii** $f(\tfrac{1}{2}x) = \sqrt{2}^{\,x}$
   b

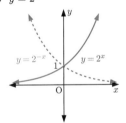

12 **a** **i** $y = 2^x$ has been reflected in the x-axis, then translated by $\begin{pmatrix} 0 \\ 2 \end{pmatrix}$.

ii

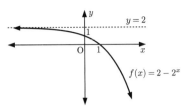

   b **i** $y = 2^x$ has been reflected in the y-axis, translated by $\begin{pmatrix} 0 \\ 1 \end{pmatrix}$, then stretched vertically with invariant x-axis and scale factor $\tfrac{1}{3}$.

   ii

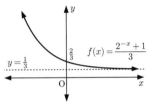

   c **i** $y = 2^x$ has been reflected in the y-axis, stretched vertically with invariant x-axis and scale factor 2, then translated by $\begin{pmatrix} 0 \\ 1 \end{pmatrix}$.

   ii

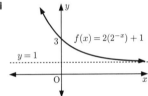

13 **a**   **b**

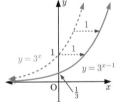
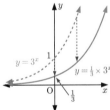

   c $3^{x-1} = 3^{-1} \times 3^x$
            $= \tfrac{1}{3} \times 3^x$

   d If $y = a^x$ is translated by $\begin{pmatrix} h \\ 0 \end{pmatrix}$, then the resulting function
          is $y = a^{x-h}$
                $= a^x a^{-h}$
                $= \dfrac{1}{a^h}\, a^x$

          which is a stretch with invariant x-axis and scale factor $\dfrac{1}{a^h}$.

14 For example, if $x = \tfrac{1}{2}$, $(-2)^{\frac{1}{2}} = \sqrt{-2}$ which is undefined.

15 **a** $a = \tfrac{3}{2}$, $k = 20$ **b** $a = \tfrac{11}{10}$, $k = 1600$
       c $a = \tfrac{1}{5}$, $k = 400$ **d** $a = \tfrac{1}{3}$, $k = 216$

EXERCISE 28D

1 **a** $x = 1$ **b** $x = 2$ **c** $x = 3$ **d** $x = 0$
    e $x = -1$ **f** $x = -1$ **g** $x = -4$ **h** $x = 0$
    i $x = -4$ **j** $x = -2$ **k** $x = 6$ **l** $x = 2$
    m $x = -\tfrac{3}{4}$ **n** $x = \tfrac{7}{2}$ **o** $x = 0$ **p** $x = 4$

2 a $x=3$ **b** $x=0$ **c** $x=-2$ **d** $x=3$
e $x=-5$ **f** $x=-2$ **g** $x=\frac{2}{7}$ **h** $x=\frac{1}{3}$
i $x=1$ **j** $x=1$ **k** no solution **l** $x=-1$ or 3

3 $a=6,\ n=2$ **4** $b=\frac{1}{4},\ t=5$ **5** $x=-1,\ y=2$

6 a $x\approx 6.644$ **b** $x\approx -1.884$ **c** no solution
d $x\approx 1.292$ **e** $x\approx -1.611$ **f** $x\approx 4.192$
g $x\approx -4.583$ **h** $x\approx -1.848$ **i** $x\approx 4.858$
j $x\approx 2.064$ **k** $x\approx 2.991$ **l** $x\approx 291.825$
m $x\approx 0.262$ **n** $x\approx 1.441$ **o** $x\approx 0.415$

EXERCISE 28E

1 a 40 mongooses
b **i** ≈ 61 mongooses **ii** ≈ 162 mongooses
iii ≈ 2650 mongooses
c
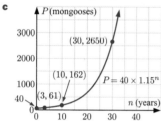
d ≈ 6.56 years (6 years 7 months)

2 a 50 echidnas
b **i** ≈ 100 echidnas **ii** ≈ 400 echidnas
iii ≈ 5090 echidnas
c
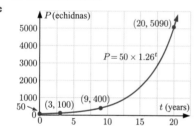
d ≈ 4.75 years (4 years 9 months)

3 a $G_0=28$
b **i** ≈ 29
ii ≈ 31
iii ≈ 34
d ≈ 198 years
c
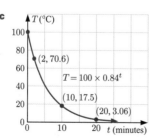

4 a $100°C$
b **i** $\approx 70.6°C$
ii $\approx 17.5°C$
iii $\approx 3.06°C$
d ≈ 4.21 min (4 min 13 s)
c
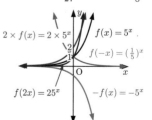

5 a 2.3 g
b **i** ≈ 1.02 g
ii ≈ 0.449 g
iii ≈ 0.199 g
d $\approx 55.8\%$ loss
c
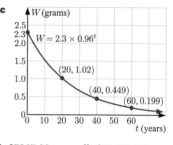

6 a $5800 **b** **i** $7367.38 **ii** $12\,873.97
c ≈ 8.69 years

7 a $500 **b** **i** $445.64 **ii** $199.11
c ≈ 62.8 months (5 years 3 months)

8 a no
b The area covered each week is 1.2 times greater than the area covered in the previous week, and the initial area covered is 40 cm^2.
c
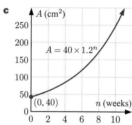
d 69.12 cm^2
e ≈ 5.03 weeks

9 a $b=5000$ **b** $10\,000$ bacteria **c** $m=3$
d **e** $20\,480\,000$ bacteria
f ≈ 2.21 days (2 days 5 hours)

EXERCISE 28F

1 a $P\approx 25.1\times 1.32^x$ **b** $N\approx 5.70\times 0.815^t$
2 a $V\approx 216\,000\times 1.02^t$ dollars
b **i** $\approx \$237\,000$ **ii** $\approx \$284\,000$
c Our estimate for 2014 is more likely to be accurate since it is an interpolation.
3 a $C\approx 300\times 0.349^t$ micrograms/ml **b** ≈ 13.5 minutes

REVIEW SET 28A

1 a $5^{\frac{1}{2}}$ **b** $7^{-\frac{1}{3}}$ **c** $51^{\frac{1}{4}}$ **d** $47^{-\frac{1}{5}}$
2 a 8 **b** $\frac{1}{5}$ **c** $\frac{1}{27}$ **d** $\frac{1}{8}$
3 a **i** $(\frac{1}{5})^x$
ii -5^x
iii 2×5^x
iv 25^x
b

4 a 0   **b** 26   **c** $-\frac{2}{3}$ **d** $-\frac{8}{9}$

5 a 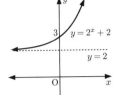   **b**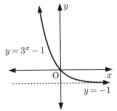

c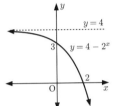

6 $y = 5^{x+2} - 5$

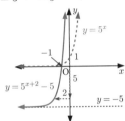

7 $a = \frac{5}{4}$, $k = 1024$

8 a $x = -4$ **b** $x = -1$ **c** $x = 4$
d $x = 2$ **e** $x = -5$ **f** $x = -\frac{4}{5}$

9 $k = 576$, $n = -2$

10 a $x \approx 2.80$ **b** $x \approx 1.36$ **c** $x \approx 6.61$

11 a i 10 people   **ii** ≈ 29 people   **iii** ≈ 82 people
b   **c** ≈ 11.4 weeks

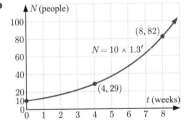

12 a $N \approx -4.83t + 529$
Since $r^2 \approx 0.996$, this seems like an appropriate model.
b $N \approx 529 \times 0.990^t$
Since $r^2 \approx 0.998$, this is an even better fit for the data. This model is more appropriate since it shows a realistic population decline in the long run.
c ≈ 445 chicks

REVIEW SET 28B

1 a ≈ 2.924 **b** ≈ 2.512 **c** ≈ 1.971
2 a $\frac{1}{4}$ **b** 32   **c** 16   **d** $\frac{1}{243}$
3 a 2   **b** $\frac{2}{3}$ **c** $\frac{2}{9}$ **d** 6   **e** 18

4 a i $(\frac{1}{2})^x$ **b**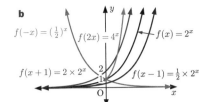
ii 4^x
iii 2×2^x
iv $\frac{1}{2} \times 2^x$

5 a 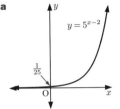   **b**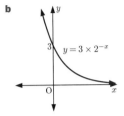

c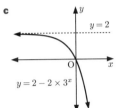

6 a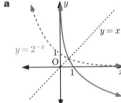

b Yes, $y = 2^{-x}$ is one-to-one, so its reflection in the line $y = x$ is its inverse function.

7 $a = \frac{2}{3}$, $k = 324$

8 a $x = -3$ **b** $x = -\frac{1}{6}$ **c** $x = 2$ **d** $x = \frac{3}{2}$
e $x = -\frac{7}{2}$ **f** $x = 2$ or -1

9 $x = -1$, $y = -2$

10 a $x \approx 2.73$ **b** no solutions   **c** $x \approx 11.33$

11 a 130 kg   **b i** ≈ 2.83 kg   **ii** ≈ 8.29 kg
c ≈ 15.2 weeks

12 a \$3500
b The value of the investment is multiplied by 1.0375 each year. The interest earned in one time period also earns interest in the next time period.
c ≈ 9.69 years

EXERCISE 29A

1 a $\log_3 9 = 2$ **b** $\log_4 16 = 2$ **c** $\log_5 25 = 2$
d $\log_5 125 = 3$ **e** $\log_{10} 10\,000 = 4$ **f** $\log_7(\frac{1}{7}) = -1$
g $\log_3(\frac{1}{27}) = -3$ **h** $\log_{27} 3 = \frac{1}{3}$ **i** $\log_5(\frac{1}{25}) = -2$
j $\log_2(\frac{1}{\sqrt{2}}) = -\frac{1}{2}$ **k** $\log_2(4\sqrt{2}) = 2.5$
l $\log_{10}(0.001) = -3$

2 a $2^3 = 8$ **b** $2^0 = 1$ **c** $5^4 = 625$ **d** $2^{-1} = \frac{1}{2}$
e $2^{\frac{1}{2}} = \sqrt{2}$ **f** $2^{-\frac{1}{2}} = \frac{1}{\sqrt{2}}$ **g** $(\sqrt{2})^2 = 2$ **h** $9^{\frac{1}{2}} = 3$

3 **a** 2 **b** 3 **c** 1 **d** 0 **e** 3
f -1 **g** -3 **h** 7 **i** -1 **j** -2
k $\frac{1}{2}$ **l** $\frac{3}{2}$ **m** $\frac{1}{3}$ **n** $\frac{5}{2}$ **o** 2
p $-\frac{5}{2}$ **q** -2 **r** 4 **s** -2 **t** $-\frac{5}{2}$

4 **a** $\log_4 y = x$ **b** $\log_9 y = x$ **c** $\log_a y = x$
d $\log_{\sqrt{3}} y = x$ **e** $\log_2 y = x + 1$ **f** $\log_3 y = 2n$
g $\log_2 y = -x$ **h** $\log_3 \left(\dfrac{y}{2}\right) = a$

5 **a** $2^y = x$ **b** $3^y = x$ **c** $a^y = x$
d $m^y = b$ **e** $5^T = \dfrac{a}{2}$ **f** $3^{2M} = p$
g $b^{\frac{G}{5}} = m$ **h** $(\sqrt{b})^P = n$

6 **a** $x = 7^y$ **b** $x = \log_3 y$ **c** $x = \log_{0.5} y$
d $x = \log_5 z$ **e** $x = 2^t$ **f** $x = \dfrac{\log_2 y}{3}$
g $x = 2\log_5 y$ **h** $x = \dfrac{3^w}{2}$ **i** $x = \log_3(2z)$
j $x = \log_4(5y)$ **k** $x = -\log_2(10D)$ **l** $x = \log_3 G - 1$

7 **a** As $a^0 = 1$ for all $a > 0$, then $\log_a 1 = 0$.
b As $a^1 = a$ for all $a > 0$, then $\log_a a = 1$.

8 **a** $x = 4$ **b** $x = \frac{1}{25}$ **c** $x = 2$ **d** $x = \frac{1}{10}$

EXERCISE 29B

1 **a**

x	-3	-2	-1	0	1	2	3
y	$\frac{1}{8}$	$\frac{1}{4}$	$\frac{1}{2}$	1	2	4	8

b

y	-3	-2	-1	0	1	2	3
x	$\frac{1}{8}$	$\frac{1}{4}$	$\frac{1}{2}$	1	2	4	8

c

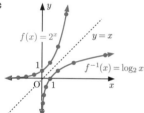

d $x = 0$
e Domain is $\{x \mid x > 0\}$
Range is $\{y \mid y \in \mathbb{R}\}$

2 **a** **I** $f^{-1}(x) = \log_4 x$
ii

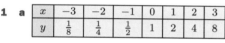

iii $y = 4^x$ has horizontal asymptote $y = 0$, $y = \log_4 x$ has vertical asymptote $x = 0$.
iv For $y = 4^x$:
Domain is $\{x \mid x \in \mathbb{R}\}$
Range is $\{y \mid y > 0\}$
For $y = \log_4 x$:
Domain is $\{x \mid x > 0\}$
Range is $\{y \mid y \in \mathbb{R}\}$

b **I** $f^{-1}(x) = -\log_3 x$
ii

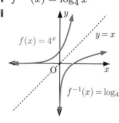

iii $y = 3^{-x}$ has horizontal asymptote $y = 0$, $y = -\log_3 x$ has vertical asymptote $x = 0$.
iv For $y = 3^{-x}$:
Domain is $\{x \mid x \in \mathbb{R}\}$
Range is $\{y \mid y > 0\}$
For $y = -\log_3 x$:
Domain is $\{x \mid x > 0\}$
Range is $\{y \mid y \in \mathbb{R}\}$

3 **a** $f^{-1}(x) = \log_{10} x$ **b** $f^{-1}(x) = \log_3\left(\dfrac{x}{2}\right)$
c $f^{-1}(x) = -\log_3(2x)$ **d** $f^{-1}(x) = 7^x$
e $f^{-1}(x) = 2^{\frac{x}{3}}$ **f** $f^{-1}(x) = 3^{\frac{x}{5}}$

EXERCISE 29C

1 **a** $\log_3 16$ **b** $\log_2 3$ **c** $\log_5 72$ **d** $\log_3 14$
e $\log_3 12$ **f** $\log_3 45$ **g** $\log_7 21$ **h** $\log_4\left(\frac{36}{125}\right)$
i $\log_3(m^2 n^7)$ **j** $\log_2\left(\dfrac{k^5}{n^3}\right)$

2 **a** $p + q$ **b** $q - p$ **c** $2p$ **d** $3q$
e $p - 2q$ **f** $p + 2q$ **g** $p + 3 - 2q$ **h** $q + p - 2$

3 **a** $y = u^3$ **b** $y = \dfrac{u^3}{v}$ **c** $y = u^2 v^3$ **d** $y = 2^{u+v}$
e $y = \dfrac{2^u}{v}$ **f** $y = \dfrac{1}{u}$ **g** $y = 7v^2$ **h** $y = \dfrac{\sqrt{v}}{u^2}$
i $y = \dfrac{36}{\sqrt[3]{u}}$ **j** $y = 3v\sqrt{u}$

4 **a** 2 **b** 2 **c** -2 **d** -2

EXERCISE 29D

1 **a** $\approx 10^{0.903}$ **b** $\approx 10^{1.903}$ **c** $\approx 10^{2.903}$
d $\approx 10^{-0.0969}$ **e** $\approx 10^{-2.0969}$ **f** $\approx 10^{-0.523}$
g $\approx 10^{-1.523}$ **h** $\approx 10^{-4.523}$ **i** $\approx 10^{1.699}$
j $\approx 10^{-3.301}$

2 **a** $\log 30$ **b** $\log 5$ **c** $\log 12$ **d** $\log(\frac{5}{4})$ **e** $\log 1 = 0$
f $\log 30$ **g** $\log 4$ **h** $-\log 6$ or $\log(\frac{1}{6})$
i $\log(\frac{1}{512})$ **j** $\log 2000$ **k** $\log(\frac{64}{125})$ **l** $\log 20$
m $\log 5$ **n** $\log 20$ **o** $\log 14\,000$

3 $\log 30 = \log(3 \times 10)$ $\log(0.3) = \log(\frac{3}{10})$
$\qquad = \log 3 + \log 10$ $\qquad = \log 3 - \log 10$
$\qquad = \log 3 + 1$ $\qquad = \log 3 - 1$

4 **a** 3 **b** 2 **c** $\frac{2}{3}$ **d** -1 **e** -1 **f** $-\frac{3}{2}$
g $\dfrac{b}{3}$ **h** $\dfrac{2}{a}$

5 **a** $\log 8 = \log 2^3$ **b** $\log 32 = \log 2^5$
$\qquad = 3\log 2$ $\qquad = 5\log 2$
c $\log(\frac{1}{7}) = \log(7^{-1})$ **d** $\log(\frac{1}{4}) = \log(2^{-2})$
$\qquad = -\log 7$ $\qquad = -2\log 2$
e $\log\sqrt{5} = \log 5^{\frac{1}{2}}$ **f** $\log\sqrt[3]{2} = \log 2^{\frac{1}{3}}$
$\qquad = \frac{1}{2}\log 5$ $\qquad = \frac{1}{3}\log 2$
g $\log(\frac{1}{\sqrt{3}}) = \log(3^{-\frac{1}{2}})$ **h** $\log 5 = \log 10 - \log 2$
$\qquad = -\frac{1}{2}\log 3$ $\qquad = 1 - \log 2$
i $\log 500 = \log 1000 - \log 2$
$\qquad = 3 - \log 2$

EXERCISE 29E

1 **a** $\log y = \log a + 2\log b$ **b** $\log y = 2\log a - \log b$
c $\log y = \log d + \frac{1}{2}\log p$ **d** $\log M = 2\log a + 5\log b$
e $\log P = \frac{1}{2}(\log a + \log b)$ **f** $\log Q = \frac{1}{2}\log m - \log n$
g $\log R = \log a + \log b + 2\log c$
h $\log T = \log 5 + \frac{1}{2}(\log d - \log c)$
i $\log M = \log a + 3\log b - \frac{1}{2}\log c$

2 a $Q = 10^{x+2}$ or $Q = 100 \times 10^x$
  b $J = 10^{2x-1}$ or $J = \frac{1}{10} \times 100^x$
  c $M = 10^{2-x}$ or $M = \dfrac{100}{10^x}$
  d $P \approx 10^{0.301+x}$ or $P \approx 2 \times 10^x$
  e $R \approx 10^{x+1.477}$ or $R \approx 30 \times 10^x$
  f $K \approx 10^{\frac{1}{2}x+1}$ or $K \approx 10 \times 10^{\frac{x}{2}}$

3 a $M = ab$ **b** $N = \dfrac{d}{e}$ **c** $F = x^2$ **d** $T = \sqrt{p}$
  e $D = \dfrac{1}{g}$ **f** $S = \dfrac{1}{b^2}$ **g** $A = \dfrac{B}{C^2}$ **h** $p^2 q = s$
  i $\dfrac{m^3}{d} = \dfrac{n}{p^2}$ **j** $\dfrac{m}{\sqrt{n}} = p^2$ **k** $N = 10t$ **l** $P = \dfrac{100}{x}$

4 a $x = 28$ **b** $x = \frac{8}{25}$ **c** $x = \frac{81}{8}$ **d** $x = 2\sqrt{15}$

5 a $x \approx 2.59$ **b** $x \approx 3.27$ **c** $x \approx 0.0401$ or ≈ 1.22
  d $x \approx 0.137$ or 1 **e** $x \approx 1.32$ **f** $x \approx 0.0103$ or 1

6 a $5^x = 13$ **b** $\log(5^x) = \log 13$
    $\therefore\ x \log 5 = \log 13$
    $\therefore\ x = \dfrac{\log 13}{\log 5} = \log_5 13 \approx 1.59$

7 a Taking the logarithm in base a of both sides, $x = \log_a b$.
  b $\log a^x = \log b$
  c Using **b**, $\ x \log a = \log b$
    $\therefore\ x = \dfrac{\log b}{\log a}$
  and using part **a**, $x = \log_a b = \dfrac{\log b}{\log a}$
  d **i** ≈ 1.77 **ii** ≈ 5.32 **iii** ≈ 3.23

EXERCISE 29F

1 a $x \approx 1.903$ **b** $x \approx 3.903$ **c** $x \approx -1.602$
  d $x \approx 2.659$ **e** $x \approx -0.057\,30$ **f** $x \approx -3.747$
2 a $x \approx 1.585$ **b** $x \approx 3.322$ **c** $x \approx 8.644$
  d $x \approx -7.059$ **e** $x \approx 4.292$ **f** $x \approx -0.099\,97$
  g $x \approx 6.511$ **h** $x \approx 4.923$ **i** $x \approx 49.60$
  j $x \approx 4.376$ **k** $x \approx 8.497$ **l** $x \approx 230.7$
3 a $x \approx 1.46$ **b** $x \approx 3.58$ **c** $x \approx 1.19$
4 a ≈ 17.0 hours **b** ≈ 64.6 hours
5 a ≈ 17.6 hours **b** ≈ 36.9 hours
6 a **i** ≈ 9.25 years ≈ 9 years 3 months
    ii ≈ 18.6 years ≈ 18 years 7 months
  b Rearranging the equation, we find $n = \log\left(\dfrac{V}{8500}\right)$, where
  V is the value of the investment after n years.

REVIEW SET 29A

1 a $\log_a a^x = x$ **b** $y = b^x \Leftrightarrow x = \log_b y$
2 a 4 **b** -1 **c** $\frac{5}{2}$ **d** $\frac{3}{2}$
3 a $\log_5 y = x$ **b** $\log_7 y = -x$
4 a $3^y = x$ **b** $n = 4^{3T}$
5 a
  b A reflection in the line $y = x$.
  c Domain is $\{x \mid x > 0\}$ Range is $\{y \mid y \in \mathbb{R}\}$

6 a $f^{-1}(x) = \log_5\left(\dfrac{x}{4}\right)$ **b** $f^{-1}(x) = 3^{\frac{x}{2}}$
7 a $\log 6$ **b** $\log 36$ **c** $\log_2 1125$
8 a $a + b$ **b** $b - a$ **c** $1 + b$
9 a $y = u^4$ **b** $y = \dfrac{1}{v^2}$ **c** $y = v\sqrt{u}$
10 a $T = \dfrac{1000}{10^x}$ **b** $N = \dfrac{c^2}{d}$
11 a $x \approx 1.533$ **b** $x \approx 0.9149$ or ≈ 4.284
12 ≈ 2.4649
13 a $x \approx 3.3219$ **b** $x \approx -4.9829$ **c** $x \approx 105.03$
14 a ≈ 492 wasps **b** ≈ 52.8 days

REVIEW SET 29B

1 a $\frac{1}{2}$ **b** $-\frac{3}{2}$ **c** 6 **d** $\frac{3}{2}$
2 a $x = \log_4 y$ **b** $n = -\log_a y$
3 a $x = 3^y$ **b** $x = \dfrac{b^T}{3}$ **c** $x = -1 + \log_2\left(\dfrac{3t}{5}\right)$
4 a $x = \frac{1}{9}$ **b** $x = \frac{49}{2}$
5 a
  b For $y = 3^x$:
  Domain is $\{x \mid x \in \mathbb{R}\}$
  Range is $\{y \mid y > 0\}$
  For $y = \log_3 x$:
  Domain is $\{x \mid x > 0\}$
  Range is $\{y \mid y \in \mathbb{R}\}$
  c $y = 3^x$ has horizontal asymptote $y = 0$, $y = \log_3 x$ has vertical asymptote $x = 0$.
6 a $f^{-1}(x) = \log_6 x$ **b** $f^{-1}(x) = 5^{2x}$
7 a $\log_2 15$ **b** $\log_3 4$ **c** $\log(\frac{5}{2})$ **d** $\log_2(\frac{25}{2})$
8 a $b - a$ **b** $a + b$ **c** $a - 1$
9 a $y = c^2$ **b** $y = \dfrac{\sqrt[3]{c}}{d^2}$
10 a $\log D = 2 - 2\log n$ **b** $2\log G = 3\log c + \log d$
11 a $M = 10^{2x+1}$ or $M = 10 \times 100^x$ **b** $G = \dfrac{\sqrt{d}}{10}$
12 a $x = \frac{1}{45}$ **b** $x = \dfrac{1}{\sqrt[3]{12}}$ **13** ≈ 2.723
14 a **i** $\$400$ **ii** $\approx \$15\,200$ **b** ≈ 53.1 years

EXERCISE 30A

1 a A$(\cos 67°, \sin 67°)$, B$(\cos 148°, \sin 148°)$,
  C$(\cos 281°, \sin 281°)$, D$(\cos(-24°), \sin(-24°))$
  b A$(0.391, 0.921)$, B$(-0.848, 0.530)$,
  C$(0.191, -0.982)$, D$(0.914, -0.407)$
  c $\tan 281° \approx -5.14$ which is the gradient of OC.
  $\tan(-24°) \approx -0.445$ which is the gradient of OD.
2 a
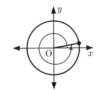
  same point on unit circle
  $\therefore$ same x-coordinate
  $\therefore$ $\cos 380° = \cos 20°$
  b same point on unit circle
  $\therefore$ same y-coordinate
  $\therefore$ $\sin 413° = \sin 53°$

c

same y-coordinate on unit circle
$\therefore$ $\sin 160° = \sin 20°$

d

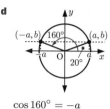

$\cos 160° = -a$
$\qquad = -\cos 20°$

e

same x-coordinate on unit circle
$\therefore$ $\cos 310° = \cos 50°$

f

OP and OP$'$ have the same gradient
$\therefore$ $\tan 25° = \tan 205°$

3 a $\cos 0° = 1$, $\sin 0° = 0$ **b** $\cos 90° = 0$, $\sin 90° = 1$
   c $\cos 360° = 1$, $\sin 360° = 0$
   d $\cos 450° = 0$, $\sin 450° = 1$
   e $\cos(-90°) = 0$, $\sin(-90°) = -1$
   f $\cos(-180°) = -1$, $\sin(-180°) = 0$

4 a $154°$ **b** $135°$ **c** $111°$ **d** $94°$
5 a $82°$ **b** $53°$ **c** $24°$ **d** $12°$
6 a $154°$ **b** $135°$ **c** $111°$ **d** $94°$
7 a $82°$ **b** $53°$ **c** $24°$ **d** $12°$
8 a $\cos 49°$ is positive, $\sin 49°$ is positive, $\tan 49°$ is positive.
   b $\cos 158°$ is negative, $\sin 158°$ is positive, $\tan 158°$ is negative.
   c $\cos 207°$ is negative, $\sin 207°$ is negative, $\tan 207°$ is positive.
   d $\cos 296°$ is positive, $\sin 296°$ is negative, $\tan 296°$ is negative.

9 a

Quadrant	Degree measure	$\cos\theta$	$\sin\theta$	$\tan\theta$
1	$0° < \theta < 90°$	$+$ ve	$+$ ve	$+$ ve
2	$90° < \theta < 180°$	$-$ ve	$+$ ve	$-$ ve
3	$180° < \theta < 270°$	$-$ ve	$-$ ve	$+$ ve
4	$270° < \theta < 360°$	$+$ ve	$-$ ve	$-$ ve

   b i 3 and 4   **ii** 1 and 4   **iii** 3   **iv** 4

10 $\tan(180° - \theta) = \dfrac{\sin(180° - \theta)}{\cos(180° - \theta)} = \dfrac{\sin\theta}{-\cos\theta} = -\tan\theta$

11 a P$(\cos\theta, \sin\theta)$
   b i Q$(\cos(-\theta), \sin(-\theta))$ **ii** Q$(\cos\theta, -\sin\theta)$
   c $\cos(-\theta) = \cos\theta$, $\sin(-\theta) = -\sin\theta$
   d $\tan(-\theta) = -\tan\theta$

12

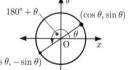

   a $\sin(180° + \theta) = -\sin\theta$
   b $\cos(180° + \theta) = -\cos\theta$
   c $\tan(180° + \theta) = \tan\theta$

13 a $\sin\theta = \dfrac{4}{5}$ **b** $\sin\theta = -\dfrac{\sqrt{15}}{4}$ **c** $\sin\theta = \dfrac{\sqrt{7}}{4}$
   d $\sin\theta = -\dfrac{12}{13}$

14 a $\cos\theta = -\dfrac{\sqrt{55}}{8}$ **b** $\tan\theta = \dfrac{3}{\sqrt{55}}$

EXERCISE 30B

1 a $\sin 30° = \dfrac{1}{2}$, $\cos 30° = \dfrac{\sqrt{3}}{2}$, $\tan 30° = \dfrac{1}{\sqrt{3}}$
   b $\sin 45° = \dfrac{1}{\sqrt{2}}$, $\cos 45° = \dfrac{1}{\sqrt{2}}$, $\tan 45° = 1$
   c $\sin 135° = \dfrac{1}{\sqrt{2}}$, $\cos 135° = -\dfrac{1}{\sqrt{2}}$, $\tan 135° = -1$
   d $\sin 120° = \dfrac{\sqrt{3}}{2}$, $\cos 120° = -\dfrac{1}{2}$, $\tan 120° = -\sqrt{3}$
   e $\sin 210° = -\dfrac{1}{2}$, $\cos 210° = -\dfrac{\sqrt{3}}{2}$, $\tan 210° = \dfrac{1}{\sqrt{3}}$
   f $\sin 240° = -\dfrac{\sqrt{3}}{2}$, $\cos 240° = -\dfrac{1}{2}$, $\tan 240° = \sqrt{3}$
   g $\sin 315° = -\dfrac{1}{\sqrt{2}}$, $\cos 315° = \dfrac{1}{\sqrt{2}}$, $\tan 315° = -1$
   h $\sin 300° = -\dfrac{\sqrt{3}}{2}$, $\cos 300° = \dfrac{1}{2}$, $\tan 300° = -\sqrt{3}$

2 a $\dfrac{1}{2}$ **b** $\dfrac{1}{4}$ **c** $\dfrac{1}{3}$ **d** $\dfrac{3}{4}$ **e** $\dfrac{1}{4}$ **f** 3
3 a $30°$ and $150°$ **b** $30°$ and $330°$ **c** $45°$ and $135°$
   d $210°$ and $330°$ **e** $270°$ **f** $150°$ and $210°$
   g $45°$ and $225°$ **h** $30°$ and $210°$ **i** $120°$ and $300°$

EXERCISE 30C

1 a ≈ 55.2 cm^2 **b** ≈ 347 km^2 **c** ≈ 1.15 m^2
2

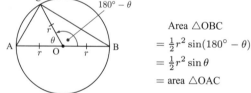

In $\triangle$PQR,
$\sin(180° - C) = \dfrac{h}{b}$
$\qquad \therefore$ $h = b\sin(180° - C)$
$\qquad \therefore$ $h = b\sin C$
But, area $\triangle$PRS $= \frac{1}{2}ah$
$\qquad\qquad = \frac{1}{2}ab\sin C$

3 a ≈ 13.6 cm^2 **b** ≈ 58.6 m^2 **c** ≈ 5.81 m^2
4 a ≈ 41.6 cm^2 **b** ≈ 36.7 m^2 **c** ≈ 7.70 cm^2
5 ≈ 50.0 cm^2 **6** $x \approx 21.9$ **7** ≈ 13.1 cm
8

Area $\triangle$OBC
$= \frac{1}{2}r^2\sin(180° - \theta)$
$= \frac{1}{2}r^2\sin\theta$
$=$ area $\triangle$OAC

9 $\theta = 30°$ or $150°$ **10** $\widehat{\text{ABC}} \approx 41.6°$ or $\approx 138.4°$
11 a i Area $= \frac{1}{2}bc\sin A$ **ii** Area $= \frac{1}{2}ab\sin C$
   b From **a**, $\frac{1}{2}bc\sin A = \frac{1}{2}ab\sin C$
   Divide both sides by $\frac{1}{2}abc$, and so on.

EXERCISE 30D.1

1 a $x \approx 11.05$ **b** $x \approx 11.52$ **c** $x \approx 5.19$
2 a $x \approx 9.43$ **b** $x \approx 11.9$ **c** $x \approx 6.37$
3 ≈ 10.2 cm^2 **4 a** $a \approx 28.4$ cm   **b** $b \approx 52.2$ cm

EXERCISE 30D.2

1 a $\widehat{\text{ACB}} \approx 72.9°$ or $\approx 107°$ **b**

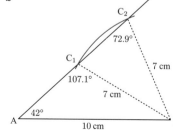

2 a Using the sine rule, $\widehat{PRQ} \approx 33.9°$ or $146.1°$.
In the case of $146.1°$, $42° + 146.1°$ is already $> 180°$.
$\therefore$ $\widehat{PRQ} \approx 33.9°$ only.

b

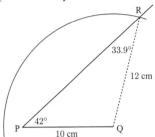

3 a $\theta \approx 31.4°$ **b** $\theta \approx 77.5°$ or $102°$
    c $\theta \approx 43.6°$ or $136°$ **d** $\theta \approx 40.8°$

4 a $\widehat{A} \approx 49.1°$ **b** $\widehat{B} \approx 71.6°$ or $108°$ **c** $\widehat{C} \approx 44.8°$

EXERCISE 30E

1 a ≈ 2.66 cm   **b** ≈ 9.63 m   **c** ≈ 10.6 m
   d ≈ 27.5 cm   **e** ≈ 4.15 km   **f** ≈ 15.2 m

2 a $\theta \approx 36.3°$ **b** $\theta \approx 53.2°$ **c** $\theta \approx 115.6°$

3 a $\widehat{A} \approx 51.8°$, $\widehat{B} \approx 40.0°$, $\widehat{C} \approx 88.3°$
   b $\widehat{P} \approx 34.0°$, $\widehat{Q} \approx 96.6°$, $\widehat{R} \approx 49.3°$

4 a $\approx 43.0°$ **b** $120°$

5 a $\cos\theta = \dfrac{m^2 + c^2 - a^2}{2cm}$

   b $\cos(180° - \theta) = \dfrac{m^2 + c^2 - b^2}{2cm}$

   c Hint: $\cos(180° - \theta) = -\cos\theta$

   d i $x \approx 9.35$ **ii** $x \approx 4.24$

6 b $x = 5 \pm \sqrt{6}$

   c

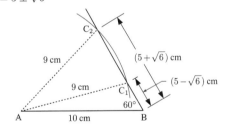

7 a ≈ 2.90 cm^2 **b** ≈ 9.92 cm^2

EXERCISE 30F

1 ≈ 14.3 km   **2** ≈ 1300 m   **3** $\theta \approx 13.4°$

4 $\widehat{BCA} \approx 107°$ **5 a** $\widehat{A} \approx 35.69°$ **b** ≈ 4 ha

6 ≈ 100 m   **7** ≈ 19.6 km in direction $106°$ **8** $\approx 214°$

9 ≈ 11.3 cm and ≈ 17.0 cm   **10** ≈ 14.1 cm

11 a We consider the coordinates of the points on the unit circle.

   b i ≈ 3.89 ha   **ii** ≈ 521 m   **iii** $\approx 32.6°$

12 a

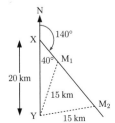

   b $XM_1 \approx 7.59$ km
       $XM_2 \approx 23.0$ km

13 $CD \approx 15.6$ m   **14** $x \approx 12.2$ **15** $\approx 129°$

16 a $\widehat{ATB} = 4°$ **b i** $\approx 11\,300$ m   **ii** $\approx 10\,400$ m
   c ≈ 6790 m
   d Hint: Start by substituting into the RHS and show that
         RHS = LHS.

17 ≈ 63.4 m

18 $AB \approx 6.43$ m, $BC \approx 9.85$ m, $AC \approx 8.66$ m

EXERCISE 30G

1 a

θ	0°	30°	60°	90°	120°	150°	180°
y	1	$\frac{\sqrt{3}}{2}$	$\frac{1}{2}$	0	$-\frac{1}{2}$	$-\frac{\sqrt{3}}{2}$	-1

θ	210°	240°	270°	300°	330°	360°
y	$-\frac{\sqrt{3}}{2}$	$-\frac{1}{2}$	0	$\frac{1}{2}$	$\frac{\sqrt{3}}{2}$	1

b

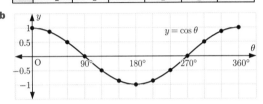

c 1 when $\theta = 0°$ or $360°$ **d** -1 when $\theta = 180°$

2 a

θ	0°	30°	60°	90°	120°	150°	180°
y	0	$\frac{1}{\sqrt{3}}$	$\sqrt{3}$	undefined	$-\sqrt{3}$	$-\frac{1}{\sqrt{3}}$	0

θ	210°	240°	270°	300°	330°	360°
y	$\frac{1}{\sqrt{3}}$	$\sqrt{3}$	undefined	$-\sqrt{3}$	$-\frac{1}{\sqrt{3}}$	0

b $\theta = 90°$, $\theta = 270°$

c

EXERCISE 30H

1 a 0.5   **b** -0.5 **c** -0.5 **d** 0.5

2 a $x = 50°, 130°, 410°, 490°$
   b $x = 45°, 135°, 405°, 495°$
   c $x = 10°, 170°, 370°, 530°$

3 a $x = 25°, 335°, 385°, 695°$
   b $x = 90°, 270°, 450°, 630°$
   c $x = 70°, 290°, 430°, 650°$

4 a $x = 20°, 200°, 380°$ **b** $x = 55°, 235°, 415°$
   c $x = 80°, 260°, 440°$

5 a $x = 0°, 180°, 360°, 540°,$ or $720°$
   b $x \approx 17°, 163°, 377°,$ or $523°$
   c $x \approx 53°, 127°, 413°,$ or $487°$
   d $x \approx 204°, 336°, 564°,$ or $696°$

6 a $x = 0°, 360°,$ or $720°$ **b** $x \approx 46°, 314°, 406°,$ or $674°$
   c $x \approx 78°, 282°, 438°,$ or $642°$
   d $x = 120°, 240°, 480°,$ or $600°$

7 a $x \approx 72°, 252°,$ or $432°$ **b** $x \approx 117°, 297°,$ or $477°$
   c $x \approx 84°, 264°,$ or $444°$

8 a

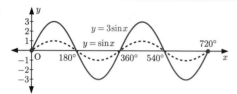

b $x = 45°, 225°, 405°, 585°$

EXERCISE 30I

1 a

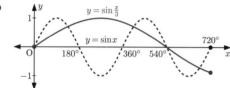

b

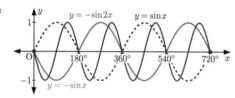

c

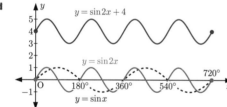

d

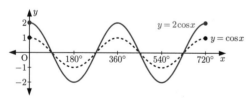

2 a

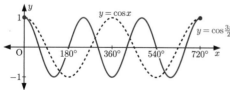

b

c

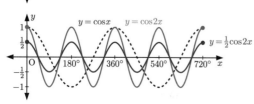

d

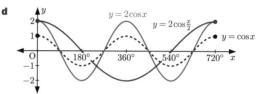

3 a 4   **b** 2   **c** $\frac{1}{3}$ **4 a** 120°   **b** 90°   **c** 720°

5 a $y = -3$ **b** $y = 5$ **c** $y = 0$

6 a

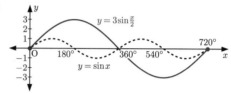

b

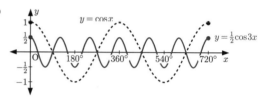

c

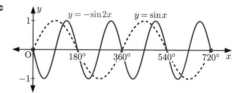

d

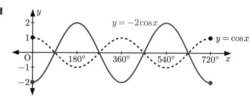

7 a $x \approx 21.8°$ or $158.2°$ **b** $x \approx 132.3°$ or $227.7°$
   c $x \approx 12.6°, 77.4°, 192.6°,$ or $257.4°$
   d $x \approx 76.0°$ or $256.0°$
   e $x \approx 23.5°, 96.5°, 143.5°, 216.5°, 263.5°,$ or $336.5°$
   f $x \approx 139.6°$ or $220.4°$

8 a $a = 2, \ b = 1$ **b** $a = -1, \ b = 1$ **c** $a = 1, \ b = 2$
   d $a = 1, \ b = \frac{1}{3}$ **e** $a = \frac{1}{2}, \ b = 1$ **f** $a = \frac{3}{2}, \ b = 2$

9 a $a = -1, \ b = 1$ **b** $a = 1.6, \ b = 1$ **c** $a = 1, \ b = \frac{1}{2}$
   d $a = 2, \ b = 2$ **e** $a = 2.5, \ b = 3$ **f** $a = -2, \ b = 3$

REVIEW SET 30A

1 a P(cos 296°, sin 296°)   **b** P(0.438, −0.899)
   c tan 296° ≈ -2.05 which is the gradient of OP.

2 a $\frac{\sqrt{3}}{2}$ **b** 1   **c** $-\frac{1}{\sqrt{3}}$

3 a ≈ 77 m²   **b** ≈ 15.9 m   **4** $x = 14$

5 a a **b** b **c** b **d** $-a$

6 ≈ 337 m in the direction $\approx 138°$

7 $\widehat{ACB} \approx 68.3°$ or $\approx 112°$ **8 a** $x \approx 223$ **b** $x \approx 99.4$

9 a DC ≈ 10.2 m   **b** BE ≈ 7.00 m   **c** ≈ 82.0 m²

10 a

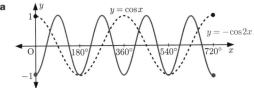

b

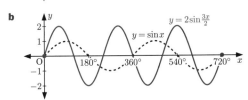

11 $x \approx 76.2°$ or $\approx 644°$

12 a $y = a \sin bx$ **b** $a = 2$, $b = 1$

REVIEW SET 30B

1 a $Q(\cos 152°, \sin 152°)$ **b** $Q(-0.8829, 0.4695)$
   c $\tan 152° \approx -0.532$ which is the gradient of OQ.

2 a $142°$ **b** $128°$ **3** $\theta \approx 23.4°$

4 a $\phi \approx 115°$ **b** $x \approx 50.8$ or ≈ 129 **c** $x \approx 89.5$

5 $x \approx 2.83$ or ≈ 15.6 **6 a** ≈ 76.1 km   **b** $\approx 053.0°$

7 ≈ 69.3 m^2 **8** $x \approx 5.25$

9 a $\approx 10\,600$ m^2 **b** ≈ 1.06 ha

10 a

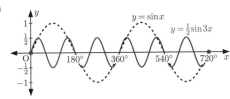

b

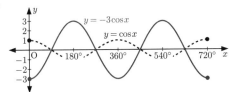

11 $y = \frac{3}{2}$ **12** $a = 2$, $b = \frac{1}{2}$

13 a $\cos \widehat{BQP} = \dfrac{2^2 + 5^2 - 4^2}{2 \times 2 \times 5} = \dfrac{13}{20}$

   b $\cos \widehat{BQR} = \cos(180° - \widehat{BQP}) = -\cos \widehat{BQP} = -\dfrac{13}{20}$

   c $BR^2 = 2^2 + 5^2 - 2 \times 2 \times 5(-\frac{13}{20})$
     $= 2^2 + 5^2 + 13$ and so on

EXERCISE 31A

1 a $\widehat{OBA} = y°$, $\widehat{OBC} = x°$
   b $2x + 2y = 180$ {angles in a triangle}
     $\therefore$ $x + y = 90$
     and $\widehat{ABC} = (x + y)° = 90°$

2 a $x = 38$ **b** $x = 30$ **c** $x = 37$

3 Hint: Show that the triangles are equiangular.

4 a $x = 8$ **b** $x = \sqrt{74}$ **5** $\dfrac{\sqrt{157}}{2} \approx 6.26$ cm

6 6 cm   **7** $6\sqrt{2} \approx 8.49$ cm   **8** $4\sqrt{3} \approx 6.93$ cm

9 a $x = 40$ **b** ≈ 7.83 cm

10 Hint: Use the "angle in a semi-circle" theorem.

11 a $\widehat{BXA} = \widehat{BXC} = 90°$ {angles in a semi-circle}
   b A, X, and C are collinear.   **c** yes
   d yes (Repeat **a** to **c** using semi-circles with diameter AD and CD.)

EXERCISE 31B

1 a Hint: Show congruency by RHS.

2 a $x \approx 5.83$ **b** $x \approx 3.61$ **c** $x \approx 9.80$

3 6.3 cm   **4** 5.0 cm   **5** 9.2 cm

6 $(8 - 4\sqrt{3})$ cm ≈ 1.07 cm   **7** 10.25 cm

8 $a = 3$, $b \approx 36.9$ **9** $m = 56$ **10** $\widehat{AOB} \approx 106°$

EXERCISE 31C

1 a $x = 90$ **b** $x = 49$ **c** $x = 35$
   d $x \approx 8.7$ **e** $x \approx 6.4$ **f** $x \approx 5.9$

2 ≈ 7.48 cm   **3** ≈ 9.75 cm   **4** $\frac{\pi}{4} \approx 78.5\%$

5 a $x = 30$ {radius-tangent, angles in a triangle theorems}
   b $a = 40$ {angles in a triangle}
     $b = 50$ {radius-tangent theorem}
   c $a = 60$ {angle in a semi-circle theorem}
     $b = 40$ {angles in a triangle, radius-tangent theorems}

6 ≈ 10.05 m   **7** ≈ 1.42 cm   **8** 9π m^2 **9** $AD = 16$ cm

EXERCISE 31D

1 a Hint: $\widehat{OAP} = \widehat{OBP} = 90°$.   **b Hint:** $OA = OB$.

2 a $x = 7$ **b** $x = 8$, $y = 6$ **c** $x = y = 50$
   d $x = 68$, $y = 56$ **e** $x = 8$, $y = 30$ **f** $x = 25$

3 Hint: $AB + CD = (AP + PB) + (DR + CR)$
                $= AS + QB + DS + CQ$, and so on.

4 Hint: Let $\widehat{BAP} = \alpha$.

5 a ≈ 5.03 m   **b** $AB \approx 7.71$ m   **6** 1 cm   **7** 40 cm

8 a Hint: Show that
     $A = r(a + b + c)$.

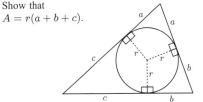

EXERCISE 31E

1 a $x = 80$ {angles in a triangle,
           angle between a tangent and a chord}
   b $x = 70$ {angle between a tangent and a chord,
           angles in an isosceles triangle}
   c $x = 40$ {angle between a tangent and a chord,
           angles in an isosceles triangle}

2 Hint: Let $\widehat{ACT} = \alpha$.

3 Hint: Use the "angle between a tangent and a chord" theorem.

4 $x = 72.5$ {angles on a straight line,
              angles in an isoceles triangle,
              angle between a tangent and a chord theorems}

EXERCISE 31F

1 a $x = 64$ {angle at the centre}
   b $x = 94$ {angle at the centre}
   c $x = 70$ {angle at the centre,
           angles in an isosceles triangle}
   d $x = 45$ {angles in an isosceles triangle,
           angle at the centre}

e $x = 66$ {angle at the centre}

f $x = 25$ {angle at the centre,
  base angles of isosceles triangle}

2 **a** OA, OP, and OB are radii of the circle. These lengths are equal, hence $\triangle OAP$ and $\triangle OBP$ are isosceles.

b **i** $A\hat{P}O = a$ **ii** $B\hat{P}O = b$ **iii** $A\hat{O}X = 2a$
   iv $B\hat{O}X = 2b$ **v** $A\hat{P}B = (a + b)$
   vi $A\hat{O}B = (2a + 2b) = 2(a + b)$

c $A\hat{O}B = 2A\hat{P}B$

d We need to consider when:
  • the centre lies on the triangle

  • the centre lies outside the triangle

  • P lies on the minor arc AB.

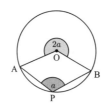

3 **a** **i** $X\hat{O}Y = \alpha$ **ii** $A\hat{X}O = 2\alpha$ **iii** $X\hat{A}O = 2\alpha$
   iv $X\hat{O}B = 4\alpha$ **v** $B\hat{O}Y = 3\alpha$

b $B\hat{O}Y = 3 \times Y\hat{O}X$

EXERCISE 31G

1 **a** $x = 46$ {angles subtended by the same arc}
b $x = y = 55$ {angles subtended by the same arc}
c $a = 50, \ b = 40$ {angles subtended by the same arc}
d $a = 55, \ c = 70$ {angles subtended by the same arc}
e $a = 80$ {angles subtended by the same arc}
  $b = 200$ {angles at the centre, angles at a point}
f $x = 75$ {angles subtended by the same arc}
  $y = 118$ {exterior angle of a triangle}
g $x = 25$ {angles in a semi-circle,
   base angles of isosceles triangle,
   angles subtended by the same arc}
h $x = 25$ {angle in a semi-circle, angles in a triangle,
   angles subtended by the same arc}

2 **a** $A\hat{O}B = 2\alpha$ **b** $A\hat{C}B = \alpha$ **c** $A\hat{D}B = A\hat{C}B$

3 **a** **i** $T\hat{A}X = 90°$ **ii** $A\hat{C}X = 90°$
b **i** $90° - \alpha$ **ii** α **iii** α **c** $T\hat{A}C = C\hat{B}A$

4 **Hint:** Use vertically opposite angles and the "angles subtended by the same arc" theorem.

5 **Hint:** Let AQ cut the circle at R. Find $A\hat{R}B$. Use exterior angles of a triangle.

EXERCISE 31H

1 **a** **i** $D\hat{O}B = 2a$ **ii** reflex $D\hat{O}B = 2b$
b $2a + 2b = 360°$ $\therefore$ $a + b = 180°$

2 **Hint:** Use the properties of isosceles triangles.

3 **Hint:** Use angles on a straight line.

4 **a** $x = 107$ {opposite angles of cyclic quadrilateral}
b $x = 60$ {opposite angles of cyclic quadrilateral}
c $x = 70$ {opposite angles of cyclic quadrilateral,
   supplementary co-interior angles}
d $x = 81$ {exterior angles of cyclic quadrilateral}
e $x = 90$ {exterior angles of cyclic quadrilateral}
f $x = 125$ {base angles of isosceles triangle,
   angle in a semi-circle theorem,
   exterior angles of cyclic quadrilateral}

5 **a** $x = 110, \ y = 100$ **b** $x = 40$ **c** $x = 65, \ y = 115$
d $x = 80$ **e** $x = 45, \ y = 90$ **f** $x = 105, \ y = 150$

6 **Hint:** Use co-interior angles and "opposite angles of a cyclic quadrilateral".

7 **a** **i** $B\hat{C}D = 90°$ **ii** $B\hat{D}C = 45°$
b From **a**, $C\hat{B}D = 45°$ {angles in a triangle}
  $\therefore$ $\triangle BCD$ is isosceles.
c $D\hat{E}F = 65°$

8 $B\hat{A}D = 95°$, $A\hat{D}C = 65°$, $D\hat{C}B = 85°$, $A\hat{B}C = 115°$

EXERCISE 31I

1 **a** Yes, one pair of opposite angles are supplementary.
b Yes, AD subtends equal angles at B and C.   **c** No
d Yes, opposite angles are supplementary.
e Yes, exterior angle equal to opposite interior angle.
f Yes, AD subtends equal angles at B and C.

2 **Hint:** Construct OD. Use opposite angles of a parallelogram, corresponding angles, base angles of an isosceles triangle.

3 **Hint:** Use "one side subtends equal angles at the other two vertices".

4 **Hint:** Use the tangents from an external point theorem.

5 **Hint:** Use corresponding angles.

6 **Hint:** Use "one side subtends equal angles at the other two vertices".

7 **Hint:** Use congruent triangles.

8 **Hint:** Join PX and use "angles subtended by the same arc".

9 **Hint:** Consider the 3 cyclic quadrilaterals, ABCR, APBC, and BQCA.

10 **Hint:** Use the exterior angle of a cyclic quadrilateral theorem.

REVIEW SET 31A

1 **a** $a = 54$ **b** $a = 62$ **c** $a = 61$ **d** $a = 80$
e $a = 63$ **f** $a = 45$

2 $\alpha + \beta + \gamma = 180°$

3 **a** $x = 38$ **b** $x = 94$ **c** $x = 104$

4 **a** $x = 2\sqrt{5} \approx 4.47$ **b** $x = \sqrt{171} \approx 13.1$

5 **a** **Hint:** Use the "tangents from an external point" theorem.
b **Hint:** Let $A\hat{C}M = \alpha$ and $B\hat{C}M = \beta$. Use the isosceles triangle theorem to show that $\alpha + \beta = 90°$.

6 **a** 8 cm   **b** 2 cm

7 **Hint:** Construct PB and XB. Use "angle between a tangent and a chord" and "angles subtended by the same arc" to show that alternate angles are equal.

8 Further hint: Use the "angle at the centre" theorem (twice) and the "angles in a triangle" theorem.

9 a The angle between a tangent and a chord through the point of contact is equal to the angle subtended by the chord in the alternate segment.

   b **i** $P\widehat{Q}B = \alpha$, $P\widehat{Q}A = \beta$, $A\widehat{Q}B = (\alpha + \beta)$

     ii Hint: Use the angles in a triangle theorem.

10 Hint: Use "angle between a tangent and a chord", and alternate angles.

REVIEW SET 31B

1 a $x = 86$ **b** $x = \sqrt{34} \approx 5.83$ **c** $x = 9$

  d $x = 45$ **e** $x = 83$ **f** $x = 79$

2 56 cm   **3 a** $x = 55$ **b** $x = 55$ **c** $x \approx 7.68$

4 Hint: Use the isosceles triangle theorem and the "angles subtended by the same arc" theorem.

5 Hint: Use the "angles subtended by the same arc" theorem and the "angles in a triangle" theorem.

6 $6\sqrt{5} \approx 13.4$ cm

7 a **i** $P\widehat{S}R = 2\alpha$ **ii** $P\widehat{Q}R = 2\alpha$ **c** $Q\widehat{R}S = 90°$

  d RS is a diameter of the circle.

8 Hint: Use the chords of a circle theorem.

9 Hint: Use angle in a semi-circle, and "one side subtends equal angles at the other two vertices".

10 Hint: Use the angle at the centre theorem.

11 a Hint: Let $X\widehat{T}A = \alpha$, $X\widehat{P}A = \beta$. Use "angle between a tangent and a chord", and sum of angles of a triangle.

  b Hint: Show $\alpha = \beta$.

EXERCISE 32A

1 a not likely to happen

  b slightly more than equal chance of happening

  c very unlikely to happen

2 a impossible   **b** not likely to happen

  c likely to happen   **d** certain   **e** very likely to happen

  f equal chance of happening as not happening

3 a B **b** A

4 a equal chance of happening as not happening

  b certain   **c** impossible   **d** very unlikely to happen

5 a Patricia   **b** Rob

  c $100\% = 1$, which means it is certain that one of the students will win the race.

  d $35\% = 0.35$

  e It is very unlikely that Rob will win the race.

  f **i** $P(E) = 0.22$

     ii E' is the event that Edward will *not* win the race.

     iii $P(E') = 0.78$

6 a S' is the event that it will *not* snow tomorrow.

  b $P(S') = 0.97$

  c **i** very unlikely to happen   **ii** very likely to happen

EXERCISE 32B

1 a 0.47   **b** 0.53   **2** ≈ 0.84 **3** ≈ 0.256

4 ≈ 0.235

5 a 5235 tickets   **b**

  c ≈ 0.207

Ticket type	Freq	Rel Freq
Adult	3762	0.719
Concession	1084	0.207
Child	389	0.074
Total	5235	1

6 a 200 people   **b**

  c **i** ≈ 0.23

     ii ≈ 0.195

     iii ≈ 0.31

Brand	Freq	Rel Freq
Silktouch	62	0.31
Super	53	0.265
Just Soap	46	0.23
Indulgence	39	0.195
Total	200	1

7 a ≈ 0.487 **b** ≈ 0.0513 **c** ≈ 0.731

8 a $x = 7$, $y = 8$ **b** ≈ 0.475

9 a **i** ≈ 0.771 **ii** ≈ 0.779

  b Melia's estimate is more likely to be accurate since her experiment had a larger number of trials.

10 a

	Like	Dislike	Total
Junior students	87	38	125
Senior students	129	56	185
Total	216	94	310

  b **i** ≈ 0.281 **ii** ≈ 0.416 **iii** ≈ 0.303

  c The total is 1. This is because the three probabilities in **b** cover all possible outcomes that could occur.

11 a 100 students

  b **i** ≈ 0.29 **ii** ≈ 0.08 **iii** ≈ 0.26 **iv** ≈ 0.68

12 a ≈ 0.957 **b** ≈ 0.0889 **c** ≈ 0.00615 **d** ≈ 0.370

EXERCISE 32C

1 65 days   **2** 13 of them   **3** 26 backs

4 a 0.11   **b** **i** 3140 points   **ii** 31.4 points

5 a 300 people   **b** **i** ≈ 0.55 **ii** ≈ 0.29 **iii** ≈ 0.16

  c **i** 4125 people   **ii** 2175 people   **iii** 1200 people

6 a

Size	Frequency	Relative frequency
Small	34	0.425
Medium	28	0.35
Large	18	0.225

  b 203

EXERCISE 32D

1 a $U = \{1, 2, 3, 4, 5, 6\}$ **b** $A = \{2, 3, 5\}$

2 a $U = \{$A, B, C, D, E, F, G, H, I, J, K, L, M, N, O, P, Q, R, S, T, U, V, W, X, Y, Z$\}$

  b **i** $A = \{$B, C, D, F, G, H, J, K, L, M, N, P, Q, R, S, T, V, W, X, Y, Z$\}$

     ii $B = \{$E, N, T, V$\}$

3 a {A, B, C, D}

  b **i** {BB, BG, GB, GG}

     ii {GGG, GGB, GBG, BGG, GBB, BGB, BBG, BBB}

  c {ABCD, ABDC, ACBD, ACDB, ADBC, ADCB, BACD, BADC, BCAD, BCDA, BDAC, BDCA, CABD, CADB, CBAD, CBDA, CDAB, CDBA, DABC, DACB, DBAC, DBCA, DCAB, DCBA}

  d **i** {HH, HT, TH, TT}

     ii {HHH, HHT, HTH, THH, HTT, THT, TTH, TTT}

     iii {HHHH, HHHT, HHTH, HTHH, THHH, HHTT, HTHT, HTTH, THHT, THTH, TTHH, HTTT, THTT, TTHT, TTTH, TTTT}

4 a

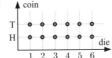

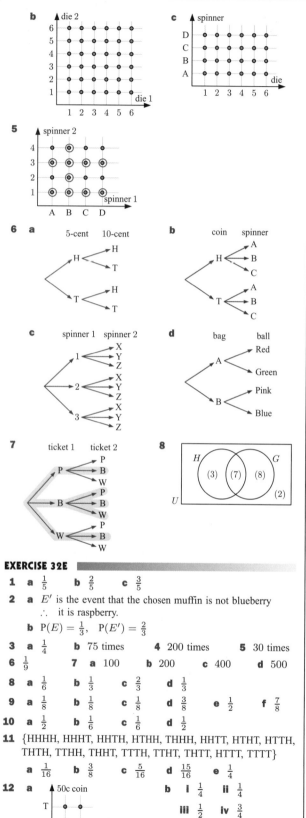

b

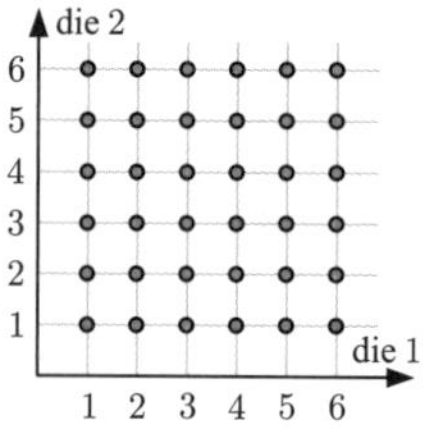
die 2
6
5
4
3
2
1
die 1
1 2 3 4 5 6

c

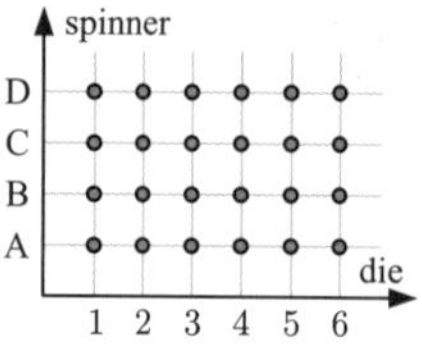
spinner
D
C
B
A
die
1 2 3 4 5 6

5

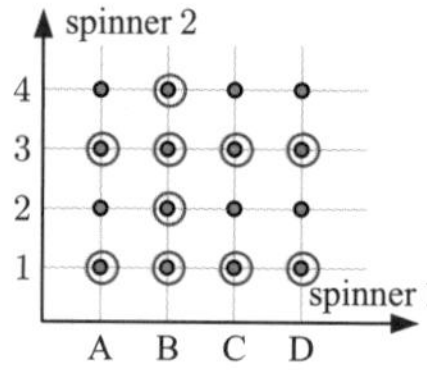
spinner 2
4
3
2
1
spinner 1
A B C D

6 **a**

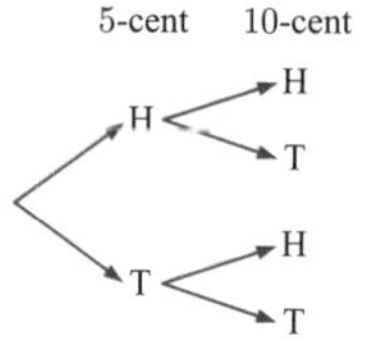
5-cent
10-cent
H
T
H
T
H
T

b

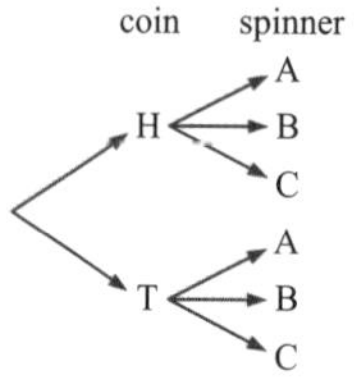
coin
spinner
H
T
A
B
C
A
B
C

c

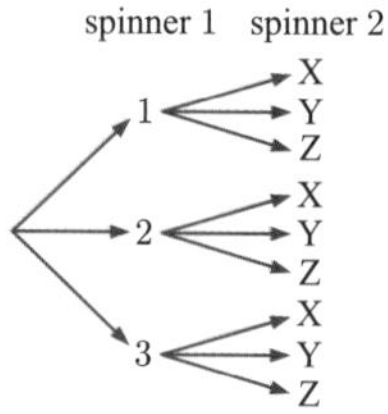
spinner 1
spinner 2
1
2
3
X
Y
Z

d

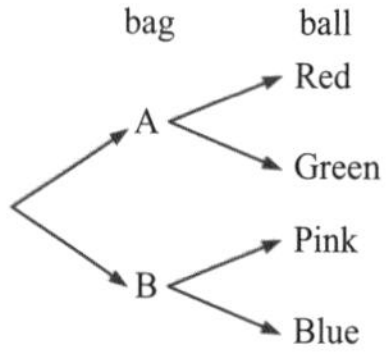
bag
ball
A
B
Red
Green
Pink
Blue

7

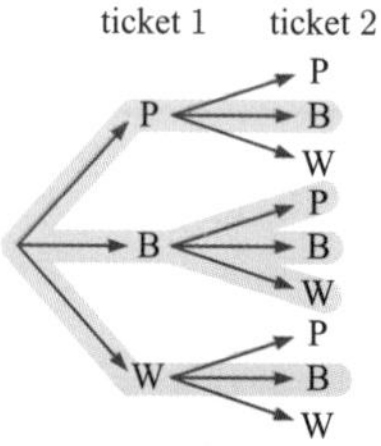
ticket 1
ticket 2
P
B
W

8

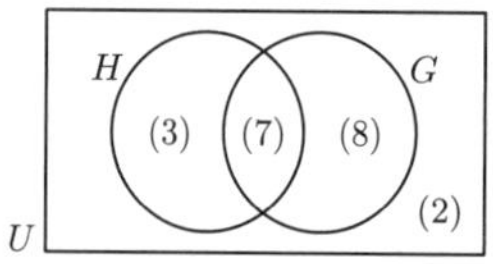
H
G
(3)
(7)
(8)
(2)
U

EXERCISE 32E

1 **a** $\frac{1}{5}$ **b** $\frac{2}{5}$ **c** $\frac{3}{5}$

2 **a** E' is the event that the chosen muffin is not blueberry
$\therefore$ it is raspberry.

b $\text{P}(E) = \frac{1}{3}$, $\text{P}(E') = \frac{2}{3}$

3 **a** $\frac{1}{4}$ **b** 75 times **4** 200 times **5** 30 times

6 $\frac{1}{9}$ **7** **a** 100 **b** 200 **c** 400 **d** 500

8 **a** $\frac{1}{6}$ **b** $\frac{1}{3}$ **c** $\frac{2}{3}$ **d** $\frac{1}{3}$

9 **a** $\frac{1}{8}$ **b** $\frac{1}{8}$ **c** $\frac{1}{8}$ **d** $\frac{3}{8}$ **e** $\frac{1}{2}$ **f** $\frac{7}{8}$

10 **a** $\frac{1}{2}$ **b** $\frac{1}{6}$ **c** $\frac{1}{6}$ **d** $\frac{1}{2}$

11 {HHHH, HHHT, HHTH, HTHH, THHH, HHTT, HTHT, HTTH, THTH, TTHH, THHT, TTTH, TTHT, THTT, HTTT, TTTT}

a $\frac{1}{16}$ **b** $\frac{3}{8}$ **c** $\frac{5}{16}$ **d** $\frac{15}{16}$ **e** $\frac{1}{4}$

12 **a**

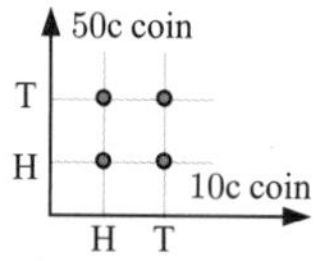
50c coin
T
H
10c coin
H T

b **i** $\frac{1}{4}$ **ii** $\frac{1}{4}$ **iii** $\frac{1}{2}$ **iv** $\frac{3}{4}$

13 **a**

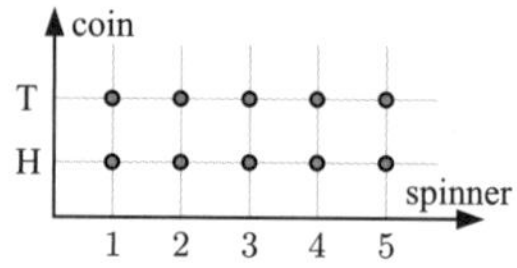
coin
T
H
spinner
1 2 3 4 5

b **i** $\frac{1}{10}$ **ii** $\frac{3}{10}$ **iii** $\frac{2}{5}$ **iv** $\frac{3}{5}$

14 **a**

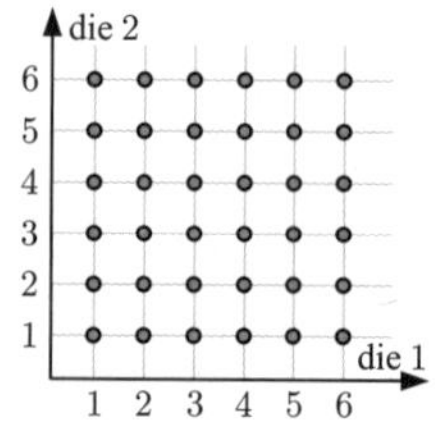
die 2
6
5
4
3
2
1
die 1
1 2 3 4 5 6

b **i** $\frac{1}{18}$ **ii** $\frac{1}{6}$ **iii** $\frac{11}{36}$ **iv** $\frac{5}{9}$ **v** $\frac{1}{4}$ **vi** $\frac{1}{6}$

15 **a** **i** $\frac{1}{15}$ **ii** $\frac{2}{15}$ **iii** $\frac{7}{15}$ **iv** $\frac{1}{3}$

b $\text{P(odd)} = \frac{6}{15}$, $\text{P(even)} = \frac{9}{15}$ $\therefore$ even **c** 80 times

16 **a** $\frac{1}{13}$ **b** $\frac{1}{52}$ **c** $\frac{1}{4}$ **d** $\frac{3}{13}$ **e** $\frac{1}{26}$ **f** $\frac{1}{2}$ **g** $\frac{4}{13}$ **h** 0

17 **a** 33 students **b** **i** $\frac{17}{33}$ **ii** $\frac{5}{33}$ **iii** $\frac{8}{11}$ **iv** $\frac{19}{33}$

18 **a** $\frac{3}{8}$ **b** $\frac{1}{8}$ **19** **a** $\frac{4}{15}$ **b** $\frac{3}{10}$ **c** $\frac{7}{10}$

20 **a** $\frac{11}{50}$ **b** $\frac{29}{50}$

21 **a**

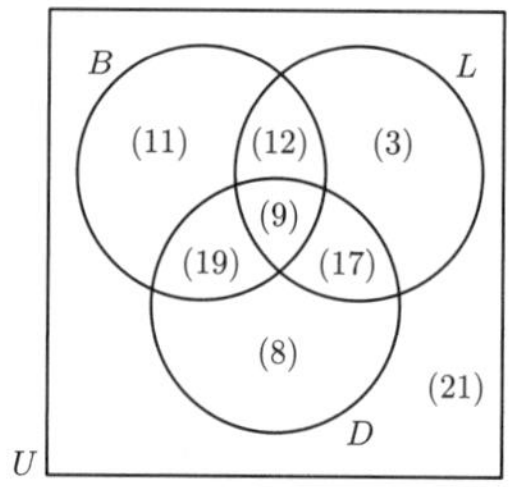
B
L
(11)
(12)
(3)
(9)
(19)
(17)
(8)
(21)
D
U

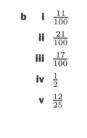

b **i** $\frac{11}{100}$ **ii** $\frac{21}{100}$ **iii** $\frac{17}{100}$ **iv** $\frac{1}{2}$ **v** $\frac{12}{25}$

EXERCISE 32F

1 **a** A and B, A and D, A and E, A and F, B and D, B and F, C and D

b **i** $\frac{2}{3}$ **ii** $\frac{5}{6}$ **iii** $\frac{2}{3}$ **iv** $\frac{1}{2}$ **v** 1 **vi** $\frac{5}{6}$

2 **a**

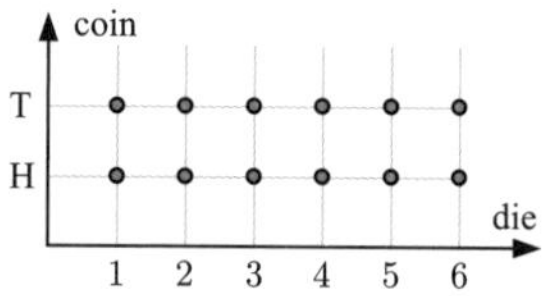
coin
T
H
die
1 2 3 4 5 6

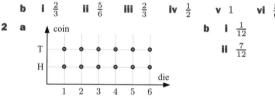

b **i** $\frac{1}{12}$ **ii** $\frac{7}{12}$

c $\text{P(H)} + \text{P(5)} - \text{P(H and 5)} = \frac{6}{12} + \frac{2}{12} - \frac{1}{12}$
$= \frac{7}{12} = \text{P(H or 5)}$

3 **a**

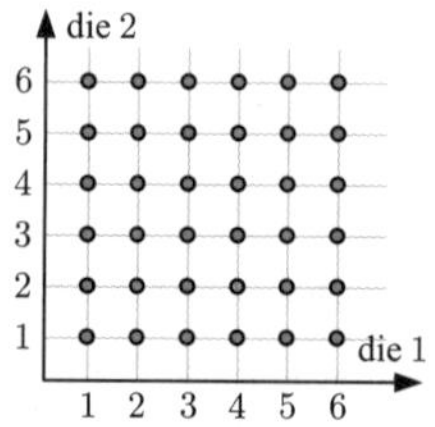
die 2
6
5
4
3
2
1
die 1
1 2 3 4 5 6

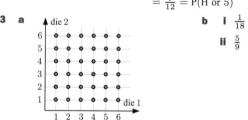

b **i** $\frac{1}{18}$ **ii** $\frac{5}{9}$

c $\text{P(3)} + \text{P(4)} - \text{P(3 and 4)} = \frac{11}{36} + \frac{11}{36} - \frac{2}{36}$
$= \frac{5}{9} = \text{P(3 or 4)}$

4 **a** mutually exclusive **b** not mutually exclusive, $\frac{1}{52}$

c mutually exclusive **d** not mutually exclusive, $\frac{1}{26}$

5 $P(A \cup B) = \frac{11}{15}$

6 a No, since $P(A \cap B) \neq 0$. **b** 0.75 **7** $P(Y) = 0.4$

8 If C and D were mutually exclusive, then
$P(C$ or $D) = 0.6 + 0.7 = 1.3$, which is not possible.

EXERCISE 32G

1 a $\frac{1}{3}$ **b** $\frac{1}{6}$ **2 a** $\frac{1}{10}$ **b** $\frac{1}{5}$ **3 a** $\frac{3}{14}$ **b** $\frac{4}{21}$

4 a 0.0441 **b** 0.6241 **5 a** $\frac{8}{21}$ **b** $\frac{1}{7}$ **c** $\frac{2}{7}$

6 a 0.0096 **b** 0.8096

7 a $\frac{1}{49}$ **b** $\frac{10}{49}$ **c** $\frac{25}{49}$

8 a ≈ 0.0545 **b** ≈ 0.0584 **c** ≈ 0.441 **d** ≈ 0.0840

9 a ≈ 0.366 **b** ≈ 0.0231 **10** $\frac{2}{5}$

11 a

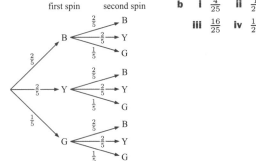

b i $\frac{4}{25}$ **ii** $\frac{1}{25}$

iii $\frac{16}{25}$ **iv** $\frac{16}{25}$

12 a

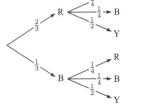

b i $\frac{1}{4}$ **ii** $\frac{3}{4}$

iii $\frac{5}{12}$

13 a

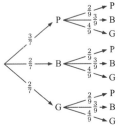

b i $\frac{2}{9}$ **ii** $\frac{20}{63}$

iii $\frac{29}{63}$

c 1; this is because every possible outcome is covered by these three events.

14 a

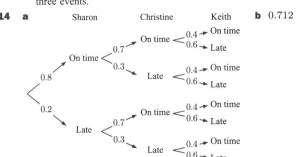

b 0.712

EXERCISE 32H

1 a $\frac{10}{21}$ **b** $\frac{5}{21}$

2 a i $\frac{2}{15}$ **ii** $\frac{1}{3}$ **iii** $\frac{4}{15}$ **iv** $\frac{4}{15}$

b 1. This is the sum of all possible outcomes.

3 a i $\frac{1}{3}$ **ii** $\frac{4}{15}$ **iii** $\frac{8}{15}$

b The possibilities are: WW, WY, YW, YY.
The 3 events do not cover all these possibilities.
So, the probability sum should not be 1.

4 a

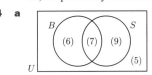

b $\frac{4}{39}$

5 $\frac{1}{5}$ **6 a** $\frac{17}{32}$ **b** $\frac{13}{28}$

7 a

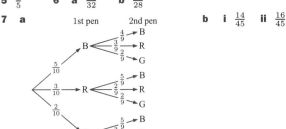

b i $\frac{14}{45}$ **ii** $\frac{16}{45}$

8 a M is the event of Matt playing in a game.
W is the event of his team winning.

b 0.6

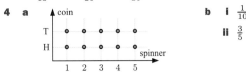

9 0.665 **10** $\frac{5}{6}$ **11 a** $\frac{1}{14}$ **b** $\frac{1}{56}$ **c** $\frac{1}{28}$ **12** $\frac{59}{120}$

13 $\frac{519}{847} \approx 0.613$ **14** 0.448 **15 a** $\frac{13}{75}$ **b** $\frac{26}{75}$ **c** $\frac{12}{25}$

REVIEW SET 32A

1 a very likely to happen
b slightly less than equal chance of happening

2 a ≈ 0.422
b The accuracy of the estimate can be improved by using a larger sample size.

3 a $\frac{1}{13}$ **b** $\frac{7}{26}$ **c** $\frac{7}{26}$

4 a

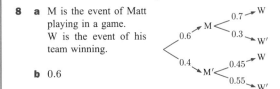

b i $\frac{1}{10}$

ii $\frac{3}{5}$

5 a 156 teenagers

b

Reason	Frequency	Relative frequency
Homework	29	≈ 0.186
Social networking	43	≈ 0.276
Playing games	15	≈ 0.0962
Streaming music	69	≈ 0.442
Total	156	≈ 1

c i ≈ 0.186 **ii** ≈ 0.558

6 ≈ 62 waves **7** $\frac{5}{33}$ **8 a** 0.73 **b** ≈ 266 long showers

9 a $\frac{318}{450} \approx 0.707$ **b** $\frac{132}{450} \approx 0.293$ **c** $\frac{21}{450} \approx 0.0467$

10 0.697

11 **a**

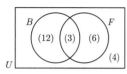

b **i** $\frac{4}{25}$

ii $\frac{12}{25}$

12 **a** 0   **b** 0.14   **13** $\frac{41}{90}$

REVIEW SET 32B

1 If two events are independent then the occurrence of one does not affect the occurrence of the other.

2 **a** ≈ 0.60 **b** ≈ 0.40

3 **a** $x = 3$ **b** **i** ≈ 0.0263 **ii** ≈ 0.289 **iii** ≈ 0.5

4 **a**

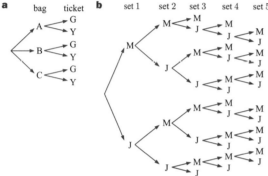

5 **a** 0.2375   **b** 0.0375   **c** 0.0125   **d** 0.7125

6 **a**

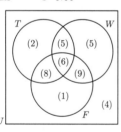

b $\frac{11}{20}$

7 6 goals   **8** 0.66

9 **a**

b $\frac{7}{195}$

10 $P(X \cup Y) = 0.8$

11 **a**

die 2

b **i** $\frac{1}{36}$ **ii** $\frac{11}{36}$

iii $\frac{1}{6}$ **iv** $\frac{1}{4}$

c 375 times

12 **a** $\frac{13}{55} \approx 0.236$

b **i** Increases, as the number of tickets of the desired colour does not decrease with each draw.

ii $\frac{37}{121} \approx 0.306$

13 **a** **i** 0.21 **ii** 0.28 **iii** 0.3

b P(Ihor wins) $= 0.238$ which is > 0.21

∴ the strategy increases his chance of winning.

EXERCISE 33A.1

1 **B** (a straight line through O)

2 **a** **i**

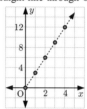

b **i**

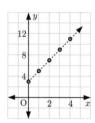

ii directly proportional $k = 3$

ii not directly proportional

c **i**

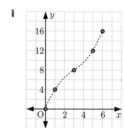

d **i**

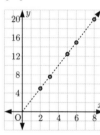

ii not directly proportional

ii directly proportional $k = 2.5$

3 **a**

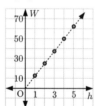

b The graph of W against h is a straight line through the origin.

c $W = 12.5h$

4 **a**

Time (t minutes)	0	2	4	6	8	10
Volume of water leaked (V ml)	0	20	40	60	80	100

b

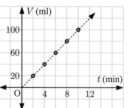

c yes, $k = 10$

5 **a**

Number of items (n)	0	1	2	3	4	5
Cost ($\$C$)	0	3.20	6.40	9.60	11.80	14

b

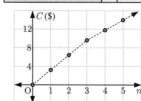

c no

6 **a** y is doubled   **b** y is trebled
   c x is doubled   **d** x is halved
   e y is increased by 20%   **f** x is decreased by 30%
   g cannot be determined   **h** cannot be determined
7 **a** 2π is a constant so the graph of C against r is a straight line through the origin.
   b $k = 2\pi$
   c **i** C is doubled   **ii** r is increased by 50%

EXERCISE 33A.2

1 **a** $y = 140$ **b** $x = 1$ **2** **a** $y = 60$ **b** $x = 21$

3

x	5	15	30
y	20	60	120

4 **a** 4 litres   **b** 121.5 km

5 **a** **i** $R = 0.006l$ **ii** 0.3 ohms   **iii** 500 cm

   b
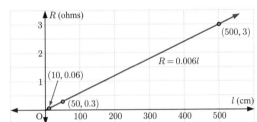

6 **a** 45 m²   **b** 9 litres   **7** **a** $4l$ lollies   **b** $\dfrac{150}{l}$ days

8 **a** 78.4 m/s   **b** ≈ 10.2 s   **9** **a** 10.5 cm   **b** 1.2 m

EXERCISE 33B

1 **a** $A \propto t^2$, $k = 4.9$ **b** $K \propto x^3$, $k = 2$
   c $T \propto \sqrt{l}$, $k = \frac{1}{5}$ **d** $V \propto t^4$, $k = 500$
   e $P \propto \sqrt[3]{x}$, $k = 4$ **f** $V \propto r^3$, $k = \frac{4}{3}\pi$

2 **a**

x^2	4	9	25
y	16	36	100

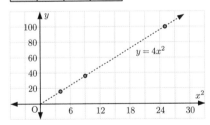

The graph is a straight line through the origin. $\therefore$ $y \propto x^2$
The rule is $y = 4x^2$

   b

x^2	1	9	16	25
y	3	27	48	75

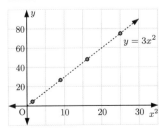

The graph is a straight line through the origin. $\therefore$ $y \propto x^2$
The rule is $y = 3x^2$

3 **a**

x^3	1	8	27
y	5	40	135

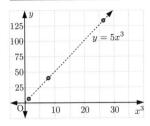

The graph is a straight line through the origin.
$\therefore$ $y \propto x^3$
The rule is $y = 5x^3$
   $\therefore$ $k = 5$

   b

x^3	8	27	125
y	4	13.5	62.5

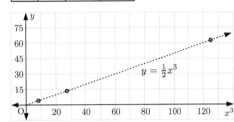

The graph is a straight line through the origin.
$\therefore$ $y \propto x^3$
The rule is $y = \frac{1}{2}x^3$
   $\therefore$ $k = \frac{1}{2}$

4 **a** $P = 48$ **b** $a = 15$ **5** **a** $M = 81$ **b** $x \approx 3.42$
6 270 hp   **7** $312.50   **8** ≈ 8.9 cm
9 ≈ 10.1 seconds   **10** **a** ≈ 12.2 km   **b** 2.4 m
11 **a** 1.21   **b** 36% reduction
12 **a** 27.1% reduction   **b** $\approx 26.0\%$ increase
13 **a** $V \propto h$ **b** $V \propto r^2$ **c** 22.4% increase

EXERCISE 33C

1 **a, d**

x	1	2	4	8
$\dfrac{1}{x}$	1	$\frac{1}{2}$	$\frac{1}{4}$	$\frac{1}{8}$
y	40	20	10	5
xy	40	40	40	40

   b
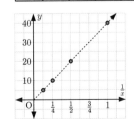

   c The points of $y = \dfrac{1}{x}$ form a straight line through the origin,
   $\therefore$ y is directly proportional to $\dfrac{1}{x}$
   $\therefore$ y is inversely proportional to x.

2 a $xy = 12$ **c** $xy = 84$

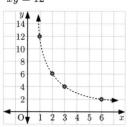

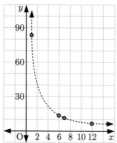

b not inversely proportional

3 B and **C**

4 a If d is fixed, s is **inversely** proportional to t.
   b If t is fixed, s is **directly** proportional to d.
   c If s is fixed, d is **directly** proportional to t.

5 a y is multiplied by $\frac{1}{4}$ **b** y is multiplied by $\frac{9}{7}$
   c x is multiplied by $\frac{3}{8}$

6 a $y = 8$ **b** $x = \frac{2}{5}$ **7 a** $p = 18$ **b** $n = 12$

8

x	6	10	50
y	25	15	3

9 8 days   **10 a** 3750 chairs   **b** 16 hours

11 a The area of a rectangle is fixed.
   $\therefore$ $xy = 60$, $\therefore$ inversely proportional.

b

x	5	6	15
y	12	10	4

c

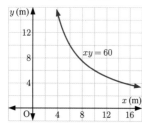

12 a 20 units   **b** 4 cm^3 **c** $P = \dfrac{400}{V}$

d

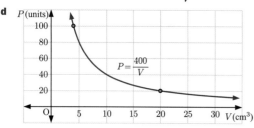

13 a 23 min 20 s   **b** 8 players   **c** 40 min

EXERCISE 33D

1 a $y = 16$ **b** $x = 4$

2 a $F = \frac{20}{\sqrt{3}} \approx 11.5$ **b** $c = \frac{44}{9} \approx 4.89$

3 a ≈ 0.115 seconds   **b** 400 units   **4** 56.25% increase

5 a 3.275 cm   **b** ≈ 3.46 cm   **c** ≈ 300 cm^3

6 ≈ 8.94 m away

EXERCISE 33E

1 a

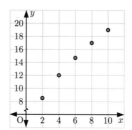

b $d = 0.2 \times t^2$
   $r^2 = 1$, so the model fits the data exactly. It is reasonable to conclude that $d \propto t^2$.

c i 1.25 cm   **ii** 7.2 cm

2 a

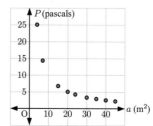

b $y \approx 6.01 \times x^{0.500}$
   $r^2 \approx 1$, so the fit is very good. It is reasonable to conclude that $y \propto \sqrt{x}$.

c i $y \approx 24.0$ **ii** $y \approx 32.9$

3 a $y \approx 2.83 \times x^{3.00}$
   r^2 is very close to 1, and the power is very close to 3, so it is reasonable to conclude that $y \propto x^3$.

b $y \approx 13.2 \times x^{-0.104}$
   $r^2 \approx 0.03$, so this is *not* a reasonable model.

4 a

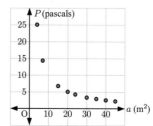

b $P \approx 100 \times a^{-1.00}$ $\left(\text{or } P \approx \dfrac{100}{a}\right)$
   r^2 is very close to 1, and the power is very close to -1, so it is reasonable to conclude that $P \propto \dfrac{1}{a}$.

c ≈ 10.0 pascals

5 a $D \approx 4.92 \times t^{1.99}$
   r^2 is very close to 1, and the power is very close to 2, so it is reasonable to conclude that $D \propto t^2$.

b ≈ 78.7 m   **c** ≈ 6.38 s

6 a $R \approx 1.00 \times T^{0.667}$
   r^2 is very close to 1, so the model seems reasonable. We suspect that $R \propto T^{\frac{2}{3}}$.

b $R^3 \approx T^2$ **c** ≈ 30.1 Earth units

REVIEW SET 33A

1 B (a straight line through the origin)

2 a

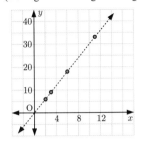

b The graph of y against x is a straight line through the origin.
∴ $y \propto x$

c $y = 3x$

3

x	12	60	80
y	3	15	20

4 a $xy = 650$ **b** $y \approx 54.2$ **c** $x \approx 4.33$

5 72 people   **6** 36 days   **7 a** $M = 60$ **b** $t = 9$

8 a The surface area is multiplied by 9.
b The radius is increased by $\approx 9.54\%$.

9 a i $E \propto m$ if v is constant.
ii $E \propto v^2$ if m is constant.
iii $m \propto \dfrac{1}{v^2}$ if E is constant.

b If m is constant, $E \propto v^2$.
∴ E decreases by $\approx 22.6\%$.

10 a

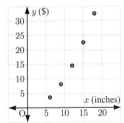

b $y \approx 0.0996 \times x^{2.00}$
r^2 is very close to 1, and the power is very close to 2, so it is reasonable to conclude that $y \propto x^2$.

REVIEW SET 33B

1 $a = 14$, $b = 21$ **2** ≈ 229 km

3 a $k = 19$ **b** $y = 119.7$

4 a not inversely proportional   **b** $y = \dfrac{36}{x}$

5 If y is increased by 25%, then y is multiplied by 1.25.
∴ x is divided by 1.25.
Now $\dfrac{x}{1.25} = 0.8x$
So, x is decreased by 20%.

6 27 minutes   **7** $y = 98$

8 a ≈ 30.6 m/s   **b** 324 m

9 a The volume is multiplied by 4.
b The radius is increased by $\approx 26.5\%$.

10 a $m \approx 0.120 \times h^{3.00}$
r^2 is very close to 1, and the power is very close to 3, so it is reasonable to conclude that $m \propto h^3$.
b ≈ 3.24 kg

EXERCISE 34A

1 a *Scale:*
1 cm ≡ 10 km/h

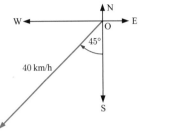

b *Scale:*
1 cm ≡ 10 m/s

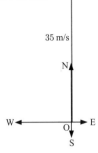

c

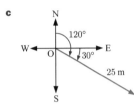

Scale: 1 cm ≡ 10 m

d

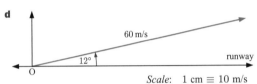

Scale: 1 cm ≡ 10 m/s

2 a *Scale:* 1 cm ≡ 15 Newtons

b *Scale:* 1 cm ≡ 15 Newtons

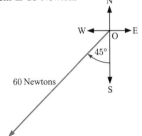

3 a *Scale:*
1 cm ≡ 20 km/h

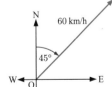

b *Scale:*
1 cm ≡ 10 km

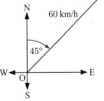

c *Scale:*
1 cm ≡ 30 km/h

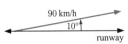

d *Scale*:
1 cm ≡ 10 kg m/s

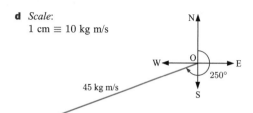

EXERCISE 34B

1 **a** a, c, and e; b and d   **b** a, b, c, and d
   c a and b; c and d   **d** none are equal   **e** a and c; b and d
2 **a** b   **b** −a   **c** a   **d** −b   **e** −a   **f** −b
3 **a** true   **b** false   **c** false   **d** true   **e** false   **f** true
   g true   **h** false

EXERCISE 34C

1 **a** 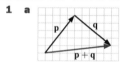   **b**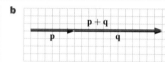

   c 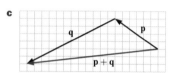   **d**

   e 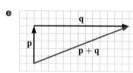   **f**

2 **a** $\overrightarrow{QS}$ **b** $\overrightarrow{PR}$ **c** $\overrightarrow{PQ}$ **d** $\overrightarrow{PS}$

3 **a** **i**   **ii**

   b For any two vectors **p** and **q**, we can form a parallelogram.

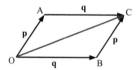

   Now, $\overrightarrow{OA} + \overrightarrow{AC} = \overrightarrow{OC}$ and $\overrightarrow{OB} + \overrightarrow{BC} = \overrightarrow{OC}$
   ∴ $\overrightarrow{OA} + \overrightarrow{AC} = \overrightarrow{OB} + \overrightarrow{BC}$
   ∴ **p** + **q** = **q** + **p**

4 **a** $\overrightarrow{PS}$ = a + b   **b** $\overrightarrow{PR}$ = a + c   **c** $\overrightarrow{QT}$ = c + d
   d $\overrightarrow{PT}$ = a + c + d
5 **a** c   **b** f   **c** g   **d** g   **e** g
6 **a** 600 km/h due north   **b** 400 km/h due north
   c 510 km/h at a bearing of ≈ 011.3°
7 **a** 0 km/h   **b** 20 km/h due east   **c** ≈ 14.1 km/h north-east
8 The aircraft is travelling at a speed of ≈ 404 km/h at a bearing of ≈ 098.5°.

EXERCISE 34D

1 **a**   **b**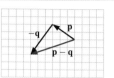

   c 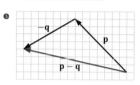   **d**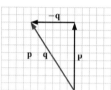

   e 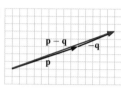   **f**

2 **a** $\overrightarrow{QS}$ **b** $\overrightarrow{PR}$ **c** 0 (zero vector)   **d** $\overrightarrow{RQ}$ **e** $\overrightarrow{QS}$
   f $\overrightarrow{RQ}$
3 **a** $\overrightarrow{AB} = \overrightarrow{AO} + \overrightarrow{OB}$ **b** **i** $\overrightarrow{BC}$ = c − b
        = (−a) + b   **ii** $\overrightarrow{CA}$ = a − c
        = b − a
4 **a** d   **b** g   **c** d   **d** a   **e** −c   **f** −g
5 The plane must fly ≈ 4.57° west of north at ≈ 502 km/h.
6 **a** The boat must head ≈ 25.5° west of north.
   b ≈ 28.3 km/h
7 **a**   **b** The current will push Holger to the right of the point he is paddling towards.

   c Speed is 13 km/h, direction is ≈ 22.6° to the right.
   d Holger should face ≈ 24.6° left of where he is aiming.

EXERCISE 34E

1 **a**   **b**   **c**   **d**

2 **a** $\binom{4}{2}$ **b** $\binom{0}{-3}$ **c** $\binom{-3}{-4}$ **d** $\binom{-6}{0}$
   e $\binom{-6}{4}$ **f** $\binom{2}{-4}$
3 **a** $\sqrt{17}$ units   **b** 6 units   **c** $\sqrt{13}$ units
   d $\sqrt{26}$ units   **e** $\sqrt{20}$ units   **f** $\sqrt{37}$ units
4 **a** $\binom{3}{4}$ **b** $\binom{-4}{-2}$ **c** $\binom{-2}{1}$ **d** $\binom{3}{-3}$ **e** $\binom{1}{5}$
5 **a** **i** $\binom{-2}{-3}$ **ii** $\sqrt{13}$ units
   b **i** $\binom{5}{-2}$ **ii** $\sqrt{29}$ units
   c **i** $\binom{-3}{-4}$ **ii** 5 units
   d **i** $\binom{-12}{5}$ **ii** 13 units

6 a $k = -4$ **b** $k = -1$ **c** $k = 4$ **7** $k = \pm 4$

8 a $\approx \begin{pmatrix} 52.0 \\ -30 \end{pmatrix}$ **b** $\approx \begin{pmatrix} -9.84 \\ -11.3 \end{pmatrix}$ **c** $\approx \begin{pmatrix} 158 \\ 25.0 \end{pmatrix}$

EXERCISE 34F

1 a $\begin{pmatrix} 3 \\ 8 \end{pmatrix}$ **b** $\begin{pmatrix} 4 \\ 10 \end{pmatrix}$ **c** $\begin{pmatrix} 7 \\ -1 \end{pmatrix}$ **d** $\begin{pmatrix} -2 \\ 5 \end{pmatrix}$

  e $\begin{pmatrix} -4 \\ -6 \end{pmatrix}$ **f** $\begin{pmatrix} -8 \\ -2 \end{pmatrix}$

2 a $\begin{pmatrix} 5 \\ -4 \end{pmatrix}$ **b** $\begin{pmatrix} 5 \\ -4 \end{pmatrix}$ **c** $\begin{pmatrix} 1 \\ -4 \end{pmatrix}$ **d** $\begin{pmatrix} 1 \\ -4 \end{pmatrix}$

  e $\begin{pmatrix} 0 \\ -6 \end{pmatrix}$ **f** $\begin{pmatrix} 0 \\ -6 \end{pmatrix}$ **g** $\begin{pmatrix} 4 \\ -6 \end{pmatrix}$ **h** $\begin{pmatrix} 3 \\ -7 \end{pmatrix}$

3 a $\begin{pmatrix} 4 \\ 2 \end{pmatrix}$ **b** $\sqrt{20}$ units **c** $\begin{pmatrix} -3 \\ -4 \end{pmatrix}$ **d** $\begin{pmatrix} -1 \\ 2 \end{pmatrix}$

4 a $\begin{pmatrix} 6 \\ 2 \end{pmatrix}$ **b** $\begin{pmatrix} 5 \\ 2 \end{pmatrix}$ **c** $\begin{pmatrix} -4 \\ 5 \end{pmatrix}$ **d** $\begin{pmatrix} -6 \\ -4 \end{pmatrix}$

  e $\begin{pmatrix} 8 \\ -3 \end{pmatrix}$ **f** $\begin{pmatrix} 11 \\ -3 \end{pmatrix}$

5 a $\begin{pmatrix} 1 \\ 6 \end{pmatrix}$ **b** $\begin{pmatrix} -5 \\ 1 \end{pmatrix}$ **c** $\begin{pmatrix} -6 \\ 4 \end{pmatrix}$ **d** $\begin{pmatrix} -2 \\ 10 \end{pmatrix}$

  e $\begin{pmatrix} -4 \\ -2 \end{pmatrix}$ **f** $\sqrt{104}$ units

6 $\begin{pmatrix} 1 \\ 8 \end{pmatrix}$ **7** $\begin{pmatrix} -3 \\ -3 \end{pmatrix}$ **8** $\begin{pmatrix} -4 \\ 9 \end{pmatrix}$

9 a $\overrightarrow{SA} = \begin{pmatrix} -2 \\ 2 \end{pmatrix}$, $\overrightarrow{AB} = \begin{pmatrix} 2 \\ 5 \end{pmatrix}$, $\overrightarrow{BC} = \begin{pmatrix} 5 \\ 3 \end{pmatrix}$, $\overrightarrow{CD} = \begin{pmatrix} 4 \\ -2 \end{pmatrix}$,

  $\overrightarrow{DE} = \begin{pmatrix} 0 \\ -5 \end{pmatrix}$, $\overrightarrow{EF} = \begin{pmatrix} -4 \\ 0 \end{pmatrix}$, $\overrightarrow{FG} = \begin{pmatrix} -4 \\ 2 \end{pmatrix}$, $\overrightarrow{GS} = \begin{pmatrix} -1 \\ -5 \end{pmatrix}$

  b $\begin{pmatrix} 0 \\ 0 \end{pmatrix}$ The finishing point is the same as the starting point, that is, we are back where we started.

EXERCISE 34G

1 a $\begin{pmatrix} 6 \\ 15 \end{pmatrix}$ **b** $\begin{pmatrix} -5 \\ 20 \end{pmatrix}$ **c** $\begin{pmatrix} -12 \\ 0 \end{pmatrix}$ **d** $\begin{pmatrix} 2 \\ 7 \end{pmatrix}$

  e $\begin{pmatrix} 8 \\ -28 \end{pmatrix}$ **f** $\begin{pmatrix} -3 \\ \frac{2}{3} \end{pmatrix}$ **g** $\begin{pmatrix} 7 \\ 11 \end{pmatrix}$ **h** $\begin{pmatrix} 10 \\ -13 \end{pmatrix}$

2 a i **b i**

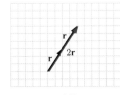

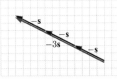

  ii $2\mathbf{r} = \begin{pmatrix} 4 \\ 6 \end{pmatrix}$ **ii** $-3\mathbf{s} = \begin{pmatrix} -12 \\ 6 \end{pmatrix}$

  c i **d i**

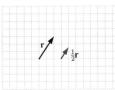

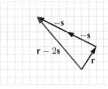

  ii $\frac{1}{2}\mathbf{r} = \begin{pmatrix} 1 \\ \frac{3}{2} \end{pmatrix}$ **ii** $\mathbf{r} - 2\mathbf{s} = \begin{pmatrix} -6 \\ 7 \end{pmatrix}$

  e i **f i**

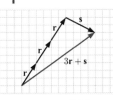

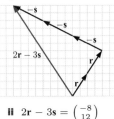

  ii $3\mathbf{r} + \mathbf{s} = \begin{pmatrix} 10 \\ 7 \end{pmatrix}$ **ii** $2\mathbf{r} - 3\mathbf{s} = \begin{pmatrix} -8 \\ 12 \end{pmatrix}$

g i **h i**

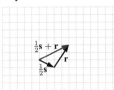

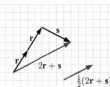

  ii $\frac{1}{2}\mathbf{s} + \mathbf{r} = \begin{pmatrix} 4 \\ 2 \end{pmatrix}$ **ii** $\frac{1}{2}(2\mathbf{r} + \mathbf{s}) = \begin{pmatrix} 4 \\ 2 \end{pmatrix}$

3 a **b** **c**

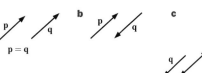

  d **e**

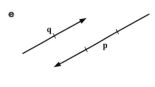

4 a $2\mathbf{a}$ **b** $-2\mathbf{b}$ **c** $\mathbf{a} - \mathbf{b}$

5 a $\begin{pmatrix} 9 \\ -8 \end{pmatrix}$ **b** $\begin{pmatrix} -5 \\ 2 \end{pmatrix}$ **c** $\begin{pmatrix} -2\frac{2}{3} \\ \frac{1}{3} \end{pmatrix}$ **d** $\begin{pmatrix} -2\frac{1}{2} \\ 1 \end{pmatrix}$

6 a $|k\mathbf{a}| = \left| \begin{pmatrix} ka_1 \\ ka_2 \end{pmatrix} \right| = \sqrt{(ka_1)^2 + (ka_2)^2}$

$\qquad = \sqrt{k^2 a_1^2 + k^2 a_2^2}$

$\qquad = \sqrt{k^2(a_1^2 + a_2^2)}$

$\qquad = \sqrt{k^2} \sqrt{a_1^2 + a_2^2}$

$\qquad = |k||\mathbf{a}|$ {since $\sqrt{k^2} = |k|$}

  b From **a**, $\left| \dfrac{1}{|\mathbf{a}|} \mathbf{a} \right| = \dfrac{1}{|\mathbf{a}|} |\mathbf{a}| = \dfrac{1}{|\mathbf{a}|} |\mathbf{a}| = 1$

  and $\dfrac{1}{|\mathbf{a}|} \mathbf{a}$ is of the form $k\mathbf{a}$ where $k > 0$ (since $|\mathbf{a}|$ is always positive).

  $\therefore \dfrac{1}{|\mathbf{a}|} \mathbf{a}$ is in the same direction as **a**.

  $\therefore \dfrac{1}{|\mathbf{a}|} \mathbf{a}$ is a vector of length 1 in the direction of **a**.

EXERCISE 34H

1 a $t = -12$ **b** $t = 6$ **c** $t = 20$ **d** $t = -10$

2 $a = -\frac{12}{5}$ or 2 **3** $t = -1$

4 a **p** is twice as long as **q**, and they have the same direction.
  b **p** is half as long as **q**, and they have the same direction.
  c **p** is three times as long as **q**, but has the opposite direction.
  d **p** is one third of the length of **q**, but has the opposite direction.

5 $\overrightarrow{PQ} = \begin{pmatrix} 5 \\ -4 \end{pmatrix}$, $\overrightarrow{SR} = \begin{pmatrix} 5 \\ -4 \end{pmatrix}$ $\Rightarrow$ $\overrightarrow{PQ}$ is parallel to $\overrightarrow{SR}$ and

  $|\overrightarrow{PQ}| = |\overrightarrow{SR}|$. $\therefore$ PQRS is a parallelogram.

6 a $\overrightarrow{AB} = \begin{pmatrix} -3 \\ 2 \end{pmatrix}$, $\overrightarrow{CD} = \begin{pmatrix} -6 \\ 4 \end{pmatrix}$

  b $\overrightarrow{CD} = 2\overrightarrow{AB}$, which implies that $\overrightarrow{CD}$ and $\overrightarrow{AB}$ have the same direction and $\therefore$ are parallel.

  c $k = -7$

7 $k = 5$

8 a q **b** 2q **c** p + q **d** p + 2q
e −p − 2q **f** p + q

9 a i a − b **ii** $\frac{1}{2}$a

b $\overrightarrow{MN} = \frac{1}{2}\overrightarrow{OA}$ that is, MN is parallel to OA and has half its length.

c i $\overrightarrow{OM} = \frac{1}{2}$b **ii** $\overrightarrow{ON} = \frac{1}{2}$a + $\frac{1}{2}$b **iii** $\frac{1}{2}$b + $\frac{1}{4}$a

10 a i $\frac{1}{2}$p **ii** $\frac{1}{3}$p + $\frac{2}{3}$q **iii** p − q **iv** $\frac{1}{3}$p − $\frac{1}{3}$q

b As $\overrightarrow{DP} = \frac{1}{3}\overrightarrow{DB}$, DP is parallel to DB and $\frac{1}{3}$ its length. Thus, D, P, and B are collinear and DP : PB = 1 : 2.

REVIEW SET 34A

1 a

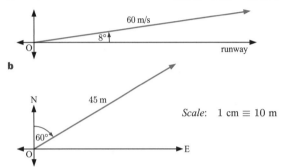

Scale: 1 cm ≡ 10 m/s

b

Scale: 1 cm ≡ 10 m

2 a $\overrightarrow{CA} = -$c **b** $\overrightarrow{AB} = -$a + b **c** $\overrightarrow{OC} = $a + c
d $\overrightarrow{BC} = -$b + a + c

3 a $\overrightarrow{AD}$ **b** $\overrightarrow{BD}$ **c** 0 (the zero vector)

4 Speed is ≈ 12.3 km/h at a bearing of ≈ 145°.

5 a is parallel to b, a is one third of the length of b, and they have the same direction.

6 a $\binom{11}{1}$ **b** $\binom{1}{12}$ **c** $\sqrt{34}$ units

7 a 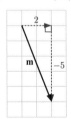 **b** $\sqrt{29}$ units **c** ≈ 158°

8 a $\binom{4}{-3}$ **b** 5 units **9** $k = -4$

10 a $\overrightarrow{DC} = 3$q **b** $\overrightarrow{CB} = -$p − q **c** $\overrightarrow{BT} = \frac{2}{3}$(p + q)

REVIEW SET 34B

1 a They have the same length.
b p is twice as long as q, and they have the same direction.

2 a He must fly ≈ 11.3° south of east. **b** ≈ 204 km/h

3 a $\binom{6}{-6}$ **b** $\binom{7}{-16}$ **c** $\binom{0}{2}$

4 a $\binom{-1}{-9}$ **b** $\sqrt{34}$ units

5 a **b i** $\binom{5}{-1}$ **ii** $\binom{5}{7}$ **iii** $\binom{18}{-2}$

6 $t = 6$ **7 a** $\binom{3}{-4}$ **b** 5 units **8** $k = 2$

9 a 2p **b** p + q **c** q − p

10 a i $\overrightarrow{UX} = \frac{4}{5}$v **ii** $\overrightarrow{OX} = $u + $\frac{4}{5}$v

b i $\overrightarrow{VY} = \frac{5}{4}$u

ii $\overrightarrow{VW} = $u and $\overrightarrow{VY} = \frac{5}{4}$u ∴ $\overrightarrow{VY} = \frac{5}{4}\overrightarrow{VW}$

Thus VY is parallel to VW and $1\frac{1}{4}$ times its length. That is, V, Y, and W are collinear and VW : WY = 4 : 1.

EXERCISE 35A

1 a $S \leqslant 40$ **b** $A \geqslant 18$ **c** $a > 3$ **d** $b \leqslant -3$
e $d < 5$ **f** $-20 \geqslant x$ **g** $4 < y$ **h** $z \geqslant 0$

2 a $x > 2$ **b** $b < 5$ **c** $c \geqslant 2\frac{1}{2}$ **d** $d \leqslant -7$
e $a < -19$ **f** $p > -3$

3 a 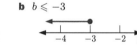 **b** $x = 3$

4 a 16 **b** 55

EXERCISE 35B

1 a $a > 2$ **b** $b \leqslant -3$
c $s < 6$ **d** $c < 10$
e $x \geqslant 5$ **f** $b < -4$
g $t > -5$ **h** $k < -6$

2 a $x > 3$ **b** $a \geqslant \frac{10}{3}$
c $a < -2$ **d** $b > 5$
e $s > -2$ **f** $b \geqslant \frac{1}{3}$
g $n < -2$ **h** $x < 13$
i $b \geqslant \frac{7}{4}$

3 a $x > 9$ **b** $x \leqslant -5$

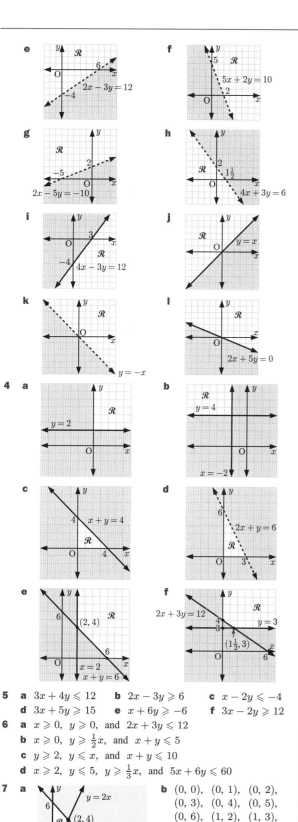

e $2x - 3y = 12$, $\mathcal{R}$

f $5x + 2y = 10$, $\mathcal{R}$

g $2x - 5y = -10$, $\mathcal{R}$

h $4x + 3y = 6$, $\mathcal{R}$

i $4x - 3y = 12$, $\mathcal{R}$

j $y = x$, $\mathcal{R}$

k $y = -x$, $\mathcal{R}$

l $2x + 5y = 0$, $\mathcal{R}$

4 a $y = 2$, $\mathcal{R}$

b $y = 4$, $x = -2$, $\mathcal{R}$

c $x + y = 4$, $\mathcal{R}$

d $2x + y = 6$, $\mathcal{R}$

e $(2, 4)$, $x = 2$, $x + y = 6$, $\mathcal{R}$

f $2x + 3y = 12$, $y = 3$, $(1\frac{1}{2}, 3)$, $\mathcal{R}$

5 a $3x + 4y \leqslant 12$ **b** $2x - 3y \geqslant 6$ **c** $x - 2y \leqslant -4$
   d $3x + 5y \geqslant 15$ **e** $x + 6y \geqslant -6$ **f** $3x - 2y \geqslant 12$

6 a $x \geqslant 0$, $y \geqslant 0$, and $2x + 3y \leqslant 12$
   b $x \geqslant 0$, $y \geqslant \frac{1}{2}x$, and $x + y \leqslant 5$
   c $y \geqslant 2$, $y \leqslant x$, and $x + y \leqslant 10$
   d $x \geqslant 2$, $y \leqslant 5$, $y \geqslant \frac{1}{3}x$, and $5x + 6y \leqslant 60$

7 a $y = 2x$, $(2, 4)$, $\mathcal{R}$, $x + y = 6$

b $(0, 0)$, $(0, 1)$, $(0, 2)$, $(0, 3)$, $(0, 4)$, $(0, 5)$, $(0, 6)$, $(1, 2)$, $(1, 3)$, $(1, 4)$, $(1, 5)$, $(2, 4)$

8 a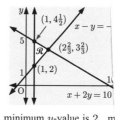
$(1, 4\frac{1}{2})$, $x - y = -$, $(2\frac{2}{3}, 3\frac{2}{3})$, $\mathcal{R}$, $(1, 2)$, $x + 2y = 10$

b minimum y-value is 2, m

9 $235x - 30y \leqslant -16\,197$,   42
   $495x + 700y \geqslant -20\,227$

REVIEW SET 35A

1 a $x \leqslant 5$ **b** $x <$

2 a $x \leqslant \frac{7}{2}$

   c $x \leqslant -\frac{4}{7}$

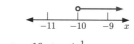

3 a $x > -10$

   c $-10 < x \leqslant \frac{1}{3}$

4 $x = -6$

5 a

6 a $-6 < x < -2$ **b** $x \leqslant -9$

7 $x \leqslant -2$ or $x \geqslant \frac{3}{4}$

8 a $x \leqslant 0.861$ **b** $x < -4.24$

9 a $x > 2$ and $y \leqslant -3$
   b $x \geqslant 0$, $y \geqslant 0$, $x + 3y \geqslant 6$,

10 a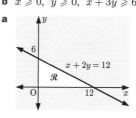
$x + 2y = 12$, $\mathcal{R}$

REVIEW SET 35B

1 a $x > 9$ **b** $x \geqslant \frac{4}{3}$ **c**

2 a $x \leqslant \frac{3}{2}$ **b** $x < 10$ **c**

3 a

4 a $-7 < x < 5$ **b** $x \leqslant -5$ or

5 $-9 < x < 3$

c

g value is $4\frac{1}{2}$
   -7825,

i x

   c $x \geqslant 20$

4 a $x \leqslant 4$

   c $x > -4$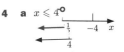

   e $x < 1$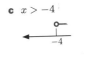

5 a $x > 2$

   c $x < -1$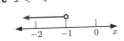

   e $x \leqslant -3$

   g $x \leqslant \frac{3}{2}$

   i $x < \frac{7}{17}$

6 a $x < -\frac{17}{3}$ **b** $x \geqslant 13$
   d $x > 3$ **e** $x \geqslant 2$

7 a **i** $x = 10$ **ii** $x = -7$
   b **i** $x = 9$ **ii** $x = 29$

8 $x = -2, -1, 0, 1, 2$

EXERCISE 35C

1 a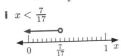

b

d

f $x \geqslant$

h $x < -$

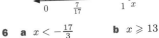

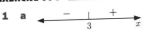

6 **a**

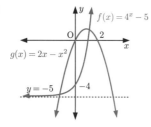

$f(x) = 4^x - 5$

$g(x) = 2x - x^2$

$y = -5$

b $-1.42 \leqslant x \leqslant 1.28$

7 **a**

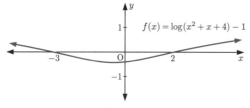

$f(x) = \log(x^2 + x + 4) - 1$

b $-3 \leqslant x \leqslant 2$ **c** $k < -0.426$

8 **a**   **b**

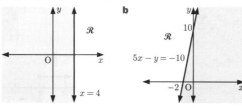

$x = 4$ $5x - y = -10$

9 **a** $x \leqslant -2$ and $y < 2$
   b $x \geqslant 0$, $y \geqslant 1$, $2x + y \leqslant 4$, and $3x + 4y \leqslant 12$

10 **a**   **b** $\frac{4}{3}$

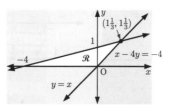

$(1\frac{1}{3}, 1\frac{1}{3})$ $x - 4y = -4$ $y = x$

CHAPTER 36

Cambridge Assessment International Education bears no
responsibility for the example answers to questions taken from its
past question papers which are contained in this publication.

1 **a** $\approx 66\,000$ cm^3 **b** **i** 16.4 cm   **ii** 120 g
2 **a** 16 : 15   **b** **i** 30%   **ii** \$24.30 interest
   c **i** \$48   **ii** 13 months
3 **a** The balls can be packed 5 long, 4 wide, and 1 high.
      $5 \times 4 \times 1 = 20$ balls
   b ≈ 14.1 cm^3 **c** ≈ 283 cm^3 **d** $\approx 2.83 \times 10^2$ cm^3
   e $\approx 52.4\%$
4 **a** ≈ 2.83 m^2 **b** $2\cos^{-1}\left(\frac{0.7}{0.9}\right) \approx 77.9°$ **c** ≈ 5980 litres
5 **a** **i** $f(g(x)) = 9x^2 - 39x + 36$
      ii $g(g(x)) = 9x - 8$ **iii** $g(f(2)) = -38$
   b **i** $x = \frac{1}{3}$ or 4   **ii** $\frac{4}{3} \leqslant x \leqslant 3$
6 **a** ≈ 9.83 cm   **b** $\approx 59.2°$ **c** ≈ 85.4 cm^2
7 **a** $\begin{pmatrix} 6 \\ -2 \end{pmatrix}$ **b** $-\frac{1}{3}$ **c** $y = -\frac{1}{3}x + 5$
   d $(9, 10)$ **e** $(15, 8)$ **f** 8 units
8 **a** $120°$ **b** ≈ 17.3 cm   **c** ≈ 779 cm^2
   d $\approx 40.3\%$ **e** ≈ 0.481

9 **a** $(6x + 1)^2 = (2x - 1)^2 + (5x + 4)^2$
      which simplifies to $7x^2 - 24x - 16 = 0$
   b $(x - 4)(7x + 4)$
   c Using $x = 4$, $A = \frac{1}{2} \times 24 \times 7$ **d** $y \approx 8.22$
                                $= 84$ cm^2
10 **a**   **b** positive, linear
                                                            correlation
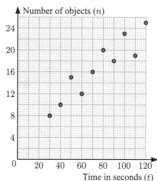

Number of objects (n)

Time in seconds (t)

   c **i** 75 s
      ii 16.6 objects

   d **i** $n \approx 0.168t + 3.96$ **ii** ≈ 18 objects
11 **a** 5   **b** $2x + 2$ **c** $\dfrac{3x + 2}{(2x + 3)(x - 1)}$ **d** $x = -\frac{9}{10}$
    e $x = 1 \pm \sqrt{5}$
12 **a** 2   **b** 10   **c** 3   **d** 5   **e** ≈ 4 **f** ≈ 0.0685
13 **a** $\sqrt{34}$ units   **b** $2\sqrt{15}$ units   **c** $\frac{10}{7} + \frac{5}{7}\sqrt{11}$ **d** D$(\frac{16}{3}, 0)$
14 **a** $x = 72$ **b** $x = -3$, $y = -4$
15 **a** $(1, -4)$ **b** $(-1, -4)$ **c** $(x, -y)$
    d A reflection in the x-axis.
16 **a** $4\sqrt{5}$ units
    b **Hint:** Show that
                $(x + 2)^2 + (y + 1)^2 = (x - 6)^2 + (y - 3)^2$.
    c P$(\frac{5}{3}, \frac{5}{3})$
17 **a** **i** 25 days   **ii** 32 days   **b** $\approx 5.56\%$ **c** 5 : 8
    d $\frac{25}{324} \approx 0.0772$
18 **a** ≈ 19.9 m   **b** AC $= \dfrac{30}{\tan 68°} \approx 12.1$ m   **c** $\approx 301°$
19 **a** P$(-\frac{3}{5}, \frac{4}{5})$,   Q$\left(\frac{2}{\sqrt 5}, -\frac{1}{\sqrt 5}\right)$ **b** $\theta \approx 126.9°$
    c $\sqrt{2 + \frac{4}{5}\sqrt 5}$ units   **d** $P\widehat{O}Q \approx 153.4°$
    e **i** $\frac{3}{4}$ **ii** 2
20 **a** **i** \$3374.59   **ii** 8 years
    b **i** \$3450   **ii** 7 years   **c** 12 years
21 **a, d**

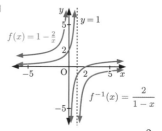

$y = 1$

$f(x) = 1 - \frac{2}{x}$

$f^{-1}(x) = \dfrac{2}{1 - x}$

    b $0 < x < 2$ **c** $f^{-1}(x) = \dfrac{2}{1 - x}$
    e A reflection in the line $y = x$.
22 **a** **Hint:** Compare the formulae for the area of a sector with
                that for the length of an arc.
    b 8 m   **c** $\approx 90.9\%$
23 **a** **i** n^2 **ii** $3n + 4$ **b** $n^2 + 3n + 4$ **c** $k = 11$

24 **a** 6.75 cm **b** 3 cm **c** $w \approx 8.49$

25 **a** $f = \dfrac{300}{L}$ **b** ≈ 107 Hz **c** ≈ 857 m

26 **a** $\widehat{ACD} = 51°$ **b** ≈ 19.7 cm^2

27 **a** $S_n = 3n + 2$ **b** $-3, 4, 15, 30$ **c** $u_n = 2n - 3$

d $u_n + s_n = 5n - 1 = 501$
$$\therefore \quad 5n = 502$$
$$n = \tfrac{502}{5}$$

but as n must be an integer, 501 is not a term of the sequence.

28 **a**

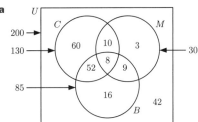

b **i** $\dfrac{21}{100}$

ii $\dfrac{9}{200}$

c **i** $\dfrac{87}{3980}$

ii $\dfrac{48}{995}$

29 **a** $25^2 = 35^2 + x^2 - 2 \times 35 \times x \times \cos 20°$
$$\therefore \quad x^2 - 65.78x + 600 = 0$$

b **i** $x \approx 10.94$ or 54.84 **ii** 54.84 km **c** 1 h 28 min

30 **a** **i** ≈ 44.2 cm^2 **ii** ≈ 0.0042 m^2

iii **Hint:** If the inner circle radius is r, then
$$\pi r^2 = \tfrac{1}{4}\pi \times 15^2.$$

b **i** ≈ 26.8 cm **ii** ≈ 303 cm^2

CHAPTER 37

Cambridge Assessment International Education bears no responsibility for the example answers to questions taken from its past question papers which are contained in this publication.

A INVESTIGATION QUESTIONS

1 **a** $k = 6$

b $n = 2$: LHS $= 5$, RHS $= \dfrac{2 \times 3 \times 5}{6} = 5$ ✓

$n = 3$: LHS $= 14$, RHS $= \dfrac{3 \times 4 \times 7}{6} = 14$ ✓

c 338 350 **d** 171 700 **e** 166 650 **f** -5050

2 **a, b**

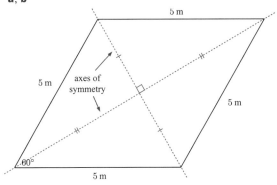

The axes of symmetry bisect each other at right angles.

c a rhombus **d** $\dfrac{25\sqrt{3}}{2} \approx 21.7$ m^2

e Area is a maximum of 25 m^2 when the angle is 90°, that is, when the rhombus is a square. This is because when 60° is replaced by θ, area $= (\tfrac{1}{2} \times 5^2 \times \sin\theta) \times 2 = 25 \sin\theta$ which is maximised when $\sin\theta = 1$.

3 **a** $5 = 2 + 3$ is one example

b **i** $16 = 3 + 13 = 5 + 11$

ii 38 can only be written as $7 + 31$

c $16 = 2 + 3 + 11$

4 **a** **i**

Shape number	1	2	3	4		7		n
Number of rods	4	8	12	16		28		$4n$
Number of squares enclosed	1	3	5	7		13		$2n - 1$

ii 199 squares

b **i** 40 rods **ii** $n(n + 3)$

5 **a** **i**

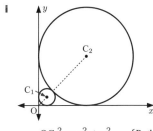

$$OC_1{}^2 = r^2 + r^2 \quad \{\text{Pythagoras}\}$$
$$\therefore \quad OC_1 = r\sqrt{2}$$
and $\quad OC_2{}^2 = R^2 + R^2 \quad \{\text{Pythagoras}\}$
$$\therefore \quad OC_2 = R\sqrt{2}$$
Now $\quad OC_1 + r + R = OC_2$
$$\therefore \quad r\sqrt{2} + r + R = R\sqrt{2}$$

b **i**

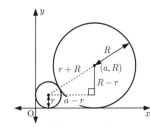

$$(a - r)^2 + (R - r)^2 = (r + R)^2 \quad \{\text{Pythagoras}\}$$
which simplifies to $\quad a^2 + r^2 = (2a + 4R)r$

ii $r = 14 - 4\sqrt{10} \approx 1.35$ units

iii $\dfrac{r}{R} = 3 - 2\sqrt{2}$, which is the same as our result in **a ii**.

iv

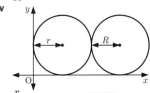

$a = 3R$

v $\dfrac{r}{R} = k + 2 - 2\sqrt{k + 1}$

6 **a** **i** 9 squares **ii** 13 squares **iii** 7 squares

b **i**

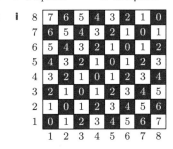

ii The number of possible squares it can move in the $\nearrow$ direction is maximised at 7, when $|x-y|=0$ becauses $|x-y|=0$ lies on the longest diagonal and the longest diagonal has 8 squares.

iii There are $8-|x-y|$ squares on the $\nearrow$ diagonal passing through (x,y). The bishop can move to $7-|x-y|$ squares in the $\nearrow$ direction.

iv Similarly to part **ii**, the longest diagonal in the $\searrow$ direction has maximum 7 squares that can be moved to. The number of squares that can be moved to decreases by 1 for each step taken from the longest diagonal. On the longest diagonal $x+y=9$, on the next longest $x+y=8$, and so on.
Hence, the bishop can move to $7-|9-(x+y)|$ in the $\searrow$ direction.

v $14-|x-y|-|9-(x+y)|$
At $(2,3)$, $14-|-1|-|4|=9$ ✓
At $(5,5)$, $14-|0|-|-1|=13$ ✓
At $(8,1)$, $14-|7|-|0|=7$ ✓

c i $2(n-1)-|x-y|-|n+1-(x+y)|$
   ii 131 possible squares

d i (1) 23 squares   **(2)** 27 squares   **(3)** 21 squares
   ii (1) $28-|x-y|-|9-(x+y)|$
   (2) $4(n-1)-|x-y|-|n+1-(x+y)|$

7 a i 1 4 6 4 1   **ii** 1 5 10 10 5 1
  b i sum of row $0=1$ **ii** sum of terms in row $n=2^n$
     sum of row $1=2$ **iii** 1 048 576
     sum of row $2=4$
     sum of row $3=8$
     sum of row $4=16$
  c i (1) 3   **(2)** 7   **(3)** 15   **(4)** 31
   ii Sum of terms up to and including row $n=2^{n+1}-1$
   iii 2 147 483 647

B MODELLING QUESTIONS

1 a $a=5$, $b=4$, $c=30$ **b** $d=5+4\sin(420°)\approx 8.46$
  c ≈ 1.54 m   **d** 9 m   **e** at 0300 and 1500   **f** 1 m

2 a

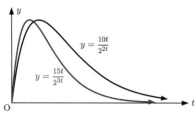

$y=\dfrac{10t}{2^{2t}}$

$y=\dfrac{15t}{2^{3t}}$

  b i $a=25$, $b=\frac{1}{2}$ **ii** $r=18.75$, $s\approx 4.69$
   iii Maximum effect ≈ 26.5 units at $t\approx 2.89$ hours
   iv between 48 min and 7 h 9 min

3 a i

$y=3$

$y=\dfrac{3\times 2^{\frac{1}{2}t}}{2^{\frac{1}{2}t}+2}$

ii The horizontal asymptote $y=3$ suggests that the limiting value is 3.

b i $a=20$, $b\approx 0.799$, $B(t)=\dfrac{20\times 2^{0.799t}}{2^{0.799t}+1}$
  ii $B(2)\approx 15.03$ ✓   **iii** 20 units
  iv If t is very large, $2^{bt}\approx 2^{bt}+c$
     $\therefore\ y\approx a$

4 a ii scale factor is $\sqrt{2}$
   iii A rotation of $45°$ about centre C, followed by an enlargement with scale factor $\sqrt{2}$ and centre C.

  b ii scale factor $=\dfrac{1+\sqrt{5}}{2}$

  c ii Hint: $\widehat{ABC}=\dfrac{180(n-2)}{n}$
   iii Scale factor is 1. The triangles are congruent.
   iv (1) ≈ 1.902 **(2)** ≈ 1.996 **(3)** ≈ 1.999
   v As the number of sides of the polygon increases, the scale factor gets closer and closer to 2.

5 a i $b_1=49$ **ii** 122.5 m
   iii 10 seconds since being projected.
  b i 98 m
   ii (1) Hint: The equation of the axis of symmetry of
     $$y=ax^2+bx+c\ \text{ is } x=\dfrac{-b}{2a}.$$
   (2) maximum $H_2=\frac{5}{98}b_2^2$ m
   (3) $b_2\approx 43.8$, ≈ 8.94 s between the first and second bounces.
  c $t_3=8$ s
  d No, the time interval between two bounces is $\sqrt{0.8}\approx 0.894$ times the previous time interval.
  e $10\times 0.8^{\frac{n}{2}}$ s   **f** 4 times

6 a $P=3x+5y$
  b There are 2 bats in each set. The number of bats produced each hour is $2x+2y$, which must be less than or equal to 560.
  c $x\geqslant 0$, $y\geqslant 0$, $3x+5y\leqslant 1080$, $y\leqslant 180$
  d

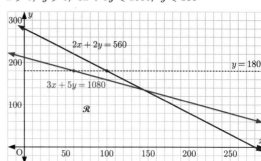

  e There are many possible answers, one solution is to produce 60 of set A and 180 of set B. In this case bats are under-utilised because only 480 are used out of the possible 560.

INDEX

absolute value 415
addition law of probability 564
adjacent angles 110
algebraic equation 83
algebraic fraction 319
algebraic product 42
alternate angles 112
amplitude 515
angle at the centre theorem 535
angle between a line and a plane 368
angle between a tangent and
a chord theorem 534
angle in a semi-circle theorem 524
angle of depression 360
angle of elevation 360
angle theorems 110
angles subtended by the
same arc theorem 537
apex 119
arc length 168, 169
area 172
area of a sector 176
arithmetic sequence 462
asymptote 420
average speed 237
axis of symmetry 444
bar chart 58
base 14
base angle 119
biased sample 272
bimodal 284
bivariate statistics 306
cancelling common factors 321
capacity 197
Cartesian plane 220
categorical data 57
categorical variable 273
census 272
centre 397
centre of data 283, 284
certain event 550
chain percentage 211
chords of a circle theorem 527
circumference 168
class interval 280
co-interior angles 112
coefficient of determination 313
collinear points 233
column vector 601
common difference 462
common factor 42
common ratio 462
complement 90, 96

complementary angles 110
complementary events 551
component form 601
composite bar chart 63
composite function 414
compound interest 215
concyclic 539
continuous numerical data 57
continuous quantitative variable 274
converse of Pythagoras' theorem 146
correlation 306
corresponding angles 112
cosine rule 509
counting numbers 92
critical value 617
cubic function 450
cumulative frequency 295
cyclic quadrilateral 539, 542
data 57
density 199
dependent events 569
dependent variable 306
difference between two squares 34
difference method 463
direct proportion 576
direct variation 576
discrete numerical data 57
discrete quantitative variable 274
discriminant 381
disjoint 91, 564
distance between two points 222
distance-time graph 240
distributive law 30
domain 408
element 87, 408
empty set 88
enlargement 390, 398
equal set 88
equal vectors 595, 603
equation 73
equation of a line 246
event 557
expansion 43
expectation 556
experimental probability 553
exponent 14
exponent laws 17
exponent notation 14
exponential equation 477
exponential function 473
exponential regression 481
exterior angle 124
extrapolation 310
factorisation 43
finite set 88
formula 155

frequency 552
frequency histogram 281
fully factorised 43
function 410
fundamental theorem
of arithmetic 15
general form 250
general term 458
geometric sequence 462
gradient 227
gradient formula 228
gradient-intercept form 249
highest common factor 42
hypotenuse 142
identity 83
image 390
impossible event 550
independent events 565
independent variable 306
index 14
infinite set 88
integer 92
interest 213
interest rate 213
interpolation 310
interquartile range 290
intersection 91, 97
interval notation 94
invariant line 399
inverse function 427
inverse of a transformation 402
inverse operation 75
inverse proportion 583
inverse trigonometric functions 358
irrational number 93
isosceles triangle 119
laws of logarithms 489
least squares regression line 312
length of a vector 594, 602
line graph 66
linear equation 76
linear inequality 614
linear regression 312
local maximum 421
local minimum 421
logarithm 485
logarithmic function 487
loss 210
lower quartile 290
lowest common denominator 81
magnitude 594, 602
many-to-many 408
many-to-one 408
mapping diagram 407
mass 199
maximum point 515

mean	284	
mean line	515	
mean point	309	
median	284	
member	87	
midpoint	225	
minimum point	515	
modal class	280	
mode	284	
modulus	415	
multiple bar chart	63	
mutually exclusive	564	
natural numbers	92	
negative exponent law	21	
negatively skewed	276	
nth term	458	
null factor law	377	
number sequence	458	
numerical data	57	
object	390	
one-to-many	408	
one-to-one	408	
ordered pair	220	
origin	220	
outcome	552	
parallel line theorems	114	
parallel lines	231	
Pearson's correlation coefficient	312	
percentage	205	
percentile	295, 296	
perfect square	36	
perimeter	167	
period	515	
periodic function	515	
perpendicular lines	231	
pictogram	59	
pie chart	59	
point of intersection	262	
pole	310	
population	272	
position vector	594, 602	
positively skewed	276	
power	14	
power equation	131	
power model	587	
prime factorisation	15	
principal	213	
principal axis	515	
probability	550	
profit	210	
projection	368	
proper subset	88	
proportionality constant	576	
Pythagoras' theorem	142	
quadrant	221	
quadratic equation	375	

quadratic formula	381	
quadratic function	434	
quadratic inequality	619	
quadratic trinomial	50	
quantitative variable	274	
quartile	290	
radical	129	
radical conjugate	138	
radius-tangent theorem	529	
range	408	
range of a data set	298	
rational equation	81	
rational number	93	
rationalising the denominator	137	
raw data	272	
real number	93	
rearranging formulae	159	
reciprocal function	419	
rectangular hyperbola	419	
reduction	390, 398	
reflection	390, 392	
relative frequency	552	
right angled triangle	142	
rotation	390, 395	
sample	272	
sample space	557	
scalar	593	
scale factor	397	
scatter diagram	306	
scientific notation	23	
set	87	
set identity	99	
set notation	88	
sign diagram	617	
similar	334	
similar triangles	337	
simple interest	213	
simplest form	134	
simultaneous equations	261	
sine rule	506	
solid of uniform cross-section	191	
solution	74	
solution by elimination	265	
standard form	23	
statistics	272	
stem plot	275	
strength of correlation	307, 313	
stretch	390, 399	
subject	155	
subset	88, 97	
substitution	157, 264	
supplementary angles	110	
surd	130	
surface area	183	
survey	272	
symmetrical distribution	276	

table of values	247
tally-frequency table	275
tangents from an external point theorem	531
tapered solid	194
term	458
theoretical probability	559
transformation	389
translation	390
translation vector	390
travel graph	240
triangle	116
trigonometry	351
true bearing	366
turning point	421
union	91, 97
unit circle	498
universal set	90
upper quartile	290
vector	593
velocity	593
Venn diagram	96
vertex	445
volume	190, 191
x-axis	220
x-coordinate	220
x-intercept	247
y-axis	220
y-coordinate	220
y-intercept	247
zero exponent law	21
zero vector	595
zeros of a function	421